Society of

Exploration Geophysicists'

Mining Geophysics

Volume II, Theory

Compiled and Edited by

The SEG Mining Geophysics Volume Editorial Committee

DON A. HANSEN, Associate Editor

WALTER E. HEINRICHS, JR., Associate Editor

RALPH C. HOLMER, Associate Editor

ROBERT E. MACDOUGALL, Associate Editor

GEORGE R. ROGERS, Associate Editor

JOHN S. SUMNER, Associate Editor

STANLEY H. WARD, Associate Editor

Published by
THE SOCIETY OF EXPLORATION GEOPHYSICISTS
P. O. Box 3098
Tulsa, Oklahoma

Composed and Printed by
George Banta Company, Inc.
Menasha, Wisconsin

To Donald J. Salt and Peter S. White

FOREWORD

Mining Geophysics has advanced significantly in recent years, and it has thus been difficult for its proponents to keep pace with new developments. To ease this burden the Mining Volume Committee was given approval by the Executive Committee of the Society of Exploration Geophysicists to proceed with the preparation of a special volume devoted to mining geophysics. It ensued from discussions that the theory and practice of the electromagnetic and induced polarization methods were lacking in textbook literature. In addition it was observed that although the theory of the magnetic method is well documented, a general exploration treatment was not available under one cover. Selected papers on the gravity method also seemed appropriate. Sequential applications of geophysical methods as applied to geologic mapping and in the search for massive sulfides, disseminated sulfides, and iron ore were virtually unrecorded. Thus the assignment was passed to your *Mining Geophysics* Editorial Committee to prepare a volume or volumes which would satisfy these needs.

It is hoped that interest in this work will extend well beyond the exploration geophysicist, and that geologists and exploration managers and those who set mining policies will find useful information herein. To that end, *Mining Geophysics* has been arranged in two volumes. Volume I contains applied papers and case histories that do not rely heavily on mathematical presentations. Descriptions of various techniques applied to actual field problems are presented. Volume contains predominantly theoretical papers for those who wish to delve more deeply into the basis of the various geophysical methods. We wish to note that the Mining Volume Committee and the Editorial Committee of *Mining Geophysics* have not presumed to present a complete treatise on mining geophysics. Rather we were interested in filling the obvious gaps in the published literature.

We believe that the information provided will be of value both to industry and education.

The future for mining geophysics and for the earth sciences appears enviably bright. Regardless of synthetic and substitute materials, man's insatiable demand for basic resources will surely continue to expand, and will accelerate as the populous underdeveloped nations begin to emerge. The types of raw materials that will be needed require careful scrutiny, but there is no doubt as to the need.

As consumption grows, the incentive to find new resources to replace the mined material grows also. As new mines are put into production, favorable areas for economic resources become harder to find. It then becomes necessary to take greater risks on poorer indications, and to rely more heavily on technical methods for finding ore. No hypothesis or anomaly can ever rank as high as does visible ore in place, but such exploration guides are becoming increasingly more rare. This trend can be expected to become more acute.

Geophysics seldom gives a unique indication in the effort to discover concealed or obscured deposits of economic material. In his effort to look beneath the surface of the earth the practicing geophysicist has had many humbling experiences. With infra-red, radar, and microwave image techniques, we can "photograph" the earth's surface from altitudes either at night or through cloud cover, and even draw inferences regarding the nature of the outer few centimeters of the surface of the moon. At the same time it is difficult to learn very much about an inhomogeneity buried only a few feet below the surface of the earth unless excavation work is done. This is the inherent problem of electrical "skin depth" and the electromagnetic spectrum. To obtain resolution and detail, very short wavelengths must be used and these will not penetrate very far into a body as conductive as the earth. To obtain significant penetration, very long wave lengths must be used and these are incapable of revealing any detail. Even so, in recent years some very significant progress has been achieved. This has been largely due to the patient, continuing effort by industry and to the contributions of educators who recognized the needs. In these volumes some of these achievements are recorded and documented in the hope that such information may be of benefit to all who are striving to keep mankind supplied with the material needed for continuing progress.

Each paper in these volumes has been indexed by the Chapter Editor using the Key Word system, and these words are given in the Table of Contents at the start of each chapter. This indexing procedure has been successfully used for briefly describing articles in *Geophysics* and other scientific publications. The KWIC (Key Word in Context) system can then be used for data retrieval by computer methods.

The Editorial Committee wishes to thank the authors and their sponsoring organizations for their contributions, and for their patience during the process of gathering this material together. Without their efforts this work would not be possible.

The Editors of Mining Geophysics wish to thank SEG Editor Robert VanNostrand and the SEG Publication Staff for their assistance and encouragement in assembling these volumes.

D. A. HANSEN
R. E. MacDOUGALL
G. R. ROGERS
J. S. SUMNER
S. H. WARD

November 1966

TABLE OF CONTENTS
Volume II

Chapter I

Chapter II
ELECTRICAL METHODS

Chapter III
MAGNETIC METHOD

Contents

Chapter IV

GRAVITY METHODS

Chapter I

INTRODUCTION

INTRODUCTION

S. H. WARD* AND G. R. ROGERS‡

The relative merits of any geophysical method in a given situation can be predicted by careful study of the expected message-to-noise[1] ratio. For example, let us draw or deduce from the subsequent text, the anomaly formulas due to a spherical inhomogeneity in the subsurface:

gravity

$$\Delta g = \left(\frac{4}{3}\pi G\right)(R^3)(\rho_2 - \rho_1)\frac{z}{r^3}$$

magnetics

$$\Delta \mathbf{H} = (H_0)(R^3)\left(\frac{\mu_2 - \mu_1}{\mu_2 + 2\mu_1}\right)$$
$$\cdot\left(\frac{(2x^2 - z^2 - y^2)\mathbf{i} + 3xy\mathbf{j} + 3xz\mathbf{k}}{r^5}\right)$$

resistivity

$$\Delta \mathbf{E} = (E_0)(R^3)\left(\frac{\sigma_2 - \sigma_1}{\sigma_2 + 2\sigma_1}\right)$$
$$\cdot\left(\frac{(2x^2 - y^2 - z^2)\mathbf{i} + 3xy\mathbf{j} + 3xz\mathbf{k}}{r^5}\right)$$

electromagnetics

$$\Delta \mathbf{H} = (H_0)(R^3)(M - iN)$$
$$\cdot\left(\frac{(2x^2 - y^2 - z^2)\mathbf{i} + 3xy\mathbf{j} + 3xz\mathbf{k}}{r^5}\right)$$

induced polarization (disseminated deposit)

$$\Delta_f(\Delta \mathbf{E}) = (E_0)(R^3)\left[\Delta_f\left(\frac{\sigma_2 - \sigma_1}{\sigma_2 + 2\sigma_1}\right)\right]$$
$$\cdot\left[\frac{(2x^2 - y^2 - z^2)\mathbf{i} + 3xy\mathbf{j} + 3xz\mathbf{k}}{r^5}\right]$$

[1] Throughout this chapter we use "message" to indicate the information sought and reserve the word "signal" for the summation of message and noise.

Each of these anomalies constitutes a *message* of the form

$$A = (IF)(SF)(PPF)(GF)$$

where

A = anomaly
IF = inducing field
SF = size factor
PPF = physical property factor
GF = geometric factor

and the symbols in each formula are explained in the text. The gravity, magnetic, resistivity, and induced-polarization surveys all are volume dependent, whereas the electromagnetic method is dependent only upon the area of the inhomogeneity, normal to the inducing field. Thus, a thin disk can give nearly the same electromagnetic anomaly as a sphere of the same radius.

If we can make a reasonable estimate of the physical property contrast anticipated to exist between ore and host, we can then predict the anomaly magnitude expected from the sphere, when buried at any given depth, via the geometric factor. Note that from this viewpoint, given the maximum or saturation value of unity for the physical property factor, the magnetic and resistivity methods theoretically give the same percent anomaly due to a sphere. The physical property function $M - iN$ for the electromagnetic method has a maximum value of one half for a sphere while the change with frequency of the electrical resistivity contrast

$$\Delta_f\left(\frac{\sigma_2 - \sigma_1}{\sigma_2 + 2\sigma_1}\right)$$

is not readily predicted but probably has a maximum of one half (assume $\sigma_2 \gg \sigma_1$ at one frequency and that $\sigma_2 \ll \sigma_1$ at a second

Department of Mineral Technology, University of California, Berkeley.
Phelps Dodge Corporation, Douglas, Arizona.

frequency). Thus, except for a factor of two, the magnetic, resistivity, electromagnetic, and induced-polarization methods should give the same maximum anomaly. Note that the geometry of the anomalous fields for each of these methods is an induced dipole with a resultant fall-off of peak anomaly proportional to the inverse cube of the depth to the center of the sphere below the measuring plane. In contrast, the gravity method exhibits an inverse second power fall-off due to an induced monopole. The density contrast between ore and host sometimes exhibits a maximum value of two. Thus from a maximum message viewpoint, one would be inclined to rate the methods in the order given above. However, we need to counter this bias by considering expected values of the physical property factor and the noise for any given geologic situation.

Let us look, then, at iron ore, massive sulfides, and disseminated sulfides, items treated in Volume I. We should expect the following physical property ranges:

Table 1

Physical property factor	Iron ore	Massive sulfides	Disseminated sulfides
$\rho_2 - \rho_1$	0.5–2.0 gm/cm³	1.0–2.0	0.02–1.0
$\dfrac{\mu_2 - \mu_1}{\mu_2 + 2\mu_1}$	0.0004–0.8	0.0001–0.025	0–0.0001
$\dfrac{\sigma_2 - \sigma_1}{\sigma_2 + 2\sigma_1}$	0–1.0	0.5–1.0	0–0.1
$\lvert M - iN \rvert$	0–0.25	0.25–0.5	0–0.25
$\Delta_f\left(\dfrac{\sigma_2 - \sigma_1}{\sigma_2 + 2\sigma_1}\right)$	0–0.5	0 (Formula neglects the effect of bounding surface.)	0.01–0.5

A very wide range of properties is evident and hence the prediction of an anomaly magnitude looks hopeless. On the other hand, if our geologic knowledge of an area is such that we can say that we are seeking massive magnetite in limestone for the iron ore, that the massive sulfides are largely pyrrhotite in a sediment-volcanic complex and that the disseminated mineralization expected is percent total pyrite and chalcopyrite in quartz porphyry intrusive, then the much more diagnostic set of figures is:

Table 2

Physical property factor	Massive magnetite	Massive sulfides mostly pyrrhotite	3 percent pyrite-chalcopyrite
$\rho_2 - \rho_1$	1.5–2.0 gm/cm³	1.3–1.8 gm/cm³	0.05 gm/cm³
$\dfrac{\mu_2 - \mu_1}{\mu_2 + 2\mu_1}$	3.5–10.0	0.029–0.91	0
$\dfrac{\sigma_2 - \sigma_1}{\sigma_2 + 2\sigma_1}$	0.5–1.0	0.5–1.0	0
$\lvert M - iN \rvert$	0.1–0.25	0.5	0
$\Delta_f\left(\dfrac{\sigma_2 - \sigma_1}{\sigma_2 + 2\sigma_1}\right)$	0	0	3–10%

With these figures, one can predict the maximum anomaly to be expected for spherical targets at any depth of burial. At this stage, however, we must evaluate the noise in order to determine the message-to-noise ratio.

Noise, encountered in geophysical survey

is of three types: instrument noise, disturbance field noise, and terrain noise. With any of the methods we have discussed, instrument noise can be, and has been, made lower than the threshold of other noise sources. Hence we shall not discuss this noise source. Disturbance field noise can be identified for each of the methods as follows:

gravity—earth tides

magnetics—geomagnetic disturbance fields such as diurnal variation, magnetic storms, bays, sudden impulses and micropulsations, and possible power line interference.

resistivity—telluric currents or power line interference, i.e. the electrical equivalent of the disturbance magnetic fields.

electromagnetics—sferic, power line fields.

induced polarization—as for resistivity.

The periods of earth tides are such that we eliminate their effects through a drift correction, obtained by repeating a given station at half-hourly or hourly intervals. The same procedure is used to eliminate geomagnetic disturbances during magnetic surveys. However, in the resistivity, electromagnetic, and induced-polarization methods, natural electric and magnetic field noise in the frequency band from 0.01 cps to 5000 cps often limit application of these methods. High power generators and phase-lock receivers can help to minimize, but never eliminate, the effects of these noise sources.

The terrain noise for each method would include geologic noise and topographic noise, plus location and sensor orientation errors. We have tabulated these sources for each method, assuming the survey is concerned with the direct search for massive sulfides, disseminated sulfides, or iron ore.

Table 3

Method	Geologic noise	Topographic noise	Location and orientation errors
gravity	—local density inhomogeneities —regional gradients —bedrock relief	incomplete topographic correction due to lack of detailed knowledge of subsurface density distribution	elevation errors, latitude correction errors
magnetics	—local susceptibility inhomogeneities —regional gradients —bedrock relief —remanence inhomogeneities	topographic correction extremely difficult to make with any assurance due to irregular magnetization of irregular shapes	usually are insignificant except irregular terrain clearance in airborne surveys
resistivity	—local conductivity inhomogeneities —regional gradients —bedrock relief —buried contacts —broad shear zones —graphite horizons —masking effect of highly conductive or highly resistive overburden	topographic correction extremely difficult to make with any assurance due to irregular distribution of subsurface conductivities	usually are insignificant but see under induced polarization
electro-magnetics	—local conductivity inhomogeneities —faults, shears —graphite horizons —masking effect of highly conductive overburden	usually are insignificant in inductive methods but same as for resistivity with conductive methods	erroneous orientation of transmitting coil relative to receiving coil
induced polarization	—minor magnetite in country rock or overburden —graphite horizons —clay minerals in overburden or country rock —masking effect of highly conductive or highly resistive overburden	usually insignificant but all our theory assumes electrodes on flat earth. Gullies can and do give resistivity and induced polarization anomalies.	usually insignificant but all our theory assumes electrodes placed on flat earth. Must correct for irregular surface if theory to be strictly applicable.

The terrain noise sources place practical but unknown limits on all of the methods, such that most mining geophysicists produce the vague answer that each of the exploration methods discussed above has a practical depth of exploration in mining applications, of the order of 500 ft. Some geophysicists are inclined to suggest a practical limit of the order of 1,000 ft or greater for both the induced-polarization method and Afmag. The fact remains that no geophysicist knows the limiting depth of exploration for any method since terrain noise varies from location to location and very few have attempted to define and evaluate it. Definition, evaluation, and subsequent elimination of terrain noise, perhaps with the aid of statistical communication theory, is one of the greatest challenges facing the mining geophysicist today.

Despite our current technological limitation in being unable to define the limiting noise for any of our methods, we must make decisions concerning the method or methods to be used to solve a given geological problem. Our experience enables us to make an educated guess that on the average terrain noise is, say 0.05 mgals for gravity, 25γ for magnetics, 5.0 percent of primary electric field for resistivity, two degrees of dip angle, or 3.5 percent of primary field for electromagnetics, and 2.0 percent for frequency effect in induced polarization. We place these, or other, fixed limits for the minimum anomaly we can detect. Then we can, via the sphere formulation for example, compute the maximum depth at which any given sphere might be buried in order to be just detectable above the noise level. We could do the same for any other target shape, provided we can obtain, by calculation or by scale model experiment, the formulation for the anomaly due to that shape.

In general, we can estimate the message-to-noise level for any of the methods for any given geologic problem. Based upon this and upon cost estimates for each method, we can then list the methods in order of "profit ratio" where the latter term for the present instance is meant to convey the ratio of probability of detection of a target divided by the cost of the survey. Unfortunately, the limiting noise is seldom randomly distributed over the surveyed area nor does its spectrum of spatial wavelengths lie outside the spectrum due to the message sought. This spectral overlap and nonrandom noise renders uncertain the profit ratio for any method. The extraneous anomalies really constitute noise although seldom do we appreciate this in the field. In the search for massive sulfides by airborne electromagnetic methods, only about one anomaly in 5,000 is an ore body, but as many as one anomaly in 100 is due to massive sulfides. From another viewpoint, massive sulfide "messages" are outweighed by extraneous anomalies by two orders of magnitude. However, by using a sequence of methods, wherein the noise sources for one method do not contribute noise for another method and vice versa, we are able to give a very high probability of detection for some targets. In the search for massive sulfides, the sequence may be electromagnetics, magnetics, and gravity, and this sequence is given better than a 95 percent chance of finding massive sulfides (not necessarily oregrade) in the Canadian Shield. For magnetic iron ore in the Cordilleran the sequence is magnetics and gravity, and it has been remarkably efficient. The sequence for disseminated ores is not so well established, nor so successful; it relies principally upon the induced-polarization method.

The geophysical methods are but a part of an overall exploration sequence which might involve field geological study, photogeology, trace element geochemistry, drilling, stripping & trenching, or underground development. The engineering approach to exploration is to place all of the available ore search aids in an efficient and balanced sequence and to refine this sequence as new information develops regarding the geological problem at hand. This, then, is *modern exploration* which has located an amazing tonnage of ore in many countries of the world since 1950, when the concept of sequential exploration began to be developed in earnest.

The mining geophysicist must have a firm grasp of the underlying theory to be able to predict message and noise under many different geologic environments. He must be aware of the statistics of ore search. He must have a sound knowledge of geology and he must temper all of his textbook knowledge with sagacity derived from experience.

To illustrate the importance of geophysics and the role of the geophysicist in modern mining exploration, we offer the following suggested sequence for a hypothetical broad scale search for massive sulfides.

Motivation for preparation of Volume II of *Mining Geophysics* stemmed from the lack of a textbook with a comprehensive treatment of the theory of those electrical methods most commonly employed in mining geophysics. While the natural field electrical methods, namely self-potential, Afmag, tellurics, and magnetotellurics are employed in special situations, the bulk of electrical pros-

1. Preliminary office study
   —geologic digest
   —photogeologic interpretation
   —statistical, logistics, & cost study
     for airborne surveys
   —study of geophysical parameters

2. Field geologic reconnaissance
   —check rock types & properties
   —cover unmapped areas
   —correct photogeologic interpretation
   —possibly conduct a geological reconnaissance
   —geochemical reconnaissance & orientation
     surveys

3. Airborne electromagnetic & magnetic survey
   —conduct survey
   —initial interpretation of data
   —adjust survey in progress if necessary

4. Classification & correlation of anomalies
   —quantitative electrical interpretation
   —quantitative magnetic anomalies interpretation
   —rate combined anomalies
   —correlate with geology anomalies where
     known or assumed
   —select best anomalies for ground examination

5. Ground electromagnetic & magnetic
   delineation of best anomalies
   —locate & delineate
   —evaluate conductivity & susceptibility
   —note obvious causes
   —reject obviously extraneous anomalies

6. Geologic & geochemical examination of
   vicinity of remaining anomalies
   —map outcrop & float
   —take soil & stream samples for analysis
   —reject obviously extraneous anomalies

7. Gravity profiles over remaining anomalies
   —two or three profiles over center of
     electromagnetic-magnetic anomaly
   —reject obviously extraneous anomalies
   —quantitative interpretation & geologic
     correlation of remainder

8. Diamond drilling

9. Geological & geophysical study of drill core
   —economic evaluation
   —explain all anomalies

10. Reevaluation of all anomalies

11. Recycle best remaining anomalies

pecting now rests on electromagnetic surveys and combined resistivity-induced polarization surveys. The standard texts by Heiland (1940), Jakosky (1940), Eve and Keys (1954), Dobrin (1960), and others do not contain the theory and methodology of these methods as practiced today. The texts by Grant and West (1965) and Keller and Frischknecht (1966) have gone a long way towards filling this gap, but it is of such broad scope that a detailed treatment of the electromagnetic and resistivity-induced polarization methods was not possible. Thus the Mining Volume Committee of the Society chose to sponsor a text wherein the theoretical basis and modern technology of these methods were treated.

However, it was decided that since the gravity and magnetic methods play such an important role in mining geophysics, that a "Mining Volume" would be incomplete without at least a summary of the theory for these methods with special emphasis on the problems arising in mining geophysics.

Finally, the Mining Volume Committee was concerned that any theory presented be a natural complement to the case histories presented in Volume I of this set.

It is admitted that these are rather un-usual guidelines for the development of a volume to be published by a professional society which relies solely upon voluntary technical contributions from its members. Thus it should not be surprising that the resulting text is unbalanced in its presentation. We offer no apologies for this since we, representing both practicing mining geophysicists and educators, know that the material presented herein is desperately needed by both the student and practitioner of mining geophysics. We trust that others will also benefit from the material presented.

References

Dobrin, Milton B., 1960, Introduction to geophysical prospecting: New York, McGraw-Hill Book Company, Inc.

Eve, A. S., and Keys, D. A., 1954, Applied geophysics: Cambridge University Press.

Grant, F. S., and West, G. F., 1965, Interpretation theory in applied geophysics: New York McGraw-Hill Book Company, Inc.

Heiland, C. A., 1940, Geophysical exploration New York, Prentice-Hall, Inc.

Jakosky, J. J., 1940, Exploration geophysics Newport Beach, Trija Publishing Company.

Keller, G. V., and Frischknecht, F. C., 1966 Electrical methods in geophysical prospecting London, Pergamon Press.

Chapter II

ELECTRICAL METHODS

Chapter II

PART A—ELECTROMAGNETIC THEORY FOR GEOPHYSICAL APPLICATIONS

Table of Contents

* Professor of Geophysical Engineering, Department of Mineral Technology, University of California, Berkeley.

Contents

PREFACE

An attempt has been made in Part A of Chapter 2 to collect together sufficient electromagnetic theory to provide the theoretical basis for the electrical methods of geophysical prospecting. The material has been drawn from standard reference texts and the periodical literature; a few original developments have been added. In preparing the material, two guiding principles have been utilized: a consistent nomenclature should be used and the presentation should always be such that senior undergraduate students or first year graduate students can follow the developments readily. In a few places, it has been an editorial convenience to depart from strict consistency in nomenclature. Whether or not I have achieved the clarity of presentation desired will remain to be seen; most of the material has been tested in senior undergraduate and first year graduate courses in the College of Engineering, University of California, Berkeley.

In attempting to meet the needs of students, I hope that I have also met the needs of the practicing geophysical engineer. More detail has been included in the problem developments than would normally appear in periodicals or a standard text and perhaps this feature will prove beneficial to all. On the other hand, the fundamental electromagnetic theory of Section 1 is necessarily abbreviated.

It is impractical to include in this volume all of the theoretical developments which might be of interest to applied geophysicists. I have selected for inclusion those developments which I consider to be most useful. To aid those interested in a broader number of topics in electromagnetic induction, I have prepared an extensive list of additional references. Texts and journals consulted in preparing this list are those which adorn my own bookshelves. Presumably, then, these texts and journals are readily available to the applied geophysicist. The items have been selected with the intent of providing a reference list which does substantially extend and support the theoretical developments contained herein. I have tried to be selective so that no attempt at completeness has been made.

I am indebted to many of my graduate students for diligence in pointing out errors, omissions, and desirable modifications. Especially, I wish to acknowledge assistance received from Douglas C. Fraser, Douglas P. O'Brien, and H. Frank Morrison. Mr. O'Brien developed formulation for the plane-wave impedance of an n-layered anisotropic earth. Preparation of this manuscript has, in part, accompanied research in geoelectromagnetic phenomena sponsored by the National Science Foundation, the American Petroleum Institute, and the Office of Naval Research.

PART A. ELECTROMAGNETIC THEORY FOR GEOPHYSICAL APPLICATIONS

1. Fundamentals

1-I. *Introduction*

We are concerned in this section with establishing the basic material upon which the subsequent sections of the chapter depend. Thus we must establish the Maxwell field equations and the wave potentials in the unitary system to be utilized (mks), and follow this with solutions of the wave equation pertinent to some of the later development. This abbreviated summary of electromagnetic fundamentals then permits us to follow the subsequent presentations of specific problems in electromagnetic theory; the problems chosen are essential to our comprehension of the electrical methods.

Throughout we shall use a harmonic time dependency $e^{-i\omega t} = \cos \omega t - i \sin \omega t$ and in general follow Stratton (1941) in the earlier development.

1-II. *Fundamental Electromagnetic Quantities*

An electromagnetic field may be defined as the domain of the four vectors $\mathbf{E}$, $\mathbf{B}$, $\mathbf{D}$, $\mathbf{H}$ where

$\mathbf{E}$ = the electric field intensity in volts/meter,
$\mathbf{B}$ = the magnetic induction, or flux density, in weber/m²,
$\mathbf{D}$ = the dielectric displacement in coulomb/m²,
$\mathbf{H}$ = the magnetic field intensity in ampere-turn/m.

The experimental evidence of Coulomb, Ampere, and Faraday leads to the four Maxwell equations relating these vectors to their sources, a distribution of electric charge density ρ (coulombs/m³) and of electric current density $\mathbf{J}$ (amp/m²), as follows:

$$\nabla \times \mathbf{E} + \frac{\partial \mathbf{B}}{\partial t} = 0, \quad \text{(Faraday's Law)} \tag{A1}$$

$$\nabla \times \mathbf{H} - \frac{\partial \mathbf{D}}{\partial t} = \mathbf{J}, \quad \text{(Ampere's Law)} \tag{A2}$$

$$\nabla \cdot \mathbf{B} = 0, \quad \text{(\textbf{B} solenoidal)} \tag{A3}$$

$$\nabla \cdot \mathbf{D} = \rho, \quad \text{(Coulomb's Law)}. \tag{A4}$$

Equation (A2) demonstrates that the quantity $\partial \mathbf{D}/\partial t$ has the dimensions of a current density. Thus it is given the name *displacement current density* ($\mathbf{J}_D$). By analogy, the quantity $\partial \mathbf{B}/\partial t$ of (A1) is sometimes given the name *magnetic current density* ($\mathbf{J}_m$) and hence the rate of change of magnetic flux $\partial \phi/\partial t$ has the dimensions of magnetic current K and is so called Schelkunoff, 1943).

To these four equations may be added the equation of continuity

$$\nabla \cdot \mathbf{J} + \frac{\partial \rho}{\partial t} = 0 \tag{A5}$$

Although (A5) is not independ   (A3) and (A4) are specified, or vice-versa.

In free space we find that there   linear functional dependency between $\mathbf{D}$ and $\mathbf{E}$ and between $\mathbf{H}$ and $\mathbf{B}$ such that we may write

$$\mathbf{D} = \epsilon_0 \mathbf{E}, \quad \epsilon_0 = 8.854 \times 10^{-12} \text{ farad/m} \tag{A6}$$

$$H = \frac{1}{\mu_0} B, \qquad \mu_0 = 4\pi \times 10^{-7} \text{ henry/m.} \tag{A7}$$

For an isotropic linear medium other than free space these relations become

$$D = \epsilon E, \tag{A8}$$

$$H = \frac{1}{\mu} B. \tag{A9}$$

The quantities ϵ_0, μ_0, ϵ, μ are called the inductive capacities of the medium. The dielectric constant is defined as the dimensionless quantity

$$K_e = \epsilon/\epsilon_0 \tag{A10}$$

and the magnetic permeability as the dimensionless quantity

$$K_m = \mu/\mu_0. \tag{A11}$$

Nonlinear behavior of earth materials is usually a second order effect so that the relations (A8) and (A9) are in general adequate for our purposes. However, anistropy is common in rocks and hence at times it becomes necessary to express the $D-E$, $H-B$ relations in tensor form

$$D_j = \epsilon_{jk} E_k \tag{A12}$$

$$H_j = \frac{1}{\mu_{jk}} B_k. \tag{A13}$$

Although the five vectors E, B, D, H, J plus the scalar ρ are adequate to describe electromagnetic phenomena, we frequently find it convenient to introduce the electric and magnetic polarization vectors through the definitions

$$P = D - \epsilon_0 E \tag{A14}$$

$$M = \frac{1}{\mu_0} B - H. \tag{A15}$$

For linear isotropic media we then find that P and M are linearly dependent upon E and H according to

$$P = \chi_e \epsilon_0 E \tag{A16}$$

$$M = \chi_m H \tag{A17}$$

where χ_e and χ_m are the electric and magnetic susceptibilities. Hence,

$$\chi_e = K_e - 1 \tag{A18}$$

$$\chi_m = K_m - 1. \tag{A19}$$

In conducting linear media, it is found that J is dependent upon E

$$J_j = \sigma_{jk} E_k \tag{A20}$$

where

$$\sigma_{jk} = \text{conductivity in mhos/m} = \frac{1}{(\rho_0)_{jk}} = \frac{1}{\text{resistivity in ohm-m}} .$$

The dc resistance of a homogeneous bar of uniform cross section A and length l is

$$R = \rho_0 \frac{l}{A} \text{ ohms.} \tag{A21}$$

In rocks in situ the **J-E** relation is usually linear, but in rock samples in the laboratory where high current densities may be achieved readily, such is not necessarily true.

1-III. *The Electromagnetic Potentials and the Wave Equations*

Frequently it is convenient to solve a problem in electromagnetic theory in terms of potential functions from which the fields may be derived by differentiation. Equation (A3) asserts that the vector **B** is solenoidal and hence derivable as the curl of another arbitrary vector **A**,

$$\mathbf{B} = \nabla \times \mathbf{A}. \tag{A22}$$

Substituting (A22) in (A1) yields

$$\nabla \times \left(\mathbf{E} + \frac{\partial \mathbf{A}}{\partial t} \right) = 0. \tag{A23}$$

Hence the vector $\mathbf{E} + (\partial \mathbf{A}/\partial t)$ is irrotational and so derivable as the gradient of an arbitrary scalar function ϕ, thus

$$\mathbf{E} + \frac{\partial \mathbf{A}}{\partial t} = - \nabla \phi$$

or

$$\mathbf{E} = - \nabla \phi - \frac{\partial \mathbf{A}}{\partial t} \tag{A24}$$

The functions **A** and ϕ are the vector and scalar potentials of the field.

If the medium is linear, homogeneous, and isotropic, then by (A8) (A9) (A22) and (A24) we may convert equations (A2) and (A4) to

$$\nabla \times \nabla \times \mathbf{A} + \mu\epsilon\nabla \frac{\partial \phi}{\partial t} + \mu\epsilon \frac{\partial \mathbf{A}}{\partial t^2} = \mu \mathbf{J} \tag{A25}$$

and

$$\nabla^2 \phi + \nabla \cdot \frac{\partial \mathbf{A}}{\partial t} = - \frac{1}{\epsilon} \rho. \tag{A26}$$

In equation (A25), the vector **J** may be considered to arise from two sources, one produced by the external electromotive force $\mathbf{J}' = \sigma \mathbf{E}'$ and the other $\mathbf{J} = \sigma \mathbf{E}$ induced by the electric fields in conducting media. The latter gives rise to the potential contributions

$$\mu\sigma \left(- \nabla \phi - \frac{\partial \mathbf{A}}{\partial t} \right)$$

so that (A25) may be rewritten,

$$\nabla \times \nabla \times \mathbf{A} + \mu\epsilon\nabla \frac{\partial \phi}{\partial t} + \mu\epsilon \frac{\partial^2 \mathbf{A}}{\partial t^2} + \mu\sigma\nabla\phi + \mu\sigma \frac{\partial \mathbf{A}}{\partial t} = \mu \mathbf{J}'. \tag{A27}$$

When use is made of the vector identity

$$\nabla \times \nabla \times \mathbf{A} \equiv \nabla\nabla\cdot\mathbf{A} - \nabla\cdot\nabla\mathbf{A} \qquad \text{(applicable only to Cartesian coordinates),} \qquad \text{(A28)}$$

and when the Lorentz condition

$$\nabla\cdot\mathbf{A} + \mu\epsilon\frac{\partial\phi}{\partial t} + \mu\sigma\phi = 0 \qquad \text{(A29)}$$

is imposed on our choice of the somewhat arbitrary vector $\mathbf{A}$, then (A27) reduces to

$$\nabla^2\mathbf{A} - \mu\epsilon\frac{\partial^2\mathbf{A}}{\partial t^2} - \mu\sigma\frac{\partial\mathbf{A}}{\partial t} = -\mu\mathbf{J}'. \qquad \text{(A30)}$$

Similarly equation (A26) converts, upon application of the Lorentz condition, to

$$\nabla^2\phi - \mu\epsilon\frac{\partial^2\phi}{\partial t^2} - \mu\sigma\frac{\partial\phi}{\partial t} = -\frac{\rho'}{\epsilon}. \qquad \text{(A31)}$$

The Lorentz condition, while appearing arbitrary, actually is only a limitation on the choice of otherwise arbitrary functions and offers the remarkable advantage of introducing complete symmetry between the scalar and vector potentials, i.e. it makes both potentials satisfy the same wave equation as that obeyed by the fields.

Note that the form of this equation is that of the inhomogeneous wave equation, solution of which, subject to appropriate boundary conditions, is then the fundamental problem in geophysical applications of electromagnetic theory. However, some problems may be solved most readily by introduction of a single potential, the Hertz vector, and others by solving the wave equation for the field vectors themselves.

Considering the first alternative, let us assume

$$\mathbf{A} = \mu\epsilon\frac{\partial\boldsymbol{\pi}}{\partial t} + \mu\sigma\boldsymbol{\pi} \qquad \text{(A32)}$$

and

$$\phi = -\nabla\cdot\boldsymbol{\pi}. \qquad \text{(A33)}$$

With these substitutions and introduction of the identity $\mathbf{J}' \equiv \partial\mathbf{P}'/\partial t$ equation (A30) becomes

$$\mu\sigma\left[\nabla^2\boldsymbol{\pi} - \mu\epsilon\frac{\partial^2\boldsymbol{\pi}}{\partial t^2} - \mu\sigma\frac{\partial\boldsymbol{\pi}}{\partial t}\right] + \mu\epsilon\frac{\partial}{\partial t}\left[\nabla^2\boldsymbol{\pi} - \mu\epsilon\frac{\partial^2\boldsymbol{\pi}}{\partial t^2} - \mu\sigma\frac{\partial\boldsymbol{\pi}}{\partial t}\right] = -\mu\frac{\partial\mathbf{P}'}{\partial t}. \qquad \text{(A34)}$$

Two simplifications of this equation are of particular interest to us; the first occurs when sources are excluded, i.e. $\mathbf{P}' = 0$; in which case we may write

$$\nabla^2\boldsymbol{\pi} - \mu\epsilon\frac{\partial^2\boldsymbol{\pi}}{\partial t^2} - \mu\sigma\frac{\partial\boldsymbol{\pi}}{\partial t} = 0. \qquad \text{(A35)}$$

This is the homogeneous wave equation in terms of the potential $\boldsymbol{\pi}$.

The second simplification of interest to us arises when $\sigma = 0$, i.e. in regions of nonconductors. Then

$$\frac{\partial}{\partial t}\left[\nabla^2\boldsymbol{\pi} - \mu\epsilon\frac{\partial^2\boldsymbol{\pi}}{\partial t^2} - \mu\sigma\frac{\partial\boldsymbol{\pi}}{\partial t}\right] = -\frac{1}{\epsilon}\frac{\partial\mathbf{P}'}{\partial t}$$

and

$$\nabla^2 \pi - \mu\epsilon \frac{\partial^2 \pi}{\partial t^2} = -\frac{P'}{\epsilon} \tag{A36}$$

except for a constant of integration which may be ignored. This is the inhomogeneous **wave** equation in terms of the potential π.

Similarly with the introduction of $\rho' \equiv -\nabla \cdot P'$, equation (A31) will yield either (A35) **or** (A36) depending upon the choice of $P' = 0$ or $\sigma = 0$. It is interesting to note that the **two** forms of the wave equation (A35) and (A36) are in a sense mutually exclusive in any **single** region, for if σ is finite then the density of free charge is always zero in the interior of **the** medium after transients have dissipated. This decay of transients is governed by the relaxation time (Stratton, 1941, p. 15) $\tau = \epsilon/\sigma$ which is of order 10^{-6} sec for distilled water and as small as 2×10^{-10} sec for sea water. For most geologic media we may ignore free charge.

In air, of course, the low value of σ excludes the application of equation (A35) and **we** may employ (A36) when sources are present. When the conductivity is negligible **and** sources are excluded, then (A35) and (A36) reduce to the same equation.

Thus only one general form of the wave equation

$$\nabla^2 \pi - \mu\epsilon \frac{\partial^2 \pi}{\partial t^2} - \left(\mu\sigma \frac{\partial \pi}{\partial t} \right) = -\left(\frac{P'}{\epsilon} \right) \tag{A37}$$

is necessary for a complete description of electromagnetic phenomena through the **Hertz** vector. The fields are obtained from the auxiliary equations

$$B = \mu\epsilon \nabla \times \frac{\partial \pi}{\partial t} + \mu\sigma \nabla \times \pi \tag{A38}$$

and

$$E = \nabla \nabla \cdot \pi - \mu\epsilon \frac{\partial^2 \pi}{\partial t^2} - \mu\sigma \frac{\partial \pi}{\partial t} \tag{A39}$$

which are derived from equations (A22) and (A24) by direct substitution of equations (A32) and (A33).

The use of the identities $\rho' \equiv -\nabla \cdot P'$ and $J \equiv \partial P'/\partial t$ is justified on the basis of the satisfaction of the equation of continuity (A5) and the physical interpretation of the charge and current sources in terms of electric dipoles. ($P' \equiv$ dipole moment per unit volume).

In a like manner one could write

$$\nabla^2 \pi^* - \mu\epsilon \frac{\partial^2 \pi^*}{\partial t^2} - \mu\sigma \frac{\partial \pi^*}{\partial t} = -M' \tag{A40}$$

where the sources are expressed in terms of magnetic dipoles ($M' \equiv$ dipole moment per unit volume). The Hertz vector in the latter instance is of magnetic type and in the former instance is of electric type. The derivation of (A40) stems from the introduction of the potentials A^* and ϕ^* rather than A and ϕ. We commence the development by introducing the vector potential A^* through

$$D = -\nabla \times A^* \quad \text{or} \quad E = -\frac{1}{\epsilon} \nabla \times A^*. \tag{A41}$$

We wish then to insert (A20) and (A41) into (A2) to obtain

$$\nabla \times \mathbf{H} + \frac{\partial}{\partial t}(\nabla \times \mathbf{A}^*) = -\frac{\sigma}{\epsilon} \nabla \times \mathbf{A}^*$$

or

$$\nabla \times \left[\mathbf{H} + \left(\frac{\partial}{\partial t} + \frac{\sigma}{\epsilon} \right) \mathbf{A}^* \right] = 0, \tag{A42}$$

indicating that the term in the square brackets is derivable from a gradient of a scalar:

$$\mathbf{H} + \left(\frac{\partial}{\partial t} + \frac{\sigma}{\epsilon} \right) \mathbf{A}^* = -\nabla \phi^*$$

or

$$\mathbf{H} = -\nabla \phi^* - \frac{\partial \mathbf{A}^*}{\partial t} - \frac{\sigma}{\epsilon} \mathbf{A}^*. \tag{A43}$$

Inherent in the replacement of $\mathbf{J}$ by $\sigma \mathbf{E}$ in equation (A2) is the assumption that induced currents may be present, but that no electric dipole sources are present. On the other hand, we do wish to recognize the presence of magnetic sources which are not *obviously* present in Maxwell's equations. To indicate the presence of the magnetic sources, we divide $\mathbf{B}$ into a true induction and a source contribution according to

$$\mathbf{B} = \mu \mathbf{H} + \mu \mathbf{M}'. \tag{A44}$$

Equation (A44) implies that the total magnetic field $\mathbf{H}$ is composed of an induced part $1/\mu \mathbf{B}$ and a part due to external sources $\mathbf{M}'$. The induction $\mathbf{B}$ is the one referred to, in this instance, in the Maxwell equation $\nabla \cdot \mathbf{B} = 0$. Then when we apply $\nabla \cdot \mathbf{B} = 0$ we obtain

$$\nabla \cdot \mathbf{H} = -\nabla \cdot \mathbf{M}'. \tag{A45}$$

Equation (A44) also permits us to write the first of Maxwell's equations in the form

$$\nabla \times \mathbf{E} + \mu \frac{\partial \mathbf{H}}{\partial t} = -\mu \frac{\partial \mathbf{M}'}{\partial t}. \tag{A46}$$

Now we may substitute (A41) and (A43) in (A45) and (A46) to yield

$$\nabla^2 \mathbf{A}^* - \mu \epsilon \frac{\partial^2 \mathbf{A}^*}{\partial t^2} - \mu \sigma \frac{\partial \mathbf{A}^*}{\partial t} = -\mu \epsilon \frac{\partial \mathbf{M}'}{\partial t} \tag{A47}$$

and

$$\nabla^2 \phi^* - \mu \epsilon \frac{\partial^2 \phi^*}{\partial t^2} - \mu \sigma \frac{\partial \phi^*}{\partial t} = \nabla \cdot \mathbf{M}', \tag{A48}$$

through use of a Lorentz condition of the form

$$\nabla \cdot \mathbf{A}^* + \epsilon \mu \frac{\partial \phi^*}{\partial t} = 0. \tag{A49}$$

The Hertz vector π^* is introduced through the relations

$$\mathbf{A}^* = \mu\epsilon \frac{\partial \pi^*}{\partial t} \tag{A50}$$

and

$$\phi^* = -\nabla \cdot \pi^* \tag{A51}$$

whereupon the inhomogeneous wave equations (A47) and (A48) each reduce to the single equation

$$\nabla^2 \pi^* - \mu\epsilon \frac{\partial^2 \pi^*}{\partial t^2} - \mu\sigma \frac{\partial \pi^*}{\partial t} = -\mathbf{M}'$$

as required. For many geophysical problems the sources may be excluded from the region of study so that the homogeneous equations

$$\nabla^2 \pi^* - \mu\epsilon \frac{\partial^2 \pi^*}{\partial t^2} - \mu\sigma \frac{\partial \pi^*}{\partial t} = 0 \tag{A52}$$

$$\nabla^2 \pi - \mu\epsilon \frac{\partial^2 \pi}{\partial t^2} - \mu\sigma \frac{\partial \pi}{\partial t} = 0 \tag{A53}$$

are applicable. In the general case, when both electric and magnetic sources are present, although not included in the region under study, the fields may be derived from

$$\mathbf{H} = \epsilon\nabla \times \frac{\partial \pi}{\partial t} + \sigma\nabla \times \pi + \nabla\nabla \cdot \pi^* - \mu\epsilon \frac{\partial^2 \pi^*}{\partial t} - \mu\sigma \frac{\partial \pi^*}{\partial t} \tag{A54}$$

$$\mathbf{E} = \nabla\nabla \cdot \pi - \mu\epsilon \frac{\partial^2 \pi}{\partial t^2} - \mu\sigma \frac{\partial \pi}{\partial t} - \mu\nabla \times \frac{\partial \pi^*}{\partial t}. \tag{A55}$$

The last four equations, then, permit us to solve any electromagnetic problem in terms of Hertz vectors in a source-free region.

The wave equations for the field vectors are obtained rather simply; take the curl of (A1) and make the substitution $\mathbf{B} = \mu\mathbf{H}$, then

$$\nabla \times \nabla \times \mathbf{E} = -\frac{\partial}{\partial t}(\nabla \times \mu\mathbf{H}). \tag{A56}$$

But from (A2),

$$\nabla \times \mu\mathbf{H} = \mu\left(\mathbf{J} + \frac{\partial \mathbf{D}}{\partial t}\right) = \mu\left(\sigma\mathbf{E} + \epsilon\frac{\partial \mathbf{E}}{\partial t}\right) \tag{A57}$$

so that (A56) becomes

$$\nabla \times \nabla \times \mathbf{E} = -\mu\sigma \frac{\partial \mathbf{E}}{\partial t} - \mu\epsilon \frac{\partial^2 \mathbf{E}}{\partial t^2}. \tag{A58}$$

Upon application of the identity (A28), equation (A58) yields

$$\nabla^2 \mathbf{E} - \mu\epsilon \frac{\partial^2 \mathbf{E}}{\partial t^2} - \mu\sigma \frac{\partial \mathbf{E}}{\partial t} = 0 \tag{A59}$$

or, if we introduce $c = (1/\sqrt{\epsilon_0 \mu_0})$, the velocity of light, we obtain

$$\nabla^2 \mathbf{E} - \frac{K_e K_m}{c^2} \frac{\partial^2 \mathbf{E}}{\partial t^2} - \mu \sigma \frac{\partial \mathbf{E}}{\partial t} = 0 \tag{A60}$$

Similarly,

$$\nabla^2 \mathbf{H} - \frac{K_e K_m}{c^2} \frac{\partial^2 \mathbf{H}}{\partial t^2} - \mu \sigma \frac{\partial \mathbf{H}}{\partial t} = 0. \tag{A61}$$

1-IV. *Harmonically varying fields, sources excluded*

In problems involving fields varying with time, the introduction of the cissoidal (or general harmonic) time function simplifies the analysis; e.g.

$$\mathbf{E} = |\mathbf{E}| e^{-i\omega t} = |\mathbf{E}| (\cos \omega t - i \sin \omega t)$$

Upon substitution of this type of time dependency for all field vectors and upon elimination of $e^{-i\omega t}$ from both sides of all equations, Maxwell's equations become for conductive media

$$\nabla \times \mathbf{E} - i\omega\mu\mathbf{H} = 0 \tag{A62}$$
$$\nabla \times \mathbf{H} + (i\omega\epsilon - \sigma)\mathbf{E} = 0 \tag{A63}$$
$$\nabla \cdot \mathbf{H} = 0 \tag{A64}$$
$$\nabla \cdot \mathbf{E} = 0. \tag{A65}$$

In effect we have absorbed the time factor $e^{-i\omega t}$ in the field vectors, so that in the remainder of this chapter, the designations $\mathbf{E}$ and $\mathbf{H}$ will infer $|\mathbf{E}| e^{-i\omega t}$ and $|\mathbf{H}| e^{-i\omega t}$ unless otherwise stated. This holds similarly for all other vector quantities. The solution may be extended to arbitrary nonsinusoidal variations by appropriate Laplace or Fourier transforms as shown later.

Under a harmonic time variation the wave equations for potentials and fields (A30) (A31) (A52) (A53) (A47) (A48) becomes, in rectangular coordinates,

$$\nabla^2 \mathbf{A} + k^2 \mathbf{A} = 0 \tag{A66}$$
$$\nabla^2 \mathbf{A}^* + k^2 \mathbf{A}^* = 0 \tag{A67}$$
$$\nabla^2 \phi + k^2 \phi = 0 \tag{A68}$$
$$\nabla^2 \phi^* + k^2 \phi^* = 0 \tag{A69}$$
$$\nabla^2 \pi + k^2 \pi = 0 \tag{A70}$$
$$\nabla^2 \pi^* + k^2 \pi^* = 0, \tag{A71}$$

where

$$k^2 = \mu\epsilon\omega^2 + i\mu\sigma\omega, \tag{A72}$$

The complex quantity $k = \alpha + i\beta$ is called the propagation constant; its real part,

$$\alpha = \omega \left[\frac{\mu\epsilon}{2} \left(\sqrt{1 + \frac{\sigma^2}{\epsilon^2\omega^2}} + 1 \right) \right]^{1/2} \tag{A73}$$

is known as the phase constant; its imaginary part,

$$\beta = \omega \left[\frac{\mu\epsilon}{2} \left(\sqrt{1 + \frac{\sigma^2}{\epsilon^2\omega^2}} - 1 \right) \right]^{1/2} \tag{A74}$$

is known as the attenuation constant.

The reasons for these names will become evident upon consideration of solutions of the wave equation. The fields may be expressed in terms of the potentials by the expressions

$$\mathbf{E} = \nabla\nabla\cdot\boldsymbol{\pi} + k^2\boldsymbol{\pi} + i\omega\mu\nabla\times\boldsymbol{\pi}^* \tag{A75}$$

$$\mathbf{E} = -\nabla\phi + i\omega\mathbf{A} - \frac{1}{\epsilon}\nabla\times\mathbf{A}^* \tag{A76}$$

and

$$\mathbf{H} = (\sigma - i\omega\epsilon)\nabla\times\boldsymbol{\pi} + \nabla\nabla\cdot\boldsymbol{\pi}^* + k^2\boldsymbol{\pi}^* \tag{A77}$$

$$\mathbf{H} = \frac{1}{\mu}\nabla\times\mathbf{A} - \nabla\phi^* + i\omega\mathbf{A}^* - \frac{\sigma}{\epsilon}\mathbf{A}^*. \tag{A78}$$

Finally the field vectors for a harmonic time dependency satisfy the wave equations

$$\nabla^2\mathbf{E} + k^2\mathbf{E} = 0 \tag{A79}$$

and

$$\nabla^2\mathbf{H} + k^2\mathbf{H} = 0. \tag{A80}$$

For many geophysical problems, the constants of the medium are such that in the expressions for α and β, $(\sigma^2/\epsilon^2\omega^2)\gg1$. This pertains when the conduction current greatly predominates over the displacement current. Then

$$\alpha = \beta = \sqrt{\frac{\omega\mu\sigma}{2}}. \tag{A81}$$

1-V. *The Schelkunoff symmetrical wave potentials*

The vector magnetic potential $\mathbf{A}$ above was somewhat arbitrarily inserted because the divergence of magnetic induction $\mathbf{B}$ is zero (A3), permitting us to write $\mathbf{B}=\text{curl }\mathbf{A}$ (A22). We may also use a similar substitution for the $\mathbf{E}$ vector in those instances where div $\mathbf{E}$ is identically zero, i.e. $\rho=0$. Schelkunoff (1943) among others, recognizes the symmetry of the potentials for magnetic and electric sources by writing

$$\mathbf{E} = \mathbf{E}' + \mathbf{E}'' \tag{A82}$$

and

$$\mathbf{H} = \mathbf{H}' + \mathbf{H}'' \tag{A83}$$

where the field $(\mathbf{E}', \mathbf{H}')$ is produced by electric currents $\mathbf{J}$ and $(\mathbf{E}'', \mathbf{H}'')$ by magnetic currents $\mathbf{J}_M$. We have already demonstrated this symmetry, in a less obvious fashion, in section III.

Maxwell's first two equations, when only magnetic current sources are recognized, become

$$\nabla\times\mathbf{E}'' + \mathbf{J}_M = -\mathbf{J}_M'' \tag{A84}$$

$$\nabla \times \mathbf{H}'' - \frac{\partial \mathbf{D}''}{\partial t} = \sigma \mathbf{E}'' \tag{A85}$$

where $\mathbf{J}_M = \partial \mathbf{B}/\partial t$ is the induced magnetic current density and the fields are both induced. For harmonically varying fields e^{-iwt} (A84) and (A85) become

$$\nabla \times \mathbf{E}'' = -\mathbf{J}_M'' + i\omega\mu\mathbf{H}'' \tag{A86}$$

$$\nabla \times \mathbf{H}'' = (\sigma - i\omega\epsilon)\mathbf{E}''. \tag{A87}$$

Equations (A86) and (A87) yield the second two of Maxwell's equations when the divergence operator is applied to each:

$$\nabla \cdot \mathbf{H}'' = \frac{\nabla \cdot \mathbf{J}_M''}{i\omega\mu} \tag{A88}$$

$$\nabla \cdot \mathbf{E}'' = 0. \tag{A89}$$

Similarly, when only electric current sources $\mathbf{J}'$ are considered,

$$\nabla \times \mathbf{E}' + \frac{\partial \mathbf{B}'}{\partial t} = 0 \tag{A90}$$

$$\nabla \times \mathbf{H}' - \frac{\partial \mathbf{D}'}{\partial t} = \sigma \mathbf{E}' + \mathbf{J}' \tag{A91}$$

which for $e^{-i\omega t}$ time dependency become

$$\nabla \times \mathbf{E}' = i\omega\mu\mathbf{H}' \tag{A92}$$

$$\nabla \times \mathbf{H}' = \mathbf{J}' + (\sigma - i\omega\epsilon)\mathbf{E}'. \tag{A93}$$

The second two Maxwell's equations are then

$$\nabla \cdot \mathbf{H}' = 0 \tag{A94}$$

and

$$\nabla \cdot \mathbf{E}' = -\frac{\nabla \cdot \mathbf{J}'}{\sigma - i\omega\epsilon}. \tag{A95}$$

Equations (A89) and (A94) show that $\mathbf{H}'$ and $\mathbf{E}'$ can be represented as the curls of two vectors $\mathbf{G}$ and $\mathbf{F}$ as follows:

$$\mathbf{H}' = \nabla \times \mathbf{G} \tag{A96}$$

$$\mathbf{E}'' = -\nabla \times \mathbf{F}. \tag{A97}$$

Obviously the vector potential $\mathbf{A}$ used previously is related to the "electric" vector potential $\mathbf{G}$ through $\mathbf{A} = \mu\mathbf{G}$. The "magnetic" vector potential $\mathbf{F}$ is related to $\mathbf{A}^*$, previously used, by $\mathbf{A}^* = \epsilon\mathbf{F}$.

Substituting (A96) and (A97) in (A92) and (A87) respectively leads to

$$\nabla \times \mathbf{E}' = i\omega\mu\nabla \times \mathbf{G} \tag{A98}$$

and

$$\nabla \times \mathbf{H}'' = -(\sigma - i\omega\epsilon)\nabla \times \mathbf{F}. \tag{A99}$$

Thus the vectors **E**, **G** and **H**, **F** are related through

$$\mathbf{E}' = i\omega\mu\mathbf{G} - \nabla V \tag{A100}$$

and

$$\mathbf{H}'' = -(\sigma - i\omega\epsilon)\mathbf{F} - \nabla U \tag{A101}$$

where V and U are two new scalar functions introduced because the equality of the curls of two vectors does not imply that the vectors are identical. By comparing (A100) with (A24) and (A101) with (A43), we recognize that V is identical with the electric scalar function ϕ used previously, while U is identical with ϕ^*.

The substitution of (A100) and (A96) in (A93) and of (A101) and (A97) in (A86) yields

$$\nabla \times \nabla \times \mathbf{G} = \mathbf{J}' + k^2\mathbf{G} - (\sigma - i\omega\epsilon)\nabla V \tag{A102}$$

and

$$\nabla \times \nabla \times \mathbf{F} = \mathbf{J}_M'' + k^2\mathbf{F} + i\omega\mu\nabla U. \tag{A103}$$

Upon application of the identity (A28) to the vectors **G** and **F** there results

$$\nabla\nabla\cdot\mathbf{G} - \nabla\cdot\nabla\mathbf{G} = \mathbf{J}' + k^2\mathbf{G} - (\sigma - i\omega\epsilon)\nabla V \tag{A104}$$

and

$$\nabla\nabla\cdot\mathbf{F} - \nabla\cdot\nabla\mathbf{F} = \mathbf{J}_M'' + k^2\mathbf{F} + i\omega\mu\nabla U. \tag{A105}$$

Lorentz conditions may be imposed upon the sets of electric and magnetic potentials as follows:

$$\nabla\cdot\mathbf{G} = -(\sigma - i\omega\epsilon)V \tag{A106}$$

and

$$\nabla\cdot\mathbf{F} = i\omega\mu U. \tag{A107}$$

Whereupon (A104) and (A105) reduce to

$$\nabla^2\mathbf{G} + k^2\mathbf{G} = -\mathbf{J}' \tag{A108}$$

and

$$\nabla^2\mathbf{F} + k^2\mathbf{F} = -\mathbf{J}_M''. \tag{A109}$$

The expressions for the fields (A82) and (A83) produced by a given distribution of impressed currents are then,

$$\mathbf{E} = i\omega\mu\mathbf{G} - \nabla V - \nabla \times \mathbf{F} \tag{A110}$$

$$\mathbf{H} = \nabla \times \mathbf{G} - \nabla U - (\sigma - i\omega\epsilon)\mathbf{F}. \tag{A111}$$

These expressions are found to be very useful in solving electromagnetic prospecting problems where the sources are always current distributions which may be looked upon as electric or magnetic dipoles or as linear current elements.

For a region containing no sources the wave equations (A108) and (A109) assume the forms

$$\nabla^2\mathbf{G} + k^2\mathbf{G} = 0 \tag{A112}$$

$$\nabla^2\mathbf{F} + k^2\mathbf{F} = 0 \tag{A113}$$

agreeing identically with the wave equations for $\mathbf{A}$, $\mathbf{A}^*$, ϕ, ϕ^*, π, and π^* as they should. While the Schelkunoff symmetrical wave potentials are almost identical with $\mathbf{A}$, $\mathbf{A}^*$, ϕ, and ϕ^*, their specific symmetric development for harmonic fields is most attractive and apparently for this reason this notation is used frequently.

1-VI. *Solutions of the wave equations*

(A) *Boundary conditions.*—Electromagnetic problems arising in the physics of the solid earth generally deal with the resultant current, field intensity, or potential in response to an impressed or primary field. The primary field gives rise to a secondary distribution of charges and currents and, hence, to a secondary field. The resultant field is the sum of the primary and secondary fields. Each of the fields must satisfy Maxwell's equations, or equations derived therefrom, plus appropriate boundary conditions. The problems we meet most frequently, therefore, are referred to as boundary value problems. Let us consider now the manner in which these boundary conditions are established.

(i) *Normal* $\mathbf{B}$.—First we shall consider the continuity of the normal component of magnetic induction $\mathbf{B}$. The third of Maxwell's equations states that $\nabla \cdot \mathbf{B} = 0$ the divergence theorem (e.g. Reitz and Milford, 1960 p. 13) states that for any vector $\mathbf{F}$ we may write:

$$\int_V \nabla \cdot \mathbf{F} dv = \oint_S \mathbf{F} \cdot \mathbf{n} da, \tag{A114}$$

or in words, the integral of the divergence of a vector over a volume V is equal to the surface integral of the normal component of the vector over the surface bounding V. Applied to the vector $\mathbf{B}$, the divergence theorem permits us to write

$$\oint_S \mathbf{B} \cdot \mathbf{n} da = 0 \tag{A115}$$

indicating now that the magnetic flux through any closed surface is zero.

Now let us consider two media of differing electrical properties, in contact as illustrated in Figure 1. We wish to determine the behavior of the fields at the boundary S between the media described by the sets of physical parameters $\epsilon_1 \mu_1 \sigma_1$ and $\epsilon_2 \mu_2 \sigma_2$. For this purpose we construct a small "pillbox" of height Δl and area Δa in which the surface is enclosed, i.e. its upper surface is in medium 2 while its lower surface is in medium 1. We now may evaluate the integral (A115) over the walls and ends of the "pillbox." If the ends, Δa, are made sufficiently small we may assume that $\mathbf{B}$ has a constant value $\mathbf{B}_1$ over the end in the lower medium and a constant value $\mathbf{B}_2$ over the end in the upper medium. We may then approximate (A115) by

$$(\mathbf{B}_2 \cdot \mathbf{n}_2 + \mathbf{B}_1 \cdot \mathbf{n}_1)\Delta a + \text{contributions from the walls} = 0. \tag{A116}$$

Since the contribution of the walls to the surface integral is directly proportional to Δl, we may neglect it as $\Delta l \rightarrow 0$. Then equation (A116) becomes

$$\mathbf{B}_2 \cdot \mathbf{n}_2 + \mathbf{B}_1 \cdot \mathbf{n}_1 = 0. \tag{A117}$$

The normals $\mathbf{n}_2$ and $\mathbf{n}_1$ are directed outward and hence we may write

$$\mathbf{n}_2 = \mathbf{n} = -\mathbf{n}_1 \tag{A118}$$

and (A117) becomes

$$(\mathbf{B}_2 - \mathbf{B}_1) \cdot \mathbf{n} = 0. \tag{A119}$$

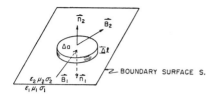

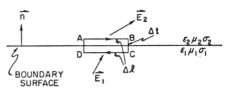

Fig. 1. Normal **B** continuous. Pillbox enclosing surface between two media in contact. Media (1) and (2) of constants $\epsilon_1\mu_1\sigma_1$ and $\epsilon_2\mu_2\sigma_2$, respectively. Magnetic induction in (1) is $\mathbf{B}_1$ and in (2) is $\mathbf{B}_2$. $\mathbf{n}_1$ and $\mathbf{n}_2$ are outward directed normals to bottom and top surfaces, respectively, of pillbox.

Fig. 2. Tangential **E** continuous. Closed contour of integration spans surface between media in contact, constants $\epsilon_1\mu_1\sigma_1$ and $\epsilon_2\mu_2\sigma_2$. Electric vectors $\mathbf{E}_1$ and $\mathbf{E}_2$ in media (1) and (2) respectively.

Equation (A119) states that the normal component B_n of **B** is continuous across an interface, i.e., $B_{n_1} = B_{n_2}$,

(ii) *Normal* **D**.—The vector **D** may be considered similarly, but in this case we have, from Coulomb's law for charge density, $\nabla \cdot \mathbf{D} = \rho$,

$$\int_V \nabla \cdot \mathbf{D} dv = \oint_S \mathbf{D} \cdot \mathbf{n} da = \int_V \rho dv = q. \qquad (A120)$$

Equation (A120), known as Gauss' law, states that the surface integral of the normal component of **D** over a closed surface is equal to the total charge q contained within it. We may replace the total charge q by the volume integral of charge density, ρ;

$$q = \int_V \rho dv = \rho \Delta l \Delta a. \qquad (A121)$$

It is convenient now to replace the product $\rho \Delta l$ by a surface charge density ω, defined as the charge per unit area. Thus we find [cf. (A118)]

$$(\mathbf{D}_2 \cdot \mathbf{n}_2 + \mathbf{D}_1 \cdot \mathbf{n}_1)\Delta a = \omega \Delta a \qquad (A122)$$

$$(\mathbf{D}_2 - \mathbf{D}_1) \cdot \mathbf{n} = \omega. \qquad (A123)$$

Equation (A123) informs us that the normal component D_n of the vector **D** is discontinuous at an interface due to the accumulation of a surface charge density ω. At the surface of a conductor the surface charge dissipates quickly (Stratton 1941 p. 15). Hence, across an interface involving all but the poorest conductors, normal **D** is continuous, i.e., $D_{n_1} = D_{n_2}$.

(iii) *Tangential* **E**.—Maxwell's first equation

$$\nabla \times \mathbf{E} + \frac{\partial \mathbf{B}}{\partial t} = 0$$

may be integrated over any boundary surface to give

$$\int_S (\nabla \times \mathbf{E}) \cdot \mathbf{n} da + \int_S \frac{\partial \mathbf{B}}{\partial t} \cdot \mathbf{n} da = 0 \qquad (A124)$$

where **n** is the unit normal to the surface S. Now Stokes' theorem (e.g. Reitz & Milford 1960 p. 16), applied to an arbitrary vector **F**, tells us that the line integral of **F** around a closed curve is equal to the integral of the normal component of curl **F** over any surface bounded by the curve, i.e.,

$$\oint_C \mathbf{F} \cdot d\mathbf{l} = \int_S (\nabla \times \mathbf{F}) \cdot \mathbf{n} \, da. \tag{A125}$$

This theorem suggests that we can convert the first surface integral of (A124) into a line integral around a suitably chosen contour C. Let us choose the contour as shown in Figure 2. Thus we may write

$$-\int_S \frac{\partial \mathbf{B}}{\partial t} \cdot \mathbf{n} \, da = \int_C \mathbf{E} \cdot d\mathbf{l} = \mathbf{E}_2 \cdot \Delta\mathbf{l} + \mathbf{E}_1 \cdot (-\Delta\mathbf{l}) + \text{(contributions from the ends)} \tag{A126}$$

where $\mathbf{E}_2 \cdot \Delta\mathbf{l}$ and $\mathbf{E}_1 \cdot \Delta\mathbf{l}$ are the tangential components of **E** in the media (1) and (2). Equation (A126) yields, when the L.H.S. is similarly approximated,

$$-\frac{\partial \mathbf{B}}{\partial t} \cdot \mathbf{n} \Delta t \Delta l = (\mathbf{E}_2 - \mathbf{E}_1) \cdot \Delta\mathbf{l}. \tag{A127}$$

In the limit, as the height $\Delta t \to 0$, L.H.S.$\to 0$, so that across the boundary surface, the tangential component E_t of **E** is continuous, i.e. $E_{t_1} = E_{t_2}$. The vector $\mathbf{n} \times \mathbf{E}$, where **n** is the unit normal to the boundary surface, will immediately give the tangential component, as reference to Figure 2 will attest. Hence, we usually find this boundary condition written in the form

$$\mathbf{n} \times (\mathbf{E}_2 - \mathbf{E}_1) = 0. \tag{A128}$$

(iv) *Tangential* **H.**—Maxwell's second equation

$$\nabla \times \mathbf{H} - \frac{\partial \mathbf{D}}{\partial t} = \mathbf{J}$$

may be integrated and Stokes' theorem applied to the first integral on the left to yield, in a manner analogous to the derivation of (A126),

$$\oint_C \mathbf{H} \cdot d\mathbf{l} - \int_S \frac{\partial \mathbf{D}}{\partial t} \cdot \mathbf{n} \, da = \int_S \mathbf{J} \cdot \mathbf{n} \, da. \tag{A129}$$

The contour for integration of **H** is the same as that shown in Figure 2. Then, by using just the components of **H** tangential to the boundary surface and by proceeding to the limit of a contour of negligible height Δt, we are able to rewrite (A129) as

$$\mathbf{n} \times (\mathbf{H}_2 - \mathbf{H}_1) = \lim_{\Delta t \to 0} \left(\frac{\partial \mathbf{D}}{\partial t} + \mathbf{J} \right) \Delta t. \tag{A130}$$

The first term on the right of (A130) vanishes at $\Delta t \to 0$ because **D** and its derivatives are bounded (by assumption). For a finite current density **J**, the second term also vanishes. There may be a surface current

$$\mathbf{K} \equiv \lim_{\substack{\Delta t \to 0 \\ \mathbf{J} \to \infty}} \mathbf{J} \Delta t \tag{A131}$$

so that the boundary condition on tangential $\mathbf{H}$ becomes

$$\mathbf{n} \times (\mathbf{H}_2 - \mathbf{H}_1) = \mathbf{K} \qquad \text{(surface current exists).} \qquad (A132)$$

If the conductivities of the two media are finite then $\mathbf{E} \equiv \mathbf{J}/\sigma$ must be finite and no surface current $\mathbf{K}$ can exist, so that the boundary condition becomes

$$\mathbf{n} \times (\mathbf{H}_2 - \mathbf{H}_1) = 0 \qquad \text{(finite conductivity).} \qquad (A133)$$

When the conductivity σ is assumed to be infinite, $\mathbf{J}$ could also be infinite and not violate our basic assumption that $\mathbf{E}$, as well as the other three field vectors, is bounded. Under these conditions we should employ the boundary condition (A132).

(v) *Continuity of current.*—The currents entering and leaving a pillbox spanning two conductive media, as in Figure 3, consist partly of tangential and partly of normal components. As the pillbox height is collapsed to zero, the normal component, i.e. the current crossing the interface, may be computed either as

$$I = \mathbf{J}_2 \cdot \mathbf{n} \Delta a$$

or as

$$I = \mathbf{J}_1 \cdot \mathbf{n} \Delta a.$$

Thus, the normal component J_n of $\mathbf{J}$ must be continuous across an interface, i.e.

$$(\mathbf{J}_2 - \mathbf{J}_1) \cdot \mathbf{n} = 0 \qquad (A134)$$

or

$$J_{n1} = J_{n2}.$$

This equation can be derived directly from the equation of continuity

$$\nabla \cdot \mathbf{J} + \frac{\partial \rho}{\partial t} = 0$$

applied to the steady state, i.e. the state when ρ has reached equilibrium or $\partial \rho/\partial t = 0$. Under this condition $\nabla \cdot \mathbf{J} = 0$ and hence, we may then follow the procedure used in deriving equation (A117) for continuity of normal $\mathbf{B}$. We thus are instructed that (A134) applies only to the steady state for conductive media in contact.

(vi) *Continuity of potentials—static fields.*—In electrostatic and magnetostatic problems involving linear media described by the constitutive relations $\mathbf{J} = \sigma \mathbf{E}$, $\mathbf{D} = \epsilon \mathbf{E}$, $\mathbf{B} = \mu \mathbf{H}$, we use the potentials ϕ and ϕ^* defined by

$$\mathbf{E} = -\nabla \phi \qquad \mathbf{H} = -\nabla \phi^*$$

so that we may rewrite (A119) (A123) (A128) (A133) and (A134) in terms of these potentials as follows.

$$\mu_2 \left(\frac{\partial \phi^*}{\partial n}\right)_2 - \mu_1 \left(\frac{\partial \phi^*}{\partial n}\right)_1 = 0 \qquad (A135)$$

$$\epsilon_2 \left(\frac{\partial \phi}{\partial n}\right)_2 - \epsilon_1 \left(\frac{\partial \phi}{\partial n}\right)_1 = \omega \qquad (A136)$$

$$\left(\frac{\partial \phi}{\partial t}\right)_2 - \left(\frac{\partial \phi}{\partial t}\right)_1 = 0 \tag{A137}$$

$$\left(\frac{\partial \phi^*}{\partial t}\right)_2 - \left(\frac{\partial \phi^*}{\partial t}\right)_1 = 0, \tag{A138}$$

$$\sigma_2 \left(\frac{\partial \phi}{\partial n}\right)_2 - \sigma_1 \left(\frac{\partial \phi}{\partial n}\right)_1 = 0 \tag{A139}$$

where $\partial/\partial n$ and $\partial/\partial t$ are, respectively, the normal and tangential derivatives. We could develop similar boundary conditions for the vector potentials, such as $\mathbf{A}$ and $\boldsymbol{\pi}$, but we shall find it convenient to do so only when the need arises in subsequent problems.

In the absence of sources, the potentials ϕ and ϕ^* must be continuous across a boundary surface, for the work required to carry a small electric charge or magnetic pole from infinity to either of two adjacent points located on opposite sides of the surface must be the same. Hence

$$\phi_1 = \phi_2 \quad \text{and} \quad \phi_1^* = \phi_2^*. \tag{A140}$$

(B) *The source problem*

(i) *The inhomogeneous wave equations.*—We have shown in section 1-III that the scalar and vector potentials are related to the electric and magnetic sources through the following equations, repeated here for convenience:

$$\nabla^2 \mathbf{A} - \mu\epsilon \frac{\partial^2 \mathbf{A}}{\partial t^2} - \mu\sigma \frac{\partial \mathbf{A}}{\partial t} = -\mu \mathbf{J}' \tag{A30}$$

$$\nabla^2 \phi - \mu\epsilon \frac{\partial^2 \phi}{\partial t^2} - \mu\sigma \frac{\partial \phi}{\partial t} = -\frac{\rho'}{\epsilon} \tag{A31}$$

$$\nabla^2 \mathbf{A}^* - \mu\epsilon \frac{\partial^2 \mathbf{A}^*}{\partial t^2} - \mu\sigma \frac{\partial \mathbf{A}^*}{\partial t} = -\mu\epsilon \frac{\partial \mathbf{M}'}{\partial t} \tag{A47}$$

$$\nabla^2 \phi^* - \mu\epsilon \frac{\partial^2 \phi^*}{\partial t^2} - \mu\sigma \frac{\partial \phi^*}{\partial t} = \nabla \cdot \mathbf{M}' \tag{A48}$$

$$\nabla^2 \boldsymbol{\pi} - \mu\epsilon \frac{\partial^2 \boldsymbol{\pi}}{\partial t^2} - \left(\mu\sigma \frac{\partial \boldsymbol{\pi}}{\partial t}\right) = -\left(\frac{\mathbf{P}'}{\epsilon}\right) \tag{A37}$$

$$\nabla^2 \boldsymbol{\pi}^* - \mu\epsilon \frac{\partial^2 \boldsymbol{\pi}^*}{\partial t^2} - \mu\sigma \frac{\partial \boldsymbol{\pi}^*}{\partial t} = -\mathbf{M}'. \tag{A40}$$

For harmonically varying fields with an $e^{-i\omega t}$ time dependency these equations become

$$\nabla^2 \mathbf{A} + k^2 \mathbf{A} = -\mu \mathbf{J}' \tag{A30a}$$

$$\nabla^2 \phi + k^2 \phi = -\frac{\rho'}{\epsilon} \tag{A31a}$$

$$\nabla^2 \mathbf{A}^* + k^2 \mathbf{A}^* = i\mu\epsilon\omega \mathbf{M}' \tag{A47a}$$

$$\nabla^2 \phi^* + k^2 \phi^* = \nabla \cdot \mathbf{M}' \tag{A48a}$$

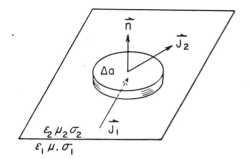

FIG. 3. Normal $\mathbf{J}$ continuous. Pillbox enclosing surface between two media in contact, constants $\epsilon_1\mu_1\sigma_1$ and $\epsilon_2\mu_2\sigma_2$. Current densities are J_1 in (1) and J_2 in (2).

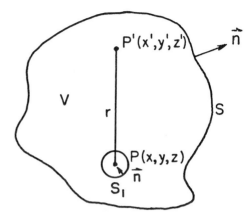

FIG. 4. Volume distribution of charge density $\rho'(x', y', z')$ at P'. Point of observation $P(x, y, x)$. $\mathbf{n}$ are outward drawn normals to bounding surfaces S, S_1.

(A37a)
$$\nabla^2\boldsymbol{\pi} + k^2\boldsymbol{\pi} = \frac{i\omega\mathbf{P}'}{\sigma - i\epsilon\omega}$$

(A40a)
$$\nabla^2\boldsymbol{\pi}^* + k^2\boldsymbol{\pi}^* = -\mathbf{M}'.$$

We must note that equation (A37a) is derived directly from equation (A34) and not from equation (A37). In this use, $\mathbf{P}'$ contains both bound *and* free source charges since we identified $\mathbf{P}'$ through $\mathbf{J}' \equiv \partial\mathbf{P}'/\partial t$ and $\rho' = -\nabla\cdot\mathbf{P}'$. From section 1-V we note that, for harmonically varying fields,

(A108)
$$\nabla^2\mathbf{G} + k^2\mathbf{G} = -\mathbf{J}'$$

(A109)
$$\nabla^2\mathbf{F} + k^2\mathbf{F} = -\mathbf{J}_M''.$$

Since the Schelkunoff scalar potentials are related to the Schelkunoff vector potentials through the Lorentz conditions [equations (A106) and (A107)]:

$$\nabla\cdot\mathbf{G} = -(\sigma - i\omega\epsilon)V$$

$$\nabla\cdot\mathbf{F} = i\mu\omega U$$

we may obtain the following two equations by taking the divergence of (A108) and (A109) and substituting for V and U:

$$\nabla^2 V + k^2 V = \frac{\nabla\cdot\mathbf{J}'}{\sigma - i\omega\epsilon} \tag{A141}$$

$$\nabla^2 U + k^2 U = -\frac{\nabla\cdot\mathbf{J}_M''}{i\mu\omega}. \tag{A142}$$

Similar inhomogeneous wave equations may be obtained for the field vectors $\mathbf{E}$ and $\mathbf{H}$, directly from Maxwell's equations (A1) through (A4). For example, in (A2) we may assume that the vector $\mathbf{J}$ consists of a source part $\mathbf{J}'$ and an induced part $\mathbf{J} = \sigma\mathbf{E}$. Then taking the curl of (A1), we obtain

$$\nabla\times\nabla\times\mathbf{E} = -\frac{\partial}{\partial t}(\nabla\times\mu\mathbf{H}) \tag{A143}$$

and from (A2) we may write

$$\nabla \times \mu \mathbf{H} = \mu \left(\mathbf{J}' + \sigma \mathbf{E} + \epsilon \frac{\partial \mathbf{E}}{\partial t} \right). \tag{A144}$$

Substitution of (A144) in (A143) yields

$$\nabla \times \nabla \times \mathbf{E} = - \mu \frac{\partial \mathbf{J}'}{\partial t} - \mu \sigma \frac{\partial \mathbf{E}}{\partial t} - \mu \epsilon \frac{\partial^2 \mathbf{E}}{\partial t^2}$$

or upon application of the identity (A28), with no charge accumulation, i.e. $\nabla \cdot \mathbf{E} = 0$,

$$\nabla^2 \mathbf{E} - \mu \epsilon \frac{\partial^2 \mathbf{E}}{\partial t^2} - \mu \sigma \frac{\partial \mathbf{E}}{\partial t} = \mu \frac{\partial \mathbf{J}'}{\partial t} \tag{A145}$$

which relates the electric fields to source currents. We can, of course, relate the electric field directly to a charge distribution through Coulomb's law (A4)

$$\nabla \cdot \mathbf{E} = \frac{\rho}{\epsilon} \tag{A146}$$

and the magnetic field to magnetic current density through the analogous equation (A88)

$$\nabla \cdot \mathbf{H}'' = \frac{\nabla \cdot \mathbf{J}_M''}{i \mu \omega}.$$

The magnetic field may be related to the source electric current density $\mathbf{J}'$ through the equation

$$\nabla^2 \mathbf{H} - \mu \epsilon \frac{\partial^2 \mathbf{H}}{\partial t^2} - \mu \sigma \frac{\partial \mathbf{H}}{\partial t} = - \nabla \times \mathbf{J}' \tag{A147}$$

obtained by taking the curl of (A2), separating $\mathbf{J}$ into source and induced parts, and substituting for $\nabla \times \mathbf{E}$ from (A1).

(ii) *Green's theorem.*—Clearly, the above discussion demonstrates that we are obliged to solve the inhomogeneous wave equation, in appropriate form, if we are to obtain the field distribution from any given source configuration. In order to find solutions of the inhomogeneous wave equation, we shall find it necessary to introduce Green's theorem. The proof of Green's theorem is included here for clarity of understanding in what follows.

Let us start with the identities

$$\nabla \cdot (\psi \nabla \phi) = \nabla \psi \cdot \nabla \phi + \psi \nabla \cdot \nabla \phi = \nabla \psi \cdot \nabla \phi + \psi \nabla^2 \phi \tag{A148}$$

and

$$\nabla \cdot (\phi \nabla \psi) = \nabla \phi \cdot \nabla \psi + \phi \nabla \cdot \nabla \psi = \nabla \psi \cdot \nabla \phi + \phi \nabla^2 \psi \tag{A149}$$

where ϕ and ψ are any scalar functions of position which are continuous throughout an arbitrary closed volume V and on a surface S bounding V. The first and second derivatives of ϕ and ψ are also continuous throughout V and over S.

We now subtract (A149) from (A148) and integrate over the volume V.

$$\int_V \nabla \cdot \{\psi \nabla \phi - \phi \nabla \psi\} \, dv = \int_V \{\psi \nabla^2 \phi - \phi \nabla^2 \psi\} \, dv. \tag{A150}$$

The left hand side of (A150) may be converted to a surface integral by the divergence theorem, which applied to an arbitrary vector $\mathbf{A}$ is

$$\int_V \nabla \cdot \mathbf{A} \, dv = \int_S \mathbf{A} \cdot \mathbf{n} \, ds. \tag{A151}$$

Thus, (A150) becomes

$$\int_S \left\{ \psi \frac{\partial \phi}{\partial n} - \phi \frac{\partial \psi}{\partial n} \right\} ds = \int_V \left\{ \psi \nabla^2 \phi - \phi \nabla^2 \psi \right\} dv. \tag{A152}$$

Note that $\nabla \phi \cdot \mathbf{n} = \partial \phi / \partial n$ where $\partial \phi / \partial n$ is the derivative in the direction of the positive normal. Equation (A152) is known as Green's theorem.

(iii) *Static fields.*—We first wish to apply Green's theorem to Poisson's equation:

$$\nabla^2 \phi = -\frac{\rho'}{\epsilon} \tag{A153}$$

which is the reduced form of (A31) obtained when dealing with electrostatic problems, i.e., $\partial / \partial t = 0$. Upon solution of (A153) we shall then be prepared to consider the more difficult source problems wherein time derivatives of fields and potentials are not negligible.

A charge distribution $\rho'(x, y, z)$ is assumed to exist in the volume V of Figure 4, although the surface S does not necessarily contain all of the charge, and in fact, ρ' could assume zero value throughout V. A point of observation P is defined by the coordinates x, y, z while the point $P'(x', y', z')$ is any point within V at which charge is assumed to exist. The potential at P, $\phi(x, y, z)$, will be used as one of the functions in Green's theorem. For the other, let us choose the spherically symmetric solution of Laplace's equation (i.e., the homogeneous counterpart of Poisson's equation),

$$\psi = \frac{1}{r} \tag{A154}$$

and

$$\nabla^2 \psi = 0 \tag{A155}$$

where

$$r = \sqrt{(x - x')^2 + (y - y')^2 + (z - z')^2}. \tag{A156}$$

The function ψ has a singularity at $r = 0$, i.e. at P, and to exclude it we draw a small sphere S_1 of radius r_1, about P. The volume V is then bounded externally by S and internally by S_1. Thus, for these particular functions ϕ and ψ, Green's theorem (A152) gives

$$\int_V \frac{\nabla^2 \phi}{r} \, dv = \int_{S+S_1} \left\{ \frac{1}{r} \frac{\partial \phi}{\partial n} - \phi \frac{\partial}{\partial n} \left(\frac{1}{r} \right) \right\} ds. \tag{A157}$$

The normal outward from the volume V is directed radially toward P over S_1, so that

$$\frac{\partial \phi}{\partial n} = -\frac{\partial \phi}{\partial r} \tag{A158}$$

and the normal derivative of the function ψ must then be

$$\frac{\partial}{\partial n}\left(\frac{1}{r}\right)\bigg|_{r=r_1} = \frac{1}{r_1^2}.$$ (A159)

The surface integral of (A157) over the sphere is then

$$\mathcal{g} = -\frac{1}{r_1}\int_{S_1}\frac{\partial\phi}{\partial r}\,ds - \frac{1}{r_1^2}\int_{S_1}\phi ds.$$ (A160)

If the sphere is contracted so that ϕ is sensibly constant over the surface S_1, then (A160) becomes

$$\mathcal{g} = -\frac{1}{r_1}4\pi r_1^2\frac{\partial\phi}{\partial r} - \frac{1}{r_1^2}4\pi r_1^2\phi.$$ (A161)

As $r_1 \to 0$, the expression (A161) reduces to

$$\mathcal{g} = -4\pi\phi.$$ (A162)

This value for the surface integral may now be substituted into (A157) and there results,

$$\int_V \frac{\nabla^2\phi}{r}\,dv = \int_S \left\{\frac{1}{r}\frac{\partial\phi}{\partial n} - \phi\frac{\partial}{\partial n}\left(\frac{1}{r}\right)\right\}\,ds - 4\pi\phi$$

or

$$\phi(x,\,y,\,z) = -\frac{1}{4\pi}\int_V \frac{\nabla^2\phi}{r}\,dv + \frac{1}{4\pi}\int_S \left\{\frac{1}{r}\frac{\partial\phi}{\partial n} - \phi\frac{\partial}{\partial n}\left(\frac{1}{r}\right)\right\}\,ds.$$ (A163)

The surface integral in (A163) must represent the contribution from all charges exterior to the volume V, for if V contains no charge (i.e. $\rho'=0$) then because $\nabla^2\phi=-\rho'/\epsilon$ from (A153),

$$-\frac{1}{4\pi}\int_V \frac{\nabla^2\phi}{r}\,dv = \frac{1}{4\pi\epsilon}\int_V \frac{\rho'}{r}\,dv$$ (A164)

must be identically zero so that the potential $\phi(x,\,y,\,z)$ at P is contributed entirely by the surface integral of (A163). When there are no charges external to the surface S, then we may express the solution of Poisson's equation in the form

$$\phi(x,\,y,\,z) = \frac{1}{4\pi\epsilon}\int_V \frac{\rho'}{r}\,dv.$$ (A165)

This is the form we most frequently use in electrical prospecting problems since we may nearly always draw a closed surface around the source. However, in application of the magnetic method, we frequently use upward and downward continuation, and then the surface integral of (A163) becomes of importance. If the values of ϕ and its normal derivative over S are known, the potential at any interior point can be determined by integration. Thus

$$\phi(x,\,y,\,z) = \frac{1}{4\pi}\int_S \left\{\frac{1}{r}\frac{\partial\phi}{\partial n} - \phi\frac{\partial}{\partial n}\left(\frac{1}{r}\right)\right\}\,ds$$ (A166)

may be interpreted as a solution of Laplace's equation within a volume V devoid of charge. Normally, for continuation problems, the surface S is the plane bounding the earth's surface or bounding that horizon in the earth about which sources do not exist; the volume V is then the half space above S. The electric field $\mathbf{E}(x, y, z)$ may be obtained by taking the negative gradient of (A165), assuming no sources external to V,

$$\mathbf{E} = -\nabla\phi = \frac{1}{4\pi\epsilon} \int_V \rho' \nabla\left(\frac{1}{r}\right) dv. \tag{A167}$$

This relation is applicable to a homogeneous charge distribution as is (A165).

For the vector potential $\mathbf{A}$ appropriate to the electrostatic case, equation (A30) reduces to

$$\nabla^2 \mathbf{A} = -\mu \mathbf{J}'$$

and by direct analogy with (A165) we may write down its solution as [cf. (A30) and (A31)]

$$\mathbf{A} = \frac{\mu}{4\pi} \int \frac{\mathbf{J}'}{r} dv. \tag{A168}$$

The integral solution (A168) applies to each of the rectangular components of $\mathbf{A}$ and $\mathbf{J}$.

(iv) *Time variant fields.*—Thus, for the time variant cases depicted by equations (A30) and (A31) we are led to suspect solutions of the form

$$\phi = \frac{1}{4\pi\epsilon} \int \frac{[\rho']}{r} dv \tag{A169}$$

and

$$\mathbf{A} = \frac{\mu}{4\pi} \int \frac{[\mathbf{J}']}{r} dv \tag{A170}$$

where now the potentials $\phi(x, y, z, t)$ and $\mathbf{A}(x, y, z, t)$ are functions of time and arise in sources $\rho'(x, y, z, t)$ and $\mathbf{J}'(x, y, z, t)$. As before, the vector solution (A170) and all succeeding vector solutions are obtained by considering, in turn, each rectangular component of the vector. The potentials observed at the point of observation P at time t must have arisen in a source event occurring some time t' earlier at P'; a finite time $\Delta t = |t' - t|$ is taken for the wave to travel from P' to P. Thus

$$t' = t - \frac{r}{v} \tag{A171}$$

where v is the velocity of propagation and, as before, r is the distance from P' to P. The expressions given by (A169) and (A170) are referred to as *retarded potentials* since they are calculated from charge and current density at a time prior to the time of observation by an amount r/v.

Similarly, we may write the retarded Hertz potential, involving the electric polarization vector $\mathbf{P}$,

$$\pi = \frac{-i\omega}{4\pi(\sigma - i\epsilon\omega)} \int_V \frac{[\mathbf{P}']}{r} dv \tag{A172}$$

derived from (A37) by analogy with the development of (A169) from (A31) which is consistent with (A32) and (A170). Then from (A108) and (A141) we should also be able to write

$$G = \frac{1}{4\pi} \int \frac{[J']}{r} \, dv \tag{A173}$$

$$V = -\frac{1}{4\pi(\sigma - i\epsilon\omega)} \int \frac{[\nabla \cdot J']}{r} \, dv. \tag{A174}$$

These electric source solutions are all similar (and the magnetic source cases are strictly analogous), but we have as yet to define the terms in the square brackets. At this point we must acknowledge that we are only seeking harmonic propagating solutions, so that, for example, for the general representation of the scalar potentials and the rectangular components of the vector potentials

$$\psi = \psi'(x', y', z')e^{-i\omega(t - r/v)}. \tag{A175}$$

Now, the propagation constant is, in the general case, given by

$$k^2 = \mu\epsilon\omega^2 + i\mu\sigma\omega = \frac{\omega^2}{v^2}$$

and we may write

$$\psi = \psi'(x', y', z')e^{-i\omega t + ikr} \tag{A176}$$

so that the solution for the Hertz vector π is of the form

$$\pi(x, y, z, t) = \frac{-i\omega e^{-i\omega t}}{4\pi(\sigma - i\epsilon\omega)} \int_V P'(x', y', z') \frac{e^{ikr}}{r} \, dv \tag{A177}$$

where t indicates the time at which the disturbance reaches the point of observation. $P(x, y, z)$ and hence is our normal reference time.

Since, for harmonically varying fields, $J \equiv -i\omega P$, we may also write (A177) in the form

$$\pi(x, y, z, t) = \frac{e^{-i\omega t}}{4\pi(\sigma - i\epsilon\omega)} \int_V J'(x', y', z') \frac{e^{ikr}}{r} \, dv.$$

In similar fashion we could establish the following integral solutions for the various inhomogeneous wave equations:

$$A = \frac{\mu e^{-i\omega t}}{4\pi} \int_V J' \frac{e^{ikr}}{r} \, dv \tag{A178}$$

$$\phi = \frac{e^{-i\omega t}}{4\pi\epsilon} \int_V \rho' \frac{e^{ikr}}{r} \, dv \tag{A179}$$

$$A^* = -\frac{\mu\epsilon e^{-i\omega t}}{4\pi} \int_V \frac{\partial M'}{\partial t} \frac{e^{ikr}}{r} \, dv \tag{A180}$$

$$\phi^* = -\frac{e^{-i\omega t}}{4\pi} \int_V \nabla \cdot M' \frac{e^{ikr}}{r} \, dv \tag{A181}$$

$$\pi = \frac{e^{-i\omega \cdot}}{4\pi(\sigma - i\epsilon\omega)} \int_V \mathbf{J}' \frac{e^{ikr}}{r} dv \tag{A182}$$

$$\pi^* = \frac{e^{-i\omega t}}{4\pi} \int_V \mathbf{M}' \frac{e^{ikr}}{r} dv$$

$$= \frac{1}{-i\mu\omega 4\pi} e^{-i\omega t} \int \mathbf{J}_M'' \frac{e^{ikr}}{r} dv \tag{A183}$$

$$\mathbf{G} = \frac{e^{-i\omega t}}{4\pi} \int_V \mathbf{J}' \frac{e^{ikr}}{r} dv \tag{A184}$$

$$\mathbf{F} = \frac{e^{-i\omega t}}{4\pi} \int_V \mathbf{J}_M'' \frac{e^{ikr}}{r} dv \tag{A185}$$

$$V = \frac{-e^{-i\omega t}}{4\pi(\sigma - i\omega\epsilon)} \int_V \nabla \cdot \mathbf{J}' \frac{e^{ikr}}{r} dv \tag{A186}$$

$$U = \frac{e^{-i\omega t}}{4\pi i\mu\omega} \int_V \nabla \cdot \mathbf{J}_M'' \frac{e^{ikr}}{r} dv. \tag{A187}$$

Throughout the above development the notation used is that adhered to in earlier sections. We note that the following relations pertain for harmonically varying fields,

$$\mathbf{A} = \mu\mathbf{G}, \qquad \mathbf{A}^* = \epsilon\mathbf{F}, \qquad U = \phi^*, \qquad \mathbf{A} = \frac{k^2}{i\omega} \pi$$

$$\mathbf{A}^* = -i\mu\epsilon\omega \pi^*, \qquad \mathbf{F} = -i\mu\omega \pi^*, \qquad \mathbf{G} = \frac{k^2}{i\mu\omega} \pi.$$

The function $1/4\pi r$ used in equation (A165) and the function $e^{ikr}/4\pi r$ used in equations (A178) through (A187) inclusive, are part of a class of functions referred to as *Green's functions*. It is to be noted that in each of the solutions (A178) through (A187) the Green's function appears as a multiplier of the term under the integral which describes the source. The basic problem when dealing with source problems is to find an appropriate expression —and usually an expansion—of the Green's function.

We may write Poisson's and Laplace's equations in the combined form

$$\nabla^2\phi = -\frac{\rho'}{\epsilon} \delta(r) \tag{A188}$$

so that if the point of observation $P(x, y, z)$ coincides with the location of charge at $P'(x', y', z')$, then Poisson's equation pertains, while otherwise Laplace's equation pertains. The delta function $\delta(r)$ is defined in the usual manner of unit value at $r=0$ and zero elsewhere.

Now let us write the solution (A165) as it pertains to a unit point charge,

$$\phi = \frac{1}{4\pi\epsilon} \frac{1}{r} \tag{A189}$$

which results when $\rho'=1$ and the volume V becomes infinitesimally small. Substitution of (A189) into (A188) yields

$$\nabla^2\left(\frac{1}{r}\right) = -4\pi\delta(r)$$

or

$$\nabla^2 G = -\delta(r) \tag{A190}$$

The function $G=1/4\pi r$ is the Green's function as before. Now in the propagating field case, if we consider that there is only one time that it can take for a disturbance to propagate from the source to the point of observation, then we might generalize (A190) to

$$(\nabla^2 + k^2)G(r, t) = -\delta(r)\delta(-t). \tag{A191}$$

Let us assume then that we were seeking solutions of the inhomogeneous wave equation

$$(\nabla^2 + k^2)\psi(r, t) = -g(r, t). \tag{A191a}$$

The solution of (A191a) may then be synthesized as a superposition of solutions of (A191) for unit point sources. At all points other than $r=0$, equation (A191) will be of the form

$$(\nabla^2 + k^2)G(r, t) = 0$$

or

$$\frac{1}{r}\frac{d^2(rG)}{dr^2} + k^2G = 0.$$

In spherical coordinates with a retarded solution, G may be written

$$G = \frac{A}{r}e^{ikr-i\omega t}.$$

To evaluate the constant A, we integrate equation (A191) over the neighborhood of the singular point $r=0$. Here G behaves as A/r so that, in spherical coordinates, (A191) becomes, except for the time dependency,

$$\int_V \nabla^2\left(\frac{A}{r}\right) dv + k^2 \int_V \frac{A}{r} dv = -\int_V \delta(r) dv.$$

The first integral on the left has the value $-4\pi A$ while the second integral goes to zero as r tends to zero since $dv \propto r^2$. The integral on the right has the value unity. Thus

$$G = \frac{e^{ikr-i\omega t}}{4\pi r}.$$

Note that Green's function is a solution of the homogeneous version of the wave equation in direct analogy with $1/4\pi r$ as a solution of Laplace's equation for the electrostatic case.

    We can, of course, integrate the field equations, (A145) and (A147), directly as Stratton (p 466) demonstrates clearly. The solutions for electric current sources only are

$$\mathbf{E} = \frac{1}{4\pi}\int_V i\mu\omega\mathbf{J}\frac{e^{jkr}}{r}dv$$

$$\mathbf{H} = \frac{1}{4\pi}\int_V \mathbf{J}\times\nabla\frac{e^{ikr}}{r}dv.$$

(C) *Examples of source problems*

(i) *The field of an electric dipole.*—As an example of the application of the integral solutions above, consider an infinitesimal electric dipole in an infinite nonconducting medium. This dipole gives rise to the potentials

$$\mathbf{A} = \frac{\mu I d\mathbf{s}}{4\pi} \frac{e^{ikr}}{r} e^{-i\omega t} \tag{A192}$$

and

$$\boldsymbol{\pi} = \frac{iI d\mathbf{s}}{4\pi\epsilon\omega} \frac{e^{ikr}}{r} e^{-i\omega t} \tag{A193}$$

where ds is an element of length and $\mathbf{J}dv = Id\mathbf{s}$ dimensionally. Because of the finite time necessary for propagation of an electromagnetic wave, the potentials ϕ, ϕ^*, $\mathbf{A}$, $\mathbf{A}^*$, $\boldsymbol{\pi}$, $\boldsymbol{\pi}^*$, and $\mathbf{G}$, $\mathbf{F}$, V, U, are computed at the time t due to excitation at the source at time $t-(r/v)$ as mentioned above. To illustrate, one may write

$$\boldsymbol{\pi}(x, y, z, t) = \frac{ie^{-i\omega t}}{4\pi\epsilon\omega} \int_v \mathbf{J}'(x, y, z) \frac{e^{ikr}}{r} \, dv \tag{A194}$$

where r is the distance between source and point of observation. To evaluate the retarded Hertz integral, one must frequently resort to some form of series expansion. The nature of this expansion will be governed by the frequency and the geometry of the current distribution as will be seen from the example to follow.

(ii) *The field of a magnetic dipole.*—In this example we wish to calculate the field of a closed loop of wire carrying an alternating current. While we could use an elemental magnetic dipole expression similar to (A192), for instructional purposes we shall carry out a detailed analysis. Some of the techniques applicable to this type of problem are thereby illustrated. We commence with the equation for the retarded Hertz vector at the point of observation P in terms of the current density $\mathbf{J} = \mathbf{J}_0(\xi)e^{-i\omega t}$ at the point ξ (Figure 5) on the boundary of the origin-centered loop. The problem, as usual, is to find a suitable expansion of the function e^{ikr}/r, for the region under consideration, enabling

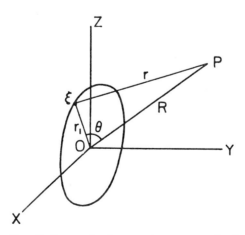

Fig. 5. Loop of wire carrying current density $\mathbf{J} = \mathbf{J}_0(\xi)e^{-i\omega t}$ at point ξ. Point of observation $P(X, Y, Z)$ at distance $R = (X^2 + Y^2 + Z^2)^{1/2}$ from origin O of loop.

the integral to be evaluated. In prospecting with the electromagnetic method we are usually concerned with measuring the field at a point which is considerably removed from the source loop so that we may assume first that $r_1 \ll R$ and secondly because of the low frequencies used, $R \ll \lambda$ where λ is the wavelength of the propagated wave. An elementary but useful expansion is

$$\frac{e^{ikr}}{r} = \frac{1}{r}\left[1 + ikr + \frac{(ikr)^2}{2!} + \frac{(ikr)^3}{3!} + \cdots\right] \tag{A195}$$

which is convergent for all values of ikr. The condition $r_1 \ll R$ enables us to write $r \approx R - r_1 \cos\theta$, so that

$$\frac{e^{ikr}}{r} = \frac{1}{R - r_1 \cos\theta} + ik - \frac{k^2}{2!}(R - r_1 \cos\theta) + \cdots. \tag{A196}$$

To obtain a simple expression for e^{ikr}/r we wish to ignore terms past the second in (A196) and this may be done if $kR \ll 1$ which we shall use in the form:

$$R \ll \frac{1}{k}. \tag{A197}$$

Another justifiable assumption at this stage is that conduction currents are negligible, $(\sigma_0^2/\epsilon_0^2\omega^2) \ll 1$, so that

$$k^2 = \mu_0\epsilon_0\omega^2 = \left(\frac{\omega}{c}\right)^2 \quad \text{or} \quad k = \frac{2\pi}{\lambda}.$$

Hence (A197) becomes

$$R \ll \frac{\lambda}{2\pi}. \tag{A198}$$

This (A198) is but a slightly more stringent form of one of our two basic assumptions. Thus (A196) becomes to a first approximation

$$\frac{e^{ikr}}{r} \sim \frac{1}{R - r_1 \cos\theta} + ik \sim \frac{1}{R}\left(1 + \frac{r_1}{R}\cos\theta\right) + ik. \tag{A199}$$

Then the retarded Hertz potential becomes

$$^1\boldsymbol{\pi} = \frac{ie^{-i\omega t}}{4\pi\epsilon\omega}\int_V \mathbf{J}_0(\xi)\left[\frac{1}{R} + \frac{\mathbf{r}_1 \cdot \mathbf{R}}{R^3} + ik\right]dv \tag{A200}$$

Note that $\int_V \mathbf{J}_0 dv$ is the integral of the current density over the volume of the wire of the loop. Thus

$$\mathbf{J}_0 dv = I_0 d\mathbf{s} \tag{A201}$$

[1] The Hertz vector $\boldsymbol{\pi}$ rather than $\boldsymbol{\pi}^*$ is used here because we are concerned with the integrated effects of a distribution of infinitesimal electric dipoles.

where ds is an element of length along the wire and I_0 is a current amplitude. Also, since $1/R$ and ik are constants with respect to integration over the volume of the wire, then

$$\int_V J_0 \left[\frac{1}{R} + ik\right] dv = \int_C I_0 \left[\frac{1}{R} - ik\right] ds = 0. \tag{A202}$$

Thus, (A200) becomes

$$\pi = \frac{ie^{-i\omega t}}{4\pi\epsilon\omega} \int_V J_0(\xi) \frac{\mathbf{r}_1 \cdot \mathbf{R}}{R^3} dv. \tag{A203}$$

Physical evaluation of the integral of (A203) requires a suitable conversion of the product $(\mathbf{r}_1 \cdot \mathbf{R})/R^3$. Hence, let us introduce the identity

$$(\mathbf{r}_1 \times \mathbf{J}_0) \times \mathbf{R} \equiv -\mathbf{R} \times (\mathbf{r}_1 \times \mathbf{J}_0) = -\mathbf{r}_1(\mathbf{R} \cdot \mathbf{J}_0) + \mathbf{J}_0(\mathbf{R} \cdot \mathbf{r}_1). \tag{A204}$$

From this last equation we are permitted to write

$$\mathbf{J}_0(\mathbf{R} \cdot \mathbf{r}_1) = (\mathbf{r}_1 \times \mathbf{J}_0) \times \mathbf{R} + \mathbf{r}_1(\mathbf{R} \cdot \mathbf{J}_0) \tag{A205}$$

and

$$2\mathbf{J}_0(\mathbf{R} \cdot \mathbf{r}_1) = (\mathbf{r}_1 \times \mathbf{J}_0) \times \mathbf{R} + \mathbf{r}_1(\mathbf{R} \cdot \mathbf{J}_0) + \mathbf{J}_0(\mathbf{R} \cdot \mathbf{r}_1) \tag{A206}$$

whereupon (A203) becomes

$$\pi = \frac{ie^{-i\omega t}}{8\pi\epsilon\omega R^3} \left[\int_V (\mathbf{r}_1 \times \mathbf{J}_0) \times \mathbf{R} dv + \int_V \{\mathbf{J}_0(\mathbf{r}_1 \cdot \mathbf{R}) + \mathbf{r}_1(\mathbf{R} \cdot \mathbf{J}_0)\} dv \right]. \tag{A207}$$

If in the right-hand integral of (A207) we substitute $I_0 d\mathbf{s}$ for $\mathbf{J}_0 dv$, we obtain

$$\mathbf{C} = \int_V \{\mathbf{J}_0(\mathbf{r}_1 \cdot \mathbf{R}) + \mathbf{r}_1(\mathbf{R} \cdot \mathbf{J}_0)\} dv = I_0 \oint \{(\mathbf{r}_1 \cdot \mathbf{R}) d\mathbf{s} + \mathbf{r}_1(\mathbf{R} \cdot d\mathbf{s})\}. \tag{A208}$$

Now let $\mathbf{R} = R\mathbf{n}$ where $\mathbf{n}$ is the unit vector in the direction of R. Then

$$\mathbf{C} = I_0 R \oint \{(\mathbf{r}_1 \cdot \mathbf{n}) d\mathbf{s} + \mathbf{r}_1(\mathbf{n} \cdot d\mathbf{s})\} \tag{A209}$$

which, upon rotation of axes such that $\mathbf{R}$ has the new direction z, takes on the value

$$\mathbf{C} = I_0 R \oint (z_1 d\mathbf{s} + \mathbf{r}_1 dz). \tag{A210}$$

The quantity z_1, is the z component of $\mathbf{r}_1$. The x component of (A210) is

$$C_x = I_0 R \oint (z_1 dx + x_1 dz) = 0 \tag{A211}$$

since the integral is a perfect differential. Similarly for the other components, and so (A207) reduces to

$$\pi = \frac{ie^{-i\omega t}}{8\pi\epsilon\omega R^3} \int_V (\mathbf{r}_1 \times \mathbf{J}_0) \times \mathbf{R} dv. \tag{A212}$$

Now we *define* the magnetic dipole moment of a circuit by

$$\mathbf{m} = \frac{I_0}{2}\oint \mathbf{r}_1 \times ds = \frac{1}{2}\int_V \mathbf{r}_1 \times \mathbf{J}_0 dv. \tag{A213}$$

then we may write

$$\boldsymbol{\pi} = \frac{ie^{-i\omega t}}{4\pi\epsilon\omega R^3}\mathbf{m} \times \mathbf{R} \tag{A214}$$

which is the retarded Hertz potential for a current loop of arbitrary shape.

Since we are interested in a plane circular loop, confined to the zy plane for which m is directed perpendicular to the face of the loop, we may write

$$\mathbf{m} \times \mathbf{R} = -\mathbf{j}m_z Z + \mathbf{k}m_z Y \tag{A215}$$

where Z and Y are the z and y components of $\mathbf{R}$. For this orientation the Hertz vector then lacks an x component. According to (A77), the field components are given by

$$H_x = -i\omega\epsilon\left(\frac{\partial \pi_z}{\partial y} - \frac{\partial \pi_y}{\partial z}\right) = \frac{me^{-i\omega t}}{4\pi}\frac{2X^2 - Y^2 - Z^2}{R^5} \tag{A216}$$

$$H_y = -i\omega\epsilon\left(-\frac{\partial \pi_z}{\partial x}\right) = \frac{me^{-i\omega t}}{4\pi}\frac{3XY}{R^5} \tag{A217}$$

$$H_z = -i\omega\epsilon\left(\frac{\partial \pi_y}{\partial x}\right) = \frac{me^{-i\omega t}}{4\pi}\frac{3XZ}{R^5}. \tag{A218}$$

The electric field is negligible as may be established from (A75):

$$\mathbf{E} = \nabla\nabla\cdot\boldsymbol{\pi} + \mu\epsilon\omega^2\boldsymbol{\pi}.$$

First, $\mu\epsilon\omega^2 = (\omega/c)^2$, where c is the velocity of light, becomes for a nominal audio frequency of 1,000 cps,

$$\left(\frac{\omega}{c}\right)^2 = \left(\frac{2\pi \times 10^3}{3 \times 10^8}\right)^2 \approx 4 \times 10^{-10}$$

so that we may neglect the second term of (A73) and write

$$\mathbf{E} \approx \nabla\nabla\cdot\boldsymbol{\pi}. \tag{A219}$$

The x component of (A219) is

$$E_x = \frac{\partial}{\partial x}\left[\frac{\partial \pi_y}{\partial y} + \frac{\partial \pi_z}{\partial z}\right]. \tag{A220}$$

Since $\pi \propto 1/R^2$, then $E_x \propto 1/R^4$ whereas $H_x \propto 1/R^3$. Thus $\mathbf{E}$ will be negligible compared to $\mathbf{H}$ beyond about 50 m from the source.

In the expression for the dipole moment

$$\mathbf{m} = \frac{I_0}{2}\oint \mathbf{r}_1 \times ds,$$

the quantity $\mathbf{r}_1 \times d\mathbf{s}$ is twice the area of a triangle bounded by a radius r_1 of the current loop and an element $d\mathbf{s}$ of the circumference of the loop. Hence $\oint \mathbf{r}_1 \times d\mathbf{s}$ is twice the area of the loop, so that $\mathbf{m}$ equals $I_0 A$ for a single turn and we have

$$m = NAI_0 \tag{A221}$$

for N turns. Thus the field of a circular coil of N turns may be written

$$H = \frac{NAI}{4\pi} e^{-i\omega t} \frac{(2X^2 - Y^2 - Z^2)\mathbf{i} + 3XY\mathbf{j} + 3XZ\mathbf{k}}{R^5} \tag{A222}$$

where

$$R = (X^2 + Y^2 + Z^2)^{1/2}.$$

The range over which (A222) is valid may be obtained by noting that our expansion (A199) neglected terms past the second, for

$$\frac{1}{R - r_1 \cos\theta} = \frac{\dfrac{1}{R}}{1 - \dfrac{r_1}{R}\cos\theta} = \frac{1}{R}\left[1 + \frac{r_1}{R}\cos\theta + \left(\frac{r_1}{r}\cos\theta\right)^2 + \cdots\right]. \tag{A223}$$

If we assume that we never measure closer to the coil than 10 coil radii, $r_1/R < (1/10)$ and $(r_1/R)^2 < (1/100)$. Hence, the greatest error might be one percent by neglecting terms past the second. The inner limit of the validity range for (A222) is then about 10 coil radii. The outer limit depends upon (A198), that $R \ll (\lambda/2\pi)$. For the nominal 1,000 cps frequency $\lambda = 3 \times 10^2$ km. Thus, the outer limit of the range poses no problem in practical prospecting.

(D) *Basic forms and solutions of the wave equation*
   (i) *Orthogonal cartesian coordinates*
      (a) *Uniform plane waves harmonic in time.*—In all our work in electromagnetic prospecting we rarely meet a physical situation where a true plane electromagnetic wave exists. Yet it is from the study of such simple special solutions of the wave equation [(A79) (A80)] that we are able to learn to apply waves in general. We shall study in this section, solutions of the wave equation which describe uniform plane harmonic waves and thereby learn of orthogonality of the E, H, and propagation vectors, phase velocity, wave impedance, elliptic polarization, etc. These concepts will all prove useful in subsequent sections of the book.

A *plane wave* is a wave whose surfaces of constant phase form a family of parallel planes. That is, the peak intensity of the oscillating **H** vector for example, is reached simultaneously for all points on an infinite plane surface. In a *uniform plane wave* the field intensities are independent of the coordinates in each equiphase plane and so we may write

$$\frac{\partial}{\partial x}[\mathbf{E}, \mathbf{H}] = \frac{\partial}{\partial y}[\mathbf{E}, \mathbf{H}] = 0$$

for a plane wave propagated in the positive z direction.

With this restriction, Maxwell's equations (A62 and A63) yield,

$$
\text{from (A62)}
\begin{cases}
\dfrac{\partial E_x}{\partial z} - i\mu\omega H_y = 0 & \text{(A224)} \\[2mm]
\dfrac{\partial E_y}{\partial z} + i\mu\omega H_x = 0 & \text{(A225)} \\[2mm]
H_z = 0 & \text{(A226)}
\end{cases}
$$

$$
\text{from (A63)}
\begin{cases}
\dfrac{\partial H_x}{\partial z} - (\sigma - i\omega\epsilon) E_y = 0 & \text{(A227)} \\[2mm]
\dfrac{\partial H_y}{\partial z} + (\sigma - i\omega\epsilon) E_x = 0 & \text{(A228)} \\[2mm]
E_z = 0. & \text{(A229)}
\end{cases}
$$

Thus, uniform plane waves infer that $\mathbf{E}$ and $\mathbf{H}$ are contained in a plane perpendicular to the direction of propagation; they are said to be transverse electromagnetic. The four transverse components of (A224) (A225) (A227) and (A228) apparently are divided into two independent pairs E_x, H_y and E_y, H_x.

The wave equations (A79) and (A80) then become

$$
\frac{\partial^2 \mathbf{E}}{\partial z^2} + k^2 \mathbf{E} = 0 \tag{A230}
$$

and

$$
\frac{\partial^2 \mathbf{H}}{\partial z^2} + k^2 \mathbf{H} = 0. \tag{A231}
$$

Both E_x and E_y satisfy (A230) since $\mathbf{E} = iE_x + jE_y$ while both H_x and H_y satisfy (A231). Since all four transverse components are known to depend upon z and t only, particular solutions of (A230) and (A231) are readily constructed as follows:

$$
E_x = E_{1x} e^{i(kz-\omega t)} + E_{2x} e^{-i(kz+\omega t)} \tag{A232}
$$

$$
E_y = E_{1y} e^{i(kz-\omega t)} + E_{2y} e^{-i(kz+\omega t)} \tag{A233}
$$

$$
H_x = H_{1x} e^{i(kz-\omega t)} + H_{2x} e^{-i(kz+\omega t)} \tag{A234}
$$

$$
H_y = H_{1y} e^{i(kz-\omega t)} + H_{2y} e^{-i(kz+\omega t)} \tag{A235}
$$

Those components containing $e^{i(kz-\omega t)}$ represent a wave traveling in the positive z direction while components containing $e^{-i(kz-\omega t)}$ represent a wave traveling in the negative z direction.

In the general case E_{1x}, E_{2x}, $\cdots$, H_{2y} are complex constants and combine to form the complex vector amplitudes.

$$
\mathbf{E}_1 = E_{1x}\mathbf{i} + E_{1y}\mathbf{j} \tag{A236}
$$

$$
\mathbf{E}_2 = E_{2x}\mathbf{i} + E_{2y}\mathbf{j} \tag{A237}
$$

$$
\mathbf{H}_1 = H_{1x}\mathbf{i} + H_{1y}\mathbf{j} \tag{A238}
$$

$$
\mathbf{H}_2 = H_{2x}\mathbf{i} + H_{2y}\mathbf{j}. \tag{A239}
$$

Hence we may write

$$E = E_1 e^{i(kz-\omega t)} + E_2 e^{-i(kz+\omega t)} \tag{A240}$$

$$H = H_1 e^{i(kz-\omega t)} + H_2 e^{-i(kz+\omega t)} \tag{A241}$$

When (A232) and (A235) are introduced into (A224) there results

$$ikE_{1x}e^{i(kz-\omega t)} - ikE_{2x}e^{-i(kz+\omega t)} - i\omega\mu H_{1y}e^{i(kz-\omega t)} - i\omega\mu H_{2y}e^{-i(kz+\omega t)} = 0. \tag{A242}$$

The coefficients of the exponentials e^{ikz} and e^{-ikz} must vanish independently and hence

$$H_{1y} = \frac{k}{\omega\mu} E_{1x} \tag{A243}$$

and

$$H_{2y} = \frac{-k}{\omega\mu} E_{2x}. \tag{A244}$$

Similarly

$$H_{1x} = \frac{-k}{\omega\mu} E_{1y} \tag{A245}$$

and

$$H_{2x} = \frac{k}{\omega\mu} E_{2y}. \tag{A246}$$

Thus, the independent pair E_{1x} and H_{1y}, representing one component of a positive traveling wave, are orthogonal as are all other pairs; the electric and magnetic vectors of a uniform plane wave are orthogonal to each other.

Let us now restrict our attention to positive traveling waves only

$$(E_{2x} = E_{2y} = H_{2x} = H_{2y} = 0).$$

Since E_{1x}, E_{1y}, H_{1x}, H_{1y} are complex, we may write

$$E_{1x} = ae^{i\theta} \tag{A247}$$

$$E_{1y} = be^{i\psi} \tag{A248}$$

where θ and ψ are real. Thus from (A232)

$$E_x = ae^{i(kz-\omega t+\theta)} \tag{A249}$$

and

$$E_y = be^{i(kz-\omega t+\psi)}. \tag{A250}$$

(b) *Phase, phase angle, and phase velocity.*—The propagation constant $k = \alpha + i\beta$, α and β being defined by (A73) and (A74). Thus (A249) and (A250) become

$$E_x = ae^{-\beta z}e^{i(\alpha z-\omega t+\theta)} = ae^{-\beta z}\big[\cos(\omega t - \alpha z - \theta) - i\sin(\omega t - \alpha z - \theta)\big] \tag{A251}$$

$$E_y = be^{-\beta z}e^{i(\alpha z-\omega t+\psi)} = be^{-\beta z}\big[\cos(\omega t - \alpha z - \psi) - i\sin(\omega t - \alpha z - \psi)\big] \tag{A252}$$

The components of the associated magnetic field are found from (A243) and (A245)

$$H_x = -\frac{k}{\omega\mu} b e^{-\beta z} e^{j(\alpha z - \omega t + \psi)} = -\frac{k}{\omega\mu} b e^{-\beta z}[\cos(\omega t - \alpha z - \psi) - i\sin(\omega t - \alpha z - \psi)] \quad \text{(A253)}$$

$$H_y = \frac{k}{\omega\mu} a e^{\beta z} e^{i(\alpha z - \omega t + \theta)} = \frac{k}{\omega\mu} a e^{-\beta z}[\cos(\omega t - \alpha z - \theta) - i\sin(\omega t - \alpha z - \theta)] \quad \text{(A254)}$$

The argument $\phi_1 = \omega t - \alpha z - \psi$ or $\phi_2 = \omega t - \alpha z - \theta$ is called the phase and the angle ψ or θ the phase angle. Since on any plane containing **E** and **H** we have made the assumption that phase is constant, then we find

$$\phi_1 = \omega t - \alpha z - \psi = \text{constant.} \quad \text{(A255)}$$

Hence there results

$$\frac{d\phi_1}{dt} = \omega - \alpha\frac{dz}{dt} = 0. \quad \text{(A256)}$$

The equiphase surfaces therefore, are propagated with the velocity

$$v = \frac{dz}{dt} = \frac{\omega}{\alpha} \quad \text{(A257)}$$

and v is called the *phase velocity* of the wave. Note that it is a velocity associated with a given phase or frequency.

(c) *Group and phase velocity.*—If a wave train of infinite duration exists, we may describe it by

$$\psi(z, t) = A e^{ikz - i\omega t} \quad \text{(A258)}$$

and compute the *phase velocity*. We find, as above

$$v_p = \frac{dz}{dt} = \frac{\omega}{\alpha} \quad \text{(A259)}$$

where $k = \alpha + i\beta$. Frequently, this is written

$$v_p = \frac{\omega}{k} \quad \text{(A260)}$$

in which case we infer that k is real.

A wave train of finite length cannot be expressed by (A258) and hence the term "phase velocity" loses its precise significance of defining the planes of constant phase through (A255). In these instances we use the concept of *group velocity*. To visualize this concept, let us consider the superposition of two harmonic waves which differ slightly in frequency and propagation constant:

$$\psi_1 = \cos(kz - \omega t)$$
$$\psi_2 = \cos[(k + \delta k)(z - (\omega + \delta\omega)t]. \quad \text{(A261)}$$

The sum of ψ_1 and ψ_2 is

$$\psi = \psi_1 + \psi_2 = 2\cos\tfrac{1}{2}(z\delta k - t\delta\omega)\cos\left[\left(k + \frac{\delta k}{2}\right)z - \left(\omega + \frac{\delta\omega}{2}\right)t\right]. \quad \text{(A262)}$$

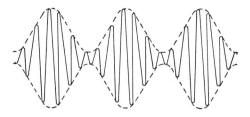

BEATS

Fig. 6. "Beats" resulting from superposition of two
signals of nearly identical frequencies.

The field ψ oscillates at a frequency $\omega+(\delta\omega/2)$ which is negligibly different from ω by assumption. The amplitude of the oscillation is

$$A = 2 \cos \tfrac{1}{2}(z\delta k - t\delta\omega) \tag{A263}$$

indicating that it is time dependent and in fact represents the "beat" periodicity. This is illustrated in Figure 6. Now the surfaces over which the group amplitude A is constant are defined by

$$z\delta k - t\delta\omega = C \tag{A264}$$

so that

$$v_G = \frac{\delta\omega}{\delta k} \tag{A265}$$

the group velocity. Strictly speaking, (A265) should be defined as

$$v_G = \frac{\delta\omega}{\delta\alpha} \tag{A266}$$

but is usually found in the literature in the form (A265).

In general, α is defined as before by

$$\alpha = \omega \left[\frac{\mu\epsilon}{2} \left(\sqrt{1 + \frac{\sigma^2}{\epsilon^2\omega^2}} + 1 \right) \right]^{1/2} \tag{A267}$$

and β by

$$\beta = \omega \left[\frac{\mu\epsilon}{2} \left(\sqrt{1 + \frac{\sigma^2}{\epsilon^2\omega^2}} - 1 \right) \right]^{1/2}. \tag{A268}$$

Two cases now arise:

(1) $(\sigma^2/\epsilon^2\omega^2) \ll 1$ the displacement current predominates over the conduction current. Then

$$v_P = \frac{1}{\sqrt{\mu\epsilon}} \tag{A269}$$

which for free space becomes

$$v_P = \frac{1}{\sqrt{\mu_0\epsilon_0}} = c \tag{A270}$$

where c is the velocity of light. The group velocity becomes

$$v_G = \frac{\delta\omega}{\delta\alpha} = \frac{\delta\omega}{\delta\omega/v_P} = v_P. \tag{A271}$$

(2) $(\sigma^2/\epsilon^2\omega) \gg 1$ the conduction current predominates over the displacement current. Then

$$\alpha = \beta = \sqrt{\frac{\omega\mu\sigma}{2}} \tag{A272}$$

and

$$v_P = \frac{\omega}{\alpha} = \sqrt{\frac{2\omega}{\mu\sigma}}. \tag{A273}$$

An increase in frequency increases v_P, but an increase in either μ or σ decreases v_P. The group velocity is

$$v_G = \frac{\delta\omega}{\delta\alpha} = \frac{\omega_1 - \omega_2}{\sqrt{\omega_1} - \sqrt{\omega_2}}\sqrt{\frac{2}{\mu\sigma}}. \tag{A274}$$

The group velocity departs from the phase velocity. A medium in which the phase velocity v_P is a function of frequency is said to be *dispersive*.

(d) *Polarization.*—If we choose the origin of time such that $\theta=0$, then the particular value of ψ at that time will represent the relative phase of E_y with respect to E_x in equation (A251) and (A252). Taking the real part of (A251) at $z=0$ we may write

$$E_x = E_1 \cos \omega t \tag{A275}$$

$$E_y = E_2 \cos (\omega t - \psi) \tag{A276}$$

where $E_1 = a$ and $E_2 = b$ for convenience. Unless $\psi=0$ or π, the vector representing the resultant intensity will rotate. One special case, arising in the electromagnetic prospecting method, occurs when $\psi=\pi/2$; i.e. the component intensities are in quadrature. Then

$$E_x = E_1 \cos \omega t \qquad E_y = E_2 \sin \omega t. \tag{A277}$$

The locus of the end point of the vector is found by eliminating t from (A277) by squaring:

$$\left(\frac{E_x}{E_1}\right)^2 + \left(\frac{E_y}{E_2}\right)^2 = 1. \tag{A278}$$

This equation represents an ellipse and the wave is said to be elliptically polarized. When $E_1 = E_2$ the wave is circularly polarized, and when $\psi=0$, the wave is linearly polarized since then the locus of the vector $\mathbf{E} = E_x\mathbf{i} + E_y\mathbf{j}$ is a straight line.

(ii) *Cylindrical coordinates.*—Geophysical prospecting frequently involves dipolar and linear current sources whose symmetry suggest solutions in cylindrical coordinates. When the sources themselves are excluded, we may deal with the homogeneous wave equation in cylindrical coordinates:

$$\frac{1}{r}\frac{\partial}{\partial r}\left(r\frac{\partial\psi}{\partial r}\right) + \frac{1}{r^2}\frac{\partial^2\psi}{\partial\phi^2} + \frac{\partial^2\psi}{\partial z^2} + k^2\psi = 0. \tag{A279}$$

To solve (A279) we may employ the separation-of-variables technique wherein it is assumed that the solution may be written as the product of three functions, each involving only one of the variables:

$$\psi = R(r)\Phi(\phi)Z(z). \tag{A280}$$

If we now substitute (A280) into (A279) and divide by $R\Phi Z$, we have

$$\frac{1}{rR}\frac{d}{dr}\left(r\frac{dR}{dr}\right) + \frac{1}{r^2\Phi}\frac{d^2\Phi}{d\phi^2} + \frac{1}{Z}\frac{d^2Z}{dz^2} + k^2 = 0. \tag{A281}$$

Since all the terms except the third are independent of z, the third term must also be independent of z; thus

$$\frac{1}{Z}\frac{d^2Z}{dz^2} + h^2 = 0 \quad \text{or} \quad \frac{d^2Z}{dz^2} + h^2Z = 0 \tag{A282}$$

where the parameter h is merely a separation constant. However, it has a particular physical significance; comparison of (A282) and (A230) reveals that h must have the dimensions of a propagation constant and in fact *is* the propagation constant pertaining to the z dependency. This constant h remains arbitrary unless boundary conditions are imposed.

If we now substitute (A282) in (A281) and multiply by r^2, we obtain

$$\frac{r}{R}\frac{d}{dr}\left(r\frac{dR}{dr}\right) + \frac{1}{\Phi}\frac{d^2\Phi}{d\phi^2} + (k^2 - h^2)r^2 = 0. \tag{A283}$$

The first and third terms are now independent of ϕ, so that we may write

$$\frac{1}{\Phi}\frac{d^2\Phi}{d\phi^2} + m^2 = 0 \quad \text{or} \quad \frac{d^2\Phi}{d\phi^2} + m^2\Phi = 0. \tag{A284}$$

Finally, when (A284) is substituted in (A283), there results the equation

$$\frac{rd}{dr}\left(r\frac{dR}{dr}\right) + [(k^2 - h^2)r^2 - m^2]R = 0$$

or

$$r^2\frac{d^2R}{dr^2} + r\frac{dR}{dr} + [(k^2 - h^2)r^2 - m^2]R = 0. \tag{A285}$$

This is *Bessel's equation*. It is a linear differential equation of the second order and hence must have two linearly independent solutions.

If we wish to have solutions of the wave equation which are harmonic in time, then a solution of (A282) will be

$$Z = C_1 e^{ihz - i\omega t} + C_2 e^{-ihz - i\omega t}. \tag{A286}$$

For real h, this solution represents a superposition of outward- and backward-traveling waves. However, in general, the propagation constant h is complex so that the field is not necessarily periodic along the z axis.

Equation (A284) has the solution

$$\Phi = C_3 e^{im\phi} + C_4 e^{-im\phi} \tag{A287}$$

with the physical requirement that Φ remain single-valued in order that the function ψ remain single-valued at any point in space. Thus m must be limited to the integral values $n = 0, 1, 2, \cdots$, for an unbounded medium. Of course if the medium is bounded by planes at ϕ_1 and ϕ_2, then we need not concern ourselves with seeking single-valuedness. In fact, the boundary conditions will usually dictate that m assume nonintegral values.

The solutions of Bessel's equation, which are finite on the axis $r = 0$, are known as *Bessel's functions* of order m and denoted by $J_m(\sqrt{k^2 - h^2} \cdot r)$. However, if we remove the restriction of finite value on the axis $r = 0$, then we usually give the solutions the name *circular cylinder functions* and denote them by $Z_m(\sqrt{k^2 - h^2} \cdot r)$.

The standard form of the *general* solution of Bessel's equation does not simply contain $J_m(\sqrt{k^2 - h^2} \cdot r)$ nor $Z_m(\sqrt{k^2 - h^2} \cdot r)$ but rather some linear combination of circular cylinder functions. Before discussing the general formula, it is desirable to make a change of the independent variable in (A285) to $x = \sqrt{k^2 - h^2} \cdot r$, whereupon (A285) becomes

$$x^2 \frac{d^2 R}{dx^2} + x \frac{dR}{dx} + (x^2 - m^2) R = 0. \tag{A288}$$

The general solution of (A288) is

$$R = C_5 J_m(x) + C_6 Y_m(x) \tag{A289}$$

where C_5 and C_6 are arbitrary constants and the function $J_m(x)$ is called the Bessel function of order m of the first kind, and $Y_m(x)$ is the Bessel function of order m of the second kind. These functions, which are tabulated (Jahnke and Emde, 1945), behave somewhat like trigonometric functions of damped amplitude and are generated from

$$J_m(x) = \frac{(\tfrac{1}{2}x)^m}{m!} \sum_{k=0}^{\infty} \frac{1}{k!} \frac{m!}{(n+k)!} \left(\frac{ix}{2}\right)^{2k} \tag{A290}$$

and

$$Y_m(x) \sin m\pi = J_m(x) \cos m\pi - J_{-m}(x). \tag{A291}$$

The properties of these functions are discussed in such standard texts as Watson (1944). In some problems we may require complex combinations of Bessel functions of the first and second kind. Then we use the Hankel functions:

$$H_m^{(1)}(x) = J_m(x) + i Y_m(x) \tag{A292}$$

$$H_m^{(2)}(x) = J_m(x) - i Y_m(x). \tag{A293}$$

In still other problems the Bessel equation is of the form

$$\frac{d^2 R}{dx^2} + \frac{1}{x} \frac{dR}{dx} + \left(-1 - \frac{m^2}{x^2}\right) R = 0 \tag{A294}$$

where $+1$ has been replaced by -1 in the bracket of the right hand term. Then Bessel functions of imaginary argument satisfy it, leading to the modified Bessel function of the first kind of order m:

$$I_m(x) = i^{-m} J_m(ix). \tag{A295}$$

Similarly, we may write the modified Bessel function of the second kind of order m as:

$$K_m(x) = \frac{\pi/2}{\sin m\pi} [I_{-m}(x) - I_m(x)] \qquad \text{(defined for } m \neq \text{integer).} \tag{A296}$$

Equation (A294) and its solution (A295) and (A296) arise when $x = \sqrt{k^2 - h^2} \cdot r$ becomes purely imaginary, i.e., for example, when h and k are real and $h > k$.

In determining the distribution of alternating currents in wires of circular cross section, the following differential equation is encountered:

$$\frac{d^2R}{dx^2} + \frac{1}{x}\frac{dR}{dx} - iR = 0. \tag{A297}$$

The general solution of (A297) may be written

$$R = AJ_0(i^{3/2}x) + BK_0(i^{1/2}x) \tag{A298}$$

wherein $J_0(i^{3/2}x)$ and $K_0(i^{1/2}x)$ are complex functions. When we decompose these functions into real and imaginary parts, we obtain

$$J_0(i^{3/2}x) = ber(x) + i\,bei(x) \tag{A299}$$

$$K_0(i^{1/2}x) = ker(x) + i\,kei(x). \tag{A300}$$

These latter four functions are given the names ber, bei, ker, kei, where the pronunciation is phonetic.

Any of the above values of R, Φ, Z, when substituted into (A279), constitutes a solution of the wave equation. As mentioned earlier, if we let h be a fixed constant, and if we require the potential ψ to be a single-valued function of ϕ, then m must take only integral values so that a general solution which remains finite at $r = 0$ is

$$\psi = \sum_{m=0}^{\infty} \left[e^{ihz}(A_m \cos m\phi + B_m \sin m\phi) \right.$$

$$\left. + e^{-ihz}(C_m \cos m\phi + D_m \sin m\phi) \right] J_m \sqrt{k^2 - h^2}\, re^{-i\omega t}. \tag{A301}$$

Within a homogeneous isotropic domain, every electromagnetic field can be represented by linear combinations of elementary wave functions as we have indicated by (A301). Each elementary wave is characterized by the parameters m, h, k. When $m = 0$, the field is symmetric about the axis; when $h = 0$, there is no propagation in the z direction, the propagation being strictly radial, and the field is said to be "two-dimensional." The function ψ is here used to represent any scalar potential or any component of a vector potential or field vector.

At this stage, it is well to review the point of departure for our discussion of the solutions of the wave equation in cylindrical coordinates. We *assumed* the form of the equation (A279). However, this form *derives* logically from the general form of the homogeneous wave equation, e.g. for the Hertz potential, equation (A35). We must remember that the operator $\nabla^2 \pi$ in (A35) applies to Cartesian coordinates and should be replaced [see equation (A28)] by

$$\nabla^2 \pi = \nabla\nabla \cdot \pi - \nabla \times \nabla \times \pi \tag{A302}$$

for other coordinate systems. Hence, the homogeneous wave equation for the Hertz potential in any coordinate system is

$$\nabla \times \nabla \times \pi = \nabla\nabla \cdot \pi - \mu\epsilon\frac{\partial^2 \pi}{\partial t^2} - \mu\sigma\frac{\partial \pi}{\partial t} \tag{A303}$$

The electric field is obtained by substituting the left hand side of (A303) for the first three terms of (A55) and setting $\pi^* = 0$, i.e.

$$\mathbf{E} = \nabla \times \nabla \times \pi \tag{A303a}$$

while the magnetic field is given directly by (A54) with $\pi^* = 0$, i.e.

$$\mathbf{H} = \left(\epsilon \frac{\partial}{\partial t} + \sigma \right) \nabla \times \pi. \tag{A303b}$$

Now it turns out that solutions of the vector wave equation (A303) are derivable only in a limited number of coordinate systems (Stratton, 1941, p. 349). One satisfactory solution in cylindrical coordinates stems from superposing partial fields derivable from two *scalar* Hertz potentials, π_z and π_z^*. The partial fields so derived are sufficiently general that we can, usually, satisfy a prescribed set of boundary conditions for many practical problems. If, then, we assume only a single component for π, the vector wave equation (A303) reduces to the scalar wave equation (A279) with which we commenced our discussion.

If we now wish to compute the fields for this scalar wave equation, in which $\psi = \pi_z$, we do so from equations (A303a) and (A303b) with π converted to π_z. Thus we obtain

$$
\begin{aligned}
E_r &= \frac{\partial^2 \pi_z}{\partial z \partial r} \qquad E_\phi = \frac{1}{r} \frac{\partial^2 \pi_z}{\partial z \partial \phi} \\
E_z &= -\frac{1}{r} \left[\frac{\partial}{\partial r} \left(r \frac{\partial \pi_z}{\partial r} \right) + \frac{\partial}{\partial \phi} \left(\frac{1}{r} \frac{\partial \pi_z}{\partial \phi} \right) \right]
\end{aligned}
\tag{A304}
$$

$$
\begin{aligned}
H_r &= \left(\epsilon \frac{\partial}{\partial t} + \sigma \right) \frac{1}{r} \frac{\partial \pi_z}{\partial \phi} \qquad H_\phi = -\left(\epsilon \frac{\partial}{\partial t} + \sigma \right) \frac{\partial \pi_z}{\partial r} \\
H_z &= 0
\end{aligned}
\tag{A305}
$$

Thus we have derived from a scalar function π_z an electromagnetic field for which there is no axial component of the magnetic vector. This is referred to as a *transverse magnetic field*.

Similarly, a partial field can be derived from a second Hertz vector π_z^* directed along the z axis in which case the fields are given by

$$
E_r = -\frac{\mu}{r} \frac{\partial^2 \pi_z^*}{\partial t \partial \phi} \qquad E_\phi = \mu \frac{\partial^2 \pi_z^*}{\partial t \partial r} \qquad E_z = 0 \tag{A306}
$$

$$
\begin{aligned}
H_r &= \frac{\partial^2 \pi_z^*}{\partial z \partial r} \qquad H_\phi = \frac{1}{r} \frac{\partial^2 \pi_z^*}{\partial z \partial \phi} \\
H_z &= -\frac{1}{r} \left[\frac{\partial}{\partial r} \left(r \frac{\partial \pi_z^*}{\partial r} \right) + \frac{\partial}{\partial \phi} \left(\frac{1}{r} \frac{\partial \pi_z^*}{\partial \phi} \right) \right]
\end{aligned}
\tag{A307}
$$

The field derived from π^* is characterized by the absence of a longitudinal component of $\mathbf{E}$ and is, hence, referred to as *transverse electric*. A satisfactory general solution of the wave equation is then a superposition of these two wave types.

In problems in electrostatics and magnetostatics, ω is zero so that k is zero. Also, we often find that there is no z dependency, i.e. $Z(z) = C$ in equation (A282), a situation demanding that h vanish. Then Bessel's equation (A285) reduces to

$$r^2 \frac{d^2R}{dr^2} + r \frac{dR}{dr} - m^2R = 0.$$ (A308)

A particular solution of (A308) is

$$R = Cr^m + Dr^{-m} \qquad \text{for } m \neq 0$$ (A309)

$$R = C \ln r + D \qquad \text{for } m = 0.$$ (A310)

For the ϕ dependent equation (A284), we may then write

$$\frac{d^2\Phi}{d\phi^2} + m^2\Phi = 0$$ (A311)

and the two corresponding solutions are

$$\Phi = A \cos m\phi + B \sin m\phi \qquad \text{for } m \neq 0$$ (A312)

$$\Phi = A\phi + B \qquad \text{for } m = 0.$$ (A313)

Thus, a general solution of Laplace's equation, in which there is no z dependency, in cylindrical coordinates might be

$$\psi = \sum_{m=1}^{\infty} (A_m \cos m\phi + B_m \sin m\phi)(C_m r^m + D_m r^{-m}).$$ (A314)

Note that the solution for $m=0$ is a special one and, as we shall see, pertains to induced monopoles. Since induced electric and magnetic monopoles are relatively rare in electrical geophysical problems requiring cylindrical coordinates, we seldom have occasion to concern ourselves with the special solutions (A310) and (A313). Note, however, that these solutions would be pertinent in gravitational problems.

This discussion of the $m=0$ case should be extended to cover solutions of the *wave* equation. However, we leave this until the section on a cylinder in a uniform, harmonically varying field because of the special physical aspects requiring consideration.

(iii) *Spherical coordinates.*—From equation (A302) we may write the vector wave equation for harmonic time dependency as

$$\nabla\nabla \cdot \mathbf{F} - \nabla \times \nabla \times \mathbf{F} + k^2\mathbf{F} = 0$$ (A315)

where $k^2 = \mu\epsilon\omega^2 + i\mu\sigma\omega$ as usual and $\mathbf{F}$ represents any vector potential or vector field. Stratton (1941, p. 392) indicates how vector solutions may be obtained directly. However, we frequently are concerned at any moment with a single component of the vector and then the scalar wave equation is satisfactory. In spherical coordinates this equation is

$$\frac{\partial}{\partial r}\left(r^2 \frac{\partial\psi}{\partial r}\right) + \frac{1}{\sin\theta} \frac{\partial}{\partial\theta}\left(\sin\theta \frac{\partial\psi}{\partial\theta}\right) + \frac{1}{\sin^2\theta} \frac{\partial^2\psi}{\partial\phi^2} + k^2r^2\psi = 0.$$ (A316)

The assumption of a harmonic time dependency and the utilization of the separation of variables technique for solving (A316) lead us to seek a function ψ of the form

$$\psi = R\Theta\Phi e^{-i\omega t} = RSe^{-i\omega t}.$$ (A317)

The functions R, Θ, Φ are, respectively, functions of r, θ, and ϕ only. The function $S(\theta, \phi) = \Theta\Phi$ is called a surface harmonic. The function Θ when ϕ is a constant, is called a zonal surface harmonic.

If we substitute (A317) in (A316) and divide through by RS, we have

$$\frac{1}{R}\frac{\partial}{\partial r}\left(r^2\frac{\partial R}{\partial r}\right) + \frac{1}{S\sin\theta}\frac{\partial}{\partial\theta}\left(\sin\theta\frac{\partial S}{\partial\theta}\right) + \frac{1}{S\sin^2\theta}\frac{\partial^2 S}{\partial\phi^2} + k^2 r^2 = 0. \qquad (A318)$$

The first and last terms are functions of r only, and the other terms involve only θ and ϕ. Therefore

$$\frac{1}{R}\frac{\partial}{\partial r}\left(r^2\frac{\partial R}{\partial r}\right) + k^2 r^2 = p^2$$

or

$$r^2\frac{d^2 R}{dr^2} + 2r\frac{dR}{dr} + (k^2 r^2 - p^2)R = 0 \qquad (A319)$$

and

$$\frac{1}{S\sin\theta}\frac{\partial}{\partial\theta}\left(\sin\theta\frac{\partial S}{\partial\theta}\right) + \frac{1}{S\sin^2\theta}\frac{\partial^2 S}{\partial\phi^2} = -p^2. \qquad (A320)$$

If, in (A319) we make the substitution $R=(kr)^{-1/2}f(r)$ there results the equation

$$r^2\frac{d^2 f}{dr^2} + r\frac{df}{dr} + [k^2 r^2 - (p^2 + \tfrac{1}{4})]f = 0 \qquad (A321)$$

which, upon placing $p^2 = n(n+1)$ becomes the Bessel equation of half odd integral order

$$r^2\frac{d^2 f}{dr^2} + r\frac{df}{dr} + [k^2 r^2 - (n + \tfrac{1}{2})^2]f = 0. \qquad (A322)$$

The cylindrical functions of half odd integral order satisfy (A322) so that for the original equation (A319) we may write the solution

$$R = \frac{1}{\sqrt{kr}}Z_{n+1/2}(kr). \qquad (A323)$$

If $k=0$, equation (A319) has the solution

$$R = Ar^n + Br^{-n-1} \qquad (A324)$$

which is the radial part of the solution of Laplace's equation and is applicable to electrostatic and magnetostatic problems. The complete solution of Laplace's equation in spherical coordinates may be written

$$\psi = (Ar^n + Br^{-n-1})S_n \qquad (A325)$$

where S_n is a solution of (A320) with $p^2 = n(n+1)$, and where $k=0$ in (A319).

A very important special solution of (A325) is the one in which ψ is independent of ϕ so that Φ is a constant and S_n is a function of θ only. For this case we have

$$\frac{\partial^2 S_n}{\partial\phi^2} = 0 \qquad (A326)$$

and equation (A320) reduces to

$$\frac{1}{\sin\theta}\frac{\partial}{\partial\theta}\left(\sin\theta\frac{\partial S_n}{\partial\theta}\right) + n(n+1)S_n = 0. \tag{A327}$$

If we write $x = \cos\theta$, then (A327) becomes

$$\frac{d}{dx}\left[(1-x^2)\frac{dS_n}{dx}\right] + n(n+1)S_n = 0 \tag{A328}$$

where the partial derivatives have been replaced since only one variable is now involved. This is the Legendre equation of degree n. If n is a positive integer, a solution of (A327) is given by the Legendre polynomial

$$S_n = P_n(x) = P_n(\cos\theta). \tag{A329}$$

Upon summing all such solutions and multiplying by the pertinent solutions of (A324), we obtain the general solution of (A316) as

$$\psi = \sum_{n=0}^{\infty}\frac{1}{\sqrt{kr}}Z_{n+1/2}(kr)P_n(\cos\theta) \tag{A330}$$

or

$$\psi = \sum_{n=0}^{\infty}\left(A_n r^n + \frac{B_n}{r^{n+1}}\right)P_n(\cos\theta) \tag{A331}$$

as a general solution of Laplace's equation. The quantities A_n and B_n are arbitrary constants.

For the more general case where ψ is not independent of ϕ, then a further separation of variables must be completed. Thus, in (A320) we substitute $S = \Theta\Phi$ and multiply through by $\sin^2\theta$ to obtain

$$\frac{\sin\theta}{\Theta}\frac{\partial}{\partial\theta}\left(\sin\theta\frac{\partial\Theta}{\partial\theta}\right) + \frac{1}{\Phi}\frac{\partial^2\Phi}{\partial\phi^2} + n(n+1)\sin^2\theta = 0. \tag{A332}$$

We then let

$$\frac{1}{\Phi}\frac{\partial^2\Phi}{\partial\phi^2} = -m^2 \tag{A333}$$

a solution of which is

$$\Phi = e^{im\phi}. \tag{A334}$$

There remains

$$\frac{\sin\theta}{\Theta}\frac{\partial}{\partial\theta}\left(\sin\theta\frac{\partial\Theta}{\partial\theta}\right) - m^2 + n(n+1)\sin^2\theta = 0. \tag{A335}$$

Now substitute $x = \cos\theta$ in (A335) and there results

$$(1-x^2)\frac{d^2\Theta}{dx^2} - 2x\frac{d\Theta}{dx} + \left(n(n+1) - \frac{m^2}{1-x^2}\right)\Theta = 0. \tag{A336}$$

This is the associated Legendre equation and is satisfied by

$$\Theta = (1 - x^2)^{m/2} \frac{d^m}{dx^m} P_n(x).$$ (A337)

The function Θ given in (A337) is the associated Legendre polynomial and it is denoted by $P_n{}^m(x)$. We therefore have

$$P_n{}^m(x) = (1 - x^2)^{m/2} \frac{d^m}{dx^m} P_n(x).$$ (A338)

A general solution of the wave equation in spherical coordinates is then

$$\psi = \sum_{n=0}^{\infty} \sum_{m=0}^{n} \frac{1}{\sqrt{kr}} Z_{n+1/2}(kr) P^m{}_n(\cos\theta) e^{im\phi} e^{-i\omega t}$$ (A339)

and for Laplace's equation it is

$$\psi = \sum_{n=0}^{\infty} \sum_{m=0}^{n} \left(a_{nm} r^n + \frac{b_{nm}}{r^{n+1}} \right) P^m{}_n(\cos\theta) e^{im\phi}$$ (A340)

where a_{nm} and b_{nm} are arbitrary constants.

In many problems, initial or boundary conditions will indicate that the general forms (A339) and (A340) are unnecessary and that certain special solutions are satisfactory. The reader is referred to Watson (1944) for properties of the Legendre polynomials.

A nomenclature commonly used for the cylindrical functions (A323) is that of the spherical Bessel function

$$\left. \begin{array}{ll} z_n(\rho) = \sqrt{\dfrac{\pi}{2\rho}} Z_{n+1/2}(\rho) & j_n(\rho) = \sqrt{\dfrac{\pi}{2\rho}} J_{n+1/2}(\rho) \\[3mm] y_n(\rho) = \sqrt{\dfrac{\pi}{2\rho}} Y_{n+1/2}(\rho) & h_n^{(1)}(\rho) = \sqrt{\dfrac{\pi}{2\rho}} H_{n+1/2}^{(1)}(\rho) \\[3mm] & h_n^{(2)}(\rho) = \sqrt{\dfrac{\pi}{2\rho}} H_{n+1/2}^{(2)}(\rho) \end{array} \right\}.$$ (A341)

(iv) *Integral solutions of the homogeneous wave equation.*—We have seen above, equation (A232), that elementary plane wave solutions of the wave equation in cartesian coordinates are of the form

$$\psi = (A e^{ikz} + B e^{-ikz}) e^{-i\omega t}.$$ (A342)

The coefficients A and B are arbitrary and could be functions of frequency. This suggests that the general solution of the one dimensional wave equation

$$\frac{\partial^2 \psi}{\partial z^2} + k^2 \psi = 0$$ (A343)

could be of the form

$$\psi = \sum_{\omega=0}^{\infty} (A_\omega e^{ikz} + B_\omega e^{-ikz}) e^{-i\omega t}.$$ (A344)

This form does limit the solution to the discrete frequencies $\omega = 0, 1, 2, \cdots$. For a continuous spectrum of frequencies we will want to use the integral representation

$$\psi(z, t) = \int_{-\infty}^{\infty} (A(\omega)e^{ikz} + B(\omega)e^{-ikz})e^{-i\omega t}d\omega. \tag{A345}$$

Such waves are prescribed in time since we have assumed a harmonic time dependency with frequency ω for every elementary wave function. Other waves may be prescribed in space whenever we wish to assume a harmonic space dependency. To illustrate these latter waves, let us write down the one-dimensional equivalent of (A59),

$$\frac{\partial^2 E_x}{\partial z^2} - \mu\epsilon \frac{\partial^2 E_x}{\partial t^2} - \mu\sigma \frac{\partial E_x}{\partial t} = 0. \tag{A346}$$

We have assumed that there is only an x component of the electric vector for a wave propagated in the z direction. This equation may be solved by separation of variables through

$$E_x = f_1(z)f_2(t). \tag{A347}$$

Then, substitution of (A347) in (A346) results in

$$\frac{1}{f_1} \frac{d^2 f_1}{dz^2} = \frac{\mu\epsilon}{f_2} \frac{d^2 f_2}{dt^2} + \frac{\mu\sigma}{f_2} \frac{df_2}{dt} = -k^2 \tag{A348}$$

where $-k^2$ is the separation constant. The general solution for f_1 is

$$f_1(z) = Ae^{ikz} + Be^{-ikz} \tag{A349}$$

and we shall take a particular solution for f_2;

$$f_2(t) = Ce^{-pt} \tag{A350}$$

where p satisfies the equation, obtained by substituting these solutions in (A346),

$$p^2 - \frac{\sigma}{\epsilon} p + \frac{k^2}{\mu\epsilon} = 0. \tag{A351}$$

For waves harmonic in time we select $p = i\omega$ whereupon k is determined by (A351) to be

$$k^2 = \mu\epsilon\omega^2 + i\mu\sigma\omega \tag{A352}$$

and must, in general, be complex.

Alternatively we might seek the solutions

$$f_1(z) = Ce^{ikz} \tag{A353}$$

$$f_2(t) = De^{-pt} \tag{A354}$$

which lead to the equation

$$p^2 - \frac{\sigma}{\epsilon} p + \frac{k^2}{\mu\epsilon} = 0 \tag{A355}$$

as before. We may now solve this equation for p;

$$p = \frac{\sigma}{2\epsilon} \pm i\sqrt{\frac{k^2}{\mu\epsilon} - \frac{\sigma^2}{4\epsilon^2}} \tag{A356}$$

and E_x then has the value

$$E_x = e^{-(\sigma/2\epsilon)t}(A e^{iqt} + B e^{-iqt})e^{ikz} \tag{A357}$$

where

$$q = \sqrt{\frac{k^2}{\mu\epsilon} - \frac{\sigma^2}{4\epsilon^2}}. \tag{A358}$$

Waves of this type are known as *evanescent* waves, when $(\sigma^2/4\epsilon^2) > (k^2/\mu\epsilon)$ for then the quantity iq is real, and the field is periodic in z but decreases monotonically with time. For these waves, we have an expression analogous to that of equation (A345)

$$\psi(z, t) = \int_{-\infty}^{\infty} e^{-(\sigma/2\epsilon)t}[A(k)e^{iqt} + B(k)e^{-iqt}]e^{ikz}dk. \tag{A358}$$

The integration now is with respect to k, i.e. over all k space, inferring a different k for each elementary wave. Since k is the inverse of wavelength, we can generate solutions of the type given by (A358) by superposing waves covering a complete spectrum of wavelengths.

In general, then, we can construct integral solutions of the wave equation from elementary wavelets of the form

$$\psi = e^{ik\xi - i\omega t} \tag{A359}$$

in which k and ω are either real or complex and ξ is a coordinate of arbitrary direction. The unit vector in the ξ direction is $\mathbf{n} = \mathbf{i}n_x + \mathbf{j}n_y + \mathbf{k}n_z$ as defined in a rectangular coordinate system. If $\mathbf{r} = \mathbf{i}x + \mathbf{j}y + \mathbf{k}z$ is the radius vector drawn from the origin to a point of observation whose rectangular coordinates are x, y, z (see Figure 7). Then

$$\xi = \mathbf{n} \cdot \mathbf{r} = n_x x + n_y y + n_z z. \tag{A360}$$

The direction cosines $n_x, n_y, n_z,$ of the vector $\mathbf{n}$ may be expressed in terms of the polar angles α and β

$$n_x = \sin \alpha \cos \beta \tag{A361}$$

$$n_y = \sin \alpha \sin \beta \tag{A362}$$

$$n_z = \cos \alpha. \tag{A363}$$

Thus, (A359) may be written

$$\psi = e^{ik(x \sin \alpha \cos \beta + y \sin \alpha \sin \beta + z \cos \alpha) - i\omega t}. \tag{A364}$$

Let us assume that a wavelet is associated with each α, β direction and is of amplitude $g(\alpha, \beta)$. A general solution for such a superposition of elementary plane waves is then

$$\psi(x, y, z, t) = e^{-i\omega t} \int d\alpha \int g(\alpha, \beta)e^{ik(x \sin \alpha \cos \beta + y \sin \alpha \sin \beta + z \cos \alpha)}d\beta. \tag{A365}$$

Normally, we would look upon α and β as real angles, but from a mathematical viewpoint, equation (A365) will satisfy the wave equation for complex values of α and β The physical significance of complex angles α and β is discussed by Stratton (1941, p 516) complex angles α, β are required to describe an *inhomogeneous* plane wave in which the planes of constant phase and constant amplitude are not coincident. For the present discussion, we need only think in terms of real α, β.

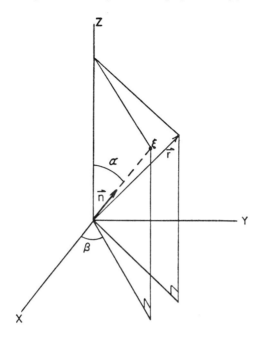

Fig. 7. Unit vector **n** in the ξ direction defined in the rectangular coordinate system (x, y, z) by the polar angles α and β.

Let us now define a *vector propagation constant*

$$\mathbf{k} = k\mathbf{n} \tag{A366}$$

whose rectangular components are

$$k_1 = k \sin \alpha \cos \beta \tag{A367}$$

$$k_2 = k \sin \alpha \sin \beta \tag{A368}$$

$$k_3 = k \cos \alpha. \tag{A369}$$

For waves harmonic in time, the elementary plane wave is now

$$\psi = e^{ik \cdot n - i\omega t} \tag{A370}$$

where the vector **k** in this usage must be distinguished from the unit coordinate vector **k**. Equation (A370) may be substituted in the wave equation

$$\frac{\partial^2 \psi}{\partial x^2} + \frac{\partial^2 \psi}{\partial y^2} + \frac{\partial^2 \psi}{\partial z^2} - \mu\epsilon \frac{\partial^2 \psi}{\partial t^2} - \mu\sigma \frac{\partial \psi}{\partial t} = 0 \tag{A371}$$

whereupon we obtain

$$k_1^2 + k_2^2 + k_3^2 = \mu\epsilon\omega^2 + i\mu\sigma\omega = k^2. \tag{A372}$$

Since, in equations (A367) through (A369), we may choose α and β arbitrarily for any given wavelet, then k_1, k_2, and k_3 are arbitrary. The only restriction on these three wave numbers is that they satisfy equation (A372). Any elementary wave function is characterized by the parameters (k_1, k_2, k_3, ω); since ω is also a variable, any three of the parameters may be selected arbitrarily whereupon the fourth is determined by (A372).

We may then represent the wave function ψ as a Fourier integral with respect to any one of the four spectral components k_1, k_2, k_3 or ω, or we may represent it even more generally as a triple Fourier integral with respect to any three spectral components. Thus, we may write

$$\psi(x, y, z, t) = \left(\frac{1}{2\pi}\right)^{3/2} \int_{-\infty}^{\infty} \int_{-\infty}^{\infty} \int_{-\infty}^{\infty} g(k_1, k_2, \omega) e^{i(k_1 x + k_2 y + k_3 z - \omega t)} dk_1 dk_2 d\omega \tag{A373}$$

in which we have chosen k_1, k_2, and ω as real variables and consequently fixed k_3 via

$$k_3^2 = \mu\epsilon\omega^2 + i\mu\sigma\omega - k_1^2 - k_2^2. \tag{A374}$$

Note that k_3 will, in general, be complex. Equation (A373) is a generalization of (A365) to allow for an arbitrary time function rather than a single time spectral parameter ω.

The amplitude function $g(k_1, k_2, \omega)$ must be a Fourier transform of another function $f(x, y, t)$ provided $f(x, y, t)$ and its first derivatives are piecewise continuous and absolutely integrable. The transform pair is

$$f(x, y, t) = \left(\frac{1}{2\pi}\right)^{3/2} \int_{-\infty}^{\infty} \int_{-\infty}^{\infty} \int_{-\infty}^{\infty} g(k_1, k_2, \omega) e^{i(k_1 x + k_2 y - \omega t)} dk_1 dk_2 d\omega \tag{A375}$$

$$g(k_1, k_2, \omega) = \left(\frac{1}{2\pi}\right)^{3/2} \int_{-\infty}^{\infty} \int_{-\infty}^{\infty} \int_{-\infty}^{\infty} f(x, y, t) e^{-i(k_1 x + k_2 y - \omega t)} dx dy dt. \tag{A376}$$

In choosing k_3 to be the fixed parameter, we have, in effect, prescribed the wave function ψ over the plane $z = 0$, for

$$\psi(x, y, 0, t) = f(x, y, t) \tag{A377}$$

as may be seen by setting $z = 0$ in (A373) and comparing it with (A375).

Alternatively, we might prescribe ψ throughout all space at time $t = 0$. Then, we may represent ψ by

$$\psi(x, y, z, t) = \left(\frac{1}{2\pi}\right)^{3/2} \int_{-\infty}^{\infty} \int_{-\infty}^{\infty} \int_{-\infty}^{\infty} g(k_1, k_2, k_3) e^{i(k_1 x + k_2 y + k_3 z - \omega t)} dk_1 dk_2 dk_3 \tag{A378}$$

in which k_1, k_2, k_3 are real variables and ω is a complex quantity obtained from (A372):

$$i\omega = \frac{\sigma}{2\epsilon} \pm i\sqrt{c^2(k_1^2 + k_2^2 + k_3^2) - \frac{\sigma^2}{4\epsilon^2}} \tag{A379}$$

$c = 1/\sqrt{\mu\epsilon}$ is the velocity of light.

The transform pair is

$$f(x, y, z) = \left(\frac{1}{2\pi}\right)^{3/2} \int_{-\infty}^{\infty} \int_{-\infty}^{\infty} \int_{-\infty}^{\infty} g(k_1, k_2, k_3) e^{i(k_1 x + k_2 y + k_3 z)} dk_1 dk_2 dk_3 \tag{A380}$$

$$g(k_1, k_2, k_3) = \left(\frac{1}{2\pi}\right)^{3/2} \int_{-\infty}^{\infty} \int_{-\infty}^{\infty} \int_{-\infty}^{\infty} f(x, y, z) e^{-i(k_1 x + k_2 y + k_3 z)} dx dy dz. \tag{A381}$$

Equations (A373) and (A378) are the *Fourier integral representation* of a generalized wave. Other integral representations are found to be useful in geophysical prospecting. One of these, the Fourier-Bessel integral is particularly useful for problems with cylindrical symmetry. In cylindrical coordinates the elementary wave function is written

$$\psi(r, \theta, z, t) = e^{in\theta}Z_n(\sqrt{k^2 - h^2} \cdot r)e^{\pm ihz - i\omega t}. \tag{A382}$$

We summed such elementary solutions to obtain the general solution given by (A301). Now we wish to find a related integral representation. In problems requiring the Fourier-Bessel integral representation we usually know $\psi(r, \theta, 0, 0) = f(r, \theta)$ over the plane $z = 0$ at time $t = 0$. We assume that $f(r, \theta)$ is a single-valued function of the variables; $f(r, \theta)$ must be periodic in θ and be expanded in a Fourier series (Wyllie, 1960 p. 263) whose coefficients are functions of r alone,

$$f(r, \theta) = \sum_{n=-\infty}^{\infty} f_n(r)e^{in\theta} \tag{A383}$$

$$f_n(r) = \frac{1}{2\pi}\int_0^{2\pi} f(r, \theta)e^{-in\theta}d\theta. \tag{A384}$$

Now let us consider a function $f(x, y)$ with the Fourier transform

$$f(x, y) = \frac{1}{2\pi}\int_{-\infty}^{\infty}\int_{-\infty}^{\infty} g(k_1, k_2)e^{i(k_1x + k_2y)}dk_1dk_2. \tag{A385}$$

To transform this function in both ξ and k space we make the substitutions

$$\left.\begin{aligned} x &= r\cos\theta \\ y &= r\sin\theta \end{aligned}\right\} \tag{A386}$$

$$\left.\begin{aligned} k_1 &= k\sin\alpha\cos\beta \\ k_2 &= k\sin\alpha\sin\beta \end{aligned}\right\}. \tag{A387}$$

The latter transformation stems from (A367) and (A368). Because $k\sin\alpha$ is common to both elements of the transformation (A387), we may simplify this transformation to

$$\left.\begin{aligned} k_1 &= \lambda\cos\beta \\ k_2 &= \lambda\sin\beta \end{aligned}\right\} \tag{A388}$$

where

$$\lambda = k\sin\alpha. \tag{A389}$$

We usually label the wavenumber in the z-direction by the letter h so that from (A369)

$$k_3 = h = k\cos\alpha.$$

Hence, by $\sin\alpha = (1/k)\sqrt{k^2 - h^2}$ we convert (A389) to

$$\lambda = \sqrt{k^2 - h^2} \quad \text{or} \quad h = \pm i\sqrt{k^2 - \lambda^2}. \tag{A390}$$

The transformation (A386) coupled with (A388) permits us to write

$$k_1x + k_2y = r\lambda\cos\beta\cos\theta + r\lambda\sin\beta\sin\theta$$
$$= \lambda r\cos(\beta - \theta). \tag{A391}$$

Thus, the Fourier integral (A385) becomes

$$f(r, \theta) = \frac{1}{2\pi}\int_0^{\infty}\lambda d\lambda\int_0^{2\pi} d\beta g(\lambda, \beta)e^{i\lambda r\cos(\beta - \theta)} \tag{A392}$$

where $\lambda d\lambda d\beta$ is an element of volume in k space analogous to $rdrd\theta$ in ξ space. The function

$$e^{i\lambda r \cos(\beta-\theta)-i\omega t} \tag{A393}$$

represents a plane wave whose propagation constant is λ, traveling in a direction which is contained in the $x-y$ plane and which makes an angle β with the x axis. Each elementary plane wave is multiplied by a *weighting function* $g(\lambda, \beta)$ and then integrated with respect to angle β and space frequency λ.

The transform of $f(x, y)$ is

$$g(k_1, k_2) = \frac{1}{2\pi} \int_{-\infty}^{\infty} \int_{-\infty}^{\infty} f(x, y)e^{-i(k_1x+k_2y)}dxdy \tag{A394}$$

which, when transformed to polar coordinates is

$$g(\lambda, \beta) = \frac{1}{2\pi} \int_{0}^{\infty} rdr \int_{0}^{2\pi} d\theta\, f(r, \theta)e^{-i\lambda r \cos(\beta-\theta)}. \tag{A395}$$

In equation (A383) each series element is described by

$$f(r, \theta) = f_n(r)e^{in\theta} \tag{A396}$$

and we may substitute this in (A395)

$$g(\lambda, \beta) = \frac{1}{2\pi} \int_{0}^{\infty} rdrf_n(r) \int_{0}^{2\pi} d\theta e^{-i\lambda r \cos(\beta-\theta)+in\theta}. \tag{A397}$$

We may now employ Sommerfeld's integral representation for Bessel functions (Jones, 1964, Stratton 1941 p. 369)

$$J_n(z) = \frac{e^{-n\pi i/2}}{2\pi} \int_{-\pi}^{\pi} e^{i(n\psi+z \cos \psi)}d\psi \tag{A398}$$

with a change of variables

$$\left. \begin{array}{l} \psi = \theta - \beta - \pi, \qquad d\psi = d\theta \\ z = \lambda r \end{array} \right\}. \tag{A399}$$

The second integral in (A397) then becomes

$$\begin{aligned} g &= \frac{1}{2\pi} \int_{\psi=-\beta-\pi}^{\psi=-\beta+\pi} e^{iz \cos \psi+in\psi}e^{in(\beta+\pi)}d\psi \\ &= e^{in(\beta+3\pi/2)}J_n(z). \end{aligned} \tag{A400}$$

Thus, (A397) assumes the value

$$g(\lambda, \beta) = e^{in(\beta+3\pi/2)} \int_{0}^{\infty} f_n(r)J_n(\lambda r)rdr = g_n(\lambda)e^{in(\beta+3\pi/2)}. \tag{A401}$$

We may substitute (A401) in (A392) to obtain

$$f(r, \theta) = f_n(r)e^{in\theta} = \frac{1}{2\pi} \int_{0}^{\infty} \lambda d\lambda g_n(\lambda) \int_{0}^{2\pi} d\beta e^{i\lambda r \cos(\beta-\theta)+in(\beta+3\pi/2)}. \tag{A402}$$

Upon making the transformation $\phi = \beta - \theta$, we observe that (A402) becomes

$$f(r, \theta) = f_n(r)e^{in\theta} = e^{in\theta} \int_0^\infty \lambda g_n(\lambda)J_n(\lambda r)d\lambda. \tag{A403}$$

From equations (A401) and (A403) we obtain the Fourier-Bessel transform pair

$$f_n(r) = \int_0^\infty g_n(\lambda)J_n(\lambda r)\lambda d\lambda \tag{A404}$$

$$g_n(\lambda) = \int_0^\infty f_n(r)J_n(\lambda r)rdr. \tag{A405}$$

Equation (A403), with a harmonic time dependency and z dependency added, and a summation effected over all elements of the Fourier series according to (A383), yields

$$\psi(r, \theta, z, t) = f(r, \theta, z)e^{-i\omega t} = e^{-i\omega t} \sum_{n=-\infty}^{\infty} e^{in\theta} \int_0^\infty g_n(\lambda)J_n(\lambda r)e^{\pm i\sqrt{k^2-\lambda^2}\cdot z}\lambda d\lambda. \tag{A406}$$

This equation (A406) is a solution of the wave equation in circular cylindrical coordinates, which at $t=0$ reduces to $f(r, \theta)$ on the plane $z=0$. If other than a harmonic time dependency is required in a problem in cylindrical coordinates, then equation (A406) may be integrated with respect to the spectral component ω.

In a similar fashion, a Fourier-Bessel integral representation may be developed for problems with spherical symmetry. The elementary wave function for spherical symmetry is, from equation (A339)

$$\psi(r, \theta, \phi, t) = \frac{1}{\sqrt{kr}} Z_{n+1/2}(kr) P_n{}^m(\cos \theta)e^{im\phi}e^{-i\omega t}. \tag{A407}$$

A solution which generalizes (A407) is now sought. Stratton (1941 p. 412) presents this solution in the form

$$\psi(r, \theta, \phi, t) = e^{-i\omega t} \sum_{n=-\infty}^{\infty} \sqrt{\frac{2}{\pi}} \int_0^\infty g_n(k)j_n(kr)k^2 dk S_n(\theta, \phi) \tag{A408}$$

where $g_n(k)$ is described by the transform pair

$$\left.\begin{aligned} f_n(r) &= \sqrt{\frac{2}{\pi}} \int_0^\infty g_n(k)j_n(kr)k^2 dk \\ g_n(k) &= \sqrt{\frac{2}{\pi}} \int_0^\infty f_n(r)j_n(kr)r^2 dr \end{aligned}\right\} \tag{A409}$$

and $S_n(\theta, \phi)$ is the surface harmonic of order n described by $S_n(\theta, \phi) = P_n{}^m(\cos \theta)e^{im\phi}$.

(v) *Selection of special functions for problems with cylindrical and spherical symmetry*
(a) *Cylinder functions.*—It is useful to have a summary guide for the applicability of the various cylinder functions. Insight into the behavior of the cylinder functions can be gained by noting their similarities to harmonic functions. For large values of the argument (kr), asymptotic series exist for the cylinder functions leading to

TABLE I

$Z_n(kr)$	ALTERNATIVE REPRESENTATION	VALUE FOR $kr \to 0$	VALUE FOR $|kr| \to \infty$	ZEROS	INFINITIES	PHYSICAL INTERPRETATION
$H_n^{(1)}(kr)$	$J_n(kr) + iY_n(kr)$	$1 - i\frac{2}{\pi}\ln\frac{2}{(\gamma kr)}$; $n=0$ $\frac{(kr)^n}{2^n n!} - i\frac{2^n(n-1)!}{\pi(kr)^n}$; $n>0$	$\sqrt{\frac{2i}{\pi kr}}\; i^{-n} e^{ikr}$	$kr \to \infty$	$kr = 0$ $kr \to -i\infty$	k REAL – OUTWARD TRAVELING WAVE k IMAGINARY – EVANESCENT FIELD k COMPLEX – ATTENUATED TRAVELING WAVE
$H_n^{(2)}(kr)$	$J_n(kr) - iY_n(kr)$	$1 + i\frac{2}{\pi}\ln\frac{2}{(\gamma kr)}$; $n=0$ $\frac{(kr)^n}{2^n n!} + i\frac{2^n(n-1)!}{\pi(kr)^n}$; $n>0$	$\sqrt{\frac{2i}{\pi kr}}\; i^{n} e^{-ikr}$	$kr \to -i\infty$	$kr = 0$ $kr \to i\infty$	k REAL – INWARD TRAVELING WAVE k IMAGINARY – EVANESCENT FIELD k COMPLEX – ATTENUATED TRAVELING WAVE
$J_n(kr)$	$\frac{1}{2}\left[H_n^{(1)}(kr)+H_n^{(2)}(kr)\right]$	1 ; $n=0$ $\frac{(kr)^n}{2^n n!}$; $n>0$	$\sqrt{\frac{2}{\pi kr}}\cos\left(kr - \frac{n\pi}{2} - \frac{\pi}{4}\right)$	INFINITE NUMBER ALONG THE REAL AXIS	$kr \to i\infty$	k REAL – STANDING WAVE k IMAGINARY – TWO EVANESCENT FIELDS k COMPLEX – LOCALIZED STANDING WAVE
$Y_n(kr)$	$\frac{1}{2i}\left[H_n^{(1)}(kr)-H_n^{(2)}(kr)\right]$	$-\frac{2}{\pi}\ln\frac{2}{(\gamma kr)}$; $n=0$ $-\frac{2^n(n-1)!}{\pi(kr)^n}$; $n>0$	$\sqrt{\frac{2}{\pi kr}}\sin\left(kr - \frac{n\pi}{2} - \frac{\pi}{4}\right)$	INFINITE NUMBER ALONG THE REAL AXIS	$kr = 0$ $kr \to \pm i\infty$	k REAL – STANDING WAVE k IMAGINARY – TWO EVANESCENT FIELDS k COMPLEX – LOCALIZED STANDING WAVE

WHEN $k=0$: $J_o=1$, $Y_o=\ln r$; $n=0$ AND $J_o=r^n$, $Y_o=r^{-n}$, $n\neq 0$; γ=EULER'S CONSTANT

$$J_n(kr) \xrightarrow[(kr)\to\infty]{} \sqrt{\frac{2}{\pi kr}} \cos (kr - \pi/4 - n\pi/2)$$

$$Y_n(kr) \xrightarrow[(kr)\to\infty]{} \sqrt{\frac{2}{\pi kr}} \sin (kr - \pi/4 - n\pi/2)$$

$$H_n^{(1)}(kr) \xrightarrow[(kr)\to\infty]{} \sqrt{\frac{2}{\pi kr}}\, e^{ikr} e^{-i(2n+1)\pi/4}$$

$$H_n^{(2)}(kr) \xrightarrow[(kr)\to\infty]{} \sqrt{\frac{2}{\pi kr}}\, e^{-ikr} e^{i(2n+1)\pi/4}$$

$$\left.\begin{array}{l} I_n(kr) \xrightarrow[(kr)\to\infty]{} \dfrac{e^{ikr}}{\sqrt{2\pi kr}} \\[2em] K_n(kr) \xrightarrow[(kr)\to\infty]{} \sqrt{\dfrac{\pi}{2kr}}\, e^{-kr} \end{array}\right\} (kr) \text{ imaginary.}$$

Thus, we observe that, except for an attenuation of $1/\sqrt{kr}$, the following qualitative analogies can be made:

$$\begin{array}{lll}
J_n(kr) & \text{analogous to} & \cos (kr) \\
Y_n(kr) & \text{analogous to} & \sin (kr) \\
H_n^{(1)}(kr) & \text{analogous to} & e^{ikr} \\
H_n^{(2)}(kr) & \text{analogous to} & e^{-ikr}.
\end{array}$$

For example, J_n and Y_n exhibit oscillatory behavior for real k, as do the sinusoidal functions. Hence, these solutions represent cylindrical standing waves. The $H_n^{(1)}$ and $H_n^{(2)}$ functions represent traveling waves for k real, as do the exponential functions. They therefore represent cylindrical traveling waves, $H_n^{(1)}$ representing outward traveling waves and $H_n^{(2)}$ representing inward traveling waves.

When k is purely imaginary, $k = i\beta$, the modified Bessel functions I_n and K_n are used. These are real when ik is real so that:

$$I_n(kr) \text{ is analogous to } e^{\beta r}$$
$$K_n(kr) \text{ is analogous to } e^{-\beta r}.$$

From these comments we conclude that the modified Bessel functions are used to represent evanescent waves.

Table 1 summarizes the properties of some of the cylinder functions.

(b) *Spherical Functions.*—The spherical Bessel functions behave qualitatively in the same manner as the corresponding cylindrical Bessel functions. For k real, $j_n(kr)$ and $y_n(kr)$ represent standing waves, $h_n^{(1)}(kr)$ represents an outward-traveling wave, and $h_n^{(2)}(kr)$ represents an inward-traveling wave. To represent a finite field outside of a sphere, we must choose outward-traveling waves to ensure proper behavior at infinity.

2. A Conducting Sphere in a Uniform Static Electric Field

We wish to determine the scalar potential ϕ of a conducting sphere in a uniform external field where the sphere possesses conductivity σ_2 and is embedded in a medium of conductivity σ_1. According to (A24) it is sufficient to consider only the scalar potential ϕ since the

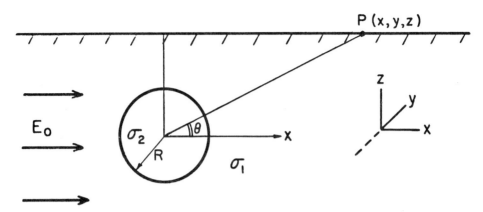

FIG. 2-1. Conducting sphere in uniform electrostatic field E_0. Conductivity of sphere, surroundings are σ_2, σ_1 respectively. Radius of sphere R. Point of observation $P(x, y, z)$. Note that θ is measured relative to the x axis in this figure and that ϕ is angular displacement about the z axis.

assumption of a static field demands that there be no time dependency in the expression for the electric field. Then

$$\mathbf{E} = - \nabla \phi \qquad (A2\text{-}1)$$

and we may ignore the magnetic field since we are interested solely in electrical measurements. We could, however, derive the magnetic field intensity H from the second Maxwell equation

$$\nabla \times \mathbf{H} = \mathbf{J} \qquad (A2\text{-}2)$$

should we so desire.

The problem, as established, is of direct interest in resistivity surveying for approximately spherical lenses of ore; an electrode array in which the current electrodes are widely spaced and fixed while the potential electrodes are close together and mobile would satisfy the conditions of the problem.

Referring to Figure 2-1, let an external field of magnitude E_0 be applied in the x direction. Then at large distances, where the influence of the sphere has disappeared, we have from (A2-1)

$$E_0 = - \frac{\partial \phi_0}{\partial x}$$

or

$$\phi_0 = - E_0 x \qquad (A2\text{-}3)$$

provided we neglect a constant of integration. According to (A31), the potential field must satisfy Laplace's equation because sources and time variations are excluded. Also, the spherical symmetry of the problem suggests that we seek solutions of Laplace's equation in spherical coordinates. Thus, according to (A340), we should seek solutions of the form (we now refer θ and ϕ to the x axis rather than the z axis in order that we might have z as vertical and x in the direction of a horizontal inducing field):

$$\phi = \sum_{n=0}^{\infty} \sum_{m=0}^{\infty} \left\{ a_{nm} r^n + \frac{b_{nm}}{r^{n+1}} \right\} P_n^m (\cos \theta) e^{im\phi}. \qquad (A2\text{-}4)$$

Furthermore, the primary potential ϕ_0 is symmetric about the x axis; consequently, it is independent of ϕ, a condition demanding $m=0$. Outside the sphere, the potential due to the sphere should be bounded at infinity, therefore positive powers of r must not appear outside. Inside the sphere, the solution must be finite at the origin so that negative powers of r must not appear there. Thus, the solution reduces to

$$\phi_e{}^a = \sum_{n=0}^{\infty} \frac{b_n}{r^{n+1}} P_n(\cos \theta) \tag{A2-5}$$

outside the sphere, and to

$$\phi_i{}^a = \sum_{n=0}^{\infty} a_n r^n P_n(\cos \theta) \tag{A2-6}$$

inside the sphere. These are the anomalous potentials $\phi_e{}^a$ and $\phi_i{}^a$. The physical requirement that the solution be finite at the origin and at infinity demands that $b_n=0$ inside the sphere, and $a_n=0$ outside the sphere.

At infinity the applied or normal potential ϕ^n is, by (A2-3),

$$\phi_\infty{}^n = - E_0 x = - E_0 r \cos \theta = - E_0 r P_1(\cos \theta). \tag{A2-7}$$

Then, in (A2-5), all b_n for $n>1$ must be zero and $a_0=b_0=0$ so that the total external potential $\phi_e = \phi_e{}^a + \phi_e{}^n$ is

$$\phi_e = \left\{ -E_0 r + \frac{b_1}{r^2} \right\} P_1(\cos \theta) \tag{A2-8}$$

where $- E_0 r \cos \theta$ represents the potential of the inducing field and $b_1/r^2 \cos \theta$ represents the potential of the induced field.

On the surface of the sphere, both the potential ϕ^s and the normal component of the current density $\mathbf{n} \cdot \mathbf{J} = \sigma \mathbf{E} \cdot \mathbf{n}$ must be continuous. For the potential to be continuous,

$$\phi_i{}^s = \phi_e{}^s$$

or

$$\sum_{n=0}^{\infty} a_n r^n P_n(\cos \theta) \Bigg|_{r=R} = \left\{ - E_0 r + \frac{b_1}{r^2} \right\} \cos \theta \Bigg|_{r=R} . \tag{A2-9}$$

Thus, $a_n=0$ for all n except $n=1$, and we obtain from (A2-9)

$$a_1 r \cos \theta \Bigg|_{r=R} = \left\{ - E_0 r + \frac{b_1}{r^2} \right\} \cos \theta \Bigg|_{r=R} . \tag{A2-10}$$

Hence we have

$$a_1 = - E_0 + \frac{b_1}{R^3} . \tag{A2-11}$$

Equation (A2-6) becomes simply

$$\phi_i{}^a = \left(- E_0 + \frac{b_1}{R^3} \right) r \cos \theta. \tag{A2-12}$$

The electric field intensity inside the sphere is

$$E_i{}^a = - \frac{\partial \phi_i{}^a}{\partial x} = - a_1 = E_0 - \frac{b_1}{R^3}. \tag{A2-13}$$

Note that it is a constant.

Since we wish to introduce the conductivities σ_1 and σ_2, it is desirable to use the continuity of the normal component of $\mathbf{J}$ at the surface of the sphere. Then

$$\mathbf{n} \cdot \mathbf{J}_1 = \mathbf{n} \cdot \mathbf{J}_2$$

$$- \sigma_2 \frac{\partial \phi_i}{\partial r} = - \sigma_1 \frac{\partial \phi_e}{\partial r}$$

$$- \sigma_2 \left(- E_0 + \frac{b_1}{R^3} \right) \cos \theta = - \sigma_1 \left\{ - E_0 - \frac{2b_1}{r^3} \right\} \cos \theta \bigg|_{r=R}. \tag{A2-14}$$

From which we obtain

$$\sigma_2 \left[E_0 - \frac{b_1}{R^3} \right] \cos \theta = \sigma_1 \left[E_0 + \frac{2b_1}{R^3} \right] \cos \theta \tag{A2-15}$$

or

$$b_1 = \left(\frac{\sigma_2 - \sigma_1}{\sigma_2 + 2\sigma_1} \right) E_0 R^3. \tag{A2-16}$$

Hence, the external potential is, from (A2-8) and (A2-16)

$$\phi_e = \left[- E_0 r + \frac{\sigma_2 - \sigma_1}{\sigma_2 + 2\sigma_1} E_0 R^3 \frac{1}{r^2} \right] \cos \theta. \tag{A2-17}$$

The applied field E_0 then leads to a normal potential $\phi_e{}^n = - E_0 r \cos \theta$ and an anomalous potential

$$\phi_e{}^a = \frac{\sigma_2 - \sigma_1}{\sigma_2 + 2\sigma_1} E_0 R^3 \frac{1}{r^2} \cos \theta.$$

In geophysical prospecting it is customary to consider the anomalous field only and to measure potential gradients. Thus, we wish to have the resulting anomalous field expressed in the form

$$\mathbf{E}^a = - \nabla \phi_e{}^a = \frac{\sigma_2 - \sigma_1}{\sigma_2 + 2\sigma_1} E_0 R^3 \left[\frac{2x^2 - y^2 - z^2}{r^5} \mathbf{i} + \frac{3xy}{r^5} \mathbf{j} + \frac{3xz}{r^5} \mathbf{k} \right]. \tag{A2-18}$$

Usually we confine our measurements to the direction of the applied field, i.e. the x direction, so that only the first term in the brackets of (A2-18) is used.

The quantity

$$P = \frac{\sigma_2 - \sigma_1}{\sigma_2 + 2\sigma_1} E_0 R^3 \tag{A2-19}$$

is the induced electric dipole moment of the sphere.

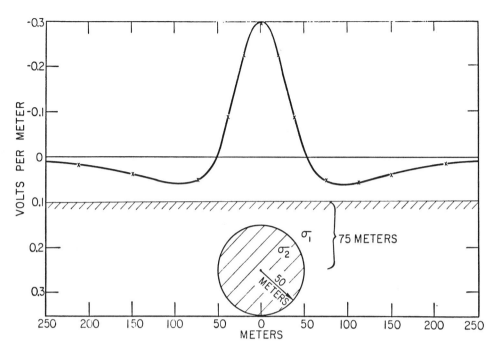

FIG. 2-2. Anomaly in electric field, in volts per meter, versus traverse distance across center of sphere of radius 50 m at depth 75 m, σ_2/σ_1, $E_0=1$ volt/meter.

Note, in this development, that the air-earth interface has been neglected.

The anomaly (A2-18) in the electric field intensity, i.e., horizontal voltage gradient, has een computed for a section through the center of the sphere and parallel to the applied eld E_0, and appears in Figure 2-2 for a ratio of $\sigma_2/\sigma_1=10$ and for $R=50$ meters, $z=75$ meters

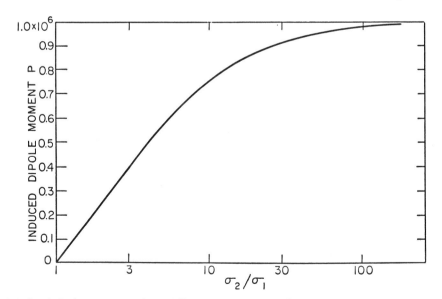

FIG. 2-3. Induced dipole moment $P=(\sigma_2-\sigma_1)/(\sigma_2+2\sigma_1)E_0R^3$ versus σ_2/σ_1 for buried sphere in electrostatic field.

and $E_0 = 1$ volt/meter. The equation (A2-18) is most conveniently used in the dimensionless form

$$E_x{}^a = \frac{\sigma_2 - \sigma_1}{\sigma_2 + 2\sigma_1} E_0 \left(\frac{R}{z}\right)^3 \left[\frac{2\left(\frac{x}{z}\right)^2 - 1}{\left\{\left(\frac{x}{z}\right)^2 + 1\right\}^{5/2}}\right] \tag{A2-20}$$

for such calculations.

The variation of the induced dipole moment (A2-19) as a function of σ_2/σ_1 for the same conditions is shown in Figure 2-3. Note that a saturation takes place at a σ_2/σ_1 ratio of about 10^2; resistivity contrasts greater than this do little to increase the dipole moment. On the other hand the dipole moment increases, without limit, as the cube of the radius of the sphere.

3. A Conducting Cylinder in a Uniform Transverse Electrostatic Field

For this problem we assume the electrostatic field to be perpendicular to the axis of a conducting cylinder of infinite length embedded in a conducting medium (Figure 3-1). Since there is no axial dependency, we are permitted to use the solution given by equation (A314) (with x now as the axial direction):

$$\phi = \sum_{n=1}^{\infty} (A_n \cos n\theta + B_n \sin n\theta)(C_n r^n + D_n r^{-n}). \tag{A3-1}$$

The applied field outside the cylinder is E_0 so that the applied potential, according to (A2-3), is

$$\phi_0 = -E_0 x = -E_0 r \cos \theta. \tag{A3-2}$$

At infinity, the potential superimposed on this, due to the induced charges on the cylinder, must vanish; no terms in r^n can therefore appear so that C_n equals zero. Further, the potential

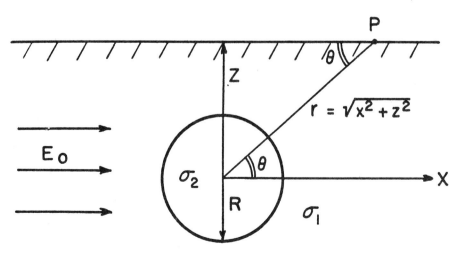

FIG. 3-1. Conducting cylinder in uniform transverse electrostatic field E_0. Conductivity of cylinder, surroundings are σ_2, σ_1 respectively. Radius of cylinder R. Point of observation $P(x, y, z)$. Note that θ is measured relative to the x axis as polar axis in this figure and that the positive y coordinate is into the page.

must be symmetric about the x axis and, hence, no terms involving $\sin n\theta$ can appear. Thus, B_n must be zero, and the potential outside the cylinder ϕ_e must be of the form

$$\phi_e = - E_0 r \cos \theta + \sum_{n=1}^{\infty} A_n{}^e r^{-n} \cos n\theta \qquad (A3\text{-}3)$$

where the constant $A_n{}^e = A_n D_n$.

Inside the cylinder, solutions involving r^{-n} must be excluded if the potential is to remain finite. Hence, we have

$$\phi_i = \sum_{n=1}^{\infty} [A_n{}^i \cos n\theta + B_n{}^i \sin n\theta] r^n \qquad (A3\text{-}4)$$

where $A_n{}^i = A_n C_n$ and $B_n{}^i = B_n C_n$.

At the boundary, where $r = R$, we must insist on the boundary conditions

$$\phi_e = \phi_i \big|_{r=R} \qquad (A3\text{-}5)$$

$$\sigma_1 \frac{\partial \phi_e}{\partial r} = \sigma_2 \frac{\partial \phi_i}{\partial r} \bigg|_{r=R}. \qquad (A3\text{-}6)$$

Boundary condition (A3-5) reveals that n must assume the value unity since the only positive power of r in equation (A3-3) is associated with the inducing potential and the power of r in that term is unity. Then

$$- E_0 R + \frac{A_1{}^e}{R} = A_1{}^i R \quad \text{and} \quad B_n{}^i = 0. \qquad (A3\text{-}7)$$

From boundary condition (A3-6) we find

$$- \sigma_1 E_0 - \frac{\sigma_1 A_1{}^e}{R^2} = \sigma_2 A_1{}^i. \qquad (A3\text{-}8)$$

Then

$$A_1{}^i = \frac{- 2\sigma_1 E_0}{\sigma_1 + \sigma_2} \qquad (A3\text{-}9)$$

and

$$A_1{}^e = E_0 R^2 \left[\frac{\sigma_2 - \sigma_1}{\sigma_2 + \sigma_1} \right]. \qquad (A3\text{-}10)$$

Therefore, the potential outside the cylinder is

$$\phi_e = - E_0 r \cos \theta + E_0 \frac{R^2}{r} \left[\frac{\sigma_2 - \sigma_1}{\sigma_2 + \sigma_1} \right] \cos \theta = \phi_e{}^n + \phi_e{}^a. \qquad (A3\text{-}11)$$

The second term in this last equation represents the anomalous or induced potential. The variation of the physical property parameter $(\sigma_2 - \sigma_1)/(\sigma_2 + \sigma_1)$ as a function of the ratio σ_2/σ_1 appears in Figure 3-3. Once again, the magnitude of the anomaly rises asymptotically to a saturation level as the ratio σ_2/σ_1 increases. As much as 82 percent of the peak anomaly is reached for a ratio σ_2/σ_1 of 10 and any further increase in conductivity contrast adds little to the magnitude of the anomaly. The anomalous potential decreases as the first power of

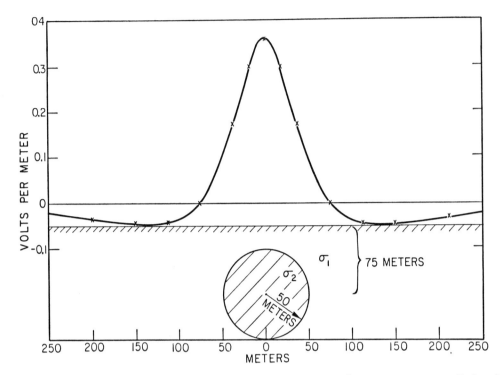

FIG. 3-2. Anomaly in electric field, in volts per meter, versus traverse distance transverse to cylinder of radius 50 m at depth 75 m, $\sigma_2/\sigma_1 = 10$, $E_0 = 1$ volt/meter.

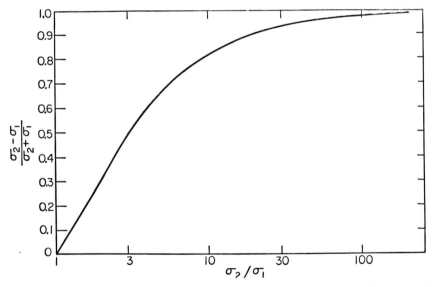

FIG. 3-3. Physical property factor $F = (\sigma_2 - \sigma_1)/(\sigma_2 + \sigma_1)$ versus σ_2/σ_1 for buried cylinder in electrostatic field.

The anomalous potential is the second term on the right of (A4-10). In magnetic prospecting we are interested in magnetic field intensity rather than magnetic potential. Hence, we obtain for the anomalous field

$$\mathbf{H}^a = -\nabla\phi_e^{*a} = \left[\frac{\mu_2 - \mu_1}{\mu_2 + 2\mu_1}\right] H_0 R^3 \left[\frac{2x^2 - y^2 - z^2}{r^5}\mathbf{i} + \frac{3xy}{r^5}\mathbf{j} + \frac{3xz}{r^5}\mathbf{k}\right]. \quad \text{(A4-11)}$$

We usually wish to express the physical property contrast in terms of susceptibilities rather than inductive capacities μ_i or permeabilities $K_m^{(i)}$. Thus, we may write

$$F = \frac{\mu_2 - \mu_1}{\mu_2 + 2\mu_1} = \frac{K_m^{(2)} - K_m^{(1)}}{K_m^{(2)} + 2K_m^{(1)}} = \frac{\chi_m^{(2)} - \chi_m^{(1)}}{\chi_m^{(2)} + 2\chi_m^{(1)} + 3}. \quad \text{(A4-12)}$$

Since (A4-12) is dimensionless, we may replace the mks $\chi_m^{(i)}$ by the cgs k_i where $\chi_m^{(i)} = 4\pi k_i$

$$F = \frac{4\pi(k_2 - k_1)}{4\pi(k_2 + 2k_1) + 3} = \frac{\frac{4\pi}{3}(k_2 - k_1)}{\frac{4\pi}{3}(k_2 + 2k_1) + 1}. \quad \text{(A4-13)}$$

This physical property factor F differs from that quoted in most texts on exploration geophysics (e.g. Heiland, p. 390). The typical formula given is

$$F' = \frac{\frac{4\pi}{3}(k_2 - k_1)}{\frac{4\pi}{3}(k_2 - k_1) + 1}. \quad \text{(A4-14)}$$

The expression (A4-14) is only correct when $k_1 = 0$, otherwise (A4-13) should be used.

The shape of the anomaly H_x^a is identical to that given in Figure 2-2 and the saturation effect for increasing ratio k_2/k_1 is shown in Figure 4-2.

5. A Permeable Cylinder in a Uniform Transverse Magnetostatic Field

If we compare equation (A2-18) and (A4-11), we observe that the anomalies in electrostatic and magnetostatic problems of the sphere in a uniform field are identical with the exception of the physical property factors

$$\frac{\sigma_2 - \sigma_1}{\sigma_2 + 2\sigma_1} \quad \text{and} \quad \frac{\mu_2 - \mu_1}{\mu_2 + 2\mu_1}.$$

Thus, when we study a permeable cylinder in a uniform transverse magnetostatic field, we anticipate that the anomaly in $\mathbf{H}$ will be identical to that in $\mathbf{E}$ [equation (A3-12)] with an appropriate change in the physical property factor. Thus, we may at once write down the anomaly in $\mathbf{H}$:

$$\mathbf{H} = -\nabla\phi_e^{*a} = \left[\frac{\mu_2 - \mu_1}{\mu_2 + \mu_1}\right] H_0 R^2 \left[\frac{(x^2 - z^2)\mathbf{i} + 2xz\mathbf{k}}{r^4}\right]. \quad \text{(A5-1)}$$

We can, of course, prove (A5-1) in the same manner that we developed (A3-18). The deductions concerning the form of the anomaly follow directly from the earlier analyses. Note that in all four of the equations (A2-18), (A3-12), (A4-11), and (A5-1) that the anomaly consists of the following four basic components:

$$A = (PPF) \cdot (IF) \cdot (SF) \cdot (GF) \tag{A5-2}$$

where

$$A = \text{anomaly}$$

$$PPF = \text{physical property factor}$$

$$IF = \text{inducing field}$$

$$SF = \text{size factor}$$

$$GF = \text{geometrical factor}$$

$$PPF = \frac{\alpha_2 - \alpha_1}{\alpha_2 + 2\alpha_1} \quad \text{for a sphere}$$

$$= \frac{\alpha_2 - \alpha_1}{\alpha_2 + \alpha_1} \quad \text{for a cylinder}$$

$$IF = H_0, E_0$$

$$SF = R^3 \quad \text{for a sphere}$$

$$= R^2 \quad \text{for a cylinder}$$

$$GF = \frac{(2x^2 - y^2 - z^2)\mathbf{i} + 3xy\mathbf{j} + 3xz\mathbf{k}}{r^5} \quad \text{for a sphere with inducing field in } x \text{ direction}$$

$$= \frac{(x^2 - z^2)\mathbf{i} + 2xz\mathbf{k}}{r^4} \quad \text{for a cylinder with inducing field in } x \text{ direction.}$$

6. A Conducting Permeable Sphere in a Harmonically Varying Magnetic Field

We wish to consider a sphere of conductivity σ_2 and inductive capacities μ_2 and ϵ_2 embedded in an infinite medium defined by the parameters σ_1, μ_1, and ϵ_1 (see Figure 6-1). A uniform alternating magnetic field

$$H = H_0 e^{-i\omega t} \tag{A6-1}$$

is applied in the x direction. For the field to be uniform in the vicinity of the sphere requires that $|k_1 R| \ll 1$ where k_1 is the propagation constant, of the infinite medium, defined by

$$k_1 = [\mu_1 \epsilon_1 \omega^2 + i\mu_1 \sigma_1 \omega]^{1/2}. \tag{A6-2}$$

The inequality $|k_1 R| \ll 1$ really implies that the wavelength in the external medium is much greater than the radius of the sphere ($k_1 = 2\pi/\lambda_1$). Under this restriction the amplitude of the inducing field is sensibly constant across the sphere. The propagation constant for the medium of the sphere is,

$$k_2 = [\mu_2 \epsilon_2 \omega^2 + i\mu_2 \sigma_2 \omega]^{1/2}. \tag{A6-3}$$

Since the source of excitation is purely magnetic we may use the Hertz vector $\boldsymbol{\pi}^*$ from which the magnetic field may be computed via equation (A77) restricted to magnetic sources solely:

$$\mathbf{H} = \nabla\nabla \cdot \boldsymbol{\pi}^* + k^2 \boldsymbol{\pi}^*. \tag{A6-4}$$

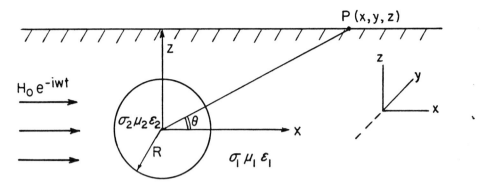

FIG. 6-1. Conducting permeable sphere in uniform alternating magnetic field $H_0 e^{-i\omega t}$. Constants of sphere, surroundings are $\sigma_2\mu_2\epsilon_2$, $\sigma_1\mu_1\epsilon_1$ respectively. Radius of sphere R. Point of observation $P(x, y, z)$.

Since the primary field is uniform, it is divergenceless, so that it may be represented simply in terms of a potential π_0^* by

$$\mathbf{H}_0 = k^2\pi_0^*. \tag{A6-5}$$

There must be symmetry about the x axis because of the uniform applied field in the x direction. Since the electric currents must be confined to the z-y plane because H_0 is perpendicular to this plane, then the electric vector is confined to the z-y plane, i.e., it is transverse. Then by analogy with equations (A306) and (A307) we need only an x component of π^* which we designate π_x^*; the vector wave equation reduces to the scalar wave equation and we may proceed to solve it as follows.

Since there is symmetry about the x axis, then we can seek solutions of the wave equation for π_x^*, in spherical coordinates, with no ϕ dependency. Thus, we might seek scalar solutions of the form given by equation (A339).

$$\pi_{x0}^* = \sum_{n=0}^{\infty} b_n h_n^{(1)}(k_1 r) P_n(\cos\theta) \tag{A6-6}$$

for traveling wave solutions finite at infinity, or

$$\pi_{x2}^* = \sum_{n=0}^{\infty} a_n j_n(k_2 r) P_n(\cos\theta) \tag{A6-7}$$

for standing wave solutions finite at the origin. Outside the sphere, then, the potential for both primary and secondary fields is

$$\pi_{x1}^* = \frac{H_0}{k_1^2} + \sum_{n=0}^{\infty} b_n h_n^{(1)}(k_1 r) P_n(\cos\theta). \tag{A6-8}$$

The boundary conditions are:

(1) $\mathbf{n} \cdot (\mathbf{B}_2 - \mathbf{B}_1) = 0$,   normal $\mathbf{B}$ is continuous.

(2) $\mathbf{n} \times (\mathbf{H}_2 - \mathbf{H}_1) = 0$,   tangential $\mathbf{H}$ is continuous.

These conditions apply at the boundary of the sphere where $r = R$. Since we have only the zeroth order Legendre Polynomial $P_0(\cos\theta) = 1$ inherent in H_0/k_1^2, then n must be limited to the zero order throughout equations (A6-7) and (A6-8) if the boundary conditions are to be satisfied. This requires that $a_n = b_n = 0$ for $n > 0$. For $n = 0$,

$$h_n^{(1)}(kr) = \frac{e^{ikr}}{ikr} \quad \text{and} \quad j_n(kr) = \frac{\sin (kr)}{kr}$$

(Harrington 1961, p. 266) so that (A6-7) and (A6-8) simplify to

$$\pi_{z1}{}^* = \frac{H_0}{k_1{}^2} + b_0 \frac{e^{ik_1r}}{r} \tag{A6-9}$$

$$\pi_{z2}{}^* = a_0 \frac{\sin k_2 r}{r} \tag{A6-10}$$

a result corresponding to that obtained by Stratton (1941, p. 405–406). Note that the constants ik_1 and k_2 have been absorbed in b_0 and a_0, respectively. Returning now to the boundary conditions, we must evaluate them in terms of the vector potential π^* via the relation

$$\mathbf{H} = \nabla\nabla \cdot \pi^* + k^2 \pi^*.$$

In spherical coordinates (Sommerfeld 1952, p. 150),

$$\nabla_r \nabla \cdot \pi^* = \cos\theta \frac{\partial^2 \pi_z{}^*}{\partial r^2}$$

$$\nabla_\theta \nabla \cdot \pi^* = -\frac{\sin\theta}{r} \frac{\partial \pi_z{}^*}{\partial r}$$

$$\nabla_\phi \nabla \cdot \pi^* = 0$$

so that

$$\mathbf{n} \cdot (\mu_2 \mathbf{H}_2 - \mu_1 \mathbf{H}_1) = \mu_2 \left(\frac{\partial^2 \pi_{z2}{}^*}{\partial r^2} + k_2{}^2 \pi_{z2}{}^* \right) - \mu_1 \left(\frac{\partial^2 \pi_{z1}{}^*}{\partial r^2} + k_1{}^2 \pi_{z1}{}^* \right) = 0$$

and

$$\mathbf{n} \times (\mathbf{H}_2 - \mathbf{H}_1) = \left(\frac{1}{r} \frac{\partial \pi_{z2}{}^*}{\partial r} + k_2{}^2 \pi_{z2}{}^* \right) - \left(\frac{1}{r} \frac{\partial \pi_{z1}{}^*}{\partial r} + k_1{}^2 \pi_{z1}{}^* \right) = 0.$$

Then the boundary condition for normal $\mathbf{B}$ continuous becomes, in terms of the potential in spherical coordinates,

$$\mu_2 \left(\frac{\partial^2 \pi_{z2}{}^*}{\partial r^2} + k_2{}^2 \pi_{z2}{}^* \right) = \mu_1 \left(\frac{\partial^2 \pi_{z1}{}^*}{\partial r^2} + k_1{}^2 \pi_{z1}{}^* \right) \Big|_{r=R}. \tag{A6-11}$$

Similarly the boundary condition for tangential $\mathbf{H}$ continuous becomes

$$\frac{1}{r} \frac{\partial \pi_{z2}{}^*}{\partial r} + k_2{}^2 \pi_{z2}{}^* = \frac{1}{r} \frac{\partial \pi_{z1}{}^*}{\partial r} + k_2{}^2 \pi_{z1}{}^* \Big|_{r=R}. \tag{A6-12}$$

We now wish to substitute equations (A6-9) and (A6-10) in (A6-11) and (A6-12). To facilitate development of the argument, we proceed as follows:

$$\pi_{x2}{}^* = a_0 \frac{\sin k_2 r}{r} \tag{A6-13}$$

$$\frac{\partial \pi_{x2}{}^*}{\partial r} = \frac{a_0 k_2 \cos k_2 r}{r} - \frac{a_0 \sin k_2 r}{r^2} \tag{A6-14}$$

$$\frac{\partial^2 \pi_{x2}{}^*}{\partial r^2} = \frac{-a_0 k_2{}^2 \sin k_2 r}{r} - \frac{a_0 k_2 \cos k_2 r}{r^2} - \frac{a_0 k_2 \cos k_2 r}{r^2} + \frac{2 a_0 \sin k_2 r}{r^3}$$

$$= \frac{-a_0 k_2{}^2 \sin k_2 r}{r} - \frac{2 a_0 k_2 \cos k_2 r}{r^2} + \frac{2 a_0 \sin k_2 r}{r^3} \tag{A6-15}$$

$$\mu_2 \left(\frac{\partial^2 \pi_{x2}{}^*}{\partial r^2} + k_2{}^2 \pi_{x2}{}^* \right) = \frac{2 a_0 \mu_2 (\sin k_2 r - k_2 r \cos k_2 r)}{r^3}. \tag{A6-16}$$

The expression (A6-16) is to be evaluated at $r = R$; to facilitate this we multiply both sides by R_3 and set $R k_2 = \alpha$.

$$R^3 \mu_2 \left(\frac{\partial^2 \pi_{x2}{}^*}{\partial r^2} + k_2{}^2 \pi_{x2}{}^* \right) = 2 a_0 \mu_2 [\sin \alpha - \alpha \cos \alpha]. \tag{A6-17}$$

Similarily

$$\pi_{x1}{}^* = \frac{H_0}{k_1{}^2} + \frac{b_0 e^{i k_1 r}}{r} \tag{A6-18}$$

$$\frac{\partial \pi_{x1}{}^*}{\partial r} = \frac{b_0 e^{i k_1 r} i k_1}{r} - \frac{b_0 e^{i k_1 r}}{r^2} \tag{A6-19}$$

$$\frac{\partial^2 \pi_{x1}{}^*}{\partial r^2} = \frac{-b_0 k_1{}^2 e^{i k_1 r}}{r} - \frac{b_0 i k_1 e^{i k_1 r}}{r^2} - \frac{b_0 i k_1 e^{i k_1 r}}{r^2} + \frac{2 b_0 e^{i k_1 r}}{r^3} \tag{A6-20}$$

$$\mu_1 \left(\frac{\partial^2 \pi_{x1}{}^*}{\partial r^2} + k_1{}^2 \pi_{x1}{}^* \right) = \frac{-\mu_1 b_0 k_1{}^2 e^{i k_1 r}}{r} - \frac{k_1 2 i \mu_1 b_0 e^{i k_1 r}}{r^2} - \frac{2 \mu_1 b_0 e^{i k_1 r}}{r^2}$$

$$+ \frac{\mu_1 k_1{}^2 b_0 e^{i k_1 r}}{r} + \mu_1 H_0. \tag{A6-21}$$

In (A6-21), we wish to evaluate the right hand side at $r = R$; to facilitate this we multiply both sides by R^3, and invoke the basic premise that $|R k_1| \ll 1$.

$$R^3 \mu_1 \left(\frac{\partial^2 \pi_{x1}{}^*}{\partial r^2} + k_1{}^2 \pi_{x1}{}^* \right) = 2 \mu_1 b_0 + \mu_1 H_0 R^3 \tag{A6-22}$$

If we now equate (A6-17) and (A6-22), which is a procedure dictated by the boundary condition (A6-11), there results

$$2 a_0 \mu_2 (\sin \alpha - \alpha \cos \alpha) = 2 \mu_1 b_0 + \mu_1 H_0 R^3 \tag{A6-23}$$

from which we obtain

$$a_0 = \frac{\mu_1}{\mu_2} b_0 \frac{1}{[\sin \alpha - \alpha \cos \alpha]} + \frac{\mu_1}{2 \mu_2} H_0 R^3 \frac{1}{[\sin \alpha - \alpha \cos \alpha]}. \tag{A6-24}$$

The second boundary condition (A6-12) yields:

$$\frac{a_0 k_2 \cos k_2 r}{r^2} - \frac{a_0 \sin k_2 r}{r^3} + k_2^2 a_0 \frac{\sin k_2 r}{r}$$

$$= \frac{b_0 i k_1 e^{i k_1 r}}{r^2} - \frac{b_0 e^{i k_1 r}}{r^3} + \frac{k_1^2 b_0 e^{i k_1 r}}{r} + H_0 \qquad \text{(A6-25)}$$

again we may invoke the premise that $|Rk_1| \ll 1$ and evaluate (A6-25) at $r = R$, multiplying through by R^3 and setting $\alpha = k_2 R$ facilitate the computation

$$a_0[\alpha \cos \alpha - \sin \alpha + \alpha^2 \sin \alpha] = - b_0 + H_0 R^3$$

or

$$a_0 = - b_0 \frac{1}{[\alpha \cos \alpha - \sin \alpha + \alpha^2 \sin \alpha]} + H_0 R^3 \frac{1}{[\alpha \cos \alpha - \sin \alpha + \alpha^2 \sin \alpha]} \cdot \qquad \text{(A6-26)}$$

We may now equate (A6-24) and (A6-26) to find an expression for b_0 in terms of the parameters of the system. We find

$$b_0 = H_0 R^3 \frac{2\mu_2[\sin \alpha - \alpha \cos \alpha] - \mu_1[\alpha \cos \alpha - \sin \alpha + \alpha^2 \sin \alpha]}{2\mu_2[\sin \alpha - \alpha \cos \alpha] + 2\mu_1[\alpha \cos \alpha - \sin \alpha + \alpha^2 \sin \alpha]} \cdot \qquad \text{(A6-27)}$$

If we now substitute $\alpha = i\beta$, we obtain the equivalent form

$$b_0 = H_0 R^3 \frac{2\mu_2[\sinh \beta - \beta \cosh \beta] + \mu_1[\sinh \beta - \beta \cosh \beta + \beta^2 \sinh \beta]}{2\mu_2[\sinh \beta - \beta \cosh \beta] - 2\mu_1[\sinh \beta - \beta \cosh \beta + \beta^2 \sinh \beta]} \qquad \text{(A6-28)}$$

which is identical, except for nomenclature, to the result obtained by Wait (1951). For computational purposes we will want to use (A6-27) in the form

$$b_0 = H_0 R^3 \frac{2\mu_2[\tan \alpha - \alpha] - \mu_1[\alpha - \tan \alpha + \alpha^2 \tan \alpha]}{2\mu_2[\tan \alpha - \alpha] + 2\mu_1[\alpha - \tan \alpha + \alpha^2 \tan \alpha]} \qquad \text{(A6-29)}$$

where

$$\alpha = k_2 R - (\mu_2 \epsilon_2 \omega^2 + i\mu_2 \sigma_2 \omega)^{1/2} R. \qquad \text{(A6-30)}$$

If we might neglect displacement currents then we may write (A6-30) as

$$\alpha = (i\mu_2 \sigma_2 \omega)^{1/2} R = (i)^{1/2}\theta \qquad \text{(A6-31)}$$

where

$$\theta = (\sigma_2 \mu_2 \omega)^{1/2} R. \qquad \text{(A6-32)}$$

Wait (1951) wrote the formula (A6-28) in the form

$$b_0 = H_0 R^3(M - iN) \qquad \text{(A6-33)}$$

for a sphere of negligible permeability. In the general case then,

$$(M - iN) = \left[\frac{2\mu_2(\tan \alpha - \alpha) - \mu_1(\alpha - \tan \alpha + \alpha^2 \tan \alpha)}{2\mu_2(\tan \alpha - \alpha) + 2\mu_1(\alpha - \tan \alpha + \alpha^2 \tan \alpha)} \right]. \qquad \text{(A6-34)}$$

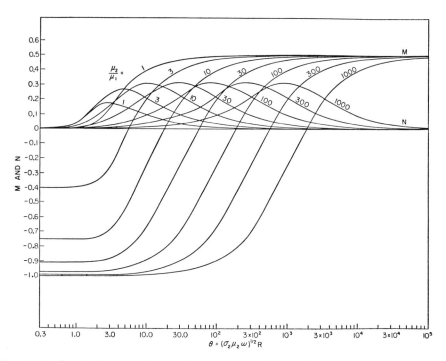

FIG. 6-2. In-phase (M) and out-of-phase (N) components of induced dipole moment of a sphere in a uniform alternating magnetic field. Signs of M and N changed for convenience.

The in-phase and quadrature functions M and N are plotted versus the dimensionless parameter θ, for various values of μ_2/μ_1, in Figure (A6-2). The permeability ratios range from one (free space) to 1,000 (steel).

The external magnetic field components are given by equation (A6-4) with π^* given by equation (A6-9). Since we customarily measure magnetic field components with reference to a Cartesian coordinate system, it becomes desirable to compute (A6-4) in such a system. This is most easily accomplished by writing the Hertz potential for the anomalous external field as

$$\pi_{x1}^* = b_0 \frac{1}{r} e^{ik_1 r} e^{-i\omega t} = b_0 \frac{1}{r} e^{i(k_1 r - \omega t)}. \tag{A6-35}$$

The geometry of the field is then obtained simply as $\nabla\nabla\cdot(1/r)$ since $e^{i(k_1 r - \omega t)}$ represents the propagation outward.

$$\nabla\nabla\cdot\left(\frac{1}{r}\right) = \frac{\partial^2\left(\dfrac{1}{r}\right)}{\partial x^2}\mathbf{i} + \frac{\partial^2\left(\dfrac{1}{r}\right)}{\partial y \partial x}\mathbf{j} + \frac{\partial^2\left(\dfrac{1}{r}\right)}{\partial z \partial x}\mathbf{k}$$

$$= \frac{(2x^2 - y^2 - z^2)\mathbf{i} + 3xy\mathbf{j} + 3xz\mathbf{k}}{r^5}. \tag{A6-36}$$

Then the Cartesian components of the external magnetic field are

$$H_x(\omega) = R^3 H_0 (M - iN) \frac{2x^2 - y^2 - z^2}{r^5} + H_0$$

$$H_y(\omega) = R^3 H_0 (M - iN) \frac{3xy}{r^5} \Bigg\}. \quad\quad\quad \text{(A6-37)}$$

$$H_z(\omega) = R^3 H_0 (M - iN) \frac{3xz}{r^5}$$

The field is that of a dipole with axis oriented in the x direction. The induced dipole moment is

$$P = R^3 H_0 (M - iN) \times 4\pi. \quad\quad\quad \text{(A6-38)}$$

It is of interest to compare the above development with that due to Wait (1951). Wait used a positive harmonic time dependency $e^{i\omega t}((e^{-i\omega t}))$ so that his propagation constant is denoted by $\gamma = (i\sigma\mu\omega - \epsilon\mu\omega^2)^{1/2}$ $((k = (i\sigma\mu\omega + \epsilon\mu\omega^2)^{1/2}))$. Further, the positive time dependency causes the wave equation to appear in the form $(\nabla^2 - \gamma^2)\psi = 0$ rather than $(\nabla^2 + k^2)\psi = 0$. The magnetic vector $\mathbf{F} = i\mu\omega\, \pi^*$ was employed by Wait rather than π^*. Because the wave equation was of the form $(\nabla^2 - \gamma^2)\psi = 0$, solutions arose in terms of modified spherical Bessel functions rather than spherical Bessel functions. The result of this last point is to lead to solutions directly in terms of hyperbolic trigonometric functions rather than the trigonometric functions employed herein. The solution obtained here is otherwise identical with that due to Wait. Note, however, that we include the factor $(-\frac{3}{2})$ in M and N.

7. A Conducting Permeable Cylinder in a Harmonically Varying Magnetic Field

7-I. *Introduction*

Let us now treat an infinite cylinder of constants $\epsilon_2\mu_2\sigma_2$ embedded in a medium of constants $\epsilon_1\mu_1\sigma_1$ on which there is incident a uniform inducing magnetic field of angular frequency ω. We wish to deal with the inducing field both transverse and parallel to the axis of the cylinder. Once we obtain these two solutions we can, if we wish, combine them to obtain the solution for an arbitrarily oriented inducing field and, in fact, for an elliptically polarized field of arbitrary orientation. The geometry of the problem is illustrated in Figure 7-1. Since the problem is two-dimensional there can be no y dependency in the solutions we seek. Because we wish to develop both the transverse and parallel cases, we shall find it convenient to use the Schelkunoff symmetrical wave potentials which we had earlier defined by the following set of equations.

(a) electric sources

$$\nabla \times \mathbf{E} = i\omega\mu\mathbf{H} \quad\quad\quad \text{(A7-1)}$$

$$\nabla \cdot \mathbf{H} = 0 \qu\quad\quad\quad \text{(A7-2)}$$

$$\mathbf{H} = \nabla \times \mathbf{G} \qu\quad\quad\quad \text{(A7-3)}$$

$$\mathbf{E} = i\omega\mu\mathbf{G} - \nabla V \qu\quad\quad\quad \text{(A7-4)}$$

$$V = -\frac{\nabla \cdot \mathbf{G}}{\sigma - i\omega\epsilon} \qu\quad\quad\quad \text{(A7-5)}$$

$$\mathbf{E} = i\omega\mu\mathbf{G} + \frac{1}{\sigma - i\omega\epsilon}\nabla\nabla \cdot \mathbf{G} \qu\quad\quad\quad \text{(A7-6)}$$

$$\nabla^2\psi + k^2\psi = 0, \quad \psi = \mathbf{G}, V \qu\quad\quad\quad \text{(A7-7)}$$

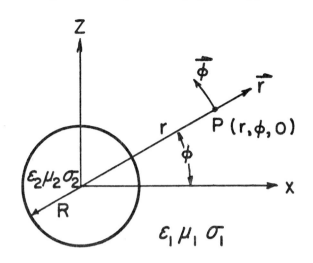

Y INTO PAGE

Fig. 7-1. Conducting permeable cylinder in uniform alternating magnetic field $H_0 e^{-i\omega t}$. Constants of cylinder, surroundings of $\sigma_2\mu_2\epsilon_2$, $\sigma_1\mu_1\epsilon_1$ respectively. Radius of sphere R. Point of observation $P(r, \phi, 0)$.

(b) magnetic sources

$$\nabla \times \mathbf{H} = (\sigma - i\omega\epsilon)\,\mathbf{E} \tag{A7-8}$$

$$\nabla \cdot \mathbf{E} = 0 \tag{A7-9}$$

$$\mathbf{E} = -\nabla \times \mathbf{F} \tag{A7-10}$$

$$\mathbf{H} = -(\sigma - i\omega\epsilon)\mathbf{F} - \nabla U \tag{A7-11}$$

$$U = \frac{\nabla \cdot \mathbf{F}}{i\omega\mu} \tag{A7-12}$$

$$\mathbf{H} = -(\sigma - i\omega\epsilon)\mathbf{F} - \frac{1}{i\omega\mu}\nabla\nabla\cdot\mathbf{F} \tag{A7-13}$$

$$\nabla^2\psi + k^2\psi = 0, \qquad \psi = \mathbf{F},\, U. \tag{A7-14}$$

7-II. *Transverse inducing field*

For a transverse field, equation (A7-3) will give the secondary fields due to electric currents induced in the cylinder by a primary field. The secondary magnetic fields are, from (A7-3)

$$H_r = \frac{1}{r}\frac{\partial G_y}{\partial \phi} - \frac{\partial G_\phi}{\partial y} \tag{A7-15}$$

$$H_\phi = \frac{\partial G_r}{\partial y} - \frac{\partial G_y}{\partial r} \tag{A7-16}$$

$$H_y = \frac{1}{r}\left[\frac{\partial}{\partial r}(rG_\phi) - \frac{\partial G_r}{\partial \phi}\right]. \tag{A7-17}$$

Since the cylinder is infinite, $H_y = 0$ and $\partial/\partial y = 0$, so that the above equations reduce to:

$$H_r = \frac{1}{r}\frac{\partial G_y}{\partial \phi} \tag{A7-18}$$

$$H_\phi = -\frac{\partial G_y}{\partial r} \tag{A7-19}$$

$$H_y = 0. \tag{A7-20}$$

Since there is only a y component of the potential **G**, the wave equation (A7-7) becomes

$$\nabla^2 G_y + k_2{}^2 G_y = 0 \qquad r \le R. \tag{A7-21}$$

We seek a solution of the physical problem in which displacement currents may be neglected so that the propagation constant for the cylinder may be written

$$k_2{}^2 = i\mu_2\sigma_2\omega. \tag{A7-22}$$

Since the field is assumed uniform, then $|k_1 R| \ll 1$ as for the sphere problem preceding, where

$$k_1{}^2 = \mu_1\epsilon_1\omega^2 + i\mu_1\sigma_1\omega. \tag{A7-23}$$

If we assume the external medium to be nonconducting, $\sigma_1 = 0$, then the contribution to the propagation comes from the displacement currents only. Since we have neglected the displacement currents relative to the conduction currents in the cylinder and since we are prepared to assume that $\epsilon_1 \sim \epsilon_2$, then we are obliged to neglect the displacement currents in the external medium; they will contribute no significant magnetic field under the assumptions made. Thus, we may set $k_1 = 0$ and we need then only seek a solution of Laplace's equation in the external medium.

$$\nabla^2 G_y = 0 \qquad r > R. \tag{A7-24}$$

The solutions of (A7-21) and (A7-24) follow directly from (A301) and (A314)

$$G_y = \sum_{n=1}^{\infty} (A_n \cos n\phi + B_n \sin n\phi) J_n(k_2 r); \qquad r \le R \tag{A7-25}$$

and

$$G_y = \sum_{n=1}^{\infty} (A_n \cos n\phi + B_n \sin n\phi)(C_n r^n + D_n r^{-n}); \qquad r > R. \tag{A7-26}$$

We have been forced to exclude $n=0$ in (A7-25) and (A7-26) in order to avoid induced monopoles [see comments subsequent to (A314)].

The primary or applied field outside the cylinder is $H = H_0 e^{-i\omega t}$, and its radial component is $H_r = H_0 \cos \phi e^{-i\omega t}$, so that the applied potential, derived from (A7-15), is

$$G_y = H_0 r \sin \phi e^{-i\omega t}. \tag{A7-27}$$

At infinity, the potential due to the secondary field must vanish; then in (A7-26) there can be no terms in r^n with the result that C_n equals zero. The potential outside the cylinder $G_y{}^e$ must be of the form

$$G_y^e = H_0 r \sin \phi + \sum_{n=1}^{\infty} [A_n^e \cos n\phi + B_n^e \sin n\phi] r^{-n} \tag{A7-28}$$

where $A_n^e = A_n D_n$ and $B_n^e = B_n D_n$.

Inside the cylinder, solutions involving r^{-n} must be excluded if the potential is to remain finite. Hence, we have

$$G_y^i = \sum_{n=1}^{\infty} [A_n^i \cos n\phi + B_n^i \sin n\phi] J_n(k_2 r). \tag{A7-29}$$

At the boundary, where $r = R$, we must insist on the boundary conditions

$$G_y^e = G_y^i|_{r=R} \qquad \text{(potential continuous)} \tag{A7-30}$$

$$\mu_1 \left(\frac{\partial G_y^e}{\partial r} \right) = \mu_2 \left(\frac{\partial G_y^i}{\partial r} \right) \Big|_{r=R} \qquad \text{(normal } B \text{ continuous)}. \tag{A7-31}$$

Boundary condition (A7-30) reveals that n must assume the value unity since the only positive power of r in equation (A7-28) is associated with the inducing potential and the power of r in that term is unity. Thus

$$A_1^e R^{-1} = A_1^i J_1(k_2 R)$$

$$H_0 R + B_1^e R^{-1} = B_1^i J_1(k_2 R). \tag{A7-32}$$

From boundary condition (A7-31) we find

$$-\mu_1 A_1^e R^{-2} = \mu_2 A_1^i \frac{d}{dr} \{J_1(k_2 r)\} \Big|_{r=R}$$

$$-\mu_1 B_1^e R^{-2} + \mu_1 H_0 = \mu_2 B_1^i \frac{d}{dr} \{J_1(k_2 r)\} \Big|_{r=R}. \tag{A7-33}$$

The differentiation formula for Bessel functions (Watson, 1944, p. 45) is now applied

$$\frac{d}{dr} \{J_n(kr)\} = k \left[J_{n-1}(kr) - \frac{n}{kr} J_n(kr) \right]. \tag{A7-34}$$

Equation (A7-33) now becomes

$$-\mu_1 B_1^e R^{-2} + \mu_1 H_0 = \mu_2 B_1^i \left[k J_0(k_2 R) - \frac{1}{R} J_1(k_2 R) \right]. \tag{A7-35}$$

Equations (A7-32) and (A7-35), constituting two equations in the two unknowns B_1^e and B_1^i, may now be solved simultaneously by application of Cramer's rule (Wylie, 1960, p. 32). Rewriting (A7-32) and (A7-35)

$$B_1^e R^{-1} - B_1^i J_1(k_2 R) = -H_0 R$$

$$B_1^e \mu_1 R^{-2} + B_1^i \mu_2 \left[k_2 J_0(k_2 R) - \frac{1}{R} J_1(k_2 R) \right] = \mu_1 H_0.$$

and

$$
B_1{}^e = \frac{
\begin{vmatrix}
-H_0R & -J_1(\alpha) \\[2mm]
\mu_1 H_0 & \mu_2\left[k_2 J_0(\alpha) - \dfrac{1}{R}J_1(\alpha)\right]
\end{vmatrix}
}{
\begin{vmatrix}
R^{-1} & -J_1(\alpha) \\[2mm]
\mu_1 R^{-2} & \mu_2\left[k_2 J_0(\alpha) - \dfrac{1}{R}J_1(\alpha)\right]
\end{vmatrix}
}, \qquad \alpha = k_2 R
$$

or

$$
B_1{}^e = R^2 H_0 \left[\frac{-\alpha J_0(\alpha) + J_1(\alpha)\left(\dfrac{\mu_1}{\mu_2}+1\right)}{\alpha J_0(\alpha) + J_1(\alpha)\left(\dfrac{\mu_1}{\mu_2}-1\right)}\right]. \tag{A7-36}
$$

Similarily

$$
B_1{}^e = \frac{2\mu_1 H_0 R}{\alpha J_0(\alpha) + J_1(\alpha)\left(\dfrac{\mu_1}{\mu_2}-1\right)}. \tag{A7-37}
$$

Simultaneous solution of the two expressions for $A_1{}^i$ and $A_1{}^e$ can only be effected for $A_1{}^e = A_1{}^i = 0$.

The fields may now be derived directly from (A7-25) and (A7-26) upon application of (A7-18) through (A7-20).

$$
H_r = \frac{1}{r} J_1(k_2 r) B_1{}^i \cos\phi; \qquad r \le R \tag{A7-38}
$$

$$
H_\phi = -\frac{d}{dr}\{J_1(k_2 r)\} B_1{}^i \sin\phi; \qquad r \le R \tag{A7-39}
$$

$$
H_r = r^{-2} B_1{}^e \cos\phi; \qquad r > R \tag{A7-40}
$$

$$
H_\phi = r^{-2} B_1{}^e \sin\phi; \qquad r > R. \tag{A7-41}
$$

In geophysical prospecting we are interested only in the external field described by equations (A7-40) and (A7-41); these may be simplified, since we now have evaluated all of the constants, to

$$
H_r = H_0 \cos\phi\, e^{-i\omega t} + H_0\left(\frac{R}{r}\right)^2 \left[\frac{-k_2 R J_0(k_2 R) + J_1(k_2 R)\left(\dfrac{\mu_1}{\mu_2}+1\right)}{k_2 R J_0(k_2 R) + J_1(k_2 R)\left(\dfrac{\mu_1}{\mu_2}-1\right)}\right]\cos\phi\, e^{-i\omega t} \tag{A7-42}
$$

$$
H_\phi = -H_0\sin\phi\, e^{-i\omega t} + H_0\left(\frac{R}{r}\right)^2 \left[\frac{-k_2 R J_0(k_2 R) + J_1(k_2 R)\left(\dfrac{\mu_1}{\mu_2}+1\right)}{k_2 R J_0(k_2 R) + J_1(k_2 R)\left(\dfrac{\mu_1}{\mu_2}-1\right)}\right]\sin\phi\, e^{-i\omega t}. \tag{A7-43}
$$

If the cylinder and its surroundings have permeabilities equal to that of free space, $\mu_2 = \mu_1 = \mu_0$, then equation (A7-42) and (A7-43) will simplify upon application of the recurrence formula (Watson 1944, p. 45)

$$\alpha J_2(\alpha) = 2J_1(\alpha) - \alpha J_0(\alpha); \qquad \alpha = k_2 R. \tag{A7-44}$$

Thus, the result we find is

$$H_r = H_0 \cos \phi e^{-i\omega t} + H_0 \left(\frac{R}{r}\right)^2 \left[\frac{J_2(\alpha)}{J_0(\alpha)}\right] \cos \phi e^{-i\omega t}; \qquad \alpha = k_2 R \tag{A7-45}$$

and

$$H_\phi = - H_0 \sin \phi e^{-i\omega t} + H_0 \left(\frac{R}{r}\right)^2 \left[\frac{J_2(\alpha)}{J_0(\alpha)}\right] \sin \phi e^{-i\omega t}. \tag{A7-46}$$

By analogy with the sphere problem we might write, from (A7-36)

$$B_1^e = - H_0 R^2 (M - iN) \tag{A7-47}$$

where

$$M - iN = \frac{\mu_2 [\alpha J_0(\alpha) - J_1(\alpha)] - \mu_1 J_1(\alpha)}{\mu_2 [\alpha J_0(\alpha) - J_1(\alpha)] + \mu_1 J_1(\alpha)}. \tag{A7-48}$$

The in-phase and quadrature functions M and N are plotted versus the dimensionless parameter θ, for various values of μ_2/μ_1, in Figure (A7-2). The permeability ratios range from one (free space) to 1,000 (steel).

It may be desirable to express the magnetic fields in terms of cartesian components H_x

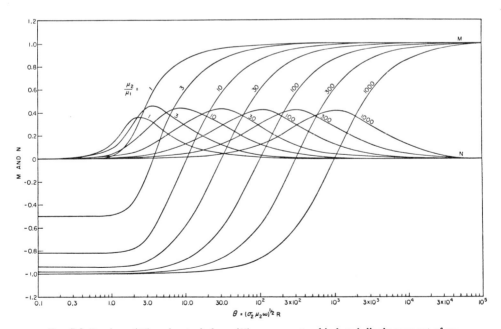

Fig. 7-2. In-phase (M) and out-of-phase (N) components of induced dipole moment of an infinite cylinder in a transverse uniform alternating magnetic field.

and H_z; these components are obtained simply from the transformations

$$H_x = H_r \cos \phi - H_\phi \sin \phi \tag{A7-49}$$

$$H_z = H_r \sin \phi + H_\phi \cos \phi \tag{A7-50}$$

and yield the equation,

$$H = H_x\mathbf{i} + H_z\mathbf{k} = H_0 e^{-i\omega t}\mathbf{i} + H_0 R^2 \frac{\mu_2[\alpha J_0(\alpha) - J_1(\alpha)] - \mu_1 J_1(\alpha)}{\mu_2[\alpha J_0(\alpha) - J_1(\alpha)] + \mu_1 J_1(\alpha)}$$

$$\cdot \left[\frac{(x^2 - z^2)\mathbf{i} + 2xz\mathbf{k}}{r^4}\right] e^{-i\omega t}. \tag{A7-51}$$

This is the field of a line of dipoles and is identical in form to the expression obtained earlier for the conducting cylinder in the electrostatic field and the magnetic cylinder in the magnetostatic field. Indeed, the formula (A7-51) reduces to the formula (A5-1), deduced for the magnetostatic problem, when the angular frequency is set identically equal to zero.

7-III. *Longitudinal inducing field*

The field will induce ring currents only in the cylinder. We are then inclined to use the vector **F** to derive a solution to the problem. Stated another way, we seek a solution for a magnetic field which physical reasoning tells us is curl free, and for an electric field which is rotational. Equation (A7-13) informs us that we need but a single component of the vector **F** since we have but a single component of **H**. The **H** field is also divergenceless. Thus

$$H_r = H_\phi = 0$$

$$H_y = -(\sigma - i\omega\epsilon)F_y.$$

Since we wish to neglect displacement currents, i.e. $\sigma \gg \omega\epsilon$, the fields are:

$$H_r = 0 \qquad\qquad E_r = 0 \tag{A7-52}$$

$$H_\phi = 0 \qquad\qquad E_\phi = \frac{\partial F_y}{\partial r} \tag{A7-53}$$

$$H_y = -\sigma F_y \qquad E_y = 0 \tag{A7-54}$$

and the wave equations are:

$$\nabla^2 F_y + k_2^2 F_y = 0 \qquad r \leq R \tag{A7-55}$$

$$\nabla^2 F_y = 0 \qquad r > R \tag{A7-56}$$

$$\text{where } k_2^2 = i\mu_2\sigma_2\omega \quad \text{and} \quad k_1^2 \approx 0. \tag{A7-57}$$

Since we are prepared to assume that the conductivity of the exterior medium is zero, then (A7-54) informs us that there will be no external anomalous magnetic field. There is, however, an anomalous internal field distribution.

7-IV *Discussion*

The above derivation follows that of Meyer (1963). It may be compared with Wait's solution for a cylindrical ore body in the field of a line source (Wait, 1952) or with Negi's solution for an inhomogeneous cylindrical ore body in a uniform harmonically varying transverse field (Negi, 1962).

8. Electrodes on the Surface of Half-Space, Direct Current

8-I. *Potential of a point source in an infinite, homogeneous, isotropic medium*

We assume that a current I enters an infinite medium at the origin O of a coordinate system (Figure 8-1). At any spherical surface S, a distance r from the origin, the current flows radially. Since the surface area of S is $4\pi r^2$, the current density at distance r is, then

$$J_r = \frac{I}{4\pi r^2} \cdot \tag{A8-1}$$

If $\rho = 1/\sigma$ is the homogeneous isotropic resistivity then we may write Ohm's Law in the form

$$E_r = J_r\rho = \frac{I\rho}{4\pi r^2} \cdot \tag{A8-2}$$

The potential V at a distance r from the electrode is given by the integral of E_r between r and infinity

$$V = \int_r^\infty E_r dr = \frac{I\rho}{4\pi r} \cdot \tag{A8-3}$$

Equation (A8-3) is the fundamental relationship for all electrical sounding in well bores.

If the source electrode is at the surface of a half-space, say the half-space below the x-y plane, then the current flows radially out through a hemispherical surface of radius r, and surface area $2\pi r^2$. Hence, the current density is

$$J_r = \frac{I}{2\pi r^2} \tag{A8-4}$$

and the potential is

$$V = \frac{I\rho}{2\pi r} \cdot \tag{A8-5}$$

This equation gives the fundamental relationship for all electrical prospecting from the surface of the earth. In subsequent developments we will refer only to electrodes on the surface of the earth, but the formulas are directly applicable to well-logging provided 2π is replaced by 4π.

8-II. *Electric dipole grounded to a homogeneous, isotropic half-space*

In this section and subsequently, we shall refer to any two-electrode array as a dipole even though that term is normally reserved for a pair of point sources an infinitesimal distance apart. This liberal use of the word "dipole" has become custom in prospecting geophysics.

The potential at any point P_1 located at distances r_1 and r_2 from source electrodes C_1 and C_2 (Figure 8-2) may be obtained by adding two potentials given by (A8-5). Thus

$$V_1 = \frac{I_1\rho}{2\pi r_1} \qquad V_2 = \frac{I_2\rho}{2\pi r_2} \tag{A8-6}$$

and

$$V = V_1 + V_2 = \frac{I_1\rho}{2\pi r_1} + \frac{I_2\rho}{2\pi r_2} \cdot \tag{A8-7}$$

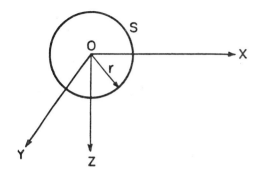

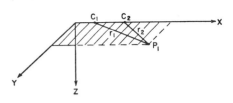

FIG. 8-2. Geometry for potential at point P_1 due to current from source electrodes C_1 and C_2 located at distances r_1 and r_2 from P_1. Electrodes and point of observation on surface of earth.

FIG. 8-1. Current I enters an infinite medium at origin O of a coordinate system (x, y, z). Current density at distance r where current flows radially through surface S is $J_r = I/4\pi r^2$.

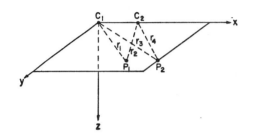

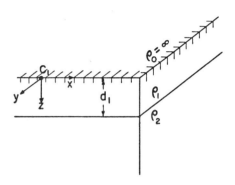

FIG. 8-3. Geometry for potential difference between two points P_1 and P_2 on surface of earth due to current sources C_1 and C_2 also on surface.

FIG. 8-4. Source electrode on surface of two layer earth. Thickness of first layer is d_1. Resistivities of layer (1) is ρ_1 and of layer (2) is ρ_2.

Let us assume that the current enters the half-space via electrode C_1 and leaves via C_2. Then we have

$$I = I_1 = -I_2 \tag{A8-8}$$

and

$$V = \frac{I\rho}{2\pi}\left[\frac{1}{r_1} - \frac{1}{r_2}\right]. \tag{A8-9}$$

Equation (A8-9) gives the potential due to a dipole on a homogeneous, isotropic half-space.

8-III. *Source and potential dipole grounded to a homogeneous, isotropic half-space*

The next problem to be solved is to find the *potential difference* between two points on the surface of the earth due to current applied through an adjacent dipolar source. The geometry is illustrated in Figure 8-3.

If V_1 and V_2 are the potentials at P_1 arising from the source electrodes C_1 and C_2, and if V_3 and V_4 are the potentials at P_2 arising from C_1 and C_2, then the potential difference may be written

$$V = (V_1 + V_2) - (V_3 + V_4) \tag{A8-10}$$

or

$$V = \frac{I\rho}{2\pi}\left[\frac{1}{r_1} - \frac{1}{r_2} - \frac{1}{r_3} + \frac{1}{r_4}\right]. \tag{A8-11}$$

The ratio of potential to current, or the mutual resistance of the electrode array, is then

$$Q = \frac{\rho}{2\pi}\left[\frac{1}{r_1} - \frac{1}{r_2} - \frac{1}{r_3} + \frac{1}{r_4}\right]. \tag{A8-12}$$

8-IV. *Electrodes on a two-layered earth*

Let us consider a two-layered earth on which an electrode C is grounded. The geometry is illustrated in Figure 8-4. Potentials in the upper and lower layers, respectively, consist of a primary and a secondary part.

$$V' = V_P + V_{S1} \tag{A8-13}$$

and

$$V'' = V_P + V_{S2} \tag{A8-14}$$

where V_P is the primary potential and V_{S1} and V_{S2} are the secondary potentials induced in the upper and lower layers, respectively. We may consider the primary potential V_P as due to a grounded electrode on a uniform earth of resistivity ρ_1 equal to that of the upper layer.

$$V_P = \frac{I\rho_1}{2\pi}(z^2 + r^2)^{-1/2} \tag{A8-15}$$

where $r^2 = x^2 + y^2$.

Reference to a table of Laplace transforms (e.g. Scott, 1955) will reveal that the direct Laplace transform of the zeroth order Bessel function of the first kind is identically equal to $(z^2 + r^2)^{-1/2}$, that is

$$(z^2 + r^2)^{-1/2} = \int_0^\infty J_0(\lambda r)e^{-\lambda z}d\lambda. \tag{A8-16}$$

Hence, the expression (A8-15) for the primary potential may be written

$$V_P = \frac{I\rho_1}{2\pi}\int_0^\infty J_0(\lambda r)e^{-\lambda z}d\lambda. \tag{A8-17}$$

From equation (A406) with $k = t = 0$ as appropriate to a problem in electrostatics, we recognize that we should seek secondary potentials of the form

$$V_{S1} = \int_0^\infty [f_1(\lambda)e^{-\lambda z} + g_1(\lambda)e^{\lambda z}]J_0(\lambda r)d\lambda \tag{A8-18}$$

$$V_{S2} = \int_0^\infty [f_2(\lambda)e^{-\lambda z} + g_2(\lambda)e^{\lambda z}]J_0(\lambda r)d\lambda. \tag{A8-19}$$

The choice of $n = 0$ in equation (A406), applied to this particular problem, is made on the physical basis that the potential should be completely independent of θ for a point electrode. The eigenvalue λ of equation (A406) has been incorporated in the eigenfunctions $f_1(\lambda)$ and $g_1(\lambda)$ assigned to each exponential.

The problem now reduces to evaluation of the eigenfunctions $f_1(\lambda)$, $f_2(\lambda)$, $g_1(\lambda)$, $g_2(\lambda)$, from the boundary conditions. The first boundary condition to be invoked is continuity of normal $\mathbf{J}$ across the interface bounding the half-space [refer to equation (A134)]. Since the normal currents are zero in air, the normal J_z must be zero in the medium at the interface where $z = 0$

$$J_z = 0 \quad \text{or} \quad \sigma E_z = 0 \quad \text{or} \quad E_z = -\frac{\partial V}{\partial z} = 0. \tag{A8-20}$$

Then, from equation (A8-18) we find, upon application of (A8-20), that

$$f_1 = g_1. \tag{A8-21}$$

The secondary V_{S2} potential due to the point electrode must tend to zero as z tends to infinity, so that, from (A8-19),

$$g_2 = 0. \tag{A8-22}$$

The third and fourth boundary conditions to be invoked are continuity of potentials and normal current densities across the boundary between medium (1) and medium (2). That is,

$$V' = V'' \big|_{z=d_1} \tag{A8-23}$$

$$\frac{1}{\rho_1} \frac{\partial V'}{\partial z} = \frac{1}{\rho_2} \frac{\partial V''}{\partial z} \bigg|_{z=d_1}. \tag{A8-24}$$

The boundary condition defined by (A8-23) leads to the equation

$$f_1(\lambda) \left[e^{-\lambda d_1} + e^{\lambda d_1} \right] = f_2(\lambda) e^{-\lambda d_1} \tag{A8-25}$$

when use is made of (A8-21) and (A8-22) in equations (A8-18) and (A8-19). From boundary condition (A8-24) applied to (A8-17), (A8-18), and (A8-19) with cognizance of (A8-21) and (A8-22), we obtain

$$\frac{\lambda}{\rho_1} \left[-\frac{I\rho_1}{2\pi} e^{-\lambda d_1} + f_1(\lambda)(-e^{-\lambda d_1} + e^{\lambda d_1}) \right] = \frac{\lambda}{\rho_2} \left[-\frac{I\rho_1}{2\pi} e^{-\lambda d_1} - f_2(\lambda) e^{-\lambda d_1} \right]. \tag{A8-26}$$

Equations (A8-25) and (A8-26) may be solved simultaneously for $f_1(\lambda)$ and $f_2(\lambda)$ to yield

$$f_1(\lambda) = \frac{I\rho_1}{2\pi} \left(\frac{-u_1 e^{-2\lambda d_1}}{1 + u_1 e^{-2\lambda d_1}} \right) \tag{A8-27}$$

$$f_2(\lambda) = \frac{I\rho_1}{2\pi} \left(\frac{-u_1(e^{-2\lambda d_1} + 1)}{1 + u_1 e^{-2\lambda d_1}} \right) \tag{A8-28}$$

where

$$u_1 = \frac{\rho_1 - \rho_2}{\rho_1 + \rho_2}.$$

Because we will measure potentials only at the surface of medium (1), we need only subsequently consider the eigenfunction $f_1(\lambda)$. A binomial expansion of the denominator of this function permits us to write (A8-27) as

$$f(\lambda) = \frac{I\rho_1}{2\pi} \left(-u_1 e^{-2\lambda d_1} + u_1^2 e^{-4\lambda d_1} - u_1^3 e^{-\phi \lambda d_1} + \cdots \right)$$

$$= \frac{I\rho_1}{2\pi} \sum_{n=1}^{\infty} (-u_1)^n e^{-2nd_1\lambda}. \tag{A8-29}$$

Thus, the secondary potential (A8-18) may be written, for the surface of the earth, where $z=0$,

$$V_{S1} = \frac{I\rho_1}{2\pi} \int_0^\infty 2 \sum_{n=1}^\infty (-u_1)^n e^{-2nd_1\lambda} J_0(\lambda r) d\lambda$$

$$= \frac{I\rho_1}{2\pi} 2 \sum_{n=1}^\infty (-u_1)^n \int_0^\infty e^{-2nd_1\lambda} J_0(\lambda r) d\lambda. \tag{A8-30}$$

In equation (A8-16) we noted the Laplace transform of the zeroth order Bessel function. The integral in (A8-30) is nothing more than this transform process, so that we may replace the integral by

$$\frac{1}{[r^2 + (2nd_1)^2]^{1/2}} \cdot$$

Then equation (A8-30) becomes

$$V_{S1} = \frac{I\rho_1}{2\pi} 2 \sum_{n=1}^\infty (-u_1)^n \frac{1}{[r^2 + (2nd_1)^2]^{1/2}} \cdot \tag{A8-31}$$

When we combine this potential with the primary potential given by (A8-15) with $z=0$ we obtain the total potential observed at the surface of the earth

$$V' = V_P + V_{S1}$$

$$= \frac{I\rho_1}{2\pi} \left[\frac{1}{r} + 2 \sum_{n=1}^\infty \frac{(-u_1)^n}{[r^2 + (2nd_1)^2]^{1/2}} \right]. \tag{A8-32}$$

Equation (A8-32) may also be expressed in integral form. When (A8-27) is substituted in (A8-18) and z set equal to zero, the secondary potential resulting is

$$V_{S1} = \frac{I\rho_1}{2\pi} \int_0^\infty \frac{-2u_1 e^{-2\lambda d_1}}{1 + u_1 e^{-2\lambda d_1}} J_0(\lambda r) d\lambda. \tag{A8-33}$$

This expression may be added to the primary potential given by (A8-17) with $z=0$,

$$V_P = \frac{I\rho_1}{2\pi} \int_0^\infty J_0(\lambda r) d\lambda \tag{A8-34}$$

o yield the total potential

$$V' = \frac{I\rho_1}{2\pi} \int_0^\infty \frac{1 - u_1 e^{-2\lambda d_1}}{1 + u_1 e^{-2\lambda d_1}} J_0(\lambda r) d\lambda. \tag{A8-35}$$

The development above and others in section 8 follow those of Sunde (1949).

If we now use the method used in 8-III above, we may immediately write down the incremental voltage ΔV observed between a pair of electrodes P_1 and P_2 due to current transferred o a two-layered earth via a pair of current electrodes C_1 and C_2,

$$\Delta V = (V_1' + V_2') - (V_3' + V_4') \tag{A8-36}$$

$$V_1' = \frac{I\rho_1}{2\pi} \left[\frac{1}{r_1} + 2 \sum_{n=1}^\infty \frac{(-u_1)^n}{[r_1^2 + (2nd_1)^2]^{1/2}} \right] \tag{A8-37}$$

$$V_2' = -\frac{I\rho_1}{2\pi}\left[\frac{1}{r_2} + 2\sum_{n=1}^{\infty}\frac{(-u_1)^n}{[r_2{}^2 + (2nd_1)^2]^{1/2}}\right] \tag{A8-38}$$

$$V_3' = \frac{I\rho_1}{2\pi}\left[\frac{1}{r_3} + 2\sum_{n=1}^{\infty}\frac{(-u_1)^n}{[r_3{}^2 + (2nd_1)^2]^{1/2}}\right] \tag{A8-39}$$

$$V_4' = -\frac{I\rho_1}{2\pi}\left[\frac{1}{r_4} + 2\sum_{n=1}^{\infty}\frac{(-u_1)^n}{[r_4{}^2 + (2nd_1)^2]^{1/2}}\right]. \tag{A8-40}$$

8-V. *Electrodes on a three-layered earth*

Referring to Figure 8-5 the potentials V' and V'' in the first two layers are as before

$$V' = V_P + V_{S1} \tag{A8-41}$$
$$V'' = V_P + V_{S2} \tag{A8-42}$$

and we may similarly represent the potential V''' in the third layer

$$V''' = V_P + V_{S3}. \tag{A8-43}$$

The four potentials V_P, V_{S1}, V_{S2}, V_{S3} may be written, following the earlier development,

$$V_P = \frac{I\rho_1}{2\pi}\int_0^{\infty} e^{-\lambda z}J_0(\lambda r)d\lambda \tag{A8-44}$$

$$V_{S1} = \int_0^{\infty}[f_1(\lambda)e^{-\lambda z} + g_1(\lambda)e^{\lambda z}]J_0(\lambda r)d\lambda \tag{A8-45}$$

$$V_{S2} = \int_0^{\infty}[f_2(\lambda)e^{-\lambda z} + g_2(\lambda)e^{\lambda z}]J_0(\lambda r)d\lambda \tag{A8-46}$$

$$V_{S3} = \int_0^{\infty}[f_3(\lambda)e^{-\lambda z} + g_3(\lambda)e^{\lambda z}]J_0(\lambda r)d\lambda. \tag{A8-47}$$

We now seek to solve for the eigenfunctions $f_1(\lambda) \cdots , g_3(\lambda)$ through application of boundary

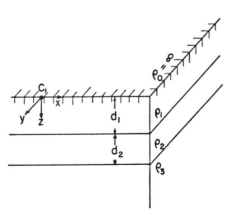

FIG. 8-5. Source electrode on surface of three layer earth. Thicknesses of first and second layers are d_1 and d_2 respectively. Resistivities of three layers are ρ_1, ρ_2. and ρ_3.

conditions. The continuity of J_z at $z=0$ again ensures that $f_1=g_1$. The condition that V_{S3} $\rightarrow 0$ as $z \rightarrow \infty$ provides for $g_3 = 0$. Thus, we have reduced the unknowns to four, which may be evaluated from the four boundary conditions.

$$V' = V''\big|_{z=d_1} \tag{A8-48}$$

$$V'' = V'''\big|_{z=d_1+d_2} \tag{A8-49}$$

$$\frac{1}{\rho_2}\frac{\partial V'}{\partial z} = \frac{1}{\rho_2}\frac{\partial V''}{\partial z}\bigg|_{z=d_1} \tag{A8-50}$$

$$\frac{1}{\rho_2}\frac{\partial V''}{\partial z} = \frac{1}{\rho_3}\frac{\partial V'''}{\partial z}\bigg|_{z=d_1+d_2} \tag{A8-51}$$

where the values of ρ and d are those of Figure 8-5. Equations (A8-48) through (A8-51), applied to equations (A8-44) through (A8-47), constitute a system of four simultaneous equations in the four unknowns $f_1(\lambda)$, $f_2(\lambda)$, $g_2(\lambda)$, $f_3(\lambda)$. The system may be solved for the unknowns by using Cramer's rule. Substitution of the eigenfunction values in equation (A8-45) permits us to find the secondary potential at the surface of the earth. When this potential V_{S1} is added to the primary potential V_P for $z=0$, we obtain

$$V' = \frac{I\rho_1}{2\pi}\int_0^\infty \frac{1 - u(\lambda)e^{-2\lambda d_1}}{1 + u(\lambda)e^{-2\lambda d_1}} J_0(\lambda r)\,d\lambda \tag{A8-52}$$

where

$$u(\lambda) = \frac{\rho_1 - \rho_2\left(\dfrac{1 - u_2 e^{-2\lambda d_2}}{1 + u_2 e^{-2\lambda d_2}}\right)}{\rho_1 + \rho_2\left(\dfrac{1 - u_2 e^{-2\lambda d_2}}{1 + u_2 e^{-2\lambda d_2}}\right)} \tag{A8-53}$$

and

$$u_2 = \frac{\rho_2 - \rho_3}{\rho_2 + \rho_3}. \tag{A8-54}$$

The potentials can be added for a dipole-dipole array as in (A8-36)

8-VI. *Electrodes on an n-layered earth*

Equation (A8-35), describing the potential at the surface of a two-layered earth may be written

$$V' = \frac{I\rho_1}{2\pi}\int_0^\infty k_{12}(\lambda)J_0(\lambda r)\,d\lambda \tag{A8-55}$$

where the *kernel* of the integral is

$$k_{12} = \frac{1 - u_{12}e^{-2\lambda d_1}}{1 + u_{12}e^{-2\lambda d_1}} \tag{A8-56}$$

and where

$$u_{12} = \frac{\rho_1 - \rho_2}{\rho_1 + \rho_2}. \tag{A8-57}$$

Similarly, the potential at the surface of a three-layered earth may be written

$$V' = \frac{I\rho_1}{2\pi} \int_0^\infty k_{123}(\lambda) J_0(\lambda r) d\lambda \qquad \text{(A8-58)}$$

and

$$k_{123} = \frac{1 - u_{123}e^{-2\lambda d_1}}{1 + u_{123}e^{-2\lambda d_1}} \qquad \text{(A8-59)}$$

$$u_{123} = \frac{\rho_1 - \rho_2 k_{23}}{\rho_1 + \rho_2 k_{23}} \qquad \text{(A8-60)}$$

$$k_{23} = \frac{1 - u_{23}e^{-2\lambda d_2}}{1 + u_{23}e^{-2\lambda d_2}} \qquad \text{(A8-61)}$$

$$u_{23} = \frac{\rho_2 - \rho_3}{\rho_2 + \rho_3} . \qquad \text{(A8-62)}$$

By inference, we can then write down the potential at the surface of an n-layered earth:

$$V_1 = \frac{I\rho_1}{2\pi} \int_0^\infty k_{12\ldots n} J_0(\lambda r) d\lambda \qquad \text{(A8-63)}$$

and

$$k_{12\ldots n} = \frac{1 - u_{12\ldots n}e^{-2\lambda d_1}}{1 + u_{12\ldots n}e^{-2\lambda d_1}} . \qquad \text{(A8-64)}$$

$$u_{12\ldots n} = \frac{\rho_1 - \rho_2 k_{23\ldots n}}{\rho_1 + \rho_2 k_{23\ldots n}} \qquad \text{(A8-65)}$$

$$k_{(m-1)m\ldots n} = \frac{1 - u_{(m-1)m\ldots n}e^{-2\lambda d_{m-1}}}{1 + u_{(m-1)m\ldots n}e^{-2\lambda d_{m-1}}} \qquad \text{(A8-66)}$$

$$u_{(m-1)m\ldots n} = \frac{\rho_{m-1} - \rho_m k_{m(m+1)\ldots n}}{\rho_{m-1} + \rho_m k_{m(m+1)\ldots n}} \qquad \text{(A8-67)}$$

$$k_{(n-1)n} = \frac{1 - u_{(n-1)n}e^{-2\lambda d_{n-1}}}{1 + u_{(n-1)n}e^{-2\lambda d_{n-1}}} , \qquad u_{(n-1)n} = \frac{\rho_{n-1} - \rho_n}{\rho_{n-1} + \rho_n} . \qquad \text{(A8-68)}$$

Once again, the potentials may be added for a dipole-dipole array as in (A8-36).

8-VII. *Use of potential formulas*

In resistivity sounding, we hope to be able to deduce the thicknesses and resistivities of the various layers in the earth. To accomplish this we usually compute *apparent* resistivity ρ_a versus electrode separation curves based on the assumption that for each electrode separation the measured resistivity is equal to that of an *apparent* homogeneous earth. Thus, from (A8-11)

$$\rho_a = 2\pi \frac{V}{I} \frac{1}{\left[\dfrac{1}{r_1} - \dfrac{1}{r_2} - \dfrac{1}{r_3} + \dfrac{1}{r_4}\right]} = 2\pi \frac{V}{I} r_0 \qquad \text{(A8-69)}$$

here

$$\frac{1}{r_0} = \frac{1}{r_1} - \frac{1}{r_2} - \frac{1}{r_3} + \frac{1}{r_4}$$

d ρ_a is plotted versus r_0 or some distance related to it. The resulting observed curves may
e compared with theoretical curves of apparent resistivity based on the two- or three-
yered earth models of equations (A8-35) and (A8-52). We may rewrite these last two
uations in the useful forms

$$\rho_a = 2\pi \frac{V}{I} r_0\rho_1 \int_0^\infty \frac{1 - u_1 e^{-2\lambda d_1}}{1 + u_1 e^{-2\lambda d_1}} [J_0(\lambda r_1) - J_0(\lambda r_2) - J_0(\lambda r_3) + J_0(\lambda r_4)] d\lambda \qquad \text{(A8-70)}$$

d

$$\rho_a = 2\pi \frac{V}{I} r_0\rho_1 \int_0^\infty \frac{1 - u(\lambda) e^{-2\lambda d_1}}{1 + u(\lambda) e^{-2\lambda d_1}} [J_0(\lambda r_1) - J_0(\lambda r_2) - J_0(\lambda r_3) + J_0(\lambda r_4)] d\lambda \qquad \text{(A8-71)}$$

here allowance has been made for all four electrodes.

We note in equations (A8-35), (A8-52) and the general form (A8-63) that the fundamental
uantity providing information concerning the layering, is the kernel $k_{12\ldots n}$; the contribu-
on from $J_0(\lambda r)$ is merely descriptive of the electrode array. Thus, the fundamental prob-
m in resistivity sounding should be determination of the kernel. The Fourier-Bessel trans-
rm pair given by equations (A404) and (A405) suggest that we might transform equation
A8-63) to yield

$$k_{12\ldots n} = \frac{2\pi\lambda}{I\rho_1} \int_0^\infty rV(r) J_0(\lambda r) dr. \qquad \text{(A8-72)}$$

hus, if we know the observed voltage function $V(r)$ for a constant current I, we may
ompute an experimental kernel for comparison with kernels derived for model earths.
ozoff (1958) has made reference to this technique.

The kernel k_{12} for a two-layered earth is, from (A8-56) and (A8-57)

$$k_{12} = \frac{1 - u_{12} e^{-2\lambda d_1}}{1 + u_{12} e^{-2\lambda d_1}}$$

r

$$u_{12} = \frac{\rho_1 - \rho_2}{\rho_1 + \rho_2}.$$

he expression for the kernel may be rewritten as

$$k_{12} = \frac{(\rho_1 + \rho_2) e^{\lambda d_1} - (\rho_1 - \rho_2) e^{-\lambda d_1}}{(\rho_1 + \rho_2) e^{\lambda d_1} + (\rho_1 - \rho_2) e^{-\lambda d_1}} \qquad \text{(A8-73)}$$

here multiplication by $(\rho_1 + \rho_2) e^{\lambda d_1}$ has been effected. Equation (A8-73) may be rearranged
ously

$$k_{12} = \frac{\rho_1(e^{\lambda d_1} - e^{-\lambda d_1}) + \rho_2(e^{\lambda d_1} + \epsilon^{-\lambda d_1})}{\rho_1(e^{\lambda d_1} + e^{-\lambda d_1}) + \rho_2(e^{\lambda d_1} - e^{-\lambda d_1})} \qquad \text{(A8-74)}$$

and when numerator and denominator are divided by $e^{\lambda d_1}+e^{-\lambda d_1}$ with the substitution

$$\tanh \lambda d_1 = \frac{e^{\lambda d_1} - e^{-\lambda d_1}}{e^{\lambda d_1} + e^{-\lambda d_1}}$$

then

$$\rho_1 k_{12} = \rho_1 \frac{\rho_2 + \rho_1 \tanh \lambda d_1}{\rho_1 + \rho_2 \tanh \lambda d_1} . \qquad (A8\text{-}75)$$

The quantity $\rho_1 k_{12}$ is directly analogous to the plane wave impedance of a two-layer earth given in the familiar form

$$Z(0) = Z_1 \frac{Z_2 + Z_1 \tanh ikh_1}{Z_1 + Z_2 \tanh ikh_1} \qquad (A8\text{-}76)$$

where

$Z(0)$ is the impedance at the surface of the earth
Z_2 is the terminal impedance
Z_1 is the characteristic impedance of the first layer
h_1 is the thickness of the first layer.

The quantity u_{12} appearing above is analogous to the square root of the reflection coefficient (Stratton, 1941, p. 512)

$$r_{12} = R_{12}^{1/2} = \frac{Z_2 - Z_1}{Z_2 + Z_1} = - r_{21}. \qquad (A8\text{-}77)$$

For a two-layered earth, the parameter u_{12} is even more fundamental than the kernel. This parameter was plotted previously in Figure 3-3 wherein we commented that a ratio of ρ_1/ρ_2 greater than 10 does not give rise to any significant change in u_{12} as a function of ρ_1/ρ_2. Equation (A8-32) then informs us that for a fixed ρ_1, the potential V' does not change significantly as ρ_2 is increased beyond $\rho_2 = 0.1 \rho_1$.

9. Electrodes on the surface of a half-space, alternating current

When alternating current, rather than direct current, is used in resistivity sounding or prospecting, inductive and capacitive coupling between the current and potential circuits arise. This coupling complicates interpretation, especially when one wishes to conduct an induced-polarization survey in an area of low resistivity. We may evaluate the inductive and capacitive coupling only for very simple earth models. Let us now consider the extraneous inductive coupling term for a homogeneous earth. Our presentation of this problem appears at this point in the text in order that we may introduce an ac source problem at the earliest possible moment. The presentation does suffer slightly as a result of this placement, but we shall round out the treatment later. Subsequent source problems are treated in greater depth at the outset.

The dipole is oriented along the x axis, as in Figure 9-1, and is located at a height h above the earth's surface. A point P in the earth or above it may be described by the cartesian coordinates (x, y, z) or by the cylindrical coordinates (ρ, θ, z). The origin is at the dipole.

We shall assume the existence of a Hertz vector $\pi(\rho, \theta, z)$ and the components of this vector must satisfy the wave equation in cylindrical coordinates (A279). An integral solution which remains finite on the axis is given by (A406). The symmetry of the electric field is illustrated in Figure 9-2; the field is symmetrical with respect to the x-z plane and anti-

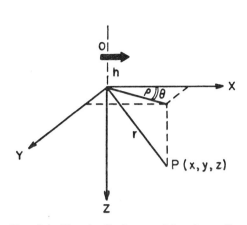

FIG. 9-1. Electric dipole at origin of coordinate system on surface of homogeneous earth. Point of observation $P(x, y, z)$ is arbitrarily located on or within earth.

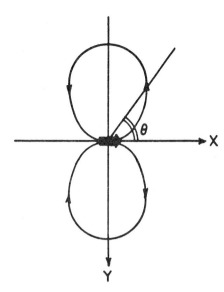

FIG. 9-2. Symmetry of electric field due to electirc dipole oriented in x-direction.

symmetrical with respect to the y-z plane. A cosine function will describe this symmetry, but a sine function will not when the angle θ is measured relative to the x axis. Thus, $e^{in\theta}$ must be replaced by $\cos n\theta$ in (A406)

$$\psi(\rho, \theta, z, t) = e^{-i\omega t} \sum_{n=-\infty}^{\infty} \cos n\theta \int_0^\infty [f_n(\lambda)e^{+i\sqrt{k^2-\lambda^2}z} + g_n(\lambda)e^{-i\sqrt{k^2-\lambda^2}z}]J_n(\lambda\rho)d\lambda \quad \text{(A9-1)}$$

where the λ under the integral of (A406) has now been incorporated in the eigenfunctions and where we have chosen to generalize the solution somewhat by introducing a separate eigenfunction for the positive and negative exponentials under the integral sign.

We have already found the potential of an infinitesimal electric dipole in an infinite medium to be, equation (A193),

$$\pi_x^P = \frac{i\mu\omega}{4\pi k_0^2} \frac{e^{ik_0 r}}{r} I ds e^{-i\omega t}; \qquad r^2 = \rho^2 + z^2. \quad \text{(A9-2)}$$

This is, then, the primary potential of an infinitesimal dipole to which we must add secondary potentials brought into existence by the presence of the earth. Once this is accomplished, we may integrate the expressions for the potentials of an infinitesimal dipole to obtain the potentials for "dipoles" of finite length. The function $e^{ik_0 r}/r$ may be converted to an integral representation. From (A406), a solution of the wave equation which is finite at the origin and has axial symmetry $(n=0)$ may be written, neglecting the time dependency,

$$\psi(\rho, 0, z) = \int_0^\infty g_0(\lambda)J_0(\lambda\rho)e^{\pm i\sqrt{k_0^2-\lambda^2}z}\lambda d\lambda. \quad \text{(A9-3)}$$

Since $e^{ik_0 r}/r$ is also a solution of the wave equation which is finite at the origin and has axial symmetry, we may equate $e^{ik_0 r}/r$ and (A9-3) and find at $z=0$

$$\frac{e^{ik_0 r}}{r} = \int_0^\infty g_0(\lambda)J_0(\lambda\rho)d\lambda. \quad \text{(A9-4)}$$

We now wish to find the value of $g_0(\lambda)$ for which this equality holds true. If (A9-4) is treated as one member of a Fourier-Bessel transform pair as in (A404) and (A405), then the other member is

$$g_0(\lambda) = \int_0^\infty e^{ik_0 r} J_0(\lambda \rho) dr. \tag{A9-5}$$

By analogy with equation (A8-16), we may convert (A9-5) to

$$g_0(\lambda) = \int_0^\infty e^{ik_0 r} J_0(\lambda \rho) dr = (\lambda^2 - k_0^2)^{-1/2}. \tag{A9-6}$$

Therefore

$$\frac{e^{ik_0 r}}{r} = \int_0^\infty \frac{\lambda}{(\lambda^2 - k_0^2)^{1/2}} e^{\pm\sqrt{\lambda^2 - k_0^2}\, z} J_0(\lambda \rho) d\lambda. \tag{A9-7}$$

The choice of the positive or negative exponential in (A9-7) depends upon the region in which the expansion is to be applied. We wish to assure that the integral representation exhibits the same behavior at infinity as $e^{ik_0 r}/r$. Since e^{ikr}/r is a spherically spreading wave, its amplitude will diminish to zero as $r \to \infty$. Thus in the integral representations, we make the real part of $\sqrt{\lambda^2 - k^2}$ always positive and choose the sign of z to lead to a wave which vanishes at infinity. Thus, for the region $z \leq 0$, the expansion is

$$\pi_x{}^P = \frac{ce^{ik_0 r}}{r} = c \int_0^\infty \frac{\lambda}{(\lambda^2 - k_0^2)^{1/2}} e^{\sqrt{\lambda^2 - k_0^2}\, z} J_0(\lambda \rho) d\lambda \tag{A9-8}$$

while for the region $h \geq z > 0$ the expansion is

$$\pi_x{}^P = c \frac{e^{ik_0 r}}{r} = c \int_0^\infty \frac{\lambda}{(\lambda^2 - k_0^2)^{1/2}} e^{-\sqrt{\lambda^2 - k_0^2}\, z} J_0(\lambda \rho) d\lambda \tag{A9-9}$$

where

$$c = \frac{i\mu\omega}{4\pi k_0^2} I ds e^{-i\omega t}. \tag{A9-10}$$

It is convenient to replace $\sqrt{\lambda^2 - k_0^2}$ by u_0 so that (A9-2) now becomes

$$\pi_x{}^P = c \int_0^\infty \frac{\lambda}{u_0} e^{u_0 z} J_0(\lambda \rho) d\lambda; \qquad z \leq 0 \tag{A9-11}$$

$$\pi_x{}^P = c \int_0^\infty \frac{\lambda}{u_0} e^{-u_0 z} J_0(\lambda \rho) d\lambda; \qquad h \geq z > 0. \tag{A9-12}$$

We assume that in the air the total potential consists of a sum of primary and secondary parts

$$\pi_{z0} = \pi_x{}^P + \pi_z{}^S \tag{A9-13}$$

while in the ground the potential consists only of a secondary part

$$\pi_{z_1} = \pi_{z_1}{}^S. \tag{A9-14}$$

While this procedure may seem arbitrary, it is equivalent to expressing the solution of the inhomogeneous wave equation in terms of a particular solution plus the solution of the homogeneous wave equation for the region above the earth, while seeking only a solution of the homogeneous wave equation for the earth.

We note that the expressions for the primary potentials (A9-11) and (A9-12), contain Bessel functions of order zero only. Thus, to meet boundary conditions at the earth's surface, we should expect that the secondary potentials contain Bessel functions of zeroth order only. Let us then turn to the boundary conditions expressed in terms of potentials.

While the primary potential has only an x component, the lack of symmetry of the problem will obligate us to employ two components for the secondary potentials. In general, then, we may write the potential as

$$\pi = i\pi_x + k\pi_z, \qquad \pi_y = 0 \tag{A9-15}$$

so that the fields are, from (A75) and (A77),

$$\mathbf{E} = \nabla\nabla\cdot\boldsymbol{\pi} + k^2\boldsymbol{\pi} \tag{A9-16}$$

$$\mathbf{H} = (\sigma - i\omega\epsilon)\nabla \times \boldsymbol{\pi}. \tag{A9-17}$$

The components of the fields may be written down directly as:

$$E_x = \frac{\partial}{\partial x}\left(\frac{\partial \pi_x}{\partial x} + \frac{\partial \pi_z}{\partial z}\right) + k^2\pi_x \tag{A9-18}$$

$$E_y = \frac{\partial}{\partial y}\left(\frac{\partial \pi_x}{\partial x} + \frac{\partial \pi_z}{\partial z}\right) \tag{A9-19}$$

$$E_z = \frac{\partial}{\partial z}\left(\frac{\partial \pi_x}{\partial x} + \frac{\partial \pi_z}{\partial z}\right) + k^2\pi_z \tag{A9-20}$$

$$H_x = (\sigma - i\omega\epsilon)\frac{\partial \pi_z}{\partial y} \tag{A9-21}$$

$$H_y = (\sigma - i\omega\epsilon)\left(\frac{\partial \pi_x}{\partial z} - \frac{\partial \pi_z}{\partial x}\right) \tag{A9-22}$$

$$H_z = -(\sigma - i\omega\epsilon)\frac{\partial \pi_x}{\partial y}. \tag{A9-23}$$

From the continuity of tangential $\mathbf{E}$ and $\mathbf{H}$ at the air-earth interface and the above expressions for the electric and magnetic fields in terms of the vector $\boldsymbol{\pi}$ we may write

$$\text{from } H_x: \quad (\sigma_0 - i\omega\epsilon_0)\frac{\partial \pi_{z0}}{\partial y} = (\sigma_1 - i\omega\epsilon_1)\frac{\partial \pi_{z1}}{\partial y}\bigg|_{z=h} \tag{A9-24}$$

$$\text{from } H_y: \quad (\sigma_0 - i\omega\epsilon_0)\left(\frac{\partial \pi_{x0}}{\partial z} - \frac{\partial \pi_{z0}}{\partial x}\right) = (\sigma_1 - i\omega\epsilon_1)\left(\frac{\partial \pi_{x1}}{\partial z} - \frac{\partial \pi_{z1}}{\partial x}\right)\bigg|_{z=h} \tag{A9-25}$$

$$\text{from } E_x: \quad \frac{\partial}{\partial x}\left(\frac{\partial \pi_{x0}}{\partial x} + \frac{\partial \pi_{z1}}{\partial z}\right) + k_0^2\pi_{x0} = \frac{\partial}{\partial x}\left(\frac{\partial \pi_{x1}}{\partial x} + \frac{\partial \pi_{z1}}{\partial z}\right) + k_1^2\pi_{x1}\bigg|_{z=h} \tag{A9-26}$$

$$\text{from } E_y: \quad \frac{\partial}{\partial y}\left(\frac{\partial \pi_{x0}}{\partial x} + \frac{\partial \pi_{z0}}{\partial z}\right) = \frac{\partial}{\partial y}\left(\frac{\partial \pi_{x1}}{\partial x} + \frac{\partial \pi_{z1}}{\partial z}\right)\bigg|_{z=h}. \tag{A9-27}$$

The relations (A9-24) through (A9-27) hold for all x and all y and can, therefore, be integrated with respect to x or y. The functions and their derivatives vanish as $x \to \infty$ and $y \to \infty$ so that the constants of integration must be zero. Thus boundary condition (A9-27) reduces to

$$\frac{\partial \pi_{x0}}{\partial x} + \frac{\partial \pi_{z0}}{\partial z} = \frac{\partial \pi_{x1}}{\partial x} + \frac{\partial \pi_{z1}}{\partial z}\bigg|_{z=h} \tag{A9-28}$$

and when this is substituted in (A9-26) there results

$$k_0^2 \pi_{x0} = k_1^2 \pi_{x1}\big|_{z=h} . \tag{A9-29}$$

From (A9-24), by integration, we obtain

$$(\sigma_0 - i\omega\epsilon_0)\pi_{z0} = (\sigma_1 - i\omega\epsilon_1)\pi_{z1}\big|_{z=h} . \tag{A9-30}$$

We may integrate (A9-24) with respect to y, differentiate the result with respect to x, and add the result to (A9-25) to obtain

$$(\sigma_0 - i\omega\epsilon_0)\frac{\partial \pi_{z0}}{\partial z} = (\sigma_1 - i\omega\epsilon_0)\frac{\partial \pi_{z1}}{\partial z}\bigg|_{z=h} . \tag{A9-31}$$

Since, according to our earlier statement, the boundary conditions will demand that only zeroth order Bessel functions enter any expression for potential, we may write for the x components of the total potentials, following (A9-1)

in air above the dipole

$$\pi_{x0}^- = \pi_{x0}^P + \pi_{x0}^S = \int_0^\infty [f_0(\lambda)e^{u_0 z} + g_0(\lambda)e^{u_0 z}]J_0(\lambda\rho)d\lambda; \qquad z \leq 0 \tag{A9-32}$$

in air below the dipole

$$\pi_{x0}^+ = \pi_{x0}^P + \pi_{x0}^S = \int_0^\infty [f_0(\lambda)e^{u_0 z} + g_0(\lambda)e^{-u_0 z}]J_0(\lambda\rho)d\lambda; \qquad h \geq z > 0 \tag{A9-33}$$

in the ground

$$\pi_{x1} = \pi_{x1}^S = \int_0^\infty [f_1(\lambda)e^{u_1 z} + g_1(\lambda)e^{-u_1 z}]J_0(\lambda\rho)d\lambda; \qquad z \geq h_1 . \tag{A9-34}$$

Note that the primary wave function in (A9-32), represented by $g_0(\lambda)e^{u_0 z}$, bears a positive exponential since for the region $z \leq 0$ the primary wave travels in the negative z direction. For equations (A9-32) and (A9-33), each potential is made up of a primary or outgoing wave represented by a negative exponential and a secondary or reflected wave represented by a positive exponential. We shall refer to this point again in later sections.

Once again we wish to evaluate the four eigenfunctions $f_0(\lambda)$, $g_0(\lambda)$, $f_1(\lambda)$, $g_1(\lambda)$. First we note that $f_1(\lambda)=0$, because π_{x1} must go to zero as z tends to infinity; there is no reflected wave in a semi-infinite earth. Next from (A9-31)

$$\frac{k_0^2}{\mu_0}\frac{\partial}{\partial z}[f_0(\lambda)e^{u_0 z} + g_0(\lambda)e^{-u_0 z}] = \frac{k_1^2}{\mu_1}\frac{\partial}{\partial z}[g_1(\lambda)e^{-u_1 z}]\big|_{z=h} \tag{A9-35}$$

or

$$\frac{k_0^2 u_0}{\mu_0}[f_0(\lambda)e^{u_0 h} - g_0(\lambda)e^{-u_0 h}] = -\frac{k_1^2}{\mu_1}u_1 g_1(\lambda)e^{-u_1 h}. \tag{A9-36}$$

Similarly from (A9-29) applied to (A9-33) and (A9-34) we find

$$k_0^2[f_0(\lambda)e^{u_0h} + g_0(\lambda)e^{-u_0h}] = k_1^2 g_1(\lambda)e^{-u_1h} \ . \tag{A9-37}$$

From (A9-36) and (A9-37), we obtain

$$g_1(\lambda) = \frac{2k_0^2}{k_1^2} \frac{u_0\mu_1}{\mu_1 u_0 + \mu_0 u_1} e^{(-u_0+u_1)h} g_0(\lambda) \tag{A9-38}$$

$$f_0(\lambda) = \frac{-u_1\mu_0 + u_0\mu_1}{u_1\mu_0 + u_0\mu_1} \epsilon^{-2u_0h} g_0(\lambda). \tag{A9-39}$$

The function $g_0(\lambda)$ must now be evaluated in terms of the constants of the system. This may be accomplished by noting that with $k_1 = k_0$, the solution of (A9-32) must reduce to the potential of the source alone since then we have an infinite medium. Comparing (A9-32) with (A9-8) we observe that

$$g_0(\lambda) = c\frac{\lambda}{u_0} \ . \tag{A9-40}$$

Therefore, from (A9-38) and (A9-39) we find

$$g_1(\lambda) = 2c\frac{k_0^2}{k_1^2} \frac{\lambda\mu_1}{\mu_1 u_0 + \mu_0 u_1} e^{(-u_0+u_1)h} \tag{A9-41}$$

$$f_0(\lambda) = \frac{c\lambda}{u_0} \frac{-u_1\mu_0 + u_0\mu_1}{u_1\mu_0 + u_0\mu_1} e^{-2u_0h}. \tag{A9-42}$$

Hence, π_{z1} and π_{z0} can now be obtained without difficulty from (A9-32) through (A9-34).

The boundary conditions for the z components of the potentials in air bear cogitation. First, we note from (A9-28) that the differentiations $\partial\pi_{z0}/\partial_x$ and $\partial\pi_{z1}/\partial_x$ require only differentiation of the zeroth order Bessel function. This may be accomplished via the formula

$$J_n'(x) = \frac{n}{x} J_n(x) - J_{n+1}(x) \tag{A9-43}$$

and since the order is zero in our problem

$$J_0'(x) = -J_1(x). \tag{A9-44}$$

Thus, only the first order Bessel functions can appear in (A9-28) so that, in general, the z components of potential can only contain the first order Bessel functions, i.e. $n=1$. Hence, the z components of potentials, consisting only of *secondary* potentials, are

in air

$$\pi_{z0} = \cos\theta \int_0^\infty [p_0(\lambda)e^{u_0z} + q_0(\lambda)e^{-u_0z}]J_1(\lambda\rho)d\lambda \tag{A9-45}$$

in the ground

$$\pi_{z1} = \cos\theta \int_0^\infty [p_1(\lambda)e^{u_1z} + q_1(\lambda)e^{-u_1z}]J_1(\lambda\rho)\lambda d \ . \tag{A9-46}$$

Again, $p_1(\lambda)=0$ because $\pi_{z1}\to0$ as $z\to\infty$; there is no reflected wave in a semi-infinite earth.

Also, we know that there would be no π_{z0} component for an infinite medium, since the dipole potential is in the x direction. Hence, $\pi_{z0} \to 0$ as $z \to -\infty$ and we must have $q_0(\lambda) = 0$. To determine the remaining two eigenfunctions $p_0(\lambda)$ and $q_1(\lambda)$ we first apply the boundary condition (A9-30) to (A9-45) and (A9-46)

$$(\sigma_0 - i\omega\epsilon_0)e^{u_0 h}p_0(\lambda) = (\sigma_1 - i\omega\epsilon_1)e^{-u_1 h}q_1(\lambda)$$

or

$$p_0(\lambda) = \frac{k_1^2\mu_0}{\mu_1 k_0^2}e^{-(u_0+u_1)h}q_1(\lambda). \tag{A9-47}$$

Equation (A9-28) involves a differentiation of a Bessel function with respect to x. Note that

$$\frac{\partial}{\partial x}\int_0^\infty J_0(\lambda\rho)d\lambda = \left[\frac{\partial}{\partial\rho}\int_0^\infty J_0(\lambda\rho)d\lambda\right]\frac{\partial\rho}{\partial x} = -\cos\theta\int_0^\infty \lambda J_1(\lambda\rho)d\lambda. \tag{A9-48}$$

where equation (A9-44) has been used. Then equation (A9-28) applied to (A9-45) (A9-46) (A9-33) and (A9-34) yields

$$-[f_0(\lambda)e^{u_0 h} + g_0(\lambda)e^{-u_0 h}]\lambda + p_0(\lambda)u_0 e^{u_0 h} = -\lambda g_1(\lambda)e^{-u_1 h} - q_1(\lambda)u_1 e^{-u_1 h}. \tag{A9-49}$$

When equations (A9-40) (A9-41) (A9-42) (A9-47) and (A9-49) are combined we find

$$q_1(\lambda) = 2c\lambda^2\frac{k_0^2}{k_1^2}\frac{\mu_1^2}{\mu_1 u_0 + \mu_0 u_1}\frac{k_1^2 - k_0^2}{u_0\mu_0 k_1^2 + u_1\mu_1 k_0^2}e^{(u_1-u_0)h} \tag{A9-50}$$

so that (A9-47) may be expressed as

$$p_0(\lambda) = 2c\lambda^2\frac{\mu_0\mu_1}{\mu_1 u_0 + \mu_0 u_1}\frac{k_1^2 - k_0^2}{u_0\mu_0 k_1^2 + u_1\mu_1 k_0^2}e^{-2u_0 h}. \tag{A9-51}$$

The latter two eigenfunctions may be substituted in (A9-45) and (A9-46) to obtain the potentials π_{z0} and π_{z1}. First note that (A9-45) may be rewritten (after setting $q_0(\lambda) = 0$ in accordance with our physical evaluation of this eigenfunction) as

$$\pi_{z0} = -\frac{\partial}{\partial x}\int_0^\infty \frac{p_0(\lambda)}{\lambda}e^{u_0 z}J_0(\lambda\rho)d\lambda \tag{A9-52}$$

and also (A9-46) may be rewritten as

$$\pi_{z1} = -\frac{\partial}{\partial x}\int_0^\infty \frac{q_1(\lambda)}{\lambda}e^{-u_1 z}J_0(\lambda\rho)d\lambda \cdot \tag{A9-53}$$

Upon substitution of (A9-50) and (A9-51) into (A9-52) and (A9-53) there results

$$\pi_{z0} = -2c\frac{\partial}{\partial x}\int_0^\infty \frac{\mu_0\mu_1}{u_0\mu_1 + u_1\mu_0}\frac{k_1^2 - k_0^2}{u_0\mu_0 k_1^2 + u_1\mu_1 k_0^2}e^{u_0(z-2h)}\lambda J_0(\lambda\rho)d\lambda \tag{A9-54}$$

and

$$\pi_{z1} = -2c\frac{\partial}{\partial x}\int_0^\infty \frac{k_0^2}{k_1^2}\frac{\mu_1^2}{\mu_1 u_0 + \mu_0 u_1}\frac{k_1^2 - k_0^2}{u_0\mu_0 k_1^2 + u_1\mu_1 k_0^2}e^{-u_1(z-h)}e^{-u_0 h}\lambda J_0(\lambda\rho)d\lambda \cdot \tag{A9-55}$$

At $h=0$ and, for $\mu_1=\mu_0$, equation (A9-54) becomes

$$\pi_{z0} = -2c \frac{\partial}{\partial x} \int_0^\infty \frac{k_1^2 - k_0^2}{(u_0 + u_1)(u_0 k_1^2 + u_1 k_0^2)} e^{u_0 z} \lambda J_0(\lambda\rho) d\lambda \qquad (A9\text{-}56)$$

which for $k_0 \smallsmile 0$, the quasi-static approximation, and therefore for $u_0 \smallsmile \lambda$, becomes

$$\pi_{z0} = -2c \frac{\partial}{\partial x} \int_0^\infty \frac{1}{\lambda + u_1} e^{\lambda z} J_0(\lambda\rho) d\lambda. \qquad (A9\text{-}57)$$

This latter result agrees with those presented by Wolf (1946) and Quon (1963). The quasi-static approximation is pertinent to low frequency propagation. It permits us to neglect displacement currents both in the air and in the ground. Since conduction currents are assumed to be zero in air, then we may place $k_0 \smallsmile 0$. We then seek solutions of Laplace's equation in air and of the wave equation in the ground.

Now that the potentials have been calculated, we may compute the fields. Our interest in a horizontal electric dipole in prospecting lies largely with the electric fields and we restrict our attention herein to them. We shall assume that $\mu_1=\mu_0$, $k_0 \smallsmile 0$, $u_0 \smallsmile \lambda$ and that $z=0$; the horizontal electric dipole lies on a homogeneous nonpermeable ground. Then the potentials, in ground, given by equations (A9-34) and (A9-55), become

$$\pi_{x1} = 2c \frac{k_0^2}{k_1^2} \int_0^\infty \frac{\lambda}{\lambda + u_1} e^{-u_1 z} J_0(\lambda\rho) d\lambda \qquad (A9\text{-}58)$$

$$\pi_{z1} = -2c \frac{k_0^2}{k_1^2} \frac{\partial}{\partial x} \int_0^\infty \frac{1}{\lambda + u_1} e^{-u_1 z} J_1(\lambda\rho) d\lambda. \qquad (A9\text{-}59)$$

Both of these integrals have been evaluated by Foster (1931). We commence our development by multiplying numerator and denominator of (A9-59) by $\lambda - u_1$ and then replacing $\lambda^2 - u_1^2$ by its equivalent k_1^2

$$\pi_{z1} = -2c \frac{k_0^2}{k_1^2} \frac{1}{k_1^2} \frac{\partial}{\partial x} \left[\int_0^\infty \lambda e^{-u_1 z} J_0(\lambda\rho) d\lambda - \int_0^\infty u_1 e^{-u_1 z} J_0(\lambda\rho) d\lambda \right]. \qquad (A9\text{-}60)$$

The first of these integrals is related to the Sommerfeld (1926) integral

$$\frac{e^{ik_1 r}}{r} = \int_0^\infty \frac{\lambda}{u_1} e^{-u_1 z} J_0(\lambda\rho) d\lambda = P. \qquad (A9\text{-}61)$$

The second integral of (A9-60) in turn is the second derivative of Foster's (1931) integral

$$N = \int_0^\infty \frac{1}{u_1} e^{-u_1 z} J_0(\lambda\rho) d\lambda = I_0 \left[\frac{\gamma}{2} (r + z) \right] K_0 \left[\frac{\gamma}{2} (r - z) \right] \qquad (A9\text{-}62)$$

I_0 and K_0 are the modified Bessel functions of order zero. Then we find

$$\pi_{z1} = 2c \frac{k_0^2}{k_1^2} \frac{1}{k_1^2} \frac{\partial}{\partial x} \left[\frac{\partial P}{\partial z} + \frac{\partial^2 N}{\partial z^2} \right]. \qquad (A9\text{-}63)$$

The form of this solution suggests that we seek a similar form for the integral of (A9-58). In fact, we can write (A9-58) as

$$\pi_{x1} = -2c \frac{k_0^2}{k_1^2} \frac{1}{k_1^2} \left[\frac{\partial^2 P}{\partial z^2} + \frac{\partial}{\partial z} \left(k_1^2 N + \frac{\partial^2 N}{\partial z^2} \right) \right]. \qquad (A9\text{-}64)$$

The electric field intensity components are then obtained by differentiation of (A9-63) and (A9-64). Thus, from equations (A9-18) and (A9-19)

$$E_x = \frac{\partial}{\partial x}\left[\frac{\partial \pi_{x1}}{\partial x} + \frac{\partial \pi_{z1}}{\partial z}\right] + k_1^2 \pi_{x1} \tag{A9-65}$$

$$E_y = \frac{\partial}{\partial y}\left[\frac{\partial \pi_{x1}}{\partial x} + \frac{\partial \pi_{z1}}{\partial z}\right] \tag{A9-66}$$

or

$$E_x = 2c\,\frac{k_0^2}{k_1^2}\left[\frac{\partial^3 N}{\partial^2 y \partial z} - \frac{\partial^2 P}{\partial z^2}\right] \tag{A9-67}$$

$$E_y = -\,2c\,\frac{k_0^2}{k_1^2}\,\frac{\partial^3 N}{\partial x \partial y \partial z}\;. \tag{A9-68}$$

These are identical to the expressions found by Foster (1931). In obtaining them, use was made of the wave equation for $\partial N/\partial z$, i.e.

$$\frac{\partial^2 \left(\frac{\partial N}{\partial z}\right)}{\partial x^2} + \frac{\partial^2 \left(\frac{\partial N}{\partial z}\right)}{\partial y^2} + \frac{\partial^2 \left(\frac{\partial N}{\partial z}\right)}{\partial z^2} + k^2\,\frac{\partial N}{\partial z} = 0\;. \tag{A9-69}$$

The use of this particular wave equation is justified since we know that π_{z1} must satisfy the wave equation and hence all derivatives and integrals of π_{z1} must also satisfy a wave equation. Refer to equations (A9-60) and (A9-62) to obtain the relationship of $\partial N/\partial z$ to π_{z1}.

At the surface of the earth where $z=0$ we find

$$\frac{\partial N}{\partial z} = -\int_0^\infty J_0(\lambda\rho)d\lambda = -\frac{1}{\rho}\;. \tag{A9-70}$$

This latter integral is the Lipschitz integral used in (A8-16). Also at the surface of the earth the integral P has the value

$$P = \frac{e^{ik_1\rho}}{\rho} \tag{A9-71}$$

where again

$$\rho^2 = x^2 + y^2$$
$$r^2 = x^2 + y^2 + z^2.$$

Thus the electric field components become

$$E_x = \frac{Ids}{2\pi\sigma_1}\left[-\frac{\partial^2}{\partial y^2}\left(\frac{1}{\rho}\right) + \frac{1 - ik_1\rho}{\rho^3}e^{ik_1\rho}\right]$$

$$= \frac{Ids}{2\pi\sigma_1\rho^3}\left[1 + (1 - ik_1\rho)e^{ik_1\rho} - \frac{3y^2}{\rho^2}\right] \tag{A9-72}$$

$$E_y = \frac{Ids}{2\pi\sigma_1}\frac{\partial^2}{\partial x \partial y}\left(\frac{1}{\rho}\right) = \frac{Ids}{2\pi\sigma_1\rho^3}\frac{3xy}{\rho^2}\;. \tag{A9-73}$$

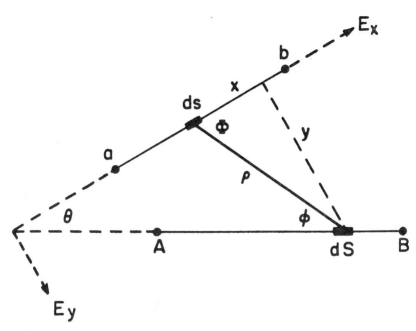

FIG. 9-3. Two adjacent current lines AB and ab on surface of homogeneous earth.

So far we have been considering the potentials and fields due to an infinitesimal electric dipole. Now let us consider two adjacent wires on the surface of the earth as in Figure 9-3. The resultant field acting along an element dS of a second wire along a path S in the same plane as s is

$$E_S = E_x \cos \theta + E_y \sin \theta \tag{A9-74}$$

and hence the voltage dV impressed on dS is

$$dV = dS(E_x \cos \theta + E_y \sin \theta). \tag{A9-75}$$

Then upon substitution of (A9-72) and (A9-73) in (A9-75) we obtain

$$dV = \frac{I\,ds\,dS}{2\pi\sigma_1}\left[\left[1 - \frac{3y^2}{\rho^2}\right]\frac{\cos\theta}{\rho^3} + \frac{3xy}{\rho^2}\frac{\sin\theta}{\rho^3} + [1 - ik_1\rho]e^{ik_1\rho}\frac{\cos\theta}{\rho^3}\right]. \tag{A9-76}$$

The mutual impedance between two infinitesimal elements ds and dS is now written as the ratio of the resulting electric force in one element to the current in the other,

$$dZ = \frac{dV}{I} = \frac{ds\,dS}{2\pi\sigma_1}\left[-\frac{3}{\rho^3}\sin\Phi\sin\phi + \frac{2\cos\theta}{\rho^3} - [1 - (1 - ik_1\rho)e^{ik_1\rho}]\frac{\cos\theta}{\rho^3}\right] \tag{A9-77}$$

where the substitutions $\cos\Phi = x/\rho$, $\sin\Phi = y/\rho$, and $\Phi = \theta + \phi$ have been made in the first two terms of (A9-76).

We wish to provide an alternate form for the first term in (A9-77). Hence we note that, for a function w,

$$\frac{dw}{dx} = \frac{\partial w}{\partial x} + \frac{\partial w}{\partial y}\frac{dy}{dx}. \tag{A9-78}$$

In Figure 9-3, x and y are independent variables while ds is directed along the x axis so that the total derivative becomes

$$\frac{dw}{dx} = \frac{\partial w}{\partial x} = \frac{\partial w}{\partial s} = \frac{dw}{ds}. \tag{A9-79}$$

Similarly we may write

$$\frac{dw}{dS} = \frac{\partial w}{\partial x}\frac{dx}{dS} + \frac{\partial w}{\partial y}\frac{dy}{dS} = \frac{\partial w}{\partial x}\cos\theta + \frac{\partial w}{\partial y}\sin\theta \tag{A9-80}$$

where S is the coordinate direction along the second wire. Then we find

$$\frac{d^2w}{dsdS} = \frac{\partial^2 w}{\partial x^2}\cos\theta + \frac{\partial^2 w}{\partial x\partial y}\sin\theta$$

$$= -\frac{\cos\theta}{\rho^3} + \frac{3x^2}{\rho^5}\cos\theta + \frac{3xy}{\rho^5}\sin\theta, \qquad \text{for } w = \frac{1}{\rho}$$

$$= \frac{2\cos\theta}{\rho^3} - \frac{3\sin^2\Phi\cos\theta}{\rho^3} + \frac{3\sin\Phi\cos\Phi\sin\theta}{\rho^3} \tag{A9-81}$$

or

$$\frac{d^2w}{dsdS} = \frac{1}{\rho^3}(2\cos\theta - 3\sin\Phi\sin\phi). \tag{A9-82}$$

Therefore, (A9-77) may be written

$$dZ = \frac{dsdS}{2\pi\sigma_1}\left[\frac{d^2}{dsdS}\left(\frac{1}{\rho}\right) - \left[1 - (1 - ik_1\rho)e^{ik_1\rho}\right]\frac{\cos\theta}{\rho^3}\right]. \tag{A9-83}$$

To follow conventional presentation, we rewrite (A9-83) as

$$dZ = dsdS\left[\frac{d^2Q(\rho)}{dsdS} + P(\rho)\cos\theta\right] \tag{A9-84}$$

where

$$Q(\rho) = \frac{1}{2\pi\sigma_1\rho} \tag{A9-85}$$

$$P(\rho) = -\frac{1}{2\pi\sigma_1\rho}\left[\frac{1 - (1 - ik_1\rho)e^{ik_1\rho}}{\rho^2}\right]. \tag{A9-86}$$

Provided we choose $P(\rho)$ and $Q(\rho)$ appropriately, equation (A9-84) is valid regardless of whether or not the earth is stratified. However, $P(\rho)$ and $Q(\rho)$ will depend on the geometry of the media and of the electrode array. Thus we may say that the mutual impedance of two wires s and S extending, respectively, from a to b and from A to B is

$$Z = \int_a^b \int_A^B \left[P(\rho)\cos\theta + \frac{d^2}{dsdS}Q(\rho)\right]dsdS. \tag{A9-87}$$

The value of $Q(\rho)$ given by (A9-85) is the potential due to a single current source. For the dipole-dipole array of Figure 9-3, we have from (A9-85)

$$Q_{(A-B)(a-b)} = Q(Aa) - Q(Ba) - Q(Ab) + Q(Bb)$$

$$= \frac{1}{2\pi\sigma_1}\left[\frac{1}{\rho_1} - \frac{1}{\rho_2} - \frac{1}{\rho_3} + \frac{1}{\rho_4}\right] \tag{A9-88}$$

where $\rho_1 = Aa$, $\rho_2 = Ba$, $\rho_3 = Ab$, and $\rho_4 = Bb$. Equation (A9-88) is identical to (A8-11) for the direct current case. We shall refer to this as resistive coupling

The other term in (A9-87) then must be the inductive coupling term. If we are prepared to neglect displacement currents, then $P(\rho)$ is given by (A9-86). Evidently, $P(\rho)$ is a function of frequency and of the electrical constants of the ground. Note that this inductive coupling term does not enter into the expression for E_y, indicating, as expected, that orthogonal linear current elements over an isotropic earth are not inductively coupled.

Madden and Cantwell (this volume) have used (A9-86) to estimate the inductive coupling for the dipole-dipole array over a homogeneous earth.

The solution can readily be extended to an n-layered earth, as we shall show subsequently. First, however, we must introduce additional theory which will lead to a unified approach to solution of problems of this kind.

10. Reflection and Refraction of Plane Waves

10-I. *Introduction*

In this section we are to be concerned with proof of Snell's Law, the development of the Fresnel equations and the development of expressions for reflection and transmission coefficients. These elementary concepts are essential to our understanding of the subsequent sections. We commence with the development of Snell's Law.

10-II. *Snell's Law*

Two media of electrical properties $\epsilon_1\mu_1\sigma_1$, and $\epsilon_2\mu_2\sigma_2$ are in plane contact as in Figure 10-1. The unit vector $\mathbf{n}$ is normal to the plane S and directed from medium (1) into medium (2). If $\mathbf{r}$ is a position vector drawn from the origin O to any point in either (1) or (2), then the plane S is defined by

$$\mathbf{n}\cdot\mathbf{r} = 0. \tag{A10-1}$$

Now assume a plane wave incident upon S travelling in the direction $\mathbf{n}_0$. The electric and magnetic vectors are given by

$$\mathbf{E}_i = \mathbf{E}_0 \exp\left[ik_2\mathbf{n}_0\cdot\mathbf{r} - i\omega t\right] \tag{A10-2}$$

$$\mathbf{H}_i = \frac{k_2}{\omega\mu_2}\mathbf{n}_0 \times \mathbf{E}_i \tag{A10-3}$$

where $\mathbf{E}_0$ is the complex amplitude of the incident wave. The plane defined by the pair of vectors $\mathbf{n}$ and $\mathbf{n}_0$ is called the *plane of incidence*.

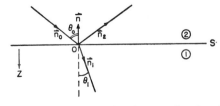

FIG. 10-1. Reflection and refraction at a plane interface.

Waves are *transmitted* through the surface S into (1) and are also *reflected* by S back into (2). Assuming the reflected and transmitted waves are also plane, we write for the transmitted wave,

$$\mathbf{E}_t = \mathbf{E}_1 \exp\left[ik_1\mathbf{n}_1\cdot\mathbf{r} - i\omega t\right] \tag{A10-4}$$

$$\mathbf{H}_t = \frac{k_1}{\omega\mu_1}\,\mathbf{n}_1 \times \mathbf{E}_t \tag{A10-5}$$

and for the reflected wave

$$\mathbf{E}_r = \mathbf{E}_2 \exp\left[ik_2\mathbf{n}_2\cdot\mathbf{r} - i\omega t\right] \tag{A10-6}$$

$$\mathbf{H}_r = \frac{k_2}{\omega\mu_2}\,\mathbf{n}_2 \times \mathbf{E}_r. \tag{A10-7}$$

Since we are assuming that the incident, transmitted, and reflected waves are all plane, then $\mathbf{E}_1$, $\mathbf{E}_2$ and $\mathbf{E}_0$ are independent of the coordinates. We may find a relation between the three wave amplitudes by invoking the boundary conditions calling for continuity of tangential $\mathbf{E}$ and tangential $\mathbf{H}$ at the surface $z=0$. First, however, these boundary conditions hold for arbitrary x and y, and for all times, so that the phase factors must all be equal at $z=0$, i.e.

$$k_2\mathbf{n}_0\cdot\mathbf{r} = k_1\mathbf{n}_1\cdot\mathbf{r} = k_2\mathbf{n}_2\cdot\mathbf{r}. \tag{A10-8}$$

We now wish to introduce the identity

$$\mathbf{r} = (\mathbf{n}\cdot\mathbf{r})\mathbf{n} - \mathbf{n} \times (\mathbf{n} \times \mathbf{r}). \tag{A10-9}$$

For $z=0$, we have $\mathbf{n}\cdot\mathbf{r}=0$, so that (A10-9) becomes

$$\mathbf{r} = -\,\mathbf{n} \times (\mathbf{n} \times \mathbf{r}) \tag{A10-10}$$

which when substituted in (A10-8) yields

$$k_2\mathbf{n}_0\cdot\mathbf{n} \times (\mathbf{n} \times \mathbf{r}) = k_2\mathbf{n}_2\cdot\mathbf{n} \times (\mathbf{n} \times \mathbf{r}) \tag{A10-11}$$

and

$$k_2\mathbf{n}_0\cdot\mathbf{n} \times (\mathbf{n} \times \mathbf{r}) = k_1\mathbf{n}_1\cdot\mathbf{n} \times (\mathbf{n} \times \mathbf{r}). \tag{A10-12}$$

Via the vector identity

$$\mathbf{A}\cdot\mathbf{B} \times \mathbf{C} = \mathbf{A} \times \mathbf{B}\cdot\mathbf{C} \tag{A10-13}$$

we may convert the equations (A10-11) and (A10-12) to

$$(\mathbf{n}_0 \times \mathbf{n} - \mathbf{n}_2 \times \mathbf{n})\cdot\mathbf{n} \times \mathbf{r} = 0 \tag{A10-14}$$
$$(k_2\mathbf{n}_0 \times \mathbf{n} - k_1\mathbf{n}_1 \times \mathbf{n})\cdot\mathbf{n} \times \mathbf{r} = 0. \tag{A10-15}$$

If we now replace the vectors in (A10-14) and (A10-15) by the following substitutes,

$$(\mathbf{n}_0 \times \mathbf{n} - \mathbf{n}_2 \times \mathbf{n}) = \mathbf{A} \tag{A10-16}$$

$$\mathbf{n} \times \mathbf{r} = \mathbf{B} \tag{A10-17}$$

$$(k_2\mathbf{n}_0 \times \mathbf{n} - k_1\mathbf{n}_1 \times \mathbf{n}) = \mathbf{C} \tag{A10-18}$$

then (A10-14) and (A10-15) become

$$A \cdot B = 0 \tag{A10-19}$$

$$C \cdot B = 0. \tag{A10-20}$$

Then the product $A \cdot B$ demands that A be perpendicular to S since B may be arbitrarily oriented in S. Thus A is parallel to n. However, A arises from two cross products, each of which contains n and each of which must then be perpendicular to n. The only way for these two conditions to be met is that $A=0$. Similarly we may establish that $C=0$. Thus we have

$$n_0 \times n = n_2 \times n \tag{A10-21}$$

and

$$k_2 n_0 \times n = k_1 n_1 \times n. \tag{A10-22}$$

The vectors represented by the left and right hand sides of (A10-21) are parallel to each other and perpendicular to n_0, n_2, and n. Similarly the left and right hand sides of (A10-23) are parallel (and equal) vectors, each of which is perpendicular to n_0, n_1, and n. Thus n_0, n_1, n_2 and n are coplanar. The planes of constant phase of both transmitted and reflected waves are normal to the plane of incidence.

With reference to Figure 10-1, we find that the magnitude of the left-hand side of (A10-21) is

$$\sin (\pi - \theta_0) = \sin \theta_0.$$

and that the magnitude of the right hand side of (A10-21) is

$$\sin \theta_2.$$

We conclude that

$$\sin \theta_2 = \sin \theta_0 \tag{A10-23}$$

or in words, the angle of incidence θ_0 is equal to the angle of reflection θ_2. From equation (A10-22), we may now write

$$k_2 \sin \theta_0 = k_1 \sin \theta_1. \tag{A10-24}$$

Equations (A10-23) and (A10-24) are *Snell's Laws* of reflection and refraction.

10-III. *Fresnel's equations*

Let us return now to the boundary conditions relating the amplitudes E_0, E_1, and E_2. From the continuity of tangential E we may write

$$n \times (E_0 + E_2) = n \times E_1 \tag{A10-25}$$

and from the continuity of tangential H we may write

$$n \times (H_0 + H_2) = n \times H_1. \tag{A10-26}$$

Now let us use equations (A10-3) (A10-5) and (A10-7) to express (A10-26) in terms of the electric vector

$$n \times (n_0 \times E_0 + n_2 \times E_2) \frac{k_2}{\mu_2} = n \times (n_1 \times E_1) \frac{k_1}{\mu_1}. \tag{A10-27}$$

The three terms of (A10-27) may be expanded by use of the vector identity,

$$A \times (B \times C) = (A \cdot C)B - (A \cdot B)C \tag{A10-28}$$

to

$$n \times (n_0 \times E_0) = (n \cdot E_0)n_0 - (n \cdot n_0)E_0 \tag{A10-29}$$

$$n \times (n_2 \times E_2) = (n \cdot E_2)n_2 - (n \cdot n_2)E_2 \tag{A10-30}$$

$$n \times (n_1 \times E_1) = (n \cdot E_1)n_1 - (n \cdot n_1)E_1. \tag{A10-31}$$

The orientation of the incident vector E_0 is arbitrary but can be resolved into a component normal to the plane of incidence and a component in the plane of incidence. Let us treat these two cases separately.

(a) *Case I.* E_0 *normal to the plane of incidence.*—Since the plane of incidence contains n, n_0, n_1, n_2 and since E_0 is normal to this plane, then

$$n \cdot E_0 = n_0 \cdot E_0 = 0. \tag{A10-32}$$

For isotropic media, E_1 and E_2 are similarly normal to the plane of incidence

$$n \cdot E_1 = n \cdot E_2 = 0. \tag{A10-33}$$

We have thus evaluated as zero, the first term on the right of each of equations (A10-29) through (A10-31). The second terms may be evaluated directly from Figure 10-1

$$n \cdot n_0 = \cos (\pi - \theta_0) = - \cos \theta_0 \tag{A10-34}$$

$$n \cdot n_1 = \cos (\pi - \theta_1) = - \cos \theta_1 \tag{A10-35}$$

$$n \cdot n_2 = \cos \theta_2. \tag{A10-36}$$

Let us now multiply (A10-25) by $n \times$

$$n \times (n \times E_0) + n \times (n \times E_2) = n \times (n \times E_1). \tag{A10-37}$$

Following (A10-29) through (A10-31) we may convert (A10-37) to

$$(n \cdot E_0)n - (n \cdot n)E_0 + (n \cdot E_2)n - (n \cdot n)E_2 = (n \cdot E_1)n - (n \cdot n)E_1 \tag{A10-38}$$

and by using (A10-32) and (A10-33) we obtain

$$E_0 + E_2 = E_1. \tag{A10-39}$$

Similarly (A10-27) yields

$$\left[-(n \cdot n_0)E_0 - (n \cdot n_2)E_2 \right] \frac{k_2}{\mu_2} = - (n \cdot n_1)E_1 \frac{k_1}{\mu_1} \tag{A10-40}$$

or

$$\cos \theta_0 E_0 - \cos \theta_2 E_2 = \frac{\mu_2 k_1}{\mu_1 k_2} \cos \theta_1 E_1. \tag{A10-41}$$

Solving (A10-39) and (A10-41) for E_1, and E_2 in terms of the primary amplitude E_0 leads to

$$E_1 = \frac{\mu_1 k_2 (\cos \theta_2 + \cos \theta_0)}{\mu_1 k_2 \cos \theta_2 + \mu_2 k_1 \cos \theta_1} E_0 \tag{A10-42}$$

$$E_2 = \frac{\mu_1 k_2 \cos \theta_0 - \mu_2 k_1 \cos \theta_1}{\mu_1 k_2 \cos \theta_2 + \mu_2 k_1 \cos \theta_1} E_0. \tag{A10-43}$$

The relative orientations of the electric, magnetic, and propagation vectors are shown in Figure 10-2.

From Snell's second law (A10-24) we compute

$$k_1 \cos \theta_1 = \sqrt{k_1^2 - k_2^2 \sin^2 \theta_0} \tag{A10-44}$$

and from Snell's first law (A10-23) we compute

$$\cos \theta_2 = \cos \theta_0. \tag{A10-45}$$

When (A10-44) and (A10-45) are substituted in (A10-42) and (A10-43) there results

$$E_1 = \frac{2\mu_1 k_2 \cos \theta_0}{\mu_1 k_2 \cos \theta_0 + \mu_2 \sqrt{k_1^2 - k_2^2 \sin^2 \theta_0}} E_0 \tag{A10-46}$$

$$E_2 = \frac{\mu_1 k_2 \cos \theta_0 - \mu_2 \sqrt{k_1^2 - k_2^2 \sin^2 \theta_0}}{\mu_1 k_2 \cos \theta_0 + \mu_2 \sqrt{k_1^2 - k_2^2 \sin^2 \theta_0}} E_0. \tag{A10-47}$$

As an example, let us take $\theta_0 = 0$ which pertains to normal incidence. Then we find

$$E_2 = \frac{\mu_1 k_2 - \mu_2 k_1}{\mu_1 k_2 + \mu_2 k_1} E_0. \tag{A10-48}$$

If k_2 pertains to free space and k_1 pertains to a conductor, i.e. $k_2 = \alpha_2$ and $k_1 = \alpha_1 + i\beta_1$, then

$$E_2 = \frac{\mu_1 \alpha_2 - \mu_2(\alpha_1 + i\beta_1)}{\mu_1 \alpha_2 + \mu_2(\alpha_1 + i\beta_1)} E_0. \tag{A10-49}$$

Evidently a phase shift exists between E_2 and E_0 at the surface of a conductor. The ratio of the reflected to the incident electric fields is termed the amplitude reflection coefficient $r_\perp$ for E_0 perpendicular to the plane of incidence. So from (A10-47) we find

$$r_\perp \equiv \frac{E_2}{E_0} = \frac{\mu_1 k_2 \cos \theta_0 - \mu_2 k_1 \sqrt{1 - \left(\frac{k_2}{k_1}\right)^2 \sin^2 \theta_0}}{\mu_1 k_2 \cos \theta_0 + \mu_2 k_1 \sqrt{1 - \left(\frac{k_2}{k_1}\right)^2 \sin^2 \theta_0}}. \tag{A10-50}$$

If we then make the substitutions

$$u_2 = ik_2 \cos \theta_0 \tag{A10-51}$$

and

$$u_1 = ik_1 \sqrt{1 - \left(\frac{k_2}{k_1}\right)^2 \sin^2 \theta_0} \tag{A10-52}$$

then $r_\perp$ may be written

$$r_\perp = \frac{\mu_1 u_2 - \mu_2 u_1}{\mu_1 u_2 + \mu_2 u_1} \tag{A10-53}$$

or, in general,

$$r_\perp = \frac{\mu_k u_j - \mu_j u_k}{\mu_k u_j + \mu_j u_k} \tag{A10-54}$$

where the wave originates in medium j and is reflected from medium k. The quantity $i = \sqrt{-1}$ is included in (A10-51) and (A10-52) for later convenience.

(b) *Case II.* $\mathbf{E}_0$ *in the plane of incidence.*—The magnetic vectors must be normal to the plane of incidence for this case, so that we may write

$$\mathbf{n} \cdot \mathbf{H}_0 = \mathbf{n} \cdot \mathbf{H}_1 = \mathbf{n} \cdot \mathbf{H}_2 = 0. \tag{A10-55}$$

Now we have written the field vectors in the form

$$\mathbf{E}_i = \mathbf{E}_0 \exp\left[ik_2 \mathbf{n}_0 \cdot \mathbf{r} - i\omega t\right] \qquad \mathbf{H}_i = \frac{k_2}{\omega \mu_2} \mathbf{n}_0 \times \mathbf{E}_i \tag{A10-56}$$

$$\mathbf{E}_t = \mathbf{E}_1 \exp\left[ik_1 \mathbf{n}_1 \cdot \mathbf{r} - i\omega t\right] \qquad \mathbf{H}_t = \frac{k_1}{\omega \mu_1} \mathbf{n}_1 \times \mathbf{E}_t \tag{A10-57}$$

$$\mathbf{E}_r = \mathbf{E}_2 \exp\left[ik_2 \mathbf{n}_2 \cdot \mathbf{r} - i\omega t\right] \qquad \mathbf{H}_r = \frac{k_2}{\omega \mu_2} \mathbf{n}_2 \times \mathbf{E}_r. \tag{A10-58}$$

The right hand members of each of (A10-56) through (A10-58) may be written

$$\mathbf{H}_i = \mathbf{H}_0 \exp\left[ik_2 \mathbf{n}_0 \cdot \mathbf{r} - i\omega t\right] \tag{A10-59}$$
$$\mathbf{H}_t = \mathbf{H}_1 \exp\left[ik_1 \mathbf{n}_1 \cdot \mathbf{r} - i\omega t\right] \tag{A10-60}$$
$$\mathbf{H}_r = \mathbf{H}_2 \exp\left[ik_2 \mathbf{n}_2 \cdot \mathbf{r} - i\omega t\right] \tag{A10-61}$$

so that

$$\mathbf{H}_0 \exp\left[ik_2 \mathbf{n}_0 \cdot \mathbf{r} - i\omega t\right] = \frac{k_2}{\omega \mu_2} \mathbf{n}_0 \times \mathbf{E}_0 \exp\left[ik_2 \mathbf{n}_0 \cdot \mathbf{r} - i\omega t\right]$$

or

$$\frac{\omega \mu_2}{k_2} \mathbf{H}_0 = \mathbf{n}_0 \times \mathbf{E}_0. \tag{A10-62}$$

We may now multiply (A10-62) by $\mathbf{n}_0 \times$

$$\frac{\omega \mu_2}{k_2} \mathbf{n}_0 \times \mathbf{H}_0 = \mathbf{n}_0 \times (\mathbf{n}_0 \times \mathbf{E}_0) = (\mathbf{n}_0 \cdot \mathbf{E}_0)\mathbf{n}_0 - (\mathbf{n}_0 \cdot \mathbf{n}_0)\mathbf{E}_0. \tag{A10-63}$$

Since $\mathbf{E}_0$ is in the plane of incidence and $\mathbf{n}_0$ is normal to it, then $\mathbf{n}_0 \cdot \mathbf{E}_0 = 0$, and (A10-62) becomes

$$\mathbf{E}_0 = -\frac{\omega \mu_2}{k_2} \mathbf{n}_0 \times \mathbf{H}_0. \tag{A10-64}$$

Similarly, we find

$$\mathbf{E}_1 = -\frac{\omega \mu_1}{k_1} \mathbf{n}_1 \times \mathbf{H}_1 \tag{A10-65}$$

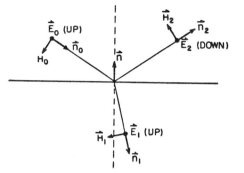

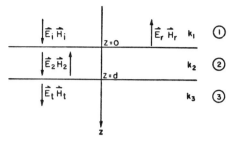

FIG. 10-3. Electromagnetic wave incident upon a three layered structure.

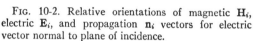

FIG. 10-2. Relative orientations of magnetic H_i, electric E_i, and propagation n_i vectors for electric vector normal to plane of incidence.

and

$$E_2 = -\frac{\omega\mu_2}{k_2} n_2 \times H_2. \tag{A10-66}$$

The boundary conditions for tangential E and H, equations (A10-25) and (A10-26), now convert, upon application of (A10-64) through (A10-66), to

$$n \times \left(-\frac{\omega\mu_2}{k_2} n_0 \times H_0 - \frac{\omega\mu_2}{k_2} n_2 \times H_2\right) = -n \times \frac{\omega\mu_1}{k_1} n_1 \times H_1 \tag{A10-67}$$

and

$$n \times (H_0 + H_2) = n \times H_1. \tag{A10-68}$$

Equation (A10-67) may be simplified via the expansions

$$n \times (n_0 \times H_0) = (n \cdot H_0)n_0 - (n \cdot n_0)H_0 = \cos\theta_0 H_0 \tag{A10-69}$$

$$n \times (n_2 \times H_2) = (n \cdot H_2)n_2 - (n \cdot n_2)H_2 = -\cos\theta_2 H_2 \tag{A10-70}$$

$$n \times (n_1 \times H_1) = (n \cdot H_1)n_1 - (n \cdot n_1)H_1 = \cos\theta_1 H_1 \tag{A10-71}$$

to

$$\cos\theta_0 H_0 - \cos\theta_2 H_2 = \frac{\mu_1 k_2}{\mu_2 k_1} \cos\theta_1 H_1. \tag{A10-72}$$

If we now multiply (A10-68) by $n\times$, we obtain

$$n \times (n \times H_0) + n \times (n \times H_2) = n \times (n \times H_1) \tag{A10-73}$$

or

$$(n \cdot H_0)n - (n \cdot n)H_0 + (n \cdot H_2)n - (n \cdot n)H_2 = (n \cdot H_1)n - (n \cdot n)H_1 \tag{A10-74}$$

which reduces to

$$H_0 + H_2 = H_1 \tag{A10-75}$$

in view of the orthogonality of n with H_1, H_2 and H_0. When equations (A10-72) and (A10-75) are combined, there results

$$H_1 = \frac{(\cos \theta_0 + \cos \theta_2)\mu_2 k_1}{\mu_1 k_2 \cos \theta_1 + \mu_2 k_1 \cos \theta_2} H_0 \tag{A10-76}$$

$$H_2 = \frac{\mu_2 k_1 \cos \theta_0 - \mu_1 k_2 \cos \theta_1}{\mu_2 k_1 \cos \theta_2 + \mu_1 k_2 \cos \theta_1} H_0. \tag{A10-77}$$

We may eliminate the angles of reflection and refraction from (A10-76) and (A10-77) by substituting (A10-44) and (A10-45),

$$H_1 = \frac{2 \cos \theta_0 \mu_2 k_1^2}{\mu_1 k_2 \sqrt{k_1^2 - k_2^2 \sin^2 \theta_0} + \mu_2 k_1^2 \cos \theta_0} H_0 \tag{A10-78}$$

$$H_2 = \frac{\mu_2 k_1^2 \cos \theta_0 - \mu_1 k_2 \sqrt{k_1^2 - k_2^2 \sin^2 \theta_0}}{\mu_2 k_1^2 \cos \theta_0 + \mu_1 k_2 \sqrt{k_1^2 - k_2^2 \sin^2 \theta_0}} H_0. \tag{A10-79}$$

There is no distinction between Case I and Case II for normal incidence, the electric vectors then being

$$E_1 = \frac{2\mu_1 k_2}{\mu_1 k_2 + \mu_2 k_1} E_0 \tag{A10-80}$$

$$E_2 = \frac{\mu_1 k_2 - \mu_2 k_1}{\mu_1 k_2 + \mu_2 k_1} E_0. \tag{A10-81}$$

The equations (A10-46) (A10-47) (A10-78) and (A10-79) are the Fresnel equations. We note that it is necessary to specify the polarization of the incident wave for all angles of incidence other than normal incidence. Reference will be made to this observation in subsequent developments. While we have developed Snell's Laws and the Fresnel Equations for real angles of incidence, it may be demonstrated (e.g. Stratton, 1941, p. 497, p. 516) that under certain physical conditions, complex values of θ_0 and θ_1 will also be required.

The ratio of the reflected to the incident magnetic fields is given by equation (A10-79); this will be the negative of the ratio of the reflected to the incident electric field as may be seen by computing the electric fields via (A10-64) and (A10-66). Thus we may write

$$r_\| = \frac{\mu_1 k_2 \sqrt{k_1^2 - k_2^2 \sin^2 \theta_0} - \mu_2 k_1^2 \cos \theta_0}{\mu_1 k_2 \sqrt{k_1^2 - k_2^2 \sin^2 \theta_0} + \mu_2 k_1^2 \cos \theta_0} \tag{A10-82}$$

or

$$r_\| = \frac{\mu_1 u_1 k_2^2 - \mu_2 u_2 k_1^2}{\mu_1 u_1 k_2^2 + \mu_2 u_2 k_1^2} \tag{A10-83}$$

and, in general

$$r_\| = \frac{\mu_k u_k k_j^2 - \mu_j u_j k_k^2}{\mu_k u_k k_j^2 + \mu_j u_j k_k^2} \tag{A10-84}$$

where the wave originates in the medium j and is reflected from medium k.

For normal incidence, $\theta_0 = 0$ and the two reflection coefficients are identical, in which case we drop the subscript, i.e.,

$$r_{jk} = \frac{\mu_k k_j - \mu_j k_k}{\mu_k k_j + \mu_j k_k} \cdot \tag{A10-85}$$

Sometimes it is convenient to write the reflection coefficients in terms of the plane wave impedances Z_j which are *defined* as the ratio of the amplitudes of the orthogonal electric and magnetic field pairs

$$Z_j \equiv \left| \frac{E_j}{H_j} \right| \tag{A10-86}$$

where the subscript refers to the medium in which the impedance is measured. Thus from equations (A243) through (A246) we learn that we may also define the impedances by

$$Z_j \equiv \frac{\omega \mu_j}{k_j} \cdot \tag{A10-87}$$

The reflection coefficients may then appear in the forms

$$r_\perp = \frac{Z_k \cos \theta_0 - Z_j \sqrt{1 - \left(\frac{k_j}{k_k} \right)^2 \sin^2 \theta_0}}{Z_k \cos \theta_0 + Z_j \sqrt{1 - \left(\frac{k_j}{k_k} \right)^2 \sin^2 \theta_0}} \tag{A10-88}$$

and

$$r_\parallel = \frac{Z_k \sqrt{1 - \left(\frac{k_j}{k_k} \right)^2 \sin^2 \theta_0} - Z_j \cos \theta_0}{Z_k \sqrt{1 - \left(\frac{k_j}{k_k} \right)^2 \sin^2 \theta_0} + Z_j \cos \theta_0} \cdot \tag{A10-89}$$

For normal incidence these expressions are identical and equal to

$$r_{jk} = \frac{Z_k - Z_j}{Z_k + Z_j} \cdot \tag{A10-90}$$

Frequently the *power reflection coefficient* is used; $R_{jk} \equiv |r_{jk}|^2$.

10-IV. *Reflection and transmission coefficients*

Let us consider a plane electromagnetic wave normally incident upon the three layered structure depicted by Figure 10-3. For the incident and reflected waves in medium (1) we may write

$$E_i = E_0 e^{ik_1 z - i\omega t} \tag{A10-91}$$

$$H_i = \frac{k_1}{\omega \mu_1} E_i \tag{A10-92}$$

$$E_r = E_1 e^{-ik_1 z - i\omega t} \tag{A10-93}$$

$$H_r = -\frac{k_1}{\omega \mu_1} E_r. \tag{A10-94}$$

Since we are dealing with normal incidence, the E_i for the cases normal and parallel to the plane of incidence are identical, permitting us to drop vector notation.

Both positive and negative travelling waves occur in medium (2)

$$E_2 = (E_2^+ e^{ik_2 z} + E_2^- e^{-ik_2 z}) e^{-i\omega t} \tag{A10-95}$$

$$H_2 = \frac{k_2}{\omega \mu_2} (E_2^+ e^{ik_2 z} - E_2^- e^{-ik_2 z}) e^{-i\omega t}. \tag{A10-96}$$

The transmitted wave is represented by

$$E_t = E_3 e^{ik_3 z - i\omega t} \tag{A10-97}$$

$$H_t = \frac{k_3}{\omega \mu_3} E_t. \tag{A10-98}$$

We introduce the intrinsic plane wave impedance via

$$E_j \equiv \pm Z_j H_j \tag{A10-99}$$

$$Z_j \equiv \frac{\omega \mu_j}{k_j} \tag{A10-100}$$

so that the magnetic components are written

$$H_i = \frac{1}{Z_1} E_i \tag{A10-101}$$

$$H_r = -\frac{1}{Z_1} E_r \tag{A10-102}$$

$$H_2 = \frac{1}{Z_2} \left[E_2^+ e^{ik_2 z} - E_2^- e^{-ik_2 z} \right] e^{-i\omega t} \tag{A10-103}$$

$$H_t = \frac{1}{Z_3} E_t. \tag{A10-104}$$

To find the relations between the amplitudes of the electric and magnetic vector amplitudes in each of the three media, we employ the usual boundary conditions of continuity of tangential **E** and tangential **H** at each of the plane surfaces $z = 0$ and $z = d$. Thus at $z = 0$

$$E_0 + E_1 = E_2^+ + E_2^- \tag{A10-105}$$

$$(E_0 - E_1) \frac{1}{Z_1} = (E_2^+ - E_2^-) \frac{1}{Z_2} \tag{A10-106}$$

and at $z = d$

$$E_2^+ e^{ik_2 d} + E_2^- e^{-ik_2 d} = E_3 e^{ik_3 d} \tag{A10-107}$$

$$(E_2^+ e^{ik_2 d} - E_2^- e^{-ik_2 d}) \frac{1}{Z_2} = E_3 e^{ik_3 d} \frac{1}{Z_3}. \tag{A10-108}$$

This system of four equations may be solved by Cramer's rule (Wylie, 1960, p. 32) to give

$$E_1 = \frac{(Z_2 - Z_1)(Z_3 + Z_2) + (Z_2 + Z_1)(Z_3 - Z_2)e^{2ik_2d}}{(Z_2 + Z_1)(Z_2 + Z_2) + (Z_2 - Z_1)(Z_3 - Z_2)e^{2ik_2d}} E_0 \qquad \text{(A10-109)}$$

$$E_3 = \frac{4e^{ik_3d}Z_2Z_3}{(Z_2 - Z_1)(Z_3 - Z_2)e^{ik_2d} + (Z_2 + Z_1)(Z_3 + Z_1)e^{-ik_2d}} E_0. \qquad \text{(A10-110)}$$

We shall now introduce the amplitude reflection coefficient for normal incidence

$$r_{jk} = \frac{Z_k - Z_j}{Z_k + Z_j} = -r_{kj} \qquad \text{(A10-111)}$$

whereupon (A10-109) and (A10-110) become

$$E_1 = \frac{r_{12} + r_{23}e^{2ik_2d}}{1 + r_{12}r_{23}e^{2ik_2d}} E_0 \qquad \text{(A10-112)}$$

$$E_3 = \frac{Z_2Z_3}{(Z_2 + Z_1)(Z_3 + Z_2)} \frac{4e^{i(k_2-k_3)d}}{1 + r_{12}r_{23}e^{2ik_2d}} E_0. \qquad \text{(A10-113)}$$

A thin sheet bounded by the same material above and below will produce a reflection unless the product $k_2d \to 0$. For if $k_2d \to 0$, then (A10-112) reduces to

$$\frac{E_1}{E_0} = \frac{r_{12} + r_{23}}{1 + r_{12}r_{23}} = \frac{r_{12} + r_{21}}{1 + r_{12}r_{21}} = \frac{r_{12} - r_{12}}{1 - r_{12}^2} = 0. \qquad \text{(A10-114)}$$

The dimensionless parameter k_2d then controls the amplitude of reflection by a thin sheet.

11. The Plane-Wave Impedance of an n-Layered Isotropic Medium

The analysis of this problem is of particular importance for the magnetotelluric method. However, it is also useful as a guide in studying propagation in layered media for nonplanar waves arising in sources of finite dimensions.

In any layer we may write the electric and magnetic fields in terms of an outgoing wave and a reflected wave. For normal incidence of a uniform plane wave upon a plane layered isotropic earth, Figure 11-1, the fields are, from equations (A236) to (A246) inclusive,

$$E_y^i = \left[A_{yx}^i e^{jk_{yx}^i(z^i-z)} + B_{yx}^i e^{-jk_{yx}^i(z^i-z)} \right] \qquad \text{(A11-1)}$$

$$H_x^i = -\frac{k_{yx}^i}{\omega\mu_0} \left[A_{yx}^i e^{jk_{yx}^i(z^i-z)} - B_{yx}^i e^{-jk_{yx}^i(z^i-z)} \right] \qquad \text{(A11-2)}$$

where

k_{yx}^i is the propagation constant in the ith layer. The subscripts y and x refer to the components of the electric and magnetic vectors respectively and are introduced at this stage to permit ready generalization to anisotropic layers.

μ_0 is the permeability of free space. All layers are assumed to have this permeability.

z^i is the vertical distance to the bottom of the ith layer.

z is any vertical distance at which the field is measured.

A_{yx}^i is the amplitude of the outgoing electric wave in the ith layer.

B_{yx}^i is the amplitude of the reflected electric wave in the ith layer.

ω is the angular frequency. A harmonic time dependency $e^{-i\omega t}$ is assumed throughout but has been omitted from the equations for convenience.

Since we have assumed a form for the electric vector and computed the magnetic vector

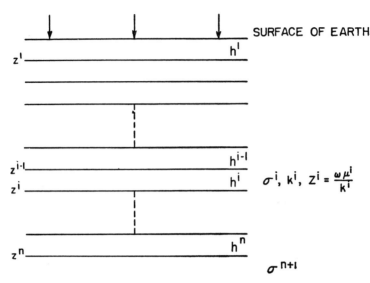

FIG. 11-1. Uniform plane electromagnetic wave normally incident upon an n-layered earth.

therefrom, we are, in effect, assuming that the electric vector is normal to the plane of incidence. At $z = z^i$ we find

$$E_y^i = A_{yx}^i + B_{yx}^i \tag{A11-3}$$

$$H_x^i = [B_{yx}^i - A_{yx}^i] \frac{1}{Z_{yx}^i} \tag{A11-4}$$

where

$$Z_{yx}^i \equiv \frac{\omega \mu_0}{k_{yx}^i} \equiv \text{intrinsic impedance of } i\text{th layer.} \tag{A11-5}$$

From (A11-3) and (A11-4) we find

$$A_{yx}^i = \tfrac{1}{2}[E_y^i - Z_{yx}^i H_x^i] \tag{A11-6}$$
$$B_{yx}^i = \tfrac{1}{2}[E_y^i + Z_{yx}^i H_x^i]. \tag{A11-7}$$

At $z = z^{i-1}$, continuity demands that

$$H_x^i = H_x^{i-1} \tag{A11-8}$$
$$E_y^i = E_y^{i-1}. \tag{A11-9}$$

Therefore we may write

$$E_y^{i-1} = [A_{yx}^i e^{jk_{yx}^i(z^i - z^{i-1})} + B_{yx}^i e^{-jk_{yx}^i(z^i - z^{i-1})}] \tag{A11-10}$$

$$H_x^{i-1} = -\frac{1}{Z_{yx}^i}[A_{yx}^i e^{jk_{yx}^i(z^i - z^{i-1})} - B_{yx}^i e^{-jk_{yx}^i(z^i - z^{i-1})}]. \tag{A11-11}$$

Now if we let

$$z^i - z^{i-1} = -h^i \tag{A11-12}$$

and substitute in (A11-10) and (A11-11) for A^i and B^i described by (A11-6) and (A11-7) we find

$$E_y{}^{i-1} = E_y{}^i \cosh jk_{yx}{}^i h^i - Z_{yx}{}^i H_x{}^i \sinh jk_{yx}{}^i h^i \tag{A11-13}$$

$$H_x{}^{i-1} = H_x{}^i \cosh jk_{yx}{}^i h^i - \frac{1}{Z_{yx}{}^i} E_y{}^i \sinh jk_{yx}{}^i h^i \tag{A11-14}$$

where use has been made of the identities

$$\cosh x = \frac{e^x + e^{-x}}{2} \quad \sinh x = \frac{e^x - e^{-x}}{2}.$$

Equations (A11-13) and (A11-14) may be written in matrix form

$$\begin{bmatrix} E_y{}^{i-1} \\ H_x{}^{i-1} \end{bmatrix} = \begin{bmatrix} \cosh jk_{yx}{}^i h^i & -Z_{yx}{}^i \sinh jk_{yx}{}^i h^i \\ -\dfrac{1}{Z_{yx}{}^i} \sinh jk_{yx}{}^i h^i & \cosh jk_{yx}{}^i h^i \end{bmatrix} \cdot \begin{bmatrix} E_y{}^i \\ H_x{}^i \end{bmatrix} \tag{A11-15}$$

and symbolically by

$$\begin{bmatrix} E_y{}^{i-1} \\ H_x{}^{i-1} \end{bmatrix} = T^i \begin{bmatrix} E_y{}^i \\ H_x{}^i \end{bmatrix}. \tag{A11-16}$$

The matrix T^i is referred to as the transfer matrix of the layer. For n layers we can find a succession of T^i from T^2 through T^{n+1}, each transfer matrix permitting us to write the fields in one layer in terms of the fields in the next layer. Thus we can readily find the matrix relationship between fields in the $(i-1)$th layer and those in the infinite medium terminating the nth layer.

$$\begin{bmatrix} E_y{}^{i-1} \\ H_x{}^{i-1} \end{bmatrix} = \prod_{2}^{n+1} T^i \begin{bmatrix} E_y{}^{n+1} \\ H_x{}^{n+1} \end{bmatrix} \tag{A11-17}$$

The product $\prod_{2}^{n+1} T^i$ of n matrices is itself a matrix S so that (A11-17) may be written

$$\begin{bmatrix} E_y{}^{i-1} \\ H_x{}^{i-1} \end{bmatrix} = S \begin{bmatrix} E_y{}^{n+1} \\ H_x{}^{n+1} \end{bmatrix} \tag{A11-18}$$

where

$$S \equiv \begin{bmatrix} \alpha_{11} & \alpha_{12} \\ \alpha_{21} & \alpha_{22} \end{bmatrix}. \tag{A11-19}$$

Then the impedance looking into the n layered medium from the surface of the ith layer is

$$Z_{yx}{}^{i-1} = -\frac{E_y{}^{i-1}}{H_x{}^{i-1}} = -\frac{\alpha_{11}E_y{}^{n+1} + \alpha_{12}H_x{}^{n+1}}{\alpha_{21}E_y{}^{n+1} + \alpha_{22}H_x{}^{n+1}}$$

$$= \frac{\alpha_{11}Z_{yx}{}^{n+1} - \alpha_{12}}{\alpha_{22} - \alpha_{21}Z_{yx}{}^{n+1}}. \tag{A11-20}$$

For an earth model consisting of one layer overlying an infinite half space (this is usually referred to as a "two-layer earth"), the impedance may be found by making the substitutions for α_{ij} from equation (A11-15), i.e.,

$$\alpha_{11} = \cosh j k_{yx}{}^1 h^1$$

$$\alpha_{12} = - Z_{yx}{}^1 \sinh j k_{yx}{}^1 h^1$$

$$\alpha_{21} = - \frac{1}{Z_{yx}{}^1} \sinh j k_{yx}{}^1 h^1$$

$$\alpha_{22} = \cosh j k_{yx}{}^1 h^1. \tag{A11-21}$$

Thus we obtain from (A11-20) the impedance $Z_{yx}{}^1 = -(E_y{}^1/H_x{}^1)$ which is defined in terms of the electric and magnetic fields measured at the surface of the earth.

$$\hat{Z}_{yx}{}^1 = Z_{yx}{}^1 \frac{Z_{yx}{}^2 + Z_{yx}{}^1 \tanh j k_{yx}{}^1 h^1}{Z_{yx}{}^1 + Z_{yx}{}^2 \tanh j k_{yx}{}^1 h^1}. \tag{A11-22}$$

We may express (A11-20) in terms of the known impedances $Z_{yx}{}^1 \cdots Z_{yx}{}^{n+1}$ the known propagation constants $k_{yx}{}^1 \cdots k_{yx}{}^{n+1}$, and the known layer thicknesses $h^1 \cdots h^{n+1}$, by computing first the impedance at the top of the first layer above the homogeneous half space. By analogy with (A11-22), this impedance will be

$$\hat{Z}_{yx}{}^n = Z_{yx}{}^n \frac{Z_{yx}{}^{n+1} + Z_{yx}{}^n \tanh j k_{yx}{}^n h^n}{Z_{yx}{}^n + Z_{yx}{}^{n+1} \tanh j k_{yx}{}^n h^n}. \tag{A11-23}$$

Once this impedance is computed, then we may use it as the terminating impedance of an equivalent homogeneous half space and write for the impedance at the top of the $(n-1)$th layer

$$\hat{Z}_{yx}{}^{n-1} = Z_{yx}{}^{n-1} \frac{\hat{Z}_{yx}{}^n + Z_{yx}{}^{n-1} \tanh j k_{yx}{}^{n-1} h^{n-1}}{Z_{yx}{}^{n-1} + \hat{Z}_{yx}{}^n \tanh j k_{yx}{}^{n-1} h^{n-1}} \tag{A11-24}$$

and so on up to the surface where

$$\hat{Z}_{yx}{}^1 = Z_{yx}{}^1 \frac{\hat{Z}_{yx}{}^2 + Z_{yx}{}^1 \tanh j k_{yx}{}^1 h^1}{Z_{yx}{}^1 + \hat{Z}_{yx}{}^2 \tanh j k_{yx}{}^1 h^1}. \tag{A11-25}$$

We have used the notation $\hat{Z}_{yx}{}^i$ to denote the impedance at the top of the ith layer and the notation $Z_{yx}{}^i = \omega \mu_0 / k_{yx}{}^i$ to denote the characteristic impedance of the ith layer. A succession of n steps is required in the computation of the impedance at the top of an n layered medium; the steps are those indicated by equations (A11-23) through (A11-25) and their counterparts for the other layers.

For the other pair of field components, the impedance equivalent to (A11-25) may be written

$$\hat{Z}_{xy}{}^1 = - Z_{xy}{}^1 \frac{\hat{Z}_{xy}{}^2 + Z_{xy}{}^1 \tanh j k_{xy}{}^1 h}{Z_{xy}{}^1 + \hat{Z}_{xy}{}^2 \tanh j k_{xy}{}^1 h^1} \tag{A11-26}$$

where $\hat{Z}_{xy}{}^1 = E_x{}^1/H_y{}^1$. Note that $\hat{Z}_{yx}{}^1 = -(E_y{}^1/H_x{}^1)$.

For normal incidence of a plane wave polarized with the electric vector normal to the plane of incidence, the reflection coefficient at an interface is, from (A10-90),

$$r_{01} = \frac{Z_1 - Z_0}{Z_1 + Z_0}. \tag{A11-27}$$

If the impedance looking into the interface is $\hat{Z}_{yx}{}^1$ rather than Z_1, then the reflection coefficient will be

$$r_{0a} = \frac{\hat{Z}_{yx}^1 - Z_0}{\hat{Z}_{yx}^1 + Z_0}. \tag{A11-28}$$

$\hat{Z}_{yx}$ is the impedance of an homogeneous earth equivalent to the n-layered model.

The above development may be generalized for an arbitrary angle of incidence. Referring to Figure 11-2, we shall first assume a plane wave incident at an angle θ_0 on a stratified medium composed of n layers with the electric vector normal to the plane of incidence, i.e. a y component only.

The wave equation for $\mathbf{E}$ in the ith layer is then

$$[\nabla^2 + (k_{xy}^i)^2]E_{iy} = 0 \tag{A11-29}$$

where

$$(k_{yx}^i)^2 = \epsilon_{yx}^i \mu_{yx}^i \omega^2 + i\mu_{yx}^i \sigma_{yx}^i \omega. \tag{A11-30}$$

This is a two dimensional wave equation which can be solved by the separation-of-variables technique. Physically, reflections can take place in the z direction but not in the x direction. Hence we seek a plane wave solution of the form, with variables separated,

$$E_{iy} = [a_i e^{u_{yx}^i z} + b_i e^{-u_{yx}^i z}]e^{i\lambda x}. \tag{A11-31}$$

Equation (A11-31) will be a solution of (A11-29) provided

$$\frac{\partial^2 E_{iy}}{\partial x^2} + \frac{\partial^2 E_{iy}}{\partial z^2} + (k_{yx}^i)^2 E_{iy} = 0 \tag{A11-32}$$

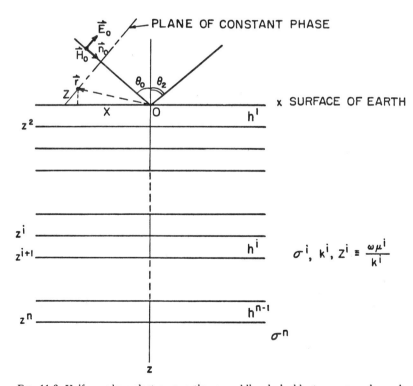

Fig. 11-2. Uniform plane electromagnetic wave obliquely incident upon an n-layered earth, electric vector in plane of incidence.

or

$$-\lambda^2 E_{iy} + (u_{yx}{}^i)^2 E_{iy} + (k_{yx}{}^i)^2 E_{iy} = 0 \tag{A11-33}$$

or

$$(u_{yx}{}^i)^2 = \lambda^2 - (k_{yx}{}^i)^2 \tag{A11-34}$$

where λ is an arbitrary factor at the moment.

There must be attenuation in the z direction since the media are assumed to be dissipative. Hence the real part of $u_{yx}{}^i$ is positive.

The incident field is

$$E_{0y}{}^{INC} = E_0 \exp\left[ik_{yx}{}^0 \mathbf{n}_0 \cdot \mathbf{r} - i\omega t\right]. \tag{A11-35}$$

Let us expand $\mathbf{n}_0 \cdot \mathbf{r}$,

$$\mathbf{n}_0 \cdot \mathbf{r} = x \sin \theta_0 + z \cos \theta_0. \tag{A11-36}$$

The incident field may thus be expressed as

$$E_{0y}{}^{INC} = E_0 \exp\left[ik_{yx}{}^0(x \sin \theta_0 + z \cos \theta_0) - i\omega t\right]. \tag{A11-37}$$

By equating (A11-31) and (A11-37) we find that

$$a_0 = E_0 \tag{A11-38}$$

$$u_{yx}{}^0 = ik_{yx}{}^0 \cos \theta_0 \tag{A11-39}$$

$$\lambda = k_{yx}{}^0 \sin \theta_0. \tag{A11-40}$$

The parameter λ is then simply defined in terms of the propagation constant of the incident medium and of the angle of incidence.

We note that, as far as reflections are concerned, we may ignore the factor $e^{i\lambda x}$ in the solution (A11-31). Hence, by comparison with (A11-1) (A11-2) and (A11-25), we may at once write down the impedance of the n layered structure to an obliquely incident wave

$$\hat{Z}_{yx}{}^1 = Z_{yx}{}^1 \frac{\hat{Z}_{yx}{}^2 + Z_{yx}{}^1 \tanh u_{yx}{}^1 h^1}{Z_{yx}{}^1 + \hat{Z}_{yx}{}^2 \tanh u_{yx}{}^1 h^1}. \tag{A11-41}$$

Wait (1962) has presented the same solution to this problem. The wave propagates with an *apparent* wavenumber $u_{yx}{}^1$ in the ith layer so that the apparent intrinsic impedance $Z_{yx}{}^i$ of the ith layer is

$$Z_{yx}{}^i = \frac{\omega \mu_{yx}{}^i}{iu_{yx}{}^i} = \frac{\omega \mu_{yx}{}^i}{i[\lambda^2 - (k_{yx}{}^i)^2]^{1/2}}. \tag{A11-42}$$

By (A11-35) and Snell's Law in the form

$$-\cos \theta_1 = \frac{1}{k_{yx}{}^1} \sqrt{(k_{yx}{}^1)^2 - (k_{yx}{}^0)^2 \sin^2 \theta_0} = \frac{i}{k_{yx}{}^1} \sqrt{(k_{yx}{}^0)^2 \sin^2 \theta_0 - (k_{yx}{}^1)^2} \tag{A11-43}$$

we may convert (A11-42) to yield the intrinsic impedance for the first layer

$$Z_{yx}{}^1 = -\frac{\omega \mu_{yx}{}^1}{k_{yx}{}^1 \cos \theta_1}. \tag{A11-44}$$

Note that for the above form of Snell's Law we have defined the surface normal $\mathbf{n}$ as positive downwards, hence the minus sign before $\cos \theta_1$.

Note that Snell's Law also informs us that at the air-earth interface, the angle of refraction is always negligible, for

$$-\cos \theta_1 = \sqrt{1 - \left(\frac{k_{yx}^0}{k_{yx}^1}\right)^2 \sin^2 \theta_0} \approx 1 \tag{A11-45}$$

since $k_{yx}^1 \gg k_{yx}^0$ for displacement currents neglected. From which we conclude that regardless of the angle of incidence of low frequency waves upon the earth the impedance Z_{yx}^1 is simply related to the physical constants of the earth through

$$Z_{yx}^1 = \frac{\omega \mu_1}{k_1}. \tag{A11-46}$$

Similarly, we find

$$u_{yx}^i = \left[\lambda^2 - (k_{yx}^i)^2\right]^{1/2} = \left[(k_{yx}^0)^2 \sin^2 \theta_0 - (k_{yx}^i)^2\right]^{1/2} \tag{A11-47}$$

and within the earth,

$$u_{yx}^i \approx i k_{yx}^i \tag{A11-48}$$

for real angles of incidence θ_0. Hence the impedance of a layered earth is simply given by (A11-26) or (A11-25) for plane waves incident at any real angle θ_0 upon the earth.

Now for the other polarization, i.e. for the electric vector *parallel* to the plane of incidence, we need to start from the equation

$$\left[\nabla^2 + (k_{xy}^i)^2\right] H_{iy} = 0 \tag{A11-49}$$

since now we have only a y component of magnetic field, and

$$(k_{xy}^i)^2 = (\epsilon_{xy}^i)^2 (\mu_{xy}^i)^2 \omega^2 + i \mu_{xy}^i \sigma_{xy}^i \omega. \tag{A11-50}$$

For this case we seek a solution of the form

$$H_{ix} = \left[a_i e^{u_{xy}^i z} + b_i e^{-u_{xy}^i z}\right] e^{i\lambda x}. \tag{A11-51}$$

Equation (A11-51) will be a solution of (A11-49) provided

$$\frac{\partial^2 H_{iy}}{\partial x^2} + \frac{\partial^2 H_{iy}}{\partial z^2} + (k_{xy}^i)^2 = 0 \tag{A11-52}$$

from which we obtain

$$(u_{xy}^i)^2 = \lambda^2 - (k_{xy}^i)^2. \tag{A11-53}$$

By analogy with (A11-37), the incident field may be written

$$H_{0y}^{INC} = H_0 \exp\left[i k_{xy}^i (x \sin \theta_0 + z \cos \theta_0) - i\omega t\right] \tag{A11-54}$$

and

$$a_0 = H_0 \tag{A11-55}$$
$$u_{xy}^0 = i k_{xy}^0 \cos \theta_0 \tag{A11-56}$$
$$\lambda = k_{xy}^0 \sin \theta_0. \tag{A11-57}$$

It is a straightforward exercise then, to obtain the impedance expression given by (A11-26). If, now, we compare (A11-39) or (A11-56) with (A10-51), we can see the physical significance of the quantities u_i we introduced in order to simplify the expressions for the reflection coefficients $r_\perp$ and $r_\parallel$. The u_i are equivalent propagation constants which precisely reduce to ik_i for normal incidence, and which approximately reduce to ik_i, regardless of the angle of incidence, for practical earth materials. When the propagation constant in the earth is much larger than the propagation constant in air, such that the $u_i \approx ik_i$ in earth, then we say that we are making the quasi-static approximation because we have neglected the propagation constant in air. We thereby reduce the wave equation in air to Laplace's equation. Note that in general $r_\perp$ and $r_\parallel$ are functions of θ_0 and hence of λ, but that for the materials and frequencies of interest in this volume, it is usually justifiable to assume they are equal and independent of λ.

12. The Plane-Wave Impedance of an *n*-Layered Anisotropic Medium

In an anisotropic medium, the propagation constant $k_{yx}{}^i$ for the (E_y, H_x) orthogonal pair will differ in general from the propagation constant $k_{xy}{}^i$ for the (E_x, H_y) orthogonal pair. Only when the measuring axes x and y are aligned along the principal directions of the anisotropy will the $k_{xy}{}'$ and $k_{yx}{}'$ assume the principal values $k_O{}^i$ and $k_E{}^i$ for that layer. The propagation constants $k_O{}^i$ and $k_E{}^i$ now pertain to the orthogonal pairs (E_O, H_E) and (E_E, H_O) where the axes (O, E) are the principal axes of the anisotropy (Figure 12-1). In general, each field component in the (x, y) directions will be made up of contributions from each of the two principal modes. In the following formulation numerous subscripts and superscripts appear both fore and aft of the amplitudes according to the legend:

E, O —"extraordinary" and "ordinary" modes
$+, -$ —incident and reflected waves, respectively
x, y —referenced to cartesian components
$\quad i$ —ith layer

Thus we note the following expressions for the field components:

$$E_y{}^i = {}^+_yE_O{}^ie^{jk_O{}^i(z-z^i)} + {}^+_yE_E{}^ie^{jk_E{}^i(z-z^i)} + {}^-_yE_O{}^ie^{-jk_O{}^i(z-z^i)} + {}^-_yE_E{}^ie^{-jk_E{}^i(z-z^i)} \quad \text{(A12-1)}$$

$$H_x = \frac{-k_O{}^i}{\omega\mu}\left[{}^+_yE_O{}^ie^{jk_O{}^i(z-z^i)} - {}^-_yE_O{}^ie^{-jk_O{}^i(z-z^i)}\right]$$
$$- \frac{k_E{}^i}{\omega\mu}\left[{}^+_yE_E{}^ie^{jk_E{}^i(z-z^i)} - {}^-_yE_E{}^ie^{-jk_E{}^i(z-z^i)}\right] \quad \text{(A12-2)}$$

$$E_x{}^i = {}^+_xE_O{}^ie^{jk_O{}^i(z-z^i)} + {}^+_xE_E{}^ie^{jk_E{}^i(z-z^i)} + {}^-_xE_O{}^ie^{-jk_O{}^i(z-z^i)} + {}^-_xE_E{}^ie^{-jk_E{}^i(z-z^i)} \quad \text{(A12-3)}$$

$$H_y{}^i = \frac{k_O{}^i}{\omega\mu}\left[{}^+_xE_O{}^ie^{jk_O{}^i(z-z^i)} - {}^-_xE_O{}^ie^{-jk_O{}^i(z-z^i)}\right]$$
$$+ \frac{k_E{}^i}{\omega\mu}\left[{}^+_xE_E{}^ie^{jk_E{}^i(z-z^i)} - {}^-_xE_E{}^ie^{-jk_E{}^i(z-z^i)}\right]. \quad \text{(A12-4)}$$

At $z=z^i$ we find

$$E_y{}^i = {}^+_yE_O{}^i + {}^+_yE_E{}^i + {}^-_yE_O{}^i + {}^-_yE_E{}^i \quad \text{(A12-5)}$$

$$H_x{}^i = -\frac{1}{Z_O{}^i}\left[{}^+_yE_O{}^i - {}^-_yE_O{}^i\right] - \frac{1}{Z_E{}^i}\left[{}^+_yE_E{}^i - {}^-_yE_E{}^i\right] \quad \text{(A12-6)}$$

$$E_x{}^i = {}^+_xE_O{}^i + {}^+_xE_E{}^i + {}^-_xE_O{}^i + {}^-_xE_E{}^i \quad \text{(A12-7)}$$

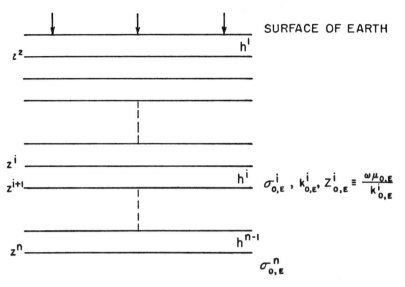

Fig. 12-1. Uniform plane electromagnetic wave normally incident upon an anisotropic n-layered earth.

$$H_y{}^i = \frac{1}{Z_O{}^i}\left[{}^+{}_xE_O{}^i - {}^-{}_xE_O{}^i\right] + \frac{1}{Z_E{}^i}\left[{}^+{}_xE_E{}^i - {}^-{}_xE_E{}^i\right]. \tag{A12-8}$$

The eight unknown amplitudes ${}^+{}_yE_O{}^1 \cdots {}^-{}_xE_E{}^1$ can be reduced to four unknown amplitudes and an angle ϕ_i by the following transformation (refer to Figure 12-2):

$$ {}^+{}_yE_O{}^i = -\tan\phi_i{}^+{}_xE_O{}^i \tag{A12-9}$$

$$ {}^+{}_xE_E{}^i = \tan\phi_i{}^+{}_yE_E{}^i \tag{A12-10}$$

$$ {}^-{}_yE_O{}^i = -\tan\phi_i{}^-{}_xE_O{}^i \tag{A12-11}$$

$$ {}^-{}_xE_E{}^i = \tan\phi_i{}^-{}_yE_E{}^i \tag{A12-12}$$

whereupon (A12-1) through (A12-4) become

$$E_y{}^i = -\tan\phi_i\left[{}^+{}_xE_O{}^i e^{jk_O{}^i(z-z^i)} + {}^-{}_xE_O{}^i e^{-jk_O{}^i(z-z^i)}\right]$$

$$ + \left[{}^+{}_yE_E{}^i e^{jk_E{}^i(z-z^i)} + {}^-{}_yE_E{}^i e^{-jk_E{}^i(z-z^i)}\right] \tag{A12-13}$$

$$H_x{}^i = \frac{1}{Z_O{}^i}\left[{}^+{}_xE_O{}^i e^{jk_O{}^i(z-z^i)} - {}^-{}_xE_O{}^i e^{-jk_O{}^i(z-z^i)}\right]\tan\phi_i$$

$$ + \frac{1}{Z_E{}^i}\left[-{}_yE_E{}^i e^{-jk_E{}^i(z-z^i)} - {}^+{}_yE_E{}^i e^{jk_E{}^i(z-z^i)}\right] \tag{A12-14}$$

$$E_x{}^i = \left[{}^+{}_xE_O{}^i e^{jk_O{}^i(z-z^i)} + {}^-{}_xE_O{}^i e^{-jk_O{}^i(z-z^i)}\right]$$

$$ + \tan\phi_i\left[{}^+{}_yE_E{}^i e^{jk_E{}^i(z-z^i)} + {}^-{}_yE_E{}^i e^{-jk_E{}^i(z-z^i)}\right] \tag{A12-15}$$

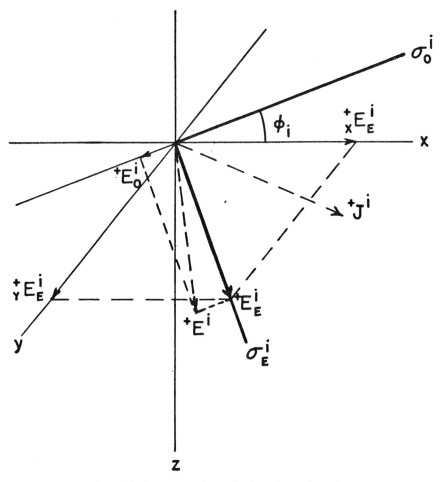

FIG. 12-2. Geometry and notation for anisotropic earth.

$$H_y{}^i = \frac{1}{Z_0{}^i}\left[+_xE_0{}^ie^{jk_0{}^i(z-z^i)} - {}_xE_0{}^ie^{-jk_0{}^i(z-z^i)}\right]$$

$$- \frac{\tan\phi_i}{Z_E{}^i}\left[-_yE_E{}^ie^{-jk_E{}^i(z-z^i)} - {}_{+y}E_E{}^ie^{jk_E{}^i(z-z^i)}\right]. \tag{A12-16}$$

Continuity of the tangential components of **E** and **H** across the interface between the ith and $(i+1)$th layer leads to the matrix equation

$$\begin{bmatrix} E_y{}^{i+1} \\ H_x{}^{i+1} \\ E_x{}^{i+1} \\ H_y{}^{i+1} \end{bmatrix} = \begin{bmatrix} E_y{}^i \\ H_x{}^i \\ E_x{}^i \\ H_y{}^i \end{bmatrix}.$$

These relations enable us to obtain a matrix formulation expressing the amplitude factors, such as $^+_xE_0{}^i$, in (A12-13) with the comparable factors, such as $^+_xE_0{}^{i+1}$ in the next layer. First, we rewrite (A12-13) through (A12-16) in the matrix form

$$
\begin{bmatrix} E_y^i \\ H_x^i \\ E_x^i \\ H_y^i \end{bmatrix}
=
\begin{bmatrix}
-\tan\phi_i e^{jk_O^i(z-z^i)} & -\tan\phi_i e^{-jk_O^i(z-z^i)} & e^{jk_E^i(z-z^i)} & e^{-jk_E^i(z-z^i)} \\[4pt]
\dfrac{\tan\phi_i e^{jk_O^i(z-z^i)}}{Z_O^i} & \dfrac{-\tan\phi_i e^{-jk_O^i(z-z^i)}}{Z_O^i} & -\dfrac{e^{jk_E^i(z-z^i)}}{Z_E^i} & \dfrac{e^{-jk_E^i(z-z^i)}}{Z_E^i} \\[4pt]
e^{jk_O^i(z-z^i)} & e^{-jk_O^i(z-z^i)} & \tan\phi_i e^{-jk_E^i(z-z^i)} & \tan\phi_i e^{-jk_E^i(z-z^i)} \\[4pt]
\dfrac{e^{jk_O^i(z-z^i)}}{Z_O^i} & -\dfrac{e^{-jk_O^i(z-z^i)}}{Z_O^i} & \dfrac{\tan\phi_i e^{jk_E^i(z-z^i)}}{Z_E^i} & -\dfrac{\tan\phi_i e^{-jk_E^i(z-z^i)}}{Z_E^i}
\end{bmatrix}
$$

$$
\cdot
\begin{bmatrix} {}^+_x E_O^i \\[4pt] {}^-_x E_O^i \\[4pt] {}^+_y E_E^i \\[4pt] {}^-_y E_E^i \end{bmatrix}.
\tag{A12-17}
$$

For the $(i+1)$th layer a similar matrix may be written,

$$
\begin{bmatrix} E_y^{i+1} \\ H_x^{i+1} \\ E_x^{i+1} \\ H_y^{i+1} \end{bmatrix}
=
\begin{bmatrix}
-\tan\phi_{i+1} e^{jk_O^{i+1}(z-z^{i+1})} & -\tan\phi_{i+1} e^{-jk_O^{i+1}(z-z^{i+1})} \\[4pt]
\dfrac{\tan\phi_{i+1} e^{jk_O^{i+1}(z-z^{i+1})}}{Z_O^{i+1}} & \dfrac{-\tan\phi_{i+1} e^{-jk_O^{i+1}(z-z^{i+1})}}{Z_O^{i+1}} \\[4pt]
e^{jk_O^{i+1}(z-z^{i+1})} & e^{-jk_O^{i+1}(z-z^{i+1})} \\[4pt]
\dfrac{e^{jk_O^{i+1}(z-z^{i+1})}}{Z_O^{i+1}} & \dfrac{-e^{-jk_O^{i+1}(z-z^{i+1})}}{Z_O^{i+1}}
\end{bmatrix}
$$

$$
\begin{bmatrix}
e^{jk_E^{i+1}(z-z^{i+1})} & e^{-jk_E^{i+1}(z-z^{i+1})} \\[4pt]
\dfrac{e^{jk_E^{i+1}(z-z^{i+1})}}{Z_E^{i+1}} & \dfrac{e^{-jk_E^{i+1}(z-z^{i+1})}}{Z_E^{i+1}} \\[4pt]
\tan\phi_{i+1} e^{jk_E^{i+1}(z-z^{i+1})} & \tan\phi_{i+1} e^{-jk_E^{i+1}(z-z^{i+1})} \\[4pt]
\dfrac{\tan\phi_{i+1} e^{jk_E^{i+1}(z-z^{i+1})}}{Z_E^{i+1}} & \dfrac{-\tan\phi_{i+1} e^{-jk_E^{i+1}(z-z^{i+1})}}{Z_E^{i+1}}
\end{bmatrix}
\cdot
\begin{bmatrix} {}^+_x E_O^{i+1} \\[4pt] {}^-_x E_O^{i+1} \\[4pt] {}^+_y E_E^{i+1} \\[4pt] {}^-_y E_E^{i+1} \end{bmatrix}.
\tag{A12-18}
$$

If the last two matrix equations are written symbolically as

$$
[A^i] = [B^i]\cdot[C^i]
\tag{A12-19}
$$

$$
[A^{i+1}] = [B^{i+1}]\cdot[C^{i+1}]
\tag{A12-20}
$$

then the boundary conditions (A12-17) permit us to compute the transfer matrix between C^i and C^{i+1},

$$
[C^i] = [C^{i+1}]\cdot[B^{i+1}]\cdot[B^i]^{-1}.
\tag{A12-21}
$$

The transfer matrix of the ith layer

$$T^i = [B^{i+1}] \cdot [B^i]^{-1} \qquad (A12\text{-}22)$$

is a four by four matrix with the elements

$$T^i = \begin{bmatrix} a_{11}{}^i & a_{12}{}^i & a_{13}{}^i & a_{14}{}^i \\ a_{21}{}^i & a_{22}{}^i & a_{23}{}^i & a_{24}{}^i \\ a_{31}{}^i & a_{32}{}^i & a_{33}{}^i & a_{34}{}^i \\ a_{41}{}^i & a_{42}{}^i & a_{43}{}^i & a_{44}{}^i \end{bmatrix} \qquad (A12\text{-}23)$$

where

$$a_{11}{}^i = \left[1 + \frac{Z_O{}^{i+1}}{Z_O{}^i}\right]\left[\frac{1 + \tan\phi_{i+1}\tan\phi_i}{2(1 + \tan^2\phi_{i+1})}\right] e^{j(k_O{}^i - k_O{}^{i+1})h^i}$$

$$a_{12}{}^i = \left[1 - \frac{Z_O{}^{i+1}}{Z_O{}^i}\right]\left[\frac{1 + \tan\phi_{i+1}\tan\phi_i}{2(1 + \tan^2\phi_{i+1})}\right] e^{-j(k_O{}^i + k_O{}^{i+1})h^i}$$

$$a_{13}{}^i = \left[1 + \frac{Z_O{}^{i+1}}{Z_E{}^i}\right]\left[\frac{\tan\phi_i - \tan\phi_{i+1}}{2(1 + \tan^2\phi_{i+1})}\right] e^{j(k_E{}^i - k_O{}^{i+1})h^i}$$

$$a_{14}{}^i = \left[1 - \frac{Z_O{}^{i+1}}{Z_E{}^i}\right]\left[\frac{\tan\phi_i - \tan\phi_{i+1}}{2(1 + \tan^2\phi_{i+1})}\right] e^{-j(k_E{}^i + k_O{}^{i+1})h^i}$$

$$a_{21}{}^i = \left[1 - \frac{Z_O{}^{i+1}}{Z_O{}^i}\right]\left[\frac{1 + \tan\phi_i\tan\phi_{i+1}}{2(1 + \tan^2\phi_{i+1})}\right] e^{j(k_O{}^i + k_O{}^{i+1})h^i}$$

$$a_{22}{}^i = \left[1 + \frac{Z_O{}^{i+1}}{Z_O{}^i}\right]\left[\frac{1 + \tan\phi_i\tan\phi_{i+1}}{2(1 + \tan^2\phi_{i+1})}\right] e^{-j(k_O{}^i - k_O{}^{i+1})h^i}$$

$$a_{23}{}^i = \left[1 - \frac{Z_O{}^{i+1}}{Z_E{}^i}\right]\left[\frac{\tan\phi_i - \tan\phi_{i+1}}{2(1 + \tan^2\phi_{i+1})}\right] e^{j(k_E{}^i + k_O{}^{i+1})h^i}$$

$$a_{24}{}^i = \left[1 + \frac{Z_O{}^{i+1}}{Z_E{}^i}\right]\left[\frac{\tan\phi_i - \tan\phi_{i+1}}{2(1 + \tan^2\phi_{i+1})}\right] e^{-j(k_E{}^i - k_O{}^i)h^i}$$

$$a_{31}{}^i = \left[1 - \frac{Z_E{}^{i+1}}{Z_O{}^i}\right]\left[\frac{\tan\phi_{i+1} - \tan\phi_i}{2(1 + \tan^2\phi_{i+1})}\right] e^{-j(k_O{}^i + k_E{}^{i+1})h^i}$$

$$a_{32}{}^i = \left[1 - \frac{Z_E{}^{i+1}}{Z_O{}^i}\right]\left[\frac{\tan\phi_{i+1} - \tan\phi_i}{2(1 + \tan^2\phi_{i+1})}\right] e^{-j(k_O{}^i + k_E{}^{i+1})h^i}$$

$$a_{33}{}^i = \left[1 + \frac{Z_E{}^{i+1}}{Z_E{}^i}\right]\left[\frac{1 + \tan\phi_i\tan\phi_{i+1}}{2(1 + \tan^2\phi_{i+1})}\right] e^{j(k_E{}^i - k_E{}^{i+1})h^i}$$

$$a_{34}{}^i = \left[1 - \frac{Z_E{}^{i+1}}{Z_E{}^i}\right]\left[\frac{1 + \tan\phi_i\tan\phi_{i+1}}{2(1 + \tan^2\phi_{i+1})}\right] e^{-j(k_E{}^i + k_E{}^{i+1})h^i}$$

$$a_{41}{}^i = \left[1 - \frac{Z_E{}^{i+1}}{Z_O{}^i}\right]\left[\frac{\tan\phi_{i+1} - \tan\phi_i}{2(1 + \tan^2\phi_{i+1})}\right] e^{j(k_O{}^i + k_E{}^{i+1})h^i}$$

$$a_{42}{}^i = \left[1 + \frac{Z_E{}^{i+1}}{Z_o{}^i}\right]\left[\frac{\tan \phi_{i+1} - \tan \phi_i}{2(1 + \tan^2 \phi_{i+1})}\right]e^{-j(ko^i - k_E{}^i)h^i}$$

$$a_{43}{}^i = \left[1 - \frac{Z_E{}^{i+1}}{Z_E{}^i}\right]\left[\frac{1 + \tan \phi_i \tan \phi_{i+1}}{2(1 + \tan^2 \phi_{i+1})}\right]e^{j(k_E{}^i + k_E{}^{i+1})h^i}$$

$$a_{44}{}^i = \left[1 + \frac{Z_E{}^{i+1}}{Z_E{}^i}\right]\left[\frac{1 + \tan \phi_i \tan \phi_{i+1}}{2(1 + \tan^2 \phi_{i+1})}\right]e^{-j(k_E{}^i - k_E{}^{i+1})h^i}.$$

Then, following (A11-17), the transfer function of the layers between the ith layer and the nth (semi-infinite) layer at the bottom, becomes

$$[C^i] = \prod_1^n T^i[C^n]. \tag{A12-24}$$

Note that for this anisotropic problem we have chosen the bottom, semi-infinite, medium as the nth medium whereas for the isotropic case we chose it as the $(n+1)$th medium. The choice of labelling is purely arbitrary; there is no change in the physics of the problem. The product $\prod_1^n T^i$ of n matrices is the matrix S^1 as before, but S^1 is now defined by

$$S^1 \equiv \begin{bmatrix} s_{11}{}^1 & s_{12}{}^1 & s_{13}{}^1 & s_{14}{}^1 \\ s_{21}{}^1 & s_{22}{}^1 & s_{23}{}^1 & s_{24}{}^1 \\ s_{31}{}^1 & s_{32}{}^1 & s_{33}{}^1 & s_{34}{}^1 \\ s_{41}{}^1 & s_{42}{}^1 & s_{43}{}^1 & s_{44}{}^1 \end{bmatrix} \tag{A12-25}$$

This matrix relates the amplitudes $^+{}_zE_0{}^1$, $^-{}_zE_0{}^1$, $^+{}_yE_E{}^1$, and $^-{}_yE_E{}^1$ to the amplitudes $^+{}_zE_0{}^n$, $^-{}_zE_0{}^n$, $^+{}_yE_E{}^n$, and $^-{}_yE_E{}^n$. However, the reflected wave is absent in the nth medium and so

$$^-{}_zE_0{}^n = {}^-{}_yE_E{}^n = 0. \tag{A12-26}$$

Once the amplitudes $^+{}_zE_0{}^1, \cdots, {}^-{}_yE_E{}^1$, pertaining to the surface of the earth, have been found, then so also are $E_x{}^1$, $E_y{}^1$, $H_x{}^1$, and $H_y{}^1$. The latter quantities are the ones normally measured. We can expect a matrix relationship between the $E_x{}^1, \cdots, H_y{}^1$, and the $E_x{}^n, \cdots, H_y{}^n$ of the form

$$\begin{bmatrix} E_y{}^1 \\ H_x{}^1 \\ E_x{}^1 \\ H_y{}^1 \end{bmatrix} = S \begin{bmatrix} E_y{}^n \\ H_x{}^n \\ E_x{}^n \\ H_y{}^n \end{bmatrix} \tag{A12-27}$$

where

$$S = \begin{bmatrix} s_{11} & s_{12} & s_{13} & s_{14} \\ s_{21} & s_{22} & s_{23} & s_{24} \\ s_{31} & s_{32} & s_{33} & s_{34} \\ s_{41} & s_{42} & s_{43} & s_{44} \end{bmatrix} \tag{A12-28}$$

is the four by four transfer matrix of the n layers. Then the impedance measured at the surface of the earth will be of the form

$$\hat{Z}_{yx}{}^{1} = -\frac{E_{y}{}^{1}}{H_{x}{}^{1}} = -\frac{s_{11}Z_{yx}{}^{n} + s_{12} + s_{13}\dfrac{E_{x}{}^{n}}{H_{x}{}^{n}} + s_{14}\dfrac{H_{y}{}^{n}}{H_{x}{}^{n}}}{s_{21}Z_{yx}{}^{n} + s_{22} + s_{13}\dfrac{E_{x}{}^{n}}{H_{x}{}^{n}} + s_{24}\dfrac{H_{y}{}^{n}}{H_{x}{}^{n}}} \cdot \qquad (A12\text{-}29)$$

Clearly, the impedance measured is a function of the polarization $H_{y}{}^{n+1}/H_{x}{}^{n+1}$ of the magnetic field at the bottom of the structure and hence will also be a function of the polarization of the downcoming wave. It is not practical to apply (A2-29) in the general case. O'Brien (1964) has, however, used this expression to find the impedance of a structure composed of an anisotropic layer upon an isotropic half space. The anisotropy introduces the extra terms involving s_{13}, s_{14}, s_{23}, and s_{24} as comparison of (A12-29) with (A11-20) will indicate.

13. The Line Source of Current Over an n-Layered Medium

13-I. *The line source in free space*

Assume an infinite line source of current directed along the y axis in an infinite medium of zero conductivity (Figure 13-1). We are here, and elsewhere in this volume, concerned with the low frequency approximation so that displacement currents can be neglected. It is necessary to solve the inhomogeneous wave equation

$$\nabla^{2}\psi - \mu\epsilon\frac{\partial^{2}\psi}{\partial t^{2}} = -g(x, y, z, t) \qquad (A13\text{-}1)$$

where the source function $g(x, y, z, t)$ is described as an infinite line of harmonically varying current of "constant" density. Further, it is convenient to use a single component π vector, directed along the current line, in seeking the solution for the fields. Thus from equation (A36) we may state that we are seeking solutions of the equation.

$$\nabla^{2}\pi_{y} + \mu\epsilon\omega^{2}\pi_{y} = \frac{P_{y}'}{\epsilon} \cdot \qquad (A13\text{-}2)$$

We also know that the solution of this equation is, from (A182),

$$\pi_{y} = \frac{-e^{-i\omega t}}{4\pi i\epsilon\omega}\int_{V} J_{y}\frac{e^{ik_{0}r}}{r}\,dv \qquad (A13\text{-}3)$$

where $k_{0} = \sqrt{\mu_{0}\epsilon_{0}}\cdot\omega$ is the propagation constant of free space. The volume integral may be replaced by a line integral involving the current,

$$\pi_{y} = \frac{ie^{-i\omega t}}{4\pi\epsilon\omega}\int_{y=-\infty}^{\infty} I\frac{e^{ik_{0}r}}{r}\,dy. \qquad (A13\text{-}4)$$

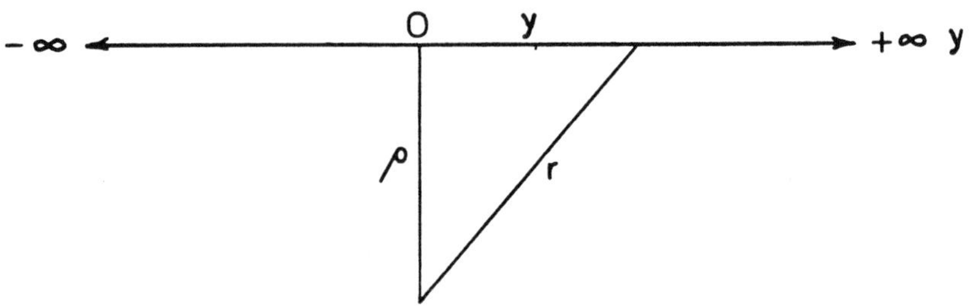

FIG. 13-1. Geometry for infinite line source in free space.

We have stated that the current is constant throughout the length of the wire, although such can only be true for zero frequency. Nevertheless, this assumption is justifiable for very low frequencies since wavelengths are very long; we need only assume that the current is constant over some interval $-y$, to y_1, such that the contribution in the integral of (A13-4) from currents outside this interval is negligible. Then we may remove I from the integral of (A13-4) and we are left with the task of evaluating the integral of the Green's function,

$$g = 2 \int_{y=0}^{\infty} \frac{e^{ik_0r}}{r} \, dy. \tag{A13-5}$$

It is desirable to effect a change of variables in order to evaluate this integral. First, from Figure (13-1), note that

$$\rho^2 + y^2 = r^2 \tag{A13-6}$$

and by differentiation

$$dy = \frac{r\,dr}{\sqrt{r^2 - \rho^2}}. \tag{A13-7}$$

The integral (A13-5) becomes

$$g = \frac{2}{\rho} \int_{r=\rho}^{\infty} \frac{e^{ik_0r}}{\sqrt{\left(\dfrac{r}{\rho}\right)^2 - 1}} \, dr. \tag{A13-8}$$

We now substitute $(r/\rho)=t$, so that

$$g = 2 \int_{1}^{\infty} \frac{e^{ik_0\rho t}}{\sqrt{t^2 - 1}} \, dt. \tag{A13-9}$$

This integral has been evaluated by Watson (1944, p. 185),

$$g = 2K_0(-ik_0\rho) \tag{A13-10}$$

where $K_0(-ik_0\rho)$ is the modified Bessel function of order zero so that the potential becomes

$$\pi_y = \frac{ie^{-i\omega t}}{2\pi\epsilon\omega} I K_0(-ik_0\rho). \tag{A13-11}$$

The fields are then derived from equations (A75) and (A77).

$$E_y = k^2\pi_y = \frac{i\mu\omega e^{-i\omega t}}{2\pi} I K_0(-ik_0\rho) \tag{A13-12}$$

$$H_\theta = -i\omega\epsilon \frac{\partial \pi_y}{\partial y} = \frac{ik_0}{2\pi} I K_1(-ik_0\rho) e^{-i\omega t} \approx -\frac{Ie^{-i\omega t}}{2\pi\rho} \tag{A13-13}$$

where use has been made of the relation (Watson 1944, p. 79)

$$K_0'(z) = -K_1(z). \tag{A13-14}$$

The θ coordinate is directed normally to y and ρ.

3-II. *The effect of the earth*

The geometry for the line source over the stratified earth is represented in Figure 13-2. The infinite line source is situated at a height h above the surface of the earth. The origin

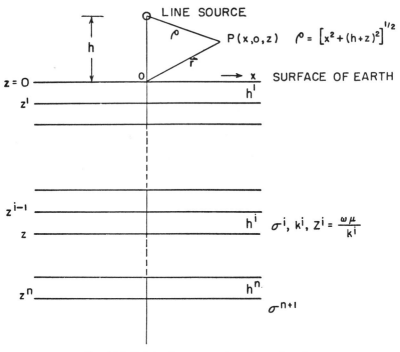

Fig. 13-2. Infinite line source above layered earth.

of a Cartesian coordinate system is vertically below the line source. Fields are observed at a point $P(x, 0, z)$.

At first glance one might intuitively seek solutions in terms of Hertzian vectors with cylindrical symmetry about the line source as we have done for the primary field. However, one can readily see that difficulties then arise in attempting to satisfy the boundary conditions at each of the $n+1$ plane interfaces in the layered earth. To avoid this problem, we represent all fields, both primary and all others, in terms of superposition of plane waves. Recall that equation (A365) represented a superposition of elementary wavelets, each with its own weighting function $g(\alpha, \beta)$. The weighting function and the angles of incidence α and β can all be complex if necessary for the field representation. Thus equation (A406) represents a superposition of elementary plane waves $e^{\pm i \sqrt{k^2 - \lambda^2} \cdot z - iwt}$ each of which is multiplied by a weighting function and integrated with respect to space frequency λ.

Now a general plane wave incident at an angle θ_0, with the electric vector normal to the plane of incidence, may be written, following equation (A11-31),

$$E_{iy} = [a_i e^{u_i z} + b_i e^{-u_i z}] e^{i\lambda x} \qquad (A13\text{-}15)$$

where

$$\lambda = k_0 \sin \theta_0 \qquad (A13\text{-}16)$$

$$(u_i)^2 = \lambda^2 - (k_i^0)^2 \qquad (A13\text{-}17)$$

$$k_i^0 = \epsilon_i \mu_i \omega^2 + i \mu_i \sigma_i \omega. \qquad (A13\text{-}18)$$

The first term in the brackets may be interpreted as an outward traveling wave in the ith layer while the second term may be interpreted as a reflected wave in the ith layer. The incident wave is

$$E_{0y} = a_0 \exp[ik_0 \mathbf{n} \cdot \mathbf{r}] = a_0 \exp[ik_0 x \sin \theta_0] \exp[ik_0 z \cos \theta_0] = a_0 \exp[i\lambda x] \exp[u_0 z] \quad \text{(A13-19)}$$

in accordance with (A11-31) (A11-34) and (A11-35).

The general solution (A13-15) may be rewritten, for the free space above the layered earth, in the form

$$E_{0y} = a_0 \left[e^{u_0 z} + \frac{b_0}{a_0} e^{-u_0 z} \right] e^{i\lambda x} \quad \text{(A13-20)}$$

or

$$E_{0y} = a_0 [e^{u_0 z} + r(\lambda) e^{-u_0 z}] e^{i\lambda x}. \quad \text{(A13-21)}$$

The reflection coefficient $r(\lambda)$ must be a function of the angle of incidence, and hence must be a function of λ.

If it is assumed that the amplitude factor a_0 is also a function of the angle of incidence, then the general form of E_{0y}, as a superposition of plane waves, is

$$E_{0y} = \int_{-\infty}^{\infty} a_0(\lambda) [e^{u_0 z} + r(\lambda) e^{-u_0 z}] e^{i\lambda x} d\lambda. \quad \text{(A13-22)}$$

Any two-dimensional field can be represented in this fashion, so that the primary field of the line source is obtained with $r(\lambda) = 0$ as pertains to an infinite medium. Then

$$\int_{-\infty}^{\infty} a_0(\lambda) e^{u_0 z} e^{i\lambda x} d\lambda = \frac{i\mu\omega I}{2\pi} K_0(-ik_0\rho) = \frac{i\mu\omega I}{2\pi} K_0[-ik_0\{x^2 + (h+z)^2\}^{1/2}]. \quad \text{(A13-23)}$$

We may treat (A13-23) as a Fourier transform and so write its inverse

$$a_0(\lambda) e^{u_0 z} = \frac{i\mu\omega I}{2\pi} \int_{-\infty}^{\infty} K_0[-ik_0\{x^2 + (h+z)^2\}^{1/2}] e^{-i\lambda x} dx. \quad \text{(A13-24)}$$

Since the kernel of the integral in (A13-24) is an even function of x, the complex integral transform can be written as the cosine transform

$$a_0(\lambda) e^{u_0 z} = \frac{i\mu\omega I}{2\pi} \cdot 2 \int_0^{\infty} K_0[-ik_0\{x^2 + (h+z)^2\}^{1/2}] \cos \lambda x \, dx$$

$$= \frac{i\mu\omega I}{2\pi} \frac{1}{2} (\lambda^2 - k_0^2)^{-1/2} e^{(z+h)(\lambda^2 - k_0^2)^{1/2}}$$

$$= \frac{i\mu\omega I}{4\pi} \frac{e^{(z+h) u_0}}{u_0}. \quad \text{(A13-25)}$$

Reference is made to Erdelyi (1954, Vol. I, p. 17, n. 27) for evaluation of the above transform. Thus we have

$$a_0(\lambda) = \frac{i\mu\omega I}{2\pi} \frac{e^{h u_0}}{u_0} \quad \text{(A13-26)}$$

and the expression for E_{0y} becomes

$$E_{0y} = \frac{i\mu\omega I}{4\pi} \int_{-\infty}^{\infty} \frac{1}{u_0} [e^{u_0(z+h)} + r(\lambda) e^{-u_0(z-h)}] e^{i\lambda x} d\lambda. \quad \text{(A13-27)}$$

The magnetic field component, H_{0x}, can be obtained from the relation

$$-i\mu\omega H_{0x} = \frac{\partial E_{0y}}{\partial z} \tag{A13-28}$$

$$i\mu\omega H_{0z} = \frac{\partial E_{0y}}{\partial x} \tag{A13-29}$$

or

$$H_{0x} = \frac{I}{4\pi} \int_{-\infty}^{\infty} e^{u_0 h} [r(\lambda)e^{-u_0 z} - e^{u_0 z}]e^{i\lambda x} d\lambda. \tag{A13-30}$$

The expressions (A13-27) and (A13-30) give the resultant fields in the space $0 > z > -h$. The reflection coefficient $r(\lambda)$ is just that for plane wave reflection of the individual spectral components. This integral representation for E_0 clearly is a superposition of plane waves, or spectral components, of generally complex angles of incidence.

We may, at this stage, introduce the reflection coefficient of (A10-54) since for this particular problem the electric vector is normal to the plane of incidence for all elementary wavelets. Further, if we make the far-field assumption, $u_{yx}{}^i \approx ik_{yx}{}^i$ and set all permeabilities equal to that of free space, then the reflection coefficient simplifies from (A10-54) to

$$r_{\perp} = \frac{k_{yx}{}^0 - k_{yx}{}^1}{k_{yx}{}^0 + k_{yx}{}^1} = \frac{\hat{Z}_{yx}{}^1 - Z_0}{\hat{Z}_{yx}{}^1 + Z_0} \tag{A13-31}$$

where

$$\hat{Z}_{yx}{}^1 = Z_{yx}{}^1 \frac{\hat{Z}_{yx}{}^2 + Z_{yx}{}^1 \tanh u_{yx}{}^1 h^1}{Z_{yx}{}^1 + \hat{Z}_{yx}{}^2 \tanh u_{yx}{}^1 h^1}. \tag{A13-32}$$

For this approximation, the $u_{yx}{}^1$, the $Z_{yx}{}^1$, and hence the $\hat{Z}_{yx}{}^1$ are all independent of λ. Thus the reflection coefficient (A13-31) is independent of λ. Therefore, we may integrate (A13-27) simply

$$E_{0y} = \frac{i\mu\omega I}{2\pi} [K_0\{-ik_{yx}{}^0[x^2 + (z + h)^2]^{1/2}\} + r(\lambda)K_0\{-ik_{yx}{}^0[x^2 + (z - h)^2]^{1/2}\}]. \tag{A13-33}$$

This relation will not hold, in general, for complex angles of incidence associated with large values of λ. Complex angles of incidence are required to obtain a plane wave superposition near the source. Provided either h or z is large, then (A13-33) is an adequate approximation.

Note that in the limiting case where $r(\lambda) = 0$, corresponding to no reflection, the solution reduces to the primary field as it should. Also for $r(\lambda) = -1$, corresponding to a perfectly conducting half space, the solution (A13-33) reduces to

$$E_{0y} = \frac{i\mu\omega I}{2\pi} [K_0\{ik_{yx}{}^0[x^2 + (z + h)^2]^{1/2}\} - K_0\{-ik_{yx}{}^0[x^2 + (z - h)^2]^{1/2}\}] \tag{A13-34}$$

13-III. The line source on a homogeneous earth

Now let us investigate a more exact solution. Again considering that the electric vector is normal to the plane of incidence for all electromagnetic waves issuing from a uniform cylindrical source such as a line source, then we may use (A10-54) for the reflection coefficient.

Let us assume that all media have the permeability of free space, so that (A10-54) reduces to

$$r(\lambda) = \frac{u_0 - u_1}{u_0 + u_1} \tag{A13-35}$$

where u_0 pertains to free space in which the line source is situated and u_1 to a homogeneous earth beneath it. We have not at this stage made the quasi-static assumption in this particular development.

When (A13-35) is substituted in (A13-27), the following result is found

$$E_{0y} = \frac{i\mu\omega I}{2\pi} \int_0^\infty \frac{1}{u_0} \left[e^{u_0(z+h)} + \frac{u_0 - u_1}{u_0 + u_1} e^{-u_0(z-h)} \right] \cos \lambda x d\lambda \tag{A13-36}$$

where the Fourier integral transform has been changed to a Fourier cosine transform for convenience. Now when the line source is on the surface of the earth, $h=0$, and (A13-36) reduces to

$$E_{0y} = \frac{i\mu\omega I}{2\pi} \int_0^\infty \frac{e^{u_0 z}}{u_0} \left[1 + \frac{u_0 - u_1}{u_0 + u_1} e^{-2u_0 z} \right] \cos \lambda x d\lambda$$

$$= \frac{i\mu\omega I}{\pi} \int_0^\infty \frac{\cos \lambda x}{u_0 + u_1} e^{-u_0 z} d\lambda. \tag{A13-37}$$

This is the electric field above the surface of the earth. We now wish to integrate (A13-37). First note that

$$\frac{1}{u_1 + u_0} = \frac{u_1 - u_0}{u_1^2 - u_0^2} = \frac{u_1 - u_0}{k_0^2 - k_1^2} . \tag{A13-38}$$

Hence (A13-37) becomes

$$E_{oy} = \frac{i\mu\omega I}{\pi(k_0^2 - k_1^2)} \left[\int_0^\infty u_1 \cos \lambda x e^{-u_0 z} d\lambda - \int_0^\infty u_0 \cos \lambda x e^{-u_0 z} d\lambda \right]. \tag{A13-39}$$

Both the integrals in (A13-39) may be treated as Fourier cosine transforms. To evaluate them, we first note that in (A13-25) we used the following cosine transform pair

$$\int_0^\infty \frac{e^{(z+h)u_0}}{u_0} \cos \lambda x d\lambda = K_0 \left[-ik_0 \{ x^2 + (h+z)^2 \}^{1/2} \right] \tag{A13-40}$$

$$\int_0^\infty K_0 \left[-ik_0 \{ x^2 + (h+z)^2 \}^{1/2} \right] \cos \lambda x dx = \frac{e^{(z+h)u_0}}{u_0} . \tag{A13-41}$$

Since we are interested in both the line source and the point of observation on the surface of the earth, we may set $h=z=0$ in (A13-40).

$$\int_0^\infty \frac{\cos \lambda x}{u_0} d\lambda = K_0 \left[-ik_0 x \right]. \tag{A13-42}$$

Both sides of (A13-42) are now multiplied by $[k_0^2 + \partial^2/\partial x^2]$.

$$-\int_0^\infty u_0 \cos \lambda x d\lambda = \left[k_0^2 + \frac{\partial^2}{\partial x^2} \right] K_0(-ik_0 x). \tag{A13-43}$$

To evaluate the right hand side of (A13-43), we use the recurrence relations (Watson, 1944, p. 79)

$$K_0'(z) = -K_1(z) \tag{A13-44}$$

$$K_1'(z) + \frac{1}{z} K_1(z) = -K_0(z). \tag{A13-45}$$

Then from (A13-44)

$$K_0''(z) = -K_1'(z) = \frac{1}{z} K_1(z) + K_0(z) \tag{A13-46}$$

where differentiation is with respect to the variable z. In terms of the quantities appearing in equation (A13-43), the latter equation becomes

$$K_0''(-ik_0x) = \frac{1}{-ik_0x} K_1(-ik_0x) + K_0(-ik_0x) \tag{A13-47}$$

and if differentiation is carried out with respect to x rather than $(-ik_0x)$, then (A13-47) becomes

$$\frac{\partial^2 K_0(-ik_0x)}{\partial x^2} = \frac{-ik_0}{x} K_1(-ik_0x) - k_0^2 K_0(-ik_0x) \tag{A13-48}$$

with the result that (A13-43) is now simply

$$\int_0^\infty u_0 \cos \lambda x d\lambda = \frac{ik_0}{x} K_1(-ik_0x). \tag{A13-49}$$

Similarly the first integral of (A13-39) may be evaluated at $z = h = 0$

$$\int_0^\infty u_1 \cos \lambda x d\lambda = \frac{ik_1}{x} K_1(-ik_1x) \tag{A13-50}$$

whereupon the electric field is now

$$E_{0y} = \frac{i\mu\omega I}{\pi(k_0^2 - k_1^2)x^2} \left[ik_1 x K_1(-ik_1x) - ik_0 x K_1(-ik_0x) \right]. \tag{A13-51}$$

The vertical magnetic field can now be calculated from (A13-29)

$$H_{0z} = \frac{1}{i\mu\omega} \frac{\partial E_{0y}}{\partial x}$$

$$H_{0z} = \frac{I}{\pi(k_0^2 - k_1^2)x^3} \left[-2ik_0 x K_1(-ik_0x) + k_0^2 x^2 K_0(-ik_0x) + 2ik_1 x K_1(-ik_1x) \right.$$
$$\left. - k_1^2 x^2 K_0(-ik_1x) \right]. \tag{A13-52}$$

Wait (1962, p. 27 has computed H_{0z} as a fraction of the field $H_{0z}{}^P = -(I/2\pi x)$ of a line current in free space. His figure, based on the low frequency assumption that displacement currents are negligible, is reproduced in Figure 13-3.

The horizontal component of the magnetic field is, from Maxwell's equation,

$$H_{0x} = \frac{1}{-i\mu\omega} \frac{\partial E_{0y}}{\partial z} \tag{A13-53}$$

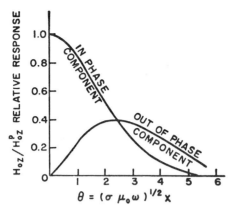

FIG. 13-3. In-phase and quadrature components of normalized vertical magnetic field due to line source on a homogeneous earth. Components plotted versus induction number $\theta = (\sigma\mu_0\omega)^{1/2}x$ with x the linear horizontal distance from line source. (After Wait, 1962.)

where E_{0y} is given by (A13-37). Hence we find

$$H_{0x} = \frac{I}{\pi} \int_0^\infty \frac{u_0}{u_0 + u_1} \cos \lambda x e^{-u_0 z} d\lambda. \tag{A13-54}$$

upon differentiating with respect to z under the integral sign of (A13-37). In the quasi-static approximation

$$u_0 = (\lambda^2 - k_0^2)^{1/2} \approx \lambda \tag{A13-55}$$

so that (A13-54) may be written

$$H_0 = \frac{I}{\pi} \int_0^\infty \frac{\lambda}{\lambda + u_1} \cos \lambda x e^{-\lambda z} d\lambda. \tag{A13-56}$$

We now multiply (A13-56) by $\lambda - u_1$, employ the identity

$$\lambda^2 - u_1^2 = k_1^2 \tag{A13-57}$$

and obtain

$$H_{0x} = \frac{I}{\pi k_1^2} \int_0^\infty \lambda(\lambda - u_1) \cos \lambda x e^{-\lambda z} d\lambda. \tag{A13-58}$$

The factor $(u_1 - \lambda)$ may be converted to an integral using a formula due to Watson (1944, p. 386, no. 7),

$$\int_0^\infty e^{-at} J_\nu(bt) \frac{dt}{t} = \frac{\{(a^2 + b^2)^{1/2} - a\}^\nu}{\nu b^\nu}. \tag{A13-59}$$

If we set $a = \lambda$, $b = -ik_1$, and $\nu = 1$, equation (A13-59) becomes

$$\int_0^\infty e^{-\lambda t} J_1(-ik_1 t) \frac{dt}{t} = \frac{\{(\lambda^2 - k_1^2)^{1/2} - \lambda\}}{-ik_1} = \frac{u_1 - \lambda}{-ik_1}. \tag{A13-60}$$

Thus the expression (A13-58) for H_{0x} is now

$$H_{0x} = -\frac{I}{\pi i k_1} \int_0^\infty \frac{J_1(-ik_1 t)}{t} \, dt \int_0^\infty \lambda e^{-\lambda t} e^{-\lambda z} \cos \lambda x d\lambda. \tag{A13-61}$$

The last integral, which we shall label $\mathcal{I}$, may be treated as a Fourier cosine transform

$$\mathcal{I} = \int_0^\infty \lambda e^{-\lambda t} e^{-\lambda z} \cos \lambda x d\lambda = \frac{t^2 - x^2}{(t^2 + x^2)^2} \tag{A13-62}$$

where reference has been made to *Tables of Integral Transforms*, Erdelyi (1954, Vol. I, p. 14, no. 5). We may place (A13-62) in an alternate form by noting that

$$\frac{\partial}{\partial x}\left(\frac{x}{t^2 + x^2}\right) = \frac{t^2 - x^2}{(t^2 + x^2)^2} \tag{A13-63}$$

with the result that

$$\mathcal{I} = \frac{\partial}{\partial x}\left(\frac{x}{t^2 + x^2}\right) \tag{A13-64}$$

and the magnetic field component H_{0x} is expressed by

$$H_{0x} = \frac{I_0}{\pi i k_1} \frac{\partial}{\partial x}\left[x \int_0^\infty \frac{J_1(-ik_1 t)}{(t^2 + x^2)t} \, dt\right]. \tag{A13-65}$$

This latter integral has been evaluated in general form by Watson (1944, p. 426) as

$$\mathcal{I} = \int_0^\infty \frac{J_\nu(at)dt}{(t^2 + b^2)t} = \frac{\pi}{2b^{\nu+1}}\left[I_\nu(ab) - L_\nu(ab)\right] \tag{A13-66}$$

where L_ν is the Nicholson's function defined in series form by Watson (1944, p. 329)

$$L_\nu(z) = \sum_{m=0}^\infty \frac{(\frac{1}{2}z)^{\nu+2m+1}}{\Gamma(m + 3/2)\Gamma(\nu + m + 3/2)}. \tag{A13-67}$$

Thus in terms of the variable $(-ik_1 x)$, the horizontal magnetic field is given as

$$H_{0x} = \frac{I}{2} \frac{\partial}{\partial x}\left[\frac{1}{-ik_1 x}\left\{I_1(-ik_1 x) - L_1(-ik_1 x)\right\}\right]. \tag{A13-68}$$

We may wish to determine the inclination of the magnetic field at any point on the surface of the earth. To obtain this inclination, we first note that both H_{0x} and H_{0z} are complex so that the field will, in general, be elliptically polarized. The ellipse of polarization may be defined in the following manner. The field components with which we are concerned are:

$$H_x e^{i\varphi x} = H_x(\cos \varphi_x + i \sin \varphi_x) \tag{A13-69}$$

$$H_z e^{i\varphi z} = H_z(\cos \varphi_z + i \sin \varphi_z) \tag{A13-70}$$

where now H_x and H_z refer to the amplitudes of the magnetic field in the x and z directions. Along any axis oriented at an angle α to the x axis, the magnetic field is

$$H_1 = [H_x \cos \varphi_x \cos \alpha + H_z \cos \varphi_z \sin \alpha] + i[H_x \sin \varphi_x \cos \alpha + H_z \sin \varphi_z \sin \alpha] \tag{A13-71}$$

while along a perpendicular axis the magnetic field is

$$H_2 = [-H_x \cos \varphi_x \sin \alpha + H_z \cos \varphi_z \cos \alpha] + i[-H_x \sin \varphi_x \sin \alpha + H_z \sin \varphi_z \cos \alpha]. \tag{A13-72}$$

We now wish to find an angle α such that $|H_1|$ is maximum while $|H_2|$ is minimum. The two directions so defined are the major and the minor axes of the ellipse of polarization. The square of the absolute magnitude of the magnetic field in the direction of the minor axis may be written as

$$
\begin{aligned}
|H_2|^2 &= H_x^2 \sin^2 \alpha + H_z^2 \cos^2 \alpha - 2H_x H_z \cos \varphi_x \cos \varphi_z \sin \alpha \cos \alpha \\
&\quad - 2H_x H_z \sin \varphi_x \sin \varphi_z \sin \alpha \cos \alpha \\
&= H_x^2 \sin^2 \alpha + H_z^2 \cos^2 \alpha - 2H_x H_z \sin \alpha \cos \alpha \cos (\varphi_x - \varphi_z).
\end{aligned}
\tag{A13-73}
$$

A minimum of $|H_2|$ will correspond to a minimum of $|H_2|^2$ so that it is sufficient to find $d|H_2|^2/d\alpha$ or

$$
2H_x^2 \sin \alpha \cos \alpha - 2H_z^2 \sin \alpha \cos \alpha - 2 \cos (\varphi_x - \varphi_z) H_x H_z (\cos^2 \alpha - \sin^2 \alpha) = 0.
\tag{A13-74}
$$

This equation is of the form

$$
A \tan^2 \alpha + B \tan \alpha + C = 0
\tag{A13-75}
$$

with

$$
\begin{aligned}
A &= 2H_x H_z \cos (\varphi_x - \varphi_z) \\
B &= 2H_x^2 - 2H_z^2 \\
C &= -2H_x H_z \cos (\varphi_x - \varphi_z)
\end{aligned}
\tag{A13-76}
$$

and has the roots

$$
\tan \alpha = \frac{-B \pm \sqrt{B^2 - 4AC}}{2A}
\tag{A13-77}
$$

corresponding to the directions of the major and minor axes. The inclination of the magnetic field in the vicinity of a line source lying on the ground may be found from (A13-77).

In summary then, the fields near a line source on a homogeneous earth are given by the expressions:

$$
E_{0y} = \frac{i\mu\omega I}{\pi(k_0^2 - k_1^2)x^2} \left[ik_1 x K_1(-ik_1 x) - ik_0 x K_1(-ik_0 x) \right] \sim \frac{i\mu\omega I}{\pi k_1 x} K_1(-ik_1 x)
\tag{A13-78}
$$

$$
\begin{aligned}
H_{0x} = \frac{I}{2} &\left[\frac{2I_1(-ik_1 x)}{ik_1 x^2} - \frac{L_1(-ik_1 x)}{ik_1 x^2} + \frac{1}{x} I_0(-ik_1 x) \right] \\
&- \frac{1}{x} \sum_{m=0}^{\infty} \frac{(m+1)\left(-\dfrac{ik_1 x}{2}\right)^{2m+1}}{\Gamma(m + 3/2)\Gamma(m + 5/2)}
\end{aligned}
\tag{A13-79}
$$

$$
\begin{aligned}
H_{0z} = \frac{I}{\pi(k_0^2 - k_1^2)x^3} &\left[-2ik_0 x K_1(-ik_0 x) + k_0^2 x^2 K_0(-ik_0 x) \right. \\
&\left. + 2ik_1 x K_1(-ik_1 x) - k_1^2 x^2 K_0(-ik_1 x) \right] \\
\sim \frac{I}{\pi x} &\left[K_0(-ik_1 x) - \frac{2}{(-ik_1 x)} K_1(-ik_1 x) \right]
\end{aligned}
\tag{A13-80}
$$

$$
\tan \alpha = \frac{-(H_x^2 - H_z^2) \pm \sqrt{(H_x^2 - H_z^2)^2 + 4H_x^2 H_z^2 \cos^2 (\varphi_x - \varphi_z)}}{2H_x H_z \cos (\varphi_x - \varphi_z)}
\tag{A13-81}
$$

where H_x and H_z in the last expressions are the amplitudes of (A13-79) and (A13-80) while φ_x and φ_z are the moduli of the same expressions.

13-IV. *The line source on an* n-*layered earth*

This problem can be treated rather simply by direct analogy with the line source over the homogeneous earth. The reflection coefficient must now be written, following (A13-35).

$$r(\lambda) = \frac{u_0 - u_a}{u_0 + u_a} \tag{A13-82}$$

where u_a is an apparent propagation constant for an equivalent homogeneous earth. Thus we may directly write down the electric field by analogy with (A13-37)

$$E_{0y} = \frac{i\mu\omega I}{2\pi} \int_0^\infty \frac{\cos \lambda x}{u_0 + u_a} e^{-u_0 z} d\lambda. \tag{A13-83}$$

The plane wave impedance of an n-layered structure, for the electric vector normal to the plane of incidence, is given by (A11-25). To simplify the repeated writing of this expression, we shall drop the subscripts and lower the superscripts to subscripts. We must, of course, remember that the altered expression, to follow, pertains only to instances where the electric vector is normal to the plane of incidence. Thus we have

$$\hat{Z}_1 = Z_1 \frac{\hat{Z}_2 + Z_1 \tanh u_1 h_1}{Z_1 + \hat{Z} \tanh u_1 h_1} \tag{A13-84}$$

with

$$Z_1 = \frac{\omega\mu_1}{iu_1} \; ; \qquad \hat{Z}_1 = \frac{\omega\mu_a}{iu_a} \tag{A13-85}$$

whereupon we may write

$$u_a = u_1 \frac{Z_1 + \hat{Z}_2 \tanh u_1 h_1}{\hat{Z}_2 + Z_1 \tanh u_1 h_1} \tag{A13-86}$$

provided $\mu_1 = \mu_a$.

For some practical prospecting problems we may introduce the far-field assumption, $u_i \approx ik_i$, so that (A13-86) becomes

$$k_a \approx k_1 \frac{Z_1 + \hat{Z}_2 \tanh jk_1 h_1}{\hat{Z}_2 + Z_1 \tanh jk_1 h_1} \approx \frac{k_1}{Q} \tag{A13-87}$$

where

$$Q \approx \frac{\hat{Z}_2 + Z_1 \tanh jk_1 h_1}{Z_1 + \hat{Z}_2 \tanh jk_1 h_1} \tag{A13-88}$$

The symbol j has been used to replace i for $\sqrt{-1}$, here and elsewhere, for convenience of notation. Then, by analogy with the field for a line source over a half space, we may write

$$E_{0y} \approx \frac{i\mu\omega I}{\pi(k_0^2 - k_a^2)x^2} \left[ik_a x K_1(-ik_a x) - ik_0 x K_1(-ik_0 x) \right]. \tag{A13-89}$$

The first term in the square bracket is negligible for $|-ik_ax| \gg 1$ since for large argument, the asymptotic form of the modified Bessel function K_1 is

$$K_n(-ik_ax) \to \sqrt{\frac{\pi}{2(-ik_ax)}} e^{ik_ax}. \tag{A13-90}$$

Then we find

$$E_{0y} \approx \frac{-i\mu\omega I}{\pi k_1^2 x^2} (-ik_0x) K_1(-ik_0x) Q^2 \tag{A13-91}$$

or

$$E_{0y} \approx \frac{i\mu\omega I k_0}{\pi k_1^2 x} K_1(-ik_0x) Q^2. \tag{A13-92}$$

Similarly we can place the electric field for the line source over the homogeneous earth in the analogous form

$$E_{0y} \approx \frac{i\mu\omega I k_0}{\pi k_1^2 x} K_1(-ik_0x). \tag{A13-93}$$

Then, as Wait (1962, p. 31) has indicated, the factor Q^2 can be interpreted as a correction factor to account for the presence of stratification in the conductive half space beneath the source. Note that $u_i \sim ik_i$ only for $\lambda = k_0 \sin\theta_0 \sim 0$ implying real θ_0; near a source this is not true, and (A13-83) must be evaluated numerically with u_a given by (A13-86).

We can convert (A13-92) to another convenient form by using the relation

$$\hat{Z}_1 = \frac{\omega\mu}{k_a} \tag{A13-94}$$

and then we find

$$E_{0y} \approx \frac{iI k_0}{\pi\mu\omega x} K_1(-ik_0x) \{\hat{Z}_1\}^2 \tag{A13-95}$$

where now the square of the plane wave impedance is used as a correction factor.

The distant horizontal magnetic field on a layered earth follows directly from (A13-68)

$$H_{0x} = \frac{I}{2} \frac{\partial}{\partial x} \left[\frac{1}{-ik_ax} \{ I_1(-ik_ax) - L_1(-ik_ax) \} \right] \tag{A13-96}$$

and the distant vertical magnetic field follows directly from (A13-52)

$$H_{0z} = \frac{I}{\pi(k_0^2 - k_a^2)x^3} \left[-2ik_0x K_1(-ik_0x) + k_0^2 x^2 K_0(-ik_0x) \right.$$
$$\left. + 2ik_a x K_1(-ik_ax) - k_a^2 x^2 K_0(-ik_ax) \right]. \tag{A13-97}$$

13-V. *Complex angles of refraction and incidence*

We have written Snell's second law as

$$k_2 \sin\theta_0 = k_1 \sin\theta_1$$

where θ_0, θ_1 are the angles of incidence and refraction respectively or

$$\sin \theta_1 = \frac{k_2}{k_1} \sin \theta_0. \tag{A13-98}$$

Now if $(k_2/k_1) \sin \theta_0 > 1$, then (A13-98) can be satisfied only by complex values of θ_1.
For dielectrics, (A13-98) may be written

$$\sin \theta_1 = \sqrt{\frac{\epsilon_2}{\epsilon_1}} \sin \theta_0 \tag{A13-99}$$

and complex angles of incidence will arise, for example, when $\epsilon_2/\epsilon_1 > 1$, that is, where the wave travels in a direction of decreasing dielectric constant.

Let us assume that this condition does exist, then we may write

$$\theta_1 = \theta_1{}^r + i\theta_1{}^i \tag{A13-100}$$

and

$$\sin \theta_1 = \sin (\theta_1{}^r + i\theta_1{}^i) = \sin \theta_1{}^r \cosh \theta_1{}^i + \cos \theta_1{}^r \sinh \theta_1{}^i.$$

Since both $\theta_1{}^i$ and $\sinh \theta_1{}^i$ can be greater than unity then it is readily apparent that $\sin \theta_1$ is greater than unity. Jahnke and Emde (1945) present a relief of the function $\sin(x+iy)$. How, then, are we to interpret complex angles of refraction in terms of the physics of the boundary value problems with which we are dealing? For $\sin \theta_1 > 1$, the cosine is a pure imaginary in dielectrics

$$\cos \theta_1 = \frac{i}{\sqrt{\epsilon_1}} \sqrt{\epsilon_2 \sin^2 \theta_1 - \epsilon_1} = in_{12}\sqrt{\sin^2 \theta_0 - n_{21}{}^2} \tag{A13-101}$$

where

$$n_{12} = \sqrt{\frac{\epsilon_2}{\epsilon_1}} = \frac{1}{n_{21}}$$

is the index of refraction.

For two media in contact at the plane $z=0$, Figure 13-4, the phase of the *transmitted* wave is

$$\mathbf{k} \cdot \mathbf{r} = \omega\sqrt{\epsilon_1\mu_1} \, (z \cos \theta_1 + x \sin \theta_1)$$
$$= \omega\sqrt{\epsilon_2\mu_2} \, (iz\sqrt{\sin^2 \theta_0 - n_{21}{}^2} + x \sin \theta_1). \tag{A13-102}$$

The transmitted electric field intensity is

$$\mathbf{E}_t = \mathbf{E}_1 \exp [\mathbf{k}_1 \cdot \mathbf{r}] = \mathbf{E}_1 \exp [-\beta_1 z + i\alpha x - i\omega t]. \tag{A13-103}$$

The amplitudes of the reflected and transmitted fields are obtained from the Fresnel equations (A10-46) (A10-47) plus (A10-78) and (A10-79) as follows:

(a) for the electric field normal to the plane of incidence

$$\mathbf{E}_1 = \frac{2 \cos \theta_0}{\cos \theta_0 + i\sqrt{\sin^2 \theta_0 - n_{21}{}^2}} \mathbf{E}_0 \tag{A13-104}$$

$$\mathbf{E}_2 = \frac{\cos \theta_0 - i\sqrt{\sin^2 \theta_0 - n_{21}{}^2}}{\cos \theta_0 + i\sqrt{\sin^2 \theta_0 - n_{21}{}^2}} \mathbf{E}_0 \tag{A13-105}$$

(b) for the electric field in the plane of incidence

$$\mathbf{n}_1 \times \mathbf{E}_1 = \frac{2n_{21} \cos \theta_0}{n_{21}^2 \cos \theta_0 + i\sqrt{\sin^2 \theta_0 - n_{21}^2}} \mathbf{n}_0 \times \mathbf{E}_0 \tag{A13-106}$$

$$\mathbf{n}_2 \times \mathbf{E}_2 = \frac{n_{21}^2 \cos \theta_0 - i\sqrt{\sin^2 \theta_0 - n_{21}^2}}{n_{21}^2 \cos \theta_0 + i\sqrt{\sin^2 \theta_0 - n_{21}^2}} \mathbf{n}_0 \times \mathbf{E}_0. \tag{A13-107}$$

The power reflection and transmission coefficients are defined by

$$R \equiv \frac{E_2^2}{E_0^2} \qquad T \equiv \sqrt{\frac{\epsilon_1}{\epsilon_2} \frac{\cos \theta_1}{\cos \theta_0} \frac{E_1^2}{E_0^2}} \tag{A13-108}$$

where the power reflected and refracted normal to the surface is computed in each instance and where it is demanded that

$$R + T = 1. \tag{A13-109}$$

It is readily established that the Fresnel equations satisfy (A13-108) and (A13-109).

Now, from (A13-106) and (A13-107) it is apparent that the transmitted and reflected waves are out-of-phase with the incident wave at the surface because the coefficients of E_0 are complex. For equations (A13-104) through (A13-107) it is readily established that

$$R = 1 \qquad T = 0. \tag{A13-110}$$

The reflection is total; there is no average energy flow into the medium of lesser dielectric constant.

Now, let us assume that medium (2) is a perfect dielectric, but medium (1) is conductive as appropriate to the air-earth interface. The propagation constants are

$$k_1^2 = \epsilon_1 \mu_1 \omega^2 + i\mu_1 \sigma_1 \omega = (\alpha_1 + i\beta_1)^2 \tag{A13-111}$$

$$k_2^2 = \epsilon_2 \mu_2 \omega^2 = \alpha_2^2. \tag{A13-112}$$

Snell's second law informs us that

$$\sin \theta_1 = \frac{k_2}{k_1} \sin \theta_0 = \frac{\alpha_2}{\alpha_1^2 + \beta_1^2} (\alpha_1 - i\beta_1) \sin \theta_0 \tag{A13-113}$$

$$= (a - ib) \sin \theta_0. \tag{A13-114}$$

We may compute $\cos \theta_1$, from (A13-114)

$$\cos \theta_1 = \sqrt{1 - (a^2 - b^2 - 2abi) \sin^2 \theta_0} = \rho e^{i\gamma}. \tag{A13-115}$$

The magnitude ρ and phase γ are found by squaring (A13-115) and equating real and imaginary parts on either side

$$\rho^2 \cos 2\gamma = \rho^2 (2 \cos^2 \gamma - 1) = 1 - (a^2 - b^2) \sin^2 \theta_0 \tag{A13-116}$$

$$\rho^2 \sin 2\gamma = 2\rho^2 \sin \gamma \cos \gamma = 2ab \sin^2 \theta_0. \tag{A13-117}$$

The phase of the transmitted wave is, as in (A13-102)

$$\begin{aligned}
\mathbf{k}_1 \cdot \mathbf{r} &= (\alpha_1 + i\beta_1)(z \cos \theta_1 + x \sin \theta_1) \\
&= z\rho(\alpha_1 \cos \gamma - \beta_1 \sin \gamma) + iz\rho(\beta_1 \cos \gamma + \alpha_1 \sin \gamma) \\
&\quad + x(a\alpha_1 + b\beta_1) \sin \theta_0 + ix(a\beta_1 - b\alpha_1) \sin \theta_0.
\end{aligned} \tag{A13-118}$$

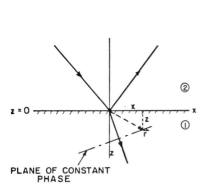

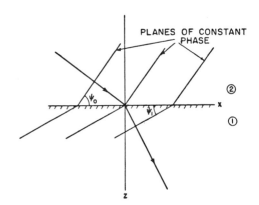

FIG. 13-4. Reflection and refraction at a plane interface, complex angle of refraction.

FIG. 13-5. Reflection and refraction at a plane interface, complex angles of incidence and refraction.

From (A13-113) and (A13-114) we find that

$$(a\alpha_1 + b\beta_1) \sin \theta_0 = \alpha_2 \sin \theta_0 \qquad \text{(A13-119)}$$

and

$$(a\beta_1 - b\alpha_1) = 0. \qquad \text{(A13-120)}$$

If, additionally, we make the following substitutions

$$p = \rho(\beta_1 \cos \gamma + \alpha_1 \sin \gamma) \qquad \text{(A13-121)}$$

$$q = \rho(\alpha_1 \cos \gamma - \beta_1 \sin \gamma) \qquad \text{(A13-122)}$$

then we may write the transmitted wave as

$$E_t = \mathbf{E}_1 \exp\left[-pz + i(qz + \alpha_2 x \sin \theta_0 - \omega t)\right]. \qquad \text{(A13-123)}$$

The surfaces of constant amplitude are the planes $-pz =$ constant, the surfaces of constant phase are the planes $qz + \alpha_2 \sin \theta_0 x =$ constant, and these planes do not, in general, coincide. Then we say the waves are *inhomogeneous plane waves*. The planes of constant amplitude are parallel to the surface; the direction of propagation is determined by the normal to the planes of constant phase. The angle ψ made by this wave normal to the surface is the true angle of refraction and is defined by

$$\cos \psi = \frac{q}{\sqrt{q^2 + \alpha_2^2 \sin^2 \theta_0}} \qquad \text{(A13-124)}$$

which is obtained directly from the propagation factor of (A13-123).

There will always be some reflection at an air-earth interface for real angles of incidence. If, however, complex *angles of incidence* occur, reflection can be nonexistent. The amplitude reflection coefficient for the electric vector in the plane of incidence may be obtained directly from (A10-82) with $\mu_1 = \mu_2 = \mu_0$,

$$r_{\parallel} = -\frac{\cos \theta_0 - \dfrac{k_2}{k_1} \cos \theta_1}{\cos \theta_0 + \dfrac{k_2}{k_1} \cos \theta_1}. \qquad \text{(A13-125)}$$

For no reflection we deduce that

$$\cos \theta_0 = \frac{k_2}{k_1} \cos \theta_1 \tag{A13-126}$$

and from Snell's Law, (A10-24)

$$\sin \theta_0 = \frac{k_1}{k_2} \sin \theta_1. \tag{A13-127}$$

Equations (A13-126) and (A13-127) may be combined to yield the following conditions for no reflection

$$\sin^2 \theta_0 = \frac{k_1^2}{k_1^2 + k_2^2}. \tag{A13-128}$$

Equation (A13-128) determines the condition for no reflection but with real angles of refraction. At an air-earth interface for low frequencies where displacement currents are negligible in the earth,

$$\begin{array}{ccc} in\ air & & in\ earth \\ k_2 = \mu \epsilon_2 \omega^2 & & k_1^2 = i \mu \sigma_1 \omega \end{array} \tag{A13-129}$$

and

$$\sin^2 \theta_0 = \frac{1}{1 - i \dfrac{\epsilon_2 \omega}{\sigma_1}}. \tag{A13-130}$$

The imaginary term in (A13-130) does not become appreciable until frequencies greater than 10^6 cps are employed. Thus at prospecting frequencies,

$$\sin^2 \theta_0 = 1 \tag{A13-131}$$

which advises that the only condition for zero reflection is real angles of incidence of $\pi/2$. Apparently, in the line source problem we should have no concern with complex angles of incidence since no unusual modes of propagation arise. However, let us look at the problem in more detail.

Figure 13-5 illustrates a plane wave refracted at an air-earth interface. The electric vector is in the plane of incidence, and hence the magnetic vector is normal to this plane. For continuity of tangential **H**, the amplitudes and phases of the **H** fields in (1) and (2) must be equal. Thus we may write

$$H_{2y} = H \exp \left[i k_2 (z \cos \theta_0 + x \sin \theta_0) - i \omega t \right] \tag{A13-132}$$

$$H_{1y} = H \exp \left[i k_1 (z \cos \theta_1 + x \sin \theta_1) - i \omega t \right]. \tag{A13-133}$$

As usual we will set $\lambda = k_2 \sin \theta_0$ and by Snell's Law $k_2 \sin \theta_0 = k_1 \sin \theta_1$. In general, then, λ will be complex, permitting us to write

$$\lambda = \alpha + i\beta \tag{A13-134}$$

$$i k_2 \cos \theta_0 = - i \sqrt{k_2^2 - \lambda^2} = a_2 + i b_2 \tag{A13-135}$$

$$i k_1 \cos \theta_1 = i \sqrt{k_1^2 - \lambda^2} = - a_1 + 2 b_1 \tag{A13-136}$$

where the signs of (A13-135) and (A13-136) have been chosen to lead to finite fields for

$x = \pm \infty$. Thus (A13-132) and (A13-133) become

$$H_{1y} = H \exp\left[-a_1 z - \beta x + i(b_1 z + \alpha x) - i\omega t\right] \tag{A13-137}$$

$$H_{2y} = H \exp\left[a_2 z - \beta x + i(b_2 z + \alpha x) - i\omega t\right]. \tag{A13-138}$$

Then, for the incident wave, the planes of constant phase are defined by

$$b_2 z + \alpha x = \text{constant} \tag{A13-139}$$

and the planes of constant amplitude are defined by

$$a_2 z - \beta x = \text{constant}. \tag{A13-140}$$

We conclude from (A13-139) and (A13-140) that the planes of constant amplitude do not coincide with the planes of constant phase.

The *real* angle of incidence ψ is shown in Figure 13-5 and is defined by

$$\cos \psi = \frac{b_2}{\sqrt{\alpha^2 + b_2^2}}. \tag{A13-141}$$

The planes of constant amplitude in the incident wave are defined by the angle ψ' between a normal to these planes and the negative z axis.

$$\tan \psi' = -\beta/a_2 \tag{A13-142}$$

The components of the electric vector may be calculated from

$$\mathbf{E} = \frac{i\mu\omega}{k^2} \nabla \times \mathbf{H} \tag{A13-143}$$

or

$$E_x = -\frac{i\mu\omega}{k^2} \frac{\partial H_y}{\partial z} \tag{A13-144}$$

and

$$E_z = \frac{i\mu\omega}{k^2} \frac{\partial H_y}{\partial x}. \tag{A13-145}$$

When (A13-132) and (A13-133) are substituted in (A13-144) and (A13-145) we obtain

$$E_{2x} = \frac{i\mu\omega}{k_2^2} (a_2 + ib_2) H_{2y} \tag{A13-146}$$

$$E_{2z} = \frac{\mu\omega}{k_2^2} (\alpha + i\beta) H_{2y} \tag{A13-147}$$

$$E_{1x} = -\frac{i\mu\omega}{k_1^2} (a_1 - ib_1) H_{1y} \tag{A13-148}$$

$$E_{1z} = \frac{\mu\omega}{k_1^2} (\alpha + i\beta) H_{1y}. \tag{A13-149}$$

The transverse component E_z gives rise to an energy flow[3] parallel to the plane surface divid-

---

[3] *Note:* Energy flow is given by the Poynting vector $\mathbf{S} = \mathbf{E} \times \mathbf{H}$ watts/meter² (Stratton, 1941, p. 132).

ing the media (1) and (2). Note that this mean energy flow is negligible relative to the mean energy flow into the medium provided α, β is small relative to a_1, b_1 (i.e. that λ is negligible relative to k_1 as before). We have already established that

$$\lambda = k_1 \sin \theta_1 \tag{A13-150}$$

and that $\theta_1 \approx 0$ often for an air-earth interface, so that often $k_1 \gg \lambda$. The surface mode does not contain significant energy under these circumstances.

13-VI. *The line source above an* n-*layered medium*

The discussion of section 13-V above leads us to conclude that only when $\lambda \sim 0$ may we employ the formula (A13-33) for the electric field of a line source above a homogeneous earth regardless of the altitude of the line source or height of measurement. Presumably, then, we could deduce the magnetic field components H_{ox} and H_{oz} with equal simplicity. However, it is possible to establish these formulas by a slightly more rigorous procedure. The starting point for the present development will be equation (A13-27) which we repeat here for convenience

$$E_{0y} = \frac{i\mu\omega I}{4\pi} \int_{-\infty}^{\infty} \frac{e^{u_0 h}}{u_0} \left[e^{u_0 z} + \frac{u_0 - u_1}{u_0 + u_1} e^{-u_0 z} \right] e^{i\lambda x} d\lambda. \tag{A13-151}$$

This equation involves no approximations. The magnetic field expressions for the same degree of rigor are, from Maxwell's equation

$$H_{0x} = \frac{I}{4\pi} \frac{\partial}{\partial z} \int_{-\infty}^{\infty} \frac{e^{u_0 h}}{u_0} \left[e^{u_0 z} + \frac{u_0 - u_1}{u_0 + u_1} e^{-u_0 z} \right] e^{i\lambda x} d\lambda \tag{A13-152}$$

and

$$H_{0z} = \frac{I}{4\pi} \frac{\partial}{\partial x} \int_{-\infty}^{\infty} \frac{e^{u_0 h}}{u_0} \left[e^{u_0 z} + \frac{u_0 - u_1}{u_0 + u_1} e^{-u_0 z} \right] e^{i\lambda x} d\lambda. \tag{A13-153}$$

Our task evidently reduces to evaluating the single integral

$$\mathcal{I} = \int_{-\infty}^{\infty} \frac{e^{u_0 h}}{u_0} \left[e^{u_0 z} + \frac{u_0 - u_1}{u_0 + u_1} e^{-u_0 z} \right] e^{i\lambda x} d\lambda. \tag{A13-154}$$

Since the reflection coefficient $r(\lambda)$ may be written

$$r(\lambda) = \frac{u_0 - u_1}{u_0 + u_1} = \frac{2u_0}{u_0 + u_1} - 1 \tag{A13-155}$$

then the integral (A13-154) may be split into the following three integrals

$$\mathcal{I} = \mathcal{I}_1 + \mathcal{I}_2 + \mathcal{I}_3 \tag{A13-156}$$

$$\mathcal{I}_1 = \int_{-\infty}^{\infty} \frac{e^{u_0 (h+z)}}{u_0} e^{i\lambda x} d\lambda \tag{A13-157}$$

$$\mathcal{I}_2 = 2 \int_{-\infty}^{\infty} \frac{e^{u_0 (h-z)}}{u_0 + u_1} e^{i\lambda x} d\lambda \tag{A13-158}$$

$$\mathcal{I}_3 = - \int_{-\infty}^{\infty} \frac{e^{u_0 (h-z)}}{u_0} e^{i\lambda x} d\lambda \tag{A13-159}$$

$$u_0 = (\lambda^2 - k_0^2)^{1/2}.$$

Since both ϑ_1 and ϑ_3 are even valued functions of λ, we may convert them to cosine transforms and evaluate them by reference to Erdelyi (1954, Vol. I, p. 17, no. 27) as we did in (A13-25). Thus we find,

$$\vartheta_1 = 2K_0\left[-ik_0\{x^2 + (h + z)^2\}^{1/2}\right] \tag{A13-160}$$

$$\vartheta_3 = -2K_0\left[-ik_0\{x^2 + (h - z)^2\}^{1/2}\right]. \tag{A13-161}$$

Clearly the first of these represents the primary source function, while the second represents an image located at a distance $-h$ below the surface of the earth. This would be the location of an image for a perfectly conducting earth. Thus the remaining integral ϑ_2 must account for the finite conductivity of the earth.

The integral ϑ_2 may be reduced to a cosine transform since the kernel is an even function of λ.

$$\vartheta_2 = 4\int_0^\infty \frac{e^{u_0(h-z)}}{u_0 + u_1} \cos \lambda x d\lambda. \tag{A13-162}$$

Further, the numerator and denominator may be multiplied by $u_0 - u_1$ to yield

$$\vartheta_2 = \vartheta_{21} + \vartheta_{22}$$

$$\vartheta_{21} = \frac{4}{k_1^2 - k_0^2}\int_0^\infty u_0 e^{u_0(h-z)} \cos \lambda x d\lambda \tag{A13-163}$$

$$\vartheta_{22} = \frac{-4}{k_1^2 - k_0^2}\int_0^\infty u_1 e^{u_0(h-z)} \cos \lambda x d\lambda. \tag{A13-164}$$

The first of these integrals may be evaluated by means of the technique employed to obtain (A13-49) without any approximations or we may refer directly to Campbell and Foster (1948, p. 76, no. 635). We shall choose the latter approach with the realization that we must employ the quasi-static approximation $\lambda \sim u_0$ before the evaluation. Then we find

$$\vartheta_{21} = \frac{4}{k_1^2 - k_0^2}\frac{(z - h)^2 - x^2}{[(z - h)^2 + x^2]^2}. \tag{A13-165}$$

Next we wish to rewrite (A13-164) by substituting $(e^{i\lambda x} + e^{-i\lambda x})/2$ for $\cos \lambda x$ in the integrand

$$\vartheta_{22} = \vartheta_{221} + \vartheta_{222} \tag{A13-166}$$

$$\vartheta_{221} = \frac{-2}{k_1^2 - k_0^2}\int_0^\infty (\lambda^2 - k_1^2)^{1/2}e^{\lambda[(h-z)+ix]}d\lambda \tag{A13-167}$$

$$\vartheta_{222} = \frac{-2}{k_1^2 - k_0^2}\int_0^\infty (\lambda^2 - k_1^2)^{1/2}e^{\lambda[(h-z)-ix]}d\lambda. \tag{A13-168}$$

These latter two integrals are identical in form and may be evaluated by the following integral representation of the Struve function (Erdelyi et al., 1953, Vol. I, p. 38, no. 51)

$$\Gamma(\nu + \tfrac{1}{2})[H_\nu(\xi z) - Y_\nu(\xi z)] = \frac{1}{\pi^{1/2}}(\tfrac{1}{2}\xi)^{\nu-1}z^\nu \int_0^{e^{i\beta}} e^{-zt}(1 + t^2\xi^{-2})^{\nu-1/2}dt \tag{A13-169}$$

$$\beta - \tfrac{1}{2}\pi < \arg \xi < \beta + \tfrac{1}{2}\pi; \qquad -\frac{\pi}{2} - \beta < \arg z < \frac{\pi}{2} - \beta$$

where Y_ν, and $\Gamma(\nu+\tfrac{1}{2})$ are the Bessel function of the second kind of order ν and the gamma function of order $\nu+\frac{1}{2}$. Application of (A13-169) to $\mathscr{G}_{221}$ and $\mathscr{G}_{222}$ leads to

$$\mathscr{G}_{221} = \frac{2(-ik_1)}{k_1{}^2 - k_0{}^2} \frac{\pi}{(h-z)+ix} [H_1[ik_1\{(h-z)+ix\}] - Y[ik_1\{(h-z)+ix\}]] \quad (A13\text{-}170)$$

$$\mathscr{G}_{222} = \frac{2(-ik_1)}{k_1{}^2 - k_0{}^2} \frac{\pi}{(h-z)-ix} [H_1[ik_1\{(h-z)-ix\}] - Y[ik_1\{(h-z)-ix\}]]. \quad (A13\text{-}171)$$

If we now assume that $k_0 \sim 0$, which is of course the quasi-static approximation, we can write the electric field as

$$E_{0y} = \frac{i\mu\omega I}{4\pi} [\mathscr{G}_1 + \mathscr{G}_3 + \mathscr{G}_{21} + \mathscr{G}_{221} + \mathscr{G}_{222}]$$

$$= \frac{i\mu\omega I}{2\pi} [K_0[-ik_0\{x^2 + (h+z)^2\}^{1/2}] - K_0[-ik_0\{x^2 + (h-z)^2\}^{1/2}]$$

$$+ \frac{2}{k_1{}^2} \frac{(z-h)^2 - x^2}{[(z-h)^2 + x^2]^2}$$

$$+ \frac{\pi}{k_1} \frac{1}{[-x+i(h-z)]} [H_1[k_1\{-x+i(h-z)\}] - Y[k_1\{-x+i(h-z)\}]]$$

$$+ \frac{\pi}{k_1} \frac{1}{[x+i(h-z)]} [H_1[k_1\{x+i(h-z)\}] - Y[k_1\{x+i(h-z)\}]]]. \quad (A13\text{-}172)$$

The above development follows that of Law and Fannin (1961) in a general way. This problem was solved in an approximate manner as early as 1926 by Carson (1926). The magnetic field components can now be calculated according to (A13-152) and (A13-153). However, the simplest means of obtaining all of the field expressions is by numerical evaluation of the series representations of the functions in (A13-172) and their derivatives.

Once again, we may generalize the result (A13-172) to an n-layered earth by substituting k_a for k_1 in (A13-172), valid only for large values of x,

$$E_{0y} = \frac{i\mu\omega I}{2\pi} [K_0[-ik_0\{x^2 + (h+z)^2\}^{1/2}] - K_0[-ik_0\{x^2 + (h-z)^2\}^{1/2}]$$

$$+ \frac{2}{k_a{}^2} \frac{(z-h)^2 - x^2}{[(z-h)^2 + x^2]^2}$$

$$+ \frac{\pi}{k_a} \frac{1}{[-x+i(h-z)]} [H_1[k_a\{-x+i(h-z)\}] - Y[k_a\{-x+i(h-z)\}]]$$

$$+ \frac{\pi}{k_a} \frac{1}{[x+i(h-z)]} [H_1[k_a\{x+i(h-z)\}] - Y[k_a\{x+i(h-z)\}]]] \quad (A13\text{-}173)$$

where

$$H_{0x} = -\frac{1}{i\mu\omega} \frac{\partial E_{0y}}{\partial z} \quad (A13\text{-}174)$$

$$H_{0z} = \frac{1}{i\mu\omega} \frac{\partial E_{0y}}{\partial x}. \quad (A13\text{-}175)$$

For small x (A13-151) (A13-152) and (A13-153) are to be evaluated numerically with u_a replacing u_1.

14. A Vertical Magnetic Dipole Over an *n*-Layered Medium

14-I. *The magnetic dipole source in free space*

The Schelkunoff electric wave potential for a magnetic dipole source may be derived from equation (A185)

$$\mathbf{F} = \frac{e^{-i\omega t}}{4\pi} \int_V \mathbf{J}_M'' \frac{e^{ikr}}{r} \, dv \tag{A14-1}$$

where

$$r^2 = x^2 + y^2 + z^2.$$

From a comparison of equations (A46) and (A84) we may define $\mathbf{J}_M''$ in terms of $\mathbf{M}'$.

$$\mathbf{J}_M'' = \mu \frac{\partial \mathbf{M}'}{\partial t} = -i\mu\omega\mathbf{M}' \tag{A14-2}$$

so that (A14-1) may be written in the alternate form

$$\mathbf{F} = -\frac{i\mu\omega e^{-i\omega t}}{4\pi} \int \mathbf{M}' \frac{e^{ikr}}{r} \, dv. \tag{A14-3}$$

The polarization vector $\mathbf{M}$, on the other hand, may be defined as the dipole moment per unit volume,

$$\mathbf{M} = \frac{d\mathbf{m}}{dv} = I \frac{d\mathbf{a}}{dv}$$

where $\mathbf{m}$ is the dipole moment and where $d\mathbf{a}$ is an element of area of a loop and I is the current in that loop. Then (A14-3) becomes

$$\mathbf{F} = -\frac{i\mu\omega e^{-i\omega t}}{4\pi} I \int \frac{e^{ikr}}{r} \, d\mathbf{a} \tag{A14-4}$$

which, for an elemental loop, may be written simply

$$\mathbf{F} = -\frac{i\mu\omega I d\mathbf{a}}{4\pi} e^{-i\omega t} \frac{e^{ikr}}{r} \tag{A14-5}$$

or

$$\mathbf{F} = \mathbf{c} \frac{e^{ikr}}{r} \tag{A14-6}$$

where

$$\mathbf{c} = -\frac{i\mu\omega I d\mathbf{a}}{4\pi} \tag{A14-7}$$

and the harmonic time dependency is now inferred. Then equation (A14-6) presents an expression for the primary potential of an infinitesimal magnetic dipole in free space provided $k = k_0$ where k_0 is the propagation constant of free space.

14-II. *The vertical magnetic dipole over a homogeneous earth*

A magnetic dipole, or current loop, is located at the origin of the cylindrical coordinate system (ρ, θ, z). It is oriented in the z direction and is located at a height h above the surface of a homogeneous earth as in Figure 14-1. Since the normal to the elemental area of the loop is in the z direction, then we need only a z component of primary field potential $F_z{}^P$:

$$F_z{}^P = c\,\frac{e^{ikr}}{r}.\tag{A14-8}$$

To this primary potential we must add secondary potentials brought into existence by the presence of the earth. The function $(e^{ikr})/r$ may be converted to an integral representation by equation (A9-7) as it pertains to both media.

For the region $z \leq 0$, the expansion is

$$\frac{e^{ik_0r}}{r} = \int_0^\infty \frac{\lambda}{(\lambda^2 - k_0{}^2)^{1/2}}\, e^{\sqrt{\lambda^2 - k_0{}^2}\,z} J_0(\lambda\rho)\,d\lambda\tag{A14-9}$$

while for the region $h \geq z \geq 0$, the expansion is

$$\frac{e^{ik_0r}}{r} = \int_0^\infty \frac{\lambda}{(\lambda^2 - k_0{}^2)^{1/2}}\, e^{-\sqrt{\lambda^2 - k_0{}^2}\,z} J_0(\lambda\rho)\,d\lambda\tag{A14-10}$$

and finally for the region $z \geq h$, we have

$$\frac{e^{ik_1r}}{r} = \int_0^\infty \frac{\lambda}{(\lambda^2 - k_1{}^2)^{1/2}}\, e^{-\sqrt{\lambda^2 - k_1{}^2}\,z} J_0(\lambda\rho)\,d\lambda.\tag{A14-11}$$

The positive value of the exponential has been used in equation (A14-9) to ensure proper behavior of the expansion at $z = -\infty$ while the negative value of the exponential has been

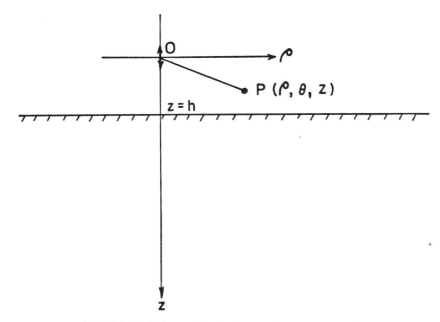

FIG. 14-1. Vertical magnetic dipole over a homogeneous earth.

used in equations (A14-10) and (A14-11) to ensure proper behavior of the expansion at $z = \infty$.

Consider now the boundary conditions at the surface of the earth. For continuity of tangential H we wish to use the expression (A111) in the form

$$\mathbf{H} = -(\sigma - i\omega\epsilon)\mathbf{F} - \frac{1}{i\mu\omega} \nabla\nabla\cdot\mathbf{F}. \tag{A14-12}$$

Since there is no tangential component of $\mathbf{F}$, we may ignore the first term in (A14-12) when computing tangential $\mathbf{H}$. The second term involves the gradient of a scalar which is computed from a divergence. In cylindrical coordinates, the gradient is

$$\nabla\psi = \frac{\partial\psi}{\partial\rho}\mathbf{i}_1 + \frac{1}{\rho}\frac{\partial\psi}{\partial\theta}\mathbf{i}_2 + \frac{\partial\psi}{\partial z}\mathbf{i}_3 \tag{A14-13}$$

where $\mathbf{i}_1$, $\mathbf{i}_2$, $\mathbf{i}_3$ are unit vectors of the ρ, θ, and z directions respectively. The tangential components must exclude the third term of (A14-13) and we know, by symmetry, that there can be no θ component of $\mathbf{H}$. Thus the gradient contribution to tangential $\mathbf{H}$ must be merely the first term in (A14-13). Now the divergence of a vector $\mathbf{F}$ in cylindrical coordinate is

$$\nabla\cdot\mathbf{F} = \frac{1}{\rho}\frac{\partial}{\partial\rho}(\rho F_\rho) + \frac{1}{\rho}\frac{\partial F_\theta}{\partial\theta} + \frac{\partial F_z}{\partial z}. \tag{A14-14}$$

Since we have only a z component of $\mathbf{F}$, only the third term in (A14-14) is retained. Thus, for continuity of tangential $\mathbf{H}$, we may substitute continuity of

$$-\frac{1}{i\mu\omega}\frac{\partial^2 F_z}{\partial\rho\partial z}. \tag{A14-15}$$

Then at the surface of the earth we may write

$$\frac{1}{i\mu_0\omega}\frac{\partial^2 F_{z0}}{\partial\rho\partial z} = \frac{1}{i\mu_1\omega}\frac{\partial^2 F_{z1}}{\partial\rho\partial z}\bigg|_{z=h}. \tag{A14-16}$$

For the continuity of tangential E we shall need to use (A110) in the form

$$\mathbf{E} = -\nabla\times\mathbf{F}$$

$$= \frac{\partial F_z}{\partial\rho}. \tag{A14-17}$$

Thus at the surface of the earth,

$$\frac{\partial F_{z0}}{\partial\rho} = \frac{\partial F_{z1}}{\partial\rho}\bigg|_{z=h}. \tag{A14-18}$$

The conditions (A14-16) and (A14-18) hold for all ρ and hence can be integrated with respect to ρ, without regard for a constant of integration. Thus the boundary conditions reduce to

$$\frac{1}{\mu_0}\frac{\partial F_{z0}}{\partial z} = \frac{1}{\mu_1}\frac{\partial F_{z1}}{\partial z}\bigg|_{z=h}. \tag{A14-19}$$

$$F_{z0} = F_{z1}\big|_{z=h}. \tag{A14-20}$$

The primary potential has only a z component expressed by (A14-8) with (A14-9) (A14-10) or (A14-11) substituted for e^{ikr}/r. Note that only the zeroth order Bessel function enters the expression, i.e. $n=0$. Hence the z components of the secondary potentials can only exist for $n=0$ if the boundary conditions (A14-19) and (A14-20) are to be met. Then we may write the z components of the total potentials, following (A9-1) as:

in air

$$F_{z0} = \int_0^\infty f_0(\lambda)e^{u_0 z} + g_0(\lambda)e^{-u_0 z}]J_0(\lambda\rho)d\lambda \qquad h \geq z \geq 0 \qquad (A14\text{-}21)$$

in the ground

$$F_{z1} = \int_0^\infty [f_1(\lambda)e^{u_1 z} + g_1(\lambda)e^{-u_1 z}]J_0(\lambda\rho)d\lambda \qquad z \geq h \qquad (A14\text{-}22)$$

where

$$u_0 = (\lambda^2 - k_0^2)^{1/2}$$

and

$$u_1 = (\lambda^2 - k_1^2)^{1/2}.$$

We wish to evaluate the four eigenfunctions $f_0(\lambda)$, $g_0(\lambda)$, $f_1(\lambda)$, $g_1(\lambda)$. First we note that $f_1(\lambda)=0$ because F_{z1} must go to zero as z tends to infinity. Next, from the boundary condition (A14-19) we find

$$\frac{1}{\mu_0}\frac{\partial}{\partial z}[f_0(\lambda)e^{u_0 z} + g_0(\lambda)e^{-u_0 z}] = \frac{1}{\mu_1}\frac{\partial}{\partial z}[g_1(\lambda)e^{-u_1 z}]\big|_{z=h} \qquad (A14\text{-}23)$$

or

$$\frac{1}{\mu_0}[u_0 f_0(\lambda)e^{u_0 h} - u_0 g_0(\lambda)e^{-u_0 h}] = \frac{1}{\mu_1}[-u_1 g_1(\lambda)e^{-u_1 h}]. \qquad (A14\text{-}24)$$

Also from the boundary condition (A14-20) there results

$$f_0(\lambda)e^{u_0 h} + g_0(\lambda)e^{-u_0 h} = g_1(\lambda)e^{-u_1 h}. \qquad (A14\text{-}25)$$

Equations (A14-24) and (A14-25) permit us to find values for $f_0(\lambda)$ and $g_1(\lambda)$ in terms of $g_0(\lambda)$.

$$f_0(\lambda) = \frac{u_0\mu_1 - u_1\mu_0}{u_0\mu_1 + u_1\mu_0}e^{-2u_0 h}g_0(\lambda) \qquad (A14\text{-}26)$$

$$g_1(\lambda) = \frac{2u_0\mu_1}{u_0\mu_1 + u_1\mu_0}e^{(u_1-u_0)h}g_0(\lambda). \qquad (A14\text{-}27)$$

The function $g_0(\lambda)$ must now be evaluated in terms of the constants of the system. This may be accomplished by noting that (A14-21) must consist of a summation of primary and secondary potentials. The only term in (A14-21) which can represent a primary potential is the second term because only this term has a negative exponential to correspond with the negative exponential of (A14-10). Thus, from (A14-21) (A14-10) and (A14-6) we may write

$$g_0(\lambda) = \frac{c\lambda}{(\lambda^2 - k_0^2)^{1/2}} = -\frac{i\mu\omega I da}{4\pi}\frac{\lambda}{u_0}. \qquad (A14\text{-}28)$$

We have now obtained the formal solution of the problem and need to evaluate the integrals of (A14-21) and (A14-22) in order to develop useful formulas for application.

14-III. *Solution for a loop lying on a homogeneous earth*

Let us assume now that $\mu_0 = \mu_1$, and that $h = 0$; the loop lies on a homogeneous non-permeable ground. Then the potential in air given by equation (A14-21) becomes

$$F_{z0} = c \int_0^\infty \left[\frac{u_0 - u_1}{u_0 + u_1} e^{u_0 z} + e^{-u_0 z} \right] \frac{\lambda}{u_0} J_0(\lambda \rho) d\lambda \qquad h \geq z \geq 0. \tag{A14-29}$$

We wish to note for future reference that the expression

$$\frac{u_0 - u_1}{u_0 + u_1} = r_\perp(\lambda) \tag{A14-30}$$

is just the reflection coefficient for amplitudes as given by equation (A13-35). Now for $z = 0$, the potential may be written

$$F_{z0} = c \int_0^\infty \frac{2\lambda}{u_0 + u_1} J_0(\lambda \rho) d\lambda. \tag{A14-31}$$

Also, when we neglect displacement currents, we find

$$u_0 = \sqrt{\lambda^2 - k_0^2} \approx \lambda \tag{A14-32}$$

so that we now wish to evaluate the integral

$$F_{z0} = c \int_0^\infty \frac{2\lambda}{u_1 + \lambda} J_0(\lambda \rho) d\lambda. \tag{A14-33}$$

We noted earlier, equation (A9-58), that this integral had been evaluated by Foster (1931) so that we may write directly

$$F_{z0} = 2c \frac{1 - (1 - k_1\rho) e^{ik_1\rho}}{-(k_1\rho)^2 \rho}. \tag{A14-34}$$

The electric field will have only a θ component, given by (A306)

$$E_\theta = -i\mu\omega \frac{\partial \pi_z^*}{\partial \rho} = \frac{\partial F_{z0}}{\partial \rho} = \frac{2c}{k_1^2 \rho^4} \left[3 - \left\{ 3 - 3ik_1\rho - k_1^2\rho^2 \right\} e^{ik_1\rho} \right] \tag{A14-35}$$

and the magnetic field has the components, according to (A307)

$$H_z = \frac{1}{i\mu\omega} \frac{1}{\rho} \left[\frac{\partial}{\partial \rho} \left(\rho \frac{\partial F_{z0}}{\partial \rho} \right) \right] \tag{A14-36}$$

and

$$H_\rho = -\frac{1}{i\mu\omega} \frac{\partial^2 F_{z0}}{\partial z \partial \rho}. \tag{A14-37}$$

In the last three expressions we have used the identity

$$F = -i\mu\omega\pi^* \tag{A14-38}$$

where π^* is the Hertz vector due to magnetic sources, and we have substituted ρ for r as he radial coordinate. Symmetry demands that there be no θ (or ϕ as used in (A306–307) lependency so that we have set $\partial/\partial\theta = 0$.

The vertical field is readily calculated from (A14-36). Note that $\partial F_{z0}/\partial\rho$ was calculated in obtaining (A14-35). Thus we find

$$H_z = \frac{-2c}{i\mu\omega k_1{}^2}\frac{1}{\rho^5}[9 - (9 - 9ik_1\rho - 4k_1{}^2\rho^2 + ik_1\rho^3)e^{ik_1\rho}]. \tag{A14-39}$$

To compute H_ρ we must use F_{z1} in the form given by (A14-22)

$$F_{z1} = \int_0^\infty 2c\,\frac{\lambda e^{-u_{1z}}}{\lambda + u_1}J_0(\lambda\rho)d\lambda \tag{A14-40}$$

vhere once again we have replaced u_0 by λ. This last equation can be written in the following orm

$$F_{z1} = \frac{-2c}{k_1{}^2}\left[\frac{\partial^2 P}{\partial z^2} - \frac{\partial}{\partial z}\left(k_1{}^2 N + \frac{\partial^2 N}{\partial z^2}\right)\right] \tag{A14-41}$$

vhere

$$P = \int_0^\infty \frac{\lambda}{u_1}e^{-u_{1z}}J_0(\lambda\rho)d\lambda = \frac{e^{ik_1r}}{r} \tag{A14-42}$$

and

$$N = \int_0^\infty \frac{1}{u_1}e^{-u_{1z}}J_0(\lambda\rho)d\lambda = I_0\left[-\frac{ik_1}{2}(r+z)\right]K_0\left[-\frac{ik_1}{2}(r-z)\right]. \tag{A14-43}$$

The integral P was introduced in (A14-11) and the integral N was developed by Foster 1931). The functions I_0 and K_0 are the modified Bessel functions of order zero. We now nay carry out the differentiations indicated by (A14-37). Let us reverse the order of lifferentiation, however:

$$H_\rho = -\frac{1}{i\mu\omega}\frac{\partial^2 F_{z1}}{\partial z\partial\rho}\bigg|_{z=0} = -\frac{1}{i\mu\omega}\frac{\partial}{\partial\rho}\left[\frac{\partial F_{z1}}{\partial z}\right]\bigg|_{z=0}. \tag{A14-44}$$

From (A14-41) we obtain:

$$\left[\frac{\partial F_{z1}}{\partial z}\right]_{z=0} = -\frac{2c}{k_1{}^2}\left[\frac{\partial^3 P}{\partial z^3} - \frac{\partial^2}{\partial z^2}\left(k^2 N + \frac{\partial^2 N}{\partial z^2}\right)\right]_{z=0}. \tag{A14-45}$$

The first term in the square bracket above is zero at $z=0$ as may be established by differentiation of e^{ik_1r}/r.

We know, further, that F_{z1} must satisfy the wave equation in cylindrical coordinates, and hat any integral or derivative of this function must also satisfy the same wave equation. Therefore

$$\frac{\partial^2 N}{\partial\rho^2} + \frac{1}{\rho}\frac{\partial N}{\partial\rho} + \frac{\partial^2 N}{\partial z^2} + k^2 N = 0. \tag{A14-46}$$

This equation permits us to write (A14-45) upon change of order of differentiation,

$$\left[\frac{\partial F_{z1}}{\partial z}\right]_{z=0} = \frac{2c}{k_1{}^2}\left[\left(\frac{\partial^2}{\partial\rho^2} + \frac{1}{\rho}\frac{\partial}{\partial\rho}\right)\left[\frac{\partial^2 N}{\partial z^2}\right]\right]_{z=0}. \tag{A14-47}$$

To compute (A14-47) we first note that

$$N = I_0\left[\frac{\gamma}{2}(r+z)\right]\cdot K_0\left[\frac{\gamma}{2}(r-z)\right] \quad \text{where} \quad \gamma = -ik_1 \tag{A14-48}$$

$$\frac{\partial N}{\partial z} = \frac{\partial I_0}{\partial z}K_0 + I_0\frac{\partial K_0}{\partial z}$$

$$= K_0\frac{\partial I_0}{\partial p}\left[\frac{\gamma}{2}\left(\frac{z}{r}+1\right)\right] + I_0\frac{\partial K_0}{\partial q}\left[\frac{\gamma}{2}\left(\frac{z}{r}-1\right)\right] \tag{A14-49}$$

where

$p = \dfrac{\gamma}{2}(r+z)$ is the argument of I_0

$q = \dfrac{\gamma}{2}(r-z)$ is the argument of K_0

$$\frac{\partial^2 N}{\partial z^2} = \frac{\partial K_0}{\partial z}\frac{\partial I_0}{\partial p}\left[\frac{\gamma}{2}\left(\frac{z}{r}+1\right)\right] + K_0\frac{\partial^2 I_0}{\partial z\partial p}\left[\frac{\gamma}{2}\left(\frac{z}{r}+1\right)\right]$$

$$+ K_0\frac{\partial I_0}{\partial p}\frac{\partial}{\partial z}\left[\frac{\gamma}{2}\left(\frac{z}{r}+1\right)\right] + \frac{\partial I_0}{\partial z}\frac{\partial K_0}{\partial q}\left[\frac{\gamma}{2}\left(\frac{z}{r}-1\right)\right]$$

$$+ I_0\frac{\partial^2 K_0}{\partial z\partial q}\left[\frac{\gamma}{2}\left(\frac{z}{r}-1\right)\right] + I_0\frac{\partial K_0}{\partial q}\frac{\partial}{\partial z}\left[\frac{\gamma}{2}\left(\frac{z}{r}+1\right)\right]$$

$$= -\frac{\gamma}{2}\left(\frac{z}{r}-1\right)\frac{\partial K_0}{\partial q}\frac{\partial I_0}{\partial p}\left[\frac{\gamma}{2}\left(\frac{z}{r}+1\right)\right]$$

$$+ \frac{\gamma}{2}\left(\frac{z}{r}+1\right)K_0\frac{\partial^2 I_0}{\partial p^2}\left[\frac{\gamma}{2}\left(\frac{z}{r}+1\right)\right]$$

$$+ K_0\frac{\partial I_0}{\partial p}\frac{\gamma}{2r}\left(1-\frac{z^2}{r^2}\right) + \frac{\gamma}{2}\left(\frac{z}{r}+1\right)\frac{\partial I_0}{\partial p}\frac{\partial K_0}{\partial q}\left[\frac{\gamma}{2}\left(\frac{z}{r}-1\right)\right]$$

$$- \frac{\gamma}{2}\left(\frac{z}{r}-1\right)I_0\frac{\partial^2 K_0}{\partial q^2}\left[\frac{\gamma}{2}\left(\frac{z}{r}-1\right)\right]$$

$$+ I_0\frac{\partial K_0}{\partial q}\frac{\gamma}{2r}\left(1-\frac{z^2}{r^2}\right). \tag{A14-50}$$

We wish now to evaluate (A14-49) and (A14-50) at $z=0$ where

$$\frac{\partial}{\partial q} = \frac{\partial}{\partial p} = \frac{\partial}{\partial t} \quad \text{and} \quad t = \frac{\gamma\rho}{2}$$

is the common variable for both I_0 and K_0. Then we find

$$\left.\frac{\partial N}{\partial z}\right|_{z=0} = \frac{\gamma}{2}\left[K_0 I_0' - I_0 K_0'\right] \tag{A14-51}$$

$$\left.\frac{\partial^2 N}{\partial z^2}\right|_{z=0} = \frac{\gamma^2}{4}\left[-K_0' I_0' + K_0 I_0'' - I_0' K_0' + I_0 K_0'' + \frac{1}{t}(K_0 I_0' + I_0 K_0')\right] \tag{A14-52}$$

where the primes indicate differentiation with respect to t. These latter two expressions may be converted to equivalent expressions involving only Bessel functions of zeroth and first order. To do this we use the recurrence relations (Watson, 1944, p. 79)

$$I_0'' = I_1' = I_0 - \frac{1}{t} I_1 \qquad\qquad I_0' = I_1$$

$$K_0'' = -K_1' = K_0 + \frac{1}{t} K_1 \qquad K_0' = -K_1$$

and the Wronskian for modified Bessel functions (Watson, 1944, p. 80)

$$I_0' K_0 - I_0 K_0' = \frac{1}{t}.$$

We find

$$\left.\frac{\partial N}{\partial z}\right|_{z=0} = \frac{1}{\rho} \tag{A14-53}$$

and

$$\left.\frac{\partial^2 N}{\partial z^2}\right|_{z=0} = \frac{\gamma^2}{2} [I_0 K_0 + I_1 K_1]. \tag{A14-54}$$

The functions I_0 and K_0 are now of the variable $t = \gamma\rho/2$. The next step in our development is computation of the derivatives with respect to ρ.

$$\frac{\partial}{\partial \rho} [I_0 K_0 + I_1 K_1] = -\frac{2}{\rho} I_1 K_1 \tag{A14-55}$$

and

$$\frac{\partial^2}{\partial \rho^2} [I_0 K_0 + I_1 K_1] = \frac{6}{\rho^2} I_1 K_1 + \frac{\gamma}{\rho} [I_1 K_0 - I_0 K_1]. \tag{A14-56}$$

Thus we find, from (A14-44) (A14-47) (A14-54) (A14-55) and (A14-56)

$$H_\rho = \frac{1}{i\mu\omega} 2c \frac{\partial}{\partial \rho} \left[\frac{4}{\rho^2} I_1 K_1 + \frac{\gamma}{\rho} \{I_1 K_0 - I_0 K_1\} \right] \tag{A14-57}$$

and upon carrying out the differentiation there results

$$H_\rho = -\frac{1}{i\mu\omega} \frac{c}{\rho^3} [\gamma^2 \rho^2 (I_1 K_1 - I_0 K_0) + 4\gamma\rho(I_1 K_0 - I_0 K_1) + 16 I_1 K_1] \tag{A14-58}$$

or

$$H_\rho = -\frac{1}{i\mu\omega} \frac{c}{\rho^3} [-k_1^2 \rho^2 (I_1 K_1 - I_0 K_0) - 4 i k_1 \rho (I_1 K_0 - I_0 K_1) + 16 I_1 K_1]. \tag{A14-59}$$

The formulas (A14-35) (A14-39) and (A14-59) are individually useful but they may be combined in various ways to provide additional useful formulas. As in the case of a line source over a homogeneous earth, we may compute the tilt of the magnetic vector in a radial plane using the horizontal, or radial component H_ρ, and the vertical component H_z as follows:

$$\alpha = \tan^{-1} \frac{-B \pm \sqrt{B^2 - 4AC}}{2A} \tag{A14-60}$$

$$A = 2H_\rho H_z \cos(\varphi_\rho - \varphi_z)$$
$$B = 2(H_\rho^2 - H_z^2)$$
$$C = -2H_\rho H_z \cos(\varphi_\rho - \varphi_z)$$

with H_ρ and H_z from (A14-59) and (A14-39) respectively. An advantage of measuring the angle α is that source current variations do not affect the measurement. Other examples of useful functions are the "wave impedances"

$$Z_{\theta\rho} = -\frac{E_\theta}{H_\rho} = -\frac{1}{2i\mu\omega k_1^2\rho}$$
$$\cdot \left[\frac{3 - \{3 - ik_1\rho - k_1^2\rho^2\}e^{ik_1\rho}}{-k_1^2\rho^2(I_1K_1 - I_0K_0) - 4ik_1\rho(I_1K_0 - I_0K_1) + 16I_1K_1} \right] \tag{A14-61}$$

$$Z_{\theta z} = -\frac{E_\theta}{H_z} = \frac{1}{i\mu\omega\rho} \left[\frac{3 - \{3 - 3ik_1\rho - k_1^2\rho^2\}e^{ik_1\rho}}{9 - \{9 - 9ik_1\rho - 4k_1^2\rho + ik_1^2\rho^3\}e^{ik_1\rho}} \right] \tag{A14-62}$$

or perhaps more conventionally we may compute the mutual impedance between one loop and an adjacent one. At a distance ρ from the first loop let us assume that we have a second loop of area dA. The voltage induced in this loop, if it is horizontal is

$$e = -\frac{d\Phi_z}{dt} = i\mu\omega H_z dA. \tag{A14-63}$$

The quantity

$$Z = \frac{i\mu\omega H_z dA}{I} \tag{A14-64}$$

where I is the current in the first loop of area da, is known as the mutual impedance between the two loops. Hence we find

$$Z = \frac{i\mu\omega da\, dA}{2\pi k_1^2\rho^5} \left[9 - (9 - 6ik_1\rho - 4k_1^2\rho^2 + ik_1^3\rho^3)e^{ik_1\rho} \right]. \tag{A14-65}$$

Since the mutual impedance of two coplanar loops in an infinite medium would be

$$Z_0 = -\frac{i\mu\omega da\, dA}{4\pi\rho^3} \tag{A14-66}$$

then we may write (A14-65) in the more convenient form

$$\frac{Z}{Z_0} = -\frac{2}{k_1^2\rho^2} \left[9 - (9 - 9ik_1\rho - 4k_1^2\rho^2 + ik_1^3\rho^3)e^{ik_1\rho} \right]. \tag{A14-67}$$

Wait (1955) has computed this impedance ratio as a function of the dimensionless parameter $\theta = (\sigma_1\mu\omega)^{1/2}\rho$ where $k_1 = (i\mu\sigma_1\omega)^{1/2}$. The coupling curve for this and other cases is presented in Figure 14-2.

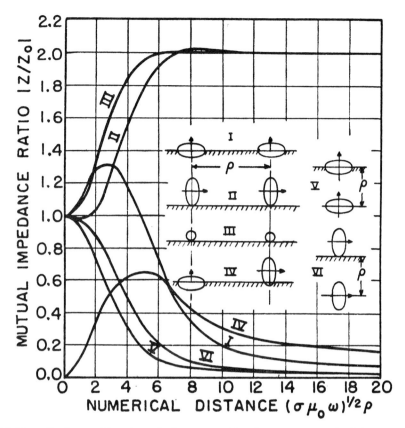

FIG. 14-2. Normalized mutual impedance for loops on and in a homogeneous earth. (After Wait, 1955.)

To produce the fourth curve in Wait's drawing (Figure 14-2), we need to find the coupling between a vertical source dipole and a radial horizontal dipole. In free space this coupling is zero, but in the presence of the homogeneous earth it will be given by

$$Z = \frac{i\mu\omega}{I} H_\rho dA$$

$$= \frac{i\mu\omega da\, dA}{4\pi\rho^3}\left[-k_1^2\rho^2(I_1K_1 - I_0K_0) - 4ik_1\rho(I_1K_0 - I_0K_1) + 16I_1K_1\right] \quad (A14\text{-}68)$$

and if we arbitrarily define Z_0 by (A14-66), there results the impedance ratio

$$\frac{Z}{Z_0} = -\left[-k_1^2\rho^2(I_1K_1 - I_0K_0) - 4ik_1\rho(I_1K_0 - I_0K_1) + 16I_1K_1\right] \quad (A14\text{-}69)$$

which is identical to the result found by Wait (1955).

The above development in principle follows those of Wait (1951) and Meyer (1962). Others to work on this problem include Gordon (1951) and Bhattacharyya (1959).

14-IV. *Solution for a loop lying on an* n-*layered earth*

When dealing with a line source over a stratified earth, we noted that account could be taken of the stratification by introducing an apparent propagation constant u_a where

$$u_a \approx u_1 \frac{Z_1 + \hat{Z}_2 \tanh u_1 h_1}{\hat{Z}_2 + Z_1 \tanh u_1 h_1} \tag{A14-70}$$

The same result can be accomplished for the magnetic dipole source by first replacing u_1 by u_a in the key integrals (A14-31) and (A14-40) which is, in effect, introducing the reflection coefficient

$$r_\perp(\lambda) = \frac{u_0 - u_a}{u_0 + u_a} \tag{A14-71}$$

as before. Then throughout equations (A14-35) (A14-39) and (A14-59), we replace k_1 by $k_a = k_1/Q$ and find the far-field solutions.

$$E_\theta = \frac{2cQ^2}{k_1{}^2 \rho^4} \left[3 - \{3 - ik_a\rho - k_a{}^2\rho^2\} e^{ik_a\rho} \right] \tag{A14-72}$$

$$H_z = \frac{-2cQ^2}{i\mu\omega k_1{}^2 \rho^5} \left[9 - \{9 - ik_a\rho - 4k_a{}^2\rho^2 + ik_a{}^3\rho^3\} e^{ik_a\rho} \right] \tag{A14-73}$$

$$H_\rho = -\frac{1}{i\mu\omega} \frac{c}{\rho^3} \left[-k_a{}^2\rho^2(I_1K_1 - I_0K_0) - 4ik_a\rho(I_1K_0 - I_0K_1) + 16I_1K_1 \right]. \tag{A14-74}$$

Equation (A14-73) simplifies, for $|-ik_a\rho| \gg 1$, to

$$H_z \approx \frac{9daIQ^2}{2\pi k_1{}^2 \rho^5}. \tag{A14-75}$$

Solutions valid for all ρ are obtained numerically from (A14-29) with u_a in place of u_1.

15. A Horizontal Magnetic Dipole Over an n-Layered Medium

15-I. *A horizontal magnetic dipole over a homogeneous earth*

A magnetic dipole of strength

$$\mathbf{c} = -\frac{i\mu\omega I da}{4\pi} \tag{A15-1}$$

is situated at the origin and oriented in the x direction of a cartesian coordinate system. We infer by (A15-1) that the source of the dipole is a small circular current loop of area da carrying a current I with the plane of the loop normal to the x axis. The loop is located at a height h above the earth as in Figure 15-1.

As for a horizontal electric dipole on the earth, we will require both a z and an x component for the Hertz vector from which we derive the fields. The appropriate Hertz vector is the one arising in magnetic sources π^*; alternatively we may use the Schelkunoff potential $\mathbf{F} = -i\mu\omega\,\pi^*$. If we select the latter alternative the potentials are:

$$\mathbf{F} = iF_x + kF_z, \qquad F_y = 0 \tag{A15-2}$$

and the fields are, from (A97), (A101) and (A107):

$$\mathbf{E} = -\nabla \times \mathbf{F} \tag{A15-3}$$

$$\mathbf{H} = -(\sigma - i\omega\epsilon)\mathbf{F} - \frac{1}{i\mu\omega} \nabla\nabla \cdot \mathbf{F}. \tag{A15-4}$$

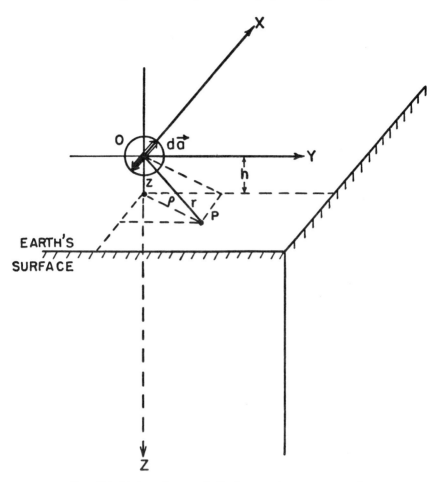

FIG. 15-1. Horizontal magnetic dipole over a homogeneous earth.

The components of the fields may then be written down directly as:

$$
\left.
\begin{aligned}
E_x &= -\frac{\partial F_z}{\partial y} & H_x &= -(\sigma - i\omega\epsilon)F_x - \frac{1}{i\mu\omega}\frac{\partial}{\partial x}\left(\frac{\partial F_x}{\partial x} + \frac{\partial F_z}{\partial z}\right) \\
E_y &= \frac{\partial F_z}{\partial x} - \frac{\partial F_x}{\partial z} & H_y &= -\frac{1}{i\mu\omega}\frac{\partial}{\partial y}\left(\frac{\partial F_x}{\partial x} + \frac{\partial F_z}{\partial z}\right) \\
E_z &= \frac{\partial F_x}{\partial y} & H_z &= -(\sigma - i\omega\epsilon)F_z - \frac{1}{i\mu\omega}\frac{\partial}{\partial z}\left(\frac{\partial F_x}{\partial x} + \frac{\partial F_z}{\partial z}\right)
\end{aligned}
\right\}. \quad \text{(A15-5)}
$$

This problem was originally studied by Sommerfeld (1926) and later developed by Wait (1953) and Quon (1963). We wish to introduce a little more generality and yet, following the theme of this Volume, include all of the pertinent steps of the development. We shall start with a consideration of the boundary conditions at the surface of the earth. From the continuity of tangential **E** and **H** and the expressions of (A15-5) for the electric and magnetic fields in terms of the vector **F** we may write:

from H_x:

$$(\sigma_0 - i\omega\epsilon_0)F_{x0} + \frac{1}{i\mu_0\omega}\frac{\partial}{\partial x}\left(\frac{\partial F_{x0}}{\partial x} + \frac{\partial F_{z0}}{\partial z}\right)$$

$$= (\sigma_1 - i\omega\epsilon_1)F_{x1} + \frac{1}{i\mu_1\omega}\frac{\partial}{\partial x}\left(\frac{\partial F_{x1}}{\partial x} + \frac{\partial F_{z1}}{\partial z}\right)\Bigg|_{z=h} \quad \text{(A15-6)}$$

from H_y:

$$\frac{1}{i\mu_0\omega}\frac{\partial}{\partial y}\left(\frac{\partial F_{x0}}{\partial x} + \frac{\partial F_{z0}}{\partial x}\right) = \frac{1}{i\mu_1\omega}\frac{\partial}{\partial y}\left(\frac{\partial F_{x1}}{\partial x} + \frac{\partial F_{z1}}{\partial z}\right)\Bigg|_{z=h} \quad \text{(A15-7)}$$

from E_x:

$$\frac{\partial F_{z0}}{\partial y} = \frac{\partial F_{z1}}{\partial y}\Bigg|_{z=h} \quad \text{(A15-8)}$$

from E_y:

$$\frac{\partial F_{z0}}{\partial x} - \frac{\partial F_{x0}}{\partial z} = \frac{\partial F_{z1}}{\partial x} - \frac{\partial F_{x1}}{\partial z}\Bigg|_{z=h}. \quad \text{(A15-9)}$$

The relations (A15-6) through (A15-9) hold for all x and all y and can therefore be integrated with respect to x or y. The functions and their derivatives vanish as $x \to \infty$ and $y \to \infty$ so that the constants of integration must be zero. Thus the boundary conditions (A15-7) and (A15-8) reduce to

$$\frac{1}{\mu_0}\left(\frac{\partial F_{x0}}{\partial x} + \frac{\partial F_{z0}}{\partial z}\right) = \frac{1}{\mu_1}\left(\frac{\partial F_{x1}}{\partial x} + \frac{\partial F_{z1}}{\partial z}\right)\Bigg|_{z=h} \quad \text{(A15-10)}$$

and

$$F_{z0} = F_{z1}\big|_{z=h} \quad \text{(A15-11)}$$

which may then be utilized to reduce (A15-6) and (A15-9) to

$$(\sigma_0 - i\omega\epsilon_0)F_{x0} = (\sigma_1 - i\omega\epsilon_1)F_{x1}\big|_{z=h} \quad \text{(A15-12)}$$

and

$$\frac{\partial F_{x0}}{\partial z} = \frac{\partial F_{x1}}{\partial z}\Bigg|_{z=h}. \quad \text{(A15-13)}$$

Equations (A15-10) through (A15-13) then constitute the boundary conditions for the potentials F_x, F_z. The primary potential has only an x component

$$F_x{}^P = c\frac{e^{ikr}}{r} \quad \text{(A15-14)}$$

where

$$r^2 = \rho^2 + z^2$$

which satisfies the inhomogeneous wave equation as noted earlier. This expression for potential may be placed in a convenient form using the identities (A14-9) through (A14-11) so that

$$F_x{}^P = c \int_0^\infty \frac{\lambda}{(\lambda^2 - k_0{}^2)^{1/2}} e^{\sqrt{\lambda^2-k_0}\,z} J_0(\lambda\rho)\,d\lambda; \qquad z \leq 0 \qquad \text{(A15-15)}$$

$$F_x{}^P = c \int_0^\infty \frac{\lambda}{(\lambda^2 - k_0{}^2)^{1/2}} e^{-\sqrt{\lambda^2-k_0{}^2}\,z} J_0(\lambda\rho)\,d\lambda; \qquad h \geq z \geq 0 \qquad \text{(A15-16)}$$

$$F_x{}^P = c \int_0^\infty \frac{\lambda}{(\lambda^2 - k_1{}^2)^{1/2}} e^{-\sqrt{\lambda^2-k_1{}^2}\,z} J_0(\lambda\rho)\,d\lambda; \qquad z \geq h. \qquad \text{(A15-17)}$$

We assume that, in the air, the total potential consists of a sum of primary and secondary parts

$$F_{x0} = F_x{}^P + F_x{}^S$$

while in the ground the potential consists only of a secondary part

$$F_{x1} = F_{x1}{}^S.$$

This procedure is equivalent to expressing the solution of the inhomogeneous wave equation in terms of a particular solution plus the solution of the homogeneous wave equation for the air, while seeking only a solution of the homogeneous wave equation for the ground. Note that only the zeroth order Bessel function enters these expressions, implying $n=0$. Hence, the x components of the secondary potentials can only exist for $n=0$ if the boundary conditions (A15-12) and (A15-13) are to be met. Then we may write the x components of the total potentials, following earlier developments, as:

in air above the dipole

$$F_{x0}{}^- = F_{x0}{}^P + F_{x0}{}^S = \int_0^\infty [f_0(\lambda)e^{u_0 z} + g_0(\lambda)e^{u_0 z}]J_0(\lambda\rho)\,d\lambda; \qquad z \leq 0 \qquad \text{(A15-18)}$$

in air below the dipole

$$F_{x0}{}^+ = F_{x0}{}^P + F_{x0}{}^S = \int_0^\infty [f_0(\lambda)e^{u_0 z} + g_0(\lambda)e^{-u_0 z}]J_0(\lambda\rho)\,d\lambda; \qquad h \geq z > 0 \qquad \text{(A15-19)}$$

in the ground

$$F_{x1} = F_{x1}{}^S = \int_0^\infty [f_1(\lambda)e^{u_1 z} + g_1(\lambda)e^{-u_1 z}]J_0(\lambda\rho)\,d\lambda; \qquad z \geq h \qquad \text{(A15-20)}$$

where

$$u_0 = (\lambda^2 - k_0{}^2)^{1/2}$$

and

$$u_1 = (\lambda^2 - k_1{}^2)^{1/2}.$$

Note that the primary wave function in (A15-18) represented by $g_0(\lambda)e^{u_0 z}$ bears a positive exponential since for the region $z \leq 0$, the primary wave travels in the negative z direction. For equations (A15-19) and (A15-20), each potential is made up of a primary or outgoing wave represented by a negative exponential and a secondary or reflected wave represented by a positive exponential. This identification of primary and secondary waves with negative and positive exponentials follows logically from the selection of roots $\pm\sqrt{\lambda^2-k_0{}^2}$ chosen in equations (A15-15) through (A15-17). Of course, we should expect only an outgoing wave in the semi-infinite earth so that we shall expect to see one of the eigenfunctions take zero value. Let us then evaluate the four eigenfunctions $f_0(\lambda)$, $g_0(\lambda)$, $f_1(\lambda)$, and $g_1(\lambda)$ as we have in previous problems. First we note that $f_1(\lambda) = 0$ because $\mathbf{F}_{x1}$ must tend to zero as z tends to infinity. Next from (A15-12)

$$(\sigma_0 - i\omega\epsilon_0)\left[f_0(\lambda)e^{u_0 h} + g_0(\lambda)e^{-u_0 h}\right] = (\sigma_1 - i\omega\epsilon_1)\left[g_1(\lambda)e^{-u_1 h}\right]. \qquad \text{(A15-21)}$$

Similarly from (A15-13) we find

$$u_0\left[f_0(\lambda)e^{u_0 h} - g_0(\lambda)e^{-u_0 h}\right] = -u_1 g_1(\lambda)e^{-u_1 h}. \qquad \text{(A15-22)}$$

We may solve this latter pair of equations for $g_1(\lambda)$ and $f_0(\lambda)$ in terms of $g_0(\lambda)$:

$$g_1(\lambda) = \frac{2u_0\mu_1 k_0^2}{u_0\mu_0 k_1^2 + u_1\mu_1 k_0^2} e^{(u_1 - u_0)h} g_0(\lambda) \qquad \text{(A15-23)}$$

$$f_0(\lambda) = \frac{u_0\mu_0 k_1^2 - u_1\mu_1 k_0^2}{u_1\mu_1 k_0^2 + u_0\mu_0 k_1^2} e^{-2u_0 h} g_0(\lambda). \qquad \text{(A15-24)}$$

The function $g_0(\lambda)$ must now be evaluated in terms of the constants of the system. This may be accomplished upon noting that, with $k_1 = k_0$, the solution (A15-18) must reduce to the potential of the source alone, since then we have an infinite medium. Comparing (A15-19) and (A15-16) we observe that

$$g_0(\lambda) = c\frac{\lambda}{u_0}. \qquad \text{(A15-25)}$$

Therefore, from (A15-23) and (A15-24) we evaluate $g_1(\lambda)$ and $f_0(\lambda)$ respectively as

$$g_1(\lambda) = \frac{2c\lambda\mu_1 k_0^2}{u_0\mu_0 k_1^2 + u_1\mu_1 k_0^2} e^{(u_1 - u_0)h} \qquad \text{(A15-26)}$$

$$f_0(\lambda) = \frac{c\lambda}{u_0}\frac{u_0\mu_0 k_1^2 - u_1\mu_1 k_0^2}{u_1\mu_1 k_0^2 + u_0\mu_0 k_1^2} e^{-2u_0 h}. \qquad \text{(A15-27)}$$

Hence F_{x0}^-, F_{x0}^+ and F_{x1} can now be obtained without difficulty from (A15-18) (A15-19) and (A15-20):

in air above the dipole

$$F_{x0}^- = c\int_0^\infty \frac{1}{u_0}\left[\frac{u_0\mu_0 k_1^2 - u_1\mu_1 k_0^2}{u_1\mu_1 k_0^2 + u_0\mu_0 k_1^2}e^{-2u_0 h} + 1\right]e^{u_0 z}\lambda J_0(\lambda\rho)d\lambda; \qquad z \leq 0 \qquad \text{(A15-28)}$$

in air below the dipole

$$F_{x0}^+ = c\int_0^\infty \frac{1}{u_0}\left[\frac{u_0\mu_0 k_1^2 - u_1\mu_1 k_0^2}{u_1\mu_1 k_0^2 + u_0\mu_0 k_1^2}e^{u_0(z-2h)} + e^{-u_0 z}\right]\lambda J_0(\lambda\rho)d\lambda; \qquad h \geq z \geq 0 \qquad \text{(A15-29)}$$

in the ground

$$F_{x1} = 2c\int_0^\infty \frac{\mu_1 k_0^2}{u_0\mu_0 k_1^2 + u_1\mu_1 k_0^2} e^{(u_1 - u_0)h}e^{-u_1 z}\lambda J_0(\lambda\rho)d\lambda; \qquad z \geq h. \qquad \text{(A15-30)}$$

We note that the expression (A15-28), except for the factor $e^{-2u_0 h}$, corresponds with that found by Sommerfeld (1926) and Wait (1953); for $h=0$, our solution is identical with the earlier ones as expected. Quon finds the same form of solution except for a displacement of the origin relative to that which we have used.

The boundary conditions for the z components of the potentials may be derived next. Analogous to the situation for the horizontal electric dipole we note that the boundary condition (A15-10) implies a single differentiation of the zero order Bessel function. This differentiation yields

$$
\frac{\partial F_{x0}}{\partial x} = c \frac{\partial}{\partial x} \int_0^\infty \frac{1}{u_0} \left[\frac{u_0\mu_0 k_1^2 - u_1\mu_1 k_0^2}{u_1\mu_1 k_0^2 + u_0\mu_0 k_1^2} e^{u_0(z-2h)} + e^{-u_0 z} \right] \lambda J_0(\lambda\rho) d\lambda
$$

$$
= - c \int_0^\infty \frac{1}{u_0} \left[\frac{u_0\mu_0 k_1^2 - u_1\mu_1 k_0^2}{u_1\mu_1 k_0^2 + u_0\mu_0 k_1^2} e^{u_0(z-2h)} + e^{-u_0 z} \right] \lambda^2 J_1(\lambda\rho) \cos\theta d\lambda .
$$

Thus, only first order Bessel functions can appear in (A15-10) so that the z components of potentials, since they consist only of secondary potentials, may be written:

in air

$$
F_{z0} = \cos\theta \int_0^\infty [p_0(\lambda)e^{u_0 z} + q_0(\lambda)e^{-u_0 z}] J_1(\lambda\rho) d\lambda \tag{A15-31}
$$

in the ground

$$
F_{z1} = \cos\theta \int_0^\infty [p_1(\lambda)e^{u_1 z} + q_1(\lambda)e^{-u_1 z}] J_1(\lambda\rho) d\lambda . \tag{A15-32}
$$

We deduce that $p_1(\lambda) = 0$ because $F_{z1} \to 0$ as $z \to \infty$. Also, we know that there would be no F_{z0} component for an infinite medium, since the source potential is in the x direction. Hence, $F_{z0} \to 0$ as $z \to -\infty$ and we must have $g_0(\lambda) = 0$. To determine the remaining two eigenfunctions $p_0(\lambda)$ and $q_1(\lambda)$ we first apply the boundary condition (A15-11) to (A15-31) and (A15-32)

$$
p_0(\lambda)e^{u_0 h} = q_1(\lambda)e^{-u_1 h} . \tag{A15-33}
$$

Then from the boundary condition (A15-10), with the potentials F_{x0}^+, F_{z0}, F_{x1}, F_{z1} obtained from (A15-29) (A15-30) (A15-31) and (A15-32), we find the following relation

$$
\frac{-c\lambda^2}{u_0\mu_0} e^{-u_0 h} \left[\frac{u_0\mu_0 k_1^2 - u_1\mu_1 k_0^2}{u_1\mu_1 k_0^2 + u_0\mu_0 k_1^2} + 1 \right] + \frac{u_0}{\mu_0} p_0(\lambda)e^{u_0 h}
$$

$$
= - \frac{2c\lambda^2}{\mu_1} \left[\frac{\mu_1 k_0^2}{u_0\mu_0 k_1^2 + u_1\mu_1 k_0^2} \right] e^{-u_0 h} - \frac{u_1}{\mu_1} [q_1(\lambda)e^{-u_1 h}] \tag{A15-34}
$$

from which we obtain

$$
p_0(\lambda) = \frac{2c\lambda^2 \mu_0\mu_1}{u_0\mu_1 + u_1\mu_0} \frac{k_1^2 - k_0^2}{u_0\mu_0 k_1^2 + u_1\mu_1 k_0^2} e^{-2u_0 h} \tag{A15-35}
$$

$$
q_1(\lambda) = \frac{2c\lambda^2 \mu_0\mu_1}{u_0\mu_1 + u_1\mu_0} \frac{k_1^2 - k_0^2}{u_0\mu_0 k_1^2 + u_1\mu_1 k_0^2} e^{(u_1 - u_0) h} . \tag{A15-36}
$$

The latter two eigenfunctions may be substituted in (A15-31) and (A15-32) to obtain the potentials F_{z0} and F_{z1}. First, let us note that (A15-31) and (A15-32) may be rewritten as

$$
F_{z0} = - \frac{\partial}{\partial x} \int_0^\infty \frac{p_0(\lambda)}{\lambda} e^{u_0 z} J_0(\lambda\rho) d\lambda \tag{A15-37}
$$

and

$$F_{z1} = -\frac{\partial}{\partial x}\int_0^\infty \frac{q_1(\lambda)}{\lambda} e^{-u_1 z}J_0(\lambda\rho)d\lambda.$$ (A15-38)

Upon substitution of (A15-35) and (A15-36) into (A15-37) and (A15-38) there results

$$F_{z0} = -2c\frac{\partial}{\partial x}\int_0^\infty \frac{\mu_0\mu_1}{u_0\mu_1 + u_1\mu_0}\frac{k_1^2 - k_0^2}{u_0\mu_0 k_1^2 + u_1\mu_1 k_0^2} e^{u_0(z-2h)}\lambda J_0(\lambda\rho)d\lambda$$ (A15-39)

and

$$F_{z1} = -2c\frac{\partial}{\partial x}\int_0^\infty \frac{\mu_0\mu_1}{u_0\mu_1 + u_1\mu_0}\frac{k_1^2 - k_0^2}{u_0\mu_0 k_1^2 + u_1\mu_1 k_0^2} e^{-u_1(z-h)}e^{-u_0 h}\lambda J_0(\lambda\rho)d\lambda.$$ (A15-40)

At $h=0$ and for $\mu_1=\mu_0$, equation (A15-39) becomes identical to that found by Wait (1953):

$$F_{z0} = -2c\frac{\partial}{\partial x}\int_0^\infty \frac{k_1^2 - k_0^2}{(u_0 + u_1)(u_0 k_1^2 + u_1 k_0^2)} e^{u_0 z}\lambda J_0(\lambda\rho)d\lambda.$$ (A15-41)

Note, however, the difference in variables from Wait's solution to the above

$$\left[\gamma_1^2,\ \gamma_0^2,\ -z,\ \frac{\partial}{\partial y}\right] = \left[-k_1^2,\ -k_0^2,\ z,\ \frac{\partial}{\partial x}\right].$$

Wait   This volume

We have, in obtaining the potentials F_{z0}^-, F_{z0}^+, F_{z0}, F_{z1}, and F_{z1}, found the formal solution of the problem with a minimum of restrictions. Now we seek to obtain expressions for the fields for a horizontal dipole *on* the surface of a homogeneous earth.

15-II. *A horizontal magnetic dipole on a homogeneous earth*

Let us assume now that $\mu_1=\mu_0$, and that $h=0$; the horizontal magnetic dipole lies on a homogeneous nonpermeable ground. Then the potentials in air, given by equations (A15-28) and (A15-39), become

$$F_{z0}^- = 2c\int_0^\infty \frac{k_1^2}{u_1 k_0^2 + u_0 k_1^2} e^{u_0 z}\lambda J_0(\lambda\rho)d\lambda; \qquad z \leq 0$$ (A15-42)

$$F_{z0} = -2c\frac{\partial}{\partial x}\int_0^\infty \frac{k_1^2 - k_0^2}{(u_0 + u_1)(u_0 k_1^2 + u_1 k_0^2)} e^{u_0 z}\lambda J_0(\lambda\rho)d\lambda; \qquad z \leq 0.$$ (A15-43)

The divergence of $\mathbf{F}_0$ may then be computed

$$\nabla\cdot\mathbf{F}_0 = \frac{\partial F_{z0}^-}{\partial x} + \frac{\partial F_{z0}}{\partial z}$$

$$= 2c\frac{\partial}{\partial x}\int_0^\infty \frac{(u_1 k_1^2 + u_0 k_0^2)e^{u_0 z}}{(u_0 + u_1)(u_0 k_1^2 + u_1 k_0^2)}\lambda J_0(\lambda\rho)d\lambda.$$ (A15-44)

In the quasi-static approximation pertinent to low frequency propagation, we may neglect k_0^2 and seek solutions of Laplace's equation in air and of the wave equation in the ground. We have seen in previous sections that this approximation leads to $u_0\sim\lambda$, and hence equation (A15-44) may be simplified to

$$\Phi = - \nabla \cdot F_0 = - 2c \frac{\partial}{\partial x} \int_0^\infty \frac{u_1 e^{\lambda z}}{u_1 + \lambda} J_0(\lambda \rho) d\lambda.$$
(A15-45)

The vertical magnetic field may now be derived from (A15-45) with $\sigma_0 = \epsilon_0 \approx 0$

$$H_z = \frac{1}{i\mu\omega} \frac{\partial \Phi}{\partial z} = - \frac{2c}{i\mu\omega} \frac{\partial^2}{\partial x \partial z} \int_0^\infty \frac{u_1 e^{\lambda z}}{u_1 + \lambda} J_0(\lambda \rho) d\lambda$$
(A15-46)

at the surface of the earth where $z = h = 0$, H_z has the value

$$H_z = - \frac{2c}{i\mu\omega} \frac{\partial}{\partial x} \int_0^\infty \frac{\lambda u_1}{u_1 + \lambda} J_0(\lambda \rho) d\lambda.$$
(A15-47)

To (A15-47) we may add

$$\int_0^\infty \lambda J_0(\lambda \rho) d\lambda = 0$$
(A15-48)

a result obtained as a special case of a formula given by Watson (1944, p. 386, no. 6) with $\mu = \nu = 0$. Then we find

$$H_z = - \frac{c}{i\mu\omega} \frac{\partial}{\partial x} \int_0^\infty \frac{u_1 - \lambda}{u_1 + \lambda} \lambda J_0(\lambda \rho) d\lambda.$$
(A15-49)

The evaluation of this integral involves several steps which have been elucidated by Wait 1953). First the quantity $(u_1 - \lambda)/(u_1 + \lambda)$ may be expressed as an integral via the relation Watson, 1944, p. 386, no. 7)

$$\int_0^\infty e^{-at} J_\nu(bt) \frac{dt}{t} = \frac{\{(a^2 + b^2)^{1/2} - a\}^\nu}{\nu b^\nu}.$$
(A15-50)

If we set $a = \lambda$, $b = -ik_1$, and $\nu = 2$, equation (A15-50) becomes

$$\int_0^\infty e^{-\lambda t} J_2(-ik_1 t) \frac{dt}{t} = \frac{\{(\lambda^2 - k_1^2)^{1/2} - \lambda\}^2}{-2k_1^2} = \frac{(u_1 - \lambda)^2}{2(u_1^2 - \lambda^2)} = \frac{u_1 - \lambda}{2(u_1 + \lambda)} \cdot$$
(A15-51)

Thus equation (A14-49) may be converted to

$$H_z = \frac{-2c}{i\mu\omega} \frac{\partial}{\partial x} \int_0^\infty \int_0^\infty e^{-\lambda t} J_2(-ik_1 t) J_0(\lambda \rho) \lambda \frac{dt}{t} d\lambda.$$
(A15-52)

Now the integration with respect to λ may be carried out by employing a formula derived from the Lipschitz integral (Watson, 1944, p. 384)

$$\int_0^\infty e^{-t\lambda} J_0(\lambda \rho) d\lambda = \frac{1}{(t^2 + \rho^2)^{1/2}} \cdot$$
(A15-53)

If this integral is differentiated with respect to t under the integral sign it yields

$$\int_0^\infty \lambda e^{-t\lambda} J_0(\lambda \rho) d\lambda = \frac{t}{(t^2 + \rho^2)^{3/2}} = - \frac{1}{\rho} \frac{\partial}{\partial \rho} \left\{ \frac{t}{(t^2 + \rho^2)^{1/2}} \right\}.$$
(A15-54)

Equation (A15-54) substituted in (A15-52) gives

$$H_z = \frac{2c}{i\mu\omega} \frac{\partial}{\partial x} \frac{1}{\rho} \frac{\partial}{\partial \rho} \int_0^\infty \frac{J_2(-ik_1 t) dt}{(t^2 + \rho^2)^{1/2}} \cdot$$
(A15-55)

Watson (1944, p. 435) evaluates this infinite integral so that we may write

$$H_z = \frac{2c}{i\mu\omega} \frac{\partial}{\partial x} \frac{1}{\rho} \frac{\partial}{\partial\rho} \left[I_1\left(\frac{-ik_1\rho}{2}\right) K_1\left(\frac{-ik_1\rho}{2}\right) \right]. \tag{A15-56}$$

For convenience we may write both differentiations in terms of ρ via

$$\rho^2 = x^2 + y^2, \qquad \frac{\partial\rho}{\partial x} = \frac{x}{\rho}.$$

Thus we find

$$\frac{\partial}{\partial x} = \frac{\partial\rho}{\partial x}\left[\frac{\partial}{\partial\rho} = \frac{x}{\rho}\frac{\partial}{\partial\rho}\right]$$

and

$$H_z = \frac{2cx}{i\mu\omega\rho} \frac{\partial}{\partial\rho} \frac{1}{\rho} \frac{\partial}{\partial\rho} \left[I_1\left(\frac{-ik_1\rho}{2}\right) K_1\left(\frac{-ik_1\rho}{2}\right) \right]. \tag{A15-57}$$

The differentiations in (A15-57) can be carried out using the recurrence relations between Bessel functions.

$$H_z = -\frac{1}{i\mu\omega} \frac{cx}{\rho^4} \left[-k_1^2\rho^2(I_1K_1 - I_0K_0) - 4ik_1\rho(I_1K_0 - I_0K_1) + 16I_1K_1 \right]. \tag{A15-58}$$

This result is, of course, directly obtained by reciprocity from the x component of the magnetic field due to a z-directed magnetic dipole [equation (A14-59)].

The components of the tangential magnetic field at the earth's surface may be obtained from (A15-5) with $\sigma_0 = \epsilon_0 = 0$ and

$$H_x = \frac{1}{i\mu\omega} \frac{\partial\Phi}{\partial x} \qquad H_y = \frac{1}{i\mu\omega} \frac{\partial\Phi}{\partial y}. \tag{A15-59}$$

Thus we wish to evaluate Φ for $z=0$. From (A15-45) we find, after differentiation,

$$\Phi_{z=0} = \frac{2cx}{\rho} \int_0^\infty \frac{\lambda u_1}{\lambda + u_1} J_1(\lambda\rho)d\lambda \tag{A15-60}$$

which can be rewritten in the form

$$\Phi_{z=0} = \frac{2cx}{-k_1^2\rho} \int_0^\infty (u_1 - \lambda)\lambda u_1 J_1(\lambda\rho)d\lambda \tag{A15-61}$$

by use of the identity $u_1^2 = \lambda^2 - k_1^2$. This integral can be composed of the following three integrals:

$$\Phi_{z=0} = \frac{2cx}{-k_1^2\rho} \left[\int_0^\infty \lambda^3 J_1(\lambda\rho)d\lambda - k_1^2 \int_0^\infty \lambda J_1(\lambda\rho)d\lambda - \int_0^\infty \lambda^2 u_1 J_1(\lambda\rho)d\lambda \right]. \tag{A15-62}$$

The first and second integrals are derivable from the Lipschitz integral

$$\int_0^\infty e^{-\lambda z} J_0(\lambda\rho)d\lambda = \frac{1}{(\rho^2 + z^2)^{1/2}}. \tag{A15-63}$$

If we differentiate this integral once with respect to ρ, then twice with respect to z, and set $z=0$, we obtain the first integral of (A15-62).

$$\int_0^\infty \lambda e^{-\lambda z} J_1(\lambda \rho) d\lambda = \frac{\rho}{(\rho^2 + z^2)^{3/2}} \tag{A15-64}$$

$$\int_0^\infty \lambda^3 e^{-\lambda z} J_1(\lambda \rho) d\lambda \Big|_{z=0} = -\frac{3}{\rho^4} \cdot \tag{A15-65}$$

The second integral of (A15-62) is obtained by differentiating (A15-63) with respect to ρ with z set equal to 0

$$\int_0^\infty \lambda J_1(\lambda \rho) d\lambda = -\frac{1}{\rho^2} \cdot \tag{A15-66}$$

The third integral in (A15-62) derives from Sommerfeld's (1926) integral valid for $z \leq 0$ [see equation (A15-15)]

$$\int_0^\infty \frac{\lambda}{u_1} e^{u_1 z} J_0(\lambda \rho) d\lambda = \frac{e^{ik_1 r}}{r}; \qquad r^2 = \rho^2 + z^2 \cdot \tag{A15-67}$$

This integral is differentiated once with respect to ρ then twice with respect to z before setting $z=0$.

$$-\int_0^\infty \frac{\lambda^2}{u_1} e^{u_1 z} J_1(\lambda \rho) d\lambda = \frac{i\rho k_1}{r^2} e^{ik_1 r} - \frac{\rho e^{ik_1 r}}{r^3} \tag{A15-68}$$

$$-\int_0^\infty \lambda^2 e^{u_1 z} J_1(\lambda \rho) d\lambda = -\frac{2iz\rho k_1^2 e^{ik_1 r}}{r^4} - \frac{\rho k^2 z e^{ik_1 r}}{r^3} + \frac{3\rho z e^{ik_1 r}}{r^5} - \frac{\rho z i k_1 e^{ik_1 r}}{r^4} \tag{A15-69}$$

$$-\int_0^\infty \lambda^2 u_1 J_1(\lambda \rho) d\lambda = \left[-\frac{3ik_1}{\rho^3} - \frac{k_1^2}{\rho^3} + \frac{3}{\rho^4} \right] e^{ik_1 \rho}. \tag{A15-70}$$

When we substitute (A15-65) (A15-66) and (A15-70) in (A15-62) we obtain

$$\Phi_{z=0} = \frac{2cx}{-k_1^2 \rho^5} \left[-3 - k_1^2 \rho^2 + (3 - k_1^2 \rho^2 - 3ik_1 \rho) \right] e^{ik_1 \rho}. \tag{A15-71}$$

The H_x and H_y components of the magnetic field on the surface of the earth can be found by differentiation of Φ with respect to x and y, respectively, as indicated by (A15-59). Following Wait (1953), the expression (A15-71) may be placed in the convenient form

$$\Phi_{z=0} = -\frac{cx}{\rho} M \tag{A15-72}$$

where

$$M = \frac{2}{k_1^2 \rho^4} \left[-3 - k_1^2 \rho^2 + (3 - k_1^2 \rho^2 - 3ik_1 \rho) e^{ik_1 \rho} \right] \tag{A15-73}$$

from which we obtain the field components as

$$H_y = \frac{c}{i\mu\omega} M \frac{xy}{\rho^3} - \frac{c}{i\mu\omega} \frac{\partial M}{\partial \rho} \frac{xy}{\rho^2} \tag{A15-74}$$

$$H_x = -\left[\frac{c}{i\mu\omega} M \frac{y^2}{\rho^3} + \frac{c}{i\mu\omega} \frac{\partial M}{\partial \rho} \frac{x^2}{\rho^2} \right] \tag{A15-75}$$

where

$$\frac{\partial M}{\partial \rho} = \frac{-2}{k_1^2 \rho^5} \left[(ik_1^3 \rho^3 - 5k_1^2 \rho^2 - 12ik_1\rho + 12)e^{ik_1\rho} - 12 - 2k_1^2\rho^2 \right]. \tag{A15-76}$$

The form of expression (A15-75) is particularly useful when one wishes to obtain the H_x field on either the x or y axis; then only the first or only the second term of (A15-75) appears.

The electric fields may be obtained by applying (A15-5) to (A15-42) and (A15-43) with $\lambda \sim u_0$, $k_0^2 \sim 0$. First the potentials are

$$F_{x0}^- = 2c \int_0^\infty e^{\lambda z} J_0(\lambda\rho) d\lambda \tag{A15-77}$$

and

$$F_{z0} = -2c \frac{\partial}{\partial x} \int_0^\infty \frac{1}{\lambda + u_1} e^{\lambda z} J_0(\lambda\rho) d\lambda. \tag{A15-78}$$

The latter integral may be multiplied by $\lambda - u_1$; using the identity $\lambda^2 - u_1^2 = k_1^2$, we obtain

$$F_{z0} = \frac{-2c}{k_1^2} \frac{\partial}{\partial x} \int_0^\infty \lambda e^{\lambda z} J_0(\lambda\rho) d\lambda + \frac{2c}{k_1^2} \frac{\partial}{\partial x} \int_0^\infty u_1 e^{\lambda z} J_0(\lambda\rho) d\lambda. \tag{A15-79}$$

The first integral on the right of (A15-79) at $z=0$ has the value zero as we noted in equation (A15-48). Since none of the electric field components contain the z derivatives of F_{z0}, it is permissible to substitute $z=0$ in (A15-79) at this juncture. The second integral may be evaluated at $z=0$ by differentiating Foster's integral (Foster, 1931) twice with respect to z and setting $z=0$, thus

$$\int_0^\infty \frac{1}{u_1} e^{u_1 z} J_0(\lambda\rho) d\lambda = I_0 \left[\frac{\gamma}{2} (r + z) \right] K_0 \left[\frac{\gamma}{2} (r - z) \right] = N \tag{A15-80}$$

$$\int_0^\infty u_1 J_0(\lambda\rho) d\lambda = \frac{\partial^2 N}{\partial z^2} \bigg|_{z=0}. \tag{A15-81}$$

The z component of potential is then

$$F_{z0} = \frac{2c}{k_1^2} \frac{\partial^3 N}{\partial x \partial z^2} \bigg|_{z=0}. \tag{A15-82}$$

The integral appearing in the expression (A15-77) for the x component of potential is, of course, the Lipschitz integral so that we may write

$$F_{x0}^- = \frac{2c}{(\rho^2 + z^2)^{1/2}}. \tag{A15-83}$$

The field components are now readily computed from

$$E_x = -\frac{\partial F_{z0}}{\partial y} \tag{A15-84}$$

$$E_y = \frac{\partial F_{z0}}{\partial x} - \frac{\partial F_{x0}^-}{\partial z} \tag{A15-85}$$

$$E_z = \frac{\partial F_{x0}^-}{\partial y}. \tag{A15-86}$$

Upon substitution of (A15-82) and (A15-83) in (A15-84) (A15-85) and (A15-86) we find

$$E_x = - \frac{2c}{k_1^2} \frac{\partial^4 N}{\partial x \partial y \partial z^2} \bigg|_{z=0} = - \frac{2c}{k_1^2} \frac{xy}{\rho^2} \frac{\partial^4 N}{\partial \rho^2 \partial z^2} \bigg|_{z=0} \tag{A15-87}$$

$$E_y = \frac{2c}{k_1^2} \frac{\partial^4 N}{\partial x^2 \partial z^2} \bigg|_{z=0} = \frac{2c}{k_1^2} \frac{x^2}{\rho^2} \frac{\partial^2 N}{\partial \rho^2 \partial z^2} \bigg|_{z=0} \tag{A15-88}$$

$$E_z = - \frac{2cy}{\rho^3} . \tag{A15-89}$$

Of course, the function $\partial^4 N/\partial \rho^2 \partial z^2$ was evaluated in the section on the vertical magnetic dipole and is given except for a factor of $\gamma^2/2$ by equation (A14-56). Thus we have

$$\frac{\partial^4 N}{\partial \rho^2 \partial z^2} \bigg|_{z=0} = \frac{\gamma^2}{2} \left[\frac{6}{\rho^2} I_1 K_1 + \frac{\gamma}{\rho} (I_1 K_0 - I_0 K_1) \right] \tag{A15-90}$$

and

$$E_x = \frac{cxy}{\rho^4} \left[6 I_1 K_1 - ik_1 \rho (I_1 K_0 - I_0 K_1) \right] \tag{A15-91}$$

$$E_y = - \frac{cx^2}{\rho^4} \left[6 I_1 K_1 - ik_1 \rho (I_1 K_0 - I_0 K_1) \right] \tag{A15-92}$$

are the tangential electric fields on the surface of the earth.

We may now combine the formulas (A15-58) (A15-74) (A15-75) (A15-89) (A15-91) and (A15-92) in various combinations depending upon the application. First let us collect these formulas:

$$H_x = - \frac{c}{i\mu\omega} \left[M \frac{y^2}{\rho^3} + \frac{\partial M}{\partial \rho} \frac{x^2}{\rho^2} \right] \tag{A15-93}$$

$$H_y = \frac{c}{i\mu\omega} \left[M \frac{xy}{\rho^3} - \frac{\partial M}{\partial \rho} \frac{xy}{\rho^2} \right] \tag{A15-94}$$

$$H_z = - \frac{c}{i\mu\omega} \frac{x}{\rho^4} \left[-k_1^2 \rho^2 (I_1 K_1 - I_0 K_0) - 4ik_1 \rho (I_1 K_0 - I_0 K_1) + 16 I_1 K_1 \right] \tag{A15-95}$$

$$E_x = c \frac{xy}{\rho^4} \left[6 I_1 K_1 - ik_1 \rho (I_1 K_0 - I_0 K_1) \right] \tag{A15-96}$$

$$E_y = - c \frac{x^2}{\rho^4} \left[6 I_1 K_1 - ik_1 \rho (I_1 K_0 - I_0 K_1) \right] \tag{A15-97}$$

$$E_z = - 2c \frac{y}{\rho^3} \tag{A15-98}$$

where

$$M = \frac{2}{k_1^2 \rho^4} \left[-3 - k_1^2 \rho^2 + (3 - k_1^2 \rho^2 - 3ik_1 \rho) e^{ik_1 \rho} \right] \tag{A15-99}$$

$$\frac{\partial M}{\partial \rho} = \frac{-2}{k_1^2 \rho^5} \left[(ik_1^3 \rho^3 - 5k_1^2 \rho^2 - 12ik_1 \rho + 12) e^{ik_1 \rho} - 12 - 2k_1^2 \rho^2 \right]. \tag{A15-100}$$

The angle defined by

$$\tan \alpha = \frac{-(H_x^2 - H_z^2) \pm \sqrt{(H_x^2 - H_z^2)^2 + 4H_x^2 H_z^2 \cos^2 (\varphi_x - \varphi_z)}}{2H_x H_z \cos (\varphi_x - \varphi_z)} \qquad \text{(A15-101)}$$

is zero on the y axis, but has a finite value on the x axis given by substituting (A15-93) and (A15-95) in (A15-101). It has the approximate value

$$\tan \alpha \approx \frac{|H_z|}{|H_x|} \qquad \text{(A15-102)}$$

for a large range of values of $\phi_x - \phi_z$.

Measurement of this angle as a function of x will provide information on the subsurface conductivity and could be quite useful in estimating the influence of overburden on vertical loop electromagnetic data. The following "wave impedances" are of interest in studying layering of sedimentary strata:

$$Z_{xy} = \frac{E_x}{H_y}, \qquad Z_{yx} = -\frac{E_y}{H_x}. \qquad \text{(A15-103)}$$

Additionally, we may wish to measure

$$Z_{xz} = -\frac{E_x}{H_z} \quad \text{or} \quad Z_{yz} = -\frac{E_y}{H_z}$$

as a measure of the uniformity of the field; these latter two impedances will lead to the free space impedance at distances sufficiently far from the dipole.

For some electromagnetic prospecting systems we may wish to know the mutual impedance between a pair of horizontal dipoles. Following the development of section 14, we may write the mutual impedance for both coaxial and coplanar coils as

$$Z = \frac{i\mu\omega H_x dA}{I} \qquad \text{(A15-104)}$$

for an x-directed dipole. Assume the second coil is of area da.

If the coils are coaxial, the magnetic field H_x is computed from (A15-93) with y set equal to zero. Hence we find

$$Z = \frac{i\mu\omega da\, dA}{4\pi} \frac{\partial M}{\partial \rho}. \qquad \text{(A15-105)}$$

The mutual impedance of two coaxial loops in an infinite medium would be computed using the formula (A222) with $y=z=0$, i. e.

$$Z_0 = \frac{2i\mu\omega da\, dA}{4\pi x^3}. \qquad \text{(A15-106)}$$

Thus the impedance ratio Z/Z_0 is given by

$$\frac{Z}{Z_0} = -\frac{1}{k_1^2 \rho^2} \left[(ik_1^3 x^3 - 5k_1^2 x^2 - 12ik_1 x + 12)e^{ik_1 x} - 12 - 2k_1^2 x^2 \right]. \qquad \text{(A15-107)}$$

On the other hand, if the coils are coplanar, the magnetic field is computed from (A15-93) with x set equal to zero so that we find

$$Z = \frac{i\mu\omega dad A}{4\pi} \frac{M}{y}.$$ (A15-108)

The mutual impedance of two coplanar coils is [equation (A14-66)]

$$Z_0 = -\frac{i\mu\omega dad A}{4\pi y^3}$$ (A15-109)

so that the impedance ratio Z/Z_0 is given by

$$\frac{Z}{Z_0} = -\frac{2}{k_1^2 y^2}\left[-3 - k_1^2 y^2 + (3 - k_1^2 y^2 - 3ik_1 y)e^{ik_1 y}\right]$$ (A15-110)

which is the same result as that found by Wait (1955).

15-III. *A horizontal magnetic dipole on an* n-*layered earth*

From equation (A15-29) we note that the reflected wave represented by the positive exponential $e^{u_0(z-2h)}$ is multiplied by the factor

$$r_\parallel(\lambda) = \frac{u_0\mu_0 k_1^2 - u_1\mu_1 k_0^2}{u_1\mu_1 k_0^2 + u_0\mu_0 k_1^2}.$$ (A15-111)

This is, of course, the amplitude reflection coefficient for the magnetic vector with the electric vector parallel to the plane of incidence as derived in (A11-84). For a layered earth this reflection coefficient will be,

$$r_\parallel(\lambda) = \frac{u_0\mu_0 k_a^2 - u_a\mu_a k_0^2}{u_a\mu_a k_0^2 + u_0\mu_0 k_a^2}$$ (A15-112)

where k_a is the apparent propagation constant in an equivalent homogeneous earth and μ_a is the apparent permeability for this same earth. The quantity u_a is then to be derived from

$$u_a = \sqrt{\lambda^2 - k_a^2}.$$ (A15-113)

Thus the solution we have already obtained for a homogeneous earth may be adapted readily to the layered earth problem. For example, we wish to substitute k_a for k_1 and u_a for u_1 in the expression (A15-41) for the z component of potential, and in the streaming potential Φ given by (A15-45). Hence, from (A15-93) through (A15-100) we may directly write down the far fields:

$$H_x = -\frac{c}{i\mu\omega}\left[M\frac{y^2}{\rho^3} + \frac{\partial M}{\partial\rho}\frac{x^2}{\rho^2}\right]$$ (A15-114)

$$H_y = \frac{c}{i\mu\omega}\left[M\frac{xy}{\rho^3} - \frac{\partial M}{\partial\rho}\frac{xy}{\rho^2}\right]$$ (A15-115)

$$H_z = -\frac{c}{i\mu\omega}\frac{x}{\rho^4}\left[-k_a^2\rho^2(I_1K_1 - I_0K_0) - 4ik_a\rho(I_1K_0 - I_0K_1) + 16I_1K_1\right]$$ (A15-116)

$$E_x = \frac{cxy}{\rho^4}\left[6I_1K_1 - ik_a\rho(I_1K_0 - I_0K_1)\right]$$ (A15-117)

$$E_y = -c\frac{x^2}{\rho^4}\left[6I_1K_1 - ik_a\rho(I_1K_0 - I_0K_1)\right]$$ (A15-118)

$$E_z = -2 \frac{cy}{\rho^3} \tag{A15-119}$$

where

$$M = \frac{2}{k_a^2 \rho^4} \left[-3 - k_a^2 \rho^2 + (3 - k_a^2 \rho^2 - 3ik_a \rho)e^{ik_a \rho} \right] \tag{A15-120}$$

$$\frac{\partial M}{\partial \rho} = -\frac{2}{k_a^2 \rho^5} \left[(ik_a^3 \rho^3 - 5k_a^2 \rho^2 - 12ik_a \rho + 12)e^{ik_a \rho} - 12 - 2k_a^2 \rho^2 \right] \tag{A15-121}$$

$$k_a = k_1/Q.$$

Exact expressions for the fields for all values of ρ must be obtained by numerical integration of (A15-45) with u_a replacing u_1.

16. Magnetic Dipoles Above an n-Layered Earth

16-I. *Introduction*

In dealing with electric and magnetic dipoles on a layered earth, we have met some common integrals which have been readily solved in closed form. When the dipoles are raised above the earth, solution of the related integrals can only be carried out numerically. Quon (1963) has given an excellent presentation of this subject and has treated horizontal and vertical dipoles of both electric and magnetic type. His work is a logical extension of Sommerfeld's (1926) classical paper. In this volume we have been concerned with three of the four cases discussed by Quon and Sommerfeld, omitting only the vertical electric dipole example.

In electromagnetic prospecting we are primarily concerned with magnetic dipoles above a layered earth and it is only these sources that will be considered in this section.

16-II. *A vertical magnetic dipole over an* n-*layered earth*

From the vertical magnetic dipole discussion of Section 14-II, we find that the potentials in the air and in the ground may be written, following equations (A14-21) (A14-22) (A14-26) (A14-27) and (A14-28),

in air above the dipole

$$F_{z0}^- = -\frac{i\mu\omega I da}{4\pi} \int_0^\infty \left[\frac{\lambda}{u_0} \frac{u_0\mu_1 - u_1\mu_0}{u_0\mu_1 - u_1\mu_0} e^{-2u_0 h} e^{u_0 z} + \frac{\lambda}{u_0} e^{u_0 z} \right] J_0(\lambda\rho) d\lambda \tag{A16-1}$$

in the air below the dipole

$$F_{z0}^+ = -\frac{i\mu\omega I da}{4\pi} \int_0^\infty \left[\frac{\lambda}{u_0} \frac{u_0\mu_1 - u_1\mu_0}{u_0\mu_1 + u_1\mu_0} e^{-2u_0 h} e^{u_0 z} + \frac{\lambda}{\mu_0} e^{-u_0 z} \right] J_0(\lambda\rho) d\lambda \tag{A16-2}$$

in the ground

$$F_{z1} = -\frac{i u\omega I da}{4\pi} \int_0^\infty \left[\frac{2u_0\mu_1}{u_0\mu_1 + u_1\mu_0} e^{(u_1 - u_0)h} \frac{\lambda}{u_0} e^{-u_1 z} \right] J_0(\lambda\rho) d\lambda. \tag{A16-3}$$

These expressions can be placed in a more convenient form provided we make the usual assumptions of $\lambda \sim u_0$ and $\mu_1 = \mu_0$ and provided we translate the origin from the dipole to the surface of the earth. Then we have

In air above the dipole

$$F_{z0}^- = c \int_0^\infty \left[\frac{\lambda - u_1}{\lambda + u_1} e^{\lambda(z-h)} + e^{\lambda(z-h)} \right] J_0(\lambda\rho) d\lambda \qquad \text{(A16-4)}$$

In air below the dipole

$$F_{z0}^+ = c \int_0^\infty \left[\frac{\lambda - u_1}{\lambda + u_1} e^{\lambda(z-h)} + e^{-\lambda(z+h)} \right] J_0(\lambda\rho) d\lambda \qquad \text{(A16-5)}$$

In the ground

$$F_{z1} = c \int_0^\infty \frac{2\lambda}{\lambda + u_1} e^{\lambda(z-h)} J_0(\lambda\rho) d\lambda \qquad \text{(A16-6)}$$

where

$$c = -\frac{i\mu\omega I da}{4\pi}.$$

The magnetic field components in air and in the ground may be calculated from these last three equations using the relations

$$H_\rho = -\frac{1}{i\mu\omega} \frac{\partial^2 F_z}{\partial z \partial \rho} \qquad \text{(A16-7)}$$

and

$$H_z = \frac{1}{i\mu\omega} \frac{1}{\rho} \left[\frac{\partial}{\partial \rho} \left(\rho \frac{\partial F_z}{\partial \rho} \right) \right]. \qquad \text{(A16-8)}$$

Now the wave equation in cylindrical coordinates, for F_z, is obtained from (A285) with $\gamma^2 = -u^2$ and $m = 0$.

$$\frac{1}{\rho} \frac{\partial}{\partial \rho} \left(\rho \frac{\partial F_z}{\partial \rho} \right) + (k^2 + u^2) F_z = 0$$

or

$$\frac{1}{\rho} \frac{\partial}{\partial \rho} \left(\rho \frac{\partial F_z}{\partial \rho} \right) = -\lambda^2 F_z. \qquad \text{(A16-9)}$$

Hence there results:

In the air above the dipole

$$H_\rho = \frac{Ida}{4\pi} \int_0^\infty \lambda^2 [r(\lambda) e^{\lambda(z-h)} + e^{\lambda(z-h)}] J_1(\lambda\rho) d\lambda \qquad \text{(A16-10)}$$

$$H_z = \frac{Ida}{4\pi} \int_0^\infty \lambda^2 [r(\lambda) e^{\lambda(z-h)} + e^{\lambda(z-h)}] J_0(\lambda\rho) d\lambda \qquad \text{(A16-11)}$$

In air below the dipole

$$H_\rho = \frac{Ida}{4\pi} \int_0^\infty \lambda^2 [r(\lambda) e^{\lambda(z-h)} - e^{-\lambda(z+h)}] J_1(\lambda\rho) d\lambda \qquad \text{(A16-12)}$$

$$H_z = \frac{Ida}{4\pi} \int_0^\infty \lambda^2 [r(\lambda)e^{\lambda(z-h)} + e^{-\lambda(z+h)}] J_0(\lambda\rho) d\lambda \tag{A16-13}$$

in the ground

$$H_\rho = \frac{Ida}{4\pi} \int_0^\infty \frac{2\lambda^3}{\lambda + u_1} e^{\lambda(z-h)} J_1(\lambda\rho) d\lambda \tag{A16-14}$$

$$H_z = \frac{Ida}{4\pi} \int_0^\infty \frac{2\lambda^3}{\lambda + u_1} e^{\lambda(z-h)} J_0(\lambda\rho) d\lambda \tag{A16-15}$$

where

$$r(\lambda) = \frac{\lambda - u_1}{\lambda + u_1}. \tag{A16-16}$$

For an n-layered earth we merely need to replace u_1 by u_a and redefine the reflection coefficient by

$$r(\lambda) = \frac{\lambda - u_a}{\lambda + u_a}. \tag{A16-17}$$

then the equations (A16-10) through (A16-15) still pertain. Note that in equations (A16-10) through (A16-13), only two types of integrals are involved. Thus, for example, if we wish to compute the fields at the surface of the earth, the integrals to be evaluated are

$$N(\mu, \nu) = \int_0^\infty \lambda^\mu J_\nu(\lambda\rho) e^{-\lambda h} d\lambda \tag{A16-18}$$

and

$$T(\mu, \nu) = \int_0^\infty \lambda^\mu r(\lambda) J_\nu(\lambda\rho) e^{-\lambda h} d\lambda \tag{A16-19}$$

where $\mu = 2$ and $\nu = 0, 1$. Then we might express the fields in air below the dipole as

$$H_\rho = \frac{Ida}{4\pi} [T(2, 1) - N(2, 1)] \tag{A16-20}$$

$$H_z = \frac{Ida}{4\pi} [T(2, 0) + N(2, 0)]. \tag{A16-21}$$

This is the nomenclature used by Quon (1963) who followed Wait (1958) in solving the integrals involved. First, Quon noted that

$$N(0, 0) = \int_0^\infty J_0(\lambda\rho) e^{-\lambda h} d\lambda \tag{A16-22}$$

is the Lipschitz integral and has the value

$$N(0, 0) = \frac{1}{(\rho^2 + h^2)^{1/2}}. \tag{A16-23}$$

Then, the integral

$$N(0, 1) = \int_0^\infty J_1(\lambda\rho)e^{-\lambda h}d\lambda \tag{A16-24}$$

has been evaluated by Watson (1944, p. 386, no. 8) so that

$$N(0, 1) = \frac{(\rho^2 + h^2)^{1/2} - h}{\rho(\rho^2 + h^2)^{1/2}} . \tag{A16-25}$$

Then $N(\mu, \nu)$ with $\mu \to 0$ can be evaluated as follows

$$N(\mu, 0) = (-1)^\mu \frac{\partial^\mu}{\partial h^\mu} \int_0^\infty J_0(\lambda\rho)e^{-\lambda h}d\lambda = (-1)^\mu \frac{\partial^\mu}{\partial h^\mu}\left[\frac{1}{(\rho^2 + h^2)^{1/2}}\right] \tag{A16-26}$$

and

$$N(1, 1) = -\frac{\partial}{\partial\rho} \int_0^\infty J_0(\lambda\rho)e^{-\lambda h}d\lambda = -\frac{\partial}{\partial\rho}\left[\frac{1}{(\rho^2 + h^2)^{1/2}}\right] \tag{A16-27}$$

so that

$$N(\mu + 1, 1) = (-1)^{\mu+1} \frac{\partial^\mu}{\partial h^\mu}\left(\frac{\partial}{\partial\rho} \frac{1}{(\rho^2 + h^2)^{1/2}}\right) = -\frac{\partial}{\partial\rho} N(\mu, 0). \tag{A16-28}$$

The integral $T(\mu, \nu)$ can be expressed in terms of the integral $N(\mu, \nu)$ by expanding $r(\lambda)$ in a power series of the form

$$r(\lambda) = \sum_{l=0}^\infty a_l\lambda^l \tag{A16-29}$$

so that $T(\mu, \nu)$ becomes

$$T(\mu, \nu) = \sum_{l=0}^\infty a_l N(\mu + l, \nu). \tag{A16-30}$$

The coefficients a_l can be found by Taylor's expansion about 0 in which a_l is given by

$$a_l = \frac{1}{l!}\left[\frac{d^l}{d\lambda^l} r(\lambda)\right]_{\lambda=0} \tag{A16-31}$$

provided that all derivatives of $r(\lambda)$ exist at $\lambda=0$. The first four coefficients are

$$a_0 = -1$$

$$a_1 = -\frac{2i}{k_a}$$

$$a_2 = \frac{2}{k_a^2}$$

$$a_3 = \frac{2i}{k_a^3} \tag{A16-32}$$

where we have assumed an n-layered earth with

$$r(\lambda) = \frac{\lambda - u_a}{\lambda + u_a}$$

and $u_a = ik_a$ at $\lambda = 0$. Then we find

$$T(2, 0) = \sum_{l=0}^{\infty} a_l N(2 + l, 0)$$

$$= - N(2, 0) - \frac{2i}{k_a} N(3, 0) + \frac{2}{k_a{}^2} N(4, 0) + \cdots. \tag{A16-33}$$

$$T(2, 1) = \sum_{l=0}^{\infty} a_l N(z + l, 1) = - N(2, 1) - \frac{2i}{k_a} N(3, 1) + \frac{2}{k_a{}^2} N(4, 1). \tag{A16-34}$$

Thus the fields are expressible in terms of the function $1/(\rho^2+h^2)^{1/2}$ and its derivatives, since all four functions $T(2, 1)$, $N(2, 1)$, $T(2, 0)$, and $N(2, 0)$ are derived therefrom via (A16-26) (A16-28) (A16-33) and (A16-34). For small ρ, $T(\mu, \nu)$ is evaluated by computer directly.

When measurements are made at a height z above the surface of the earth, the integrals to be evaluated are:

$$N_1(\mu, \nu) = \int_0^{\infty} \lambda^\mu J\nu(\lambda\rho)e^{\lambda(z-h)}d\lambda \tag{A16-35}$$

$$N_2(\mu, \nu) = \int_0^{\infty} \lambda^\mu J_\nu(\lambda\rho)e^{-\lambda(z+h)}d\lambda \tag{A16-36}$$

$$T(\mu, \nu) = \int_0^{\infty} \lambda^\mu r(\lambda)J_\nu(\lambda\rho)e^{\lambda(z-h)}d\lambda \tag{A16-37}$$

and the latter integral is evaluated through

$$T(\mu, \nu) = \sum_{l=0}^{\infty} a_l N_1(\mu + l, \nu). \tag{A16-38}$$

The asymptotic expansion for $T(\mu, \nu)$ converges rapidly only for small values of k_a. For many practical problems $k_a \ll 1$ and we need only use the first three or four terms. Quon (1963) discusses alternate means of evaluating $T(\mu, \nu)$.

16-III. *A horizontal magnetic dipole over an n-layered earth*

From the discussion of Section 15-I, we obtain the following expressions for the potentials in air below the dipole and in the ground

$$F_{x0}{}^+ = c \int_0^{\infty} [r_\|(\lambda)e^{\lambda(z-h)} + e^{-\lambda(z+h)}]J_0(\lambda\rho)d\lambda \tag{A16-39}$$

$$F_{x1} = 2c \int_0^{\infty} \frac{k_0{}^2}{\lambda k_1{}^2 + u_1 k_0{}^2} e^{-\lambda h}e^{-u_1 z}\lambda J_0(\lambda\rho)d\lambda \tag{A16-40}$$

$$F_{z0} = - 2c \frac{\partial}{\partial x} \int_0^{\infty} \frac{1}{\lambda + u_1} \frac{k_1{}^2 - k_0{}^2}{\lambda k_1{}^2 + u_1 k_0{}^2} e^{\lambda(z-h)}\lambda J_0(\lambda\rho)d\lambda \tag{A16-41}$$

$$F_{z1} = - 2c \frac{\partial}{\partial x} \int_0^{\infty} \frac{1}{\lambda + u_1} \frac{k_1{}^2 - k_0{}^2}{\lambda k_1{}^2 + u_1 k_0{}^2} e^{-u_1 z}e^{-\lambda h}\lambda J_0(\lambda\rho)d\lambda \tag{A16-42}$$

where we have assumed $\mu_0 \sim \lambda$, $\mu_1 = \mu_0$, and where we have translated the z axis so that origin occurs at the surface of the earth. The function $r_{||}(\lambda)$ is defined for homogeneous and layered earths, by

$$r_{||}(\lambda) = \frac{\lambda k_1{}^2 - u_1 k_0{}^2}{u_1 k_0{}^2 + \lambda k_1{}^2}, \qquad r_{||}(\lambda) = \frac{\lambda k_a{}^2 - u_a k_0{}^2}{u_a k_0{}^2 + \lambda k_a{}^2}. \tag{A16-43}$$

These expressions may be further reduced by carrying throughout the assumption that $k_0 \sim 0$, whereupon we find

$$F_{z0}{}^+ = c \int_0^\infty \left[e^{\lambda(z+h)} + e^{-\lambda(z+h)} \right] J_0(\lambda\rho) \, d\lambda \tag{A16-44}$$

$$F_{z1} = 0 \tag{A16-45}$$

$$F_{z0} = -2c \frac{\partial}{\partial x} \int_0^\infty \frac{1}{\lambda + u_1} e^{\lambda(z-h)} J_0(\lambda\rho) \, d\lambda \tag{A16-46}$$

$$F_{z1} = -2c \frac{\partial}{\partial x} \int_0^\infty \frac{1}{\lambda + u_1} e^{-u_1 z} e^{-\lambda h} J_0(\lambda\rho) \, d\lambda. \tag{A16-47}$$

The divergence of $\mathbf{F}_0$ may then be computed for the air space below the dipole as

$$\begin{aligned}
\nabla \cdot \mathbf{F}_0 &= \frac{\partial F_{X0}{}^+}{\partial x} + \frac{\partial F_{z0}}{\partial z} \\
&= c \frac{\partial}{\partial x} \int_0^\infty \frac{u_1 - \lambda}{u_1 + \lambda} e^{\lambda(z-h)} J_0(\lambda\rho) \, d\lambda + c \frac{\partial}{\partial x} \int_0^\infty e^{-\lambda(z+h)} J_0(\lambda\rho) \, d\lambda \\
&= -c \frac{\partial}{\partial x} \int_0^\infty r(\lambda) e^{\lambda(z-h)} J_0(\lambda\rho) \, d\lambda + c \frac{\partial}{\partial x} \int_0^\infty e^{-\lambda(z+h)} J_0(\lambda\rho) \, d\lambda. \tag{A16-48}
\end{aligned}$$

The field components are most conveniently expressed in Cartesian coordinates as, according to (A110) and (A111),

$$\left.\begin{aligned}
\mathbf{E} &= -\nabla \times \mathbf{F}_0 \\
i\mu_0\omega\mathbf{H} &= -\nabla\nabla\cdot\mathbf{F}_0 - k_0{}^2\mathbf{F}_0 = \nabla\Phi - k_0{}^2\mathbf{F}_0; \qquad \Phi = -\nabla\cdot\mathbf{F}_0 \\
E_x &= -\frac{\partial F_{z0}}{\partial y} \qquad\qquad i\mu_0\omega H_x = -k_0{}^2 F_{z0}{}^+ + \frac{\partial\Phi}{\partial x} \\
E_y &= -\frac{\partial F_{z0}{}^+}{\partial z} + \frac{\partial F_{z0}}{\partial x} \qquad i\mu_0\omega H_y = \frac{\partial\Phi}{\partial y} \\
E_z &= \frac{\partial F_{z0}{}^+}{\partial y} \qquad\qquad i\mu_0\omega H_z = -k_0{}^2 F_{z0} + \frac{\partial\Phi}{\partial z}
\end{aligned}\right\}. \tag{A16-49}$$

We first wish to compute the field components at $z=0$, i.e. at the surface of the earth. We note that at $z=0$, we have

$$F_{z0}{}^+ = 2c \int_0^\infty e^{-\lambda h} J_0(\lambda\rho) \, d\lambda; \qquad z = 0 \tag{A16-50}$$

$$F_{z0} = -2c \frac{\partial}{\partial x} \int_0^\infty \frac{1}{\lambda + u_1} e^{-\lambda h} J_0(\lambda\rho) d\lambda; \quad z = 0$$

$$= 2c \frac{x}{\rho} \int_0^\infty \frac{\lambda}{\lambda + u_1} e^{-\lambda h} J_1(\lambda\rho) d\lambda; \quad z = 0 \quad\quad \text{(A16-51)}$$

$$= \frac{cx}{\rho} \int_0^\infty [r(\lambda) + 1] e^{-\lambda h} J_1(\lambda\rho) d\lambda; \quad z = 0$$

$$\nabla \cdot \mathbf{F}_0 = \frac{cx}{\rho} \int_0^\infty \lambda r(\lambda) e^{-\lambda h} J_1(\lambda\rho) d\lambda - \frac{cx}{\rho} \int_0^\infty \lambda e^{-\lambda h} J_1(\lambda\rho) d\lambda; \quad z = 0. \quad \text{(A16-52)}$$

These last three expressions may be inserted in (A16-49) to obtain the fields. We shall need to use the following in calculating the fields:

$$\frac{\partial}{\partial x} \left[\frac{x}{\rho} f(\rho) \right] = \left(\frac{1}{\rho} - \frac{x^2}{\rho^3} \right) f(\rho) + \frac{x^2}{\rho^2} \frac{\partial}{\partial\rho} f(\rho) \quad\quad \text{(A16-53)}$$

$$\frac{\partial}{\partial y} \left[\frac{x}{\rho} f(\rho) \right] = -\frac{xy}{\rho^3} f(\rho) + \frac{xy}{\rho^2} \frac{\partial}{\partial\rho} f(\rho) \quad\quad \text{(A16-54)}$$

and

$$\frac{\partial}{\partial\rho} [J_1(\lambda\rho)] = \lambda J_0(\lambda\rho) - \frac{1}{\rho} J_1(\lambda\rho). \quad\quad \text{(A16-55)}$$

Thus we find

$$E_x = 2c \frac{xy}{\rho^3} \int_0^\infty [r(\lambda) + 1] e^{-\lambda h} J_1(\lambda\rho) d\lambda$$

$$- \frac{cxy}{\rho^2} \int_0^\infty \lambda [r(\lambda) + 1] e^{-\lambda h} J_0(\lambda\rho) d\lambda \quad\quad \text{(A16-56)}$$

$$E_y = c \left(\frac{1}{\rho} - \frac{2x^2}{\rho^3} \right) \int_0^\infty [1 + r(\lambda)] e^{-\lambda h} J_1(\lambda\rho) d\lambda$$

$$+ \frac{cx^2}{\rho^2} \int_0^\infty [1 + r(\lambda)] e^{-\lambda h} \lambda J_0(\lambda\rho) d\lambda \quad\quad \text{(A16-57)}$$

$$E_z = -2 \frac{cy}{\rho} \int_0^\infty \lambda e^{-\lambda h} J_1(\lambda\rho) d\lambda \quad\quad \text{(A16-58)}$$

$$i\mu_0 H_x = c \left(\frac{1}{\rho} - \frac{2x^2}{\rho^3} \right) \int_0^\infty [1 - r(\lambda)] \lambda e^{-\lambda h} J_1(\lambda\rho) d\lambda$$

$$+ \frac{cx^2}{\rho^2} \int_0^\infty [1 - r(\lambda)] \lambda^2 e^{-\lambda h} J_0(\lambda\rho) d\lambda \quad\quad \text{(A16-59)}$$

$$i\mu_0 H_y = \frac{cxy}{\rho^3} \int_0^\infty [r(\lambda) - 1] \lambda e^{-\lambda h} J_1(\lambda\rho) d\lambda$$

$$+ \frac{cxy}{\rho^2} \int_0^\infty [r(\lambda) - 1] \lambda^2 e^{-\lambda h} J_0(\lambda\rho) d\lambda \quad\quad \text{(A16-60)}$$

$$i\mu_0 H_z = -\frac{cx}{\rho}\int_0^\infty \lambda^2[r(\lambda)+1]e^{-\lambda h}J_1(\lambda\rho)\,d\lambda. \tag{A16-61}$$

We may now use the notation of Section 16-II, and the values for the integrals developed therein, to express equations (A16-56) through (A16-61) in the simple forms

$$E_x = -\frac{i\mu_0\omega I da}{4\pi}\frac{xy}{\rho^3}[T(0,1)+N(0,1)] + \frac{i\mu_0\omega I da}{4\pi}\frac{xy}{\rho^2}[T(1,0)+N(1,0)] \tag{A16-62}$$

$$E_y = -\frac{i\mu_0\omega I da}{4\pi}\left(\frac{1}{\rho}-\frac{2x^2}{\rho^3}\right)[T(0,1)+N(0,1)]$$
$$-\frac{i\mu_0\omega I da}{4\pi}\frac{x^2}{\rho^2}[T(1,0)+N(1,0)] \tag{A16-63}$$

$$E_z = \frac{2i\mu_0\omega I da}{4\pi}\frac{y}{\rho}N(1,1) \tag{A16-64}$$

$$H_x = \frac{I da}{4\pi}\left(\frac{1}{\rho}-\frac{2x^2}{\rho^3}\right)[T'(1,1)-N(1,1)] + \frac{I da}{4\pi}\frac{x^2}{\rho^2}[T(2,0)-N(2,0)] \tag{A16-65}$$

$$H_y = \frac{I da}{4\pi}\frac{xy}{\rho^3}[N(1,1)-T(1,1)] + \frac{I da}{4\pi}\frac{xy}{\rho^2}[N(2,0)-T(2,0)] \tag{A16-66}$$

$$H_z = \frac{I da}{4\pi}\frac{x}{\rho}[T(2,1)+N(2,1)]. \tag{A16-67}$$

These formulas agree with those given by Quon (1963). As in section 16-II, the functions T and N are defined by

$$N(\mu,\nu) = \int_0^\infty \lambda^\mu J_\nu(\lambda\rho)e^{-\lambda h}\,d\lambda \tag{A16-68}$$

$$T(\mu,\nu) = \int_0^\infty \lambda^\mu r(\lambda)J_\nu(\lambda\rho)e^{-\lambda h}\,d\lambda \tag{A16-69}$$

with

$$r(\lambda) = \frac{\lambda-u_1}{\lambda+u_1} \tag{A16-70}$$

for a homogeneous earth, and

$$r(\lambda) = \frac{\lambda-u_a}{\lambda+u_0} \tag{A16-71}$$

for a layered earth. As before, $T(\mu,\nu)$ can be expressed in terms of the known integral $N(\mu,\nu)$ by expanding $r(\lambda)$ in a power series of the form

$$r(\lambda) = \sum_{l=0}^\infty a_l\lambda^l. \tag{A16-72}$$

That is, we may write

$$T(\mu, v) = \sum_{l=0}^{\infty} a_l N(u + l, v).\tag{A16-73}$$

When measurements are made at a height z above the surface of the earth, the integrals to be evaluated are:

$$N_1(\mu, v) = \int_0^\infty \lambda^\mu J_v(\lambda\rho) e^{\lambda(z-h)} d\lambda \tag{A16-74}$$

$$N_2(\mu, v) = \int_0^\infty \lambda^\mu J_v(\lambda\rho) e^{-\lambda(z+h)} d\lambda \tag{A16-75}$$

$$T(\mu, v) = \int_0^\infty \lambda^\mu r(\lambda) J_v(\lambda\rho) e^{\lambda(z-h)} d\lambda \tag{A16-76}$$

and the latter integral is evaluated through

$$T(\mu, v) = \sum_{l=0}^{\infty} a_l N_1(\mu + l, v).\tag{A16-77}$$

The asymptotic expansions used previously are again applicable, but with $(z \pm h)$ replacing h.

17. A Horizontal Electric Dipole on an n-Layered Earth

In Section 9 we computed the tangential electric field components E_x and E_y for an electric dipole over a homogeneous earth. We also computed the mutual impedance between a pair of linear current elements on the surface of a homogeneous earth. These expressions may be generalized for an n-layered earth by substituting σ_a for σ_1 and k_a for k_1 in equations (A9-72) (A9-73) (A9-86) and (A9-88). Thus we obtain, for large values of ρ

$$E_x = \frac{Ids}{2\pi\sigma_a\rho^3}\left[1 + (1 - ik_a\rho)e^{ik_a\rho} - \frac{3y^2}{\rho^2}\right]\tag{A17-1}$$

$$E_y = \frac{Ids}{2\pi\sigma_a\rho^3}\frac{3xy}{\rho^2}\tag{A17-2}$$

$$Q(\rho) = -\frac{1}{2\pi\sigma_a\rho}\tag{A17-3}$$

$$P(\rho) = \frac{i\mu\omega}{2\pi\rho}\frac{1 - (1 - ik_a\rho)e^{ik_a\rho}}{-(k_a\rho)^2}\tag{A17-4}$$

where $k_a \approx k_1/Q$, $\sigma_a \approx \sigma_1/Q$ and

$$Q = \frac{Z_1 + \hat{Z}_2 \tanh jk_1 h_1}{\hat{Z}_2 + Z_1 \tanh jk_1 h_1}.$$

18. Summary of Mutual Coupling Expressions for Loops over an n-Layered Earth

The mutual impedance between two loops over an n-layered ground can be expressed simply in terms of the integrals $N_1(\mu, v)$, $N_2(\mu, v)$, and $T(\mu, v)$ given in Section 16. By equation (A14-64) we defined the mutual impedance between two loops as

$$Z = \frac{i\mu\omega H dA}{I}\tag{A18-1}$$

where I is the current in the first loop of area da and H is the magnetic field component normal to the plane of the second loop. The mutual impedance of two coplanar loops in an infinite medium is

$$Z_0 = -\frac{i\mu\omega dad A}{4\pi\rho^3} \tag{A18-2}$$

where ρ is the separation between the centers of the loops. We are assuming here that the

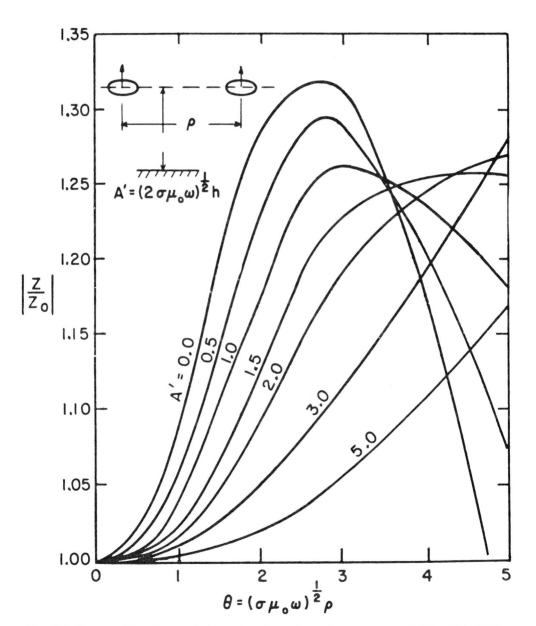

F<small>IG</small>. 18-1. The mutual impedance ratio for coplanar loops above a homogeneous earth (after Wait, 1955).

radii of the loops are both small relative to ρ. Previously we have computed the normalized mutual impedance

$$\frac{Z}{Z_0} = - \frac{4\pi H \rho^3}{Ida} .$$ (A18-3)

Four cases of special interest arise:

(a) *Coplanar loops with axes vertical*

For this case we need the formula for the vertical magnetic field of a vertical magnetic dipole above a layered earth, specialized for $x=y=0$. This may be drawn from (A16-21) and inserted in (A18-3)

$$Z/Z_0 = - \rho^3[T(2, 0) + N(2, 0)].$$ (A18-4)

(b) *The first loop has its axis vertical and the second loop has its axis parallel to the ground along a radius from the first loop*

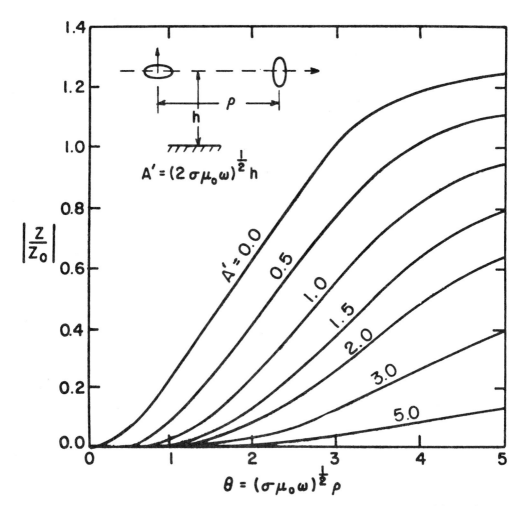

FIG. 18-2. The mutual impedance ratio for perpendicular loops above a homogeneous earth (after Wait, 1955).

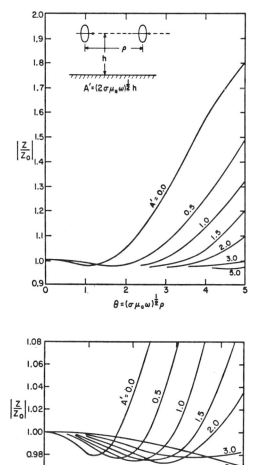

FIG. 18-3. The mutual impedance ratio for coaxial loops with axes parallel to a homogeneous earth (after Wait, 1956).

For this case we need the radial magnetic field of a vertical magnetic dipole above a layered earth, specialized for $z = h$. Thus we may substitute (A16-20) in (A18-3) to obtain

$$Z/Z_0 = \rho^3 [T(2, 1) - N(2, 1)]. \tag{A18-5}$$

(c) *Coaxial loops with axes horizontal*

For this case we need the axial magnetic field component of a horizontal magnetic dipole over a layered earth, specialized for $z = h$ and $y = 0$. Thus we may substitute (A16-65) in (A18-3)

$$Z/Z_0 = -\rho^3 \left(\frac{1}{\rho^2} - \frac{2x^2}{\rho^3} \right) [T(1, 1) - N(1, 1)]$$

$$- \rho^3 \frac{x^2}{\rho^2} [T(2, 0) - N(2, 0)] \tag{A18-6}$$

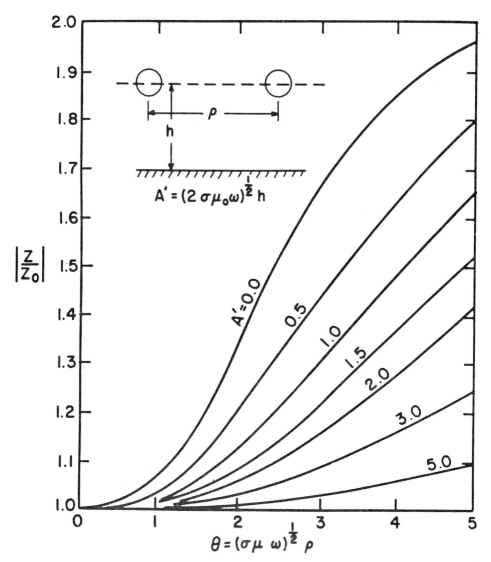

FIG. 18-4. The mutual impedance ratio for coplanar loops with axes parallel to a
homogeneous earth (after Wait, 1956).

(d) *Coplanar loops with axes horizontal.*

For this case we require the x component of the magnetic field of a horizontal magnetic
dipole, specialized for $z=h$ and for $x=0$. Thus we may substitute (A16-65) in (A18-3)

$$Z/Z_0 = \rho^2[T(1,1) - N(1,1)]. \tag{A18-7}$$

Wait (1955 & 1956) has computed the normalized impedances for the four cases listed
from formulation similar to that given here. The graphical results of this computation are
given in Figures 18-1 through 18-4.

References

A. Texts

Campbell, G., and Foster, R. M., 1948, Fourier integrals for practical application: Van Nostrand Co., Ltd.

Erdelyi, A., 1954, Tables of integral transforms: McGraw-Hill Book Co , Inc.

Harrington, R. F., 1961, Time-harmonic electromagnetic fields: McGraw-Hill Book Co., Inc.

Heiland, C. A., 1940, Geophysical exploration: Prentice-Hall, Inc.

Jahnke, E., and Emde, F., 1945, Tables of functions: Dover Publications.

Jones, D. S., 1964, The theory of electromagnetism: The Macmillan Company.

Reitz, J. R., and Milford, F. J., 1960, Foundations of electromagnetic theory: Addison-Wesley Publishing Co., Inc.

Schelkunoff, S. A., 1943, Electromagnetic waves: D. Van Nostrand Co., Inc.

Scott, E. J., 1955, Transform calculus: Harper and Brothers.

Sommerfeld, A., 1949, Partial differential equations in physics: Academic Press, Inc.

―――― 1952, Electrodynamics, Volume III of Lectures on theoretical physics: Academic Press, Inc.

Stratton, J. A., 1941, Electromagnetic theory: McGraw-Hill Book Co.

Sunde, E. D., 1949, Earth conduction effects in transmission systems: D. Van Nostrand Co., Inc.

Wait, J. R., 1962, Electromagnetic waves in stratified media: The Macmillan Company.

Watson, G. N., 1944, A treatise on the theory of Bessel functions: Cambridge University Press.

Wylie, C. R., 1960, Advanced engineering mathematics: McGraw-Hill Book Co., Inc.

B. Journal Articles

Bhattacharyya, B. K., 1959, Electromagnetic fields of a transient magnetic dipole on the earth's surface: Geophysics, v. 24, p. 89–108.

Carson, J. R., 1926, Wave propagation in overhead wires: Bell System Technical Journal, p. 539.

Foster, R. M., 1931, Mutual impedance of grounded wires lying on the surface of the earth: Bell System Technical Journal, v. 10, p. 408–419.

Gordon, A. N., 1951, The field induced by an oscillating magnetic dipole outside a semi-infinite conductor: Quart. Jour. Mechanics and Applied Mathematics, v. 4, p. 106–115.

Law, P. F., and Fannin, B. M., 1961, Radiation from a current filament above a homogeneous earth, with application to micropulsations: J. G. R., v. 66, no. 4, p. 1049–1060.

Madden, T. R., and Cantwell, T. 1967, This Volume.

Meyer, J., 1962, Elektromagnetische induktion eines vertikalen magnetischen dipols über einem leitenden homogenen halbraum: Mitt Max-Planck-Inst. f Aeronomie (s) Nr. 7.

―――― 1963, Elektromagnetische induktion in einem leitenden homogenen zylinder durch aussere magnetische und elektrische wechselfelder miteilungen aus dem: Max-Planck-Inst. f Aeronomie.

Negi, J. G., 1962, Inhomogeneous cylindrical ore body in presence of a time varying magnetic field: Geophysics, v. 27, no. 3, p. 386–392.

Nisbet, A., 1955, Hertzian electromagnetic potentials and associated gauge transformations: Proc. Roy. Soc. 231A, p. 250–263.

O'Brien, D. P., 1964, personal communication.

Quon, C., 1963, Electromagnetic fields of elevated dipoles on a two-layer earth: M.S. Thesis, University of Alberta.

Sommerfeld, A., 1926, Über die Ausbreitung der Wellen in der dratlosen Telegraphie: Annalen der Physik, 4, 81, 1135–1153.

Vozoff, K., 1958, Numerical resistivity analysis: Horizontal layers: Geophysics, v. 23, p. 536–556.

Wait, J. R. 1951, A Conducting sphere in a time varying magnetic field: Geophysics, v. 16, no. 5, p. 666–672.

―――― 1952, The cylindrical ore body in the presence of a cable carrying an oscillating current: Geophysics, v. 17, no. 2, p. 378–386.

―――― 1953, Induction by a horizontal oscillating magnetic dipole over a conducting, homogeneous earth: Trans. Amer., Geophys. Union, v. 34, p. 185–189.

―――― 1954, Mutual coupling of wire loops lying on the ground: Geophysics, v. 19, p. 290–296.

―――― 1955, Mutual electromagnetic coupling of loops over a homogeneous ground: Geophysics, v. 20, no. 3, p. 630–637.

―――― 1956, Mutual electromagnetic coupling of loops over a homogeneous ground—An additional note: Geophysics, v. 21, no. 2, p. 479–484.

―――― 1958, Induction by an oscillating magnetic dipole over a two layer ground: Appl. Sci. Res., Sec. B, v. 7, p. 73–80.

Wolf, A., 1946, Electric field of an oscillating dipole over the surface of a two layer earth: Geophysics, v. 2, no. 4, p. 518–534.

Additional References

A. *Texts*

Brekhovskik, L. M., 1960, Waves in layered media: Academic Press.

Bremmer, H., 1958, Propagation of electromagnetic waves: Handbuch der Physik, v. 16, p. 423–639.

Budden, K. G., 1951, Radiowaves in the ionosphere: Cambridge University Press.

Compagïe Generale de geophysique, 1955, Abaques de sondage electrique: Geophysical Prospecting, v. 3, Supplement 3.

Fritsch, V., 1960, Elektrische messungen an raumlich ausgedehnten, Besondere in der angewandten geoelektrik: Verlag G. Braun, Karlsruhe.

Grant, F. S., and West, G. F., 1965, Interpretation theory in applied geophysics: McGraw-Hill Book Co.

Jackson, John David, 1962, Classical electrodynamics: John Wiley and Sons, Inc.

Landau, L. D., and Lifshitz, E. M., 1960, Electrodynamics of continuous media: Addison-Wesley Publishing Co. Inc. (English translation)

Mooney, H. M., and Wetzel, W. W., 1956, The potentials about a point electrode and apparent resistivity curves for a two, three, and four layer earth: Univ. of Minnesota Press.

Morse, P. M., and Feshbach, H., 1953, Methods of theoretical physics: McGraw-Hill Book Co., Inc.

Panofsky, W. K. H., and Phillips, M. 1962, Classical electricity and magnetism, 2nd edition: Addison-Wesley Publishing Company, Inc.

Plomsey, R., and Collin, R. E., 1961, Principles and applications of electromagnetic fields: McGraw-Hill Book Co., Inc.

Ramo, S., and Whinnery, J R., 1953, Fields and waves in modern radio: John Wiley and Sons, Inc.

Smythe, W. R., 1950, Static and dynamic electricity, 2nd edition: McGraw-Hill Book Co., Inc.

Sommerfeld, A. N., 1949, Partial differential equations: New York, Academic Press.

Tarkhov, A. G., 1963, Spravochnik geofizika, Tom 3, Electrorazvedka (Handbook of Geophysics), v. 3, Electrical Surveying: Moscow, Gostoptekhizdat.

Wait, J. R., 1962, Electromagnetic waves in stratified media: The Macmillan Co.

Weeks, W. L., 1964, Electromagnetic theory for engineering applications: John Wiley and Sons, Inc.

Zaborovskiy, A. I., 1960, Peremennyye elektromagnitnoye polya v. electrorazvedke: Moscow, Izdatel'stvo Moskov Univ.

B. *Journal Articles*

Adachi, Saburo, 1960, Impedance characteristics of a uniform current loop having a spherical core: Jour. of Res., Nat. Bur. Stand., v. 64D, no. 3, p. 295–298.

Ashour, A. A., 1950, Induction of electric currents in a uniform circular disk: Quart. Jour. of Mech. and Appl. Math., v. 3, p. 119–128.

―――― 1952, The induction of electric currents in a uniform conducting circular disk by the sudden creation of magnetic poles: Quart. Jour. Mech. and Appl. Math., v. 5, p. 379.

Banos, A., and Wesley, J. P., 1953, The horizontal dipole in a conducting half-space: University of California, Marine Physical Lab, Pt. I, S10, Ref. 53-33.

―――― 1954, The horizontal dipole in a conducting half-space: University of California, Marine Physical Lab, Pt. II, S10, Ref. 54-31.

Belluigi, A., 1949, Coupling of a vertical coil with a homogeneous earth: Geophysics, v. 14, p. 501–507.

―――― 1950, The electromagnetic field due to induced currents in a conductive slab: Geophysics, v. 15, no. 4, p. 687–703.

―――― 1952, Sui campi geoelettromagnetici a bassa frequenza: Rivista di Geofisica Applicata, v. 13, p. 3–34.

Berdichevsky, M. N., and Brunelli, B. E., 1959, Theoretical premises of magneto-telluric profiling: Bull. Acad. Sci., U.S.S.R., Geophysics Series, no. 7, p. 757–762.

Bhattacharyya, B. K., 1955, Electromagnetic induction in a two-layer earth: J. G. R., v. 60, p. 279.

———— 1955, Propagation of transient electromagnetic waves in a conducting medium: Geophysics, v. 20, no. 4, p. 959–961.

———— 1957, Propagation of an electric pulse through a homogeneous and isotropic medium: Geophysics, v. 22, p. 905–921.

———— 1957, Propagation of transient electromagnetic waves in a medium of finite conductivity: Geophysics, v. 22, no. 1, p. 75–88.

———— 1959, Electromagnetic fields of a transient magnetic dipole on the earth's surface: Geophysics, v. 24, no. 1, p. 89–108.

———— 1959, Field on earth's surface due to a transient electro-magnetic disturbance: Jour. Technology, v. 1, p. 151–161.

———— 1963, Electromagnetic fields of a vertical magnetic dipole placed above the earth's surface: Geophysics, v. 28, no. 3, p. 408–425.

———— 1963, Input resistances of horizontal and vertical magnetic dipoles over a homogeneous ground: Trans. I.E.E.E., VAP-II, no. 3.

———— 1964, Electromagnetic fields of a small loop antenna on the surface of a polarizable medium: Geophysics, v. 29, no. 5, p. 814–831.

Bilinsky, Solomon, 1938, On the field due to a vertical line source of current grounded to earth: Geophysics, v. 3, no. 1, p. 58–62.

Buckner, G. O., 1954, Sub-surface electrical measurements about two plane interfaces: Geophysics, v. 19, no. 2, p. 297–309.

Burrows, C. R., 1937, Radio propagation over plane earth-field strength curves: Bell. Syst. Tech. Jour., v. 16, p. 45.

Bursian, V. R., 1936, The theory of electromagnetic fields applied in electric prospecting, Pt. 2: Gostekhteoretizdat.

Cagniard, L., 1953, Basic theory of the magneto-telluric method of geophysical prospecting: Geophysics, v. 18, p. 605–635.

Chastenet De Gery, J., and Kunetz, G., 1956, Potential and apparent resistivity over dipping beds: Geophysics, v. 21, no. 3, p. 780–793.

Cook, K. L., and Gray, R. L., 1961, Theoretical horizontal resistivity profiles over hemispherical sinks: Geophysics, v. 26, no. 3, p. 342–354.

Cook, K. L., and Van Nostrand, R. G., 1954, Interpretation of resistivity data over filled sinks: Geophysics, v. 19, no. 4, p. 761–770.

d'Erceville, I., and Kunetz, G., 1962, The effect of a fault on the earth's natural electromagnetic field: Geophysics, v. 27, p. 651–665.

D'Iakonov, B. P., 1957, A cylinder in the field of a point source of electric current: Bull. Acad. Sci., U.S.S.R., Geophysics Series, no. 1, p. 135–140.

Dmitriev, V. I., 1959, The effect of inhomogeneities in the earth on the field of a rectilinear, infinitely long cable: Bull. Acad. Sci., U.S.S.R., Geophysics Series, no. 4, p. 435–437.

———— 1960, A solution of a basic problem in the theory of the induction method of electromagnetic surveying: Bull. Acad. Sci., U.S.S.R., Geophysics Series, no. 8, p. 748–753.

———— 1962, Diffraction of electromagnetic waves at a conducting plate in a conducting medium: Bull. Acad. Sci., U.S.S.R., Geophysics Series, no. 6, p. 475–477.

Doll, H. G., 1949, Introduction to induction logging and application to logging of wells drilled with oil base mud: Journal of Petroleum Technology, v. 1, no. 6, p. 148–162.

Douloff, A. A., 1961, The response of a disk in a dipole field: Geophysics, v. 26, no. 4, p. 452–464.

Duesterhoeft, W. C., 1961, Propagation effects in induction logging: Geophysics, v. 26, no. 2, p. 192–204.

Duesterhoeft, W. C., and Smith, H. W., 1962, Propagation effects on radial response in induction

D'Yakonov, B. P., 1959, The diffraction of electromagnetic waves by a circular cylinder in a homogeneous half-space: Bull. Acad. Sci., U.S.S.R., Geophysics Series, no. 9, p. 950–955.

logging: Geophysics, v. 27, no. 4, p. 463–469.

———— 1959, The diffraction of electromagnetic waves by a sphere located in a half-space: Bull. Acad. Sci., U.S.S.R., no. 11, p. 1120–1125.

—— 1960, Asymptotic expressions for electromagnetic fields caused by a cylindrical inhomogeneity: Bull. Acad. Sci., U.S.S.R., Geophysics Series, no. 7, p. 636–638.

—— 1960, The influence of the earth's surface on the electromagnetic field of a cylindrical inhomogeneity: Bull. Acad. Sci., U.S.S.R., Geophysics Series, no. 5, p. 488–492.

Eckart, G., and Martin, H., 1963, Some problems in the theory of diffraction and refraction in stratified media: Publication A.D. 404 897, U. S. Dept. of Commerce.

Ehrenburg, D. O., and Watson, R. J., 1932, Mathematical theory of electrical flow in stratified media with horizontal, homogeneous, and isotropic layers: Trans. A.I.M.E., Geophysical Prospecting, p. 423–442.

Enenshtein, B. S., 1957, Method of interpreting curves for electromagnetic soundings: Bull. Acad. Sci., U.S.S.R., Geophysics Series, no. 12, p. 102–108.

Evjen, H. M., 1938, Depth factors and resolving power of electrical measurements: Geophysics, v. 3, no. 1, p. 78–95.

—— 1949, Theory and practice of low-frequency electromagnetic exploration: Geophysics, v. 13, no. 4, p. 584–594.

Flathe, H., 1955, A practical method of calculating geoelectrical model graphs, for horizontally stratified media: Geophys. Prosp., v. 3, no. 3, p. 268–294.

—— 1963, Five-layer master curves for the hydrogeological interpretation of geoelectrical resistivity measurements above a two-storey aquifer: Geophys. Prosp., v. 11, no. 4, p. 471–508.

Fraser, D. C., and Ward, S. H., 1965, Resolution of two-layer earth structure from dipole-dipole resistivity and induced polarization data: Proc. Symp. on Computers and Computer Applications in Mining and Exploration, University of Arizona, p. PP-1 to PP-43.

Frolov, P. P., 1963, On the establishment of an electromagnetic field: Bull. Acad. Sci., U.S.S.R., Geophysics Series, no. 7, p. 656–658.

—— 1965, On the asymptotic behaviour of magnetic field buildup in a layered medium: Bull. Acad. Sci., U.S.S.R., Geophysics Series, Physics of the Solid Earth, no. 1, p. 33–36.

Galbraith, J. N., Jr., and Cantwell, T., 1963, Resistivity calculations: Report under contract NONR-4198(00) by Geoscience Incorporated.

Gordon, A. N., 1951, Electromagnetic induction in a uniform semi-infinite conductor: Quart. Jour. Mech. and Applied Math, v. 8, p. 116.

Gray, M., 1934, Mutual impedance of grounded wires lying on the surface of the earth when the conductivity varies exponentially with depth: Physics, v. 5, p. 76–80.

Groskopf, J., and Vogt, K., 1940, On the measurement of earth conductivity: Telegrapher und Fernspech Funk Fernseh Technik, v. 29, p. 164–172.

Hack, F., 1908, The propagation of electromagnetic waves over a plane conductor: Annalen der Physik, v. 27, p. 43.

Harrington, R. R., 1964, Magnetic components radiated by a horizontal dipole at V. L. F.: U. S. Navy Electronics Lab, San Diego, Research Rpt. 1221.

Hallof, P. G., 1957, On the interpretation of resistivity and induced polarization results: Ph.D. thesis, M.I.T. Dept. of Geology and Geophysics.

Hedstrom, H., 1932, Electrical prospecting for auriferous quartz veins and reefs: Mining Magazine, v. 46, p. 201–213.

Horton, C. W., 1946, On the use of electromagnetic waves in geophysical prospecting: Geophysics, v. 11, no. 4, p. 505–517.

Hummel, J. N., 1932, A theoretical study of apparent resistivity in surface potential methods: A.I.M.E. Geophysical Prospecting, p. 392–422.

Ivanov, A. G., 1957, Approximate formula for a calculation of the variable magnetic field over a lode: Bull. Acad. Sci., U.S.S.R., Geophysics Series, no. 2, p. 91–97.

—— 1957, Frequency investigations in detailed electrical prospecting: Bull. Acad. Sci., U.S.S.R., Geophysics Series, no. 1, p. 43–56.

Ivanov, A. G., Nikitana, V. N., and Skugarevskaya, O. A., 1964, Spectral interpretation of electromagnetic field build-up curves: Bull. Acad. Sci., U.S.S.R., Geophysics Series, no. 3, p. 210–213.

Jackson, C. M., Wait, J. R., and Walters, L. C., 1962, Numerical results for the surface impedance of a stratified conductor: Technical Note No. 43, Nat. Bur. Stand.

Jain, S., 1964, A method of quantitative interpretation of the electrical fields of infinitely long sinks and horizontal circular cylindrical bodies: Geophys. Prosp., v. 12, no. 3, p. 290–297.

Kamenetskii, F. M., Kaufman, A. A., and Iakubovskii, I. U. V., 1957, On the choice of the optimum frequency in the induction method of electrical prospecting: Bull. Acad. Sci., U.S.S.R., Geophysics Series, no. 2, p. 80–90.

Kertz, W., 1960, Leitungsfahiger zylinder im transversalen magnetischen Wechselfeld: Gerl. Beitr. Geophys., 69, 4–28.

Koefoed, O., 1955, Resistivity curves for a conducting layer of finite thickness embedded in an otherwise homogeneous and less conducting earth: Geophysical Prospecting, v. 3, no. 3.

—— 1965, A semi-direct method of interpreting resistivity observations: Geophys. Prosp., v. 13, no. 2.

Koroleva, K. P., Nikitina, V. N., and Skugarevskaya, O. A., 1956, Buildup of an electric field in an homogeneous half-space in the case of a submerged source: Bull. Acad. Sci., U.S.S.R., Geophysics Series, Physics of the Solid Earth, no. 2, p. 106–110.

Koroleva, K. P., and Skugarevskaya, O. A., 1965, Buildup of a magnetic field excited by a horizontal electric dipole in a homogeneous conducting half-space: Bull. Acad. Sci., U.S.S.R., Geophysics Series, Physics of the Solid Earth, no. 2, p. 99–105.

Kosenkov, O. M., 1963, The electromagnetic field of a circular loop at the earth-air boundary: Bull. Acad. Sci., U.S.S.R., Geophysics Series, no. 12, p. 1122–1126.

Kozulin, Yu. N., 1960, The electromagnetic field of a transmitter for large values of the product of the complex wave number and transmitter-to-receiver distance: Bull. Acad. Sci., U.S.S.R., Geophysics Series, no. 10, p. 1006–1007.

—— 1960, On the theory of electromagnetic frequency sounding of multilayered structures: Bull. Acad. Sci., Geophysics Series, no. 8, p. 798–803.

Kraichman, M. B., 1960, Basic experimental studies of the magnetic field from electromagnetic sources immersed in a semi-infinite conducting medium: Jour. Res. Nat. Bur. Stand., v. 64D, no. 1, p. 21–25

—— 1962, Impedance of a circular loop in an infinite conducting medium: Jour. Res. Nat. Bur. Stand., v. 66D, no. 4, p. 499–504.

—— 1962, Induction in a small loop moving with a magnetostatic dipole toward a conducting half-space: Jour. Res. Nat. Bur. Stand., v. 66D, p. 731–735.

Krajcovic, S., 1962, O telurickom anomalnom poli kruhoveno valca (On the telluric anomaly field of a circular cylinder): Geol. Prace, Zpravy 24, p. 237–247.

Lahiri, B. N., and Price, A. T., 1939, Electromagnetic induction in non-uniform conductors, and the determination of the conductivity of the earth from terrestrial magnetic variations: Roy. Soc. Phil. Trans., Ser. A, v. 237, p. 509–540.

Lien, R. H., 1953, Radiation from a horizontal dipole in a semi-infinite dissipative medium: J. Appl. Phys., v. 24, p. 1–5.

Lien, R. H., and Wait, J. R., 1953, Radiation from a horizontal dipole in a semi-infinite dissipative medium: J. Appl. Phys., v. 24, p. 958–959.

Lipskaya, N. V., 1949, The field of a point electrode observed on the earth's surface near a buried conducting sphere: Bull. Acad. Sci., U.S.S.R., Geophysics Series, v. 13, p. 409–427.

Logn, O., 1954, Mapping nearly vertical discontinuities by earth resistivities: Geophysics, v. 19, no. 4, p. 739–760.

Lowndes, J. S., 1957, A transient magnetic dipole source above a two-layer earth: Quart. Jour. Mech. and Appl. Math., v. 10, p. 79.

Lowrie, W., and West, G. F., 1965, The effect of a conducting overburden on electromagnetic prospecting methods: Geophysics, v. 30, no. 4, p. 624–632.

Maeda, Katsuro, 1955, Apparent resistivity for dipping beds: Geophysics, v. 20, no. 1, p. 123–139.

Maillet, Raymond, 1947, The fundamental equations of electrical prospecting: Geophysics, v. 12, no. 4, p. 529–556.

Mal, A. K., 1962, On the field of an electric dipole in presence of a layered media: Zeitschr. Geophysik, v. 28, no. 5, p. 209–218.

March, H. W., 1953, The field of a magnetic dipole in the presence of a conducting sphere: Geophysics, v. 18, p. 671.

Matveev, B. K., and Shkabarnya, N. G., 1959, Electrical profiling above a sphere situated near the boundary between two media: Bull. Acad. Sci., Geophysics Series, no. 10, p. 1060–1064.

Meier, A. A., 1964, The potential of a point source of current in a semi-infinite inhomogeneous medium with conductivity varying in a direction parallel to the surface: Bull. Acad. Sci., U.S.S.R. Geophysics Series, no. 3, p. 235–236.

Moore, R. K., 1951, Theory of radio communication between submerged submarines: Ph.D. Thesis, Cornell University.

Moore, R. K., and Blair, W. E., 1961, Dipole radiation in a conducting half-space: Jour. Res. Nat. Bur. Stand., v. 65D, no. 6, p. 547–563.

Moran, J. H., and Kuntz, K. S., 1962, Basic theory of induction logging and application to study of two-coil sondes: Geophysics, v. 27, no. 6, p. 829–858.

Muskat, M., and Evinger, H. H., 1941, Current penetration in direct current prospecting: Geophysics, v. 6, no. 4, p. 397–427.

Negi, J. G., 1961, Radiation resistance of a vertical magnetic dipole over an inhomogeneous earth: Geophysics, v. 26, no. 5, p. 635–642.

―――― 1962, Diffraction of electromagnetic waves by an inhomogeneous sphere: Geophysics, v. 28, no. 4, p. 480–492.

―――― 1965, Radiation resistance of a horizontal circular loop over a finitely conducting ground and application of results to geophysical exploration of conducting sheet-type deposits: Geophysics, v. 30, no. 2, p. 234–245.

Nikitina, V. N., 1956, Anomalies in electromagnetic fields over cylindrical inhomogeneities: Trans. (Trudy) Inst. Geophys. Acad. Sci., U.S.S.R., no. 32, p. 159.

―――― 1960, The calculation of a variable electromagnetic field over a sloping vein: Bull. Acad. Sci., U.S.S.R., Geophysics Series, no. 3, p. 328–334.

―――― 1960, The general solution of an axially symmetrical problem in induction logging theory: Bull. Acad. Sci., U.S.S.R., Geophysics Series, p. 607–616.

―――― 1962, Some calculations of electromagnetic fields for the method of radioscopy: Bull. Acad. Sci., U.S.S.R., Geophysics Series, no. 7, p. 596–600.

Norton, K. A., 1936, The propagation of radio waves over the surface of the earth and in the upper atmosphere: Pt. I., Proc. I.R.E., v. 24, p. 1367–1387.

―――― 1937, Propagation of radio waves over the surface of the earth and in the upper atmosphere: Pt. II., Proc. I.R.E., v. 25, p. 1203–1236.

Onodera, Seibe, 1963, Numerical analysis of relative resistivity for a horizontally layered earth: Geophysics, v. 28, no. 2, p. 222–231.

Orsinger, A., and Van Nostrand, R., 1954, A field evaluation of the electromagnetic reflection method: Geophysics, v. 19, no. 3, p. 478–489.

Pekeris, C. L., 1940, Direct method of interpretation in resistivity prospecting: Geophysics, v. 5, no. 1, p. 32–42.

Peters, L. J., and Bardeen, John, 1932, Some aspects of electrical prospecting applied in locating oil structures: American Physical Society (Geophysics), Trans. Soc. of Pet. Geophysicists, v. 2, p. 1–20.

Phillips, R. J., 1965, Computer utilization in analyzing telluric data of structure in sedimentary basins: Proc. Symp. on Computers and Computer Applications in Mining and Exploration, University of Arizona, p. QQ-1 to QQ-13.

Pirson, S. J., 1935, Effect of anisotropy on apparent resistivity curves: Bull. A.A.P.G., v. 19, no. 1, p. 37–57.

Price, A. T., 1950, Electromagnetic induction in a semi-infinite conductor with a plane boundary: Quart. Jour. Mech. and Appl. Math., v. 3, p. 385.

Pris, G. V., 1961, Parameters of cylindrical conductors in inductive prospecting: Bull. Acad. Sci., U.S.S.R., Geophysics Series, no. 11, p. 1070–1074.

―――― 1965, Magnetic-field sources which have a directional effect: Bull. Acad. Sci., U.S.S.R., Geophysics Series, Physics of the solid earth, no. 1, p. 37–41.

Rice, S. O., 1937, Series for the wave function of a radiating dipole at the earth's surface: Bell System Tech. Jour., v. 16, p. 101–109.

Richards, P. I., 1958, Transients in conducting media: Trans. I.R.E., v. AP-6, p. 178–182.

Rikitake, T., and Sawada, M., 1962, Electromagnetic induction within an anisotropic plane sheet over a non-conductor and underlain by a uniform semi-infinite conductor: Bull. Earthquake Research Institute, University of Tokyo, v. 40, Pt. 4, p. 657–684.

———— 1965, Electromagnetic induction in a semi-infinite conductor having a undulatory surface: Bull. Earthquake Research Institute, University of Tokyo, v. 43, p. 161–166.

Rikitake, T., and Whitham, K., 1964, Interpretation of the Alert anomaly in geomagnetic variations: Canadian Journal of Earth Sciences, v. 1, p. 35–62.

Riordan, J., 1931, Transients in grounded wires lying on the earth's surface: Bell Syst. Tech. Jour., v. 10, p. 420–431.

Riordan, J., and Sunde, E. D., 1933, Mutual impedance of grounded wires for stratified two-layer earth: Bell. Syst. Jour., v. 12, p. 162–177.

Roden, R. B., 1964, The effect of an ocean on magnetic diurnal variations: The Geophysical Journal, v. 8, no. 4, p. 375–388.

Roman, Irwin, 1933, The calculation of electrical resistivity for a region underlying two uniform layers: Terr. Mag. and Atmos. Elect., v. 38, p. 117–140 and 185–202.

———— 1959, An image analysis of multiple-layer resistivity problems: Geophysics, v. 24, no. 3, p. 485–509.

———— 1963, The kernel function in the surface potential for a horizontally stratified earth: Geophysics, v. 28, no. 2, p. 232–249.

Roy, A., and Jain, S., 1961, A simple integral transform and its applications to some problems in geophysical interpretation: Geophysics, v. 26, no. 2, p. 229–241.

Schaub, Yu. B., 1962, The influence of the specific resistance of the surrounding medium on the form of anomaly curves obtained in aerial electrical prospecting: Bull. Acad. Sci., U.S.S.R., Geophysics Series, no. 5, p. 423–426.

———— 1963, The determination of the distribution of specific electrical conductivity in a horizontally layered medium by aerial electric induction exploration: Bull. Acad. Sci., U.S.S.R., Geophysics Series, no. 9, p. 837–841.

Schlumberger, C., 1920, Etude sur la prospection electrique du sous sol, Paris: Gauthier-Villars, Chapt. VIII.

Seigel, H. O., 1952, Ore body size determination in electrical prospecting: Geophysics, v. 17, no. 4, p. 907–914.

———— 1959, Mathematical formulation and type curves for induced polarization: Geophysics, v. 24, no. 3, p. 547–565.

Shakhsuvarov, D. N., 1956, Method for interpreting the results of observations on an electromagnetic field for dipole soundings: Bull. Acad. Sci., U.S.S.R., Geophysics Series, no. 5.

———— 1956, Method of interpreting dipole sounding data for electromagnetic fields: Bull. Acad. Sci., U.S.S.R., Geophysics Series, no. 5.

Shakhsuvarov, D. N., and Rybakova, E. V., 1960, On the application of the expressions of a distant zone for electromagnetic frequency soundings: Bull. Acad. Sci., U.S.S.R., Geophysics Series, no. 11, p. 1072–1073.

Skalskaya, I. P., 1948, The field of a point source of current situated on the earth's surface above an inclined plane: Jour. Technical Physics, U.S.S.R., v. 18, p. 1242–1254.

Slichter, L. B., 1932, Observed and theoretical electromagnetic model response of conducting spheres: A.I.M.E. Trans., v. 97, p. 443–459.

———— 1933, An inverse boundary value problem in electrodynamics: Physics, v. 4, p. 411.

———— 1933, The interpretation of the resistivity prospecting method for horizontal structures: Physics, v. 4. p. 307–322.

———— 1951, An electromagnetic interpretation problem in geophysics: Geophysics, v. 16, p. 431–449.

———— 1952, An electromagnetic interpretation problem for the sphere: Proc. Roy. Soc. London, v. A214, p. 356–370.

Slichter, L. B., and Knopoff, Leon, 1959, Field of an alternating magnetic dipole on the surface of a layered earth: Geophysics, v. 24, no. 1, p. 77–88.

Sommerfeld, A., 1897, Über verzweigte potentiale im Raum: Proc. Lond. Math. Soc., v. 28, p. 395–429.

———— 1909, Über die Ausbrutung der wellen in der drahtlosen telegraphie: Ann. der Physik, v. 28, p. 665–737.

Stefanesco, S. S., 1942, Das elektromagnetische normalfeld des waagerechten dipols: Angewandte Geophysik, v. 9, p. 201.

Stefanesco, S., Schlumberger, C., and Schlumberger, M., 1930, Sur la distribution electrique potentielle autour d'une prise de terre ponctuelle dans un terrain a couches horizontales, homogenes et isotropes: Jour. Physique et Radium, tome 1, p. 132–140.

Sumi, F., 1953, On the possibility of determining the dip of the contact between two geologic formations by the geoelectric method: Srbije Zavoid Geol i Geofiz. Instrazivanjz Vesnik, Kniga, 10, p. 273–280.

———— 1956, Geoelectrical exploration of inclined thin beds: Geophys. Prosp., v. 4, no. 2, p. 194–204.

Tagg, G. F., 1930, The earth resistivity method of geophysical prospecting: Some theoretical considerations: Mining Magazine, v. 43, p. 150–158.

———— 1934, Interpretation of resistivity measurements: A.I.M.E. Trans., v. 166.

Tai, C. T., 1947, Hertzian dipole immersed in a dissipative medium: Cruft. Lab. Report No. 21, Harvard University.

Tikhonov, A. N., 1942, The effect of inhomogeneity of the earth's crust on the field of terrestrial currents: Bull. Acad. Sci., U.S.S.R., Geophysics Series, v. 5, p. 207–218.

———— 1946, The establishment of an electric current in a homogeneous conducting halfspace: Bull. Acad. Sci., U.S.S.R., Ser. Geogr. and Geophys., no. 3.

———— 1950, The establishment of an electric current in an inhomogeneous layered medium: Bull. Acad. Sci., U.S.S.R., Ser. Geogr. and Geophys., no. 3.

Tikhonov, A. N., and Dimitriev, V. I., 1959, On the possibility of using the induction method of electrical prospecting from the air for geological map-making, Bull. Acad. Sci., U.S.S.R., Geophysics Series, no. 10, p. 1053–1055.

Tikhonov, A. N., and Shakhsuvarov, D. N., 1954, The application of electromagnetic fields from radio transmitters in geophysical exploration: Trans. (Trudy). Inst. Geophys. Acad. Sci., U.S.S.R., no. 9.

———— 1956, Method for calculating electromagnetic fields produced by an alternating current in stratified media: Bull. Acad. Sci., U.S.S.R., Geophysics Series, no. 3.

———— 1959, The electromagnetic field produced by a dipole at points in distant zones: Bull. Acad. Sci., U.S.S.R., Geophysics Series, no. 7, p. 672–677.

————1959, The distant electromagnetic field of a dipole: Bull. Acad. Sci., U.S.S.R., Geophysics Series, no. 7, p. 946.

Tikhonov, A. N., Shakhsuvarov, D. N., and Rybakova, E. V., 1959, The properties of the electromagnetic field of a dipole activated in a layer lying on an insulator: Bull. Acad. Sci., U.S.S.R., Geophysics Series, no. 11, p. 1173–1174.

Tikhonov, A. N., and Skugarevskaya, O. A., 1951, The establishment of an electric current in an inhomogeneous layered medium III: Bull. Acad. Sci., U.S.S.R., Geophysics Series, no. 6.

———— 1958, The interpretation of the process of establishing an electric field in layered media: Bull. Acad. Sci., Geophysics Series, no. 3, p. 197–199.

———— 1959, The asymptotic behaviour of the process of generating an electromagnetic field: Bull. Acad. Sci., U.S.S.R., Geophysics Series, no. 6, p. 573–578.

———— 1959, The asymptotic behaviour of the process of generating an electromagnetic field in a laminated medium: Bull. Acad. Sci., U.S.S.R., Geophysics Series, no. 7, p. 667–671.

Tuman, V. S., 1951, The telluric method of prospecting and its limitations under certain geologic conditions: Geophysics, v. 16, p. 102–114.

Unz, M., 1964, Superposition in resistivity prospecting: Geophys. Prosp., v. 12, no. 1, p. 1–48.

Van Dam, J. C., 1965, A simple method for the calculation of standard graphs to be used in geoelectrical prospecting: Geophys. Prosp., v. 13, no. 1, p. 37–65.

Van Nostrand, R. G., 1953, Limitations on resistivity methods as inferred from the buried sphere problem: Geophysics, v. 18, p. 423–433.

Van Nostrand, R. G., and Cook, K. L. 1955, Apparent resistivity for dipping beds: Geophysics, v. 20, no. 1, p. 140–147.

Vogler, L. E., and Noble, J. L., 1963, Curves of ground proximity loss for dipole antennas (a digest): Jour. Res., Nat. Bur. Stand., v. 67D, no. 5, p. 567–575.

Wait, J. R., 1951, The magnetic dipole over the horizontally stratified earth: Can. Jour. Phys., v. 29, p. 577–592.

———— 1951, Transient electromagnetic propagation in a conducting medium: Geophysics, v. 16, p. 213–221.

———— 1952, Current-carrying wire loops in simple inhomogeneous region: Jour. Appl. Phys., v. 23, p. 297.

———— 1952, The magnetic dipole antenna immersed in a conducting medium: Proc. Inst. Radio Engrs., v. 40, no. 10, p. 1244–1245.

———— 1952, A transient magnetic dipole source in a dissipative medium: Jour. Appl. Phys., v. 24, no. 3, p. 341–343.

———— 1953, A conducting permeable sphere in the presence of a coil carrying an oscillating current: Can. Jour. Phys., v. 31, p. 670.

———— 1953, Electromagnetic coupling between a circular loop and a conducting sphere: Geophysics, v. 18, no. 4, p. 971–972.

———— 1953, Induction in a conducting sheet by a small current-carrying loop: Appl. Sci. Res., Sec. B, v. 3, p. 230–236.

———— 1953, Propagation of radio waves over a stratified ground: Geophysics, v. 18, no. 2, p. 416–422.

———— 1953, Radiation resistance of a small circular loop in the presence of a conducting ground: Jour. Appl. Phys., v. 54, no. 5, p. 646–649.

———— 1953, Transient coupling in grounded circuits: Geophysics, v. 18, p. 138–141 and p. 971.

———— 1956, Shielding of a transient electromagnetic dipole field by a conducting sheet: Can. Jour. Phys., v. 34, p. 888–890.

———— 1957, Insulated loop antenna immersed in a conducting medium: Jour. Res., Nat. Bur. Stand., v. 59, no. 2, p. 133–137.

———— 1957, The transient behaviour of the electromagnetic ground wave over a spherical earth: Trans. I.R.E., v. AP-5, p. 198–202.

———— 1958, Induction by an oscillating magnetic dipole over a two-layer ground: Appl. Sci. Res., v. B-7, p. 73–80.

———— 1959, On the electromagnetic response of an imperfectly conducting thin-dyke: Geophysics, v. 14, p. 167–171.

———— 1959, Radiation from a small loop immersed in a semi-infinite conducting medium: Can. J. Phys., v. 37, p. 672–674.

———— 1960, Propagation of electromagnetic pulses in a homogeneous conducting earth: Appl. Sci. Res., Sec. B, v. 8, p. 213–253.

———— 1960, Some solutions for electromagnetic problems involving spheroidal, spherical, and cylindrical bodies: Jour. of Res., Nat. Bur. Stand., v. 64B, no. 1, p. 15–32.

———— 1962, A note on the electromagnetic response of a stratified earth: Geophysics, v. 27, no. 3, p. 382–385.

Wait, J. R., and Campbell, L. Lorne, 1953, The fields of an electric dipole in a semi-infinite conducting medium: J. G. R., v. 58, no. 1, p. 21–28.

———— 1953, Fields of an oscillating magnetic dipole immersed in a semi-infinite conducting medium: J.G.R., v. 58, p. 167.

Wait, J. R., and Spies, K. P., 1964, A note on the insulated loop antenna immersed in a conducting medium: Jour. Res., Nat. Bur. Stand., v. 68D, no. 11, p. 1249–1250.

Ward, S. H., 1953, Electrical conductivity of diamond drill core specimens: Geophysics, v. 23, p. 434–447.

———— 1959, Unique determination of conductivity, susceptibility, size and depth in multi-frequency electromagnetic exploration: Geophysics, v. 24, no. 3, p. 531–546.

Wesley, J. P., 1958, Response of dyke to oscillating dipole: Geophysics, v. 23, p. 128–133.

———— 1958, Response of a thin dyke to oscillating dipole: Geophysics, v. 23, p. 134–143.

West, G. F., 1960, Quantitative interpretation of electromagnetic prospecting measurements: Ph.D. Thesis, University of Toronto, Canada.

West, S. S., 1940, Three-layer resistivity curves for the eltran electrode configuration: Geophysics, v. 5, no. 1, p. 43–46.

———— 1943, The mutual impedance of collinear grounded wires: Geophysics, v. 8, no. 2, p. 157–164.

Wetzel, W. W., and McMurry, H. V., 1951, A set of curves to assist in the interpretation of the three layer resistivity problem: Geophysics, v. 2, no. 4, p. 329–341.

Wise, W. H., 1937, The physical reality of the Zenneck surface wave: Bell System Tech. Jour., v. 13.

———— 1937, The physical reality of the Zenneck surface wave: Bell System Tech. Jour., v. 16, p. 35–44.

Wolf, A., 1942, The impedance of a grounded wire: Geophysics, v. 7, p. 414–418.

Yost, W. J., 1952, The interpretation of electromagnetic reflection data in geophysical exploration, Pt. I, General theory: Geophysics, v. 17, no. 1, p. 89–105.

Yost, W. J., Beard, C. I., McClure, C. D., and Skomal, E. M., 1952, Interpretation of electromagnetic reflection data in geophysical exploration: Geophysics, v. 17, no. 4, p. 806–826.

Yungul, S. H., 1961, Magneto-telluric sounding three-layer interpretation curves: Geophysics, v. 26, no. 4, p. 465–473.

Zakharov, V. Kh., 1964, The interpretation of anomalies of electromagnetic dipole profiling taken above solids of revolution (spheres, cylinders): Bull. Acad. Sci., U.S.S.R., Geophysics Series no. 4, p. 339–342.

Zenneck, J., 1907, The propagation of plane electromagnetic waves over a flat earth and its application to wireless telegraphy: Annalen der Physik, vol. 23, p. 846.

Zitron, N. R., 1960, Shielding of transient electromagnetic signals by a thin conducting sheet: Jour. Res., Nat. Bur. Stand., v. 64D, no. 5, p. 563–567.

Chapter II

PART B—CONDUCTION OF ELECTRICITY IN ROCKS

S. H. WARD* AND D. C. FRASER†

Table of Contents

* Professor of Geophysical Engineering, Department of Mineral Technology, University of California, Berkeley.
† Chief Geophysicist, Geophysical Engineering and Surveys Limited, Toronto, Canada.

PART B. CONDUCTION OF ELECTRICITY IN ROCKS

1. Basic Concepts of Electrical Conduction

Electrical conductivity is the movement of electrical charge from one location to another. Because the charge may be carried by ions or electrons, whose mobilities vary from material to material, there is a full spectrum of conductivities ranging from highly conducting metals to nearly perfect insulators, as illustrated in Figure 1.

Electrical conductivity can be derived from the relation

$$\sigma = ne\mu$$

where n is the number of charge carriers in a material, e is the charge carried by each, and μ is the mobility of the carriers. The mobility is defined as the drift velocity per unit electric field. Since the charge carriers may be ions or electrons (or "holes" as we shall see later), we classify conduction in solids as *ionic* or *electronic* within the range 1 to 10^8 mho/m. Below this range of conductivity, materials may be semiconductors or insulators. For porous media, such as rocks at the earth's surface, conductors extend into the range normally covered by solid semiconductors.

Ionic conductivity involves the ordered movement of ions in an electrolyte upon application of an external electric field. In the absence of an electric field, the ions move randomly as a result of thermal agitation and collisions with other ions and atoms. Since both cations and anions are present in an electrolyte, the conductivity can be expressed as

$$\sigma = e\left[n^+\mu^+ + n^-\mu^-\right]$$

where the numbers and mobilities of the positive and negative ions are indicated by superscript signs. A temperature increase results in a conductivity increase since the mobility of both ion species is increased with

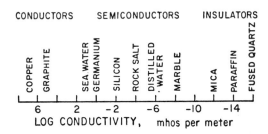

FIG. 1. Spectrum of conductivities.

temperature. Any force which modifies the mobilities of cations and anions *differentially* will cause a change in the ratio of contributions to the conductivity made by each ion species.

Ionic conductivity and electronic conductivity are analogous to the extent that the random motion of particles is affected by an applied field. In electronic conduction, the random motion of valence electrons among the atoms is ordered by application of an external electric field. The electrons then travel with a drift velocity through the solid. Further elucidation of the mechanism of electronic conduction is facilitated by reference to energy level diagrams (Figure 2) for electrons surrounding a nucleus. These electrons are grouped into shells with distinct energy levels; energy increases from the inner (K) shell to the outer (valence) shell. Only those electrons in the K-shell have identical energies. Electrons occupying other shells

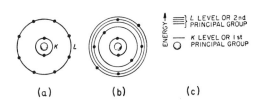

FIG. 2. Electron energy levels for neon; (a) energy shells, (b) energy levels, (c) energy level plot (after Van Vlack, 1959).

exist at discrete energy levels within the shells. Van Vlack (1959) summarizes several important principles which apply to electrons within any one isolated atom as follows:

"(1) There are specific electronic energy levels around each atom. Electrons cannot occupy spaces between these levels.

"(2) Electrons fill the lowest energy levels first. A specific quantity of energy, called a *quantum* of energy, must be supplied to move an electron to the next higher level.

"(3) At most, only two electrons may occupy any one energy level.

"(4) These two electrons with equal energy values are 'mirror images' of each other; that is, their characteristics indicate that one 'spins' in one direction and the other in the opposite direction," (Figure 3).

The principles listed above pertain as long as an atom is isolated sufficiently from its neighbors to behave independently. When this is not the case, then interaction of the valence or outermost electrons of adjacent atoms occurs. New sublevels arise and constitute an *energy band* corresponding to an energy level in a single atom. Each band contains one sublevel for each atom in the material. The sublevels are not all occupied (Figure 4), however, when the valence shell is only partly filled.

Where valence is determined by the outer two shells of a single atom, two valence bands arise. These bands can overlap as in Figure 5. Electrons will fill the lowest energy sublevels of the second valence band while leaving vacant the uppermost sublevels of the first valence band.

An electron will move from one location to another if energy is supplied from the ex-

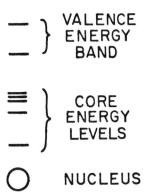

Fig. 4. Partially filled valence band of sodium for many atoms close together.

terior to raise it to a position of higher energy in the energy models shown above. An external electric field can supply the energy to raise an electron from one sublevel to a higher one in a given band or even from one band to another. This will permit the electron to "drift" and decelerate to a new, lower energy site, provided a site is available. The drift will be in a direction dictated by the applied field. When one electron is raised to a higher energy level, it leaves a "hole" which may then be occupied by an electron moving under thermal agitation against the external electric field. A contribution to conduction can thus be made by "holes" as well as by electrons.

In some materials the valence energy bands do not overlap so that an *energy gap* exists. If all sublevels are filled in an inner valence band, the only means for conduction is to supply enough energy to raise an electron across an energy gap to the first energy band which is not completely filled. The larger the energy gap, the more resistive is

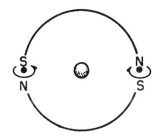

Fig. 3. Opposed electron spins (after Van Vlack, 1959).

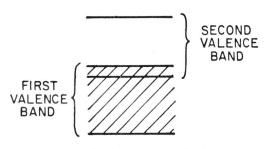

Fig. 5. Overlapping valence bands.

the material. Insulators are materials with exceptionally large energy gaps. Semiconductors are intermediate between conductors and insulators both in size of energy gaps and electrical conductivity.

We have indicated above that electrons are distributed over a number of shells. Our illustrations necessitated consideration only of two or three shells, while, in fact, electrons for some atoms are distributed over seven shells labelled K, L, M, N, O, P, and Q. They may be characterized by the principal quantum number $n = 1, 2, 3, 4, 5, 6, 7$. The maximum number of electrons which each shell can contain is $2n^2$. Furthermore, we have noted the fine structure of the shells, which we may label subshells s, p, d, and f corresponding to the azimuthal quantum numbers $l = 0, 1, 2, 3$. The maximum number of electrons in a subshell is then $2(2l+1)$. The electron shells of the elements are shown in Table 1. Note that the subshells refer to the isolated atom and are not synonomous with the sublevels of energy bands arising when adjacent atoms interact. The outer electrons may then be slightly rearranged by minor variations in the surrounding conditions as we indicated earlier.

For many discussions it is convenient to represent the energy diagram in a manner other than as shown in Figure 2. The alternate presentation is illustrated in Figure 6. The curved lines in Figure 6(a) depict the potential in the neighborhood of an atomic nucleus, and the horizontal lines indicate the permitted energy levels. In this example, the lower levels K and L are completely filled. In the M-level, the subshell s normally contains the valence electron while p is a subshell which could be occupied. A monovalent metal has one electron in the s subshell, a bivalent metal has two electrons in the s subshell, while a trivalent metal has two electrons in the s subshell and one electron in the p subshell.

If the atoms come close enough together for reaction, the rim of the potential trough is depressed (Figure 6(b)). The energy gap which an electron must traverse in order to become free is thus lower for the solid material than for the free atom. Criteria for electronic conduction thus become:

(a) An incomplete s band
(b) Overlapping s and p bands
(c) A potential barrier lowered to beneath the upper boundary of the filled band.

Table 1

Shell	K	L		M			N				O				P			Q
Subshell	1s	2s	2p	3s	3p	3d	4s	4p	4d	4f	5s	5p	5d	5f	6s	6p	6d	7s
1H–2He	1–2																	
3Li–4Be	2	1–2																
5B–10Ne	2	2	1–6															
11Na–12Mg	2	2	6	1–2														
13Al–18A	2	2	6	2	1–6													
19K–20Ca	2	2	6	2	6		1–2											
21Sc–30Zn	2	2	6	2	6	1–10	2											
31Ga–36Kr	2	2	6	2	6	10	2	1–6										
37Rb–38Sr	2	2	6	2	6	10	2	6			1–2							
39Y–48Cd	2	2	6	2	6	10	2	6	1–1		2							
49In–54Xe	2	2	6	2	6	10	2	6	10		2	1–6						
55Cs–56Ba	2	2	6	2	6	10	2	6	10		2	6			1–2			
57La	2	2	6	2	6	10	2	6	10		2	6	1		2			
58Ce–71Lu	2	2	6	2	6	10	2	6	10	1–14	2	6	1		2			
72Hf–78Pt	2	2	6	2	6	10	2	6	10	14	2	6	4–10					
79Am–80Hg	2	2	6	2	6	10	2	6	10	14	2	6	10		1–2			
81Tl–86Rn	2	2	6	2	6	10	2	6	10	14	2	6	10		2	1–6		
87Fr–88Ra	2	2	6	2	6	10	2	6	10	14	2	6	10		2	6		1–2
89Ac	2	2	6	2	6	10	2	6	10	14	2	6	10		2	6	1	2
90Th–103	2	2	6	2	6	10	2	6	10	14	2	6	10	1–14	2	6	1	2

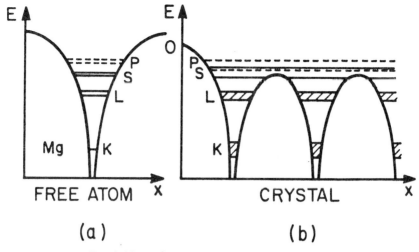

FIG. 6. Alternative representation of energy diagram.

2. Normal Mode of Conduction in Rocks

Conduction in most surface rocks, however, is largely electrolytic, taking place in the pore spaces and not significantly through the mineral grains. The ions which conduct the current result from the dissociation of salts, such dissociation occurring when salts are dissolved in water. Since each ion is able to carry only a definite quantity of charge, it follows that the more ions that are available in a solution and the faster they travel, the greater will be the charge that can be carried. Hence, the solution with the larger number of ions will have the higher conductivity. Thus, in general, a rock which contains saline water within its pores will have a greater conductivity when the salinity of the water is high than when it is low; salinity is a major factor in determining the resistivity of a rock.

An increase in temperature lowers the viscosity of water, with the result that ions in the water become more mobile. The increased mobility of the ions results in an observed resistivity decrease with increase in temperature.

Considering these factors alone, temperature should cause resistivity to decrease with depth from the surface of the earth while decreasing salinity with depth should increase resistivity. Anomalies in both of these dependencies should be expected, however,

and the effect of pressure on resistivity must also be evaluated, as we shall see. Most connate waters possess resistivities in the range 10 to 100 ohm-m, indicating salinities of the order of 0.001 N to 0.01 N. Surface waters may possess resistivities over the range 10 to 10^3 ohm-m unless stagnant, in which case the resistivity may be considerably lower.

3. Dependency of Rock Resistivity Upon Rock Texture

Even though most rock-forming minerals are essentially nonconductive, they dictate the porosity and pore distribution and, hence, the lengths and cross-sectional areas of the electrolytic paths through a specimen. It is a matter of some interest to develop a model representative of purely ionic conduction in rocks. The "bundle of capillaries" model is adequate for this purpose, since we are concerned with electrical analogs rather than with actual pore configurations. Our desire, then, is to develop a model containing a single electrolyte path, the model being equivalent electrically to actual rock specimens.

For a particular electrolyte-saturated rock core specimen, characterized by interconnected pore paths (e.g., sandstones), the length and cross-sectional area of a single electrolyte path, which is equivalent electrically to the summation of the total paths, can be computed as shown. From the definition of resistivity,

$$X = \rho L / A \qquad \begin{array}{l} X = \text{resistance} \\ \rho = \text{resistivity} \end{array} \qquad (B1)$$

we obtain the ratio

$$L/A = X/\rho. \qquad (B2)$$

For porous nonmineralized rocks containing highly saline electrolyte, we can assume that all the electrical conduction is via the electrolyte paths, i.e., via the equivalent single path. Therefore, the resistance X of the specimen is determined solely by the resistivity of the pore electrolyte and by the geometry of the pore spaces. Thus, the "conducting pore space geometric ratio" is, following equation (B2),

$$L_e / A_e = X / \rho_e \qquad (B3)$$

where L_e and A_e represent the length and cross-sectional area of the equivalent electrolyte path and ρ_e is the resistivity of the saturating electrolyte.

The quantities on the right hand side of equation (B3) are directly measurable electrically. Consequently, the conducting pore space geometric ratio can be determined readily. This ratio does not permit insight, per se, into both the length and cross-sectional area of the equivalent electrolyte path. However, these values may be obtained with additional information provided by measurement of pore volume.

The porosity is determined as the fractional volume of water in the saturated rock,

$$\phi = V_e / V_r \qquad (B4)$$

where V_e and V_r represent the measured volumes of water[1] and the rock core, respectively. For rocks containing little or no dead end pore volume (e.g., sandstones),

$$V_e = L_e A_e \qquad (B5)$$

then, from equation (B4)

$$L_e A_e = \phi V_r. \qquad (B6)$$

[1] This may be computed by comparing the dry weight of the specimen with its electrolyte-saturated weight.

We can combine equations (B3) and (B6) to give

$$L_e = \sqrt{\frac{\phi X V_r}{\rho_e}} \qquad (B7)$$

$$A_e = \sqrt{\frac{\phi V_r \rho_e}{X}}. \qquad (B8)$$

It is obvious that L_e and A_e will be dependent on the dimensions of the rock core specimens. Hence, it is useful to "normalize" these values by relating them to the actual dimensions of the specimens. By this means, we obtain the following two coefficients:

(1) The tortuosity coefficient (Pirson, 1958)

$$t = L_e / L_r \qquad (B9)$$

is used to describe the excess length of the equivalent electrolyte path relative to the rock length. This excess length is the result of electrolyte path contortion as caused by the solid framework of the rock system.

(2) The diminution coefficient (Fraser and Ward, 1963)

$$d = A_e / A_r \qquad (B10)$$

is used to describe the constriction of the equivalent electrolyte path cross-sectional area relative to the rock area. This constriction is likewise due to the solid framework of the specimen. Both the tortuosity and diminution coefficients reduce the ease with which electricity is conducted ionically through the rock system. This reduction varies directly with the tortuosity coefficient and inversely with the diminution coefficient.

In the petroleum industry, the ratio of rock resistivity ρ_r to saturating electrolyte resistivity ρ_e has proven to be a very useful parameter in electric log interpretations. This parameter is termed the formation factor, defined by Archie (1942) to be:

$$F = \rho_r / \rho_e. \qquad (B11)$$

In the example developed above, we considered a nonconducting rock framework, and so all the conduction is ionic, taking lace through the pore space geometry. In uch a case, ρ_r is directly proportional to ρ_e, o that the ratio ρ_r/ρ_e is independent of the ctual magnitude of ρ_e. Hence, the formation actor F of a rock, computed from equation B11), is a unique property of the specimen, ependent solely on the rock pore space eometry, *if* that specimen is entirely barren f conducting solids. It is related to the toruosity and diminution coefficients as folows:

$$F = t/d. \qquad \text{(B12)}$$

Also, it can be shown (Fraser and Ward, 963) that

$$t = \sqrt{F\phi} \qquad \text{(B13)}$$

$$d = \sqrt{\phi/F}. \qquad \text{(B14)}$$

Normally, t and d are computed directly rom equations (B13) and (B14), rather than y means of the defining equations (B9) and B10). It is again emphasized that all the bove relations depend on the assumption hat the solid rock framework is nonconlucting and, therefore, that the conduction is urely ionic.

From equation (B11) it can be seen that, ince the effect of conducting solids will be to lecrease ρ_r, then F decreases and becomes no onger solely dependent on the electrical pore pace geometry. In such a case, the F calcuated from equation (B11) is referred to as an apparent formation factor," F_a, the magniude of which is dependent on the resistivity f the saturating electrolyte. This concept nay be clarified by an examination of equaion (B15), which describes the apparent ormation factor of a rock containing conducive solids

haps even small amounts of disseminated metallics, can be subdued by introducing saturating electrolytes of very high salinity (e.g., 1.0 N NaCl). This problem is discussed in detail by Patnode and Wyllie (1950), Wyllie (1954) and Wyllie (1955), wherein it is shown that the "true formation factor" F_o of a porous rock is equivalent to the inverse of the slope of the straight line portion of a *rock conductivity* versus *saturating electrolyte conductivity* linear plot (e.g., Figure 7). Hence, the following equation should be used to determine the true formation factor of a rock

$$F_o = \frac{\sigma_{e_1} - \sigma_{e_2}}{\sigma_{r_1} - \sigma_{r_2}} \qquad \text{(B16)}$$

where the conductivities σ_{e_1} and σ_{e_2} pertain to two different pore electrolyte normalities both greater than 0.5 normal. The true formation factor, therefore, is solely dependent on the electrical pore space geometry, and it is this value which should be used in computing the tortuosity and diminution coefficients by means of equations (B13) and (B14).

Before leaving the subject of electrical pore space description, it is worthwhile to examine the concept of the "direction" of the equivalent electrolyte path (Fraser and Ward, 1963). We can define an "angle of divergence" θ which describes the angle at which the direction of the equivalent electrolyte path deviates from the direction of mean current flow (Figure 8).

The angle of divergence is *defined*, from Figure 8, to be

$$\theta = \cos^{-1}(R_e/R_p) \qquad \text{(B17)}$$

where R_e represents the true radius of the

$$F_a = \frac{\rho_r}{\rho_e} \equiv \frac{\sigma_e}{\sigma_r} = \frac{\text{electrolyte conductivity}}{\text{rock conductivity (ionic and conductive solids components)}} \cdot \qquad \text{(B15)}$$

From equation (B15) we see that a greater alinity leads to a greater ionic conductivity omponent and, hence, a decrease in the effect f the conductive solids component on the otal conductivity of the rock. Therefore, the ffect of conducting clay particles, and per-

circular equivalent electrolyte path area and R_p designates the semimajor axis of the elliptical area of the electrolyte path perpendicular to the direction of mean current flow (see Figures 8 and 9).

It turns out that this angle is related to the

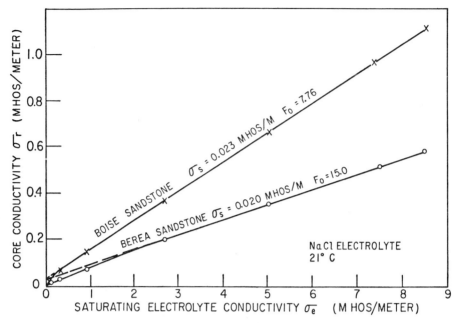

Fig. 7. Core conductivity versus saturating electrolyte conductivity.

tortuosity coefficient t as shown by equation (B18):

$$\theta = \cos^{-1}(1/t). \qquad (B18)$$

The proof of equation (B18) is interesting, as it depends on the equivalence (Wyllie, 1954; Pirson, 1958) of surface porosity and volume porosity.

Surface porosity ϕ_s is defined as the ratio of the cross-sectional area of the pore space voids to the total cross-sectional area of the rock specimen. Hence, in Figure 8 (cf. Figure 9), the surface porosity describes the ratio of the elliptical cross-sectional area[2] $\pi R_e R_p$ of the equivalent electrolyte path to the cross-sectional area of the core πR_r^2, i.e.,

$$\phi_s = \frac{R_p R_e}{R_r^2}. \qquad (B19)$$

The volume porosity ϕ_v describes the ratio

[2] Perpendicular to the core axis.

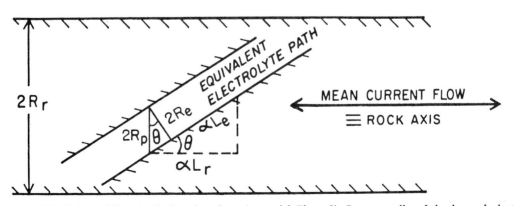

Fig. 8. Idealistic partial longitudinal section of a rock core (cf. Figure 9). R_e = true radius of circular equivalent electrolyte path area; R_p = major axis of elliptical area of electrolyte path perpendicular to mean current flow; R_r = radius of rock core.

of the total volume of the pore paths to that of the rock, i.e.,

$$\phi_v = \frac{\pi R_e^2 L_e}{\pi R_r^2 L_r}. \qquad \text{(B20)}$$

The right hand sides of equations (B19) and (B20) can be equated to obtain the identity

$$R_e/R_p = L_r/L_e. \qquad \text{(B21)}$$

Since, by definition, $\theta = \cos^{-1}(R_e/R_p)$ and $t = L_e/L_r$, it follows that equation (B18) is valid.

Thus, we see that the equating of surface porosity to volume porosity necessitates that the divergence angle θ be an alternative representation of the tortuosity coefficient t. This concept is indicated in Figure 8, where we have made

$$\cos\theta = \frac{2R_e}{2R_p} = \frac{\alpha L_r}{\alpha L_e} \equiv \frac{L_r}{L_e} = 1/t. \qquad \text{(B22)}$$

Figure 8 can also be used to illustrate the relation between porosity and the diminution coefficient. From equation (B10), we see that the latter may be represented as

$$d = \frac{\pi R_e^2}{\pi R_r^2} = \frac{R_e^2}{R_r^2}. \qquad \text{(B23)}$$

Compare this with the surface porosity as given by equation (B19). We see that the porosity ϕ will always be larger than the diminution coefficient d except for the one case where the angle of divergence is zero; in this case R_e and R_p will be identical as will be ϕ and d.

The foregoing has demonstrated that the pore geometry of a porous rock can be described in terms of t, d and θ. Figure 9, for example, represents an actual rock core specimen described by Fraser and Ward (1963). In this figure, the accordian-like pore structure is defined by t, d and θ, and is equivalent electrically to the actual pore structure.

4. Relations between Porosity and Formation Factor

The formation factors of rocks, as defined by equation (B11), are observed to increase as

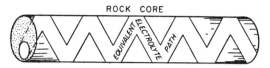

FIG. 9. Graphical representation of electrical pore space geometry of Bandera sandstone; $t = 2.28$, $d = 0.074$, $\theta = 64°$.

the porosities decrease. This is logical since a less porous (saturated) rock contains less conducting electrolyte than a more porous rock. However, the formation factors of a suite of rocks are not related uniquely to their corresponding porosities. In fact, two rocks of identical porosity can have formation factors which vary by 30 percent or more. This is due to the many pore configurations possible for a given pore volume.

In spite of this inherent complication, it has been found that the formation factors of a suite of rocks can be crudely related to their corresponding porosities according to the following equation:

$$F = \phi^{-m}. \qquad \text{(B24)}$$

This is known as Archie's Law and seems to be a reasonable approximation for many rocks. The cementation factor is called "m." The greater the cementation, the larger the value of m between the practical limits $1.3 < m < 2.3$.

Usually we find the following:

> For slightly consolidated sandstones $F = \phi^{-1.4}$
> For consolidated sandstones $F = \phi^{-1.7}$
> For limestones and dolomites $F = \phi^{-2.0}$

A more general relation is the Winsauer equation

$$F = c\phi^{-k}. \qquad \text{(B25)}$$

F and ϕ may be obtained in the laboratory on cores. The Archie and Winsauer equations have found more utility in petroleum engineering than in mineral exploration. However, they do demonstrate the importance of porosity in determining resistivity for any rock.

Since ϕ is pressure dependent, then both F and ρ_r are pressure dependent. Thus, ρ_r can be expected to increase with depth below the

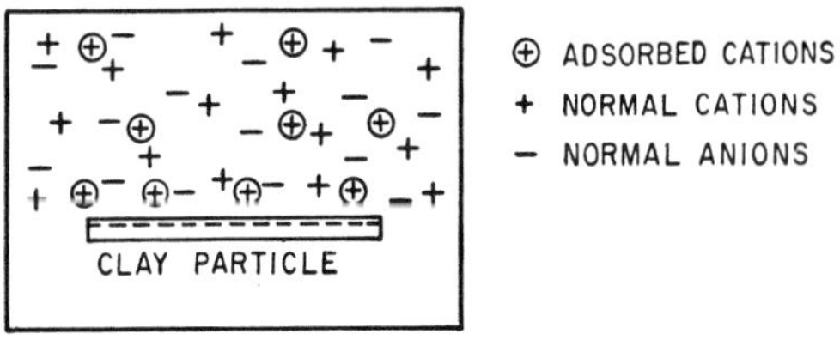

FIG. 10. Diagrammatic representation of ions adsorbed on clay particle.

surface until a horizon is reached where the rock minerals become semiconductive by virtue of a high temperature (in the order of 1,100°C). This would appear to occur at a depth of about 70–80 km (Cantwell, 1960).

5. The Effect of Clay on Rock Resistivity

At this juncture we will consider only the classical petroleum engineering approach to sedimentary rocks containing clay particles (i.e., "dirty sands"). Later the concept will be broadened. A clay or shale particle acts as a separate conducting path additional to the solution path. At the low frequencies of alternating current employed in petroleum well logging, it is customary to consider the impedance of the clay as being purely resistive. This resistance is usually substantially lower than the mineral grain resistance. The origin of this abnormally high clay mineral conductivity lies in the double layer of adsorbed cations as shown in Figure 10. The cations are required to balance the charge due to substitution within the crystal lattice, and to broken bonds (Grim, 1953). The finite size of the cations prevents the formation of a single layer. Rather, a "double layer" is formed; it consists of a "fixed layer" immediately adjacent to the clay surface and a "diffuse layer" which drops off in density exponentially with distance from the fixed layer. The diffuse layer, in contrast to the fixed layer, is free to move under the influence of an applied electric field. The cations of the diffuse layer add to the normal ion concentration and thus increase the density of charge carriers. The net result is an increased "surface conductivity." Although clay minerals exhibit this property to a high degree because of their large ion exchange capacity, all minerals exhibit it to a minor extent. All rocks con-

taining clay minerals possess an abnormally high conductivity on this account.

The effect of disseminated clay or shale on rock resistivities becomes increasingly important as the conductance through the pores diminishes. Increased alteration, such as chloritization, kaolinitization, serpentinization, gives rise to increased surface conductivity. This is particularly evident in sheared serpentinite and other ultrabasic rocks, but is rarely evident in granitoid rocks which, when sheared, suffer mylonitization, i.e., production of minimum surface area per unit volume of mineral grains.

The conductivity of clay minerals is dependent on both solution composition and normality (Berg, 1952; Wyllie, 1955). However, above a certain normality characteristic of the rock specimen, the conductivity of the clay minerals apparently becomes constant; this value represents the maximum conductivity of the clay minerals. If we could measure directly this actual maximum clay mineral conductivity, the value could be designated σ_{s_0}. However, in rocks, we can only measure the apparent maximum value σ_s.

Returning to Figure 7, we see that there is a linear relation between rock conductivity and saturating electrolyte conductivity, for large values of electrolyte salinity, although not for low salinities. This plot implies that the projected straight line intercept on the ordinate represents the observed or apparent maximum conductivity of the conductive solids σ_s since, at this point, the rock is saturated with pure nonconducting water. The equation which fits the straight line portions of the curves of Figure 7 is as follows:

$$\sigma_r = \frac{\sigma_e}{F_o} + \sigma_s \qquad (B26)$$

where σ_r, σ_e and σ_s represent the observed conductivities of the rock, electrolyte, and *conductive solids as distributed in the core*, respectively, and F_o (the inverse of the slope) is termed the true formation factor of the rock.

Equation (B26) states that the actual conductivity of the rock is equal to the theoretical rock conductivity assuming only ionic conduction *plus* the conductivity of the conductive solids. This means that, empirically, the conductive solids are in parallel with the electrolyte paths for clay-containing sandstones.

It is important to realize that the σ_s from Figure 7 does not give a true conductivity σ_{s0} for the conductive solids. This is because a maze of interconnected tortuous paths composed of a complex series-parallel arrangement of electrolytic and solid conducting components *cannot* permit the true conductivity of the conductive solids σ_{s0} to be determined by any method of interpretation of monofrequency electrical data. Rather, this value of σ_s is simply the *excess* conductivity of the rock system with respect to the saturating electrolyte. Empirically, this excess conductivity acts in parallel with the normal rock ionic conductivity and becomes increasingly significant at low electrolyte conductivities.

6. Frequency-Dependence of Conductivity: Induced Polarization

To this point in our discussion it has been tacitly assumed that resistivity—or its inverse, conductivity—is independent of the frequency of the applied electric field. In many sedimentary rocks this is true, but in most igneous and metamorphic rocks and in sedimentary rocks containing clay or metallic minerals it is not true. The causes of this frequency dependence or dispersion include normal dielectric effect, electrokinetic response of air bubbles in the rock pores, electrode polarization, and membrane polarization (Mayper, 1959). The normal dielectric effect is usually not appreciable. The electrokinetic effect may be minimized in the laboratory by vacuum saturation of rock specimens (Keevil, 1961), while in the field it is an unknown but probably unimportant contributor because of the increased solubility of air in water as hydrostatic head is increased with depth. Hence only two phenomena shall be described herein: electrode polarization and membrane polarization (Madden and Marshall, 1958; Madden and Marshall,

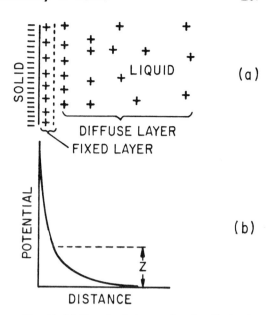

FIG. 11. (a) Hypothetical anomalous ion distribution near a solid-liquid interface; (b) Corresponding potential distribution.

1959a, b, Marshall and Madden, 1959; Keevil, 1961; Keevil and Ward, 1962).

(a) Electrode polarization

Whenever there is a change in the mode of current conduction, e.g. from ionic to metallic, energy is required to cause the current to flow across the interface. This energy barrier can be considered to constitute an electrical impedance. To visualize it, let us digress and consider the ionic double layer which exists at any interface between a solid and a liquid.

The surfaces of most solids possess a very small net attraction for either cations or anions, as we mentioned earlier for clay minerals. Let us now study this in more detail. Immediately adjacent to the outermost solid layer is adsorbed a layer of essentially fixed ions, one or a few molecular layers in thickness (Figure 11(a)). These are not truly exchangeable and, hence, constitute the "fixed layer," although they can often be removed upon application of a strong physical force.

Adjacent to the fixed layer of adsorbed ions there is a group of relatively mobile ions, either of the same or opposite charge, known as the diffuse layer. The *anomalous* number of ions in this zone decreases exponentially from the fixed layer outward to the normal ion concentration of the liquid. (The normal balanced distribution of anions and cations has been deleted from Figure 11(a) for clarity.) The particular distribution of ions shown is only one of several possible distributions, but it is the most common. The electrical potential across the double layer has been plotted also; the potential drop across the diffuse layer is known as the Zeta potential (Z).

While the fixed layer is relatively stable, the diffuse layer thickness is a function of temperature, ion concentration in the "normal" electrolyte, valency of the ions, and the dielectric constant of the medium. Most of the anomalous charge is contained within a plane distance d from the surface, where (Grahame, 1947)

$$d = [K_e kT/8\pi ne^2 v^2]^{1/2} \quad (B27)$$

n = normal ion concentration of the electrolyte
v = valence of the normal ions
e = elementary charge
K_e = the dielectric constant of the medium
k = Boltzman's constant
T = temperature

The thickness is, therefore, governed by the balance between the attraction of unlike charges at the solid surface and the thermal redistribution of ions. Obviously, increasing n, the salinity, or v, the valence, *decreases* the double layer thickness.

Returning now to polarization at electrodes, it may be stated that there are two paths by which current may be carried across an interface between an electrolyte and a metal (Figure 12). These are called the faradaic and nonfaradaic paths. Current passage in the faradaic path is the result of an electrochemical reaction such as the oxidation or reduction of some ion, and involves diffusion of the ions toward or away from the interface. The charge is carried physically across the interface by conversion of atom to ion or vice versa. In the latter (nonfaradaic) case, charged particles do not cross the interface; rather, current is carried by the charging and

discharging of the double layer. (Recall that the diffuse layer is mobile and may be "thinned" out momentarily by the application of an electric field.) The double layer then behaves as a condenser in series with the resistance of the solution. The nonfaradaic component, thus, may be represented by a simple capacitance insofar as the variation of its impedance with frequency is concerned. However, the nonfaradaic path may become frequency-independent at very high frequencies, when the inertia of the ions inhibits their sympathetic oscillation with frequency.

In the faradaic path, the ion diffusion impedance is not representable in so simple a fashion and, in fact, may not be adequately represented by any combination of fixed capacitors and resistors. It is customarily referred to as the Warburg impedance W and its magnitude varies inversely with the square root of the electrical frequency.

The interfacial impedances of many metal-electrolyte interfaces may be described roughly as follows. Above 1,000 cps, the major part of the electric current is carried across the interface by means of the nonfaradaic path; hence, the interfacial impedance varies with frequency as approximately f^{-1}. As the frequency is lowered, more and more current is carried via the faradaic path, and so the low frequency impedance varies with frequency in the range $f^{-1/2}$ to f^0 depending on the magnitude of the impedance ratio W/R.

Note that the impedance of the circuit of Figure 12 is infinite at zero frequency because the Warburg impedance is expressed

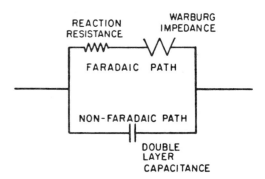

Fig. 12. Circuit analog of interfacial impedance.

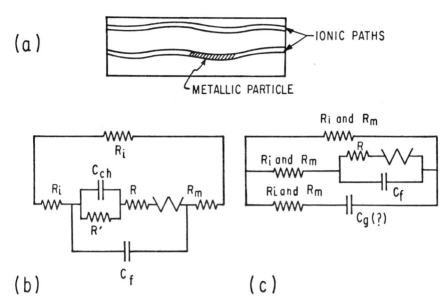

Fig. 13. Simplified representation of mineralized rock (a), and the corresponding equivalent circuit (b); (c) equivalent circuit representative of all mineralized rocks, massive to disseminated.

as $k(1+i)/\sqrt{f}$, where k is a constant, and the capacitive reactance, of course, as $i/2\pi fC$. It is important not to confuse zero frequency with direct current in this circuit, since its resistance to dc is not infinite, but is finite and indeterminate. The ambiguity lies in the derivation (Grahame, 1952) of the Warburg impedance, wherein it is assumed that the reaction products at the interface have no effect on the diffusion impedance and so can be omitted from the derivation. The derivation assumes that it is impossible to carry on such a reaction indefinitely in the same direction because the products of the reaction will accumulate and stop the reaction. Therefore, the interfacial impedance is not defined for direct current by the circuit of Figure 12.

All of the above discussion applies to a pure electrode in a pure electrolyte. The concepts, however, are important in understanding the processes occurring when current is passed through a rock. Any rock sample is "dirty" from the viewpoint of the physical chemist since the electrodes (metallic mineral grains) and electrolytes (pore solutions) are anything but pure. Nevertheless we perhaps are justified in employing equivalent circuits based on pure systems

since a phenomenological explanation for rock behavior results. With this caution, one might suggest the equivalence of the elementary rock system of Figure 13(a) with the equivalent circuit of Figure 13(b), where

W = Warburg impedance
$\quad = k(1+i)/\sqrt{f}$; k is a constant
C_F = double layer capacitance
C_{CH} = chemical capacitance
R = reaction resistance
R' = a resistance representing second and higher order reactions
R_i = resistance of ionic path
R_m = resistance of metallic vein path or particle

In noting these circuit elements, it must be appreciated that one chemical reaction at the interface may lead to a chain of subsequent reactions involving electrons, ions, and molecules of all reaction products present. At each point of the reaction chain, the accumulation of the reaction product represents a capacitance C_{CH} to the electrode. The escape of the product is achieved either by diffusion, represented by a Warburg impedance W, or by a reaction represented by a resistor R. The product of this reaction in turn follows a

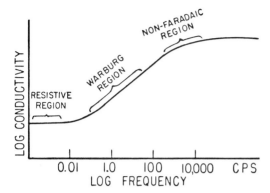

FIG. 14. Idealized conductivity-freqeuncy dependency for mineralized rock.

similar circuit behavior which we have omitted for simplicity (except to lump all such products as R').

If the circuit shown above is valid for a typical rock, then conductivity-frequency spectra should have the form shown in Figure 14. This spectral shape results as follows: At very high frequencies (e.g., $> 10,000$ cps), the capacitive reactance of C_f is very much less than R_m and R_i [i.e., in the lower branch of Figure 13(b)] and, hence, the impedance of the rock is governed largely by the magnitude of the purely resistive components R_m and R_i. Hence, at the very high frequencies, the rock becomes purely resistive, i.e., frequency-independent. On the other hand, at the very low frequencies (e.g., < 0.01 cps), the magnitudes of the capacitive reactances and of the Warburg impedance becomes very large; here, the impedance of the rock is governed by the magnitude of the purely resistive component R_i [in the upper branch of Figure 13(b)]. Again the rock is purely resistive. However, for the intermediate frequencies 1,000 to 0.1 cps, the rock is frequency-dependent. In accordance with our above remarks on pure electrodes, it would appear that most of the current is transferred across the metal-electrolyte interfaces by means of the C_f component (nonfaradaic region) at, say, 100 to 1,000 cps, and, at the lower frequencies, by means of the faradaic path which contains the Warburg impedance.

Rocks containing disseminated mineralization may have another phenomenon super-imposed on the above, i.e., that of an intergranular capacitance which may result from capacitive coupling between the discrete metallic particles. This capacitive coupling may become important above a frequency of 30 to 100 cps.

To conclude this analog discussion, we offer Figure 13(c) as an over-simplified circuit representative of any mineralized rock. Second and higher order reaction components [as shown in Figure 13(b)] are included in the first order components. The added component C_g describes possible (if questionable) intergranular capacitance. The significance of the various components of Figure 13(c) will depend, of course, on the rock in question.

Other models of a rock can be and have been employed to explain the frequency dependence of rock conductivity. However, all models are based upon similar reasoning. Metallic particles contributing to electrode polarization include pyrite, pyrrhotite, chalcopyrite, magnetite, galena, etc.; graphite also yields an appreciable frequency-dependent conductivity.

The idealized conductivity-frequency spectrum of Figure 14 bears considerable similarity to actual spectra, as shown by Figure 15. However, we see that the conductivity

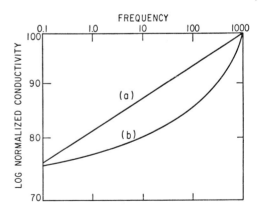

FIG. 15. Conductivity-frequency spectra of rock specimens: (a) 10 percent veined plus disseminated magnetite-chalcopyrite in skarn saturated with 1.0 N NaCl; the porosity is 1.7 percent and the 1,000 cps conductivity is 3.7×10^{-2} mho/meter. (b) 4 percent disseminated sulfides in diorite saturated with 10^{-3} N NaCl; the porosity is 1.0 percent and the 1,000 cps conductivity is 2.4×10^{-4} mho/m.

spectra may appear displaced with respect to the frequency axis of Figure 14.

The effect of salinity on the electrode polarization of mineralized rocks is complex. Referring to the circuits of Figure 13, we can generalize by stating that an increase in salinity will increase the value of C_f (since a salinity increase will suppress the double layer thickness) and will decrease the value of R_i. The consequent effect of this salinity increase on the polarization magnitude depends upon the interplay of at least these two changes. A salinity increase usually decreases the magnitude of the observed polarization in weakly disseminated mineralized rocks [Figure 16(a)], but does not change the polarization in rocks containing veined plus disseminated mineralization [Figure 16(b)]. The spectral types (i.e., concave-up and linear) of Figure 16 are distinctive for the described geometry of the conducting minerals (Fraser, Keevil, and Ward, 1964).

(b) Membrane polarization

In rocks containing a few percent clays distributed throughout the rock matrix, membrane polarization is of importance. Membrane polarization arises chiefly in porous rocks in which clay particles (membranes) partially block ionic solution paths [Figure 17(a)]. The diffuse "cloud" of cations (double layer) in the vicinity of a clay surface is characteristic of clay-electrolyte systems. On application of an electrical potential, positive charge carriers easily pass through the cationic cloud but negative charge carriers accumulate[3] [Figure 17(b)]; an ion-selective membrane, therefore, exists. Consequently, a surplus of both cations and anions occurs at one end of the membrane zone, while a deficiency occurs at the other end. This is because the number of positive charges cannot deviate significantly from the number of negative charges at any one point in space due to the large electric fields which would result if they did so deviate. These ion concentration gradients oppose the flow of current. The overall mobility of anions is

[3] In geologic materials, we do not expect zones of cation-blocking properties to exist (Madden and Marshall, 1959b).

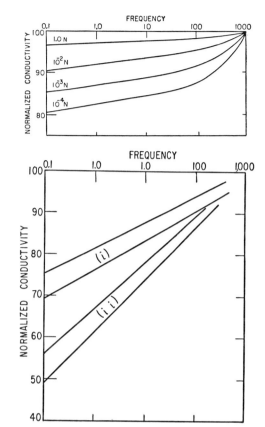

FIG. 16. (above) 4 percent disseminated metallics in diorite, illustrating polarization decrease with salinity increase; (below) 10 percent metallics [specimen (i)] and 25 percent metallics [specimen (ii)] disseminated +veined in skarn rock, illustrating a polarization which is relatively independent of normality in the range 10^{-4} to 1.0 N.

reduced by this process. This reduction in mobility is most effective for potential variations which are slow (e.g., 0.1 cps) with respect to the time of diffusion of anions between adjacent membrane zones. For potential variations which are fast (e.g., 1,000 cps) with respect to the diffusion time, the mobility of anions is not substantially reduced. Hence, the conductivity of a membrane system increases as electrical frequency increases. Note that this model puts a limit on the quantity of polarization that can occur in membrane systems. Since the unrestricted cations can carry only a fixed quantity of current, then the maximum dc impedance of an NaCl-saturated specimen, for example,

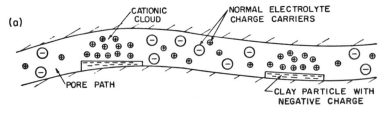

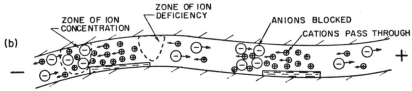

FIG. 17. Membrane polarization caused by negatively charged clay particles along pore paths of a sandstone. (a) Pore path before application of an electrical potential. (b) Pore path after application of a direct current driving force.

can be only approximately $2\frac{1}{2}$ times that of the high frequency impedance.[4] This maximum will occur only if *all* the anions are blocked completely by membranes at dc. In natural membrane systems, however, we can expect some leakage of anions through the cationic clouds, especially where the pore capillary paths are of large diameter.

Membrane polarization due to clays decreases as salinity of the pore electrolyte increases. The cationic clouds of Figure 17(a) are of smaller dimensions as electrolyte salinity increases and, hence, block fewer anions. Examples of membrane polarization in a saturated clay-containing sandstone are shown in Figure 18.

Marshall and Madden (1959) have stated that a large quantity of clay in a rock (e.g., > 30 percent) results in less polarization than if a smaller quantity (say, 10 percent) were present. This is because the clay membrane zones have to be separated by purely resistive zones in order to yield a significant frequency effect. For a given percentage of clays, the quantity of polarization will depend partly on the type of clay present. Since kaolinite particles produce diffuse layers only at their surfaces, these clay particles must occur in very narrow rock pore capillaries in

order that their membrane effect be significant. Otherwise, the membranes will be bypassed by purely resistive paths. For montmorillonite particles, electrolyte exists between the aluminosilicate layers. Conduction through this interior electrolyte, which is cation-selective, thus is less dependent on the geometry of the pores or capillaries within the sandstone. This, in conjunction with the large surface effects also present in montmorillonite, implies that the existence of montmorillonite clay particles in a rock may produce a larger polarization than a like amount of other clay materials.

The clay particles must be fixed in position, otherwise their drift will permit ready

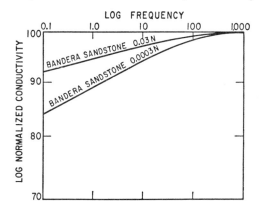

FIG. 18. Conductivity-frequency spectra of a clay-containing sandstone.

---

[4] This figure is calculated from the equivalent conductances of Na^+ (i.e., 50.9) and Cl^- (75.5).

movement of all ions and no polarization will result. Broken bonds on silica and other mineral grains may also produce minor membrane polarization.

An equivalent circuit used to describe membrane polarization is presented in Figure 19. The Warburg impedance represents the frequency-dependent diffusion impedance resulting from the presence of membrane zones. In this analog, R_i describes the resistance of unblocked ionic sections of pore paths. Phenomenologically, the series resistance represents the electrolyte path in series with the cationic clouds of Figure 17, and the bypass resistance represents leakage of charge carriers around these zones. The leakage should be more prevalent as the pore radius increases. The relative importance of the three components in the analog of Figure 19 can be indicated by varying their magnitudes in order to obtain model spectra similar to actual rock and clay spectra. For example, the following components, corresponding to Figure 19, yield spectra matching within one percent the normalized conductivities of the Bandera spectra of Figure 18. For Bandera-0.03 N: series resistance = 1,000 ohms; bypass resistance = 100 ohms; Warburg impedance = 120 $(1+i)$ $(f)^{-1/2}$, where f is the frequency. For Bandera = 0.0003 N: series resistance = 1,000 ohms; bypass resistance = 250 ohms; Warburg impedance = 170 $(1+i)$ $(f)^{-1/2}$.

The quantity of membrane polarization has been correlated with the permeability of clay-containing sandstones (Dakhnov, 1959; Kumar, 1962). The purpose of attempting such a correlation is based on the fact that permeability tends to vary inversely with specific surface (which is the quantity of grain-void interfaces per cm³ of rock) while membrane polarization tends to vary directly with it. The dependence of both permeability and polarization on specific surface is not exact; rather, it must be considered only as a general trend. Hence, we find that laboratory polarization measurements on a wide variety of sandstones may yield only an order-of-magnitude estimate of permeability. However, this is as good as other electrical methods, such as permeability-formation

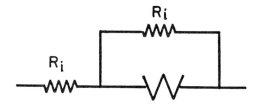

FIG. 19. Equivalent circuit for membrane polarization model. R_i = ionic solution resistance; W = Warburg impedance.

factor correlations (e.g., see Archie, 1942). Induced-polarization measurements have to date not been used in the field as a method of permeability estimation.

7. "Abnormal Dielectric Constant" versus "Variable Conductivity"

Due to electrode and/or membrane polarization, we find that the current through and voltage across a rock sample are not, in general, in-phase. Hence we may write Ohm's Law as

$$\mathbf{J} = [\sigma(\omega) - i\omega\sigma_p(\omega)]\mathbf{E}. \quad (B28)$$

As frequency increases, there is an apparent increase in conductivity defined by

$$\left|\frac{\mathbf{J}}{\mathbf{E}}\right| = [\sigma^2(\omega) + \omega^2\sigma_p^2(\omega)]^{1/2}. \quad (B29)$$

Thus the propagation constant

$$k^2 = (\alpha + i\beta)^2 = \mu\omega(\epsilon\omega + i\sigma) \quad (B30)$$

could be modified to

$$k^2 = (\alpha + i\beta)^2$$
$$= \mu\omega[\epsilon\omega + i(\sigma(\omega) - i\omega\sigma_p(\omega))]. \quad (B31)$$

This is the variable conductivity concept of a rock, with both real and imaginary components of conductivity being frequency-dependent. Alternatively, we could write

$$k^2 = \mu\omega[(\epsilon + \sigma_p(\omega))\omega + i\sigma(\omega)]$$
$$= \mu\omega[\epsilon'\omega + i\sigma(\omega)] \quad (B32)$$

and so consider an abnormally high dielectric constant as contributing to observed polarization. Obviously the two concepts are identical mathematically. However, the abnormal dielectric constant concept does lead to amazingly high values of dielectric constant. For example, following the conventional approach, the highest dielectric constant $K_e = \epsilon/\epsilon_0$ is 81.1 (for water). Yet Evjen (1948) reports K_e of 10^5 for some rocks. The use of the concept of frequency-dependent conductivity or the concept of abnormal dielectric constant seems to be a matter of personal preference. Perhaps the only physical argument against the abnormal dielectric constant lies in the classical acceptance of two basic causes of polarization (Panofsky and Phillips, 1962, p. 39):

    1) the lengthening of the bonds between atoms

    2) the preferred orientation of molecules along the direction of the field as opposed to the random orientations brought about by thermal motions.

Both of these phenomena are microscopic, whereas the polarization at electrodes and membranes occurring in rocks is macroscopic by comparison.

While we have assumed $\sigma = \sigma(\omega) - i\omega\,\sigma_p(\omega)$, the Warburg impedance concept suggests that the conductivity is not proportional to ω as predicted by

$$\left|\frac{J}{E}\right| = \sigma(\omega)\left[1 + \omega^2\left(\frac{\sigma_p(\omega)}{\sigma(\omega)}\right)^2\right]^{1/2} \quad (B33)$$

$$\left|\frac{J}{E}\right| = \sigma(\omega)\left[1 + \frac{1}{2}\,\omega\,\frac{\sigma_p(\omega)}{\sigma(\omega)} + \cdots\right] \quad (B34)$$

i.e. $\Delta\left|\dfrac{J}{E}\right| \propto \omega$

       to a first order approximation.   (B35)

Actually, for a substantial range of frequencies it is found that

$$\Delta\left|\frac{J}{E}\right| \propto \omega^{1/2} \quad (B36)$$

which infers that $\sigma(\omega)$ is a slowly varying function of frequency, and possibly that $\sigma(\omega)$ is dependent on the square root of frequency, over some frequency range. Hence, we have written, following Collett (1959),

$$J = [\sigma(\omega) - i\omega\sigma_p(\omega)]E. \quad (B37)$$

With use of this latter expression, four-electrode voltage and current measurements on a rock sample in the laboratory can yield $\sigma(\omega)$ and $\sigma_p(\omega)$. Again, following Collett (1959), a uniform current $I(\omega)$ is passed through a specimen of length l and cross-sectional area A. Then, since $J = I/A$ and $V_R = E_R l$, where V_R is the voltage across the rock specimen and E is the electric field intensity,

$$\frac{V_R}{I(\omega)} = \frac{l}{[\sigma(\omega) - i\omega\sigma_p(\omega)]A}. \quad (B38)$$

If a parallel R-C circuit, with calibrated variable components, is placed in series with the rock specimen, and the voltage V_s across it is adjusted by varying R and C so that $V_s = V$, then at balance,

$$\frac{l}{[\sigma(\omega) - i\omega\sigma_p(\omega)]A} = \frac{1}{\dfrac{1}{R} - i\omega C}. \quad (B39)$$

The conductivity $\sigma(\omega)$ and the equivalent dielectric constant $\sigma_p(\omega)$ are then given by

$$\sigma(\omega) = \frac{l}{RA} \quad (B40)$$

$$\sigma_p(\omega) = \frac{lC}{A} \quad (B41)$$

and the phase angle by

$$\tan\alpha = \frac{\omega\sigma_p(\omega)}{\sigma(\omega)}. \quad (B42)$$

The latter formula agrees with the inverse of the loss tangent given by Keller and Licastro (1959, p. 261). Note, however, that we should allow for the normal dielectric constant, as well, so that equations (B40–B42) should be rewritten

$$\sigma(\omega) = \frac{l}{RA} \quad (B43)$$

$$\sigma_p(\omega) + \epsilon = \frac{lC}{A} \quad (B44)$$

$$\tan\alpha = \frac{\omega[\sigma_p(\omega) + \epsilon]}{\sigma(\omega)} = \frac{\omega\epsilon'}{\sigma(\omega)}. \quad (B45)$$

There have been no reports in the literature of large phase angles. This implies that both $\epsilon'(\omega)$ and $\sigma_p(\omega)$ vary sympathetically.

8. Attenuation of Plane Waves in a Polarizable Medium

It is interesting to note the effect of polarizable material on the attenuation of electromagnetic waves. The attenuation of a plane wave in a uniformly polarizable medium may be obtained by equating

$$k^2 = (\alpha + i\beta)^2 \quad \text{to} \quad \mu\omega[\epsilon'\omega + i\sigma]$$

and separating into real and imaginary parts to yield

$$\alpha^2 - \beta^2 = \mu\omega^2\epsilon' \tag{B46}$$

$$2\alpha\beta = \mu\omega\sigma \tag{B47}$$

or

$$\beta = \omega\left[\frac{\mu\epsilon'}{2}\left(\sqrt{1 + \frac{\sigma^2}{(\epsilon'\omega^2)}} - 1\right)\right]^{1/2}. \tag{B48}$$

Keller (1959) lists low-frequency values of ϵ/σ ranging from about 3 for some glacial tills, sandstones, and rhyolite tuffs to about 0.0003 for some ultrabasic rocks. For a rhyolite tuff, for example, we might observe a dielectric constant K_e of 7×10^7 and a conductivity of 10^{-3} mho/m, yielding a ratio ϵ/σ of 0.62. For the lower values of ϵ/σ we find that

$$\left(\frac{\sigma}{\epsilon\omega}\right)^2 \gg 1$$

at frequencies in the vicinity of 1 cps and the attenuation constant is then:

$$\beta = \sqrt{\frac{\omega\mu\sigma}{2}}. \tag{B48a}$$

On the other hand, for the higher values of ϵ/σ we find that

$$\left(\frac{\sigma}{\epsilon\omega}\right)^2 \ll 1$$

or frequencies in the vicinity of 1 cps and the attenuation constant is given by

$$\beta = 188.3\sigma\sqrt{\frac{Km}{K_e}} \tag{B48b}$$

The attenuation for low values of dielectric constant and frequencies of the order of 1 cps is then independent of dielectric constant but is a function of frequency, whereas for high values of dielectric constant it is independent of frequency but is inversely proportional to the square root of the dielectric constant. Attenuation clearly is dependent upon the degree of polarization in a rock.

9. Effect of Frequency on Formation Factor

The formation factor of a rock was defined originally by Archie (1942) to be the ratio of the saturated rock resistivity ρ_r to the resistivity of the saturating electrolyte ρ_e, i. e.,

$$F = \rho_r/\rho_e \equiv \sigma_e/\sigma_r \tag{B49}$$

where σ is the conductivity. As mentioned earlier, F should represent only the pore geometry of the specimen. If there is a solids conductivity component in the rock, then obviously the F calculated from equation (B49) will not depend solely on ionic conduction through the pore space geometry. In this case, the F calculated from equation (B49) is referred to as an "apparent formation factor" F_a. The apparent formation factor is not only dependent on the resistivity of the saturating electrolyte but also on the frequency of the applied potential. This concept may be clarified by a further examination of equation (B15). We note that the conductive solids component is frequency dependent while the ionic component is, of course, not frequency dependent. Hence, if F is calculated from equation (B49), and conductive solids are present in the rock, then the apparent formation factor must be frequency dependent.

The formation factors of a suite of rocks can be crudely related to their corresponding porosities according to the equation of Winsauer,

$$F = C\phi^{-k} \tag{B50}$$

where C and k are constants characteristic of the particular suite of rocks studied. When F represents the apparent formation factor F_a (rather than the true formation factor

F_0), then C and k are no longer true constants, and depend on both the salinity of the saturating electrolyte and the frequency of the applied potential. In such a case, we can adapt the Winsauer equation as follows:

$$F_a(n, f) = C(n, f)\phi^{k(n,f)} \qquad (B51)$$

where $C(n, f)$ and $k(n, f)$ are slowly varying functions of both salinity n and frequency f, and F_a is the apparent formation factor. Equation (B51) may be considered applicable for a suite of clay-containing sandstones, for example. On the other hand, equation (B52) may be used to describe the apparent formation factor of a single clay-containing sandstone or, for that matter, a single mineralized rock [refer to equation (B15)].

$$F_a(n, f) = \frac{\sigma_e(n)}{\sigma_r(n, f)} . \qquad (B52)$$

Since neither equation (B51) nor equation (B52) have practical applications, the importance of avoiding the use of an apparent formation factor F_a [as calculated from equation (B49)], is emphasized. In any serious work on porous rock conductivity, the true formation F_0 always should be computed from equation (B16).

10. Computation of "Metal Factors"

Measurements of induced polarization are of particular importance in mineral exploration for disseminated metallics (Hallof, 1961) and in the recognition of "dirty aquifers" in ground water surveys (Vacquier, Holmes, Kintzinger, and Lavergne, 1957). Hence, some means of expressing the frequency-dependent part of the rock resistivity is desirable. This cannot be done completely, but some useful approximations arise. The

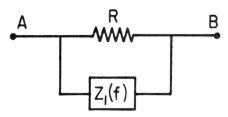

FIG. 20. Simplified equivalent circuit for a mineralized rock.

circuit shown in Figure 13(b) may be simplified to that of Figure 20.

The impedance between the points AB of Figure 20 is

$$Z(f) = \frac{R Z_1(f)}{R + Z_1(f)} \qquad (B53)$$

which for two frequencies a and b becomes $(a < b)$,

$$Z(a) = \frac{R Z_1(a)}{R + Z_1(a)} \qquad (B54)$$

and

$$Z(b) = \frac{R Z_1(b)}{R + Z_1(b)} . \qquad (B55)$$

Upon forming the normalized difference, we obtain

$$\frac{Z(a) - Z(b)}{Z(a) \cdot Z(b)}$$

$$= \frac{\dfrac{R Z_1(a)}{R + Z_1(a)} - \dfrac{R Z_1(b)}{R + Z_1(b)}}{\dfrac{R Z_1(a)}{R + Z_1(a)} \cdot \dfrac{R Z_1(b)}{R + Z_1(b)}}$$

$$= \frac{R Z_1(a)[R + Z_1(b)] - R Z_1(b)[R + Z_1(a)]}{R Z_1(a) R Z_1(b)}$$

$$\approx \frac{Z_1(a) - Z_1(b)}{Z_1(a) Z_1(b)}$$

$$= \mu$$

"Metal Factor" MF is taken to be

$$\text{MF} = 2\pi \times 10^5 \mu. \qquad (B56)$$

Thus, the parallel ionic paths are eliminated by this expression but the series ionic paths remain. While μ emphasizes the frequency dependence, it is very markedly dependent upon the salinity, valence, and temperature of the solution filling the series pores. That is, the reactive portions $Z_1(a)$ and $Z_1(b)$ are functions of salinity, temperature, and valence, as well as of frequency. For metallic particles in a rock μ may increase, remain constant, or decrease with salinity and valence, while for a rock with clay particles it decreases with salinity and valence, because the electrode and membrane effects are altered in this manner. Further, the purely resistive portions of $Z_1(a)$ and $Z_1(b)$ also depend upon salinity, valence, and temperature. To compensate for this, the "percent frequency effect" is often calculated ($\rho =$ "resistivity")

$$PFE = \left[\frac{Z_1(a) - Z_1(b)}{Z_1(b)}\right] 100$$

$$\approx \left[\frac{\rho(a) - \rho(b)}{\rho(b)}\right] 100 \quad (B57)$$

and it is sometimes much less sensitive to the nature of the solution.[5] To reduce this latter expression to a common decade base between frequencies a and b, we take the normalized PFE

$$NPFE = \left[\frac{Z_1(a) - Z(b)}{\log b/a \cdot Z_1(b)}\right] 100$$

$$\approx \left[\frac{\rho(a) - \rho(b)}{\log b/a \cdot \rho(b)}\right] 100. \quad (B58)$$

While any of these expressions is capable of indicating qualitatively the percent metallic or percent clay minerals present, none is quantitatively related to these percentages. "Salinity" as used here should be interpreted broadly to mean ion concentration and, hence, acidic solutions are included in the considerations above.

11. Frequency Domain versus Time Domain

In all of the above discussion of polarization, the phenomena have been described in the frequency domain, and perhaps this has led to the subtle inference that measurements of such are made solely in the frequency domain. This inference is not intended since, in practice, measurements are made in both domains.

In the frequency domain we have mea-

[5] An original definition of this was

$$PFE = \left[\frac{\rho(a) - \rho(b)}{\rho(a)}\right] 100,$$

(Editor).

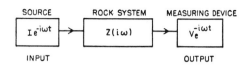

FIG. 21. Input-output relation in frequency domain.

sured an output of a system due to a known input, the system being the rock medium as illustrated in Figure 21.

The relation between measured output voltage and input current for a sinusoidal source is

$$Ve^{-i\omega t} = ZIe^{-i\omega t} \quad (B59)$$

or

$$V(i\omega) = Z(i\omega)I(i\omega) \quad (B60)$$

where $Z(i\omega)$ is the transfer impedance of the system.

In the time domain, we apply a square wave of current and measure a quasi-exponential decay of voltage subsequent to cessation of the applied current.

Usually the output voltage is integrated over an interval and divided by the voltage applied to the current electrodes so, corresponding to the frequency domain expressions "metal factor" or "percent frequency effect," we have "chargeability" measured in millivolt-seconds per volt.

Actually, the voltage decay is more apt to be the sum of a series of exponentials

$$V = \sum_{n=1}^{\infty} A_n e^{-\alpha n t}. \quad (B61)$$

The relation between input (square current pulse) and output (exponential decay) may be shown diagrammatically as in Figure 22.

$$I(t) = 1 \quad 0 < t < a$$
$$= 0 \quad t > a, \, t < 0$$

$$V(t) = \sum_{n=1}^{\infty} A_n e^{-\alpha n t}. \quad (B62)$$

The amplitude of the pulse and the duration of the pulse are selected so that most of the decay is over before a second, reversed, pulse is transmitted. We may then write

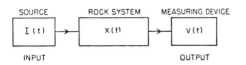

FIG. 22. Input-output relation in time domain.

$$V(t) = X(t)I(t) \qquad (B63)$$

corresponding to equation (B60).

The voltage decay subsequent to cessation of current has the inverse form of the voltage buildup at application of current, as shown in Figure 23. Thus, we can compute the form of $e(t)$ of Figure 23 by studying the response of the system to the step function $u(t)$ defined by

$$u(t) = 1 \qquad t > 0$$
$$= 0 \qquad t < 0. \qquad (B64)$$

The input-output relation may then be written

$$V(t) = A(t)I(t) \qquad (B65)$$

where $A(t)$ now describes the rock system in terms of its response to a unit step function of current, i.e., a description in the time domain. The Laplace transform relates $V(t)$ to $V(i\omega)$ and $I(t)$ to $I(i\omega)$ through

$$V(i\omega) = \mathcal{L}[V(t)] \qquad (B66)$$

$$I(i\omega) = \mathcal{L}[I(t)] \qquad (B67)$$

so that equation (B60) may be written

$$\mathcal{L}[V(t)] = \mathcal{L}[I(t)]Z(i\omega). \qquad (B68)$$

Since the Laplace transform of a unit step function, i.e. $\mathcal{L}[I(t)]_{\text{STEP}}$ is $1/i\omega$ we may write

$$\mathcal{L}[V(t)]_{\text{STEP}} = \frac{Z(i\omega)}{i\omega}. \qquad (B69)$$

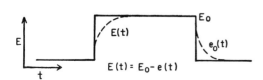

FIG. 23. Buildup and decay of voltage in polarizable medium due to square wave of current.

This, then, describes in the frequency domain the response of the system to a step function of current and, hence, must be related to $A(t)$ through the Laplace transform

$$\frac{Z(i\omega)}{i\omega} = \int_0^\infty A(t)e^{-i\omega t}dt \qquad (B70)$$

or its inverse

$$A(t) = \frac{1}{2\pi i}\int_{-i\infty}^{i\infty} \frac{Z(i\omega)}{i\omega} e^{i\omega t}d(i\omega). \qquad (B71)$$

The latter formula is obtained by taking the inverse transform of equation (B70), i.e.

$$\mathcal{L}^{-1}\mathcal{L}[V(t)]_{\text{STEP}}$$
$$= [V(t)]_{\text{STEP}} = A(t) = \mathcal{L}^{-1}\frac{Z(i\omega)}{i\omega}$$
$$= \frac{1}{2\pi i}\int_{-i\infty}^{i\infty} \frac{Z(i\omega)}{i\omega} e^{i\omega t}dt. \qquad (B72)$$

The equivalence of time and frequency measurements is, thus, demonstrated; either approach can yield information describing the rock system. Wait (1959) shows the transient response computed from frequency

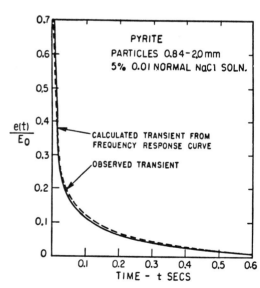

FIG. 24. Transient response computed from frequency domain data, for a synthetic mineralized rock sample, compared with the observed transient response (after Wait, 1959).

domain data, for a synthetic mineralized rock sample, compared with the observed transient response (Figure 24).

12. Semiconduction

Rocks near the surface of the crust conduct electricity by virtue of the phenomena described in the preceding sections; ionic conduction is predominant. An expected decrease in ionic conductivity with depth due to decrease of porosity and pore water salinity is counterbalanced to some extent by an increase in mobility of ions brought about by increased temperature. However, the increased temperature probably is first significantly important when it leads to semiconduction in the solids of the rock. At, or perhaps considerably before, this temperature, ionic conduction through pores becomes negligible. While semiconduction processes probably are unimportant in that portion of the crust of direct interest to the economic geophysicist, they are extremely important in studying tectonic processes in the deep crust and upper mantle.

According to Kittel (1953), "at absolute zero a pure and perfect crystal of most semiconductors would behave as an insulator; the characteristic semiconducting properties are usually brought about by thermal agitation, impurities, or lattice defects." Semiconduction can be intrinsic or extrinsic.

The electronic bands leading to intrinsic semiconduction are illustrated in Figure 25. At 0°K the conductivity is very nearly zero although, with enough field, some electrons still can be excited across the gap. Then practically all states in the valence band are filled and all states in the postulated conduction band are vacant. As temperature is increased, the conductivity increases because electrons are thermally excited part or all of the way up to the conduction band. In this state, small fields easily excite electrons across the gap. As mentioned in Section I, both *holes* in the valence band and *electrons* in the conduction band will contribute to the electrical conductivity.

The intrinsic conductivity at temperature T is computed from the relation

$$\sigma = |e| (n_e\mu_e + n_h\mu_h) \qquad (B73)$$

where n_e, n_h are the electron and hole equilibrium concentrations, and μ_e, and μ_h are the mobilities of electrons and holes respectively; e is the elemental charge.

Kinetic theory leads us to expect a temperature dependence of the form $e^{-E/kT}$ for the concentration of electrons in the conduction band. Assuming a relatively small variation of mobility with temperature, we are then led (Kittel 1953) to predict a conductivity dependence of the form

$$\sigma = \sigma_0 e^{-Eg/2kT} \qquad (B74)$$

in which Eg is the gap energy, σ_0 includes the mobility function and, in this form, is the conductivity at 0°K. Boltzmann's constant is k. Thermal, electrical, or optical excitation of electrons across the band of forbidden energy renders the solid conducting.

Impurities and imperfections in the material produce *extrinsic* conductivity. Above some temperature, impurities may be unimportant so that we define the temperature range above extrinsic conductivity as the intrinsic range in which the previous mechanism is operative.

However, below the intrinsic range, certain types of impurities and imperfections markedly alter the electrical properties of a semiconductor. Extrinsic semiconduction arises by thermal excitation of electrons, occupying intermediate energy levels in the forbidden gap produced by impurities in solid solution, into the unoccupied conduction band, or by the excitation of electrons from the occupied valence band into unoccupied impurity levels. In the first case the current is carried by electrons; in the second case by holes. If the excitation energy between the levels through which the electrons are excited is E, the electrical conductivity is given by

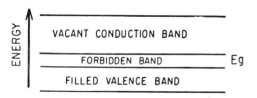

FIG. 25. Intrinsic semiconduction band scheme.

$$\sigma = \sigma_0 e^{-E/2kT} \qquad (B75)$$

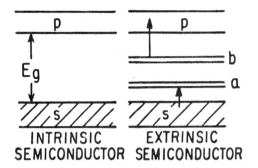

FIG. 26. Comparison of energy gaps for intrinsic and extrinsic semiconduction.

where σ_0 is proportional to the number of electrons per cc associated with the impurity levels.

The difference between extrinsic and intrinsic semiconduction can be seen from the energy diagrams of Figure 26. Conductivity in the impure semiconductor may be due to an electron which has jumped from an impurity level b to the conduction band p. This impure band is then called a donor. In other cases, the conductivity may be due to the movement of an electron from the full s band to the impurity level a; the impurity is then an acceptor. Conduction is due to the motion of the positive hole in the s band; we then speak of a p-type (positive-type) semiconductor; n-type semiconductors are those in which an electron is the current carrier.

The conductivity of all semiconductors is extremely sensitive to pressure, since pressure decreases Eg. A pressure of 20,000 atm increases the conductivity of a semiconductor by about two orders of magnitude while only increasing the conductivity of a metal by a factor of about two. The donor and acceptor levels may be due to crystal imperfections as well as to impurities.

At high temperatures, electrons cross the energy gap of Figure 26 much more readily than at low temperatures. This conduction mechanism will predominate at high temperatures, even when impurities are present, because the impurity levels contain far fewer electrons than do the valence bands. Consequently, at great depth in the earth there is a greater probability for the valence

band-conduction band transition than the transitions involving the impurity levels.

Ionic conduction in a solid occurs as a result of mobile ions moving through the crystal lattice as a result of defects in it. The simplest imperfection is a missing atom or lattice vacancy (Schottky defect). The diffusion of the vacancy through the lattice constitutes transport of charge.

In the Schottky process, two energies are of importance: i.e., half that required to produce a pair of oppositely charged lattice defects, and the height of the potential barrier separating adjacent sites occupied by the mobile ions. The excitation energy E of the process is the sum of these two energies. The conductivity is given by the equation

$$\sigma = \sigma_0{}^{-E/kT} \tag{B76}$$

in which σ_0 is proportional to the number of ion pairs per cc. A Frenkel defect may also be important in ionic conductivity; its diffusion follows the same law. Frenkel and Schottky defects are illustrated in Figure 27.

Hughes (1955) has estimated E and σ_0, for olivene, for each of the three conduction types, and hence was able to indicate the temperature range of importance of each *at ordinary pressures.* Hughes' data is given in Table 2.

The conduction mechanism above 1,100°C. is recognized as ionic because, when an iron electrode is used in contact with the magnesium orthosilicate, iron diffuses into the silicate replacing the magnesium.

The application of the above knowledge to

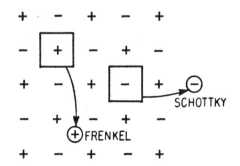

FIG. 27. Schottky and Frenkel defects; ion in box is missing in Schottky defect, ion in box is displaced in Frenkel defect (after Kittel, 1953).

Table 2

Type of Semicon- duction	σ_0	E	Range of Importance
Extrinsic	10^{-4} mho/cm	1 ev	600°C.
Intrinsic	10^{-1} mho/cm	3.3 ev	600 to 1,100°C.
Ionic	10^5 mho/cm	3.0 ev	1,100°C.

the explanation of the distribution of electrical conductivity in the mantle is clear only in a general way. The conductivity for mantle rock can be computed from laboratory values of σ_0 and E, *assuming* the temperature distribution is known. The limits of the temperature distribution are estimated in one of two ways: (a) by assuming that the material is everywhere at its melting point except in the outer 700 kms for a maximum, and (b) by assuming that the temperature gradient is adiabatic for a minimum. The gross assumptions involved leave our knowledge of the mantle temperature and conductivity on rather precarious grounds, although there is general agreement in the literature (Runcorn 1956, Lubimova 1958, Jacobs 1956, Verhoogen 1956, Uffen 1952, Lahiri and Price 1939, Tozer 1959, Noritomi 1961). The best estimates of electrical conductivity of the Mantle are derived from studies of geomagnetic fluctuations and the magnetotelluric method (Eckhardt, Larner, and Madden 1963; Srivastava, Douglass, and Ward 1963).

13. Conduction in the Earth's Core

We can reasonably expect the high-temperature conductivity of a metal to be a function of Θ_D and temperature T. Kittel (1953) gives the conductivity of a metal in the form

$$\sigma = \frac{e^2 M k \Theta_D{}^2}{2p^3 \overline{Q}_s T} \quad \text{for } T \gg \Theta_D \quad \text{(B77)}$$

where

e = charge on electron
M = mass of the lattice oscillators
k = Boltzmann constant
Θ = Debye temperature of lattice $\equiv \hbar\omega/k$
$p = \hbar k$ = electronic momentum

$\overline{Q}_s$ = mean scattering cross section for an isolated ion
$\hbar = h/2\pi$ where h = Planck's constant
ω = frequency of lattice oscillators

In deriving this formula, the wave function for the electron was taken in a form which neglected modulation by the lattice. Increased pressure will, therefore, modify the wave function so, presumably, we may write, as did Elsasser (1950)

$$\sigma = \frac{C\Theta_D{}^2}{T} \quad \text{(B78)}$$

where C lumps the constants and also assumes a dependency on pressure to account for modulation of the electronic wave function. The Debye temperature is found experimentally, and theoretically, to be proportional to the velocity of sound.

Runcorn (1956) modified Elsasser's estimate on the above formula to yield a value of $\sigma \approx 3 \times 10^4$ mhos/cm for the core of earth.

The choice of the high temperature metal theory for prediction of the electrical conductivity of the core is based on the assumption that the core consists of iron or an iron-nickel mixture.

14. Acknowledgments

The material for this article is based on research conducted over a period of years, and sponsored by the following companies and agencies:

Texas Gulf Sulphur Company
American Chemical Society, Petroleum Research Fund
Office of Naval Research
American Petroleum Institute
Craigmont Mines Limited

Appreciation is expressed to D. W. Strangway for his careful critique of this paper.

References Cited

Archie, G. E., 1942, The electrical resistivity log as an aid in determining some reservoir characteristics: A.I.M.E., Trans., v. 146, p. 54–61.
Berg, J. W., Jr., 1952, Conductivity study of aqueous kaolin NaCl mixtures: Producers Monthly, v. 16, no. 3, p. 36–41.

Cantwell, T., 1960, Detection and analysis of low frequency magnetotelluric signals: Ph.D. Thesis, Mass. Inst. of Tech.

Collett, L. S., 1959, Laboratory investigations of overvoltage, *in* Overvoltage research and geophysical applications, J. R. Wait, editor: Pergamon Press.

Dakhnov, V. N., 1959, Geophysical well logging; translated from the Russian by G. V. Keller: Colorado School of Mines, Quarterly, v. 57, no. 2, 1962, p. 374.

Eckhardt, D., Larner, K., and Madden, T., 1963, Long period magnetic fluctuations and mantle electrical conductivity estimates: J. Geophys. Res. v. 68, p. 6279.

Elsasser, W. M., 1950, The earth's interior and geomagnetism: Rev. Mod. Phys., v. 22, p. 1.

Evjen, H. M., 1948, Theory and practice of low-frequency electromagnetic exploration: Geophysics, v. 13, no. 4, p. 584.

Fraser, D. C., Keevil, N. B., Jr., and Ward, S. H., 1964, Conductivity spectra of rocks from the Craigmont ore environment: Geophysics, v. 29, no. 5, p. 832–847.

Fraser, D. C., and Ward, S. H., 1963, Electrical pore space geometry of porous media: Univ. of Calif., Inst. of Eng. Res., Rpt. No. MT-63-1, 48 p.

Grahame, D. C., 1947, The electrical double layer and the theory of electrocapillarity: Chem. Rev., v. 41, p. 441–501.

——— 1952, Mathematical theory of the faradaic admittance: Jour. Electrochem. Soc., v. 99, p. 370c–385c.

Crim, R. E., 1953, Clay mineralogy: New York, McGraw-Hill Book Co., Inc.

Hallof, P. G., 1961, Variable frequency induced polarization data compared with drilling results at four properties: Northern Miner, Nov. 30.

Hughes, H., 1955, The pressure effect on the electrical conductivity of peridot: Jour. Geophys. Res., v. 60, p. 187.

Jacobs, J. A., 1956, The earth's interior: Handbuch der Physik, Geophysik I, Springer Verlag, p. 364–400.

Keevil, N. B., Jr., 1961, A laboratory investigation of induced polarization: M.S. Thesis, University of California, Berkeley.

Keevil, N. B., Jr., and Ward, S. H., 1962, Electrolyte activity: its effect on induced polarization: Geophysics, v. 27, no. 5, p. 677–690.

Keller, G. V., 1959, Analysis of some electrical transient measurements on igneous, sedimentary, and metamorphic rocks; Overvoltage research and geophysical applications: New York, Pergamon Press.

Keller, G. V., and Licastro, P. H., 1959, Dielectric constant and electrical resistivity of natural-state cores: U. S. Geol. Surv. Bull. 1052-H.

Kittel, C., 1953, Introduction to solid state physics: New York, John Wiley and Sons, Inc.

Kumar, A., 1962, Induced polarization in sedimentary rocks: M.S. Thesis in Engineering, Univ. of Calif., Berkeley.

Lahiri, B. N., and Price, A. T., 1939, Electromagnetic induction in nonuniform conductors and the determination of the conductivity of the earth from terrestrial magnetic variations: Phil. Trans., Roy. Soc. Lond., Ser. A, v. 237, p. 509.

Lubimova, H. A., 1958, Thermal history of the earth with consideration of the variable thermal conductivity of its mantle: Geophys. Jour., v. 1, p. 115–134.

Madden, T. R., and Marshall, D., 1958, A laboratory investigation of induced polarization: M.I.T. report to A.E.C., RME 3156.

——— 1959a, Electrode and membrane polarization: M.I.T. report to A.E.C., RME 3157.

——— 1959b, Induced polarization, a study of its causes and magnitudes in geologic materials: Final M.I.T. report to A.E.C.

Marshall, D. J., and Madden, T. R., 1959, Induced polarization, a study of its causes: Geophysics, v. 24, no. 4, p. 790–816.

Mayper, V., 1959, The normal effect, *in* Overvoltage research and geophysical applications, J. R. Wait, editor: Pergamon Press, p. 125–158.

Noritomi, K., 1961, Electrical conductivity of rock and the determination of the electrical conductivity of the earth's interior: J. Min. College, Akita Univ. 1, p. 27–59.

Panofsky, W. K. H., and Phillips, Melba, 1962, Classical electricity and magnetism, 2nd Edition: Addison-Wesley Publishing Co., Inc.

Patnode, H. W., and Wyllie, M. R., 1950, The presence of conductive solids in reservoir rocks as a factor in electric log interpretation: A.I.M.E., Trans., v. 189, p. 47–52.

Pirson, S. J., 1958, Oil reservoir engineering: New York, McGraw-Hill Book Company, Inc.

Runcorn, S. K., 1956, The magnetism of the earth's body: Handbuch der Physik, Geophysik I, Springer Verlag, p. 498–532.

Srivastava, S. P., Douglass, J. L., and Ward, S. H., 1963, The application of the magnetotelluric and telluric methods in central Alberta: Geophysics, v. 28, no. 3, p. 426–446.

Tozer, D. C., 1959, Electrical properties of the earth's interior, *in* Physics and chem. of the earth, v. 3: McGraw-Hill Book Company, Inc., p. 414–436,

Uffen, R. J., 1952, A method of estimating the melting point gradient in the earth's mantle: Trans., Amer. Geophys. Union, v. 33, p. 893.

Vacquier, V., Holmes, C. R., Kintzinger, P. R., and Lavergne, M., 1957, Prospecting for groundwater by induced electrical polarization: Geophysics, v. 22, p. 660–687.

Van Vlack, L. H., 1959, Elements of materials science: Reading, Addison-Wesley Publishing Company.

Verhoogen, J., 1956, Temperatures within the earth, in Physics and chem. of the earth, v. 1: New York, McGraw-Hill Book Company, p. 17–43.

Wait, J. R., 1959, The variable-frequency method, in Overvoltage research and geophysical applications, J. R. Wait, editor: New York, Pergamon Press.

Wyllie, M. R., 1955, Role of clay in well-log interpretation, in Clays and clay technology: State of Calif., Dept. of Nat. Res., Bull. 169, p. 282–305.

—— 1954, The fundamentals of electric log interpretation: New York, Academic Press.

References for General Reading

Ananyan, A. A., 1958, Dependence of electrical conductivity on moisture content: Izvestiya, Geophysics Series, no. 4, p. 878–881.

Bleil, D. F., 1953, Induced polarization: a method of geophysical prospecting: Geophysics, v. 18, no. 3, p. 636–661.

Coster, H. P., 1946, The electrical conductivity of rocks at high temperatures: Monthly Notices of Roy. Astron. Soc. Geoph. Supp., 5, p. 193.

Henkel, J. H., 1958, Some theoretical considerations of induced polarization: Geophysics, v. 23, no. 2, p. 299–304.

Henkel, J. H., and Collins, T. C., 1961, Induced polarization in electrolyte saturated earth plugs: Geophysics, v. 22, p. 205–210.

Henkel, J. H., and Van Nostrand, R. G., 1957, Experiments in induced polarization: A.I.M.E., Trans., v. 9, p. 355–359.

Keller, G. V., 1960, Pulse-transient behavior of brine-saturated sandstones: U. S. Geol. Surv., Bull. 1083-D, p. 111–129.

Mandel, P., Jr., Berg, J. W., Jr., and Cook, K. L., 1957, Resistivity studies of metalliferous synthetic cores: Geophysics, v. 22, no. 2, p. 398–411.

McEuen, R. B., Berg, J. W., Jr., and Cook, K. L., 1959, Electrical properties of synthetic metalliferous ore: Geophysics, v. 29, no. 3, p. 510–530.

Nosske, G., 1959, Eine neue leichte Feldansruestung fuer die induzierte Polarisation mit Gleichstromimpulsen: Zeitschrift fuer angewandte Geologie, Heft 11, p. 528–533.

Parkhomenko, E. I., and Bondarenko, A. T., 1960, Effect of unilateral pressure upon electrical resistance of rock: Izvestiya, Geophysics Series, no. 2, p. 214–219.

Perkins, F. M., Jr., Osoba, J. S., and Ribe, K. H., 1956, Resistivity of sandstones as related to the geometry of their interstitial water: Geophysics, v. 21, no. 4, p. 1071–1084.

Piskunov, L. I., 1958, On a quantitative relation between the dielectric constant and the electrical resistivity of rocks: Izvestiya Geophysics Series, no. 9, p. 658–659.

Rokitansky, I. I., 1959, The nature of induced polarization of ion-conducting soils: Izvestiya, Geophysics Series, no. 7, p. 752–756.

Runcorn, S. K., 1955, The electrical conductivity of the earth's mantle: A.G.U., Trans., v. 36, p. 191.

Schufle, J. A., 1959, Cation exchange and induced electrical polarization: Geophysics, v. 24, p. 164–166.

Sumi, F., 1961, The induced polarization method in ore investigation: Geoph. Prosp., v. 19, no. 3, p. 459–477.

Volarovich, M. P., and Bondarenko, A. T., 1960, A study of electrical resistance in samples of rocks at all-round pressure up to 100 kg/cm²: Izvestiya, Geophysics Series, no. 7, p. 631–635.

Winsauer, W. O., Shearin, H. M., Jr., Masson, P. H. and Williams, M., 1952, Resistivity of brine-saturated sands in relation to pore geometry: A.A.P.G., Bull., v. 36, no. 2, p. 253–277.

Winsauer, W. O., and McCardell, W. M., 1953, Ionic double-layer conductivity in reservoir rock: A.I.M.E., Trans., v. 198, p. 129–134.

Zharkov, V. N., On the electrical conductivity and temperature of the earth's mantle: Izvestiya, Geophysics Series, no. 4, p. 260–266.

Zwikker, C., 1954, Physical properties of solid materials: Interscience Publ., 300 p.

Chapter II

PART C—THE ELECTROMAGNETIC METHOD

STANLEY H. WARD*

Table of Contents

* Professor of Geophysical Engineering, Department of Mineral Technology, University of California, Berkeley.

225

PART C. THE ELECTROMAGNETIC METHOD

I. Introduction

The conventional, or artificial field, electromagnetic method of geophysical prospecting is based on the measurement of alternating magnetic fields associated with currents artificially maintained in the subsurface. If the subsurface currents are induced by a primary alternating field, the name inductive electromagnetic method is applied. In contrast, if the subsurface currents are applied through grounded electrodes, the name given is the conductive electromagnetic method.

Inductive techniques are more common and typically involve a magnetic dipole source, or transmitter, consisting of a number of turns of wire through which an alternating current is caused to flow.

With the conductive techniques, a long wire is laid out on the surface of the earth and grounded at each end. A generator in series with the long wire provides current which flows through the subsurface via the electrodes. Also, some currents are induced in the subsurface by the alternating current flowing in the long wire.

Numerous techniques have arisen in application of the electromagnetic method, many of which will be described subsequently. Natural electromagnetic fields serve as sources of signal for solid earth studies on the one hand, or serve as sources of noise for artificial field methods on the other hand. Of the four natural field methods—telluric, magnetotelluric, magnetic variation, and Afmag—only Afmag will be described in detail. Each of these four methods depends upon the electromagnetic induction of currents in the subsurface by *natural* alternating magnetic fields.

The main function of the artificial field electromagnetic methods is the detection of bodies of exceptionally high electrical conductivity. Most frequently, the target sought is a massive sulfide ore body (ref. Chapter 3, Volume I) although the method has been employed in delineation of some iron oxides (Ward et al., 1955, Ward, 1961, Frischknecht, 1961), in delineating faults and shears, in detecting narrow vein deposits, in tracing highly conductive zones within "porphyry copper" and other disseminated deposits, in detecting and delineating graphite occurrences, and commonly for tracing underground pipes and conduits beneath city streets. Experience has shown that source frequencies in the range 50 cps to 5,000 cps provide the best distinction between anomalies due to targets sought and anomalies due to extraneous features. The choice of operating frequency or frequencies is governed by local geology and the particular technique employed.

The *telluric method* is used most commonly to indicate the depth to the first resistive horizon in a sedimentary structure (Yungul, 1961), but occasionally has been applied to mining problems (Porstendorfer, 1959, 1960). The choice of frequency for the telluric method is governed by two factors: signal frequencies of significant amplitude available in the natural fields, and depth of penetration. For penetration to a depth of 20,000 ft in a typical sedimentary section, periods in the range 1 to 100 sec are desirable. However, the natural fields usually have spectral peaks in the 15–30 sec, 50–60 sec and 90–100 sec period ranges, so these ranges, particularly the former, are most commonly used.

The *magnetotelluric method* is capable of indicating major crust and mantle discontinuities such as the sediment-basement contact and the highly conductive horizons in the mantle (Srivastava, Douglass, Ward 1963; Fournier 1963). Depth of penetration to 1,000 km is desirable for mantle studies and this requires use of fields with periods as great as 100,000 sec.

The *magnetic variation method* has been used solely for deep crust and upper mantle conductivity studies by Schmucker (1959), who has used magnetic bay disturbances with periods of one half hour to several hours. Recently Warren (1963) has studied shallow crust conductivity inhomogeneities with natural magnetic disturbances of 15–40 sec. Ward and Ruddock (1962) and Goldstein and Ward (1963) have reported on the application of geomagnetic variations to the in-situ separation of remanent from induced magnetization of magnetite deposits.

The *Afmag* (*A*udio *f*requency *m*agnetic) *method* was originally intended for detection of massive sulfides at depths greater than could be reached by the conventional electromagnetic method. While it has had some success in this regard (Paterson, Volume I, p. 194), it is also successful in tracing gouge-filled faults and shears, so that ultimately it may have more value as a structural mapping tool rather than as a direct ore finding tool. The choice of an Afmag operating frequency is governed largely by the spectrum of the natural fields. A spectral peak typically occurs somewhere in the 100 to 600 cps range so that operating frequencies are usually chosen to lie within it.

In the artificial field electromagnetic method, techniques have been developed permitting measurements to be made discontinuously and continuously on the ground (ground EM and mobile ground EM), continuously in the air (airborne or helicopter-borne EM), and continuously or discontinuously in drill holes (drill-hole EM).

Of the natural field electromagnetic methods, only Afmag has been made mobile in any sense. Airborne Afmag surveys have been carried out routinely (Ward 1959, 1960).

II. Parameters Controlling Response of Geologic Bodies

We have seen in Part A how the propagation of electromagnetic waves through a medium depends upon the electrical conductivity σ, the dielectric permittivity ϵ, the

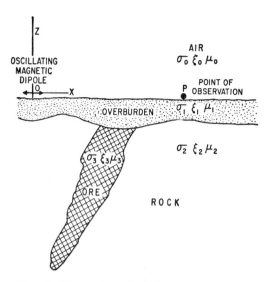

FIG. 1. The configuration of subsurface electrical parameters for the typical electromagnetic exploration problems.

magnetic permeability μ, and the frequency ω, through the propagation constant $k = \sqrt{\mu\epsilon\omega^2 + i\mu\sigma\omega}$. Further, we have seen that the response of simple models such as spheres, cylinders, and slabs is controlled by the dimensionless parameter $\theta = (\sigma\mu\omega)^{1/2}\alpha$, where α may represent one or more linear dimensions. The relative importance of the three physical properties σ, ϵ, μ requires consideration.

With reference to Figure 1, the electromagnetic exploration problem may be stated as follows: it is required to determine the nature of the total magnetic field $\mathbf{H}_T$ at the surface of the earth resulting from the superposition of the source field $\mathbf{H}_P$, the secondary field of overburden $\mathbf{H}_O$, the secondary field of the structure sought (target) $\mathbf{H}_S$, and the secondary field of the rock mass $\mathbf{H}_R$. From this total field, knowledge is required of the physical properties and geometry of the target. Each medium is characterized by the constants σ_i, ϵ_i, μ_i.

Consider now the range of values the physical parameters may take. The dielectric constant, or relative permittivity K_e, of geological materials is found to vary from one to 81 (Stratton 1941, Birch 1942). This gives a range of 8.854×10^{-12} to 718×10^{-12} farads per meter for the permittivity ϵ. The relative permeability of earth material is seldom greatly different from unity. For the most magnetic sulfide ore or the most magnetic rocks, K_m can be as high as 1.25 but is commonly much less. On the other hand, K_m for massive magnetite can reach 5 or more. Thus, the range of permeability μ encountered is $4\pi\times10^{-7}$ to $20\pi\times10^{-7}$ henrys per meter. Rocks usually possess conductivities in the range 10^{-1} to 10^{-6} mho/m. Overburden may possess conductivities as high as one mho/m, and as low as 10^{-5} mho/m. Sulfide and magnetite ore bodies exhibit a wide range of conductivities (see Table 1, Chapter 3, Vol. I) but mostly lie within the limits 10^{-1} to 10^{+4} mho/m.

With the above values of the physical parameters, it is readily shown that the neglect of displacement currents, in solving the problems of Part A, is justifiable. From Maxwell's equation the total current, conduction plus displacement, is given by the relation

$$\mathbf{J} = (\sigma - i\omega\epsilon)\mathbf{E}.$$

Displacement currents are negligible with respect to conduction currents if $\sigma\gg\omega\epsilon$. A careful choice of the maximum source frequency will ensure that the response of overburden and ore bodies is due to conduction currents and that the responses of the rock media are negligible. If, for ore, σ is taken to be the minimum 10^{-1} mho/m and ϵ is taken as high as 718×10^{-12} farads per meter, then the maximum frequency should be less than 100,000 cps if displacement currents are to be less than 0.1% of total current. For overburden or rock media, possessing a combination of high dielectric constant and low conductivity, the displacement currents would possibly equal the conduction currents, but such currents will be small compared with currents in ore targets of sufficient size to warrant investigation. This must be especially true for low audio frequencies. In any event, earth materials of poor conductivity and high dielectric constant are rarely encountered since the dielectric constant is frequently closely related to water content.

We are, of course, utilizing only normal values of dielectric constant. Rather than accept abnormal values of dielectric constant, as discussed in Part B, we will consider a frequency-dependent conductivity for macroscopically polarizable material. For example, suppose that we are dealing with a spherical body of hematite with minor magnetite, radius 1,000 m, which exhibits a frequency-dependent conductivity of the form shown in Figure 2. At 1,000 cps, the in-phase and out-of-phase responses are 0.295 and 0.035 relative units. At 100 cps, the in-phase and out-of-phase responses are 0.145 and 0.115 relative units.

On the other hand, the same four figures for a similar sphere, but of constant conductivity, are 0.295, 0.035, 0.210, and 0.090.

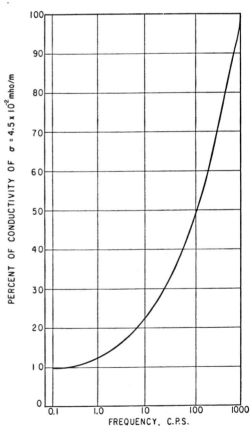

Fig. 2. Frequency-dependent conductivity for core of hematite with minor magnetite, saturated with 0.01 Normal NaCl. Four electrode cell measurement with $J\approx10^{-5}$ amps/cm^2.

Evidently, frequency-dependent conductivity could be important in interpreting electromagnetic data, although the example taken is extreme.

A change of conductivity of 10–20 percent between 1,000 cps and 100 cps is more typical for heavy sulfides and this change is not significant relative to the effect of the order of magnitude change in frequency. For a further discussion of this point, see Wait and Campbell (1953).

The assumption of macroscopic homogeneity of the physical property parameters is reasonable under many geologic conditions, although it is anticipated that there will be some gross exceptions. For example, a spherical body, radius 100 m, conductivity 10^3 mhos/m, is surrounded by a shell of lower conductivity (10^{-1} mho/m) so that the total radius of core plus shell is 200 m. At 50 cps, only the core responds with a relative in-phase peak amplitude of 0.32 relative units. At 500 cps, the whole responds with a relative in-phase peak amplitude of 0.80 relative units. For a uniform sphere of 200 m radius and 10^3 mho/m conductivity, the in-phase responses at 50 and 500 cps are identical at 2.65 relative units. Inhomogeneities obviously complicate interpretation.

For those electromagnetic systems in which a very high sensitivity is employed (typically a noise level less than one part in 25,000), variations in K_m in basic rocks cannot be ignored. Some helicopter-borne and automobile-borne systems produce negative in-phase response over basic rocks. These undesirable anomalies are often identified by their sign and by a complete lack of out-of-phase (Podolsky, Volume I, p. 204).

III. Classification of Artificial Field Techniques

The basic division of inductive versus conductive techniques is subject to further subdivision on the basis of field parameter measured, of source orientation, and on the manner of conducting a survey with any given system.

One or more of the following field parameters may be recorded with a practical electromagnetic surveying system.

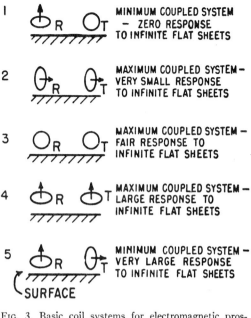

FIG. 3. Basic coil systems for electromagnetic prospecting devices.

1. Strike of the major axis of the ellipse of polarization.
2. "Dip," or more correctly pitch,[1] of the major axis of the ellipse of polarization.
3. Absolute values of amplitude of total magnetic field or any component.
4. Determination of one or more components of magnetic field intensity, measured relative to the amplitude and phase of the primary current or of the primary magnetic field.
5. Quadrature[2] magnetic field components in terms of corresponding in-phase components.
6. Magnetic field ratios and phase differences at adjacent observation points.

Most frequently, parameters 2 or 4 are used.

For ground electromagnetic systems employing a source, or transmitting, dipole, that dipole usually has either the first or fourth orientation of the coils labelled T in

[1] Some geophysicists prefer to refer to this parameter as tilt.

[2] This term is used synonymously with out-of-phase.

Figure 3. Occasionally, the orientation is that of system number two. For system number one we use the terminology, referring again to the transmitting coil, *vertical loop*, or horizontal dipole. For system number four we say that the transmitting coil is a *horizontal loop*, or vertical dipole. Thus ground electromagnetic systems are frequently classified by the orientation of the transmitting coils as *vertical loop* or *horizontal loop*. Note that some ground electromagnetic systems are not so classified, e.g., the Crone "Shootback" method described in Volume 1 of Mining Geophysics.

At times it is more convenient to consider the configuration of the transmitting and receiving coil pair, when classifying a system. Thus, system 2 (of Figure 3) would be a *coaxial system*, system 3 would be *vertical coplanar* and system 4 would be *horizontal coplanar*. Thus the plane or axis common to the coil pair is used to classify that pair.

In Figure 3, the *axis* of the transmitting coil is oriented vertically (z-directed), horizontally and aimed at the receiving coil (x-directed), or horizontally and aimed normal to the line joining transmitting and receiving coils (y-directed). Thus the transmitting coils of systems 1 and 3 are y-directed, those of systems 2 and 5 are x-directed, while that of system 4 is z-directed. Airborne electromagnetic systems employ x-, y-, and z-directed transmitting coils, plus combinations of them. The *horizontal loop* and *vertical loop* ground systems then would be classified according to the orientation of their respective transmitting coils as z-directed and y-directed.

Sometimes the transmitting and receiving coils are moved in tandem across the area to be surveyed. If the coils are both situated on the same traverse line, one ahead of the other, then the system is said to be *in-line tandem*. Most airborne systems and the *horizontal loop ground EM system*[3] are of this type. When the coils are moved in a direction perpendicular to a line joining them, the coils are said to be *broadside tandem*. Some ground EM systems are used with this array; the Rio Tinto airborne system is of this type (Pem-

[3] Described later.

berton, 1962). The *vertical loop ground EM system*[3] is frequently used with the transmitter fixed in position and only the receiver moved about the survey area. It is essential, when comparing ground EM systems, to make direct comparisons only between systems which use similar survey techniques and coil separations.

Drill-hole electromagnetic systems employ a *horizontal loop* or a *vertical loop* fixed at the collar of the hole, and a receiving coil lowered down the hole with its axis parallel to the axis of the drill hole (Ward and Harvey, 1954). Alternatively, in some drill hole systems (Elliot, 1961), both coils enter the hole and the system thereby becomes coaxial, the common axis coinciding with that of the drill hole.

With the conductive electromagnetic technique, either the phase and amplitude of the field at a point relative to the field at the transmitter, or the ratios of in-phase and quadrature components at two adjacent points, are typically measured (Frischknecht 1959).

All of the factors in the above discussion lead to a classification of systems to be described in the subsequent section. Systems in which the planes or axes of the transmitting and receiving coils are parallel are referred to as maximum coupled systems; those with the coils orthogonal are minimum coupled systems. Sometimes it is advantageous to orient the transmitting and receiving coils so that they are neither strictly maximum coupled nor minimum coupled (Paterson, 1961a; Crone, Volume I, p. 151).

IV. Methods of Electromagnetic Prospecting (Ground)

In the subsequent paragraphs we shall describe the various electromagnetic techniques in current usage and attempt to outline the advantages and limitations of each in various geologic environments. Any evaluation of artificial field electromagnetic techniques is apt to be subjective because of the number of unknowns involved. Hence, it may be wise at the outset to state that all electromagnetic systems can be employed advantageously in most geologic environments and that the following is the author's attempt at maximum objectivity. Many features common to all electromagnetic systems are discussed solely under the first subsection. Hence, the descriptions for other electromagnetic systems may be abbreviated by comparison. This is only an editorial convenience and is not intended to place more weight on the fixed transmitter vertical loop system than on others.

A. *Inductive vertical loop systems for ground surveys*

(a) *Fixed transmitter*

(i) *Modus operandi.*—The area to be surveyed is divided into blocks of convenient size and the transmitter stationed at the center of each block in turn. From any one transmitter location, lines on either side of the transmitter are surveyed as illustrated in Figure 4a.

The message-to-noise ratio at the receiver, as dictated by the transmitted field, the gain of the receiver, the level of natural magnetic noise, and the internal noise of the receiver, determines the maximum usable distance the receiver can be separated from the transmitter. Sometimes a large triangular loop 15 ft to the side, containing some tens of turns and fed by a gasoline-driven generator, is used as a transmitter. In this event, the maximum transmitter-receiver distance is frequently 2,500 ft with readily transported equipment (Figure 5). At other times, a transistor oscillator feeding . multi-turn iron-cored coil is the source f the field (Figure 6). Maximum separatic as of 1,000 ft are attained with this latter type of equipment.

Thus, the surveyed block might range from 1,000 ft×1,600 ft to 2,000 ft×2,400 ft. This particular survey technique leaves the line, on which the transmitter is situated, unsurveyed. The modification illustrated in Figure 4b obviates this limitation.

In surveying any given line, the transmitting coil is oriented so that the point of observation is contained within the plane of the coil. As the receiver is moved from

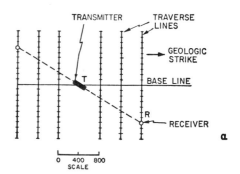

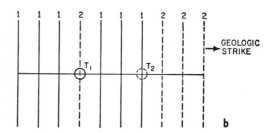

FIG. 4. Survey grid patterns for vertical loop, fixed transmitter system. (a) nonoverlapping survey block of dimensions 2,000×2,400 ft. (b) overlapping survey block of dimensions 2,000×3,600 ft. Receiving station interval 100 ft in each instance.

point to point, the transmitting coil must be rotated about a vertical axis to follow it. This rotation necessitates knowledge, on the part of the transmitter operator, of the position of the receiver operator at all times. Usually some form of orienting board or plane table is mounted on the transmitting coil to facilitate this survey control (e.g., Figure 7). The plane table is oriented by the control offered by the traverse line on which the transmitter is situated, and all stations to be surveyed are marked on the plane table map in correct relation. Lines drawn on the map between transmitter location and each receiver station are then reference lines; the transmitter is oriented parallel to each of these lines in turn. Some communication between transmitter and receiver operators is necessary for coordination of this type of survey. This communication can be provided by voice, by planning a strict time schedule for the whole operation, or in some instances by radio link.

FIG. 5. Portable vertical loop, fixed transmitter system powered by gasoline driven rotary generator.

(ii) *Special problems.*—For surveys of small areas, voice communication is customarily used. In flat country, orientation may be achieved by direct sighting or by use of an idealistic orienting card drawn on the assumption of a perfect grid of traverse lines. Seldom are the traverse lines strictly parallel and at a uniform interval, nor are

FIG. 6. Portable vertical loop, mobile transmitter system powered by transistor oscillator.

the stations usually at the precise regular intervals intended. Knowledge of the accuracy of the grid system is essential to the successful conduct of surveys in rugged terrain, as will be illustrated below.

The purpose in orienting the transmitter for each receiver station is twofold; elevation differences between transmitter and receiver produce errors in dip angles unless the orientation is perfect, and the currents induced in a uniform overburden are symmetrical about the plane of the transmitter and produce zero dip angles at a receiver situated in the plane of the transmitter. The first of these two points may be made clear by referring to the geometry of a dipole field as evident in the formula

$$\mathbf{H} = \frac{NAI}{4\pi}$$

$$\cdot \frac{(2x^2 - y^2 - z^2)\mathbf{i} + 3xy\mathbf{j} + 3xz\mathbf{k}}{r^5} \quad (C1)$$

for a coil with area A, turns N, current I, situated with its axis along the horizontal x-

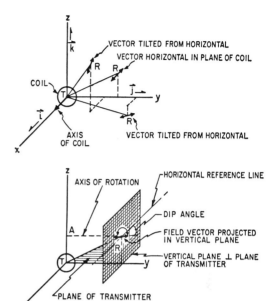

Fig. 7. Portable vertical loop, fixed transmitted system powered by transistor oscillator. Courtesy McPhar Geophysics Ltd.

Fig. 8. (*above*) Orientation of field in plane of transmitter above transmitter and displaced from plane of transmitter, and below transmitter and displaced from plane of transmitter. (*below*) Vertical plane in which receiver axis is rotated, relative to plane of transmitter. Axis of rotation of receiver axis is also shown.

direction (see Figure 8a). Then in the plane of the transmitter, i.e., $x=0$, there is only an $\mathbf{i}$ component of the field and no vertical or $\mathbf{k}$ component. In planes other than that of the transmitter, the $\mathbf{k}$ component is only zero when z is zero, i.e., when the transmitter and receiver are on the same elevation.

The symmetry of currents in a uniform overburden about the plane of the transmitting coil is illustrated in Figure 9.

(iii) *Measurements.*—The dip angles are measured with a search coil whose axis is rotated in that vertical plane which is perpendicular to the plane of the transmitter (see Figure 8b). At some particular rotation angle, the voltage induced in the receiving coil, by the transmitted or primary field, will be a minimum. The axis of the search coil is vertical unless a secondary field, due to induced subsurface currents, is present. Departures from the vertical for a minimum voltage, or "null," are recorded as tilt angles, indi-

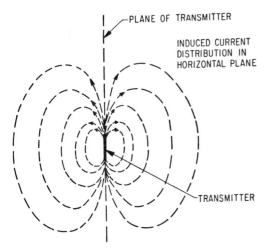

FIG. 9. Symmetrical distribution of induced currents in horizontal conductive sheet beneath transmitter. Plan View.

cating the dip of the resulting field vector from the horizontal as illustrated in Figure 10.

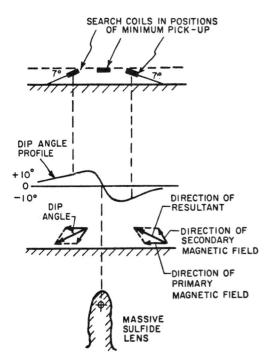

FIG. 10. Orientation of search coils for "null" in the vicinity of a conductor, resulting dip angle profile, and dip angle formed by angle resultant vector makes with horizontal.

(iv) *Depth of exploration.*—The depth of exploration obtainable with any electromagnetic method is governed by the message-to-noise ratio at the receiver. For this purpose, we define noise to include:

Instrument Noise
1. thermal agitation noise in the detection coils.
2. thermal agitation noise in the input circuit of the first amplifier.
3. tube noise in the first amplifier.
4. noise mechanically induced in the detecting coils (this may include magnetostrictive effects; vibrations of the coils and/or nearby ferrous objects in the earth's main magnetic field, plus changes in the effective area of the coils.

Disturbance Field Noise
5. fluctuations of the magnetic field in the frequency band of interest, resulting from artificial sources such as power lines, etc.
6. fluctuations of the magnetic field in the frequency band of interest, resulting from natural sources such as thunderstorms.

Terrain Noise
7. "geologic noise" or the background of minor anomalies of no significance upon which the significant anomalies are superimposed.
8. misorientation errors.

Geologic noise is fixed in amplitude and space-period for any given area once the technique and frequency of operation have been established. Natural fluctuations of the magnetic field, or *sferics*, are not subject to control and, hence, constitute a fixed reference which should govern the design of all artificial field electromagnetic systems. Correct receiver design will render instrument noise sources negligible with respect to disturbance field sources. The artificial sources are only of importance in a limited region surrounding them and must be treated specially.

Depth of exploration is most frequently limited by terrain noise; the message-to-noise ratio then is defined as the amplitude of significant anomaly divided by the amplitude of terrain noise. Goldstein and Ward (1963a) have shown that while it is possible to extract an anomaly from noise of equal amplitude, some of the information of the anomaly is lost in the process. Only when noise amplitude is less than about 50 percent of the anomaly amplitude does the destruction of anomaly information become insignificant in the extraction process. Usually the geologic noise in electromagnetic prospecting is of a much shorter space-period than the anomaly and this is of marked benefit, for then the anomaly may be recognized more readily in a low message-to-noise situation. Misorientation errors may be random or systematic and, hence, may be of any space-period.

For the vertical loop electromagnetic technique, a geologic noise of the order of two degrees is accepted as average. Misorientation errors can be controlled to any degree of precision required, but the cost of attempting this is sometimes prohibitive. For a survey control of ± 25 ft accuracy in topography exhibiting slopes to 15 degrees, the misorientation errors are usually less than one degree. A total *terrain noise level* of three degrees is considered acceptable. Hence, anomalies less than three degrees, the *threshold message level*, are not usually recognizable. One can compute the various depths, shapes, and sizes of conductors required to produce anomalies at or above the threshold level: for any coil configuration no single *depth of exploration* will result. However, most geophysicists employ a simple rule of thumb in establishing an effective depth of exploration: it is empirically established to be equal to one-half the distance between the transmitter

and a given traverse line. If this distance, or *spread*, should be chosen as 1,200 ft, the effective depth of exploration is usually taken as 600 ft. It is seldom desirable to utilize only large spreads because the maximum anomaly is obtained with a spread of the order of the largest dimension of the target.

Note, however, that this effective depth of exploration is strictly a rule of thumb for average conditions and is in no way related to the *depth of penetration* defined in Part A of this chapter.

(v) *Reduction of misorientation errors.* —If, by some error in mapping, the transmitting coil is not aligned with any given receiver location, then a misorientation error may occur. This error is dependent upon the elevational difference between transmitter and receiver as illustrated in Figure 8a. Referring to Figure 8b, the misorientation error may be reduced to one-third of its value obtained from rotations of the axis of the receiver in a vertical plane, if the rotation instead is confined to a plane perpendicular to the line TR (i.e., rotation about the axis TR rather than about the axis AR). This fact may be established as follows. The magnetic field of the dipole source of Figure 11 may be expressed in spherical coordinates, by

$$H_r = \frac{-m}{4\pi r^3} \cos \phi \sin \theta \qquad (C2)$$

$$H_\theta = \frac{m}{4\pi r^3} \frac{1}{2} \cos \phi \cos \theta \qquad (C3)$$

$$H_\phi = \frac{-m}{4\pi r^3} \frac{1}{2} \sin \phi. \qquad (C4)$$

The tilt angle in the vertical plane is given by

$$\tan \alpha = \frac{H_z}{H_\phi} = \frac{H_r \cos \theta - H_\theta \sin \theta}{H_\phi}$$

$$= -\frac{3 \cos \phi \sin \theta \cos \theta}{\sin \phi}. \qquad (C5)$$

In contrast, the tilt angle in the plane perpendicular to the line-of-sight between

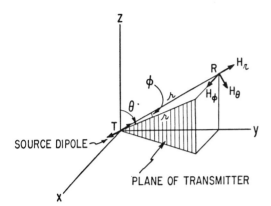

FIG. 11. Geometry for calculation of misorientation error angles α and β. The angle θ and the distance r define the elevational difference between transmitter and receiver, the angle ϕ is the orientation angle.

transmitter and receiver, i.e., perpendicular to TR, is given by

$$\tan \beta = \frac{-H_\theta}{H_\phi} = \frac{\cos \phi \cos \theta}{\sin \phi}. \quad (C6)$$

For small angles, $\tan \alpha \approx \alpha$ and $\tan \beta \approx \beta$. Also, for $\theta > 45°$ $\sin \theta$ is of order unity, so that

$$\alpha \approx 3\beta. \quad (C7)$$

A corollary to this deduction is that if the observed angle is reduced to about one-third of its value when the rotation of the receiver axis is transferred from the vertical to an inclined plane perpendicular to the transmitter-receiver line of sight, then there is a distinct possibility that the original angle was a misorientation error. Some caution must be exercised in applying this criterion, however, since dip angles due to anomalies can, under unusual circumstances, follow the same reduction law. An additional criterion for the recognition of misorientation errors then becomes desirable; such a criterion is discussed in the next subsection.

In all of our discussions so far, we have tacitly assumed that the receiver operator knew where the transmitter was located and, hence, could locate the vertical plane perpendicular to the line of sight between transmitter and receiver. In wooded terrain this may not be the case, although the receiver operator can employ a compass

and his knowledge of the survey grid to determine approximately the direction of the transmitter. If any doubt exists, the receiver axis can be placed in a horizontal plane and rotated in that plane until a null is obtained. In the null position, the axis of the receiver coil will point towards the transmitter, provided no conductors exist in the area. If a conductor is nearby, the axis of the receiver will be turned away from the transmitter-receiver line by the *strike angle* defined in Figure 12. Of course, a misorientation of the transmitter will also invalidate this scheme.

(vi) *The effect of quadrature component in the secondary field of a conductor.*—The total alternating magnetic field consisting of a primary inducing field and a secondary induced field may be written, for a primary field oriented in the x direction,

$$\mathbf{H}_T = (H_x + H_0)\mathbf{i} + H_y\mathbf{j} + H_z\mathbf{k}. \quad (C8)$$

The dip angle α is calculated from

$$\tan \alpha = \frac{H_z}{H_x + H_0}. \quad (C9)$$

The secondary field components H_x, H_y, and H_z are displaced in phase relative to the primary field H_0 so that (C9) may be written

$$\tan \alpha = \frac{\left| H_z \right| e^{-i(\omega t - \varphi)}}{\left| H_0 \right| e^{-i\omega t} + \left| H_x \right| e^{-i(\omega t - \varphi)}}$$

$$= \frac{\left| H_z \right| e^{i\varphi}}{\left| H_0 \right| + \left| H_x \right| e^{i\varphi}} \quad (C10)$$

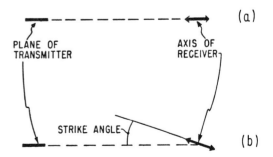

FIG. 12. (a) Orientation of receiver axis for null when no conductors present. (b) Orientation of receiver axis in presence of conductor. The strike angle is defined in the sketch.

where φ is the phase of the response of the subsurface conductor measured relative to the phase of the inducing field.[4] Note that the component in the z direction is not of the same phase as the total component in the x direction so that the field is elliptically polarized (refer to equation (A278) Part A). The phase relations are illustrated in the phase-space diagrams of Figure 13. Then the dip angle must refer to the orientation of the major axis of the ellipse.

The ellipse of polarization may be defined in the following manner. The three field components with which we are concerned are:

$$\left. \begin{array}{l} H_0 \\ H_x e^{i\varphi} = H_x(\cos\varphi + i\sin\varphi) \\ H_z e^{i\varphi} = H_z(\cos\varphi + i\sin\varphi) \end{array} \right\} . \quad (C11)$$

Along any axis, oriented at an angle α to the x axis, the magnetic field is

$$\begin{aligned} H_1 &= H_0\cos\alpha + H_x\cos\alpha + iH_x\sin\varphi\cos\alpha \\ &\quad + H_z\cos\varphi\sin\alpha + iH_z\sin\varphi\sin\alpha \\ &= [H_0\cos\alpha + H_x\cos\varphi\cos\alpha \\ &\quad + H_z\cos\varphi\sin\alpha] \\ &\quad + i[H_x\sin\varphi\cos\alpha \\ &\quad + H_z\sin\varphi\sin\alpha] \end{aligned} \quad (C12)$$

while along a perpendicular axis, the magnetic field is

$$\begin{aligned} H_2 &= [-H_0\sin\alpha - H_x\cos\varphi\sin\alpha \\ &\quad + H_z\cos\varphi\cos\alpha] \\ &\quad + i[-H_x\sin\varphi\sin\alpha \\ &\quad + H_z\sin\varphi\cos\alpha]. \end{aligned} \quad (C13)$$

We wish now to find an angle α such that $|H_1|$ is maximum while $|H_2|$ is minimum. The two directions so defined are the major and minor axes of polarization. The absolute magnitude of the magnetic field

[4] Throughout this chapter, the phase reference is the primary or inducing field, regardless of the manner in which the phase is monitored, unless otherwise noted.

in the direction of the minor axes may be written as

$$\begin{aligned} |H_2| &= [(H_x^2 + H_0^2 + 2H_0H_x\cos\varphi)\sin^2\alpha \\ &\quad + H_z^2\cos^2\alpha - (H_xH_z + H_0H_z \\ &\quad \cdot\cos\varphi)2\sin\alpha\cos\alpha]^{1/2}. \quad (C14) \end{aligned}$$

A minimum of $|H_2|$ will correspond to a minimum of $|H_2|^2$ so that it is sufficient to find $d|H_2|^2/d\alpha = 0$, or

$$\begin{aligned} &(H_x^2 + H_0^2 + 2H_0H_x\cos\varphi)2\sin\alpha\cos\alpha \\ &+ H_z^2(-2\cos\alpha\sin\alpha) \\ &- (H_xH_z + H_0H_z\cos\varphi) \\ &\quad \cdot 2(\cos^2\alpha - \sin^2\alpha) = 0. \quad (C15) \end{aligned}$$

Equation (C15) is of the form

$$A\tan^2\alpha + B\tan\alpha + C = 0 \quad (C16)$$

with

$$\left. \begin{array}{l} A = 2H_z(H_x + H_0\cos\varphi) \\ B = 2(H_x^2 + H_0^2 - H_z^2 \\ \qquad + 2H_0H_x\cos\varphi) \\ C = -2H_z(H_x + H_0\cos\varphi) \end{array} \right\} \quad (C17)$$

and has the roots

$$\tan\alpha = \frac{-B \pm \sqrt{B^2 - 4AC}}{2A} \quad (C18)$$

corresponding to the directions of the major and minor axes.

For a very large range of values of φ, in fact for $\varphi < 45°$, the $\cos\varphi$ can be neglected in (C18) without introducing serious error. We may then write

$$\tan\alpha \approx \frac{H_z}{H_x + H_0}. \quad (C19)$$

The ellipse of polarization for the components illustrated in Figure 13 has been computed and appears in Figure 14.

While a minimum signal will be obtained when the receiving coil is oriented along the major axis, it will not be a zero signal. The null is broadened by the presence of this quadrature or "out-of-phase" component. For the amplitude and phase

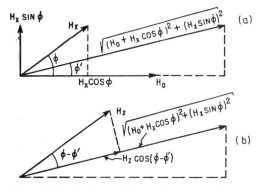

FIG. 13. Amplitude and phase relationships, in phase space, between the horizontal inducing field H_0, and the horizontal H_x and vertical H_z anomalous fields.

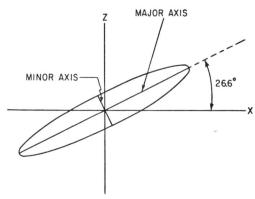

FIG. 14. The ellipse of polarization for the phases and amplitudes of H_0, H_x, H_z indicated in Figure 13.

relations exhibited in Figure 13, the output of a receiving coil will be a function of the rotation of the coil axis from the vertical, with the form (b) shown in Figure 15. For the same H_x, H_z, H_0 amplitudes but with zero phase shift, the function is of the form (a) in Figure 15. If the width of null is assumed to be $\pm 1°$ for a linearly polarized

field, the elliptical polarization of Figure 14 would lead to a width of null of $\pm 5°$. Width of null in this sense is usually taken to be the range over which the signal level remains sensibly constant to the ear, but beyond which the signal increases noticeably.

(vii) *Detailed surveys.*—Once a routine,

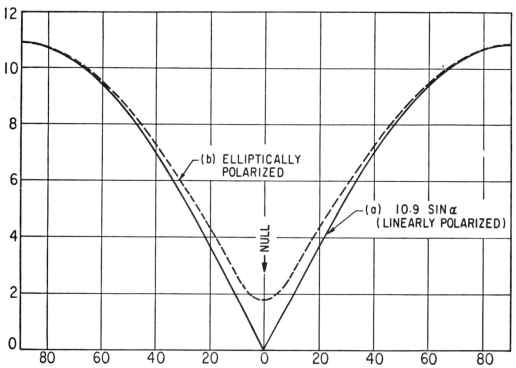

FIG. 15. Amplitude of output from receiver coil for various rotations away from null. (a) A linearly polarized field. (b) An elliptically polarized field. Ordinate is rotation angle; abscissa is dip angle in degrees.

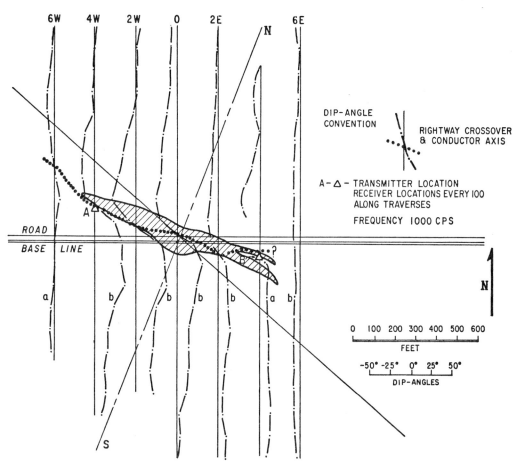

FIG. 16. Electromagnetic survey over Mobrun ore body, Clericy, Que., Canada
(after Seigel, Winkler, and Boniwell, 1958).

block by block, survey has been conducted over a mining property, it is customary to carry out detailed surveying. In this detailed work the transmitter is erected on one or more of the conductor-axes indicated by the reconnaissance survey. Traverse lines are then surveyed on either side of the transmitter. The purpose of this detailed surveying is to provide information permitting a more definitive interpretation than could be made solely from the data of the reconnaissance survey.

At this juncture it seems advisable to note one of the peculiarities of the stationary vertical loop technique. In a region in which several conductors exist, the conductor nearest the transmitter will give rise to much the largest response. This peculiarity may be considered a disadvantage in reconnaissance surveys since some large conductors may only be revealed by an inflection in an anomaly profile caused by another conductor passing near the transmitter. On the other hand, this feature may be turned to an advantage in detailed surveying where we may wish to evaluate each conductor in turn.

(viii) *Plotting the information derived from a survey.*—The observed dip angles are plotted at the receiver locations, as in Figure 16, and keyed to the appropriate transmitter location. It is essential, when interpreting data from a vertical loop survey, to take cognizance of the transmitter location in evaluating the dip angle profiles. Hence the transmitter locations are also marked on the map. For the effect of transmitter location on observed dip angle profiles, the reader is referred to section VI, Part C, Chapter II.

The convention employed in plotting the dip angle profiles varies from one geophysicist to the next. Most of the time, however, when the axis of the receiver is rotated counterclockwise from the vertical in order to reach the null position, the reading is plotted as positive. Thus, on a traverse where the transmitter is always to the west of the receiver operator, a *ccw* rotation, or positive reading, is recorded as a south dip angle while a *cw* rotation is recorded as a north dip angle. The opposite convention was employed in plotting the data of Figure 16. A linear scale of $1''$ $= 200'$ and an angular scale of $1'' = 20°$ are usually found to be entirely satisfactory for plotting the results of a vertical loop EM survey, although very high dip angles, as in Figure 16, may cause a departure from this standard.

Where dip angles change from south readings on the south of a traverse to north readings on the north, a *"proper crossover"* is exhibited by the dip angle profiles. The location of the crossover lies vertically above the axis of the current concentration in the subsurface conductor. A *"backwards crossover"* occurs when north readings on the south give way to south readings on the north. The interpretation of backwards crossovers will be discussed later. Suffice it to record here that backwards crossovers *do not*, in general, coincide with a conductor axis.

(b) *In-line tandem array*

(i) *Modus operandi.*—This use of the vertical loop system is employed in reconnaissance surveys on prospects in which cutting of a grid of lines is not planned immediately. Most often, the prospect is an airborne electromagnetic anomaly, the location of which is seldom known to an accuracy better than ± 200 ft. Traverses with the in-line array are made at an angle of 15 to 60 degrees to the anticipated strike of the conductor.

In conducting a survey with the in-line array, the transmitter and receiver travel in tandem along the same traverse, at a constant separation of 200 to 400 ft. This short range permits the use of very light weight equipment; commonly, the transmitter and receiver each weigh less than 15 lb. Readings of dip angle are made every 100 ft with the plane of the transmitter oriented to pass through the receiver station as for the fixed transmitter array. Sight or voice communication is employed in orienting the transmitter. Usually the receiver operator moves ahead of the transmitter and navigates for the survey with the pace and compass technique (Brubaker 1957).

Several traverses are made across the area of interest in this fashion. When the suspected conductor has been located by this process, a fixed transmitter or broadside array survey is made to provide information for definitive interpretation.

The tilt angle readings are plotted at the position of the receiver.

(ii) *Special problems.*—The reason for the unorthodox direction of traverse is simple: traverses perpendicular to a long linear conductor, with this array, will produce zero dip angles while traverses parallel to this type of conductor will produce constant dip angles. Neither perpendicular nor parallel traverses will yield a diagnostic dip angle profile. Even the traverse at an angle to strike results in a profile that is not always easy to interpret. Figure 17, after D. G. Brubaker (1957), shows the results of a scale model experiment over a metal sheet dipping at 60 degrees. The traverses were made at 15 degrees to the strike of the conductive sheet, in this experiment.

(iii) *Depth of exploration.*—The short spreads of 200 to 400 ft typically used for this array limit depth of exploration to about 100 to 200 ft and so they are applied to those problems where prior knowledge indicates that this depth of exploration is satisfactory. Airborne anomaly follow-up is the most customary application. The technique offers advantages of speed, economy, and flexibility where the explorer is concerned solely with location of the anomaly, and not with acquisition of information for interpretation of dip, depth, width, etc. of the source.

(c) *Expanding spread vertical loop technique.*—A technique which is a compromise between the fixed transmitter and in-line tandem techniques appears to have been introduced first by L. B. Slichter (1932). The survey procedure involves moving the receiver along lines cut at 45 degrees to the anticipated strike of the conductor while the transmitter is kept fixed at the end of the line and oriented with its plane along the line. The dip angle profiles will then be based on data from an *expanding spread* survey. Typical data from this type of survey is illustrated in Figure 18. The transmitter is set up at the end of each line in sequence.

Readings of dip angle are made at 100-ft intervals, starting 100 ft from the transmitter and extending to 2,000 ft. Two receivers are often employed simultaneously, one on either side of the transmitter. Because of the large maximum spread of 2,000 ft, a motor generator is usually used as a source to drive

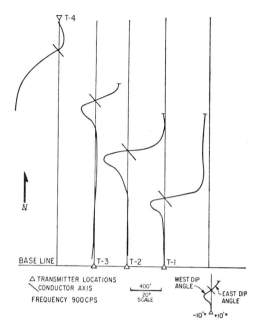

FIG. 18. Dip angle results obtained with in-line expanding spread vertical loop system (after H. V. McMurry, 1958). Near Cameron Lake, Quebec.

the large transmitting coil. This technique appears to be satisfactory for reconnaissance surveys of large areas. The data resulting from expanding spread vertical loop surveys is readily interpreted.

The depth of exploration is variable, depending upon the location of the conductor relative to the transmitter.

This technique is not commonly used, presumably because the orientation of the grid lines, at 45 degrees to strike, is generally unsatisfactory for other surveys, e.g. gravity or magnetic.

(d) *Broadside tandem array*

(i) *Modus operandi.*—The transmitter and receiver are situated on adjacent traverse lines and moved simultaneously by 100 ft, along their respective lines, between each reading. Dip angles are recorded at the receiver at each point of observation (usually every 100 ft); the plane of the transmitting coil contains the point of observation during the measurement. Visual or voice communication is maintained between transmitter and receiver operators.

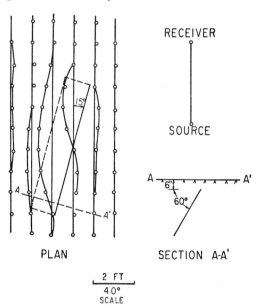

FIG. 17. Dip angle results of scale model in-line tandem survey over a metal sheet dipping at 60 degrees (after Brubaker, 1957).

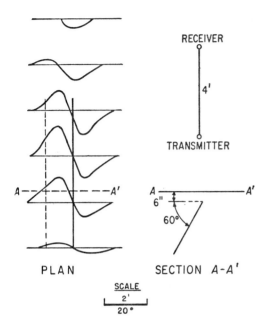

PLAN   SECTION A-A'

SCALE
2'
20°

Fig. 19. Dip angle results of scale model broadside survey over a metal sheet dipping at 60 degrees (after Brubaker, 1957).

This system may be employed in following up airborne anomalies, in prospect evaluation, and in general reconnaissance of an area. Traverses are made perpendicular to the geologic strike.

The separation between transmitter and receiver varies from 200 ft to 400 ft so that the average depth of exploration varies from 100 ft to 200 ft.

(ii) *Special problems.*—Since the transmitter and receiver operators move independently along adjacent lines, each must be concerned with navigation if the survey is conducted in heavy bush without a precut grid of lines. This tends to slow the operation down slightly. By contrast, on a precut grid the efficiency of surveying is excellent. In either event, the orientation of the transmitting coil often is in doubt and some small errors on this account frequently occur.

The resulting dip angle profiles are distinctly diagnostic, as indicated in Figure 19. These profiles were obtained in the laboratory over the same model yielding the in-line tandem data of Figure 17. Also,

the resolution of several adjacent conductors is excellent, in contrast with resolution expected from each of the previous three techniques.

A marked disadvantage of the method is that the dip angles decrease very rapidly away from the conductor as clearly indicated in Figure 19. This necessitates a close station interval that should never exceed 100 ft. Conductors 300 ft from the line joining the transmitter and receiver can readily miss detection. However, because of its resolution and clear-cut anomalies, it is often preferred to the in-line array.

B. *The inductive horizontal loop systems for ground surveys*

(a) *Modus operandi.*—The horizontal loop method was developed several decades ago in Sweden but has rapidly gained in popularity, since the mid nineteen-fifties, on the North American continent (Byers 1957, Morreau 1957, Ward and Gledhill 1959, Frischknecht 1959). The coplanar horizontal transmitting and receiving coils, of about the same dimensions, are moved in tandem either in-line or broadside. The former is by far the most common. Since the system is maximum coupled, measurement at the receiver is most conveniently made in terms of the ratios of the quadrature and in-phase voltages induced in the receiver relative to like quantities induced in a reference coil. The reference coil, usually consisting of a single turn, is mounted directly on the transmitting coil in the orientation of maximum coupling. The reference voltage and the receiver voltage are compared in a bridge or *ratiometer* circuit, the output of which is amplified and applied to earphones (Figure 20). When taking a reading, the in-phase and quadrature potentiom-

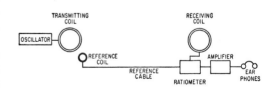

Fig. 20. Horizontal loop electromagnetic prospecting system, schematic.

FIG. 21. Horizontal loop electromagnetic prospecting system, general layout in use.

eters in the ratiometer are adjusted so that a null is obtained. The potentiometer dials are calibrated to read in percent of *normal* field. The normal field is defined as the field at the receiver when no conductors are present.

Since comparison must be made between receiver and reference voltage, a link must be established between the two. Usually this link is a cable, although it might be a radio link (Frischknecht 1959). In subsequent discussions we shall assume that a cable is used.

Depending upon the manufacturer's design, the ratiometer may be carried by the transmitter operator, the receiver operator, or mounted on the back of a third man and read by a fourth man. We shall discuss the operation on the assumption that the ratiometer is carried by the receiver operator so that only two men are involved in the survey (Figure 21).

For surveys with the in-line array, the two coils are moved in tandem along traverse lines perpendicular to geologic strike. The separation between the coils is kept constant and the readings plotted at a position midway between transmitter and receiver.

Transmitter-receiver spreads between 100 ft and 300 ft may be used with 200 ft as a general standard. Readings are taken every 100 ft.

The area to be surveyed is traversed systematically on a precut grid of lines. The spacing between the lines may range from 100 ft to 400 ft depending upon decisions reached in studying the ore search problem. The traverse lines need not be chained before the survey since the reference cable serves as a fixed length for chaining while measuring. No detailed surveying, other than traverses on lines intermediate to the basic grid lines, is necessary since no additional information can be acquired. This is common to all tandem systems and in contrast to fixed transmitter systems.

The transmitter is supplied by a battery powered electronic oscillator operating at one or more audio frequencies. The total weight of equipment, exclusive of reference cables, commonly is less than 45 lb.

(b) *Special problems.*—The reference cable, stretching between transmitter and receiver, must be kept taut so that a constant spread is maintained. An error of two percent in the

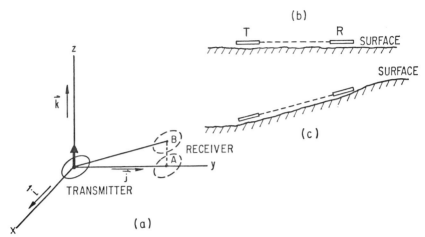

FIG. 22. Geometry of horizontal loop system. (a) Three dimensional view showing transmitter and receiver orientations relative to orthogonal reference axis. (b) Section through array as used in flat terrain. (c) Section through array as used in sloping terrain.

spread will lead to errors of six percent in the ratios, based on the field of the dipole transmitter decreasing as the cube of the distance from it. In terrain with high relief, errors from this source can become large. The in-phase ratios are greater than the normal 100 percent on this account and no quadrature readings arise.

Also in any sloping terrain, where the transmitter and receiver are apt to be on different elevations, the component of the source field along the axis of the receiving coil will be less than when the coils are on the same elevation (this change is only reflected in the in-phase ratio; no change will occur in the quadrature ratio). This point may be made clear by reference to the geometry of the dipole field described by the formula

$$\mathbf{H} = \frac{NAI}{4\pi}$$
$$\cdot \frac{3xz\mathbf{i} + 3yz\mathbf{j} + (2z^2 - y^2 - x^2)\mathbf{k}}{r^5} \quad (C20)$$

for a coil of area A, turns N, current I, situated with its axis along the vertical. At point A in Figure 22, the $\mathbf{k}$ component of the field, which is the component inducing voltage in a horizontal loop receiver, is proportional to $-y^2/r^r$ while at point B it is proportional to $(2z^2 - y^2)/r^5$. A 50-ft elevational difference be-

tween a transmitter and receiver spaced 200 ft horizontally apart will lead to a change in *normal* field of $12\frac{1}{2}$ percent. A 50-ft elevational difference in 200 ft corresponds to a 14-degree slope, a relief not uncommon in rolling terrain.

Under such conditions, it is customary to attempt to orient the transmitting and receiving coils so that they become coplanar. If this can be accomplished to an accuracy of five degrees, the elevational error will not be larger than 1.5 percent.

Through heavy brush, the reference cable is sometimes a source of annoyance when it tangles in stumps and undergrowth. Thus it is desirable to keep the cable reasonably taut even when traversing.

(c) *Depth of exploration.*—The rule of thumb depth of exploration ranges between 50 ft and 150 ft for spreads ranging from 100 ft to 300 ft. Some authors are inclined to use a rule of thumb that places the threshold level sufficiently low that the depth of exploration with a two-hundred foot spread is two hundred feet. I prefer a conservative estimate of depth of exploration and hence use the criterion for all techniques that the depth of exploration is 50 percent of the spread. This immediately raises the question of whether the elevational errors and geologic noise level are identical for all systems. This question can only be answered by reference to data from actual surveys. Hence we ask the reader to search for his own answers among the examples and case histories contained in Volume I.

A noise level of five percent of the in-phase component may be considered average for the horizontal loop method. The noise level of the out-of-phase or quadrature component depends markedly on the conductivity of the overburden in the area of survey, but an average of five percent may be expected. Further discussion of this subject will appear in the section on interpretation.

Terrain effects of any type usually do not cause deviations of more than 10 percent of normal field (e.g., Frischknecht 1959).

(d) *Plotting the information derived from a survey.*—The in-phase and quadrature components, expressed as percentages of the normal field, may be plotted in profile as in Figure 23 or plotted on maps and contoured as in Figure 24. The latter figure illustrates data taken over the same conductor that gave rise to the data of Figure 18 for the expanding spread fixed vertical coil array.

The convention employed in plotting the profiles is that increases in the in-phase component are plotted as positive readings while decreases in the in-phase are plotted as negative readings. The quadrature component follows the in-phase component in form as illustrated in Figure 23. The location of the conductor relative to the negative and positive regions of readings will be a function of the depth and attitude of the conductor. It will be discussed under the subsection on interpretation.

C. Conductive electromagnetic system

The conductive EM system in most common use today is the *Turam* system developed by Ab. Elektrisk Malmletning of Stockholm, Sweden, and described by Frischknecht (1959). Our discussion will be limited to this particular system (but see also Byers 1957).

(a) *Modus operandi.*—The energizing source is an insulated cable grounded at both ends. In a typical survey the cable, several kilometers long, is laid out parallel to the geologic strike. Current of 100 to 800 cps frequency is passed through the cable and

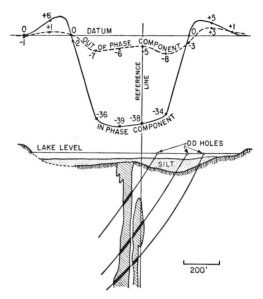

Fig. 23. Horizontal loop in-phase and out-of-phase profiles observed over a pyrite-chalcopyrite ore body. Transmitter-receiver spread 200 ft, frequency 3,600 cps (after Morreau, 1957).

the ground and drawn from a gasoline engine rotary generator (Figure 25). An area extending one or two km on each side of the cable, and within one or two km of the ends of the cable, is surveyed. Measurements are made, at intervals of 50 to 100 ft along traverses perpendicular to the cable, with two horizontal receiving coils which are 100 ft apart. The in-phase and quadrature ratios of the voltages induced in each of the two coils is measured with the aid of a ratiometer.

(b) *Special problems.*—While the grounded cable Turam technique is by definition a conductive technique, some currents are induced in subsurface conductors by induction from the cable. The ratio of inductively coupled to conductively coupled currents depends upon the local conductivity distribution. This tends to render interpretation somewhat indefinite, particularly where extensive conductive sheets occur.

However, the technique is more sensitive than strictly inductive techniques insofar as the transmitted field of the dipolar source of an inductive technique decays as the inverse cube of distance from the source; the conductive portion of the source is directly in the

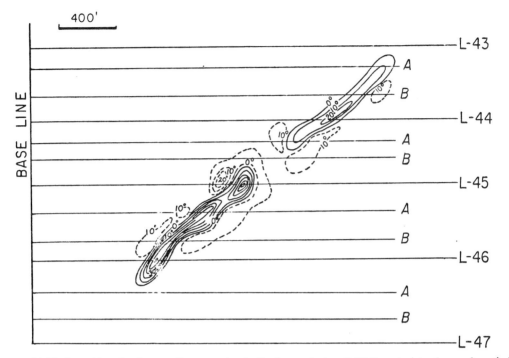

FIG. 24. Horizontal loop in-phase readings over steeply dipping conductor. Solid lines depict subnormal vertical field strength at receiver. Dashed lines depict above normal field strength at receiver. Transmitter-receiver spread 40 m, frequency 3,600 cps (after McMurry, 1958).

subsurface with Turam. Thus the Turam method has a greater depth of exploration than the inductive techniques. Under favorable circumstances conductors have been located at depths *as great as 900 ft.*

Anomalies in the vertical field due to *induced* currents are characterized by a correspondence between high values of in-phase and positive quadrature components and/or low values of the in-phase and negative quadrature components.

Anomalies due to conductive currents are characterized by a lack of correspondence between the in-phase and quadrature components. While inductive currents never give rise to negative in-phase components, conductive currents do so.

Where long linear non-ore conductors are expected, the cable may be laid out perpendicular to geologic strike so that inductive currents may predominate.

Elevational errors arise wherever topographic relief is significant. To illustrate, let us ignore conductive currents entirely and

deal solely with the inducing field of the long straight cable.

The field of a linear wire of infinite extent is given by the formula

$$H = \frac{I}{2\pi r}$$

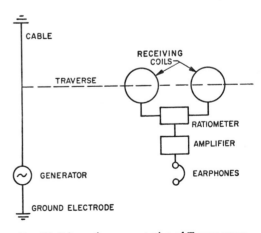

FIG. 25. Schematic representation of Turam array.

where H is the field in ampere-turns/meter, I is the current in amperes, and r is the distance, in meters, at which the field is measured. This field is directed tangential to a circle about the wire as center. In the plane of the wire, where $z=0$, the field is $H_0 = I/2\pi x$ while at an altitude of z meters above or below the wire the field is

$$H_0' = \frac{I}{2\pi(x^2 + z^2)^{1/2}} \cdot$$

The ratio of H_0' to H_0 is

$$\frac{x}{(x^2 + z^2)^{1/2}} = \frac{1}{\left[1 + \left(\dfrac{z}{x}\right)^2\right]^{1/2}} \cdot$$

If measurements are made on terrain where the slope is 15 degrees, z/x has the value of 0.268 giving rise to a ratio of H_0'/H_0 of 0.965, an error of 3.5 percent in an assumed value of H_0 if the terrain is ignored. Of course, where conductive currents predominate, the error may be entirely unpredictable. On the other hand, it is found that quadrature recordings seldom require correction.

Generally speaking, any vertically stratified anisotropic ground conductivity will lead to a channelling of much of the current into the most conductive layers. These layers may or may not correspond to the ore horizon. A reduced sensitivity to ore in a resistive rock will occur where most of the current is carried by an adjacent conductive layer. Under such circumstances, the cable should be oriented perpendicular to geologic strike. For "isotropic" ground, maximum sensitivity to ore will occur where the current flows along the strike of the ore body.

(c) *Plotting the information derived from a survey.*—The measured voltage ratios are normalized by either subtracting or dividing by normal field ratios calculated from the theoretical field of a line source grounded to a homogeneous half space. The normalized ratios are then plotted as individual profiles (the ratio curve). Additionally, the particular values of 1.00 for amplitude and zero degrees for phase are often assumed as the correct values of the field at a distance of 100 ft from

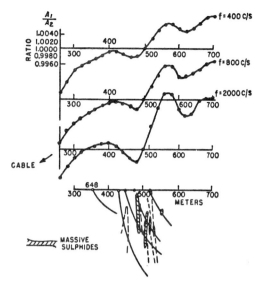

Fig. 26. Turam in-phase ratio anomalies at three frequencies (after Ivanov, 1957).

the cable. Then the ratios may be added to these values successively to yield an integrated or *field* curve.

The dip, depth, and width of a conductor are determined by comparison of observed results with model results, particularly of the in-phase component. Under conditions of favorable terrain and regular-shaped ore bodies, the error in locating the horizontal position and the depth of the top of the ore body may be less than ten percent of the true values. Usually the direction of dip can be determined, although its exact value may be in doubt with this or any other electromagnetic technique.

An example of data resulting from a Turam survey is given in Figure 26 for a situation where the cable is located at a large distance from the conductor. Observed Turam ratio and field curves for a traverse perpendicular to a long grounded cable are compared in Figure 27 with theoretical curves for a homogeneous half space.

D. *Afmag*

(a) *Introduction.*—The Afmag method (Ward et al., 1958; Ward, 1959a, 1960) is an inductive electromagnetic method in which the source is a natural audio frequency mag-

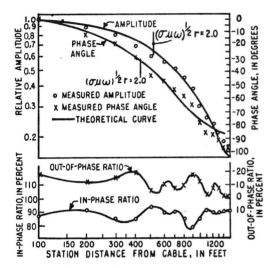

FIG. 27. Turam field and ratio curves for a traverse perpendicular to a long grounded cable. Coil separation 100 ft, frequency 500 cps. Theoretical curve is for $(\sigma\mu\omega)^{1/2}r = 2.0$ where r = distance from cable in meters (after Frischknecht, 1959).

netic field arising from atmospheric discharges. It was first made generally available in 1958 and since that time has been employed in many parts of the world. However, the literature on the method is still inadequate (Kellogg, 1960; Schaub, 1960 and 1962a; Hallof and Sutherland, 1962; Pemberton, 1962; Shaw, 1962; Jewell and Ward, 1963; Karandeev and Grinevich, 1965; Lutsenko and Pushnoi, 1965; Makowiecki, King, and Cretchley, 1965) so that the intricacies of the method are not always appreciated. The inventors of the method (McLaughlin et al., 1964) were provoked into considering its development by the desire to utilize an electromagnetic method with a depth of exploration considerably in excess of that attainable with conventional methods. The primary application of the method was considered to be the search for massive sulfides. While some success has been met in this application, certain peculiarities of the method have reduced its application in this regard, while other applications, especially fault tracing, have arisen.

(b) *Characteristics of natural audio frequency fields.*—Natural audio frequency energy at a given site may, in a first approxi-

mation, be represented by a series of delta functions of magnetic field intensity which are closely spaced in time and whose amplitude and time distributions are essentially random. The azimuthal distribution on the other hand is somewhat ordered, giving rise to an equivalent "ellipse of polarization" or "integration ellipse" provided the energy bursts are studied over a sufficient period of time. For distant sources and a perfectly and uniformly conducting earth, the plane of the ellipse is horizontal. Local sources and local conductivity inhomogeneities tilt the plane of the ellipse (Jewell and Ward, 1963). Of course, each energy burst may be elliptically polarized, in the conventional sense, either at the source or as a result of local conductivity inhomogeneities to produce a further complexity.

Some energy is always measurable in any three orthogonal directions so that, in the sense considered herein, an "integration ellipsoid of polarization" is required to provide complete definition of the mean polarization of the magnetic field. The ellipticity of the integration ellipsoid of polarization in the horizontal plane is low, often approaching unity, while the ellipticity in the vertical planes through the major and minor axes is high, sometimes as large as five. Both of these ellipticities are dependent upon the secondary fields from local conductivity inhomogeneities as well as upon the primary field character.

The azimuth of the major axis will change hourly, occasionally by as much as 90 degrees during a 24 hour interval. The tilt of the minor axis away from the vertical is remarkably stable (Ward, et al. 1958), seldom varying by more than two degrees from a mean position.

These characteristics are compatible with an atmospheric origin and worldwide propagation of the natural alternating magnetic fields. The mean spectrum of energy spanning the Afmag frequency band is indicated in Figure 28; this spectrum is merely indicative of average levels since, over much of the spectrum shown, the field strength may vary with time by as much as ±40 db from the mean. The signals in the VLF and

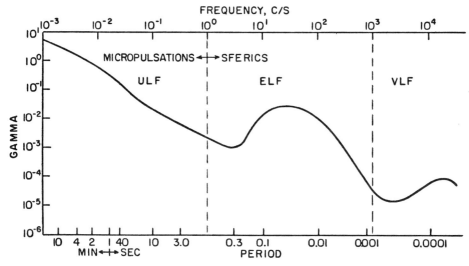

FIG. 28. Mean geoelectromagnetic sprectrum (after Bleil, 1964).

ELF band of natural atmospheric noise are usually referred to as sferics. (Bleil, 1964, is a general reference on the phenomena suggested herein.) Sources of sferics include:

1) atmospheric electrical discharges, especially lightning, propagated in the wave guide mode (Galejs, 1965; Wait, 1965) or whistler mode (Katsufrakis, 1964);
2) gyromagnetic fields due to gyration of various ion species in the earth's static magnetic field;
3) VLF and ELF emissions in the ionosphere and exosphere (Gallet, 1964);
4) VLF and ELF emissions in the turbulent region between the boundary of the magnetosphere and the standing shock wave on the sunward side of the magnetosphere (Heliwell, 1965);
5) VLF and ELF emissions in deep space; and
6) man-made noise. This latter source could include fields due to urban electrification, gyromagnetic effects from ionized blasts such as nuclear explosions, rocket engines, jet aircraft "vapor trails" etc.

World-wide thunderstorms provide by far the largest source of sferic energy. The sferic fields are propagated in a spherical wave guide bounded by the surface of the earth and the lower surface of the ionosphere. Attenuation of the wave is therefore determined by the height of the lower surface of the ionosphere and by the electrical properties of the surface layers of the earth and ionosphere. During the daytime, increased ionization of the ionosphere by ultraviolet radiation establishes a diffuse lower boundary of the D layer of the ionosphere at about 60 km, but the electron-neutral particle collisions effect absorption and attenuation of electromagnetic waves at frequencies in the ELF band and higher. At nighttime the lower boundary rises to about 90 km and is a better reflector. The net result is that an electromagnetic wave is propagated most efficiently at night by repeated reflections from the ionosphere and earth's surface.

There is some evidence that during solar minima, occurring every 11 years, reflections of sferics from the ionosphere are generally less effective, and so we might anticipate a general worldwide reduction in sferic signal strengths as a solar minimum approaches (Sutherland, 1964).

Theoretical ELF spectra for spring and winter are shown in Figure 29 (after Galejs, 1965); the spectral peaks in the 8 to 40 cps band are the well-known Schumann Resonances. Note that there are 6- and 20-db

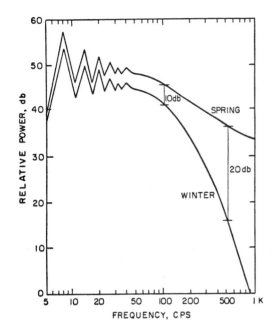

FIG. 29. Calculated sferic spectrum for local noon in the Northern Hemisphere (after Galejs, 1965).

←—◀◀◀

contrasts in power at 100 and 500 cps, respectively, between spring and winter. Experimental observations confirm the seasonal variations predicted by theory; the curve of Figure 30 was reduced from data obtained with an induction coil tuned to 500 cps. There is a 20 db change in signal strength between February and July, 1957, with the midnight field strength always greater than the midday field strength.

Most of the sferic energy arises in the principle thunderstorm centers of Central Africa, Central-South America, and the East Indies (Jewell and Ward, 1963). These centers move a few degrees northward with the approach of summer in the northern

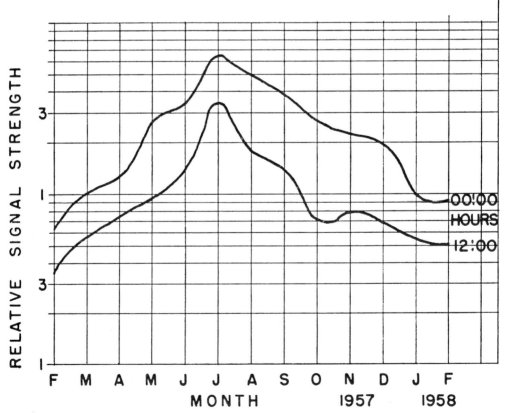

FIG. 30. Secular variation of natural magnetic fields obtained with coil tuned to 500 cps, Orangeville, Ontario, Canada, 1957-58.

hemisphere and a few degrees southward with the approach of summer in the southern hemisphere. Superimposed on these major sources are local atmospheric discharge sources distributed over the whole surface of the earth. One readily concludes that sferic energy is strongest in equatorial zones and weakest in polar regions, although, because of the geometry of the earth-ionosphere waveguide, the contrast is not as large as one might at first suspect (Figure 31). Sferic field strength measurements with Afmag units in Northern Rhodesia, Surinam, Australia, New Zealand, U.S.A. and Canada have been made at a sufficient latitude-spread of stations to confirm that sferic fields are strongest, in general, near the equator and weakest, in general, near the poles.

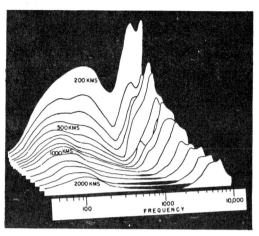

FIG. 32. Model showing source spectrum and attenuation of field of average daytime lightning stroke (after Chapman and Macario, 1956).

The average thunderstorm cell has a duration of the order of one hour in the temperate regions. Each discharge in a thunderstorm constitutes a pulse of finite duration, of the order of milliseconds, which transforms in the frequency domain to a broad band spectrum as Figure 28 suggests.

The attenuation of electromagnetic waves in the earth-ionosphere cavity is frequency dependent and the sources have a typical broadly peaked spectral distribution. The net result is, crudely, the observed spectrum of Figure 28; we limit Afmag operating frequencies to 150 cps and 510 cps to take advantage of the spectral peak near these audio frequencies. The closer to a source, the higher the ratio of 510 cps to 150 cps magnetic field strength within this band according to Chapman and Macario (1956) who presented the data of Figure 32.

(c) *Instrumentation and modus operandi*

(i) *Ground system.*—The ground survey Afmag system consists of a pair of orthogonal induction coils, double tuned nominally to 150 cps and 510 cps, and associated readout instrumentation. The output of one coil, the *reference* coil, gates the output of the other, the *signal* coil, through a phase-sensitive detector. Thus for a linearly polarized field, the instantaneous signal coil output will be positive, zero, or negative according to its orientation rela-

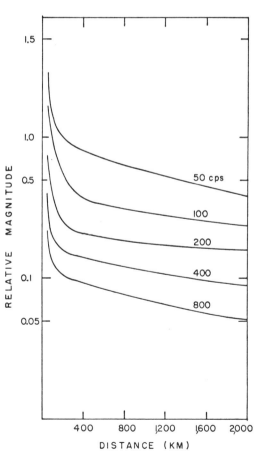

FIG. 31. Variation of magnitude of field with distance from source (after Wait, 1960).

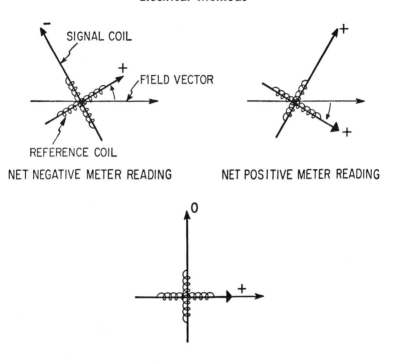

SIGNAL COIL

FIELD VECTOR

REFERENCE COIL

NET NEGATIVE METER READING   NET POSITIVE METER READING

NET ZERO METER READING

Fig. 33. Principle of Afmag phase detection system.

tive to the field vector. This concept is illustrated in Figure 33. Because a phase-sensitive detector is employed, an output will be recorded only for that part of the signal voltage which is in-phase with the reference voltage. In a field which is elliptically polarized in the conventional sense, the phase of the component along the reference coil axis governs the signal accepted by the signal coil. When the reference coil is oriented within a few degrees of the major axis of the ellipse in any plane, the signal coil will register only the projection of the major axis along the signal coil and essentially none of the projection of the minor axis along the signal coil. For a sferic field which possesses the characteristics of an integration polarization ellipsoid, some output can always be expected from the signal coil. However this output will be randomly positive and negative when the signal coil is perpendicular to the major axis in any plane. The portable detector is very sensitive to rotations rela-

tive to the ellipse of polarization in any plane, because a phase-sensitive detector exaggerates the eccentricity of the integration ellipse by effectively linearizing each elliptically polarized sferic burst. Thus it is not uncommon to be able to measure the direction of the axis in the vertical plane to an accuracy of ± 0.5 degrees and in the horizontal plane to an accuracy of ± 5 degrees. While normally operated strictly for polarization measurements, the portable detector can be used to measure field intensity in any direction. The output of the phase-sensitive detector is indicated on a meter, while the amplified output of the reference coil can be displayed on a meter or on a strip chart recorder. Because the design incorporates a phase-sensitive and not an amplitude-sensitive principle, dip angles measured with the ground Afmag unit are not subject to instrumental drift.

The unit is first placed with coil axes in horizontal plane and rotated until the azimuth of the major axis of the horizontal integration ellipse is noted. Then the unit is placed in a vertical plane passing through the major axis and rotated to determine the inclination of the major axis. These two readings are recorded as *azimuth* and *dip* of the major axis.

The internal noise level is equivalent to 10^{-6} γ for a 5 cps bandwidth at 150 cps and the time constant, introduced to reduce the dynamic range of the displayed variables, is about one second.

(ii) *Airborne system.*—Continuous recording of a magnetic field inclination for a magnetic field which varies so grossly in amplitude demands an amplitude comparison system. Airborne Afmag relies upon the amplitude comparison of the amplified outputs of two orthogonal coils mounted in a bird towed on the end of a 200-ft tether. The coils must then each be at 45 degrees to the major and minor axes of an ellipse of polarization in any plane in order to register a ratio output of unity. Rotations from this direction result in a ratio output other than unity (see Figure 34). Since no phase discrimination is used, the amplitude ratio detection system is much less sensitive to field rotation than the phase-sensitive detection system whenever the sferic fields depart grossly from linear polarization. Changes of gain in the amplifying systems following the coils can lead to drift. This drift produces a change in the output ratio which is inseparable from field rotation. Consequently a periodic drift check is desirable and can be effected by flying out of ground influence first on, say, a north track then on a south track. The gain of each channel is adjusted until the reference level on a strip chart recorder is the same for north and south tracks.

The internal noise level of the airborne system is equivalent to 10^{-6} γ for a 5 cps bandwidth at 150 cps, but rotation of the coils in the earth's field and other noise introduced through irregular motion of the bird reduce this ultimate sensitivity by at least one order of magnitude. The integration time constant is chosen to be a few

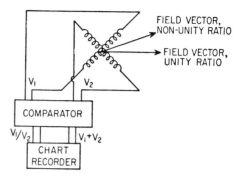

Fig. 34. Principle of Afmag amplitude ratio detection system.

seconds in order to effect reasonable smoothing of this turbulence noise.

(d) *Special problems*

(i) *Azimuth and dip vary with time.*—In practice it has been found that both the dip and azimuth of the major axis of the ellipsoid of polarization may be functions of time at any one location. To investigate this special problem, Ward et al. (1966) conducted a series of experiments designed to define the variables.

Data on the mean polarization of sferic activity in the 150 cps band were observed at sites near Gilroy, California, and Mariposa, California.

(a) *Gilroy.*—At Gilroy the aximuth and dip of the major axis of the integration ellipsoid of polarization were recorded about every fifteen minutes during nine recording intervals extending from May 2, 1963, to June 9, 1964. The results are as follows:

(b) *Diurnal variation—azimuth.* The diurnal variations of azimuth of the major axis are described in Figure 35. There are variations of azimuth in excess of 90 degrees on February 6, 1964, and in excess of 70 degrees on May 2, 1963, and July 20, 1963. The mean azimuth for any given day varies from 320°T[5] on February 6 and February 8, 1964, to 045°T on August 19, 20, 1963.

During the recording intervals, February, 1964, the mean daytime field

[5] T = azimuth from true north.

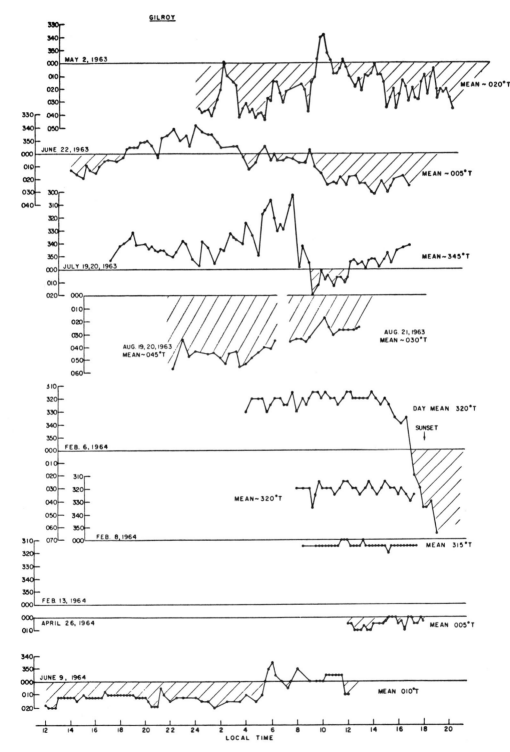

Fig. 35. Variation of azimuth with time; Gilroy, California; frequency: 150 cps.

direction tended to become steady at about 320°T. This direction is within three degrees of normal (317°T) to the direction of a major power line located 3.5 miles to the southeast of the recording site. Unquestionably the winter daytime field is primarily due to harmonics of 60 cps and/or transients arising in the powerline; the appearance of a few random natural or powerline transients can give the winter daytime field the appearance of a sferic field. It is difficult with the narrow band ground Afmag equipment alone to identify, at a single station, the source of the measured fields. Note that even the summer daytime field, observed when sferics are not especially strong, can tend toward the direction of the power line field. The accuracy of any azimuth reading in Figure 35 is typically ±5 degrees but at any time this accuracy can degenerate.

Undoubtedly some of the spring and summer variations of azimuth are due to the successive buildup and decay of the various major thunderstorm centers throughout the world (Jewell and Ward, 1963; Holzer et al., 1957).

Near sunset on February 6, 1964, the sferic field increased rapidly and apparently soon was dominating over the power line field.

(c) *Diurnal variation—dip.*—The tilt or dip of the major axis of the integration ellipsoid of polarization is due to subsurface conductivity inhomogeneities. Its variation throughout a day should then only be significant if the magnetic induction through the inhomogeneity is changed markedly by the rotation of azimuth of the major axis. Apparently the induction through the inhomogeneity causing an observed downward tilt to the south was not markedly changed, for the tilt was 5 degrees ±1 degree for more than 75 percent of the observations at Gilroy and rarely varied by more than ±2 degrees. These extremes could be caused by a transient vertical component arising in very local sources. The tilt is remarkably stable at this site.

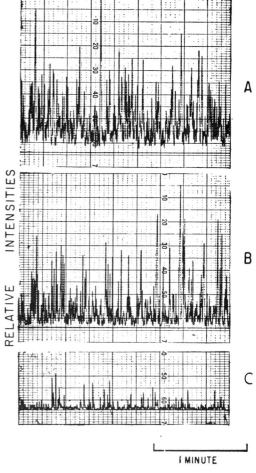

Fig. 36. Sferic signals along orthogonal principle axes of ellipsoid of polarization; Gilroy, California; approximately 1500 local time, July 23, 1963; A—major axis, 030°T; B—intermediate axis, 120°T; C—minor axis, inclined 5 degrees from vertical in direction 210°T; frequency 150 cps.

(d) *Integration ellipsoid of polarization.*—Around 1500 PST July 23, 1963, the output of the reference coil of the ground survey unit was recorded when the axis of this coil was successively placed in the major, intermediate, and minor axes of the integration ellipsoid of polarization. The result, indicating the general nature and level of the sferic field at 150 cps in each of three orthogonal directions, is shown in Figure 36. From these and other recordings of the intensity along the major axis at several gain settings, we establish the propor-

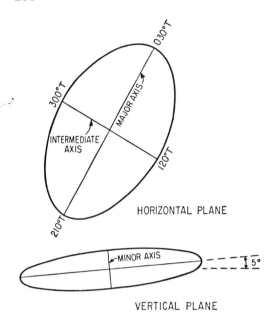

HORIZONTAL PLANE

VERTICAL PLANE

Fig. 37. Horizontal and vertical sections through ellipsoid of polarization; Gilroy, California; July 23, 1963; frequency 150 cps.

tionality of the axes of the ellipsoid to be 1: 0.6: 0.2. The major axis was oriented approximately 030°T at the time and the minor axis was tilted 5 degrees from the vertical toward 210°T. Horizontal and vertical sections through the ellipsoid are shown in Figure 37.

The estimates of intensity in each of the three orthogonal directions are not readily achieved because of the gross temporal variations in field strength. Referring to Figure 36, records A, B, C are, respectively, the intensities in the major, intermediate and minor axes at 1500 PST, July 23, 1963. By adjusting a calibrated attenuation control, we subsequently made each of these intensities approximately equal over two minutes of recording. The ratios of the axes were then the attenuation control ratios.

The dimensions of the ellipsoid permit us to predict the change in the ratio of the voltage induced in the coils of an airborne amplitude comparison system as the azimuth of the major axis changes. This is the only means by

which we can convert a ratio change to an angular rotation of the major axis and hence is a means of calibrating the airborne units. For example, assume the observed azimuth rotation of 53 degrees took place for a linearly polarized field; the ratio would change from unity to 7.1. On the other hand, for an ellipse of major and minor axes of 1.0 and 0.6. the ratio will change only from unity to 1.6 for a 53 degrees rotation. Evidently true dip angles cannot be obtained from airborne unit recordings of field ratio unless the ellipticity of the field is known.

(*e*) *Intensity.*—To record intensity as a funtion of time, we employed an airborne unit in the following manner. The sum of the voltages from the two coils was rectified and displayed on a paper chart recorder as a measure of intensity. The line bisecting one of the angles between the coil axes was set at 018°T and horizontal so that each coil was contributing about half the signal intensity throughout the recording interval.

The mean intensity, recorded as the sum of the outputs of the two coils of the recording system, is plotted as a function of time in Figure 38. The intensity was reasonably constant from 1500 to 2300 July 22, 1963. Subsequently the intensity increased sharply and remained high for about four hours, or to about sunrise. Slightly more than an hour after sunrise, the intensity dropped markedly and remained low until 1300, July 23, 1963, when once again it rapidly increased. There is no obvious correlation between intensity and the direction of the major axis on this occasion.

(*f*) *Mariposa.*—Polarization of sferics in the 150 cps band were observed at a site near Mariposa, California, during the following intervals:

(1) 0830 PST August 20, 1963, to 0200 PST August 21, 1963.

(2) 1600 PST September 3, 1963, to 1200 PST September 4, 1963.

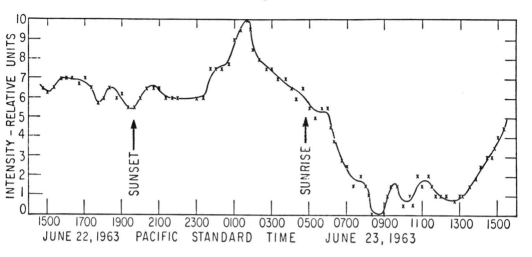

FIG. 38. Diurnal variation of mean intensity of major axis of ellipsoid of polarization obtained with airborne Afmag unit used as ground monitor; Gilroy, California; July 22, 23, 1963; frequency 150 cps.

(3) 1300 PST November 29, 1963, to 1700 PST November 30, 1963.

(g) *Diurnal variation—dip and azimuth.*—The dip and azimuth readings as functions of local time are displayed in Figures 39, 40, and 41.

For the August, 1963, recording periods, Figure 39, the azimuth rotated a maximum of 75 degrees from 030°T to 315°T. The dip of the major axis varies sympathetically from 8°N±1° to 6.5°S ±1°. This is an incredibly large change in dip. Notice that the north dips occur when the azimuth is west of north.

During the September recording period, Figure 40, the major axis of the ellipse of polarization was observed to rotate a maximum of 32 degrees from 022°T to 350°T while the dip ranged from 7°N±1 to 7°S±1. A sharp swing in azimuth from about 10°E of north to about 10°W of north between 0500 and 1000 on September 4 produces an amazingly well-correlated change in dip over the same interval with north dips again occurring almost solely when the azimuth swings west of north.

During the long November period, Figure 41, the azimuth changed quite erratically from 050°T to 335°T, a swing of 55 degrees. For the same inter-val the dips ranged from 7°N to 8°S with the northern dips tending to occur when the azimuth had swung farthest west. The weak fields in November evidently have introduced more scatter in the azimuths and dips than was observed in August or September.

There is a fine structure to dip angle and azimuth time variations; the limit of time resolution being largely determined by the time constant of the instrumentation. Unless care is taken in ground surveys, the dip variations with time can lead to erroneous results. In airborne surveys, a ground monitor is required to recognize the time variations in dip angle so that the superimposed space and time variations can be separated within the continuous recording.

(h) *Diurnal variation—ellipsoid characteristics.*—The relative intensities of the major, intermediate, and minor axes of the ellipsoid of polarization were estimated frequently during the September and November recording periods. Table I gives the results normalized to a value of unity for the major axis regardless of absolute intensity. At times of low field strengths, the minor axis could represent largely the internal noise of the system or magnetostrictive

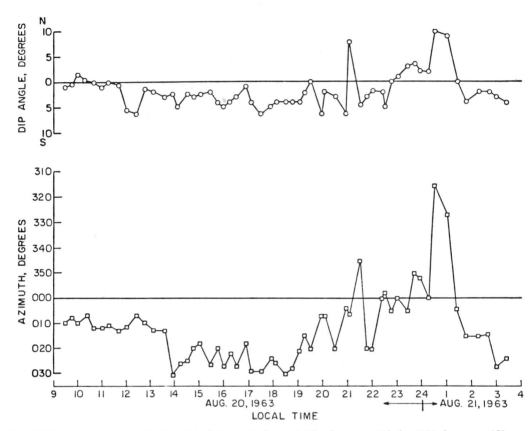

FIG. 39. Dip angle and azimuth diurnal variations; Mariposa, California; August 20, 21, 1963; frequency 150 cps.

noise due to wind. For this reason we should consider the minor axis values as maxima. The ratio of the other two axes we would estimate to be in error by no more than 0.1. The September data, taken when the fields were fairly strong, demonstrate that significant changes can occur in the shape of the integration ellipsoid of polarization over one day. It is of interest to note that the most dramatic change in the ellipsoid occurs between 0500 and 0900 September 4 when the azimuth exhibited a marked rotation from east to west of north. The dip angle was nearly zero when the largest values of intermediate and minor axes were recorded (0714–0735 and 0815–1820).

The late November values of minor axes were abnormally high, presumably representing largely internal or wind

noise at a time of low field strength. Once against the largest value of the intermediate axis occurs when the dip is nearly zero degrees, between 1800–1820.

(i) *Diurnal variation—intensity.—* The output of the reference coil of the ground survey unit was monitored periodically for the September 3–4 period. The smoothed diurnal variation of intensity is shown in Figure 40. Intensity is lowest in the early morning hours and highest in the early afternoon for the interval studied. This is just the reverse of what one would expect if waveguide attenuation were the controlling feature. Local thunderstorm activity could account for this anomalous diurnal variation of intensity. This profile would lead us to suspect that the local activity commenced about 0500 and

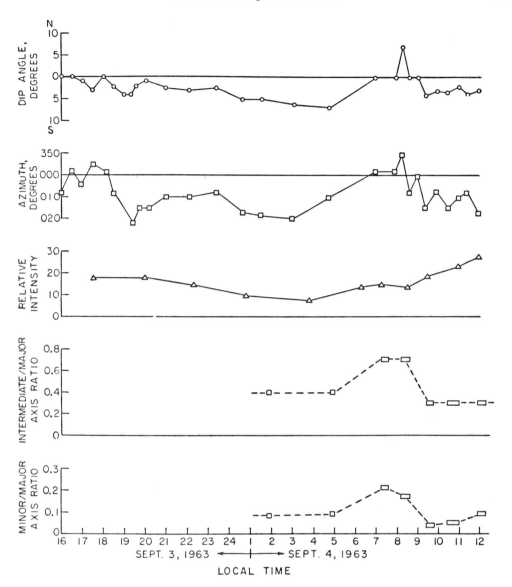

FIG. 40. Dip angle, azimuth, major axis intensity, and axis ratios as functions of local time; Mariposa, California; September 3, 4, 1963; frequency 150 cps.

sharply increased about 1000. When we couple this observation with the rotation of the azimuth, we can conclude that there were two thunderstorm cells, one which built up from 0500 to rotate the azimuth westward and the other which built up from 1000 and returned to its more normal position of about 010–015°. Alternatively, one storm moving in an arc could produce the same result.

(ii) *Theoretical and model explanation for azimuth and dip time variations.*— Certain of the problems posed by peculiar field data may be solved with the aid of theoretical or scale model analysis. The solutions of two induction problems will be presented here, one solved by theory and the other by scale model experiment.

(a) *Change of anomaly with orientation of major axis of ellipsoid of integration.*—

Table I. Mariposa, California

	Major	Intermediate	Minor
September 3, 1963			
1843–1913	1.0	0.4	0.06
2101–2128	1.0	0.4	0.06
2320–2337	1.0	0.3	0.06
September 4, 1963			
0143–0201	1.0	0.4	0.08
0447–0500	1.0	0.4	0.09
0714–0735	1.0	0.7	0.21
0815–0832	1.0	0.7	0.17
0925–0945	1.0	0.3	0.04
1026–1055	1.0	0.3	0.05
1157–1220	1.0	0.3	0.09
1318–1332	1.0	0.3	0.11
1412–1426	1.0	0.3	0.03
November 29, 1963			
1800–1820	1.0	0.8	0.4
2005–2015	1.0	0.7	0.2
2047–2052	1.0	0.5	0.3
2210–2230	1.0	0.5	0.2
November 30, 1963			
0950–1000	1.0	0.5	0.3
1157–1206	1.0	0.4	0.4
1313–1321	1.0	0.4	0.4
1517–1527	1.0	0.5	0.3

We have observed at Mariposa that the dip angle changes from 8°N as the azimuth of the major axis of the ellipsoid rotates from east to west of north. While it is evident from the areal survey of dip angles that the distribution of subsurface conductors may be complex, let us assume a very simple distribution of one North-South conductor in the area of interest and let us assume that the conductor may be represented by an infinite cylinder in free space. For an inducing field we shall assume an elliptically polarized field of major to intermediate axis ratio of 2.5:1; we assume no minor (vertical) axis of the inducing field for this analysis.

As the major axis of inducing ellipse is rotated from parallel through normal to parallel to the axis of the cylinder, i.e. the angle β changes from $-90°$ to $+90°$, the resultant horizontal ellipse changes form as Figure 42 displays. (Ward and Fraser, 1965, present a discussion of the computations involved in preparing the machine plotted ellipses.) If we now measure the inclination in the direction of the major axis of the resultant horizontal ellipse we find a systematic variation of the characteristics of the vertical ellipse, as is shown in Figure 43. The vertical sections of the latter figure rotate as the major axis of of the inducing field rotates so as to maintain a positive sign always for the dip angle as Figure 44 indicates. While this model shows the gross variation of 0 to 15 degrees of dip angle, it does not explain a reversal of dip angle. Let us then examine a second model.

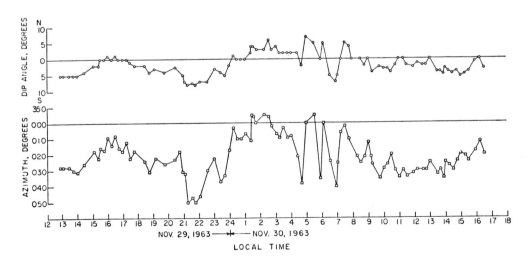

FIG. 41. Dip angle and azimuth diurnal variations; Mariposa, California; November 29, 30, 1963; frequency 150 cps.

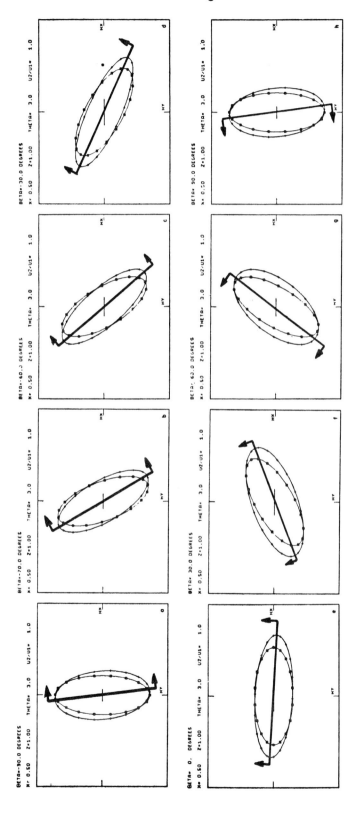

Fig. 42. Inducing (squares), secondary (dots), and resultant (crosses) ellipses in horizontal plane as function of rotation of inducing ellipse relative to axis of cylinder. Point of observation located at $x=0.50$, $z=1.00$ from axis of cylinder where x and z are horizontal and vertical distances, in arbitrary units. Theta is the induction number $\theta=(\sigma_2\mu_2\omega)^{1/2}R$ for the cylinder where σ_2 and μ_2 are conductivity and permeability of cylinder, ω is angular frequency, and R is the radius of the cylinder. The permeability ratio of cylinder to host is μ_2/μ_1.

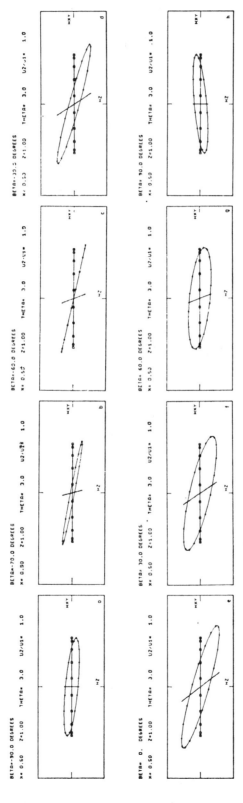

FIG. 43. Secondary (dots) and resultant (crosses) ellipses in vertical plane as function of rotation of inducing ellipse relative to axis of cylinder. $H_{xy} - H_z$ vertical plane passes through major axis of resultant ellipse.

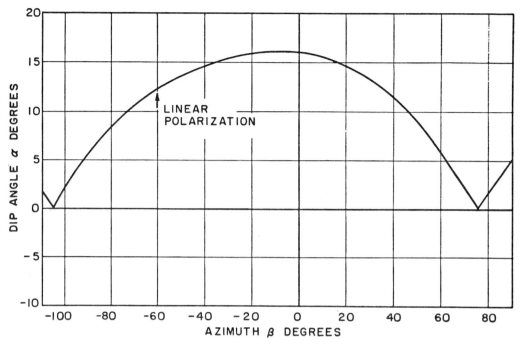

Fig. 44. Dip angle as function of rotation of inducing ellipse relative to axis of cylinder.

(b) *Change of anomaly with orientation of linearly polarized field relative to two obliquely oriented dikes.*—Two aluminum sheets, representing vertical dikes, were placed in a uniform alternating magnetic field. The dikes were oriented at 30 degrees to one another and the linearly polarized primary field rotated relative to the dikes. A traverse was made along a line normal to the bisector of the angle between the two dikes. Figure 45 portrays the geometry of dikes, fields, and traverse plus the resulting quadrature component of the vertical field measurements along the traverse. A phase reference for the measurements was obtained from a small coil wound on a remote dipole transmitter. The remoteness and small relative size of the transmitting coil virtually assured a uniform field in the vicinity of the dikes.

For primary field orientation (1), the lefthand dike is energized while the righthand one is not; the vertical field quadrature changes from positive to negative precisely where the traverse cuts the lefthand dike as expected. For primary field orientation (3), exactly the opposite occurs. However, a sign confusion can arise in interpreting data where the field is nearly parallel to structure and for this reason we employ the vector method of data presentation (Hallof and Sutherland, 1962). The direction of the vector is that of the resultant field, which we here assume to be roughly that of the inducing field. The length of the vector is proportional to the dip angle, which we here assume to be roughly proportional to the quadrature vertical field. We then can readily recognize which way the field dips and by how much. A crossover, i.e. a conductor axis, is clearly in direct coincidence with the lefthand sheet for orientation (1) of the inducing field and in direct coincidence with the righthand sheet for orientation (3) of the inducing field. For orientation (2), two crossovers occur which, by the uninitiated, might be interpreted as a proper and reverse

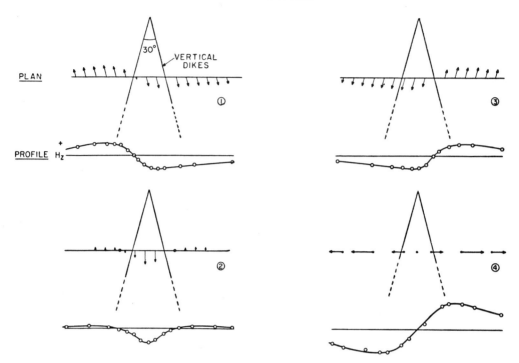

Fig. 45. Two obliquely intersecting vertical sheets in uniform horizontal linearly polarized field; vertical field profiles as function of direction of inducing field; arbitrary units.

crossover if only the profile was plotted. Note that both crossovers lie outside of either conductor! Profile (2) is very roughly the algebraic sum of profiles (1) and (3). When the field is roughly normal to the bisector between the two sheets, the resulting profile is roughly the algebraic difference between profiles (1) and (3) and the crossover is midway between the two sheets. For intermediate orientations, we would then be able to add profiles (1) and (3), with appropriate weights on each depending upon cosines of the angles the field makes with each of the sheets. This model provides a satisfactory explanation of the Mariposa observations. Obviously, there are any number of multiple-conductor models which might explain the Mariposa data and we have explored only one. The next most obvious complexity to add is an elliptically polarized field rather than a linearly polarized field.

(iii) *Overburden and topography re-* *sponse.*—It is self-evident that if we place a thin uniform horizontal conducting sheet, even of finite dimensions, in a uniform horizontal inducing field then the secondary field due to the sheet will be zero. Thus we can assert that if a uniform conducting overburden of finite extent is placed in a uniform horizontal inducing sferic field, then the response of the overburden will be almost zero unless the overburden is very thick. Several factors, however, tend to cause some concern for overburden response in practical situations as we shall attempt to elucidate.

(a) *The inducing field is not horizontal.* —We have demonstrated by the integration ellipsoids that there is usually a vertical component of the resultant field, but this is small unless an anomaly tilts the field. Thus we should not, at first glance, expect a significant anomaly from relatively uniform overburden unless the field is tilted by a nearby conductor. An extreme example of what might result from tilting is contained in

Figure 46. For this example, from Northern Quebec, Canada, a very long continuous sulfide body has tilted the field by approximately 90 degrees. Under this tilt, one could interpret that wet swampy overburden is giving rise to anomalies at locations B and C although, in this instance, there is no assurance that these "swamp" anomalies aren't due to faults or sulfides underlying the low-lying swampy ground. Dip angles of the order of 90 degrees are unusual but such steep dips are not necessary to cause an overburden response.

(b) "Telluric" currents flow in the overburden.—There are reports of Afmag anomalies due to 150 cps telluric current of differing densities in adjacent formations. Brant (1965b), cites andesite-alluvium contacts in basin and range terrain as locations for the occurrence of telluric current density contrasts. One can in fact deduce that a worldwide system of surface currents flow and that the currents arise by induction within a uniform earth by an electromagnetic wave with the electric vector having a component parallel to the earth's surface. Conversely, one can assume that the currents arise, regardless of the orientation of the inducing field electric vector, in a laterally nonuniform spherical earth. One cannot assume, logically, that audio frequency telluric currents have a source within the earth.

It is difficult to devise an experiment which will prove or disprove an alluvium origin for Afmag anomalies. However, Ware (1966) reports on one experiment intended to clarify this point. An Afmag anomaly was found in the center of a relatively narrow ($\frac{1}{2}$ mile wide, several miles long) alluvial valley in basin and range topography in Nevada. The question then arose of whether the anomaly was due to a fault or shear beneath the valley or whether it was due to a telluric current concentration in the alluvium of the valley. Several pole-dipole resistivity and induced polarization traverses

were made across and parallel to the Afmag conductor; one of the cross-profiles appears in Figure 47, beneath the observed Afmag dip angle profile. The pole-dipole sounding is readily interpreted in terms of a two layer earth model with the layer contact basin shaped. There is some evidence of a subsurface conductivity inhomogeneity at the locations of the Afmag crossover. Note from the short pole-dipole spreads that the alluvium probably has a resistivity of the order of 70 ohm-ft. The large pole-dipole spreads were not large enough to assure that the apparent resistivities reflected bedrock alone, but one assumes that the bedrock resistivity is at least 230 ohm-ft. Subsequent expander pole-dipole arrays with a 300-ft dipole suggested a bedrock resistivity of 250 ohm-ft. To be sure of this latter figure, we used a resistivity array in which the current electrodes some 4,000 ft apart straddled the valley and potential measurements were made over the central third of this distance with a 100 ft receiving dipole. (We call this the Brant array after Arthur A. Brant who introduced us to it.) This latter survey indicates a bedrock resistivity of the order of 2,200 ohm-ft and one profile from the survey is shown in Figure 47. This profile was observed about 200 ft north of the Afmag profile. Again a small resistivity anomaly coincides with the Afmag crossover. Finally we measured the telluric potentials at 150 cps both on outcrop on one side of the valley and on the alluvial fill in the center of the valley; the potentials were measured parallel to the valley. It is difficult to provide a quantitative measure of natural electric fields because of the dynamic range and changing direction of the electric vector. However, in Figure 48 we attempt to portray the range of typical voltages, a mean, and the maximum values of short transients for (a) observation on outcrop on a hillside, (b) observation on alluvium in the valley, and (c) a differential output representing the

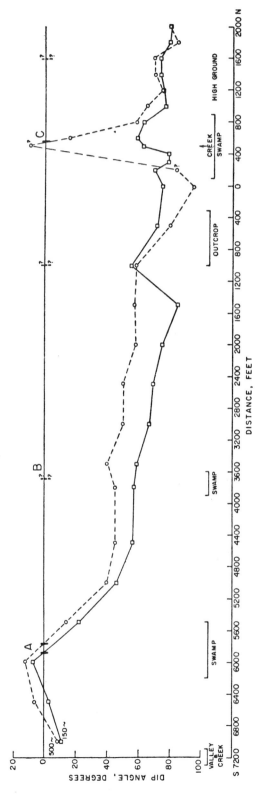

FIG. 46. Extreme tilting of major axis of ellipsoid caused by very long "Pyrrhotite dike" at location A.

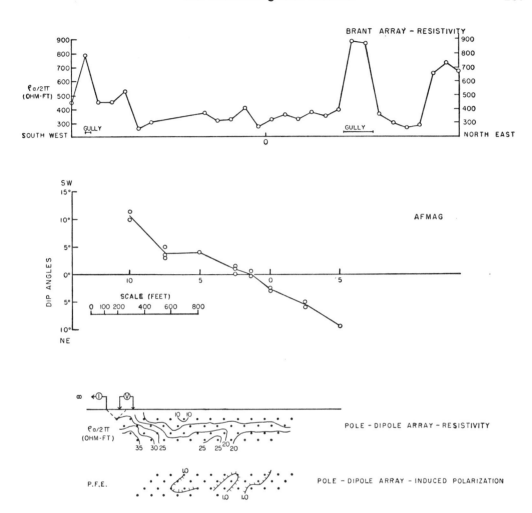

Fig. 47. Afmag anomaly and resistivity values over narrow alluvial valley; Basin and Range terrain, Nevada.

differential between voltages observed simultaneously on outcrop and alluvium. From this data we conclude that the voltages over outcrop range from about three to five times larger than those over alluvium. Since the ratio of resistivities of outcrop and alluvium is about this same order, we are inclined to deduce that there is no gross difference in telluric current density between alluvium and outcrop in this area. The Afmag anomaly present appears to be a genuine inhomogeneity in the bedrock which might even have an associated alluvial anomaly. A buried fault from which solutions are percolating upward

into alluvium is a possible cause. The valley as a whole does not seem to be producing the Afmag anomaly.

This and other examples tend to make us discredit telluric currents in bounded overburden as a cause for Afmag anomalies.

(c) *Topographic effect.*—If we study the telluric current problem in another way, we can make an elementary analysis of the possibility that topographic ridges, of the same conductivity as the plateau on which they occur, alone give rise to Afmag anomalies. Let us assume, for simplicity, a uniform plane electromagnetic wave incident upon a homo-

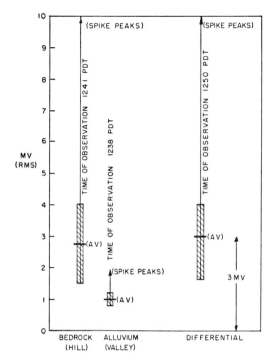

FIG. 48. Natural 150 cps potentials measured across 4,000-ft electrode spreads deployed parallel to narrow valley.

geneous isotropic conductive earth in which displacement currents are negligible. The reflection coefficient for normal incidence of plane waves is

$$R = \frac{(\alpha_1 - \alpha_0)^2 + \beta_1{}^2}{(\alpha_1 + \alpha_0)^2 + \beta_2{}^2}$$

where

$$\alpha_1 = \beta_1 = \sqrt{\frac{\omega\mu_0\sigma_1}{2}}, \quad \alpha_0 = \sqrt{\frac{\omega\mu_0\sigma_0}{2}}$$

σ_1 is the conductivity of the earth
μ_0 is the permeability of free space
σ_0 is the conductivity of air.

Since σ_0 is approximately zero, and hence α_0 is much less than α_1, the reflection coefficient has the approximate value of unity. This result pertains whenever we neglect displacement currents and assume a large contrast between the conductivity of air and the conductivity of the earth.

Then the horizontal magnetic field at the surface of the earth arises 50 percent from the source and 50 percent from reflection. The fact that reflection does occur implies that horizontal electric currents flow in the earth, i.e., a telluric sheet exists. The current density decays exponentially with distance into the earth such that approximately $\frac{2}{3}$ of the total current flow is contained within the depth of penetration.

$$\delta = \sqrt{\frac{2}{\omega\mu_0\sigma_1}}.$$

For a 150 cps electromagnetic wave incident on an earth of conductivity $\sigma_1 = 10^{-2}$ mho/m, the depth of penetration is approximately 1,200 ft. Approximately 20 percent of the current flows within the first 300 ft below the surface and, hence, about 10 percent of the measured magnetic field arises from this depth interval.

The above development assumes a plane reflecting earth surface, but the model can be used to give an order of magnitude estimate of magnetic field anomaly in terrain with relief. For example let us assume a ridge 300 ft high, then approximately 10 percent of the observed surface magnetic fields at 150 cps arise in the induced currents in the ridge. Assuming a 10 percent vertical reflected component, i.e. equal to the horizontal reflected component, could thus occur, an observed dip angle maximum of 6 degrees would be observed. The conductivity chosen for the ground is perhaps high even for basin and range terrain in the southwestern United States so our computations should, indeed, represent an anomalous situation. We stress that this is not a rigorous analysis, but we do believe that it places a reasonable upper limit on the Afmag anomaly to be expected from topography alone.

We should note that a ridge of mean conductivity 10^{-2} mho/m is seldom homogeneous so that if dip angles occur over a ridge, then in all probability they will be related to a conductive shear or fault or carbonaceous horizon within the ridge. Further, if the ridge were homogeneous, it would produce a reversed crossover for a ground survey since the currents in the ridge would be above the observer when he is off the ridge. A normal crossover would occur in an airborne survey.

(d) *Augmentation of anomalies by telluric currents.*—Brant (1965a) reports that "Afmag anomalies . . . are caused by the increased flux field resulting (a) from increased natural ground current concentrations roughly proportional to $\sigma_{zone}/\sigma_{surrounding}$, in somewhat better conducting zones or areas, and (b) from the eddy current inductive effects generated by the flux linkage of the natural earth's EM field with conducting bodies approximately proportional to $f\,(t\sigma)_{zone}$ . . . anomalies therefore can arise even when the σ_{zone} is not exceptionally high, but still higher than the surroundings."

Brant does not evaluate the relative magnitudes of the two effects but states, for a particular anomaly, that, "half this anomaly would have been contributed by fact (a) and half by (b)."

It is virtually impossible to assess the correct relative magnitudes of the effects without elaborate model experiments. We can, however, make an order of magnitude estimate of the effect (a). To do this, we assume that the inhomogeneity is not so large that it grossly modifies the telluric current distribution. Then, for a host rock conductivity of 10^{-2} mho/m, 10 percent of the surface magnetic fields are due to a "uniform" telluric sheet. The anomaly due to telluric current flow is then an anomaly in a field small relative to the inducing field. It seems probable that this contribution will be closer to 10 percent of the observed anomaly than the 50 percent that Brant suggests. Again we stress that this problem requires field and model study for solution.

(e) *Fault anomalies.*—If a semi-infinite fault separates two formations of different conductivities, the telluric currents will be of different densities in the two formations. Near the fault a vertical component of magnetic field will occur, giving rise to a spatial variation of dip angles but not a crossover. If either formation is bounded laterally, a crossover from positive to negative dip angles will occur. The width of the bounded formation determines the slope of the dip angle profile near the crossover. Telluric current density contrasts thus should lead to some Afmag anomalies, but information on the magnitude of these anomalies is lacking.

If the differing geologic units in contact have a finite depth extent, then the telluric current contrast may not be effective in producing a measurable vertical magnetic field. In particular, if the depth extent of adjacent faulted blocks is much less than a skin depth for any given frequency, then the vertical magnetic fields may be very small; telluric current density contrasts may not always produce measurable Afmag anomalies.

Similarly, an alluvial basin must have a depth of the order of a skin depth before it will lead to appreciable Afmag anomalies due to the telluric current density contrast effect.

Thus throughout this discussion of the Afmag method when mention has been made of anomalies due to faults, the reference is to the only cause we *know* to exist, i.e. currents are induced in a conductive fault zone. We do not yet commit ourselves to the deduction that a fault, by bringing two formations of different conductivities into contact, will produce an appreciable anomaly on account of the telluric current density contrast between the two formations; we do not yet have experimental evaluation of anomalies which may arise in this fashion.

(iv) *Apparent shift of crossover.*—The model results for two dikes at an oblique

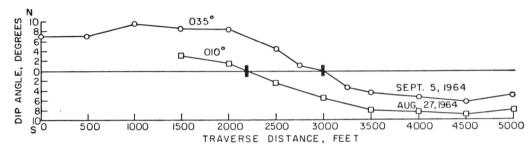

F𝒾ɢ. 49. Field example of Afmag profile in which crossover shifts 800 ft as field rotates 25 degrees.

angle, Figure 45, present an idea of the lateral distance a crossover may move, relative to the conductor-axes, when multiple conductors exist. A field example which dramatically illustrates this type of situation is illustrated in Figure 49. For this example, observed in a region of multiple intersecting faults in basin and range terrain in Nevada, the crossover moves laterally in excess of 800 ft as the major axis of the field rotates from 010°T. To 035°T. This limitation clearly must be appreciated if one is to be able to interpret correctly, that in fact both crossovers could represent conductor axes or, as Figure 45 shows, neither crossover may be a conductor axis. This problem presents the most difficulties when the field is nearly parallel to a pair of conductors intersecting at a small angle.

There seems to be a possibility that we can recognize a multiple conductor situation even when only one of the conductors is detected by the dip angle measurement. We note from Figure 45 that the problem really stems from the fact that the vertical magnetic field is an odd function of position along a traverse and that when we add two such quantities then we develop a profile which may have positive and negative regions with the crossover from positive to negative occurring anywhere relative to the two conductors. If on the other hand we add horizontal components, which are even functions, we will expect to obtain largely positive values and the peaks in these positive values will occur directly over the conductors. This analysis then indicates that if we measure the azimuth, as well as the dip, we can remove the ambiguity from the interpretation. Figure 50 exhibits two records of coincident anomalies in both azimuth and dip.

An additional piece of information is provided by the azimuth. The azimuth will rotate toward the normal to the conductor-axis and so we can deduce, from Figure 50(a), that the conductor causing the anomaly strikes more south of east than 105 degrees and yet not as far as 188 degrees. Figure 50(b) presents an example where the conductor must strike north of 092 degrees and perhaps is very close to 090 degrees. In actual fact, further dip angle profiles established that the conductor of Figure 50(a) strikes approximately 135 degrees while that of Figure 50(b) strikes roughly 090 degrees.

Unfortunately, the measurement of azimuth typically has an accuracy no better than $\pm 5°$ and this limits the usefulness of azimuth measurements. However, it is absolutely essential that azimuth measurements be made and the vector method of presenting data utilized if reliable interpretations are to be made.

(e) *Depth of exploration.*—An airborne Afmag survey over an outcropping long dikelike massive sulfide body has indicated anomalies to at least 2,000 ft above the surface as Figure 51 indicates. If this semi-infinite dike is buried, then attenuation will reduce the amplitude of the anomaly depending upon the conductivity of the host. Further the finite conductivity of the host, in electrical contact with the dike, can alter the shape and magnitude of the anomaly. We have no theoretical or model work available

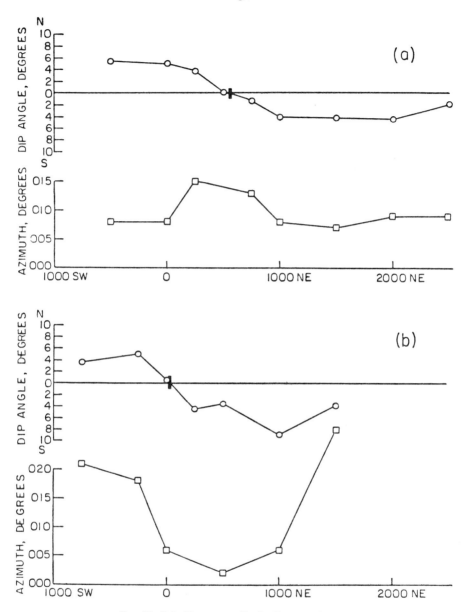

Fig. 50. Coincident anomalies in dip and azimuth.

to guide us on this problem. It seems reasonable, however, to assume that the largest targets in a resistive medium might be detected at depths of the order of 1,000 ft. Experimental confirmation of this estimate is difficult to obtain.

(f) *Plotting the information derived from a survey.*—In the most elementary representation, the observed dip angles are plotted at

the point of observation and dip angle profiles constructed therefrom as in Figure 52. The convention employed in this plot is that if the major axis of the ellipsoid dips west or south, the reading is positive; all sections are drawn either facing nominally north or west. A conductor axis is located where the readings change from positive on the left of the section to negative on the right of the sec-

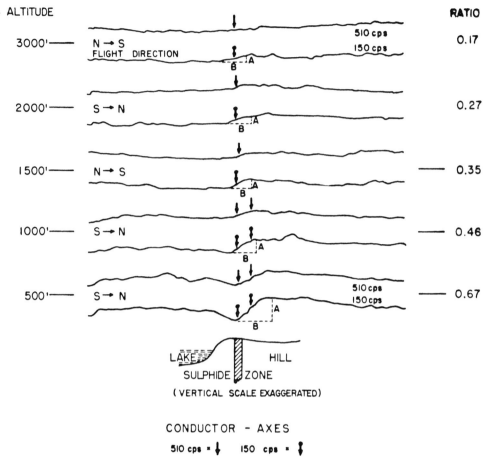

ALTITUDE

3000'—— N → S
         FLIGHT   DIRECTION

2000'—— S → N

1500'—— N → S

1000'—— S → N

500'——   S → N

LAKE   HILL
SULPHIDE ZONE
(VERTICAL   SCALE EXAGGERATED)

CONDUCTOR - AXES
510 cps = ↓   150 cps = ↓

RATIO

0.17

0.27

0.35

0.46

0.67

510 cps
150 cps

FIG. 51. Variation of anomaly with aircraft altitude over long linear conductive body. Ratio on right is A/B. Note that this crossover is in the opposite sense to that defined on page 242.

tion, i.e. at a "crossover." This method of data presentation is quite satisfactory when the major axis of the inducing ellipsoid is within ± 45 degrees of normal to the axis of the subsurface inhomogeneity. However, when the major axis of the ellipsoid is nearly parallel to the axis of the inhomogeneity, or when two or more obliquely oriented inhomogeneities are present, the vector method (Hallof and Sutherland, 1962) of plotting Afmag results should be employed. With this method, illustrated in Figure 53, the azimuth of the major axis of the ellipsoid is represented by an arrow whose length is proportional to the dip of the major axis. The sense of the arrow is most frequently chosen to be in the direction of dip. A reversal in sense then can indicate a crossover. Note from Figure 45 the importance of the vector method when dealing with two obliquely oriented conductors.

V. Methods of Electromagnetic Prospecting (Air)

A. Introduction

Many different airborne electromagnetic systems have been developed in the last seventeen years. Some of these have survived competition, others have not, but the number remaining is still very substantial. We cannot hope to discuss them all in detail and so we will outline the basic problems encountered in designing airborne electromagnetic systems suited to operation from fixed wing aircraft (AEM systems) and from helicop-

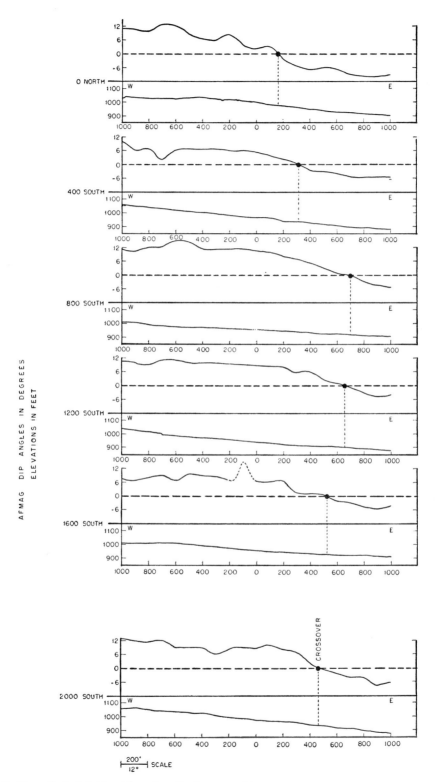

Fig. 52. Profile method of plotting Afmag data. Both topographic and dip angle profiles are shown in this example. Crossovers are marked by solid circles.

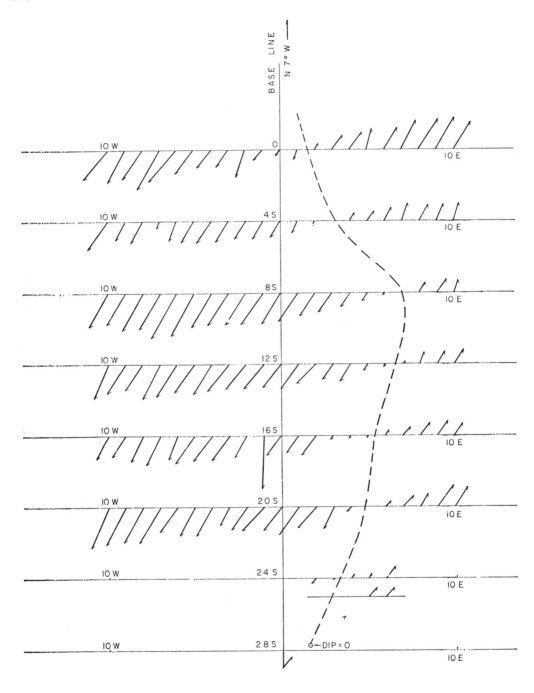

FIG. 53. Vector method of plotting Afmag data. Conductor axis marked by dashed line.

ters. We will then proceed to indicate how some of the systems have met these problems, and in the process we will provide a brief description of the design, operation, and characteristics of these systems. For a general survey of airborne electromagnetic systems the reader is referred to an article by Pemberton (1962). Definitive articles on results with specific systems have been preprepared by (Ward, 1957; Hedstrom and Parasnis, 1958; Tornquist, 1958; Ward and Barker, 1958; Cheriton, 1959; Hedstrom and Parasnis, 1959; Paterson, 1959; Tikhonov and Dmitriev, 1959 a, b; Fleming and Brooks, 1960; Joklik, 1960; MacKay and Paterson, 1960; Mizyuk, 1960; Boyd and Roberts, 1961; Khomenyuk, 1961; Paterson, 1961b; Pemberton, 1961a, b; Schaub, 1961a, b; Rattew, 1962; Schaub, 1962a, b, c; Wieduwilt, 1962.)

The first successful totally airborne electromagnetic system was placed in operation in 1950, but intensive and extensive use of such devices by more than one company was delayed until mid-1955 (Pemberton, 1962). These developments were pioneered by McPhar Engineering Co. of Canada, Ltd., who with the technical staff of the International Nickel Company of Canada, Ltd.; developed the first system. Later, the McPhar engineers responsible for this development, W. O. Cartier, H. A. Harvey, G. H. McLaughlin, and W. A. Robinson, developed the helicopter system operated in 1955 by American Metal Company, the AEM system of Aerophysics of Canada, Ltd., and the Afmag system.

The Hunting Canso system was placed in operational use in Canada in 1954 after M. Puranen, A. Kahma, and V. Ronka, working under the auspices of the Geological Survey of Finland, had spent the years 1947 to 1953 developing it.

The purpose of all of the totally airborne systems is to locate, rapidly, good conductors of electricity within the top several hundred feet of the earth's surface. Such good conductors might include graphitic schists, carbonaceous sediments, fault and shear zones, swamps, etc., as well as the primary target, massive sulfide mineralization.

Normally, an AEM system does not respond to rock type as does an airborne magnetometer. Rather, it produces discrete anomalies only over such conductive media as listed above. Thus, in the normal sense, it is not a device for mapping structure. If, however, the structure in question contains such conductive media as massive sulfides or graphite, then the structure may be mapped by virtue of this association, i.e., indirectly (Frischknecht and Ekren, 1960).

We should not design an airborne survey to detect all of the economic deposits in a given area, as a statistic-economic analysis of the ore search problem will indicate (e.g., Slichter 1955). Some interesting sulfide bodies have been missed by AEM survey simply because it is not economic to place the flight lines sufficiently close together to ensure the detection of all bodies. Further, the results of one AEM survey over any area should not be expected to duplicate the results of a second AEM survey over the same area unless the same instrument is flown at the same height, the same speed, and in the same direction, along the same flight lines for both surveys. This latter point, while evident to anyone familiar with the different characteristics of various AEM systems, has always been a source of mystery to the uninitiated. It becomes even more mystifying when it is found that all AEM systems detect an overabundance of anomalies due to extraneous sources such as swamps, faults, carbonaceous sediments, etc.

The principle of most AEM systems in operation today is the measurement of the mutual impedance between two coils as this impedance is affected by the presence of nearby naturally occurring conductive bodies. With reference to Figure 54, current I flowing in the transmitting coil causes a voltage E to appear across the receiving coil. The ratio E/I of the voltage in the receiving coil to the current in the transmitting coil is known as the mutual impedance between the two coils. If a conductive body is brought near the two coils, distributed currents I_C will flow in it. These latter currents will cause a voltage E_C to appear in the receiving coil. Then the total voltage appearing

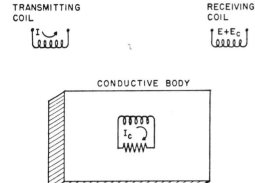

FIG. 54. Effect on mutual impedance of coil pair, with conductive body present. Schematically, the conductive body may be represented by an elementary dissipative circuit with current I_c.

across the receiving coil will be $E+E_C$, and the measured mutual impedance between the transmitting and receiving coils will be $(E+E_C)/I$; a change in measured mutual impedance occurs when the coils are brought near the conductive body. In general, E, E_C, and I will not have the same phase.

B. *Basic design problems*

The factors which must be considered in the design of an airborne electromagnetic system are numerous. Let us assume for the moment that we intend to place the transmitter in the aircraft and the receiver in a "bird" towed behind and below the aircraft. The mutual impedance between the transmitting and receiving coils is a function of the distance between the coils and of the rotation of one coil relative to the other. Since both of these quantities may vary as the bird moves relative to the aircraft, then the mutual impedance will vary in the same manner. Fictitious anomalies can arise in this fashion, which collectively may be looked upon as another source of "noise" which can obscure the "message" we seek. This source of noise, system instability noise, should be added to the list of noise sources we presented in the section on ground electromagnetic methods [Section IV A(a) (iv)]. The aircraft on which the transmitting coil is mounted will contain large metallic loops or sheets. These conductors will tend to lower the Q of the transmitting coil,

and to change the mutual impedance between transmitter and receiver. This change in mutual impedance can be time-dependent if, for example, the metal wings of the aircraft move asymmetrically relative to the transmitting coil. Another source of noise, aircraft noise, is generated in this fashion.

If the bird oscillates about its suspension axis, an alternating voltage will be induced in the receiving coil by the earth's main magnetic field. Bird noise will be developed in this fashion.

The aircraft engine can develop engine noise, i.e., stray transient magnetic fields; which must be minimized by shielding of spark plugs etc., if the bird is closer than 200 ft from the aircraft.

There will always be some response from a homogeneous plane earth for any practical EM system (see Figures 18-1, 18-2, 18-3, and 18-4 of Part A of this chapter, for a comparison of four coil configurations). This response is a function of the coil system, of the operating frequency, of the height of the aircraft above the ground and of the separation between transmitting and receiving coils. Then, if the system rotates about the towing axis, tilts relative to the ground, or if the separation changes, the response of the ground will not be independent of time. Fictitious anomalies can arise in this fashion; still another source of noise is added.

We must analyze each of these sources of noise in turn, and design a system which reduces them to a minimum. Yet, we must achieve the design without sacrificing information concerning the typical messages we seek to record. This optimization of message-to-noise ratio always results in some compromise between the various choices available to us. The distinctly different AEM systems available today represent the compromises selected by the various development groups.

Let us now analyze the problem by computing the sensitivity required of a trailing bird AEM system. We shall assume that the bird is to be towed 420 ft behind and 220 ft below the aircraft as illustrated in Figure 55 for the Hunting Canso system (Paterson, 1961a). As the aircraft traverses a conductor, an anomaly will be traced out. For a vertical half plane (sheet) conductor, the anomaly is

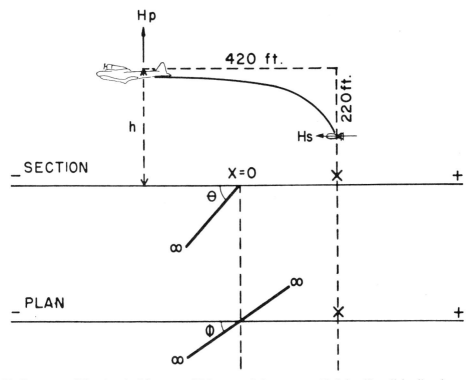

FIG. 55. Geometry of Hunting dual-frequency EM system flying over semi-infinite dike; flight direction angle ϕ relative to dike; dip of dike is θ (after Paterson, 1961a); height of aircraft is h.

described in Figure 56. Note that the anomaly amplitude decreases rapidly as the aircraft elevation increases. Height is measured from the aircraft and the readings are plotted beneath the towed receiving coil. The decrease in anomaly amplitude with aircraft height is proportional to the 4.1 power of height so that the ratio of secondary field H_S to primary field H_P is about eight parts in 1,000 at a height of 500 ft. Since we cannot expect to maintain an altitude of less than 500 ft consistently when flying over rolling terrain with a fixed wing aircraft of PBY dimensions, then clearly we will need to have sensitivity of the order of one part in 1,000 in order to recognize message over noise. It must be noted that the conductor chosen for the analysis is of infinite strike length and that the flight traverse was perpendicular to the strike of the conductor. For other flight directions and for smaller targets, we should like to improve the sensitivity by a factor of two to five. To illustrate this argument, we refer to Figure 57 which shows the theoretical

in-phase response of a disk. Thus we might consider a sensitivity of one part in 2,000 as fairly good, assuming that the Hunting system is typical, in terms of anomaly response, of all fixed wing airborne EM systems for which the transmitter-receiver separation is of order 420 ft.

Now let us consider the effects of relative

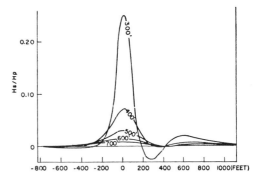

FIG. 56. Variation of in-phase anomaly with height for vertical half-plane; theoretical curves applicable to Hunting system (after Paterson, 1961a); $\phi=\theta=90°$; conductivity of dike is infinite.

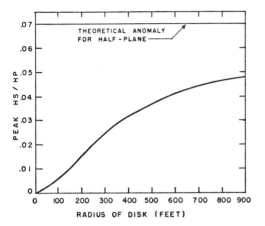

FIG. 57. Peak in-phase response over vertical disk as a function of disk radius; theoretical curve applicable to Hunting system (after Douloff, 1960a); $\phi=\theta=90°$; $h=400$ ft; conductivity of dike is infinite.

rotation between transmitting and receiving coils for some hypothetical EM system. For a minimum coupled system in which the axes of the coils are perpendicular, and one coil lies on the axis of the other the coupling is zero for true perpendicularity but varies as $\sin \alpha$ for a relative rotation of α degrees. A stability of one part in 2,000 must be obtained for our "ideal" system and this infers $\alpha=1/2,000$ or $\alpha=2$ minutes. This clearly is an impractical requirement. Note, however, that if we employ a maximum coupled system where the coils are coaxial, the rotational error varies as $\cos \alpha$; the stability requirement reduces to $\alpha=2°$. This does not appear to be an unreasonable requirement. Experience has shown, however, that obtaining a rotational stability of two degrees requires a very carefully designed "bird" operated in reasonably stable air. Aerodynamically the bird must "fly like a rock," i.e., it must present drag on one end and streamlining on the other, with small stabilizing fins but no air foil section. We should caution that the above analysis implies that the spectrum of the rotational bird noise seriously overlaps the spectra of the expected messages. If this is not the case then the rotational noise is relatively unimportant. Again experience tells us that considerable spectral overlap occurs.

The variation of the distance between transmitter and receiver must be one part in 6,000. The transmitted field as measured at the receiver is $H=K/r^3$ where K lumps the transmitting coil constants and r is the separation between transmitting and receiving coils. Then the fractional error in H to a variation in r is $\Delta H/H=3\Delta r/r$. For a 500-ft cable, this requires a position accuracy of one inch to ensure the H field stability of one part in 2,000. Restricting the flying to stable air with a well designed bird usually overcomes this problem. Oscillations of the bird in the earth's main magnetic field will lead to noise which can be minimized by good bird design and in particular by ensuring that if oscillations occur then their frequency is well outside the passband of the receiving coil system. For example, a voltage

$$ e = -N\frac{d\phi}{dt} = -N\mu H\frac{dA}{dt} $$

will be induced in the receiving coil by the alternating flux $\phi=\mu H$, where H is the earth's magnetic field, and dA/dt is the time rate of change of the area of the coil perpendicular to the field. If this area varies harmonically, the resulting voltage will be

$$ e = -\mu N H(-i\omega)Ae^{-i\omega t}. $$

The amplitude of the voltage is proportional to the frequency of oscillations and to the maximum area perpendicular to the field; the voltage is alternating at the frequency ω. As long as ω greatly differs from ω_0 the operating frequency (or harmonics) of the receiving coil system, it will not produce a high noise level.

The metallic parts of the aircraft are usually bothersome in producing fictitious anomalies only if the transmitting and receiving coils are asymmetrically placed relative to the center line of the aircraft, or if the aircraft metal parts move asymmetrically relative to the coil system. Gusts of wind can cause asymmetrical wing deflection, for example. This source of noise can only be investigated and minimized by experiment. It can be avoided by use of a wood-fiber aircraft.

For a system where the transmitter and receiver are rigidly fixed relative to one another, as is the case for helicopter electromagnetic (HEM) systems, the analysis is slightly different. The coil separation might vary from 20 ft to 60 ft. Anomaly amplitudes will now be smaller. For example, Figure 58 shows the response, as a function of height, for a 50-ft coil separation, from a dike-like body which approximates an infinite half-plane. If a helicopter flies 100 ft above the ground, a perfectly conductive half-plane at a depth of 200 ft. beneath the surface would yield an in-phase response of 50 parts per million (ppm) of the primary field. Evidently we should like to have a limiting sensitivity of the order of 10 ppm for this system to be comparable to the one discussed previously. Such a sensitivity appears to be realizable with some systems. Now the stability requirement on the coil separation becomes one part in 10^5 of field strength or about .001 inches in 50 ft of mechanical rigidity; this is a severe requirement which can only be met by mounting the coils on the ends of a rigid structure.

The engine noise level in an HEM system can be another serious problem if the rigid coil mounting is brought close to the helicopter. Magnetic shielding of magnetos and generators becomes essential if a transmitter of modest power is desired. With sufficient field strength from the transmitter this problem is not important, but seldom can we afford the weight inherent in a powerful transmitter.

The rigid boom on which we mount the coils of an HEM system may be mounted directly on the helicopter or towed from a helicopter. All such systems employ a vertical coaxial coil array. One fixed wing system retains this method in principle and a second uses vertical coplanar coils mounted on the wing tips.

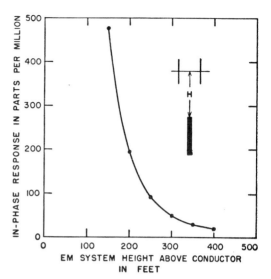

Fig. 58. Maximum in-phase response versus height of helicopter EM system above half-plane (courtesy H. V. W. Donohoo and Texas Gulf Sulphur Co.).

In the above computations of limiting sensitivity, we tacitly assumed that all recordings were of anomalous fields in-phase with the transmitted field. In several systems only the quadrature component is recorded. While the analysis differs in these cases, the end result is much the same and the stated "ideal" sensitivities for towed bird or rigid boom systems of one part in 2,000 and one part in 10^5 respectively, is about all that can be achieved. Experimental evaluation of limiting sensitivity must be established, since it is impossible to compute the ultimate noise level. This evaluation should be carried out under various air turbulence conditions and over various surface conductivities.

Thus in summary, minimization of noise sources may be accomplished in the following ways:

(a) Instrument noise

Source	*Solutions*
(1) movement of one coil relative to another, movement of receiving coil in earth's static field, movement of ferrous and or conductive objects relative to receiving coil in presence of earth's static field, microphonic noises in receiving coil.	—ensure that mechanical resonances of the coil system lie well outside of the frequency band —use coil configuration which minimizes this effect (maximum coupled systems) —remove ferrous and conductive objects from vicinity of coils —use integration, data smoothing, or other data processing scheme

	—use phase sensitive detector —fly in calm air of early morning or late afternoon
(2) ignition and electrical noise	—use spark suppression on aircraft —use magnetic shields for spark plugs and generators
(3) airframe noise	—buck out airframe anomalies
(4) thermal drift	—use ac decoupling circuit

(b) Disturbance field noise

(1) power line fundamental and harmonics	—use 60 cps band-pass rejection —choose operating frequency to be between harmonic —use phase sensitive detectors —use high dipole moment for transmitting coil
(2) sferics	—use phase sensitive detector —use high dipole moment for transmitting coil —use operating frequency of 1,000–3,000 cps where sfer signal strength is minimal —use integration, data smoothing, or other data proces ing scheme.
(c) Terrain noise (response of uniform layer of overburden)	—evaluate by use of multiple frequency operation single very low frequency —use short coil separation —use preferable coil configuration (see discussions und individual systems)

Noise evaluation is but part of the picture, however. We must, in addition, concern ourselves with the message amplitude and resolution of adjacent conductors for various coil configurations. This evaluation is simply carried out with the aid of laboratory scale model experiments and by mathematical analysis. Some concept of the anomaly amplitudes and resolution may be obtained from a subsequent section on scale modelling. It will be evident there that the highest resolution is obtained with a device of short coil separation flown at low altitudes. Resolution decreases with increase in either aircraft altitude or coil separation.

One will note that magnetometers and scintillometers are often added to an electromagnetometer in the survey aircraft. The magnetometer has proven to be especially useful in diagnostic analysis of the probable cause of airborne electromagnetic anomalies.

C. *Description of operating AEM systems*

Some literature is available on several of the AEM and HEM systems. From this literature the following descriptions are drawn.

(a) *Inco AEM System. (Prepared by the staff of The International Nickel Co. of Canada, Ltd.)*

(1) *System Basis.*—Inco's airborne electromagnetic method (AEM) consists of a means of creating alternating electromagnetic fields and a means of continuously measuring and comparing the resultant fields at a point located at a distance from the source while the fields are moved over a set path at a substantially constant speed and altitude above the terrain.

The establishment of the required fields is accomplished by the use of two air core coils mutually orthogonal, one of which contains the direction of flight in its plane and the other orthogonally mounted to the flight direction and tilted from the vertical. Each coil is excited at one or more frequencies. A similar set of coils is mounted in the towed receiver, thus providing a set of coplanar and coaxial coupled coils. The geometry of the preferred system is shown in Figure 59, although other geometric patterns have been used.

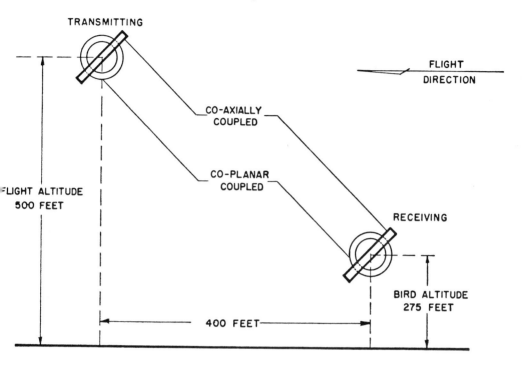

TRANSMITTING

FLIGHT DIRECTION

CO-AXIALLY COUPLED

CO-PLANAR COUPLED

FLIGHT ALTITUDE 500 FEET

RECEIVING

BIRD ALTITUDE 275 FEET

400 FEET

COIL CONFIGURATION

Fɪɢ. 59. Geometry of the Inco preferred AEM system.

The system has been successfully used with both two and three frequencies but, for the sake of simplicity, the two frequency system will be described. For the three frequency system, the third frequency is transmitted on the coplanar coupled coil.

Five channels of signal information are normally recorded. The most important channel is the main signal recording which shows the difference between the amplitudes of the received signals on the co-axial and coplanar coupled coils. The difference measurement is used as this reduces the effect of variations in relationship between the transmitters and receivers without hindering the detection of conductive material.

Two channels record the changes in amplitude for the individual fields as detected at the receivers. Although these recordings contain variations due to relative motion between receiver and trans-

mitter, it is possible under reasonable conditions to determine which field made the greatest contribution to an anomaly on the main signal channel.

Two other channels are used to record the phase relationship between the transmitted signals and received signals. This information is not used as an indication of a conductor, but rather as an additional aid in the interpretation of anomalies recorded on the main signal channel.

A photograph of the record obtained on flights over Whistle Mine on reciprocal courses in east-west directions is shown in Figure 61. Calibration marks are included at the start of the record. These marks represent one part in fifty of the received signal on the amplitude channels and one degree change in phase relation on the phase channels. Gains of the system are arbitrarily set so that these changes result in 15-mm deflections on the record. Calibration of the terrain clearance recording is

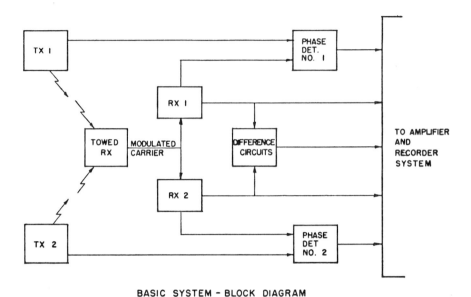

BASIC SYSTEM - BLOCK DIAGRAM

FIG. 60. Schematic representation of circuitry for Inco AEM system.

not shown on this section of record, but the values have been indicated on the photograph.

The types of anomalous responses of the coplanar and coaxial coupled coil systems can be seen from the individual amplitude or "alone" channels. Reduction of the misalignment errors in the signal channel without cancellation of the anomalous responses can be seen from a comparison of the alone and signal channels. A small sulfide deposit to the west of Whistle Mine, which has been confirmed by drilling, is indicated on the signal channel by a small arrow.

The system transmitters are held to very close frequency and amplitude tolerances.

The receiver system consists of two parts, one of which is located within the towed receiver (bird) and the other within the aircraft proper. The towed receiver contains the filters and summing circuits plus a common amplifier. A combined signal is sent to the aircraft via the tow cable as a modulation on a radio frequency carrier. Filtering circuits within the towed receiver provide a very narrow band-pass system thus reducing the noise. Within the aircraft proper, the signal is demodu-

lated, and, after suitable amplification, rectification, and filtering, the signals are applied to differencing circuits and then to the recording system as shown in Figure 60. In addition to the basic equipment, a radio altimeter and camera are carried to record terrain clearance and position relative to the ground. A magnetometer is also normally carried on survey and the data recorded coincident with the EM data. The magnetic data has not been shown in Figure 61.

(2) *Frequencies.*—Numerous frequency combinations have been used between 100 and 2,500 cps. Although various combinations of coil configurations and frequencies are possible, in the preferred system where more than two frequencies are involved, the additional frequencies are transmitted on the coplanar coupled coil.

(3) *Coil separation.*—In operation, the aircraft normally maintains an altitude of 500 ft above the terrain and the towed receiver is suspended from 500 ft of cable. The aerodynamics of the system are such that a 400-ft horizontal separation and a bird altitude of approximately 275 ft are obtained at an airspeed of approximately 110 mph.

(4) *Noise level.*—The noise level from all sources except geologic, sferic, and coil misalignment is below 1,500 ppm on the amplitude channels and less than a fifteenth of one degree on the phase channels.

Some signal anomalies of 4,000 ppm are considered worth investigating. Noise from misalignment of coils due to turbulence and to a lesser extent aircraft maneuvers must be maintained below this level on the signal channel to avoid masking valid anomalies. This precludes survey flying under rough air conditions. Misalignment noise on the alone channels is inherent and is permitted to reach levels which obscure all detail, providing cancellation on the signal channel is within required limits. Misalignment noise 'does

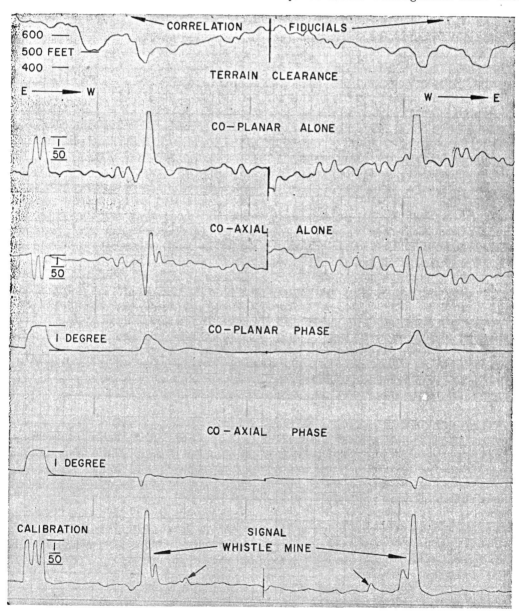

FIG. 61. Data recorded over Whistle Mine with Inco AEM system.

not affect the phase channels materially.

Geologic noise in some areas has been troublesome but has been reduced by choice of operating frequencies.

Sferics in summertime frequently reduce the quality of the recordings in particular when they occur in conjunction with air turbulence. Transmitted power levels are maintained sufficiently high that sferic noise alone seldom results in cancellation of a flight.

The noise resulting from misalignment of coils is the limiting factor on the system. Other noise could be reduced sufficiently to permit reliable detection of anomalies much less than 4,000 ppm. To do this at present, however, would entail a reduction in productive flying time in order to reduce the misalignment noise.

(5) *Equipment weight.*—The weight of the equipment as a complete system including ancilliary equipment such as a winch, camera, racks, and cables, etc., will vary between 600 and 800 lb, dependent on the frequencies and circuitry used. Complementary systems normally carried in survey aircraft, such as magnetometers, are not included in the above weights.

(6) *Aircraft.*—Up to the present time, the system has only been installed in Anson Mark V aircraft. The wooden construction of this aircraft allows interior mounting of the transmitting coils. The Anson is also very reasonable to operate from a cost standpoint and has desirable flight characteristics for airborne geophysical surveys.

The system could be used in conjunction with a metal skinned aircraft and externally mounted coils if considered desirable.

(7) *Power requirements.*—Total power requirements of the system are approximately three kilowatts and vary with the model of the installed equipment. Models using vacuum tubes require power at 115 volts, 800 cps as well as 28 volts dc, while the transistor models require only a 28 volt dc power supply.

(8) *Special features.*—Features of the system are the multiple frequency dual coil configuration used, the large separa-tion between transmitting and receiving coils, and the difference method of recording the signal.

The design of the equipment is such as to permit detection of conductive material at depth and provide sufficient data for interpretation of the relative merits of the conductors detected.

(b) *The rotary field method—Summarized from information provided by AB Elektrisk Malmletning, Sweden.*—The rotating magnetic field method was invented by Hedstrom and Tegholm in 1955. A rotating magnetic field is formed when a magnetic dipole is rotated about an axis at right angles to the dipole axis. Referring to Figure 62 the rotating field is produced by currents, 90 degrees out-of-phase with each other, flowing in a pair of orthogonal coils. This field is circularly polarized since the currents are maintained identical. Two orthogonal receiving coils are also used, each of which is coplanar with one transmitting coil. The third axis z-z^1 at the transmitter is the axis about which the field rotates; the receiving coil axes are also maintained along the z-z^1 axis. The outputs of the receiving coils are amplified then fed to phase shifters which produce a differential phase shift of 90 degrees between the voltages induced in the two coils. Because the primary field is circularly polarized about the z-z^1 axis, the voltages induced in receiving coils x-x^1 and y-y^1 will be 90 degrees out-of-phase with respect to one another. The receiving circuit phase shifters then produce outputs which are of inverse phase in the absence of subsurface conductors and so a net zero output of amplitude and phase occurs at the recorder. This cancellation is independent of the distance between transmitter and receiver. When a secondary field is present, the net output is not zero and is continuously recorded in analog form. The pair of coils x-x^1 exhibit minimum coupling with a sheet conductor normal to the z-z^1 axis so that the output from receiving coil x-x^1 is essentially the primary field. The unbalanced voltage at the output is then principally due to the change in mutual coupling between the coils y-y^1 as caused by a subsurface conductor. This unbalanced volt-age then can be expressed in percent of nor-mal field. Small changes in the distance be-tween transmitter and receiver will not grossly alter the unbalanced voltage due to secondary fields.

The distance indicator portrays the ampli-tude of the voltage in receiving coil x-x^1

which is proportional to the inverse cube of the distance between transmitter and re-ceiver. A record of this distance may thus be obtained.

The system is operated in one of two modes:

(i) receiver in bird towed behind one air-

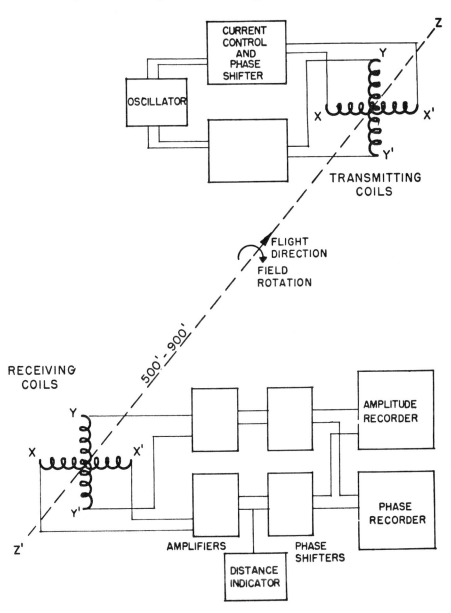

Fig. 62. Generation of circularly polarized magnetic field by orthogonal transmitting coils, and reception by orthogonal receiving coils; ABEM system.

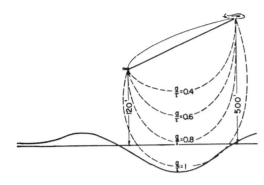

SINGLE PLANE - TOWED RECEIVER

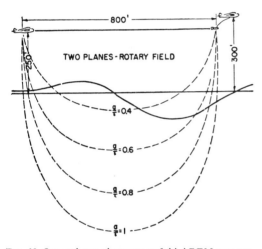

FIG. 63. One and two plane rotary field ABEM systems.

craft, transmitter in following aircraft (the two-plane system)

(ii) transmitter in aircraft, receiver in bird towed behind the one-plane system

A schematic representation of these two modes is shown in Figure 63. The former system is to be preferred because of larger anomalies and lower noise level. The anomaly, in in-phase or quadrature component, due to a conducting half-plane increases with transmitter-receiver separation for either the one-plane or two-plane system. We illustrate this feature in Figure 64 where results were obtained by scale modelling. The ratio a/τ is depth to top of conductor divided by the coil separation, critically determines the response. For a one-plane system a/τ ranges between 0.6 and 1.0 for a plane height of 500 ft; depth of exploration is thereby limited as

Figure 63 indicates. On the other hand, the two-plane system introduces larger τ, often of the order of 800 ft, thereby effectively increasing the depth of exploration according to Figure 63. Values of a/τ range from 0.4 to 0.8 with the two-plane system.

Angular rotation of the receiving coils about the z-z^1 axis does not produce a differential output since the field is circularly polarized. On the other hand, rotation of the receiving coils about either the x-x^1 or y-y^1 axes will lead to variations in output dependent upon the cosine of the angle of rotation. This would appear to be the limiting noise of the system. ABEM reports a lower noise level with the two-plane system than with the one-plane system.

Typically, with the two-plane system, the planes fly at 300 ft terrain clearance and about 800 ft apart. The latter distance is maintained reasonably constant by means of two diverging spotlight beams coming from the fuselage of the first plane.

Figure 65 contains information obtained prior to 1958 with both the one plane and two plane systems. Noise levels of the order of two percent of amplitude were evident at that time on the recordings for the two plane system. We cannot know, of course, whether this noise level represents geologic noise or system noise, but we suspect it to be the latter. Previously we suggested that one part in 2,000 or .05 percent would be a quite satisfactory noise level for the Hunting system or similar devices in which the coil separation was 420 ft. Working on an inverse cube law for primary field and assuming an approximate constant secondary field, a device with an 800-ft coil separation should require $(800/420)^3 \times 0.05$ percent or approximately 0.4 percent noise level. Apparently, then, the ABEM two-plane system is reasonably good, being at worst about half an order of magnitude less than the predicted requirement for the Hunting system.

Note that the ABEM system is basically a horizontal loop ground system converted to an airborne device by adding the vertical reference coil pair. In this sense it should respond quite well to flat lying conductors, including swamps and overburden, according to Figure 18-1 of Part A of this chapter. We shall refer to this point again under the section on interpretation.

The greatest advantage of the ABEM system unquestionably is its potential depth of exploration.

(c) *Hunting Canso System* (*Prepared from information provided by N. R. Paterson*).— The Hunting dual-frequency phase-shift system was developed by M. Puranen, A. Kahma, and V. Ronka working under the auspices of the Geological Survey of Finland during the years 1947 to 1953. In 1954 it was placed in operation in Canada by the Hunting group.

The instrument consists of a horizontal transmitting coil mounted on a Canso (PBY) aircraft, generating electromagnetic fields at 400 cps and 2,300 cps, and a vertical receiving coil located in a bird towed 420 ft behind and 220 ft below the aircraft. Figure 66 presents a pictorial description of the system. The transmitted field is inclined about 20

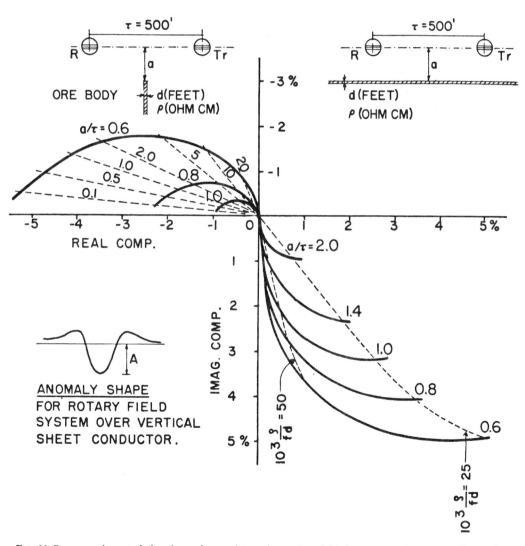

FIG. 64. Response characteristics of one-plane and two-plane rotary field electromagnetic systems. The maximum negative anomaly "A" is plotted for vertical sheets while the positive increase in mutual coupling is plotted for the horizontal sheet. The coil system is tilted from the horizontal by some 20 degrees with the one-plane system but this does not change maximum anomaly significantly.

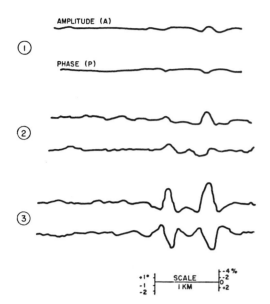

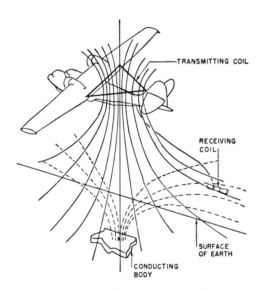

FIG. 65. Typical data obtained with ABEM rotary field systems.

FIG. 66. Pictorial description of the Hunting Canso system.

corder. As of 1960, the following system data applied:

transmitting coil: weight 75 lb, area 540 sq ft, 3 turns

power: low frequency, 80 amps at 500 watts, high frequency, 18 amps at 150 watts

receiving coil: low frequency, 12 lb, 16,000 turns, area 100 square inches, high frequency, 6 lb, 6,000 turns, area 100 square inches

bird: contains two receiving coils, preamplifier and battery

compensating coil: a small vertical coil with axis along the direction of flight is fed voltages in quadrature with the voltages of the transmitting coil in order to compensate for that quadrature field, generated by skin of aircraft, which is normal to the primary field at the receiver. The moment of the compensating coil is 0.5 percent of the moment of the transmitting coil at each frequency.

phase detectors: lock-in amplifiers are used to decrease the bandwidth to about 0.2 cps, at 400 cps, at a time constant of one second.

The vector diagram of Figure 67 illustrates that the phase angle measured is proportional, for small angles, to the quadrature component H_{sq} of the secondary field generated by subsurface conductors. Since the system measures only the changes in phase of the field component along the axis of the receiver, and since the aircraft quadrature secondary field is cancelled to first order, rotation or translation of the bird relative to the aircraft does not produce a high noise level. Paterson (1961a) claims a system noise level of 0.05 degrees or roughly one part in 1,200 of the primary field. This seems to be consistent with published flight records although this is difficult to assess because of the high geologic noise obtained in most surveys. Geologic noise is high with this sys-

degrees to the axis of the receiving coil. Phase detecting circuits in the aircraft allow the phases of the voltages generated in the receiving coils to be measured relative to the voltages across the transmitting coils; those phases are displayed on a paper chart re-

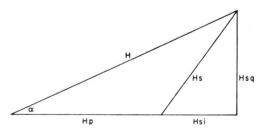

FIG. 67. Vector diagram for resultant magnetic field at receiver.

tem because flat-lying overburden gives rise to fairly large quadrature anomalies for a coil configuration consisting of one horizontal dipole and one vertical dipole (compare Figures 18-1, 18-2, 18-3, and 18-4 of Part A in this chapter). However, Paterson (1959), Paterson (1961a), and Paterson and Stam (1960) suggest interpretative means for recognizing overburden noise Figure 68 contains a record obtained in the vicinity of the Thompson Ore Body, Manitoba, Canada, where overburden is highly conductive. Here the effect of overburden is removed by inspection.

Normal flying height for the Hunting Canso system is 500 ft above mean terrain elevation. If 0.05 degrees of phase shift is the usual noise level, then Figure 56 informs us that a vertical half-plane 700 ft below the aircraft or 200 ft subsurface would respond at noise level. Evidently the aircraft must be flown as low as 400 ft in order to reach 250–300 ft subsurface.

Data presentation is unusual for this system and perhaps worthy of note. The 400 cps profile data is transferred to plan maps and "contoured." We submit that these "contours" are really form lines, since, if flight altitude changes by fifty feet from line to line, the anomaly amplitude will change by 35 percent for a half-plane and by 47 percent for a sphere. The ratio of the low frequency

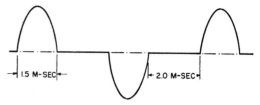

FIG. 69. Pulse shape of primary electromagnetic field for Input system.

to high frequency responses is plotted at the center of each form line closure. This ratio is related to the conductivity-thickness product of the subsurface conductor as we shall discuss under interpretation.

(d) *The Barringer Input System.*—The Input system, developed initially by A. R. Barringer under sponsorship by Selco Exploration Company Limited, is the only airborne electromagnetic system in which measurements are made in the time domain. Electromagnetic field pulses of half sine wave shape and duration 1.5 ms, are transmitted every 3.5 ms. The primary magnetic field waveform, illustrated in Figure 69, is generated by current pulses in a large loop antenna surrounding the survey aircraft. A pictorial representation of the system is presented in Figure 70. The loop is part of a pulse forming network, other components of which are located in the pulse transmitter inside the aircraft. Note that alternate pulses are of

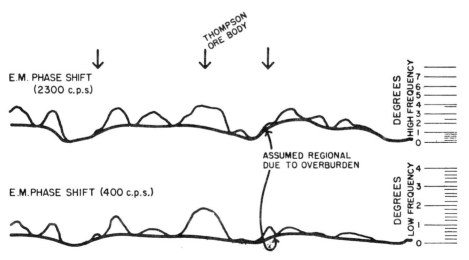

FIG. 68. Data obtained in flight with Hunting Canso system over Thompson ore body, Manitoba, Canada.

FIG. 70. Pictorial representation of Input system mounted on PBY aircraft.

opposite sign and are separated by a two ms period during which transmission does not occur. Eddy currents induced in the subsurface during the pulse period tend to decay exponentially in the subsequent interval during which no primary field transmission occurs.

Thus the secondary magnetic field associated with the induced currents may be measured, in the complete absence of primary field, in the zero transmission intervals. The secondary fields are detected by a receiving coil towed on 500 ft of cable below and behind the aircraft; the axis of the receiving coil is horizontal. The primary field detected by the receiving coil has the waveform of Figure 71 while the combined primary and

secondary field receiver waveform is as shown in Figure 72. The isolation of the secondary field from the primary field is an advantage possible in time domain systems. Note, however, that one would anticipate a dipole moment induced in the skin of the aircraft, as with the Hunting system, so that some secondary field can be expected from this source. Note too, that in some frequency domain airborne electromagnetic systems the primary field is cancelled at the receiver by the field from an auxiliary "bucking" coil so that the receiver monitors only the secondary field. Thus, one should be cautious of unqualified statements concerning the relative merits of time domain and frequency

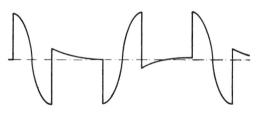

FIG. 71. Voltage measured in receiving coil due to primary field, Input system.

FIG. 72. Voltage representing combination of primary and secondary fields, as measured in receiving coil, Input system.

domain systems. However, in the Input system, compensation for transient eddy currents induced in the airframe is accomplished by feeding into each sampling channel of the receiver a signal that equals in amplitude and waveform and opposite in polarity to the signal introduced by the airframe eddy currents. The compensation signal is derived from the voltage induced in the receiving coil by the primary field and is therefore proportional to the inverse cube of the distance between the bird and the aircraft. This latter feature corrects for bird motion and consequent changes of coupling with the transmitting coil.

The voltage induced in the receiving coil is sampled at six points in time, in the Mark V version of Input, as illustrated in Figure 73. Sampling is made for a duration of 200 μsec at mean delays of 300 μsec, 500 μsec, 700 μsec, 1,100 μsec, 1,500 μsec, and 1,900 μsec. The signal information obtained at each sample position is subsequently processed in the receiver to produce four analog output voltages, recorded on a multichannel paper chart each one of which is proportional to the amplitude of the eddy current in the ground at the time in question. The time constant of the decaying eddy currents may then be obtained by comparison of the analog voltages in the six channels. This time constant is proportional to the conductivity of the subsurface inhomogeneity in which eddy currents are induced.

The primary magnetic field intensity may be written, for a single pulse,

$$H = \frac{M}{r^3} \sqrt{1 + 3 \sin^2 \theta} \sin \frac{t}{T}; \quad 0 < t < \frac{T}{2}$$

$H = 0$; for all other values of t,

where M is the magnetic moment of the source dipole, r is the distance from the center of the loop, θ is the polar angle measured from the transmitting coil axis, t is time, and T is the period of a complete sine wave.

The secondary field will be of the form

$$h(t) = \frac{e \sqrt{\frac{\mu}{\epsilon}} \, \sigma I_1 \left[\frac{\sigma}{2\epsilon} (t^2 - \rho^2 \mu \epsilon)^{1/2} \right] e^{-\sigma t/2\epsilon}}{(t^2 - \rho^2 \mu \epsilon)^{1/2}}$$

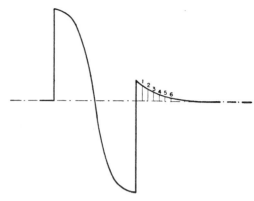

Fig. 73. Sampling of received exponential decay voltage, Input system.

for a unit impulse input, where I_1 is a modified Bessel function of the first kind of order unity. In polarizable materials the exponential term may predominate whereas in nonpolarizable materials the time dependency may be nearer to $t^{-3/2}$. Possibly one could differentiate between polarizable and nonpolarizable materials on this basis but the chances of success are not large. Bhattacharyya (1964) presents a good description of this problem for a loop *on* the ground surface and also presents some decay curves for various degrees of polarization.

Noise sources in the Input system, in addition to airframe eddy current noise, include atmospheric discharge fields, man-made electromagnetic noises especially from power lines, presumably voltages arising from motion of the receiving coil in the earth's static magnetic field, and geologic noise. Atmospherics can be troublesome in those channels where sampling occurs long after cessation of the primary pulse. However, since the secondary field pulses are of opposite polarity on alternate half cycles and since they are uniformly distributed in time, a coherent detection scheme may be employed to reject most of the atmospheric noise with frequencies differing from the pulse repetition rate of the Input transmitter. In effect the coherent detection scheme constitutes a narrow band digital filter centered about the pulse repetition frequency. An atmospheric noise gate is also introduced to clip strong atmospheric pulses.

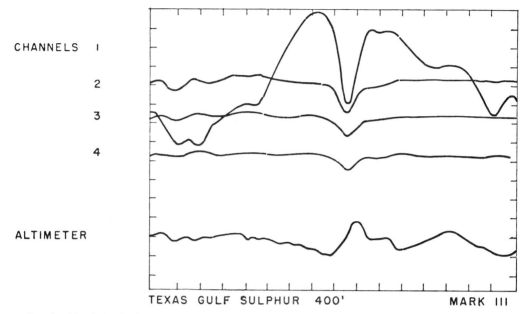

CHANNELS   1

2

3

4

ALTIMETER

TEXAS GULF SULPHUR 400'   MARK III

Fig. 74. Signal obtained with Input system over Texas Gulf Sulphur deposit near Timmins, Ontario.

The first two or three channels, since they sample in the rapidly varying portion of the exponential decay, contain responses from bodies of lower conductivity than do the last two or three channels. In fact Input has been used by the Geological survey of Canada (Collett, 1965) to map conductive clay overburden. Figure 74 contains a record over the Texas Gulf Sulphur massive sulfide deposit near Timmins, Ontario. The aircraft was at a mean terrain clearance of 400 ft. Very conductive overburden in the area leads to an irregular channel 1 recording on a Mark III Input system [Channel samplings occur at 450 μsec, 850 μsec, 1,250 μsec, and 1,650 μsec in the Mark III system]. Channel 4 accepts only the response of the sulfide deposit. Thus excellent conductors such as massive sulfides produce responses on all channels while poor conductors are limited to the first two or three channels. In this sense, when searching for massive sulfides, geologic noise is very high on the lower numbered channels while atmospheric and airframe noise tends to obscure the higher numbered channels.

It is difficult to assess the noise level of Input because of the change from geologic noise predominance on the lower channels and the atmospheric noise and airframe predominance on the higher channels. The record of Figure 75 was obtained at 700 ft mean terrain clearance above the shallow South Mystery Lake nickeliferous sulfide deposit in Manitoba, Canada. Recognition of the anomaly is just possible on channel 4. Barringer (1965) reports on detection of a magnetite deposit, with minor pyrrhotite and pyrite, at a terrain clearance of 1,100 ft with a Mark V system. Registration was primarily on channels 1, 2, and 3, those with highest geologic noise. It is apparent that the depth of exploration possible with airborne Input is at least as good as any other system and probably substantially better. Definitive comparisons are not available.

The pulse repetition frequency of 285 cps permits use of the coherent detection system. One can assume that the received signal will not change significantly in 25 ft of aircraft translation. This translation occurs in one-sixth sec for an aircraft traveling at 150 mph. During this time, nearly 50 pulse repetitions will have occurred, an adequate number to permit substantial reduction of the ratio of signal to atmospheric noise. Note, however, that the pulse repetition frequency is at the peak of the atmospheric noise spectrum (see section on Afmag).

Grant and West (1965) note that since the time derivative of the magnetic field is recorded, the anomalous fields which decay very slowly are suppressed in amplitude more than the others. They contend that since these are the fields generally associated with excellent conductors such as massive sulfides, there is an inherent weakness in the system. One might counter this argument by pointing out that the frequency response of the system may be made essentially uniform over the passband by introducing integration circuits. The problem really reduces to one of obtaining satisfactory message-to-noise ratio. In the Input system a sampling gate as narrow as 100 μse is used in the channel 1 position in order to obtain a sample which is a faithful representation of the signal amplitude at that point. In channels 5 and 6 a sampling gate of 600 μsec can be used without obtaining a distorted signal amplitude figure. An examination of the rapid change in slope of a typical transient indicates why a narrow gate must be used in channel 1 and

a wide gate can be used in channel 6. This gradation in sampling widths from channel to channel provides a significantly lower noise level in the delayed channels, upon averaging a succession of received transients, at the very place where lower noise levels are desirable due to reduced signal amplitudes. Again airframe noise enters the picture as well, but we are uncertain of its magnitude relative to atmospheric noise. Judging from recent developments, the succession of features introduced in the Mark V systems, Barringer is more concerned with atmospherics than any other form of noise.

(e) *Aerophysics of Canada, Limited, Anson System* (*description from material supplied by Spartan Air Services Limited, and from personal knowledge*).—Spartan Air Services Limited contracted with McPhar Geophysics Limited to develop an airborne electromagnetic system for quick delivery, after the Inco and Hunting Systems were operational. A very simple but limited system resulted. In this system the transmitting and receiving coils are coplanar, and in the common plane containing both the vertical and the direction of flight as in Figure 76. Only the quad-

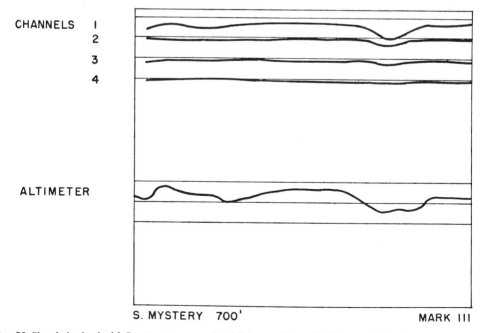

FIG. 75. Signal obtained with Input system over South Mystery Lake nickeliferous sulfide deposit in Manitoba.

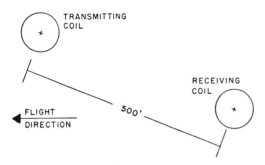

FIG. 76. Coil configuration used in Aerophysics Anson system.

rature component of the resultant field at the receiving coil was intended for interpretation although the total field is also recorded and may be used for conductivity-thickness product estimates.

The operating frequency is 140 cps and the coil separation is 500 ft. Pemberton (1962) reports that the quadrature noise level of the system is 1,000 ppm although the basis for that figure is not given. Noise level on the total signal is much higher, being dependent upon relative motion between transmitting and receiving coils following a cosine variation of relative orientation and an inverse cube law of separation. Motion in the earth's static field can also produce noise. The wooden airframe and reorganization of the electrostatic bonding in the aircraft negate airframe noise as in the Inco Anson system. The transmitting coil is entirely within the aircraft.

A peculiar feature of the system is that the coil configuration will only give a good response if flown at 30 to 60 degrees to the expected strike of subsurface conductivity inhomogeneities. The low frequency of 140 cps reduces geologic noise to an entirely acceptable level. The coil configuration is only slightly better than the Hunting system or the ABEM system for rejection of response from a conductive half-space (Figures 18-1, 18-2, 18-4, of Part A of this chapter) so that the selection of this low frequency was an important design factor.

While ostensibly the measurement of quadrature response only is a limiting feature of the system, the availability of the total signal trace largely overcomes this. Figure 77 contains copies of original records obtained over the Whistle nickel sulfide ore body near Sudbury, Ontario, Canada. Note that the ratios of quadrature units to total signal units for three flight altitudes of 460, 500 and 560 ft are 2.1, 2.1, and 2.5 although the latter ratio is obscured by high noise on the total signal recording. One might wish to compare the results of Figure 77 with those of Figure 61 for the Inco system. If the combined system and geologic (i.e. total) noise level of the Inco system is no higher than 1,500 ppm as reported herein, then the Aerophysics system, using an identical transmitter-receiver separation, must be no better than 4,500 ppm total noise, based on the quadrature data presented in Figure 77.

Note that the response of the Whistle orebody is quite asymmetrical; this is typical of this system.

(f) *Nucom Limited and Hunting Helicopter Systems (information from N. R. Paterson for Hunting system and from personal experience for Nucom system).*—The first helicopter electromagnetic system was developed by Nucom Ltd., a subsidiary of American Metal Company, and flown successfully in 1955. About one year later, Aeromagnetic Surveys Limited, a Hunting affiliate, introduced a system so similar that I choose to describe the two systems together.

The transmitting and receiving coils are mounted coaxially on either end of a twenty foot mechanically rigid lightweight bird which is towed in-line 50 ft below the helicopter which flies at 150 ft. The Hunting helicopter flies at 200 ft so a 100-ft cable connects bird and helicopter. (Hunting later used a 30-ft bird). The Nucom system records in-phase and quadrature components at 1,000 cps while the Hunting system records the same quantities at 4,000 cps.

Data obtained with the Hunting system over the Whistle Mine is shown in Figure 78. A picture of the Hunting bird beside V. Ronka, who engineered the system, is shown in Figure 79. The total noise level of the Hunting system is less than 20 ppm, and sometimes as small as one ppm (MacKay,

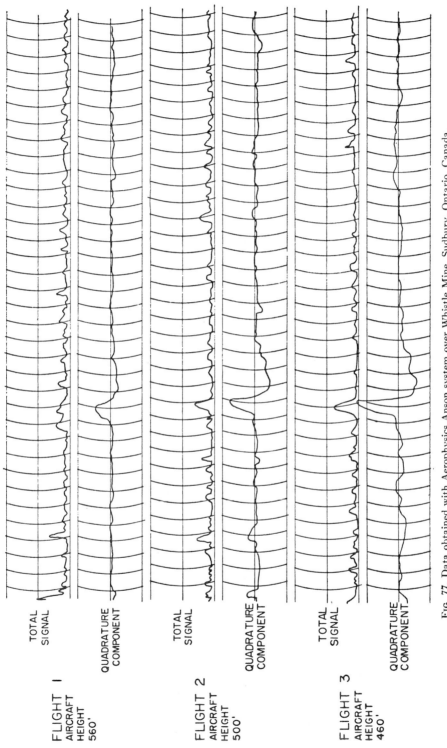

Fig. 77. Data obtained with Aerophysics Anson system over Whistle Mine, Sudbury, Ontario, Canada.

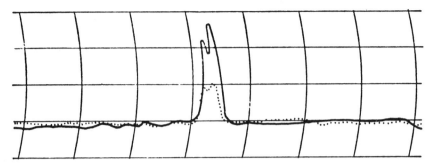

Fɪɢ. 78. Data obtained with Hunting helicopter system over Whistle Mine, Sudbury, Ontario, Canada. Solid curve is in-phase component; dotted curve is quadrature component.

1966) while the noise level of the Nucom system is about 10 ppm.

The 4,000 cps operating frequency of the Hunting system is slightly high, even for a short coil separation of 20 ft, so that some overburden response can be expected. Note from Figure 18-3, of chapter 2 part A, however, that the coil configuration gives very small response for $\theta < 2.5$; an induction number θ of 0.1 will occur from a homogeneous earth of conductivity 10^{-2} mho/m with the Hunting system and geologic noise arising therefrom is very small.

Noise sources arise primarily in relative motion between transmitting and receiving coils, provided geologic noise is small. The short separation between the coils makes it easy to obtain signals at the receiving coil which are well above atmospheric noise level. Bird design is therefore the only significant problem with this basic system.

A reference voltage is obtained from a reference coil mounted on the transmitting coil (or is obtained from a network in series with the transmitting coil) and compared with the received voltage in a quadrature

Fɪɢ. 79. Bird and helicopter used in Hunting helicopter electromagnetic system.

and in-phase bridge. Long term drift may be removed by careful source voltage and temperature balancing systems or by appropriate filtering.

The model data presented earlier indicates a half-plane can be detected 300 ft sub-aircraft by a 50-ft coaxial coil device and yield a message-to-noise ratio of 5:1 for a 10 ppm noise level. Thus the 20-ft coaxial coil instrument would need a noise level of one to two ppm to produce comparable data. Evidently this is not always achieved.

The response of a half-plane in the subsurface is a function of the conductivity of the half-plane, frequency of the source, and both separation between coils and height of the coil system above the half-plane. Thus the short-separation helicopter systems will give a much smaller response from large linear conductors of low conductivity than will the large separation towed bird fixed wing aircraft systems. To counter this, the sensitivity is made higher and the frequency can be made higher at the risk of detecting local patches of highly conductive overburden. Resolution between adjacent conductors is higher with the short separation coil configurations and this is a marked advantage of such systems.

Helicopters, because of slow operating speeds, are more expensive to operate than fixed wing aircraft so that comparable survey costs for fixed wing and helicopter systems might be in the ratio of 1:2.

(g) *Newmont/Aero Helicopter System (information from Pemberton, 1962, and from brochures released by Aero Service Corporation)*.—In 1956, Newmont Mining Corporation engineers, led by K. A. Ruddock, and A. A. Brant successfully flew the helicopter electromagnetic device subsequently known as the Newmont/Aero system. A picture of the device, mounted on Sikorsky S-55 helicopter is presented in Figure 80. The coil configuration employed is vertical coaxial, the same as that used in the Nucom and Hunting helicopter systems except that the coils are mounted rigidly fore and aft of the helicopter, permitting a coil separation of 60 ft. Further, the large helicopter readily adapts to carrying additional survey equipment including a magnetometer and a scintillometer.

System noise level on both in-phase and quadrature records is reported to be 20 ppm (Pemberton, 1962) although available data suggests that the in-phase noise level more typically is 40 ppm, suggesting either higher system noise or the addition of geologic noise. Data obtained with the system is given in Figure 81.

The operating frequency of the system is

FIG. 80. The Newmont/Aero system mounted on a Sikorsky S-55 helicopter.

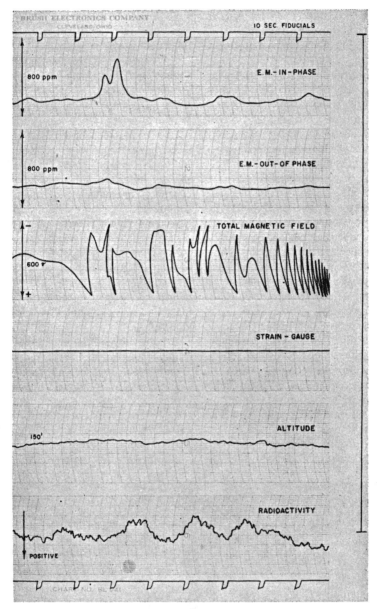

FIG. 81. Typical data portrayal for Newmont/Aero helicopter system.

390 cps and the helicopter is flown at a nominal altitude of 150 ft. Data was presented earlier that a device of this type employing a 50-ft coil separation requires a 10 ppm noise level to permit ready detection of a half-plane at 300 ft sub aircraft. Therefore a 60-ft version requires about 20 ppm noise level for the same sensitivity. We suggest that the Newmont/Aero system is quite capable of detecting a half-plane buried about 200 ft subsurface provided the helicopter flies at 100-ft terrain clearance and probably would produce a recognizable anomaly for the same conductor, when the aircraft is flown at 150 ft.

Data presentation is interesting with this

system as it is with any device with which electromagnetic and magnetic surveys are conducted simultaneously. Figures 82 and 83 demonstrate an excellent correlation between electromagnetic and magnetic data.

(h) *Varian-Texas Gulf Sulphur Helicopter System* (*information provided by Varian Associates and Texas Gulf Sulphur Co.*).— The Varian-T.G.S. helicopter system was the second of this general type engineered by K. A. Ruddock. It is a coaxial coil system operated at 400 cps with a coil separation of

50 ft. The coils are attached to a rigid tubular steel framework attached beneath a light helicopter of Bell 47G2 or Hiller 12E type as in Figure 84.

The excitation current for the transmitting coil is provided by a 250 watt, 400-cps rotary inverter driven from the aircraft 28-volt dc system. Both magnitude and frequency of the excitation current are stabilized by regulators contained within the inverter chassis.

The transmitting coil is split into two balanced halves and the system ground is at

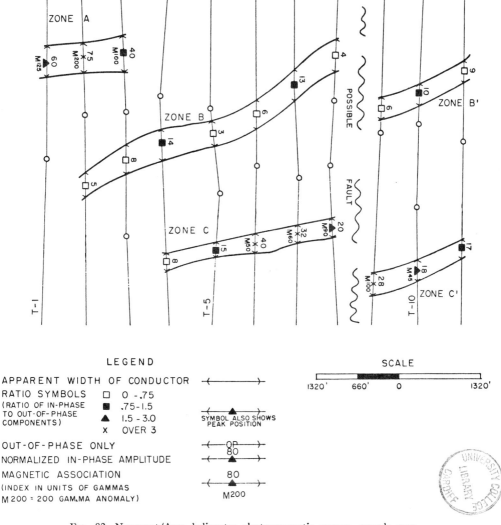

LEGEND

APPARENT WIDTH OF CONDUCTOR

RATIO SYMBOLS
(RATIO OF IN-PHASE
TO OUT-OF-PHASE
COMPONENTS)

◻ 0 -.75
◼ .75-1.5
▲ 1.5 - 3.0
× OVER 3

SYMBOL ALSO SHOWS
PEAK POSITION

OUT-OF-PHASE ONLY

NORMALIZED IN-PHASE AMPLITUDE

MAGNETIC ASSOCIATION
(INDEX IN UNITS OF GAMMAS
M 200 = 200 GAMMA ANOMALY)

SCALE

1320'   660'   0   1320'

Fig. 82. Newmont/Aero helicopter electromagnetic survey, sample area.

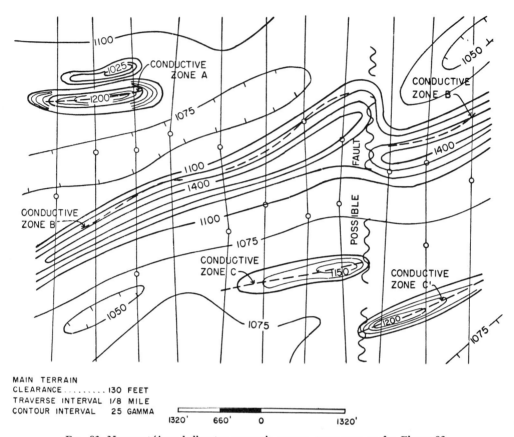

MAIN TERRAIN
CLEARANCE . . . . 130 FEET
TRAVERSE INTERVAL 1/8 MILE
CONTOUR INTERVAL 25 GAMMA

1320'   660'   0   1320'

FIG. 83. Newmont/Aero helicopter magnetic survey, same area as for Figure 82.

the center tap of this coil. In order to maintain a balanced system and to minimize capacitive coupling, the transmitter circuit is resonated by equal series capacitors between the inverter and the coil. The exciting current is maintained at about 2.2 amps and, because of the high Q, the voltage across the coil is about 3,000 volts.

A buck-out coil is connected between the split halves of the transmitting coil and is precisely located just ahead of the receiving coil to produce a region of zero net magnetic field at the location of the receiving coil. This configuration is advantageous in that the zero magnetic field condition is unaffected by variations in the transmitting coil current and/or frequency. A preamplifier with a gain of 1,000 and an amplifier with a gain of 160 follow the receiving coil.

Both in-phase and quadrature components of the secondary field are recorded. One detector has as its reference signal a voltage obtained from a pick up coil inductively coupled to the transmitting coil. This detector measures the in-phase component of the secondary magnetic field and hence is referred to as the in-phase detector.

A second detector has as its reference a voltage obtained across a resistor in series with the transmitting coil center tap. This detector measures the quadrature component of the secondary magnetic field and hence is called the quadrature detector.

The buck-out coil is carefully adjusted for proper balance as indicated by zero output from the in-phase detector. However, slight drifts occur due to changing ground effects on take-off and due to dimensional changes caused by temperature variations. Also, considerable quadrature magnetic field, resulting from eddy currents in the airframe and the supporting boom, can be expected to occur at the receiving coil. To provide a means for returning the system to the balance condition, fine adjustments can be made at the control unit in the cockpit. Small in-phase and quadrature currents in a single turn loop, closely coupled to the receiving coil, can be adjusted to reduce the voltage induced in the receiving coil to zero.

The system can also be calibrated and tested by causing known currents, either in-phase or quadrature, to flow in this single-turn loop and checking the resulting detector output as displayed on the recorder.

During survey flights, the system may depart slowly from the balance condition as a result of temperature changes, ground conductivity changes, or variations in the height above ground. It is sometimes desirable to prevent these zero drifts from appearing on the record. By inserting long time constant ac coupling networks between the detector outputs and the following filter networks, the slow dc level changes can be effectively eliminated without loss of message from subsurface inhomogeneities. To check the balance of the system the coupling can be switched from ac to dc and in fact the drift is often so slight that survey flying is carried out using dc coupling only.

The filters that follow the coupling networks are simple RC integrating networks, but they are very effective in narrowing the over-all passband of the receiver, and thus improving the message-to-noise ratio.

The filtered outputs from the in-phase and quadrature detectors are connected to the time sharing relay. A nonsymmetrical, free-running multivibrator switches this relay between two channels in such a way that the in-phase and quadrature signals are alternately fed to one channel of the recorder for periods of 250 ms and 100 ms respectively. Because of the dissimilar display times, each signal can be readily identified. The recorder has a sufficiently fast response to follow the square wave switching between the two signals. The disposition of the survey equipment around the helicopter is indicated in Figure 85 and a block diagram of the equipment is presented in Figure 86.

The field strength at the receiving coil is recorded in parts per million (ppm) and displayed continuously on the upper channel of a two-channel Brush paper chart recorder as in Figure 87. Available data suggests a system noise level of about 10 ppm. Both in-phase and quadrature departures from normal coupling are recorded on one channel by utilizing the time-sharing device as mentioned above. The scale of the deflections may be altered to record anomalous fields at 400, 1,000, 2,000, 4,000, and 8,000 ppm full scale.

Weight of the equipment, including landing gear extension is 346 lb. The boom mounted coils are less susceptible to vibrations in rough weather than if mounted rigidly to the helicopter. The boom can readily be removed to allow the helicopter to be used for other purposes. However, each new installation must be carefully tested to eliminate system noise. Engine noise level must be

Fig. 84. Picture of Varian-Texas Gulf Sulphur Co. helicopter electromagnetic system mounted on Bell 47G2 helicopter.

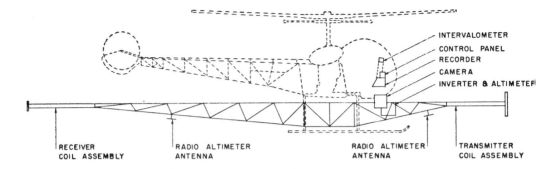

RECEIVER COIL ASSEMBLY   RADIO ALTIMETER ANTENNA   RADIO ALTIMETER ANTENNA   TRANSMITTER COIL ASSEMBLY

INTERVALOMETER
CONTROL PANEL
RECORDER
CAMERA
INVERTER & ALTIMETER

T.G.S. AIRBORNE ELECTROMAGNETIC SYSTEM

FIG. 85. Disposition of survey equipment, Varian-T. G. S. system.

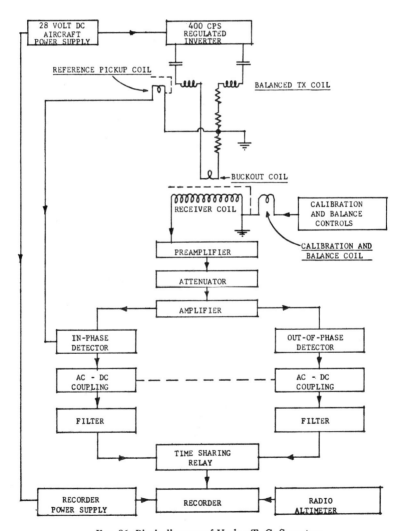

FIG. 86. Block diagram of Varian-T. G. S. system.

reduced by magnetic shielding on the magnetos and generator. Normal flight altitude is 150 ft.

The Whistle ore body near Sudbury, Ontario, Canada gave an anomaly of 30 ppm when the system was flown at an elevation of 600 ft above surface. From this information one might deduce that the system is capable of a depth of exploration of 450 ft when the aircraft is flown at 150 ft. This, very likely, is an optimistic outlook, but depths of exploration in excess of 300 feet seem to be quite reasonable.

(i) *Canadian Aero Canso System (Information from Pemberton, 1962).*—One of the latest systems to be developed was the Canadian Aero Service Ltd. adaptation of the Newmont-Aero system to a Canso aircraft. As with the Hunting and Barringer Canso systems, this unit is intended to be a "flying geophysical laboratory" as Figure 88 will attest.

As with the Newmont/Aero system, the operating frequency is 390 cps and the coil configuration is in-line coaxial. The coil separation is, however, 83 ft and the noise level reported by Pemberton to be 20 ppm. No data is available in the literature with which to check this statement.

The larger coil separation, relative to the Newmont Aero system, should give an increased depth of exploration provided the noise level is as stated. Pemberton (1962) reports a depth of exploration of the order of 200 to 275 ft for a flight altitude of 150 to 225 ft.

(j) *Canadian Aero Otter System (information from Pemberton, 1962).*—This system was introduced in Canada in 1956 by Rio Canadian Explorations and the engineering of the system was headed by D. M. Wagg. In March, 1961, Canadian Aero Service acquired the unit which is currently operated by Canadian Aero Mineral Surveys Ltd. A picture of the system is given in Figure 89.

In-phase and quadrature field components are measured at 320 cps. The coil configuration is coplanar, with the common line of the coils oriented normal, or broadside, to the flight direction. Coil separation is 62 ft and the aircraft is flown at 150–225 ft altitude. Special plastic wingtips were installed to keep the coils at an adequate distance from the flexible metal sheathing of the wing proper. A system noise level of 40 ppm is reported by Pemberton (1962), although no data are available with which to check this estimate.

The response to a homogeneous conductive earth, for this coil configuration, is depicted by Figure 18-4 in chapter 2, Part A. Note that the response is greater, for a given coil separation, than that given by a coaxial coil system as in Figure 18-3, chapter 2, Part A.

(k) *Others.*—The "long-wire" semi air-

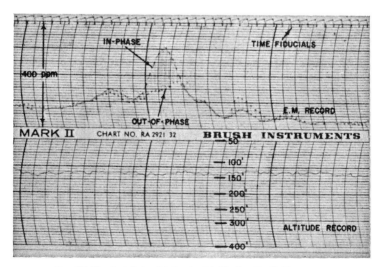

FIG. 87. Typical data obtained with Varian-T. G. S. system.

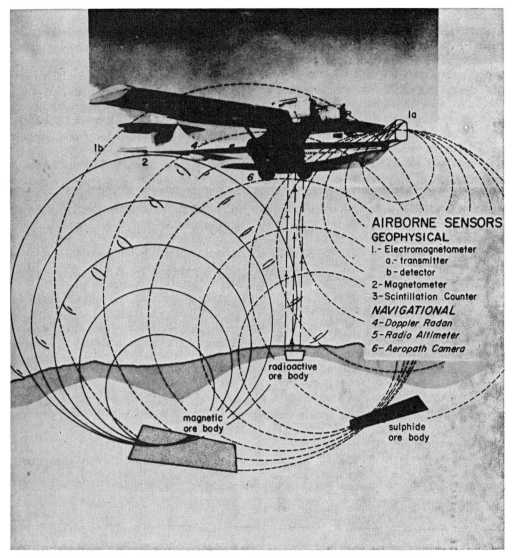

FIG. 88. Pictorial-diagrammatic representation of Canadian Aero Canso system.

borne electromagnetic method seems to have been used, at least by Geophysical Engineering Surveys Limited, at a very early date in the history of airborne electromagnetic exploration. In operation, a long straight wire of perhaps 10 miles length, laid out on the surface of the earth, is connected to a source of alternating current. A light aircraft carries a receiving coil tuned to the source frequency and is flown normal to the wire. Limitations on the system included a difficult wire-laying chore, sensitivity variable with distance from the wire, and response to any resistivity contrast regardless of absolute conductivity.

Hans Lundberg introduced a totally airborne system, about 1948, with both transmitter and receiver in a light helicopter. Few satisfactory records were obtained with the system according to Pemberton (1962).

The Anglo American Company is reported by Pemberton to have developed its own system. Pemberton also mentions a Norwegian slingram airborne electromagnetic system.

The Afmag method has been treated for both air and ground under the section on ground electromagnetic methods.

VI. Model Experiments

A. *Introduction*

Scale model experiments are frequently used to assist in interpretation of data from field geophysical surveys. Such experiments are particularly useful in electromagnetic prospecting because of the inadequacy of mathematical models for this method.

In experiments applicable to the artificial field electromagnetic methods, ore bodies are simulated by small scale models of conducting material. A large reduction in size is made to accommodate model ore bodies to the available space in the laboratory. The size reduction is offset by increasing the source frequency and/or increasing the conductivity of the various media. By appropriate scaling it is possible to simulate accurately the configurations of the lines of force. It is

advantageous to measure either the geometry of the resulting fields, the ratio of the secondary magnetic field components to the source field intensity, or the components of the resulting field. Results from the model work are then directly applicable to the full scale system despite the fact that the model and full scale sources are of far different intensities. Model experiments for electromagnetic prospecting purposes are carried out by most mining companies and by geophysical contractors. Literature references are numerous (Slichter, 1932; Bruckshaw, 1936; Hedstrom, 1940; Clark and Mungal, 1951; Ward, 1952; Burrows, 1957; Forbes, 1957; Tesche, 1951; Hedstrom and Parasnis, 1958; Dolan, 1960; Douloff, 1960b; Swanson, 1960; West, 1960; Grant and West, 1965; Lowrie and West, 1965; Strangway 1966).

Some model experiments for magnetotelluric, magnetic variation, telluric, and Afmag methods have been reported in the literature (Nagata et al., 1955; Cagniard and

FIG. 89. Canadian Aero otter system in operation.

Neale, 1957; Utzmann and Favre, 1957; Utzmann, 1959; Morin, Utzmann, and Favre, 1960; Porstendorfer, 1961; Westcott and Hessler, 1962; Roden, 1964; Parry, 1965; Rankin, Garland and Vozoff, 1965).,

B. *The theory of model systems*

(a) *General scaling conditions.*—The conditions under which a model system may reproduce accurately the geometrical configurations of the lines of force in the full scale system have been developed from the theory of similitude. The most rigorous treatment for the electromagnetic methods is due to Sinclair (1948) from which the following is largely drawn.

The differential equations (Maxwell's) describing any electromagnetic field are linear and allow linear scaling provided such nonlinear media as ferromagnetics are excluded. This necessitates, for our purposes, the assumption of a field-independent permeability of pyrrhotite and magnetite. This assumption is not unreasonable for these materials in the earth's main magnetic field. We need also assume that current conduction is linear. While we know this to be incorrect for such rectifying materials as pyrite crystals and not, in general, true at boundaries between ionic and metallic conductors, the departure from linearity is not large in earth materials. For first approximations it seems satisfactory to ignore these natural nonlinear phenomena.

Consider now a region in which there is a highly conducting ore body surrounded by a poorly conducting rock mass and overlain by a moderately conducting overburden (see Figure 1). An oscillating magnetic dipole, located at the origin of a reference frame, is generating a magnetic field. It is required to determine the conditions which must be satisfied in a model of this system to simulate configurations of the lines of force.

Let any point P in the full scale system be located by the rectangular coordinates x, y, z. Then any point P' of the model is located by the coordinates x', y', z' in a corresponding model coordinate system. The two systems are related by the transformations

$$x = px'$$
$$y = py'$$
$$z = pz' \qquad (C21)$$

where p is the mechanical scale factor.

The conditions imposed by (C21) represent the principal requirements for a mechanical model. The coordinates (x, y, z) and (x', y', z') are measured in terms of a unit of length, and the same unit of length must be used for both systems of coordinates.

Maxwell's equations for linear isotropic media in source-free regions may be written (see A62 through A65)

$$\nabla \times \mathbf{E} + \mu \frac{\partial \mathbf{H}}{\partial t} = 0$$

$$\nabla \times \mathbf{H} - \epsilon \frac{\partial \mathbf{E}}{\partial t} - \sigma \mathbf{E} = 0$$

$$\nabla \cdot \mathbf{H} = 0$$

$$\nabla \cdot \mathbf{E} = 0 \qquad (C22)$$

from which we deduce that in addition to scaling of linear distance, we must also scale $\mathbf{E}, \mathbf{H}$ and t in order that the set remains invariant under general transformation. Then the additional scaling factors α, β, γ must be considered where

$$t = \gamma t' \qquad (C23)$$

$$\mathbf{E}(x, y, z, t) = \alpha \mathbf{E}'(x', y', z', t') \quad (C24)$$

$$\mathbf{H}(x, y, z, t) = \beta \mathbf{H}'(x', y', z', t'). \quad (C25)$$

Unprimed quantities refer to the full-scale system and primed quantities to the model system.

Maxwell's equations in both full-scale and model scale systems are:

Full-scale:

$$\nabla \times \mathbf{H}(x, y, z, t)$$
$$= \sigma(x, y, z)\mathbf{E}(x, y, z, t)$$
$$+ \epsilon(x, y, z) \frac{\partial}{\partial t} [\mathbf{E}(x, y, z, t) \quad (C26)$$
$$\nabla \times \mathbf{E}(x, y, z, t)$$
$$= - \mu(x, y, z) \frac{\partial}{\partial t} [\mathbf{H}(x, y, z, t)] \quad (C27)$$

Model-scale:

$$\nabla' \times \mathbf{H}'(x', y', z', t')$$

$$= \sigma'(x', y', z')\mathbf{E}'(x', y', z', t')$$

$$+ \, \epsilon'(x', y', z') \frac{\partial}{\partial t} [\mathbf{E}'(x', y', z', t')\mathbf{C} \quad 28$$

$$\nabla' \times \mathbf{L}'(x', y', z', t')$$

$$= - \mu(x', y', z') \frac{\partial}{\partial t'} [\mathbf{H}'(x', y', z', t)]. \quad (C29)$$

The symbol $\nabla' \times$ means that the differentiations are to be performed in the primed coordinate system; so that, for example, the component of $\nabla' \times \mathbf{H}'$ directed parallel to the x' axis is:

$$[\nabla' \times]_{x'} \mathbf{H}' = \frac{\partial H_{z'}'}{\partial y'} - \frac{\partial H_{z'}'}{\partial z'} \quad (C30)$$

where $H_{z'}'$ is the component of the vector $\mathbf{H}'$ which is directed parallel to the i' axis.

If the model system is an accurate simulation of the full-scale system, then the transformations represented by (C21) and (C23) through (C25) should transform (C28) and (C29) into (C26) and (C27). When this is done, we obtain the constraints on the physical parameters of the model system. The constraints are, in fact, the transformations of the physical parameters.

From (C21) we note the following:

$$\frac{\partial H_{z'}'}{\partial y'} = \frac{\partial H_{z'}'}{\partial y} \frac{\partial y}{\partial y'} = p \frac{\partial H_{z'}'}{\partial y} \quad (C31)$$

and similarly for the other components. Hence by (C25)

$$\nabla' \times \mathbf{H}' = p \nabla \times \mathbf{H}' = \frac{p}{\beta} \nabla \times \mathbf{H} \quad (C32)$$

and similarly

$$\nabla' \times \mathbf{E}' = \frac{p}{\alpha} \nabla \times \mathbf{E}. \quad (C33)$$

Next we note from (C23) that

$$\frac{\partial}{\partial t'} = \gamma \frac{\partial}{\partial t} \quad (C34)$$

so that

$$\frac{\partial \mathbf{E}'}{\partial t'} = \gamma \frac{\partial \mathbf{E}'}{\partial t} = \frac{\gamma}{\alpha} \frac{\partial \mathbf{E}}{\partial t}. \quad (C35)$$

When we then substitute (C24) (C25) (C32) (C33) and (C35) into (C28) and (C29) we obtain

$$\frac{p}{\beta} \nabla \times \mathbf{H}(x, y, z, t)$$

$$= \sigma'(x', y', z') \frac{\mathbf{E}\,(x, y, z, t)}{\alpha}$$

$$+ \frac{\gamma}{\alpha} \epsilon'(x', y', z') \frac{\partial \mathbf{E}\,(x, y, z, t)}{\partial t} \quad (C36)$$

$$\frac{p}{\alpha} \nabla \times \mathbf{E}(x, y, z, t)$$

$$= - \mu'(x', y', z') \frac{\gamma}{\beta} \frac{\partial}{\partial t} \mathbf{H}(x, y, z, t). \quad (C37)$$

These two equations must be identical with (C26) and (C27) so that for accurate simulation we must observe the constraints

$$\frac{\beta}{p\alpha} \sigma'(x', y', z') = \sigma(x, y, z) \quad (C38)$$

$$\frac{\beta\gamma}{p\alpha} \epsilon'(x', y', z') = \epsilon(x, y, z) \quad (C39)$$

$$\frac{\alpha\gamma}{p\beta} \mu'(x', y', z') = \mu(x, y, z). \quad (C40)$$

These equations are interpreted as follows: (C38) requires the conductivity at the point $p'(x', y', z')$ in the model to be equal to $p\alpha/\beta$ times the conductivity σ at the corresponding point $p(x, y, z)$ in the full scale system. The other two equations are interpreted similarly. Therefore

$$\sigma' = \frac{p\alpha}{\beta} \sigma \quad (C41)$$

$$\epsilon' = \frac{p\alpha}{\beta\gamma} \epsilon \quad (C42)$$

$$\mu' = \frac{p\beta}{\alpha\gamma} \mu \quad (C43)$$

are the equations which represent the conditions which have to be satisfied by the media for constructing the model in order that the simulation be accurate.

(b) *Practical considerations.*—For any arbitrary choices of the four scale factors p, α, β, and γ it is mathematically possible to construct an exact model to simulate a given full-scale system. However, in practice, there are certain restrictions on the choice of scale factors which result from the limited ranges of variation of ϵ, σ, and μ available in actual media which can be used for models. For example, when ferromagnetic media are excluded from the model it is evident that the permeability of the model media cannot differ appreciably from the permeability for free space. Therefore, for all media we shall assume

$$\mu'(x', y', z')$$
$$= \mu(x, y, z)$$
$$= 4\pi \times 10^{-7} \text{ henrys/m}$$

It follows from (C43) that

$$\frac{p\beta}{\gamma\alpha} = 1. \qquad (C44)$$

A unity scaling factor often is used for permittivity because of the limited range of permittivities available and from (C42) we obtain

$$\frac{p\alpha}{\beta\gamma} = 1. \qquad (C45)$$

From (C44) and (C45) there results

$$\alpha = \beta \qquad (C46)$$

and

$$p = \gamma. \qquad (C47)$$

These conditions require that

$$\sigma' = p\sigma. \qquad (C48)$$

Thus it is apparent that for a practical model which is subject to the above restrictions there are actually only two scale factors, i.e. p and either α or β which can be arbitrarily

chosen, and that the other scale factors are fixed by (C46) and (C47).

It should be noted that the condition for conductivities required by (C48) is not necessarily satisfied by using air for the model to simulate air in the full-scale system. Actually, the air has a small conductivity which varies with frequency, and which therefore should be taken into account in designing the model and should be simulated according to (C48). However, for most frequencies the air can be considered as a perfect insulator and the error in neglecting its conductivity is generally very small.

If a definite value is assigned only to the mechanical scale factor p so that the values α or β are unknown, the model still allows the geometry of the field to be correctly simulated, only the amplitudes of **E** and **H** not being simulated. This is all that is required since, as mentioned previously, the results to be produced will apply to any size of power source.

Therefore, the important requirements to be satisfied in constructing a *geometrical* model are the following

$$\left.\begin{array}{l} x' = x/p \\ y' = y/p \\ z' = z/p \\ t' = t/p \text{ or } \omega' = p\omega \\ \epsilon' = \epsilon \\ \sigma' = p\sigma \\ \mu' = \mu \end{array}\right\} . \qquad (C49)$$

A scale factor p of 200 is typical for scaling of electromagnetic prospecting systems. Equations (C49) then inform us that the linear dimension reduction by 200 requires counter changes of an increase in frequency by 200 and an increase in conductivities by 200 with no change in ϵ and μ.

Changing both frequency and conductivity to counter the linear scale change is unnecessarily restrictive for electromagnetic prospecting. If we neglect displacement currents at the outset, we obtain more freedom in scaling as the following argument will demonstrate. Equations (C36) and (C37), with displacement currents neglected, simplify to

$$\frac{p}{\beta} \nabla \times \mathbf{H}(x, y, z, t)$$

$$= \sigma'(x', y', z') \frac{\mathbf{E}(x, y, z, t)}{\alpha} \qquad (C50)$$

$$\frac{p}{\alpha} \nabla \times \mathbf{E}(x, y, z, t)$$

$$= -\mu'(x', y', z') \frac{\gamma}{\beta} \frac{\partial}{\partial t} \mathbf{H}(x, y, z, t). \quad (C51)$$

Thus the restricting equations for α, β, γ, and p have been reduced from three in the previous case to two in the present case. We assume $\mu'(x', y', z')$ and $\mu(x, y, z)$ are identical as before. Then we find, from (C40)

$$\frac{p\beta}{\alpha\gamma} = 1. \qquad (C52)$$

If (C52) is now substituted in (C38), there results

$$\sigma'(x', y', z') = \frac{p^2}{\gamma} \sigma(x, y, z). \quad (C53)$$

Since angular frequency ω transforms according to

$$\omega' = \gamma\omega \qquad (C54)$$

we may write (C53) as

$$p^2 = \frac{\sigma'}{\sigma} \frac{\omega'}{\omega}. \qquad (C55)$$

Then we may interpret (C55) as follows: a decrease in linear scale of p may be offset by an increase in conductivity of p^2 or by an increase in frequency of p^2. Perhaps this argument can be seen more readily from the wave equation. In the full scale system the wave equation is

$$[\nabla^2 + k^2]\mathbf{H} = 0 \qquad (C56)$$

while in the model system it is

$$[(\nabla')^2 + (k')^2]\mathbf{H}' = 0. \qquad (C57)$$

If we now transform (C57) via (C21) (C23) (C24) and (C25) we obtain

$$[p^2\nabla^2 + (k')^2] \frac{\mathbf{H}}{\beta} = 0. \qquad (C58)$$

Evidently for phenomenological studies we may ignore β, but a comparison of (C56) and (C58) indicates that the wavenumber k must transform according to

$$(k')^2 = p^2 k^2 \qquad (C59)$$

or, neglecting displacement currents,

$$\sigma'\mu'\omega' = p^2\sigma\mu\omega. \qquad (C60)$$

Again, a scale factor p of 200 can be offset by a conductivity change of 4×10^4, a frequency change of 4×10^4, or by some combination of increases in conductivity and frequency whose product is 4×10^4.

(c) *Factors affecting choice of scaling conditions for present investigation.*—A 200 to 1 mechanical scaling factor is chosen to enable the apparatus and ore bodies to be handled conveniently in the laboratory. Selecting unit time or frequency in the model system to equal unit time or frequency in the full scale system permits much of the same apparatus to be used in the laboratory and the field.

Conductivity scaling is dictated by the availability of materials. Most sulfide ore bodies possess conductivities in the range 10^{-2} to 10^4 mho/m. Metals with conductivities between 10^6 and 10^8 mho/m may be used to simulate the most conducting ore bodies, provided a 4×10^4 conductivity scaling factor is employed. Graphite (10^4 mho/m) and carbon (10^3 mho/m) may be used to simulate ore bodies of lower conductivity. Aqueous solutions of NaCl of various concentrations ($\sigma < 10^2$ mho/m) may then be used to simulate rocks and overburden.

Less restrictive conditions on scaling can be achieved by consideration of the parameter controlling the response of an inhomogeneity as the following argument will reveal. We shall first note that the arguments of the response functions for a sphere and cylinder, from equations (A6-31) and (A7-44) respectively, are both kR where k is the wavenumber and R is the radius of sphere or cylinder. This parameter is dimensionless and so is referred to as the *induction number*. Dimensional arguments alone would have permitted us to predict that the response would be controlled by such a number. For example, in equation (C60) we note that

$$\sigma'\mu'\omega'(l')^2 = \sigma\mu\omega l^2 \qquad \text{(C61)}$$

where l and l' are any significant linear dimensions and are related by $p=l/l'$. Evidently $\sigma\mu\omega l^2$ must remain invariant under transformation and thus is dimensionless. We can multiply by i and then take the square root of both sides of (C61) so that the dimensionless parameter, or number, may be written kl which is identical to that obtained for sphere and cylinder provided the radii are considered as the significant linear dimension. We should expect then, for any inhomogeneity, to satisfy scaling requirements if we retain the induction number invariant under the transformation. Thus we are led to investigate the induction numbers, and significant linear dimensions, of other bodies. Grant and West (1965) note that the induction number for a thin circular disk is $\sigma\mu\omega ta$ or $kt^{1/2}a^{1/2}$ where t is the thickness and a is the radius of the disk. From equations (A10-112) we observe that the induction number for a thin sheet in a uniform field is $\sigma\mu\omega l^2$ or kl. For a line source on a homogeneous earth we note a response parameter, from equations (A13-52), of kx where x is the lateral distance from the line source. Note now that the significant linear dimension of the system is the distance, from the line source, at which we make measurements. For a line source elevated above the ground and for measurements above the ground, the argument of the response function, from equations (A13-172), is of the form $k[x+i(h-z)]$ where x is again lateral distance from source, h is height of source above the homogeneous earth, and z is height of observation. For this system, either kx or kh or kz will control the response, depending upon the relative magnitudes of x, h, and z. From the expressions for the mutual impedance of loops above an n-layered earth, given by equations (A18-4) (A18-5) (A18-6) and (A18-7), we note that the response is represented by the integrals

$$N_1(\mu, \nu) = \int_0^\infty \lambda^\mu J_\nu(\lambda\rho) e^{\lambda(z-h)} d\lambda$$

$$N_2(\mu, \nu) = \int_0^\infty \lambda^\mu J_\nu(\lambda\rho) e^{-\lambda(z+h)} d\lambda$$

$$T(\mu, \nu) = \int_0^\infty \lambda^\mu r(\lambda) J_\nu(\lambda\rho) e^{\lambda(z-h)} d\lambda.$$

If we now take one example, that of coplanar loops with axes vertical, the integrals to be evaluated are $N(2, 0)$ and $T(2, 0)$ which are given by (A16-26) and (A16-33) as

$$N(2, 0) = \frac{\partial^2}{\partial h^2}\left[\frac{1}{(\rho^2 + h^2)^{1/2}}\right]$$

$$T(2, 0) = -N(2, 0) - \frac{2i}{k_a}N(3, 0)$$
$$- \frac{2}{k_a^2}N(4, 0) + \cdots.$$

Note that the $N(2, 0)$ integral does not include any function related to the physical constants of the earth. This then directs our attention to the second term in the series expansion for $T(2, 0)$ where we note that $k_a = k_1/Q$ is the apparent propagation constant of a layered earth and where Q is a correction to the propagation factor k_1 of the first layer, to account for departure from a homogeneous earth. Then for a homogeneous earth, the second term is

$$- \frac{2i}{k}N(3, 0)$$

where

$$N(3, 0) = -1 \frac{\partial^3}{\partial h^3}\left[\frac{1}{(\rho^2 + h^2)^{1/2}}\right]$$
$$= \frac{3h(3\rho^2 - 2h^2)}{(\rho^2 + h^2)^{7/2}}. \qquad \text{(C62)}$$

If $\rho \gg h$ then the second term reduces to

$$- \frac{2i}{k}\frac{9h}{\rho^5}.$$

Since $1/\rho^3$ will be common to all terms in the expansion of $T(2, 0)$ and really is a geometrical description of the field, the effect of the earth, as indicated by the second term in the expansion, is $k\rho$ ($h\rho$ also multiplies $1/k\rho$, but it's presence merely indicates that we are concerned only with the vertical component of the magnetic field).

On the other hand, for $\rho \ll h$ the second term reduces to

$$\frac{12i}{h^3} \frac{1}{kh}$$

where now the induction number is kh. Thus for short spread airborne electromagnetic systems, the response of a homogeneous earth enters through kh whereas for ground electromagnetic systems it enters through $k\rho$.

We may use the layered earth model to obtain the induction number for a thin sheet below a double dipole system. The correction factor Q is deduced for a two-layer earth from equations (A13-84) as

$$Q = \frac{Z_2 + Z_1 \tanh jk_1 t_1}{Z_1 + Z_2 \tanh jk_1 t_1} \quad \text{(C63)}$$

where $Z_1 = \omega\mu/k_1$ and $Z_2 = \omega\mu/k_2$ are the characteristic impedances of the first and second layers, k_1 and h_1 are the propagation constant and thickness of the first layer. If we assume the second layer to be of very low conductivity relative to the first layer, then (C63) simplifies to

$$Q \approx \frac{1}{\tanh jk_1 t_1} \approx \frac{1}{k_1 t_1}.$$

Then for a ground electromagnetic system over a thin sheet we may combine this result with the earlier one for a homogeneous earth to obtain the response parameter. Previously we obtained $k\rho$ as the parameter for a homogeneous earth and this becomes $k_a \rho = k_1/Q$ $\rho = k_1^2 t_1 \rho$ for a thin layer of thickness t_1 and wavenumber k_1. We write this last expression as

$$i\sigma\mu\omega t_1 \rho$$

and thereby note that for a ground electromagnetic system of fixed ρ and ω, the response of a thin sheet is a function of the σt product of the sheet.

For a short spread airborne electromagnetic system over a thin sheet, the response parameter is $k^2 h t_1$ or $i\mu\sigma\omega t_1 h$, and once again for a fixed height and frequency the σt product determines the response. We anticipate, therefore, that the response of a half-plane would be controlled by the same parameter as for a full plane. To summarize these discussions, we list in Table 2, the response parameters for the various systems considered. Note that while the only loops discussed were a pair of horizontal coplanar loops, the same sort of result would obtain for all other loop pairs.

Thus we may scale thin overburden layers and semi-infinite veins by assuring that the σt product remains invariant under transformation. Then thin aluminum sheets or aluminum foil may be used for this purpose even though we do not scale the thickness correctly. Of course, if a steeply dipping vein has substantial thickness in the full scale system, the geometry of the field will not be scaled perfectly by a very thin aluminum sheet even though the phase relations will be.

Another freedom we may exercise arises when scaling field geometry only. Assume for example that the induction number of a half-plane is sufficiently large that eddy current saturation occurs both in the field and the model systems. Further assume that the conductivity is so high that it may be assumed to be infinite in both systems. Then we need not concern ourselves about scaling conductivity at all. Under these circumstances we need only scale geometry and in fact can make all linear distances dimension-

Table 2

Object or system	Response parameter
Sphere, uniform field	kR or $\sigma\mu\omega R^2$
Cylinder, uniform field	kR or $\sigma\mu\omega R^2$
Disk, uniform field	$kt^{1/2}a^{1/2}$ or $\sigma\mu\omega ta$
Thin sheet, uniform field	kt or $\sigma\mu\omega t^2$
Line source on homogeneous earth	kx or $\sigma\mu\omega x^2$
Line source above homogeneous earth	$k[x+i(h-z)]$
Horizontal loops on homogeneous earth	$k\rho$ or $\sigma\mu\omega\rho^2$
Horizontal loops above homogeneous earth	kh or $\sigma\mu\omega h^2$
Horizontal loops on thin layer	$kt^{1/2}\rho^{1/2}$ or $\sigma\mu\omega t\rho$
Horizontal loops above thin layer	$kt^{1/2}h^{1/2}$ or $\sigma\mu\omega th$

less by dividing by some characteristic length of the system such as spread ρ or height h. This offers advantages in data presentation and particularly in presentation of model data as we shall see subsequently.

(d) *Dimensionless presentation of model curves.*—Grant and West (1965) present a dimensional analysis of the problem of compiling a suite of model curves wherein the least number of curves is desired to display the effects of varying each of the parameters. They note that the response produced by a given electromagnetic system traversed over a subsurface inhomogeneity is usually recorded in dimensionless form, e.g. either by a dip angle or by percent of primary field. This response is a function of the known parameters of the system

$$R = f(\mu, \sigma, \omega, x, \rho, h, l_i \cdots, \alpha_i \cdots)$$

where

μ = permeability of inhomogeneity

σ = conductivity of inhomogeneity

ω = angular frequency of source

x = linear distance along traverse

ρ = spread length

h = depth of inhomogeneity below system

$l_1, l_2, \cdots$ and $\alpha_1, \alpha_2, \cdots$ = linear and angular dimensions of system other than those specifically referred to

We have noted in Table 2 that $\sigma\mu\omega$ always appear as a product and always multiplied by dimensions squared. For permeable bodies, μ also appears separately as we have learned in Part A for the sphere and cylinder. From the principles of dimensional analysis (Eshbach, 1936) we learn that the most economic arrangement of variables is dimensionless groupings which characterize the response. Hence we express the response in the form

$$R = f_g\left(\sigma\mu\omega l_1 l_2, \frac{\mu}{\mu_0}, \frac{x}{\rho}, \frac{h}{\rho}, \frac{l_i}{\rho}, \cdots, \alpha_i \cdots\right).$$

for ground electromagnetic systems since ρ is a readily measured quantity, while for airborne systems the response may be

$$R = f_a\left(\sigma\mu\omega l_1 l_2, \frac{\mu}{\mu_0}, \frac{x}{h}, \frac{l}{h}, \frac{l_i}{h}, \cdots, \alpha_i \cdots\right).$$

At saturation, the responses are independent of the induction number and of permeability so that we may write

$$R_s = f_g\left(\frac{x}{\rho}, \frac{h}{\rho}, \frac{l_i}{\rho}, \cdots, \alpha_i \cdots\right)$$

or

$$R_s = f_a\left(\frac{x}{h}, \frac{\rho}{h}, \frac{l_i}{h}, \cdots, \alpha_i \cdots\right).$$

In many instances the relative response R/R_s at induction numbers below saturation is a function only of the induction number and the relative permeability. We have noted several times that the response separates into a product of inducing field times size factor times physical property factor times geometrical factor. The fact that the geometrical factor does separate from the physical property factor (which is a function of induction number and of relative permeability) indicates that the field geometry will be identical for saturated and nonsaturated cases. Table 2 provides the guidelines for selecting l_1 and l_2; these are the two dimensions (which may collapse to one for high degrees of symmetry as in the sphere and cylinder models) which control the magnitude of the induction current multipole moments and hence the magnetic field at the receiver. We also note from Table 2 that several different parameters may affect the magnitude of the induced multipole moments. For example, a horizontal loop system on a homogeneous earth is controlled principally by $\sigma\mu\omega\rho^2$ while when the system is raised well above the earth such that $h > \rho$, then the controlling number is $\sigma\mu\omega h^2$. Evidently there is a regime where both factors must enter.

Thus families of curves may be developed

for variable induction number and where all linear distances are expressed in terms of ρ or h. Alternatively the induction number may be held constant and curve families selected for variable ρ or h. We shall see examples of this grouping subsequently.

C. *A catalog of curve types—ground electromagnetic survey*

The presentation of a comprehensive catalogue of anomaly profiles, or type curves, for any given electromagnetic method would consume a volume in itself. Accordingly I shall not attempt such an undertaking here. Rather I shall attempt to illustrate characteristic changes in type curves introduced through changes in dip, depth, depth extent, coil separation, etc. To facilitate organization of the graphical data, I shall group the curves under the ground and airborne electromagnetic methods discussed previously. Information permitting me to present this catalog has been provided by the Texas Gulf Sulphur Co., Bear Creek Mining Co., Newmont Mining Corp., McPhar Geophysics Limited, and Nucom Ltd. The doctoral dissertation by West (1960) and the open file

release by Frischknecht & Mangan (1960) have been excellent additional sources of information. I am endebted to many for assistance in obtaining type curves, and especially to Frank Frischknecht, Ralph Holmer, Van Donohoo, and Arthur Brant. Aluminum, copper, and stainless steel sheet models are used frequently and in most instances the type curves are approximately those obtained over a half-plane.

(a) *Inductive vertical loop fixed transmitter*

(i) *Effect of dip.*—A vertical sheet conductor gives rise to a symmetrical profile with a reversal, or crossover, from positive to negative angles, observed vertically above the sheet edge. The convention used herein is positive to the left and negative to the right and all profiles are plotted facing the transmitter. Figure 90 illustrates the configuration while Figure 91 contains the resulting data for sheet dips of 90, 45, and 30 degrees for each of the two spreads of 400 and 800 ft. Note that as the dip of the sheet flattens, the type curves become more asymmetrical and that *reverse* crossovers can occur. Horizon-

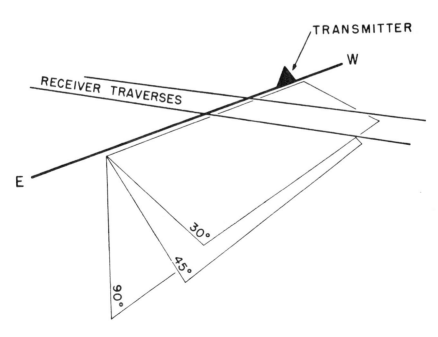

FIG. 90. Configuration of transmitter, receiver traverses and sheet conductor for study of effect of dip on vertical loop type curves.

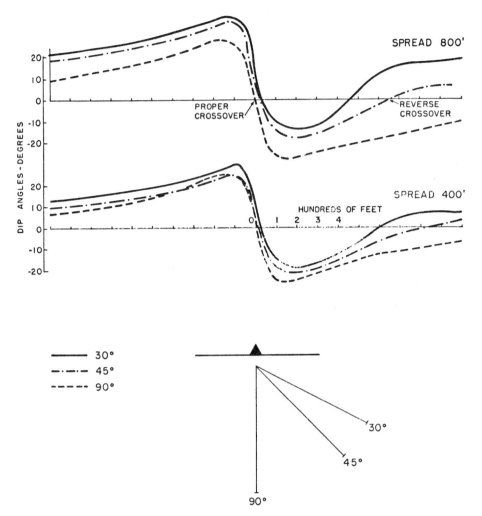

Fig. 91. Effect of dip on type curves for inductive vertical loop fixed transmitter electromagnetic method. The transmitter is located 50ft vertically above top edge and 200ft in from end of sheet conductor of dimensions 3-ft width by 1,400-ft length by 600-ft depth extent. The receiver traverses are at 400ft and 800ft from the transmitter. (Courtesy Nucom Ltd.).

tal sheet conductors, not shown here, produce type curves whose character changes dramatically as the transmitter is moved from one edge of the sheet to the other. The largest dip angles occur on the footwall and the ratio of area under curve on footwall to area under curve on hanging-wall is greater than unity.

(ii) *Effect of spread.*—Figures 90 and 91 also illustrate the effect of spread, i.e. distance between transmitter and receiver. Larger angles result with the 800-ft spread

and the asymmetry is more pronounced. Figure 91 is intended only to illustrate changes in the shape of the type curves as dip and spread are varied. However, we noted above that the response of a sheet conductor is a function of the number $\sigma\mu\omega t\rho$ and hence we expect that for conductors below eddy current saturation, increasing the spread ρ will increase the ratio of in-phase to quadrature response.

(iii) *Effect of depth.*—At this juncture we find it convenient to use the dimensionless linear distance presentation noted earlier. The geometry is given in Figure 92. In Figure 93 the depth of a thin vertical half plane is given in units of the spread ρ. The diagram then predicts the anomaly for any saturated vein of infinite conductivity, strike length, and depth extent. We may consider the spread fixed and depth h variable or vice-versa. Note that the traverse distance is given in units of depth.

From this diagram we conclude that an increase in depth will decrease the maximum observed dip angle and markedly change the slope of the profile at the crossover.

(iv) *Effect of depth extent.*—Figure 94 illustrates the configuration employed for

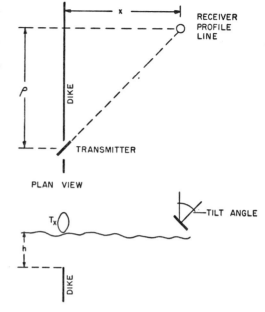

FIG. 92. Geometry for dimensionless illustration of effect of depth on dip angle profile.

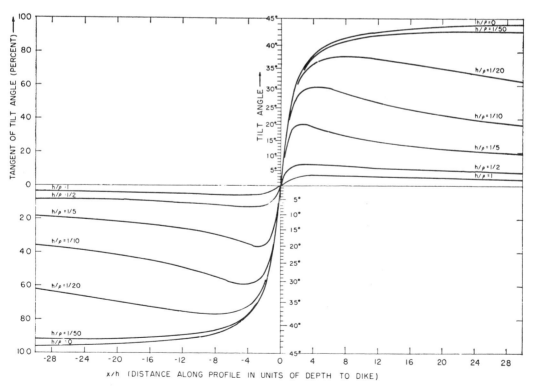

FIG. 93. Effect of depth on type curves for inductive vertical loop, fixed transmitter, electromagnetic method, dimensionless presentation. (Courtesy Newmont Mining Corp.)

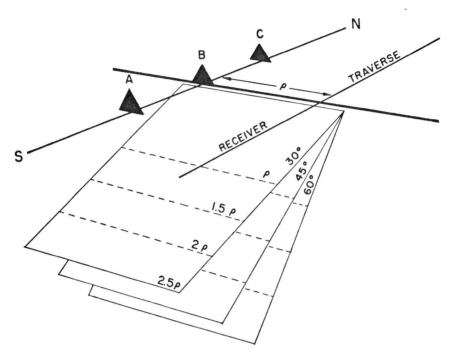

FIG. 94. Geometry for study of effect of depth extent on type curves for inductive vertical loop, fixed transmitter, electromagnetic method.

studying both the effect of finite depth extent and of offsetting the transmitter relative to the top edge of a sheet conductor. In Figure 95 the influence of down dip extent is shown for each of the three dips of 30, 45, and 60 degrees. Depth extents were ρ, 1.5 ρ, 2 ρ, and 2.5 ρ for a conductor of 1.5 ρ strike length. Depth of the conductor was 0.1 ρ, where the spread was ρ, and the transmitter was placed 0.25 ρ in from the edge of the conductor. The sheet is at saturation.

Decreasing the depth extent modifies the profile character substantially on the hanging wall side, especially for the flatter dips.

(v) *Effect of offsetting the transmitter.*— In Figure 96 the dip angle profiles for a sheet conductor of variable depth extent, 1.5 ρ strike length, 45-degree dip, spread ρ and depth 0.1 ρ are shown as a function of location of the transmitter relative to the top edge of the sheet. The sheet is at saturation. The shape of the profile and the maximum observed dip angles change

markedly with transmitter location. The crossover is essentially unmoved. The ratio of areas under the curve on footwall and hangingwall also change and if this is a criterion used to determine dip of a buried conductor, then erroneous interpretations can arise. A more dramatic result occurs when the conductor is horizontal, for then results of the type given in Figure 97 occur. Note the exceptionally large dip angles which can occur when the transmitter is located over one edge of a horizontal sheet. Spread ρ, depth 0.1 ρ, width 1.2 ρ, length 2.8 ρ; sheet is at saturation.

(vi) *Effect of multiple conductors.*—Two vertical sheet conductors spaced 0.6ρ apart were located at a depth of 0.1 ρ as in Figure 98. The spread was ρ and the identical conductor dimensions were 2.8 ρ long by 1.2 ρ depth extent and the sheets were at saturation. When the transmitter is set to one side of both sheets as in A then only one conductor is evident. It is not until the transmitter is located 0.2 ρ inside one conductor, as in D, that both conductors are

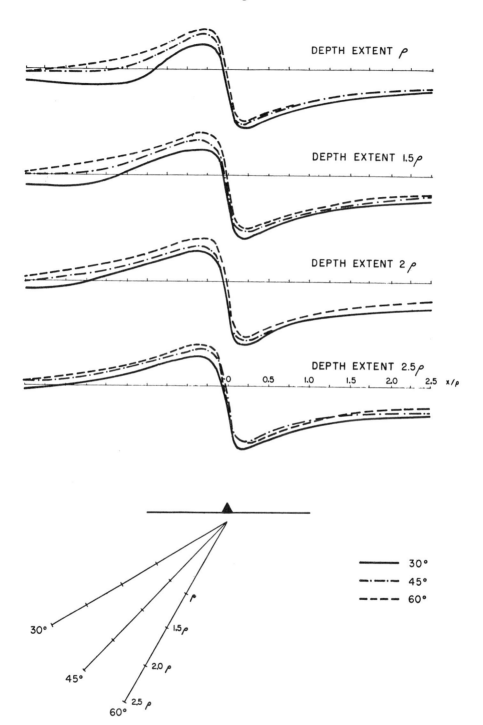

FIG. 95. Effect of depth extent on type curves for inductive vertical loop, fixed transmitter, electromagnetic method. Depth 0. 1 ρ, length 1.5 ρ, depth extent variable. Sheet at saturation. (Courtesy Nucom Ltd.)

reflected clearly. This is a peculiarity of this method and was mentioned in part C p. 240. Of course, if the ratio of depth to conductor separation is large, then the two conductors may appear as one. It is not

until the depth to separation ratio reduces that the two conductors are resolved, as Figure 99 indicates.

(vii) *Effect of conductor width.*—As the width of a vertical sheet conductor of large

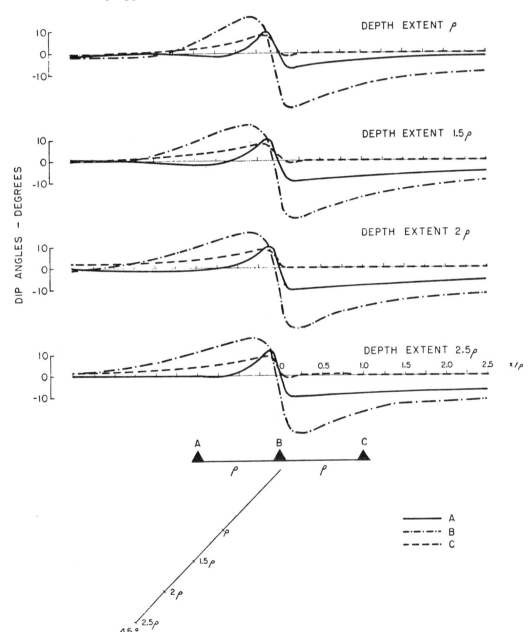

Fig. 96. Effect of transmitter offset on type curves for inductive vertical loop, fixed transmitter electromagnetic method over dipping sheet conductor. Transmitter locations designated by A, B, and C. Depth 0.1 ρ, length 1.5 ρ, depth extent variable. Sheet at saturation. (Courtesy Nucom Ltd.)

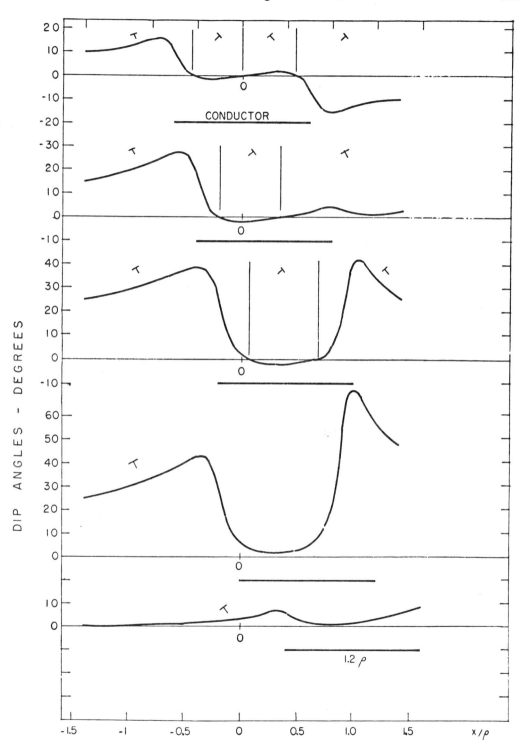

Fig. 97. Effect of transmitter offset on type curves for inductive vertical loop, fixed transmitter, electromagnetic method over horizontal sheet conductor. Transmitter ⊥ along base line which passes through 0. Depth 0.1 ρ, length 2.8 ρ, width 1.2 ρ. Sheet at saturation. (Courtesy McPhar Geophysics Ltd.)

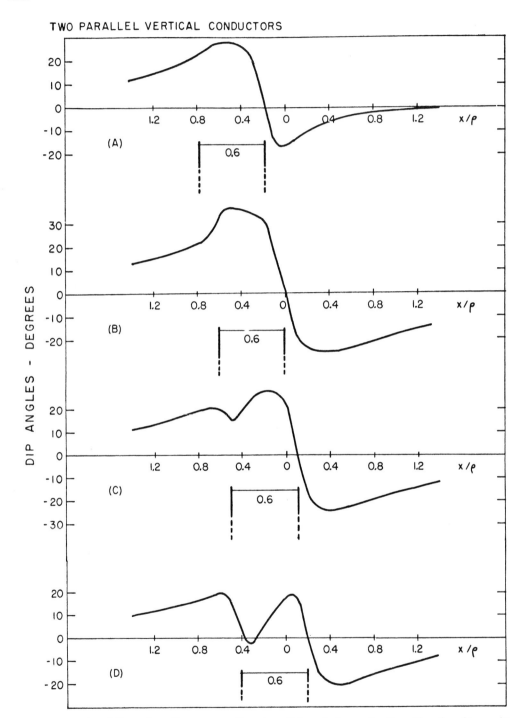

Fɪɢ. 98. Variation of dip angle profile over two adjacent parallel conductors as function of location of transmitter. Transmitter is always located at coordinate zero. Depth $h/\rho=0.1$, depth extent 1.2 ρ, length 2.8 ρ, separation of sheets 0.6 ρ. Sheets at saturation. (Courtesy McPhar Geophysics Ltd.)

depth extent is increased from a thin sheet, its response form will change from the type suggested by Figure 91 to that of Figure 97 or by Figure 98A. Seldom, however, is the conductor homogeneous so that responses of the types indicated by Figure 100 are common.

(viii) *Effect of overburden.*—One can obtain a first-order approximation to the effect of a thin infinite layer of overburden by calculating the phase shift and attenuation of a uniform plane electromagnetic wave as it passes down through the overburden to impinge on a conductor below and then calculate the attenuation and phase shift of the returning anomalous field. Alternatively, if one assumes a ubiquitous inducing field then only the upward transit needs consideration. Thus, in the first approximation, attenuation is given by equation (A10-113) with allowance made for a single transit of the thin conductive sheet in free space here used to simulate the overburden upon a very resistive bedrock (see Figure 101). Thus we find

$$\frac{H_R}{H_S} = \left[\frac{Z_2 Z_0 4 e^{ik_2 d}}{(Z_2 + Z_0)(Z_0 + Z_2)(1 - e^{2ik_2 d})} \right]$$

(C64)

where

H_R = received plane wave above surface of sheet

H_S = secondary elementary plane wave, below overburden due to target

$Z_2 = \omega \mu_0 / k_2$ = intrinsic impedance of sheet

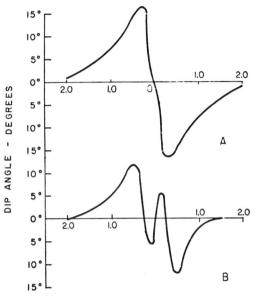

FIG. 99. Change in resolution with change in the ratio of separation to depth for two parallel conductors. Conductors identical with characteristics: length=2.25 units, depth extent=0.5 units, dip=90°, depth=0.125 units, spread=1 unit, separations A=0.25 units, and B=0.5 units. Transmitter located at zero coordinate. (Courtesy Texas Gulf Sulphur Co.)

$Z_0 = \omega \mu_0 / k_0 = 376.6\ \Omega$ is the impedance of free space

μ_0, ϵ_0 are the permeability and permittivity of free space

σ_2 is the conductivity of the thin sheet

ω is the angular frequency

d is the thickness of the sheet

For ranges of conductivity and frequency with which we are interested in geophysical exploration, $Z_0 \gg Z_2$ so that equation

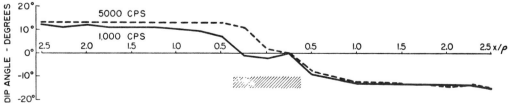

FIG. 100. Dip angle profiles over broad inhomogeneous conductor. Graphite slab simulating conductor 2.5 units long, 0.75 units wide, .0625 units depth extent, and at depth of 0.25 units. All measured relative to spread of one unit. (Courtesy Nucom Ltd.)

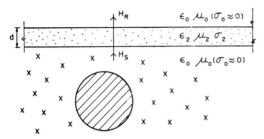

Fig. 101. Inhomogeneity in nonconductive half-space beneath thin conductive overburden of thickness d and propagation constant $k_2 = (i\sigma_2\mu_2\omega)^{1/2}$. Secondary elementary wave from inhomogeneity labelled H_S below overburden and H_R above overburden where received. Analysis applies to all elementary plane waves constituting true secondary field configuration.

(C64) reduces to

$$\frac{H_R}{H_S} = \left[\frac{Z_2 4 e^{ik_2 d}}{Z_0(1 - e^{2ik_2 d})}\right]. \quad (C65)$$

A plot of the amplitude attenuation and phase shift for variable conductivity and frequency are shown in Figure 102 for overburden thicknesses of 3, 10, 30, and 100 m. We can thus expect anomaly amplitudes to be decreased and the phases shifted to suggest a deeper body of different conductivity than that which exists. The attenuation and phase shift functions apply to each elementary plane wave arising in an anomaly source. A local inhomogeneity will give rise to a superposition of such plane waves.

Experimental checking of the theory has been achieved by Fraser (1966). In Figure 103 are plotted the vertical in-phase (H_{M_z}) and vertical quadrature H_{N_z} components over a sphere beneath a uniform thin conductive sheet for a uniform inducing field. The in-phase component is attenuated by perhaps 11 percent while the quadrature component is attenuated by approximately 53 percent as a result of the thin sheet. The field has been rotated 16 degrees towards the in-phase component and the amplitude reduced by 51 percent. The smaller amplitude suggests a deeper sphere while the phase rotation leads to a quadrature to in-phase ratio which suggests a better conductivity than actually exists accord-

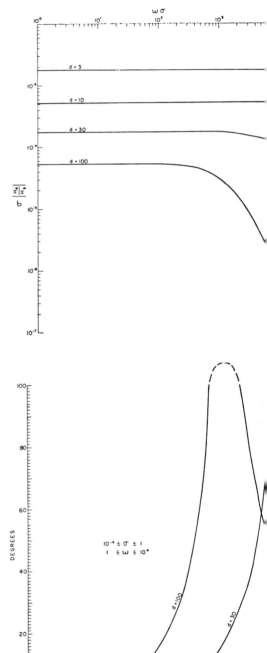

Fig. 102. Phase shift and attenuation as functions of frequency and conductivity for several thicknesses of overburden.

ing to Figure 6-2, Part A, Chapter 2. Note that the vertical component is nearly proportional to the dip angle as defined by equation (C19) so that the ratio of high frequency to low frequency dip angles will decrease due to the conductive sheet. It should be borne in mind that a uniform horizontal conducting sheet produces no response when placed in a uniform horizontal inducing field. When either the overburden is of limited extent or the field is nonuniform then a lateral anomaly may occur due to the overburden. To illustrate this point in principle, Figure 104A is included. Even though the top of a flat, poorly conductive graphite slab is 75 ft below the measuring surface, the characteristics of the anomaly are much the same as they would be for the top of the body at the measuring surface; there is a large contrast between 5,000 cps and 1,000 cps dip angle magnitudes, indicative of a small, induction number. In Figure 104B the response of a dipping copper sheet is shown, while in Figure 104C the response of the combination of carbon slab and copper sheet is given. A unity ratio of 1,000-cps dip angles to 5,000-cps dip angles characterizes the high induction number $\theta = \sigma\mu\omega t\rho$ of the copper sheet. The carbon slab, simulating overburden, makes the copper sheet appear to be of lower induction number than it really is. The phase of the copper sheet response has been rotated towards the quadrature, a result quite opposite to that found for a uniform layer of overburden. The "overburden" has decreased the slope of the profile at the zero crossing, and, as we shall see in the section on interpretation, this suggests that the sheet conductor is buried more deeply than it really is.

(b) *Inductive vertical loop in-line tandem array.*—There is not much model data available for this reconnaissance method because it is usually supplemented by the broadside tandem or fixed transmitter vertical loop methods when detailed interpretation is desired. Thus, we introduce here only sufficient model data to illustrate the basic char-

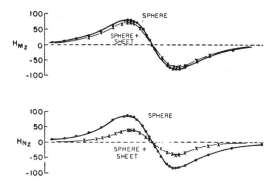

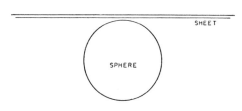

Fig. 103. Experimental attenuation of in-phase and quadrature anomalies from sphere as affected by thin conductive sheet. Uniform inducing field (after Fraser, 1966).

acteristics of the dip angle profile. Data presented has been adapted from Swanson (1960).

Figure 105 provides an indication of the change in profile form with change in direction of traverse relative to the strike of the conductor. Recall that for traverses at 90 degrees to strike, all zero dip angles will be recorded.

Figure 106 indicates two features: (a) the effect of dip on the shape of the profile and (b) the fact that the profile shape depends upon relative positions of the transmitter and receiver. Obviously any one anomaly profile form can arise from several different system-ore body configurations, and it is for this reason that the method is infrequently used when detailed interpretation is required.

(c) *Inductive vertical loop broadside array*

(i) *Effect of dip.*—A dimensionless presentation of dip angles obtained over an infinite half-plane dipping at 30, 60, and 90 degrees is contained in Figure 107.

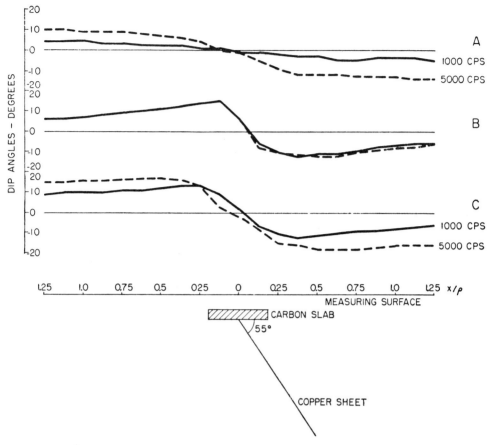

FIG. 104. Effect of finite "overburden" on response of sheet conductor: *A*—carbon slab only, *B*—copper sheet only, *C*—slab and sheet: Dimensions of sheet 700×700×1 ft: Dimensions of slab 300×1,000×50 ft; $\rho=800$ ft; $h=75$ ft.

Increasing asymmetry is introduced into the profiles by flatter dips with the peak angles largest on the footwall side. Note that for dips greater than 60 degrees, the conductor is detected only to distances of order 0.5 ρ beyond the sheet sub-outcrop. As the dip flattens, the sheet can be detected at greater distances from the sub-outcrop. In units of ρ, the depth is 0.05, while the induction number is sufficiently large to assure saturation. The plotting convention is that left dip angles are positive when facing the transmitter, indicating that the magnetic field is always dipping away from the top of the sheet.

(ii) *Effect of depth.*—The two curves presented in Figure 108 were observed over a saturated half-plane dipping at 60 degrees and at depths of 0.05 ρ, 0.12 ρ, and 0.30 ρ. The decrease in anomaly amplitude and a slight broadening of the anomaly are both evident. The slope of the profile at the crossover is reduced as depth increases. The peak amplitudes shift outward from the crossover.

(iii) *Effect of depth extent.*—In Figure 109 the effect of depth extent is evident; anomaly amplitudes decrease as the depth extent decreases. Also, the width of the peaks increases with depth extent. Curves *A* and *C* pertain to a sheet of dimensions: length 2.25 ρ, depth extent 2.0 ρ, depth 0.125 ρ, and an induction number $\sigma\mu\omega t\rho$ in excess of 100 and therefore at saturation.

Curves B and D pertain to a sheet of the same length and depth but of depth extent 0.5 ρ. Curves A and B were obtained with sheets dipping 60 degrees while curves C and D were obtained with sheets dipping 30 degrees. The induction number for curves B and D is not simply $\sigma\mu\omega t\rho$, because now the depth extent is a significant dimension. This may partially explain the decrease in amplitude of anomaly since for such a small depth extent, the induction number

$$\theta = f\left(\sigma\mu\omega, \frac{t}{\rho}, \frac{\text{depth extent}}{\rho}\right)$$

may be below saturation values.

(iv) *Effect of traverse direction.*—The dip angle profile shape changes markedly when the traverse direction changes from normal to a sheet conductor. Figure 110 contains (A) the response of a vertical half-plane when the traverse is perpendicular to the sheet and (B) the response of a vertical half-plane when the traverse is made at 60

degrees to the strike of the sheet. The profile is drawn looking from the receiver towards the transmitter, and the orientation of the half plane is such that the transmitter crosses it first when the pair of coils is moved from left to right.

When the traverse is at 120 degrees to the strike of the conductor so that the system is oriented such that the receiver crosses the sheet first, then curve C of Figure 111 is traced out. For comparison, the profiles for 60 degrees and 90 degrees are placed on the same drawing. Note the gross change in profile shape as the direction of traverse changes relative to the strike of the conductor.

The conductivity or the frequency can alter the shape of profiles obtained on oblique traverses as Figure 112 demonstrates. Curve A was obtained for a half plane of $\theta = \infty$, while curves B and C were obtained for induction numbers, θ, of 15 and 5. This change in profile shape indicates that the current distribution changes with induction number. For Figures 110,

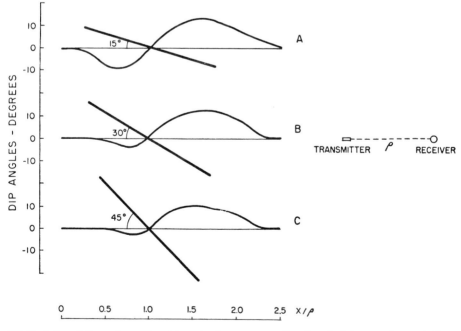

Fig. 105. Variation of dip angle profiles with angle of traverse to strike of vertical sheet conductor; in-line tandem array; conductor=1.625 units long; depth extent=0.625 units; depth=0.125 units; spread=1 unit (after Swanson, 1960).

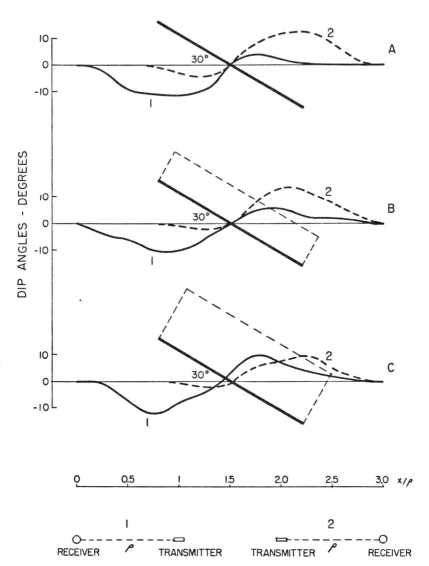

Fig. 106. Variation of dip angle profiles with dip of conductive sheet and with orientation of transmitter-receiver array; in-line tandem array; sheet conductor=1.625 units long; depth extent=0.625 units, depth=0.125 units; spread=1 unit (after Swanson, 1960).

111, and 112, the depth to the top of the sheet is 0.05 ρ. For Figures 111 and 112 the sheet is dipping 60 degrees.

(v) *Effect of multiple conductors.*—Resolution of adjacent parallel conductors is much better with the broadside array than with the fixed transmitter array. Figure 113B illustrates that two adjacent conductors 0.5 ρ apart can be resolved readily when depth of cover is 0.125 ρ. However,

when the separation to depth ratio decreases to 2:1, as in Figure 113A, the profile could be interpreted as caused by either a broad conductor or two parallel conductors.

Comparison of Figure 113 with Figure 98 demonstrates the improved resolution of the broadside method.

For Figure 113, the conductive sheets each are 2.25 ρ long, 0.5 ρ in depth extent,

0.125 ρ deep, and dipping 90 degrees. The induction number $\sigma\mu\omega t\rho$ of each sheet is approximately 100.

Grant and West (1965) discuss the coupling between sheets and its effect on the total response. When the sheets are sufficiently far apart, for a particular spread and conductor depth, the responses of the two sheets are numerically additive. As the sheets become closer together, the response of two sheets is not the sum of the individual sheets.

(vi) *Effect of conductor width.*—Figure 114 portrays the effect of varying width; profile A, B, C, and D arise from conductors of widths 0.03 ρ 0.0620ρ, 0.25 ρ, and 0.5 ρ, respectively. The conductor is 2.25 ρ

long, 0.5 ρ in depth extent and 0.125 ρ deep. The conductivity is 225 mho/m and the dip is 90 degrees. No attempt has been made to estimate the induction number since significant linear dimensions must include width, depth extent, and spread. Note that an inflection occurs near the crossover as the width increases until eventually a small reversed crossover occurs above the center of the conductor for case D. The same general type of behavior pertains to conductors of infinite strike length and depth extent.

Profile D is not unlike profile A of Figure 113 where two parallel sheets were used, emphasizing that electromagnetic methods are area sensitive, not volume

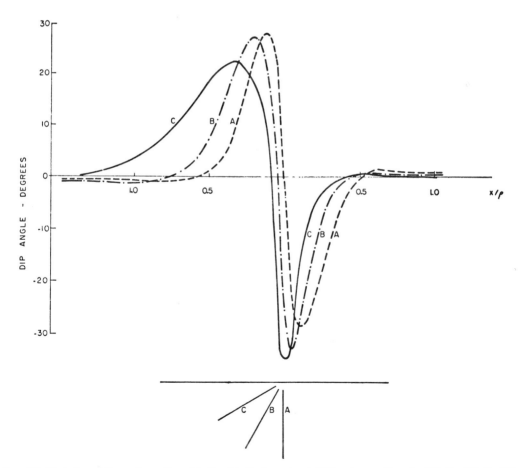

FIG. 107. Variation of dip-angle profiles with dip of half-plane; depth 0.05 ρ; $\theta = \infty$; dips: $A = 90°$, $B = 60°$, $C = 30°$; traverse normal to strike (after West, 1960). Broadside array.

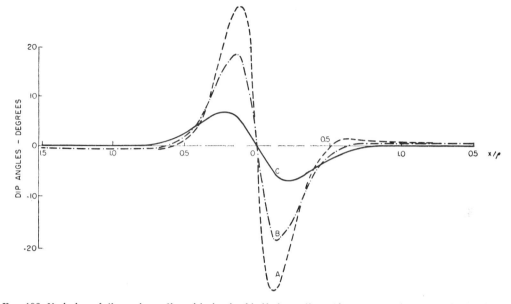

FIG. 108. Variation of dip angle profiles with depth of half-plane; dip=90°; $\theta = \infty$; depths: $A = 0.05\,\rho$, $B = 0.12\,\rho$, $C = 0.3\,\rho$; traverse normal to strike (after West, 1960). Broadside array.

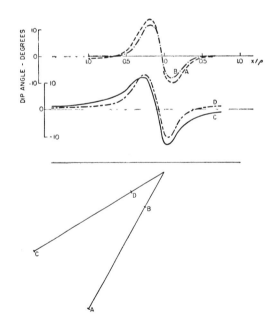

FIG. 109. Variation of dip angle profiles with depth extent of sheet conductor; dip 60 degrees; $\theta = 100$; depth $= 0.125\,\rho$; depth extents: $A = C = 2.0\,\rho$; $B = D = 0.5\,\rho$; traverse normal to strike. Broadside array. (Courtesy Texas Gulf Sulphur Co.)

sensitive. The pertinent area is that normal to the inducing field.

(vii) *Effect of conductivity.*—The lower the conductivity, the lower the response, provided the sheet conductor is below saturation. Figure 115 illustrates the decrease in amplitude with decrease in induction number $\sigma\mu\omega t\rho$. Any one of the variables σ, μ, ω, t, or ρ will bring about the variations observed in Figure 115. This data was obtained on a traverse normal to the strike, and for this orientation, only the amplitude is changed. By contrast, Figure 112 illustrates that shape as well as amplitude will change with induction number when the traverse is obliquely oriented relative to strike.

(viii) *A horizontal sheet conductor.*—A conductive sheet $3.3\,\rho$ long by one ρ wide at a depth of 0.16 ρ was traversed with the broadside array. The resulting dip angle profile is presented in Figure 116. A characteristic of the profile over a horizontal sheet is the region of small angles, often with reversed crossover, over the central two-thirds of the sheet, followed by large peaks at the edges of the sheet. The sheet used was at saturation for this experiment.

However, when the dip is increased from zero to as little as 10 degrees, the shape of the profile alters materially as Figure 117 illustrates.

(d) *Horizontal loop*

(i) *Effect of dip.*—Dips other than 90 degrees are marked by an asymmetry of the in-phase and quadrature components of the secondary field, as illustrated in Figure 118. For this test the induction number was five, the sheet conductor was essentially a half-plane, and the depth to the top of the sheet was 0.2 ρ. The traverses were normal to strike. Other induction numbers and other depths will lead to curves of different shapes.

The horizontal sheet was sufficiently large that only the effect of one edge was recorded.

(ii) *Effect of depth.*—Figure 119 contains four pairs of curves pertaining to a half-plane at the four depths 0.1 ρ, 0.2 ρ, 0.4 ρ, 0.6 ρ. The induction number $\theta = \sigma\mu\omega t\rho$ had the value 105 for these tests and the traverse was normal to strike. The amplitude decreases and the positive peaks shift outward with increasing depth, as expected.

(iii) *Effect of depth extent.*—Rather than include model profiles to illustrate this effect, a summary diagram, Figure 120, is presented instead. In this figure, the maximum in-phase response, in percent of primary field, is plotted versus depth extent for various values of depth. The maximum negative in-phase response for a vertical sheet conductor is obtained when the two coils straddle the sheet and are equidistant from it.

The data of Figure 120 were obtained over a vertical sheet of length 2.25 ρ, of

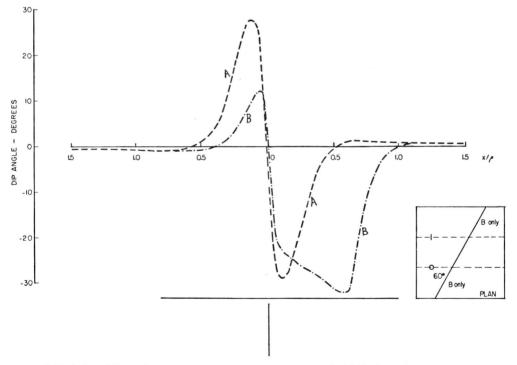

Fig. 110. Variation of dip angle profile with traverse direction over vertical half-plane: *A*—traverse 90 degrees to strike of conductor; *B*—traverse 60 degrees to strike of conductor. Depth 0.05 ρ, $\theta = \infty$. Broadside array (after West, 1960).

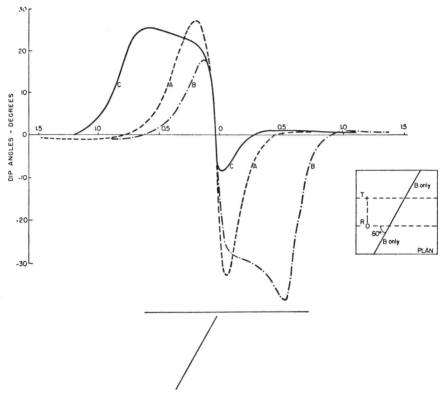

FIG. 111. Variation of dip angle profile with traverse direction over half-plane dipping 60°: *A*—traverse 90° to strike; *B*—60° to strike; *C*—120° to strike. Depth 0.05 *ρ*, *θ* = ∞. Broadside array (after West, 1960).

simulated conductivity 225 ohm-m, and of width 0.003 *ρ*. It would appear that provided the depth extent is twice the coil separation, the anomaly looks like that from a sheet of infinite depth extent.

(iv) *Effect of traverse direction.*—Figure 121 contains three in-phase profiles over a vertical sheet conductor of length 4.0 *ρ*, depth extent 2.0 *ρ*, depth 0.1 *ρ*, and thickness 0.008 *ρ*. The sheet was not at saturation. Curves A, B, and C pertain respectively to traverse directions at 45, 30, and 15 degrees to strike. As the traverse becomes more oblique to the strike of the sheet, the main negative decreases, while the side positive lobes increase and spread farther out. For traverses at angles to strike greater than 45 degrees this effect is barely discernible. This fact is illustrated in Figure 122 where the maximum nega-

tive in-phase anomaly is plotted versus the angle between traverse and strike. Data for the latter figure were obtained over a vertical sheet 3.0 *ρ* long, 2.25 *ρ* in depth extent, 0.03 *ρ* thick and nearly at saturation.

Recognition should be made of the fact that the sheet conductors used to develop Figures 121 and 122 were not closely approximating half-planes when the traverses were oblique.

(v) *Effect of multiple conductors.*—Two parallel sheet conductors of dimensions 3.0 *ρ* long, 1.0 *ρ* depth extent, and 0.008 *ρ* thickness were traversed with a horizontal loop system with depth and sheet separation as variables. Figure 123 contains the results. The two sheets can be resolved on the in-phase profile when the depth is about half the separation. Resolution on the

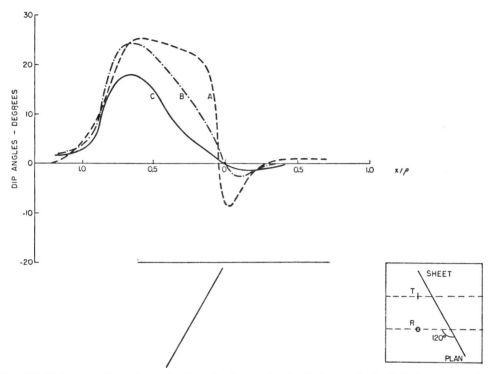

FIG. 112. Variation of dip angle profile with induction number for 60 degrees dipping half-plane traversed at 120 degrees to strike: $A-\theta=\infty$, $B-\theta=15$; $C-\theta=5$. Depth 0.05 ρ. Broadside array (after West, 1960).

quadrature profile is not evident until the depth decreases to one-fifth of the separation.

The ratio of peak negative in-phase to peak negative quadrature decreases as the sheets separate, indicating that coupling between the sheets affects the phase of the response. This observation is consistent with expectation since ultimately the two sheets will merge into one, as they are brought closer and closer together, and when merged will possess an induction number $\theta=\sigma\mu\omega t\rho$ of twice that for an individual sheet. Grant and West (1965) pre-

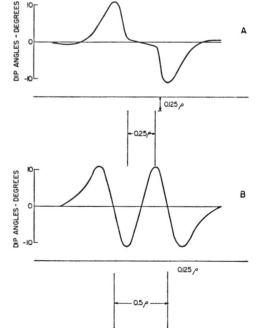

FIG. 113. Resolution of parallel sheet conductors with broadside array. Profile A pertains to two sheets 0.25 ρ apart at depth of 0.125 ρ. Profile B pertains to two sheets 0.5 ρ apart at depth of 0.125 ρ. Each sheet is dipping 90 degrees, is of induction number $\sigma\mu\omega t\rho=100$ and is of dimensions 2.25 ρ long by 0.5 ρ in depth extent. (Courtesy Texas Gulf Sulphur Co.)

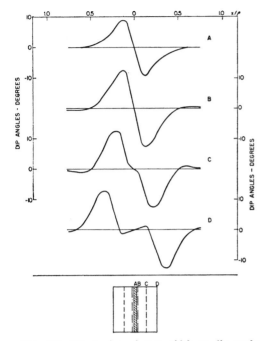

FIG. 114. Effect of conductor width on dip angle profile with broadside array. Widths are: $A=0.03\,\rho$, $B=0.0625\,\rho$, $C=0.25\,\rho$, $D=0.5\,\rho$. Conductor length $=2.25\,\rho$ and depth extent$=0.5\,\rho$ at depth $0.125\,\rho$ in all cases. Conductivity 225 mho/m. (Courtesy Texas Gulf Sulphur Co.)

sent a full discussion of the effect of coupling on the response of parallel sheet conductors as mentioned earlier.

The data of Figure 123, when compared with that of Figure 113, would indicate that the horizontal loop method is of slightly higher resolution than the broadside array vertical loop method. Further, as we shall see, the horizontal loop response for a broad conductor is quite different to that for two parallel conductors, and this was not the case for the broadside method.

(vi) *Effect of conductor width.*—The shape of the anomalous in-phase and quadrature profiles for the horizontal loop method change markedly as the width of the conductor changes relative to depth or relative to coil separation. The several characteristic profiles can be studied readily by means of theoretical calculations for a sphere. Bhattacharya and Sinha (1965) present profiles of horizontal loop response under the assumption of a uniform inducing field. This assumption is valid when the radius of the sphere is much less than the depth of burial. Figure 124 has been

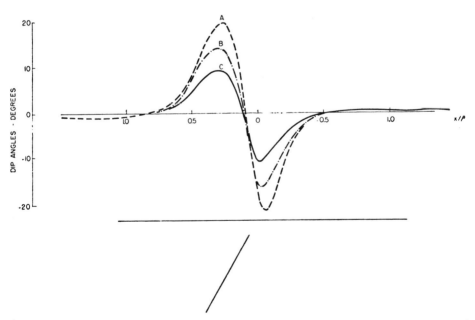

FIG. 115. Effect of induction number on dip angle profile with broadside array. Induction numbers are: $A=\infty$; $B=15$; $C=5$. Half-plane at depth $0.12\,\rho$. Dip$=60°$. Strike$=90°$ to traverse (after West, 1960).

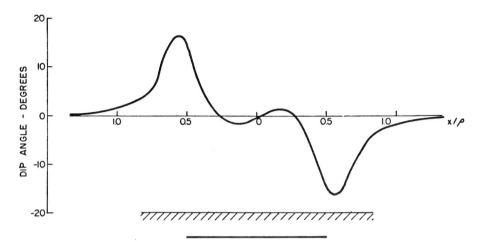

FIG. 116. Response over horizontal sheet conductor with broadside array. Length 3.3 ρ, width 1.0 ρ, depth 0.16 ρ. (Courtesy Texas Gulf Sulphur Co.)

adapted from the work of Bhattacharya and Sinha and shows five characteristic anomaly shapes as the ratio of sphere radius to depth to center varies. The quantity plotted is the geometrical factor (GF) where

$$\frac{H_{zz}}{H_{0z}} = (M - iN) \cdot \left(\frac{R}{d}\right)^3 \cdot \text{GF} \qquad \text{(C66)}$$

and where

H_{0z} = primary field at the receiving coil

H_{zz} = secondary vertical field at the receiving coil

$M - iN$ = response function depicted by Figure 6-2

R = radius of sphere

d = depth to center of sphere

GF = factor describing geometry of field

When the sphere is shallow, $d = 0.125$ ρ, then curve A pertains. As the sphere deepens the profile changes to $B(d = 0.25$ ρ$)$ through $C(d = 0.5$ ρ$)$ to $D(1.0$ ρ$)$ and $E(2.0$ ρ$)$. Curve C is not unlike those we have studied so far over vertical sheet conductors.

When the conductor is broad but lacks

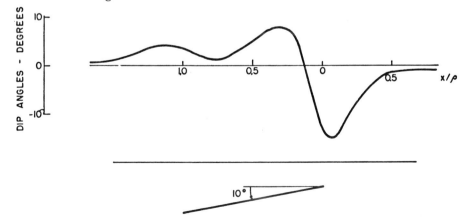

FIG. 117. Response over near horizontal sheet conductor with broadside array. Length = 3.3 ρ, width = 1.0 ρ, depth = 0.16 ρ, dip = 10°. (Courtesy Texas Gulf Sulphur Co.)

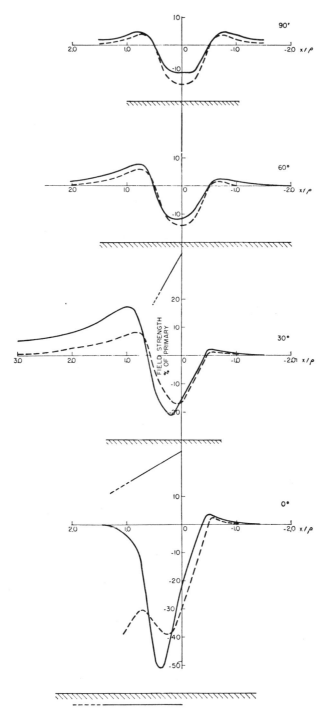

Fig. 118. Effect of dip on in-phase (solid) and quadrature (dashed) components measured with horizontal loop system. Half-plane model of $\theta = \sigma\mu\omega t\rho = 5$; depth$= 0.2 \, \rho$; traverse$= 90°$ to strike. (Courtesy Bear Creek Mining Co.)

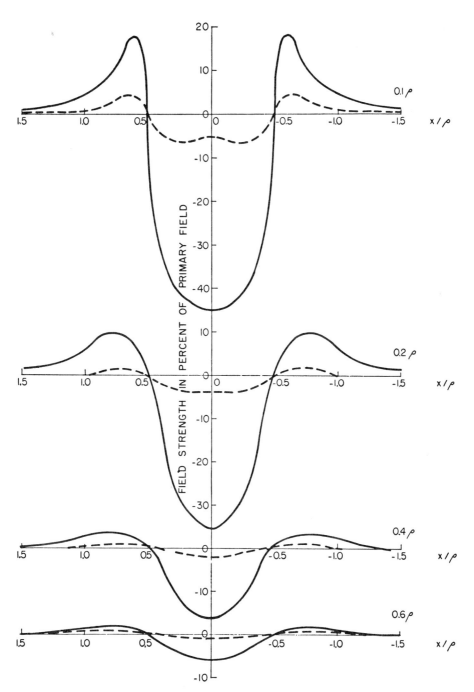

FIG. 119. Effect of depth on in-phase (solid) and quadrature (dashed) components measured with horizontal loop system. Half-plane model of $\theta = \sigma\mu\omega t\rho = 105$; traverse $= 90°$ to strike; dip $= 90°$. (Courtesy Bear Creek Mining Co.)

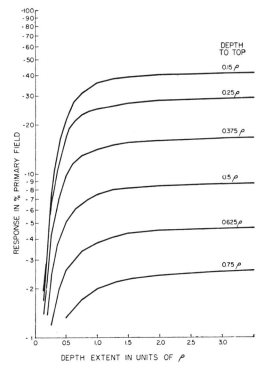

FIG. 120. Effect of depth extent on in-phase component measured with horizontal loop system. Conductor length=2.25 ρ, dip=90°, traverse normal to strike. (Courtesy Texas Gulf Sulphur Co.)

the symmetry of a sphere, the geometrical factor may not separate from the physical property factor so that the in-phase and quadrature components may not be of the same shape. Such a situation is illustrated in Figure 125 wherein the profiles were observed over a rectangular parallelepiped. Note that the in-phase curves for depths of 0.1 ρ and 0.3 ρ both are of the form of curve C of Figure 124. The quadrature curve for a depth of 0.3 cm is of the same type, but the quadrature curve for a depth of 0.1 ρ is similar to curve B of Figure 124.

In general, profiles over dike-like bodies of finite width follow the curves of Figure 124 in character.

(vii) *Effect of conductivity.*—We expect that a decrease in conductivity, such that the induction number $\theta = \sigma\mu\omega t\rho$ falls below the saturation value, will lead to a decrease

in amplitude of both in-phase and quadrature components. This expectation is borne out by the data of Figures 126 and 127. However, we note also from these latter figures that the shapes of the in-phase and quadrature profiles change with conductivity, and that the in-phase and quadrature profiles change in different manners. Evidently the induced current configuration changes with induction number, and the phase becomes a function of lateral position across the profile.

These characteristic effects are not pronounced for steeply dipping sheets, i.e. 60 to 90 degrees, but become quite noticeable for 30-degree dips.

(viii) *A horizontal sheet conductor.*—Figure 128 illustrates that a horizontal sheet conductor displays an anomaly profile characteristic which is a function of depth. The in-phase and quadrature profiles are quite different at shallow depths but become similar for depths of the order of the coil separation. Note that the sheet, being of dimensions 2.0 ρ wide by 3.0 ρ long by 0.008 ρ thick, is of comparable dimensions to the coil separation, and that this fact may have a profound influence on the characteristics of the curves. Proof of this contention is given in Figure 129 where a sheet of dimensions 0.27 ρ wide by 1.4 ρ long by 0.008 ρ thick, i.e. small width relative to coil separation, produces curves which exhibit a high flat central positive, a feature not evident in the wide sheet of Figure 128.

(ix) *Effect of overburden.*—Lowrie and West (1965) have presented a good illustration and discussion of the effect of a conducting overburden on the response of a half-plane. Figure 130 contains some of their data. An anomalous ambient response arises due to the overburden which becomes more pronounced as the induction number $\theta_0 = \sigma_0\mu\omega t_0\rho$ for the overburden increases. Superimposed on these ambients in both in-phase and quadrature components are lateral variations in both components. The in-phase response and the quadrature response change with θ_0. If we

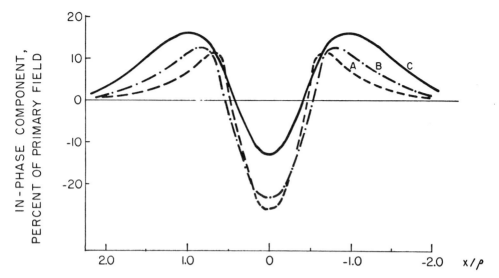

FIG. 121. Effect of traverse direction on in-phase component measured with horizontal loop system. Conductor length=4.0 ρ, depth extent=2.0 ρ, depth=0.1 ρ, thickness=0.008 ρ (after Frischknecht and Mangan, 1960).

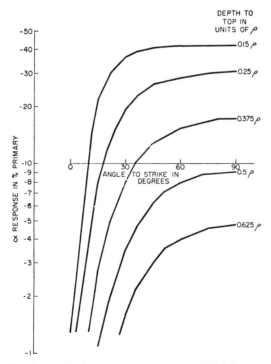

FIG. 122. Effect of traverse direction on in-phase component measured with horizontal loop system. Conductor length=3.0 ρ, depth extent=2.25 ρ, depth variable, thickness=0.03 ρ. (Courtesy Texas Gulf Sulphur Co.)

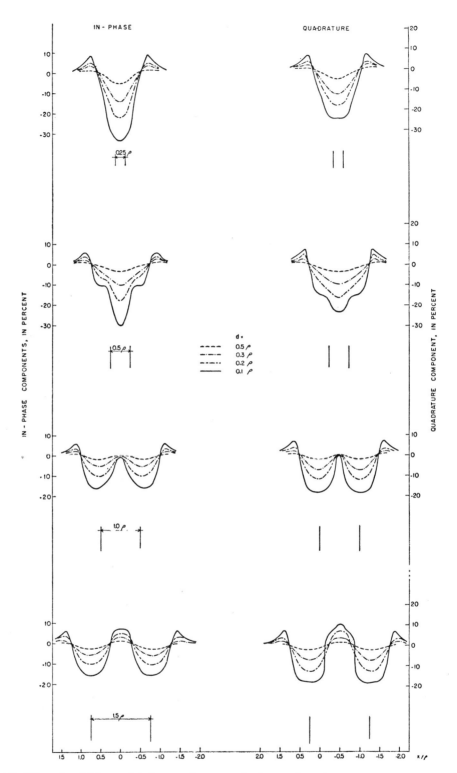

Fig. 123. Effect of multiple parallel sheet conductors on in-phase and quadrature components measured with horizontal loop system. Each sheet 0.008ρ thick, 1.0ρ in depth extent, 3.0ρ long. Depth and sheet separation variable (after Frischknecht and Mangan, 1960).

measure the peak-to-peak excursion of either component, and assign a positive or a negative to this value depending on whether the response at $x/\rho = 0$ is negative or positive relative to the response at $x/\rho > 1$, then we find that the phase of the response is rotated towards positive in-phase or even toward negative quadrature as θ_0 increases. There is only a very slight decrease in the amplitude of the total response as θ_0 increases, a decrease of in-phase component being counterbalanced by an increase in quadrature or vice-versa.

The apparent phase of the half-plane response is extremely important in interpretation as we shall see later.

(x) *Effect of strike length.*—An experiment to determine the length at which a sheet conductor appeared "infinite" was conducted over a sheet 2.25 ρ in depth extent, of thickness 0.03 ρ, of 90-degree dip, and at variable depth. The resulting

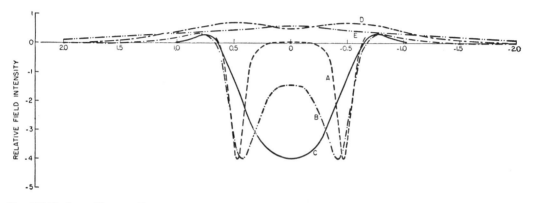

FIG. 124. Horizontal loop profile types over buried sphere. Depth to center $A = 0.125\rho$, $B = 0.25\rho$, $C = 0.50\rho$, $D = 1.0\rho$, $E = 2.0\rho$ (after Bhattacharya and Sinha, 1965).

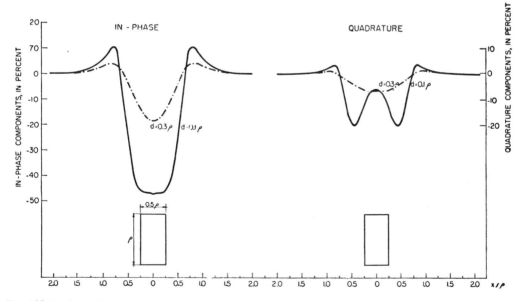

FIG. 125. Horizontal loop profiles over rectangular parallelepiped 2.0 ρ long by 1.0 ρ deep by 0.5 ρ thick. Depths 0.1 ρ and 0.3 ρ (after Frischknecht and Mangan, 1960).

IN - PHASE

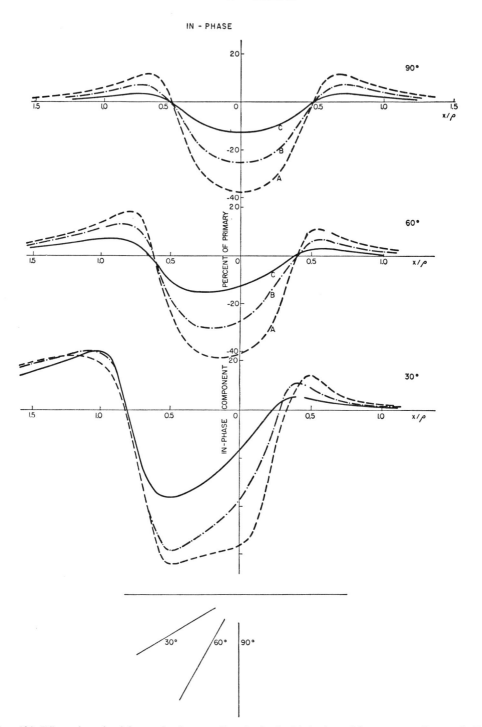

FIG. 126. Effect of conductivity on in-phase profiles obtained with horizontal loop system. Curves A, B, C pertain to induction numbers $\sigma\mu\omega t\rho$ of ∞, 15, and 5 respectively. Half-plane model at depth of 0.2 ρ (after West, 1960).

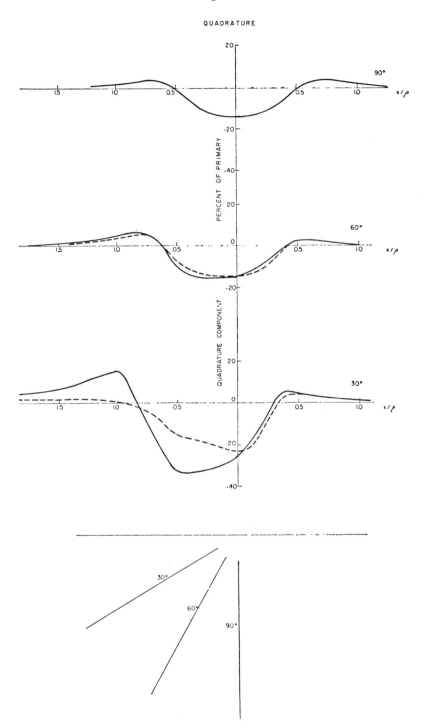

QUADRATURE

FIG. 127. Effect of conductivity on quadrature profiles obtained with horizontal loop system. Solid curves refer to an induction number $\sigma\mu\omega t\rho$ of ∞. Dashed curves refer to an induction number $\sigma\mu\omega t\rho$ of 5. Half-plane model at depth of 0.2 ρ (after West, 1960).

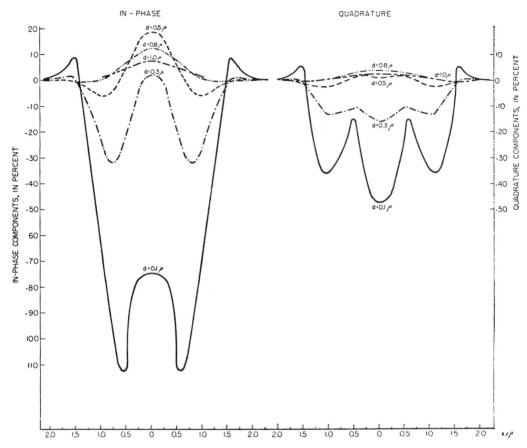

FIG. 128. Response of horizontal sheet conductor with horizontal loop system. Sheet dimensions 2.0 ρ wide by 3.0 ρ long by 0.008 ρ thick. Depth variable (after Frischknecht and Mangan, 1960).

data, portrayed in Figure 131 indicates that, provided the length is in excess of two ρ, the sheet is nearly "infinite" as far as a horizontal coil system is concerned. This criterion tends to break down for depths greater than 0.5 ρ. Thus, from this and an earlier experiment, we conclude that the minimum lateral dimension to ensure the validity of half-plane interpretation techniques is at least two ρ and preferably three ρ.

(e) Crone "Shootback" method.—In Volume I of Mining Geophysics, J. Duncan Crone has presented a description of an ingenious system suitable for reconnaissance surveying in rough terrain. Very little scale model data is available for this system and so

we resort to approximate theory to obtain an impression of the variability of anomaly characteristics. To make the problem tractable, we assume that the ratio of the radius of a spherical conductor to its depth of burial is small. We then traverse with a vertical dipole receiver and a horizontal dipole transmitter whose axis passes through the receiver as in Figure 132. A second traverse is made with the transmitter and receiver interchanged. Anomalous fields from the two traverses are added. If one studies the paper by Crone, he will see that we have established a first approximation to the Shootback method. This approximation permits us to utilize, with modifications, data presented by Bhattacharya and Sinha (1965).

Thus, in Figure 133 we see in good approxi-

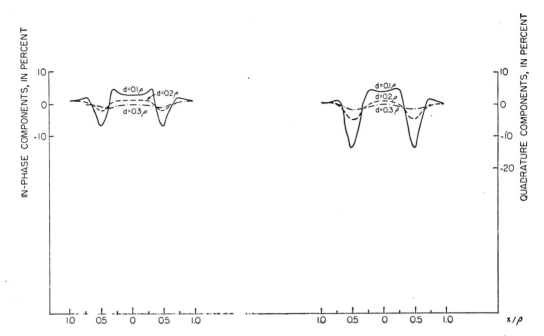

FIG. 129. Response of horizontal sheet conductor with horizontal loop system. Sheet dimensions 0.27 ρ wide by 1.4 ρ long by 0.008 ρ thick. Depth variable (after Frischknecht and Mangan, 1960).

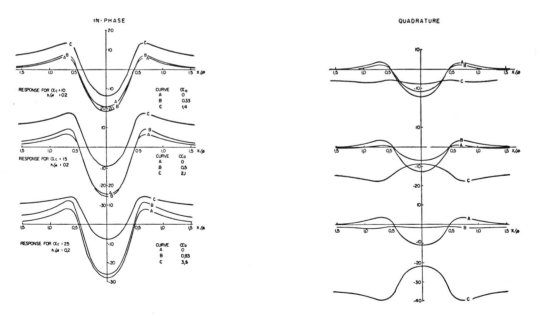

FIG. 130. Effect of overburden on in-phase and quadrature components due to half-plane in horizontal loop system. Overburden at 0.125 ρ below coil system. Half-plane 0.3 ρ below system (after Lowrie and West, 1965).

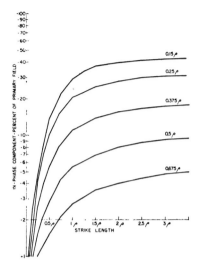

FIG. 131. Effect of strike length on in-phase component over vertical sheet 2.25 ρ depth extent, 0.03 ρ thick, variable depth, variable strike length, nearly at saturation. (Courtesy Texas Gulf Sulphur Co.)

mation the anomaly forms to be expected with the "Shootback" method when traversing a spherical conductor at variable depth.

The anomalies measured on a model bench over a vertical sheet conductor of length 3.0 ρ, depth extent 0.9 ρ, and depth 0.25 ρ are shown in Figure 134. The profile over the vertical sheet exhibits a central positive, flanked by two negatives, which form would have been predicted from curve B, Figure 133, pertaining to a sphere center depth of 0.25 ρ. Dip is indicated by the two minima being of different magnitude; the largest minimum is downdip.

The field data presented by Crone in Volume I is remarkably consistent with the anomaly types presented above.

(f) *Afmag*

(i) *Introduction.*—Parry (1965) has presented an investigation of a thin sheet in a uniform inducing field; the results are applicable to Afmag. Since only a receiver is employed, the transmitter-receiver separation, used in all other model studies as a scale length, is no longer applicable. Thus the significant linear dimension becomes the depth of burial and one could normalize all linear distances by this quantity.

We choose, instead, merely to give all linear dimensions in terms of an arbitrary unit.

Parry demonstrated that it was possible to replace a rectangular aluminum sheet by a rectangular wire loop whose dimensions were very slightly smaller than the dimensions of the sheet. This experimental observation then leads to the conclusion that the geometry of the *secondary* magnetic fields may be obtained directly by computation of the field lines about four finite line source elements, one line source corresponding to each edge of the aluminum sheet. The phase of the response can only be obtained reliably from sheet models.

Four variables have been studied in the following discussion: effect of dip, effect of depth extent, effect of depth, and the phase as a function of frequency and traverse distance. In all of these investigations the inducing field is linear and directed normal to the strike of the sheet conductor. Section CIV D contains information on the effect of elliptically polarized fields and of variable azimuth.

(ii) *Effect of dip.*—Parry measured the vertical secondary H_{sz} and horizontal secondary H_{sx} magnetic field components over a thin sheet of aluminum. Figure 135 contains profiles for dips of 30 and 60 degrees. Depth of the sheet was one unit, length was 16 units, and depth extent was 6.5 units. Dip angles are highest over the hangingwall and smallest over the

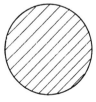

FIG. 132. Horizontal dipole transmitter (vertical loop) and vertical dipole receiver (horizontal loop) traversing sphere. Separation is ρ.

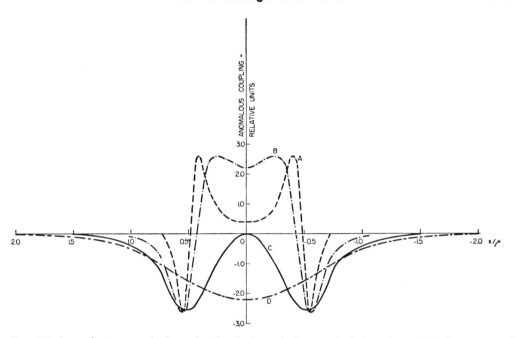

FIG. 133. Approximate anomaly forms for shootback method over spherical conductor. Depth to center of sphere: $A = 0.125\,\rho$, $B = 0.25\,\rho$, $C = 0.50\,\rho$, $D = 1.0\,\rho$. Anomalies in units of K where $K = (M - iN)(R/d)^3$. (Adapted from theoretical data by Bhattacharya and Sinha, 1965.)

footwall, the opposite to that obtained with vertical loop methods over a half-plane.

In calculating the angles Parry needed to assume a primary field to insert in the formula

$$\phi \approx \tan^{-1} \frac{H_{sz}}{H_{sx} + H_0}. \qquad (C67)$$

A wide range of H_0 will give the same profile characteristics but will, of course, cause a wide range of absolute values of the dip angle θ. Thus Figure 135 should only be used to indicate the change of anomaly form with dip.

(iii) *Effect of depth extent.*—A model consisting of two long horizontal line sources was used to simulate the top and bottom edges of a sheet conductor of depth three units and dip 60 degrees. The depth extent was varied to produce the profiles of Figure 136. As expected, the largest dip angles occur on the hanging wall side of the sheet. However, the dip angle profile becomes symmetric as the depth extent increases. This implies that the only fields

observed, for large depth extents, arise in the top line source. This would explain why most field profiles are nearly symmetric. Dip may thus be difficult to recognize from Afmag profiles.

Increased depth extent also raises the flanks of the profile.

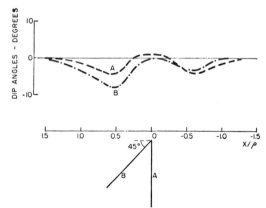

FIG. 134. "Shootback" dip angle profiles obtained over thin sheet of dimensions $3.0\,\rho$ long, $0.9\,\rho$ deep, at depth of $0.25\,\rho$. Profile A for sheet dipping 90 degrees, profile B for sheet dipping 45 degrees. (Courtesy Newmont Exploration Limited.)

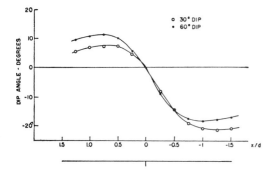

FIG. 135. Effect of dip on Afmag dip angle profile. Traverse over center of aluminum sheet of length = 16 units, depth extent = 6.5 units, depth = 1 unit (after Parry, 1965).

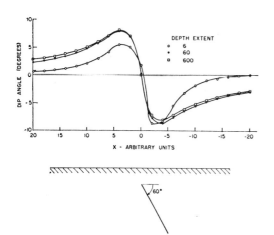

FIG. 136. Effect of depth extent on Afmag dip angle profile. Traverse over center of two horizontal wires simulating sheet of large length, depth = 3 units, dip = 60°, and variable depth extent (after Parry, 1965).

(iv) *Effect of depth.*—A model consisting of two long horizontal line sources, simulating the top and bottom edges of a sheet conductor, of depth extent 10 units and dipping 60 degrees, was used to compute the curves of Figure 137. The dip angles were computed, according to equation

(C67) with arbitrary H_0 but with calculated H_{sz} and H_{sx}, for depths of one, three, and 10 units. Thus the curves should be used for character studies only. Increased depth spreads the dip angle peaks, flattens the slope at the crossover, and raises the flanks. The asymmetry of the profile increases with increasing depth, a fact explained by noting that, for shallow depths, radiation from the top line source predominates while, for large depths, the difference in the contribution to surface fields of top and bottom line sources minimizes. Thus both depth and depth extent affect the asymmetry of the dip angle profile.

(v) *Effect of conductivity.*—This factor can be evaluated rather readily by considering a conducting disk in a uniform inducing magnetic field parallel to the axis of symmetry of the disk. Grant and West (1965) give the induced dipole moment as

$$m = \frac{8}{3} R^3 H_0 [X - iY] e^{-i\omega t} \quad \text{(C68)}$$

where

$$\theta = \sigma \mu_0 \omega t R$$

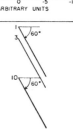

FIG. 137. Effect of depth on Afmag dip angle profile. Traverse over center of two horizontal wires simulating sheet of large length, dip = 60°, depth extent = 10 units, and variable depth (after Parry, 1965).

and R and t are the radius and thickness of the disk, respectively. At saturation the induced dipole moment has the value

$$m = \frac{8}{3} R^3 H_0 e^{-i\omega t} \qquad (C69)$$

while for values of the induction $\theta < 1$, the following approximation holds for a disk of uniform conductivity:

$$m = \frac{\pi}{15} i\sigma\mu_0\omega t R \cdot R^3 H_0 e^{-i\omega t}. \qquad (C70)$$

The function $X - iY$ is not known precisely but has been sketched by Grant and West by inference between the limiting values given in (C69) and (C70). Figure 138 contains an estimate of the in-phase and quadrature responses as functions of the induction number θ. The curve was obtained from the known resistive limit $\theta < 1$, the known inductive limit or saturation value, and the form of the response curves for the sphere. The dipole moment of a sphere at saturation is

$$m = 2\pi R^3 H_0\, e^{-i\omega t} \qquad (C71)$$

and so the ratio of dipole moments of disk and sphere is 0.425, the disk dipole moment being smaller.

From equation (C71) we determine that the conductivity enters the response only via the induction number, and from Figure 138 we observe the manner in which the response varies as a function of conductivity. The Afmag dip angles will be related mostly to the in-phase response.

(vi) *Effect of sheet size on Afmag dip angle profiles.*—The disk model enables us to determine the effect of sheet conductor size on Afmag dip angle profiles. The dipole moment given by equation (C68) indicates that the anomaly increases as radius R increases via two entries. First the physical property factor $X - iY$ increases until X reaches the value unity and Y is zero. Second, there is an increase in dipole moment proportional to the third power of the radius.

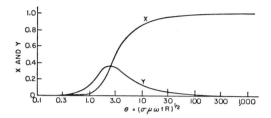

FIG. 138. Estimated in-phase and quadrature response of thin disk in uniform alternating magnetic field.

The fields near the disk may be described by

$$H_x(\omega) = R^3 H_0 [M - iN] \cdot \mathrm{GF}_x \qquad (C72)$$
$$H_y(\omega) = R^3 H_0 [M - iN] \cdot \mathrm{GF}_y \qquad (C73)$$
$$H_z(\omega) = R^3 H_0 [M - iN] \cdot \mathrm{GF}_z \qquad (C74)$$

where

$$M - iN = \frac{2}{3\pi} [X - iY]$$

and where GF_i is the geometrical factor pertaining to the ith component arising from a wire loop of radius approximately that of the disk. The dip angle at saturation then is described by

$$\begin{aligned}
\alpha &= \tan^{-1}\frac{H_z}{H_x + H_0} \\
&= \tan^{-1}\frac{\mathrm{GF}_z}{\mathrm{GF}_x + \dfrac{2}{R^3}}. \qquad (C75)
\end{aligned}$$

For very large radii $R \gg x$ and shallow depth to the top edge $R \gg z$ the dip angle will be given approximately by

$$\begin{aligned}
\alpha &= \tan^{-1}\frac{x}{z + \dfrac{2(x^2 + z^2)}{R^3}} \\
&\sim \tan^{-1}\frac{x}{z}. \qquad (C76)
\end{aligned}$$

The dip angles will quickly reach 90 degrees for $x > z$ under these assumptions, although they will not exceed 90 degrees.

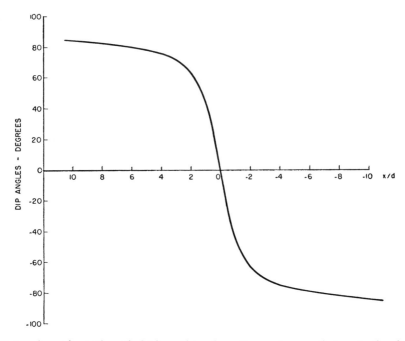

Fɪɢ. 139. Approximate theoretical Afmag dip angle profile over large vertical conductive sheet.

Such large dip angles occasionally are observed, as illustrated by Figure 46.

The disk model is all that is required in most interpretation, since Figure 138 gives the phase response and equation (C75) describes the dip angle distribution. The form of the dip angle profile for very large sheets, as given by equation (C76), is described in Figure 139.

It should be noted that, since the radius of the disk enters the induction number, saturation will be reached for many large conductors.

(vii) *Effect of overburden.*—Under our discussion of model data for the inductive vertical loop method, the effect of overburden for uniform field methods was illustrated. That discussion pertains directly to Afmag. Any body will appear deeper than it actually is if conductive overburden occurs above it.

(viii) *Effect of multiple conductors.*—Two adjacent disks are all that is necessary to model two parallel sheet conductors. Neglecting coupling, between the sheets, addition of two pertinent forms of equa-

tions (C72) and (C74) will yield the necessary field intensities to insert in (C75).

(ix) *Effect of conductor width.*—The geometry of the fields for large conductors may be predicted with sufficient accuracy by computing the fields from an infinite horizontal ribbon model placed at a depth equal to the top edge of the conductor.

D. *A catalog of curve types—airborne electromagnetic surveys*

Data is presented here for one fixed-wing towed-bird system and one helicopter mounted rigid frame system. The two categories of curves are intended to give some impression of the contrast in these two types of devices.

(a) *Hunting Canso System*

(i) *Effect of depth.*—In Figure 55 we presented the geometry pertinent to the discussion following. Then in Figure 56 the effect of depth beneath the aircraft was illustrated. Note that, in those two figures and in subsequent ones, the aircraft is flying from right to left. The direction of flight is important because the anomalies are asymmetrical. For this reason the dip is given from 0 to 180 degrees and the angle is defined as in Figure 55. The anomaly is plotted beneath the receiving coil.

The peak responses of Figure 56 are plotted versus aircraft height above a vertical half plane conductor in Figure 140. The anomaly decreases as the 4.1 power of aircraft height above the half-plane. Data for this test are from theoretical computations by G. F. West.

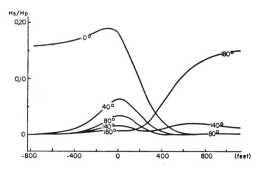

FIG. 142. Effect of dip on in-phase anomaly over half-plane. Hunting Canso system. $\phi = 90°$, $h = 500$ ft, $\sigma = \infty$ (after Paterson, 1961a).

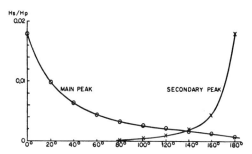

FIG. 143. Variation of peak in-phase response with dip for perfectly conducting half-plane. Strike = 90°, height of aircraft 500 ft (after Paterson, 1961a).

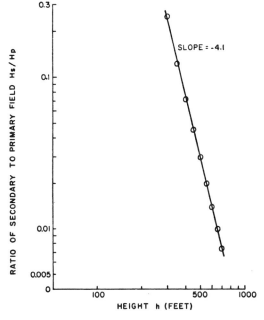

FIG. 140. Variation with aircraft height of peak in-phase response of vertical half-plane. Hunting Canso system. $\theta = 90°$, $\phi = 90°$, $\sigma = \infty$ (after Paterson, 1961a).

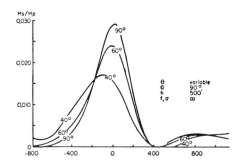

FIG. 141. Effect of strike angle on in-phase anomaly over vertical half-plane. Hunting Canso system. $\phi = 90°$, $h = 500$ ft, $\sigma = \infty$ (after Paterson, 1961a).

(ii) *Effect of strike.*—Varying the aircraft direction relative to the strike of a vertical half-plane shifts the main peak outwards away from the top of the half-plane as Figure 141 illustrates. The maximum anomaly also decreases. Herringboning in anomaly plan maps could arise from the lateral shift of the peak. The data for this test was obtained from West's (1960) theoretical solution for a half-plane.

(iii) *Effect of dip.*—The magnitude and shape of the anomaly change grossly as the dip of a half-plane is varied from zero to 180 degrees. Figure 142 contains the profiles computed for this example. At dip angles from 90 to 180 degrees a secondary peak arises as the transmitting coil passes over the upper edge of the conductor: Herringboning can arise because of this factor also. Figure 143 is a plot of the main and secondary peaks as functions of dip as obtained in scale model experiments.

The profiles presented so far have been

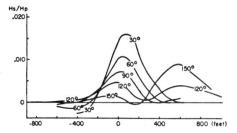

FIG. 144. Variation of quadrature anomaly with dip for finite sheet. Dip variable, strike=90°, aircraft height 500 ft, frequency 2,300 cps, conductivity 0.131 mho/m, depth extent 400 ft, thickness 100 ft (after Paterson, 1961a).

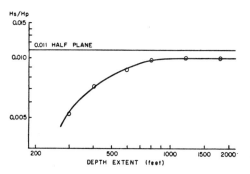

FIG. 145. Effect of depth extent of peak quadrature response obtained with Hunting Canso system. Strike =90°, dip=90°, height=500 ft, frequency 2,300 cps, conductivity 0.131 mho/m, thickness 100 ft (after Paterson, 1961a).

obtained for a perfectly conducting half-plane and hence the quadrature component is zero. Since the Hunting Canso system relies upon the quadrature component solely, it is necessary to resort to scale models. Figure 144 contains the quadrature component profiles over a sheet of finite size, finite conductivity, and dipping at various angles. Both primary and secondary peaks occur, with the secondary peak more developed than for an infinitely conducting half-plane.

(iv) *Effect of depth extent.*—The peak quadrature response was measured as a function of depth extent for a long sheet conductor of finite conductivity. From Figure 145, where the results are portrayed, one may conclude that once the conductor is about 1,000 ft in depth extent, it gives maximum response for a 500-ft flight elevation. The theoretical re-

sponse for an infinite half-plane is shown for comparison.

(v) *Effect of horizontal sheet conductor.*— Figure 146 contains profiles for in-phase response with the Hunting Canso configuration flown at 400 ft over disks of 300 ft and 600 ft radius. The response is an order of magnitude larger than for the same disks oriented vertically as reference to Figure 57 will reveal.

The peak of the anomaly is offset toward that edge of the disk which is nearest the approaching aircraft. The offset is very nearly equal to the radius of the disk. As the disk radius increases, a second peak occurs over the center of the disk, i.e. when the receiver passes over the center and the transmitter passes over the far edge.

(vi) *Effect of multiple conductors.*—Two sheet conductors of length h, depth extent $0.3h$, and conductivity-thickness product 0.0012 mhos were placed at 0, 0.345h,

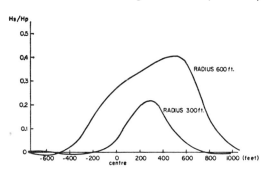

FIG. 146. In-phase anomalies due to horizontal sheet conductors (disks) obtained with Hunting Canso system. Height 400 ft, conductivity infinite (after Paterson, 1961a).

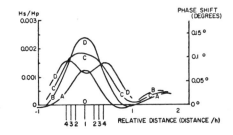

FIG. 147. Quadrature anomalies due to two parallel sheet conductors at separations $A=0$, $B=0.345$ h, $C=0.518$ h, $D=0.69$ h. Hunting Canso system. Strike =90°, dip=90°, frequency=2,300 cps, conductivity-thickness product=0.0012 mho, depth extent=0.3 h, length h, height h (after Paterson, 1961a).

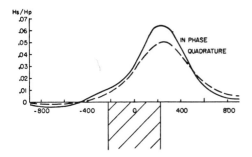

FIG. 148. Quadrature and in-phase anomalies due to broad steeply dipping conductor. Hunting Canso system. Strike=90°, dip=90°, frequency=5,000 cps, width=450 ft, depth extent=900 ft, length=1,900 ft, height 500 ft (after Paterson, 1961a).

0.578h, and 0.69h apart where h is the aircraft height. The quadrature anomalies are shown in Figure 147 from which we observe that resolution is not obtained until the sheets are separated by 0.69h. Then the anomaly is not unlike that due to a horizontal disk.

(vii) *Effect of width.*—A model conductor 1,900 ft long by 900 ft in depth extent by 450 ft width was surveyed at 500-ft aircraft altitude and the profiles of Figure 148 resulted. The peak response is

over the edge nearest the approaching aircraft. The width of the anomaly is large. A wide body will lead to herringboning on a plan map since the offset in anomaly peak will occur on opposite sides of the broad conductor when the aircraft is flown in opposite directions.

(b) *Varian-Texas Gulf Sulphur Helicopter System*

(i) *Effect of depth.*—In Figure 149 we may observe the effect of varying the depth of a sheet conductor sufficiently large to approximate a half-plane. The anomaly peak decreases rapidly with altitude. This is the data from which Figure 58 was obtained and from which we deduce that the peak in-phase anomaly decreases as the 3.3 power of height of system above the top of a half-plane.

Since this is a symmetrical system, the flight direction need not be recorded; the same profile will result from either right-to-left or left-to-right traverse of a conductor.

The coil separation is 50 ft for this system and this separation has been used as a reference distance for all measurements so

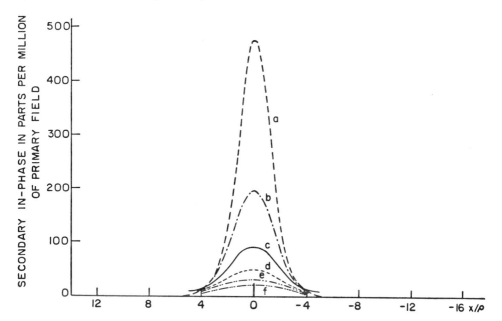

FIG. 149. Effect of depth of "half-plane" on profile obtained with Varian-T.G.S. helicopter system. Sheet 40 ρ long, 12 ρ depth extent, dip 90°, depth variable: $a=3$ ρ, $b=4$ ρ, $c=5$ ρ, $d=6$ ρ, $e=7$ ρ, $f=8$ ρ. Thickness of sheet 0.025 ρ, conductivity 565 mho/m. Courtesy Texas Gulf Sulphur Co.

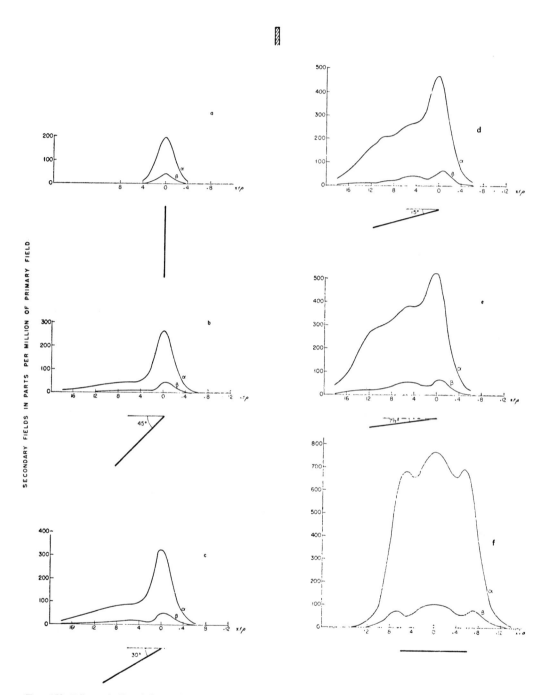

FIG. 150. Effect of dip of large sheet conductor on profiles obtained with Varian-T.G.S. helicopter system. Sheet 40 ρ long, 12 ρ depth extent, depth 4 ρ, dip variable: $a=90°$, $b=45°$, $c=30°$, $d=15°$, $e=7.5°$, $f=0$. Thickness of sheet 0.025 ρ, conductivity 565 mho/m. α is the in-phase and β the quadrature secondary fields. Courtesy Texas Gulf Sulphur Co.

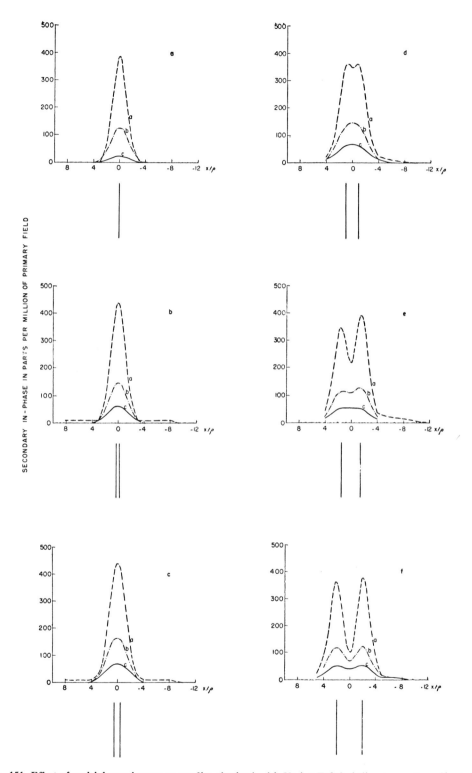

Fig. 151. Effect of multiple conductors on profiles obtained with Varian-T.G.S. helicopter system. Sheets 9 ρ
ong; 8 ρ depth extent; dip 90°; depth variable: $a = 3 ρ, b = 4 ρ, c = 6 ρ$; separation variable: 0, 0.5 ρ, ρ, 2 ρ, 3 ρ, 4 ρ,
5 ρ. Thickness 0.025 ρ, conductivity 950 mho/m. Courtesy Texas Gulf Sulphur Co.

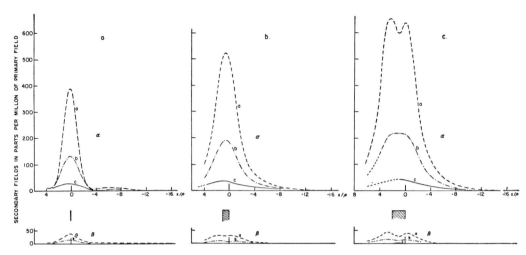

FIG. 152. Effect of conductor width on profiles obtained with Varian-T.G.S. helicopter system. Conductor length 9 ρ; depth extent 8 ρ; dip 90°; height variable: $a=3$ ρ, $b=4$ ρ, $c=6$ ρ; width variable 0.125 ρ, ρ, 2 ρ. Conductivity 565 mho-m. α is the in-phase response and β is the quadrature response. Courtesy Texas Gulf Sulphur Co.

that the curves presented might also be applicable to the Aero Canso system and to the Newmont-Aero helicopter system.

Note that the half-plane is detected at about four times the coil separation on either side of the sheet.

(ii) *Effect of strike.*—The system is relatively insensitive to the direction of flight within plus or minus 30 degrees of normal to the strike of a conductor. Since this is a reasonable tolerance to place on the selected flight direction, the effect of larger deviations from normal to strike would not appear pertinent.

(iii) *Effect of dip.*—As the dip of a large sheet conductor flattens from 90 degrees, the amplitude of the peak response increases substantially, the curve becomes asymmetrical, and three peaks gradually replace the single one.

The hangingwall of the sheet lies under the long flank of the profile and the upper edge of the conductor always lies vertically below the largest peak in the profile.

All of the above features are evident in Figure 150.

(iv) *Effect of multiple conductors.*— Resolution of adjacent sheet conductors by the Varian-T.G.S. helicopter system is indicated in Figure 151. For a system height above conductor of 3ρ, the two

sheets are not resolved until they are 2 ρ apart, while for a system height of 5 ρ the two sheets are not resolved until they are 4 ρ apart. Assuming a normal flying altitude of 150 ft and an overburden 50 ft thick, conductors 150 ft apart and greater may be resolved.

(v) *Effect of width.*—Figure 152 reveals that as width increases the peaks broaden until eventually the peak splits. Thus a wide conductor may not be differentiable from two parallel sheet conductors.

VII. Interpretation

A. *Quantitative interpretation*

The first step in electromagnetic interpretation is that of estimating quantitatively the characteristic parameters of the source such as dip, depth, depth extent, width, and conductivity. The next step usually involves correlation of the deduced parameters with independent estimates based on complementary geophysical data such as gravity and magnetics. The third step is the most difficult since it is the establishment of geologic credibility for the quantitative interpretations. With good geologic control the problem is not so severe, but usually we lack such control and must rely upon inference and experience gained from previous case histories.

Most quantitative interpretation—step I —is based on scale model observations over a half-plane or the thicker semi-infinite dike. Provided we analyze a profile over the center of a body of limited strike length, this procedure may be extended to most practical situations we meet. When the depth extent becomes very shallow or the dip very flat, then other models must be introduced. We may match a field curve with one or more members of a catalogue of field curves, or we may analyze certain characteristics of the field curves in terms of the variability of these characteristics and their relationship to source parameters as determined in scale model experiments. Usually we choose the latter procedure.

To see the manner in which quantitative interpretation is normally carried out, let us discuss each method in turn.

(a) *Fixed transmitter vertical loop ground system*

(i) *Determination of dip and depth.*— Several empirical formulas have arisen which enable us to predict the dip and the depth of a sheet conductor from the asymmetry of the dip angle profile and from the maximum dip angle observed. All of them assume that the transmitting coil is vertically above the top edge of the conductor. The most useful method for determining dip and depth is that due to Grant and West (1965). Figure 153 is a reproduction of a figure from their text. A measure of the ratio of maximum dip angle on the footwall to maximum dip angle on the hangingwall plus a measure of the peak-to-peak amplitude permits entry to the diagram. First the dip is obtained directly or by interpolation, then the depth may be

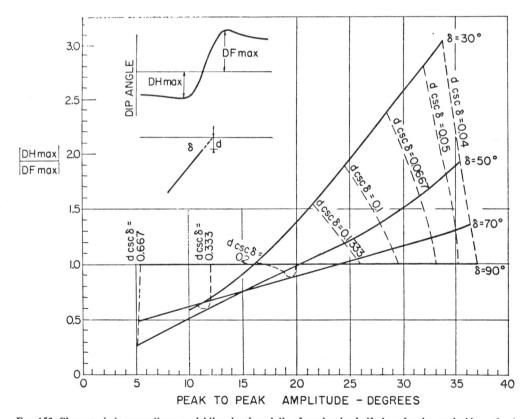

Fig. 153. Characteristic curve diagram yielding depth and dip of conductive half-plane for the vertical loop, fixed-transmitter method. The depth d is given in units of the spread ρ (after Grant and West, 1965).

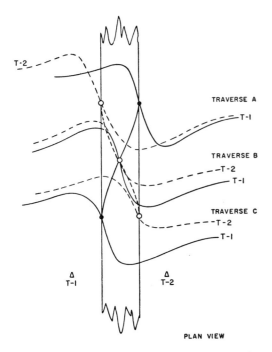

FIG. 154. Lateral shift of crossover with spread for vertical loop fixed transmitter system over broad conductor. From transmitter location T-1 the crossover follows the solid line, while from T-2 the crossover follows the dashed line.

(iii) *Determination of strike length.*—A profile containing a crossover will occur, when the transmitter is vertically above the conductor, even when the receiving coil is several hundred feet off the end of the conductor. Thus, strike length determination is usually made by setting the transmitter 400 to 800 ft off the end of the conductor, along strike, and traversing every 100 or 200 ft until a crossover is obtained. If this procedure is carried out off both ends, a minimum strike length is that between the first crossovers obtained with the strike offset transmitters. The procedure is illustrated in Figure 155.

(iv) *Determination of strike.*—Where only a single narrow conductor exists, a line joining the crossovers will trace the strike of the conductor. For broad conductors or multiple conductors, allowance must be made for the shift of the crossover with spread, with transmitter location, and with frequency. Some geologic insight is usually necessary to obtain a good idea of the reliability of strike inflections. Usu-

computed from $h \cos \delta = c$. Grant and West caution against using this characteristic curve diagram when the conductor does not approach a half-plane. It should not be used unless the length and depth are of the order of twice the spread.

(ii) *Determination of width.*—For narrow conductors there is little possibility for width estimates from a single profile. As the conductor becomes sufficiently wide a double crossover in the profile will occur, one crossover near either edge of the body. However, the most reliable means for determining width is to set the transmitter 100 or 200 ft on either side of the conductor and observe the location of the crossover as a function of spread. The crossovers will bracket the width as Figure 154 suggests. The spreads at which the crossovers occur on the near or far side of the conductors are functions of conductor width, length, and depth extent.

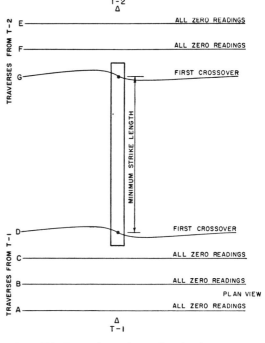

FIG. 155. Transmitter offset off ends of conductor for determination of minimum strike length.

ally it suffices to cross hatch a zone in which conductors are known to occur and thus obtain a mean strike for complex situations.

(v) *Determination of depth extent.*—Criteria for determination of depth extent are not very sensitive unless the ratio of depth extent to depth becomes very small. We have seen from the model curves that shallow depth extent manifests itself in a drop in the flanks of the dip angle profile. Usually one merely notes qualitatively that the depth extent is apt to be limited and employs gravity or magnetics to make a quantitative estimate of the depth extent.

(vi) *Determination of conductivity-thickness product.*—If we plot the ratio of peak high frequency response versus peak low frequency response for various depths and dips of a half-plane, a set of characteristic curves will result, one set for each dip. Such curve families may be obtained by means of scale model experiments and the curves for any given set are drawn for constant depth and for constant induction number $\theta = \sigma\mu\omega t\rho$. Alternatively, we may plot the peak-to-peak response versus known induction number, from model experiments, for each depth. Figure 156 is such a set of curves pertaining to a vertical sheet conductor. This set demands an

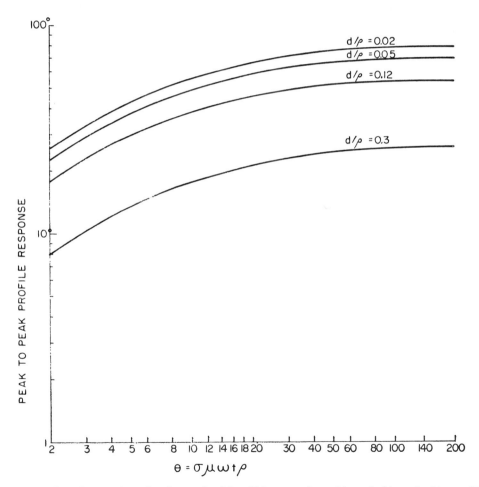

FIG. 156. Universal curves for estimating conductivity-thickness product with vertical loop, fixed transmitter electromagnetic system. Vertical half-plane model. Courtesy Newmont Exploration Ltd.

independent estimate of depth whereas the dual frequency set does not.

To use Figure 156 we note the peak-to-peak response as, say, 40 degrees. This response can arise from a thin sheet of induction number 4.4 and depth 0.02 ρ, or from an induction number of 12 and a depth of 0.12 ρ, or from any similar combination. The independent estimate of depth from Figure 153 permits us to obtain the induction number uniquely.

Since we know the frequency and spread and are prepared to assume the permeability as that of free space in most instances, then we can obtain the conductivity-thickness product. That is, for a peak-to-peak response of 40 degrees and estimated depth of 12 m a spread of 100 m, and a frequency of 100 cps,

$$\sigma t = \frac{\theta}{\mu\omega\rho}$$

$$= 15.$$

This value is rather typical of those found in electromagnetic exploration. Once an independent estimate of thickness is made by offsetting the transmitter, then the conductivity may be obtained. The conductivity should be related to sulfide concentration, oxidation, or type.

(b) *Vertical loop broadside array*

(i) *Determination of depth.*—One could develop a set of characteristic curves for depth and dip estimates pertinent to the broadside array, as Grant and West (1965) did for the fixed transmitter system. We illustrate here, for contrast, an independent depth determination.

From the model curves we note that the slope of the profile at the crossover is a function of the depth and of the conductivity. We note also that the peak-to-peak response is a function of the same two parameters. Thus if we measure both peak-to-peak response and the slope at the crossover as functions of depth and conductivity, we should be able to estimate

both parameters. However, we may note that a decrease in conductivity will lower all points by the same fraction so that the ratio of slope to peak-to-peak response should be independent of conductivity. On the other hand, increasing the depth decreases the dip angle an amount dependent upon how far the measuring station is from the conductor axis. Thus a plot of slope to peak-to-peak amplitude versus depth may be obtained from model data and used to interpret field data. Figure 157 is such a plot, the depth and the slope are normalized by the spread ρ.

(ii) *Determination of dip.*—The dip of the conductor is often crudely estimated by curve matching. The curves of Figure 107 are adequate for this purpose since they pertain to the half-plane model. The field curve will exhibit a degree of asymmetry dependent upon the departure from a vertical dip. No attempt should be made to estimate dip to an accuracy better than ±15 degrees because of the lack of sensitivity of the asymmetry criterion.

(iii) *Determination of conductivity-thickness product.*—One can rarely estimate the width reliably from broadside array data, unless the conductor is very broad. The model curves of Figure 114 illustrate this effect.

Thus we are usually content to estimate conductivity-thickness product by means of universal diagrams of the type displayed in Figure 158. A given peak-to-peak response over a half-plane can arise from any number of combinations of depth and conductivity. Hence it is necessary first to determine the depth as a fraction of the spread and then obtain the induction number from Figure 158. Once again, with ω, μ, and ρ known, the σt product can be calculated and it is usually of a diagnostic value for massive sulfides (see Strangway, Chapter 3, Volume I). Note that different sets of curves are required for each dip.

(iv) *Determination of strike, strike length, and depth extent.*—A line joining the crossovers will give a reasonable approximation to the strike throughout the length of the conductor. Strike length may be determined approximately from the termination of the line of crossovers.

Depth extent is not generally a parameter which can be obtained with the broadside array unless the depth extent is less than the spread, as Figure 109 indicates.

(c) *Horizontal loop electromagnetic system.*

—A sound basis for interpretation of horizontal loop data is contained in Strangway's article in Chapter 3 of Volume I. No additional comments are necessary.

(d) *Hunting Canso Airborne System*

(i) *Determination of conductivity-thickness product.*—An interpretation scheme for this method is contained in an article by Paterson (1961a). Some elements of that scheme follow.

First, Paterson assumed a half-plane as the basic model. Then he determined the fall-off law for the half-plane, as depicted in Figure 140. From this he constructed a correction graph by which he could convert the response at any aircraft height to

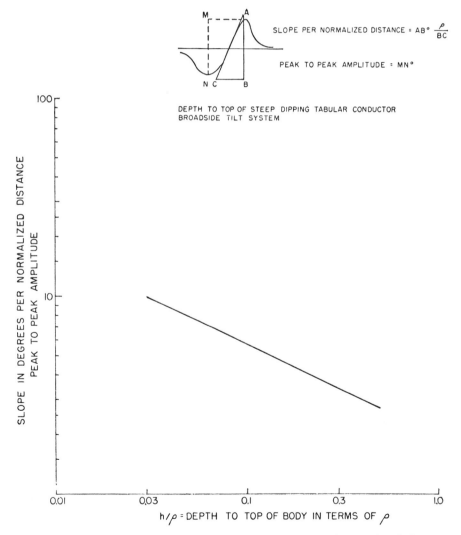

FIG. 157. Diagram for estimating depth from profiles obtained with broadside array vertical loop electromagnetic system. Vertical half-plane model. Courtesy Newmont Exploration Ltd.

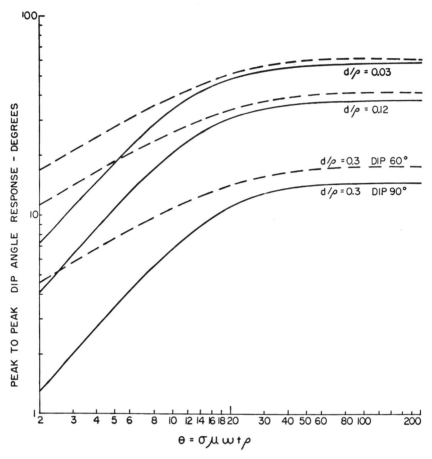

FIG. 158. Universal curves for estimating conductivity-thickness product with vertical loop, broadside array electromagnetic system. Vertical half-plane model. Courtesy Newmont Exploration Ltd.

an equivalent response at 400 ft height above conductor. The latter graph is reproduced in Figure 159. The quadrature response at 2,300 cps and 400 cps and 400-ft aircraft height over a half-plane is given, in Figure 160, as a function of the conductivity-thickness product. The ratio of 400 cps to 2,300 cps quadrature responses versus conductivity-thickness product obtained from Figure 160 is essentially independent of aircraft height and is given in Figure 161. Thus a simple means of obtaining this parameter is available. However, Paterson went further than this. He plotted the ratio of 400 cps quadrature to 2,300 cps quadrature versus 400 cps quadrature response for the half-plane

model as in Figure 162. Field data are plotted on this diagram; if the points fall on the curve then the half-plane model is applicable. If the plotted point falls to the left of the curve, it is because the conductor is of finite dimensions, or occurs at a depth greater than 400 ft; these are the conditions for an amplitude less than that given by the model. If the point falls to the right the conductor is not vertical or eddy currents in the overburden are contributing; these are the conditions for an amplitude greater than that given by the model. Thus there is a means of testing the reliability of the half-plane estimate of conductivity-thickness product. A more conventional phasor diagram for estimating the conductivity-thickness product appears in the article in Volume I, by Brant, Dolan, and Elliot.

(ii) *Determination of depth.*—If one is prepared to assume that the half-plane model is satisfactory, then the failure of a field data point to fall on the curve of Figure 162 is attributed to a depth to the

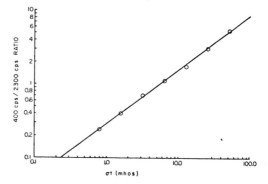

FIG. 161. Ratio of 400 cps quadrature to 2300 cps quadrature versus conductivity-thickness product. Hunting Canso System at 400 ft above conductor (after Paterson, 1961a).

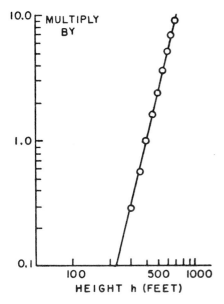

FIG. 159. Normalizing curve to convert quadrature response at aircraft height h to equivalent response at height of 400 ft above conductor. Vertical half-plane model. Hunting Canso System (after Paterson, 1961a).

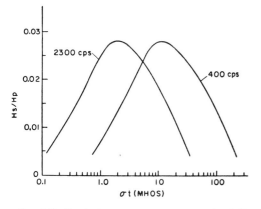

FIG. 160. Quadrature response versus conductivity-thickness product for vertical half-plane model. Hunting Canso System at 400 ft above conductor (after Paterson, 1961a).

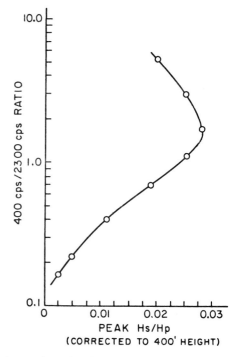

FIG. 162. Ratio of 400 cps quadrature to 2300 cps quadrature versus peak 400 cps quadrature. Hunting Canso System (after Paterson, 1961).

half-plane other than 400 ft. An amplitude multiplication factor necessary to bring the point on the line then may be computed, and reference to Figure 159 will permit converting this correction factor to a true height above conductor. From this

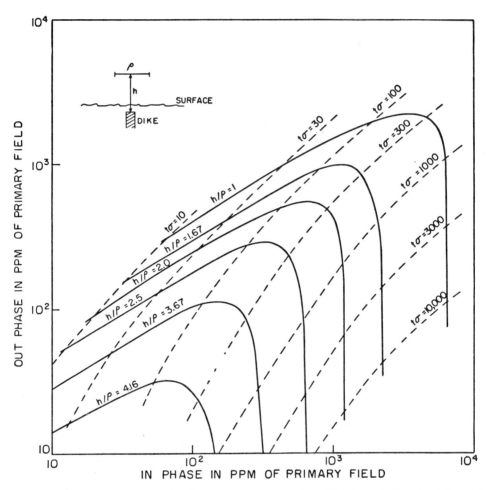

FIG. 163. Quadrature response versus in-phase response as a function of height and of conductivity-thickness product for Newmont/Aero helicopter system. Frequency 400 cps, vertical half-plane model (after Wieduwilt, 1962).

height may be subtracted the known aircraft terrain clearance to yield the subsurface depth of the body.

(iii) *Determination of dip, depth extent, width.*—Dip is estimated by curve matching with the model data of Figure 142. Depth extent is difficult to assess but the model curve of Figure 145 may aid in this endeavor.

The distance between the inflection points on the anomaly profile should be related to aircraft height, coil separation, and conductor width. At normal flying heights of 450 to 500-ft a half-plane gives anomaly widths of 275 to 300 ft. Anomaly widths greater than this may be at-tributed to finite conductor width, dip, or the effects of overburden. Usually the anomaly width is used solely as a means of evaluating whether or not the vertical thin dyke model is satisfactory for interpretion.

(iv) *Determination of strike and strike length.*—Paterson and Stam (1960) employ form lines to attempt to obtain plan configurations of anomalies. From these plan maps, strike and strike length are usually evident if the line spacing is small relative to the dimensions of the conductor.

(e) *Newmont/Aero helicopter system*

(i) *Determination of depth and conduc-*

tivity-thickness product.—Wieduwilt (1962) presented a phasor diagram for the Newmont/Aero helicopter system which we have converted for use with either this system or with the Aero Canso or Varian-T.G.S. helicopter systems. Figure 163 contains the modified phasor diagram. (Compare this diagram with the version given by Brant, Dolan, and Elliott in Volume I.) Then, given the in-phase and quadrature peak values, the depth h of a vertical half-plane below the helicopter may be read from the graph as a fraction of coil spacing. Read also from the graph is the σt product in feet$\times$mhos/meter. Since the helicopter terrain clearance is known, the depth of the conductor below ground may be calculated from h. Note that the phasor diagram given in Volume I by Podolsky for the Varian-T.G.S. system is applicable to the Newmont/Aero system.

(ii) *Determination of width (thickness).*—Usually it suffices to give estimates of just the depth and the conductivity-thickness product for steeply dipping conductors. Separation of the thickness, or width, from the conductivity in this product is not readily achieved with this system. However, an empirical relationship is available which, for thickness less than the depth below the helicopter ($t<h$) is

$$w/h = 1 + \rho/h + t/h \qquad \text{(C77)}$$

where w is the width of the anomaly as measured at the half peak points. While this relationship was derived from model experiments, it seems to be satisfactory for thickness predictions from field data. The thickness then may be computed from equation (C77) once h has been computed and w measured on the profile.

(iii) *Determination of dip.*—Dip may be estimated crudely by curve matching using the profiles of Figure 150.

(iv) *Determination of strike and strike length.*—A line joining like anomaly peaks obtained on adjacent flight lines will often yield the strike of a long conductive band. However, line-to-line correlation is often rendered difficult by large line spacing so that resorting to geologic control or to statistical correlation methods is often pre-

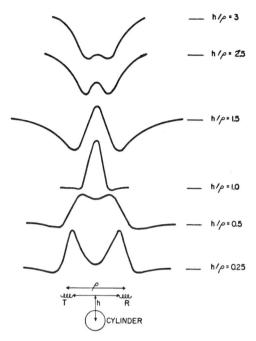

FIG. 164. Response of Newmont/Aero helicopter system over horizontal cylinder (after Dolan, 1960).

ferred. The strike length similarly will be indeterminate when the line spacing is large.

(v) *Determination of parameters for bodies of other shapes.*—If the width of the body becomes large with respect to h, then the anomaly profile form may become not unlike that over a horizontal cylinder. Figure 164 contains profiles at various heights over a horizontal cylinder, as obtained in scale model experiments conducted by Dolan. Note that both positive and negative peaks can occur. A cylinder then represents a broad body of finite depth extent. Even if the body was of large depth extent, these multiple peak profiles might result. The question then arises, as usual, of how to distinguish the broad body from two parallel conductors and how to recognize shallow depth extent. It is at this juncture that supporting parametric determinations may be made from airborne magnetic data obtained simultaneously. Thus Wieduwilt (1962) could interpret the magnetic data of Figure 165 in terms of a horizontal cylinder,

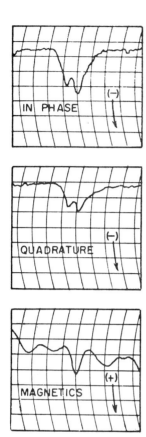

FIG. 165. Field data over broad body, obtained with Newmont/Aero helicopter system (after Wieduwilt, 1962).

and this led him to suspect that the accompanying electromagnetic data was due to a cylinder-like structure. The phasor diagram of Figure 166 then is needed for depth and conductivity-radius estimates.

(vi) *Determination of high permeability.* —Figures 6-2 and 7-2 of Part A indicate that the in-phase response for a strongly magnetic body may be of opposite sign to that obtained over a conductive body. Ward has discussed this feature in detail in two articles (Ward, 1959b; Ward, 1961). Podolsky in Volume I illustrates it as it pertains to the Varian-T.G.S. helicopter system and Wieduwilt (1962) illustrates its recognition by the Newmont/Aero helicopter system. We reproduce his example in Figure 167.

"Magnetic" anomalies of this type show up most markedly on short spread systems, such as those employed on helicopters, because the eddy current response of a dike increases with spread via the induction number $\theta = \sigma\mu\omega t\rho$. For fixed-wing-towed bird systems, ρ is so large that θ is made very large and often near eddy current saturation even for magnetic iron ores. Also the fixed wing systems usually lack the resolution and sensitivity to see the "magnetic" anomalies in the midst of a high background or in between strong conductors. Note also that the "magnetic" response occurs only on the in-phase component and hence should not be seen by most fixed-wing-towed bird systems since they rely on quadrature measurements.

B. Correlation of electromagnetic and other geophysical data

In electromagnetic surveys, numerous extraneous anomalies occur which exhibit a conductivity-thickness product characteristic of massive sulfides. Strangway in Chapter III, Volume I, provides evidence that σt is limited to the fairly narrow range of one to 30 mhos for massive sulfides, as averaged by a horizontal loop ground electromagnetic system. Paterson (1961a) notes a range of 2.2 to 12.8 mhos as averaged by the Hunting Canso system for 17 well-known sulfide bodies. Others in Volume I confirm, in general, this small range. Where widths have been determined, the apparent conductivities usually lie in the range of 0.1 to 10 mhos per meter and more frequently in the range 0.3 to 3 mho/m. Herein lies a problem in interpretation. If we assume that these apparent conductivities are real, then they are two or three orders of magnitude smaller than those typically measured in selected hand specimens as Paterson (1959) and West (1960) have noted. However, one must question the wisdom of seeking an apparent conductivity when we are using models of homogeneous conductivity to interpret field data over bodies of grossly inhomogeneous conductivity. Bosschart (1961) has presented a good discussion of this subject and concludes that it is not usually reasonable to attempt to obtain both width and conductivity explicitly from a phasor diagram, but that it is reasonable to extract the σt product as a parameter which might be used to characterize an anomaly. I agree with Bosschart.

Thus we need data from other surveys to assist in obtaining anomalous *zone* widths and in determining other parameters of anomalous zones. We have already noted several means for obtaining widths from ground electromagnetic surveys other than those means dependent upon the phasor diagram. However, Chapter 3 of Volume I contains many examples where the magnetic and gravity methods have been combined with electromagnetic methods to refine the interpretations of dip, depth, width, depth extent, etc. Ward (1959b) has given a quantitative discussion of combined electromagnetic-magnetic-gravity interpretation pertaining to a sphere model.

Airborne electromagnetic surveys ideally should be combined with simultaneous airborne magnetic surveys to assist in eliminating those extraneous electromagnetic anomalies whose susceptibilities are not typical of massive sulfides. Most massive sulfide ore bodies may be characterized by a magnetic susceptibility in the range 0.001 to 0.02 cgs units assuming either 10–100 percent pyrrhotite or 1–10 percent magnetite accompanying the other sulfides. This is seldom a bad assumption. Most nonsulfide bodies can be eliminated by this expedient alone. Nonmagnetic sulfide bodies do occur, but these are relatively rare.

Thus the two criteria, (1) σt in the range 1–30 mhos and (2) susceptibility in the range 0.001 to 0.02 cgs units, however empirical, have been employed with such success that nearly all airborne electromagnetic-magnetic anomalies drilled in the Canadian Shield since 1955 have been massive sulfides.

C. *Correlation with geology*

By far the most difficult part of interpretation of electromagnetic data is geologic reconciliation. Since we usually apply geophysical methods in relatively unexplored areas, the lack of geologic knowledge should not be too surprising. However, there are certain pieces of geologic evidence often available against which the geophysical evidence must

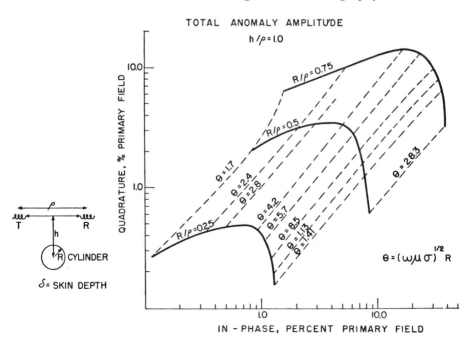

FIG. 166. Quadrature response versus in-phase response as a function of height and induction number for a horizontal cylinder. Newmont/Aero system (after Dolan, 1960).

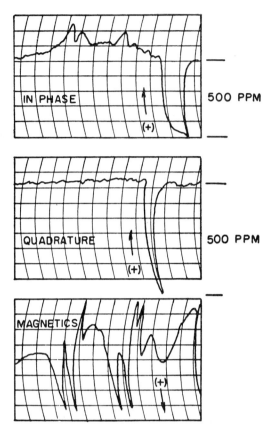

IN PHASE   500 PPM

(+)

QUADRATURE   500 PPM

(+)

MAGNETICS

(+)

FIG. 167. Field example of electromagnetic response over magnetic body. Newmont/Aero system (after Wieduwilt, 1962).

be reconciled. Either the quantitative geophysical interpretation or the imaginative geologic extrapolation from outcrop data must be reconsidered whenever there is a conflict. Opposing dip interpretations from geological and geophysical evidence are frequent. Very careful ground examination by a team consisting of a geologist and a geophysicist can usually resolve conflicts.

For this purpose it is customary to use a pocket ohmmeter to test rock conductivities, a magnet or compass to test magnetic susceptibility, and a substantial grub hoe to remove the moss and shallow soil from around key outcrops. Since sulfides often weather low, sometimes the location of the conductor must be determined by detailed electromagnetic surveys to within a matter of feet to make grub hoe stripping feasible.

At the conclusion of an aeroelectromagnetic-magnetic survey it is customary to grade or rate the anomalies on the basis of favorability of σt product, favorability of magnetic susceptibility, and favorability of known or inferred geologic setting. Letter grading of A, B, C, and D is usually sufficient for this purpose. The relative weights to apply to electromagnetic, magnetic, and geologic data is a matter of conjecture and often falls within the realm of company policy.

D. *The use of case histories*

While the quantitative and correlation interpretations are invaluable, it often is of considerable assistance to temper one's conclusions based thereon, with knowledge gained from a study of case histories. It is for this reason that Chapter 3 of Volume I has been assembled.

References

Barringer, A. R., 1965, The Barringer input airborne electromagnetic system: Sales document published by Barringer Research Limited.

Bhattacharya, P. K., and Sinha, A. K., 1965, Response of a spherical conductor to an oscillating magnetic dipole and its use in geophysical prospecting: Journal of Sci. & Engineering Research, Indian Institute of Technology, Kharagpur, v. 9, Pt. 1, p. 51–62.

Bhattacharyya, B. K., 1964, Electromagnetic fields of a small loop antenna on the surface of a polarizable medium: Geophysics, v. 29, no. 5, p. 814–831.

Birch, F., 1942, Handbook of physical constants: G.S.A. special paper no. 36.

Bleil, D. F., 1964, Natural electromagnetic phenomena below 30 Kcs.: Plenum Press.

Bosschart, R. A., 1961, On the occurrence of low resistivity geological conductors: Geophys. Prosp., v. 9, no. 2, p. 203–212.

Boyd, D., and Roberts, B. C., 1961, Model experiments and survey results from a wingtip-mounted electromagnetic prospecting system: Geophys. Prosp., v. 9, no. 3, p. 411–420.

Brant, A. A., 1965a, A review and discussion of present geophysical methods applied in mining explorations: Economic Geology, v. 60, no. 4, p. 819–821.

——— 1965b, manuscript in preparation.

Brubaker, D. G., 1957, Apparatus and procedure

for electromagnetic prospecting: Trans. A.I.M.E., v. 208, p. 777–780.

Bruckshaw, J. McG., 1936, Experiments on conducting laminae in periodic magnetic fields: Proc. Phys. Soc. 48, p. 63.

Burrows, K., 1957, An investigation into the interpretation of airborne electromagnetic data by means of scale model experiments: M.Sc. Thesis, University of Manchester.

Byers, A. R., 1957, Comparison of electromagnetic geophysical prospecting methods over known sulphide zones in the Flin Flon area, Saskatchewan: Report No. 28, Department of Mineral Resources, Metallic and Industrial Minerals Branch, Province of Saskatchewan, Canada.

Cagniard, L., and Neale, R. N., 1957, Technique nouvelle de modeles reduits pour la prospection electrique: Geophys. Prosp., v. 5, p. 259–271.

Chapman, F. W., and Macario, R. C. V., 1956, Electromagnetic phenomena of natural origin in the 1–150 cps band: Nature, v. 177, p. 930.

Cheriton, C. G., 1959, Anaconda exploration in the Bathurst District of New Brunswick, Canada: Presented at the Annual Meeting of the A.I.M.E., San Francisco.

Clark, A. R., and Mungal, A. G., 1951, Scale model experiments in electromagnetic methods of geophysical exploration: Can. Jour. of Physics, v. 29, p. 285–293.

Collett, L. S., 1965, The measurement of the resistivity of surficial deposits by airborne pulsed electromagnetic equipment: Paper presented at the 35th Annual International SEG Meeting, Dallas.

Dolan, W. M., 1960, A versatile approach to electromagnetic scale modeling: Paper presented at the 30th Annual International SEG Meeting, Galveston.

Douloff, A. A., 1960a, The response of a conducting disk in a dipolar magnetic field: M.A. Thesis, Dept. of Physics, University of Toronto, April, 1960.

——— 1960b, The response of a disk in a dipole field: Geophysics, v. 26, no. 4, p. 452–464.

Elliot, C. L., 1961, An electromagnetic drill hole instrument for the detection of conductive sulfide bodies: Presented at the 31st Annual SEG Meeting, Denver.

Eshbach, O. W., 1936, Handbook of engineering fundamentals: New York, John Wiley & Sons, Inc.

Fleming, H. W., and Brooks, R. R., 1960, Geophysical case history of the Clearwater deposit, Northumberland County, New Brunswick,

Canada: A.I.M.E. Trans., v. 217, p. 131–138.

Forbes, R. F. S., 1957, Modeling of the electromagnetic response of mineral bodies as a function of conductivity: Ph.D. Thesis, University of California, Los Angeles.

Fournier, H. G., 1963, La spectrographie directionelle magneto-tellurique: Annales de Geophysique, no. 2.

Fraser, D. C., 1966, Rotary field electromagnetic prospecting: Ph.D. Thesis, University of California, Berkeley.

Frischknecht, F. C., 1959, Scandinavian electromagnetic prospecting: A.I.M.E. Trans., v. 214, p. 932–937.

Freschknecht, F. C. and Ekren, E. B., 1960, Mapping conductive strata by electromagnetic methods, in Geological Survey research 1960: U.S.G.S. Prof. Paper, 400-B, p. B121–125.

——— 1961, Electromagnetic studies of iron formations in the Lake Superior region: Mining Engineering, v. 13, no. 10, p. 1157–1162.

Frischknecht, F. C., and Mangan, G. B., 1960, Preliminary report on electromagnetic model studies: U.S.G.S. Open File Report.

Galejs, J., 1965, Schumann resonances: Journal of Research, National Bureau of Standards, v. 69D, no. 8, p. 1043–1056.

Gallet, R. M., 1964, Whistler mode and theory of VLF emissions in natural electromagnetic phenomena below 30 Kcs.: Plenum Press, p. 167–204.

Goldstein, N. E., and Ward, S. H., 1963a, Potential field message detection: Paper presented at the 33rd Annual International SEG Meeting, New Orleans.

——— 1963b, Permeability environment on micropulsations: Presented at the 13th General Assembly, I.U.G.G., Berkeley.

Grant, F. S., and West, G. F., 1965, Interpretation theory in applied geophysics: New York, McGraw-Hill Book Company, Inc.

Hallof, P. G., and Sutherland, D. B., 1962, The vector method of plotting AFMAG results, abstract in 1962 Yearbook of Society of Exploration Geophysicists: paper available as brochure from McPhar Geophysics Limited.

Hedstrom, H., 1940, Phase measurements in electrical prospecting: A.I.M.E. Transactions, v. 138, Geophysics, p. 456–472.

Hedstrom, E. H., and Parasnis, D. S., 1958, Some model experiments relating to electromagnetic prospecting with special reference to airborne work: Geophys. Prosp., v. 6, no. 4, pp. 322–341.

——— 1959, Reply to comments by N. R. Paterson: Geophys. Prosp., v. 7, no. 4, p. 448–470.

Helliwell, R., 1964, personal communication.

Holzer, R. E., Deal, O. E., and S. Ruttenburg, 1957, Low audio-frequency natural electromagnetic signals: Symposium on the Propagation of VLF Radio Waves, VIII, NBS, paper no. 45.

Ivanov, A. G., 1957, Frequency investigations in detailed electrical prospecting: Izv. Akad. Nauk., U.S.S.R. (geofiz. ser.), v. 1, no. 39, p. 43–56.

Jewell, T. R., and Ward, S. H., 1963, The influence of conductivity inhomogeneities upon audio-frequency magnetic fields: Geophysics, v. 27, no. 2, p. 201–221.

Joklik, G. F., 1960, The discovery of a copper-zinc deposit at Garon Lake, Quebec: Economic Geology, v. 55, p. 338–353.

Karandeev, K. B., and Grinevich, F. B., 1965, On designing antennas for geophysical research by natural electromagnetic-field methods: Bull. (Izv.) Acad. Sci. U.S.S.R., Physics of the Solid Earth Series, no. 4, p. 279–281.

Katsufrakis, J., 1964, Whistlers and VLF emissions, in natural electromagnetic phenomena below 30 Kcs.: Plenum Press, p. 261–286.

Kellogg, W. C., 1960, A report on Airborne AFMAG, the theory, equipment, and operation in western United States: Paper presented to A.I.M.E. Annual Meeting, New York.

Khomenyuk, Yu. V., 1961, The double rotating field method: Bull. (Izv.) Acad. Sci. U.S.S.R, Geophys. Ser., no. 12, p. 1182–1183.

Lowrie, W., and West, G. F., 1965, The effect of a conducting overburden on electromagnetic prospecting measurements: Geophysics, v. 30, no. 4, p. 624–632.

Lutsenko, B. N., and Pushnoi, B. M., 1965, Application of the mutual correlation method for measuring the angle of polarization of the magnetic component of electromagnetic fields: Bull. (Izvestya) Acad. Sci. U.S.S.R., Physics of Solid Earth Series, no. 3, p. 212–215.

MacKay, D. G., 1966, personal communication.

MacKay, D. G., and Paterson, N. R., 1960, Geophysical discoveries in the Mattagami District, Quebec: Can. Inst. of Min. & Met. Bull., v. 53, no. 581.

Makowiecki, L. Z., King, A. J., and Cratchley, C. R., 1965, A comparison of three airborne electromagnetic methods of mineral prospecting —results of test surveys in East Africa: Geols. of Canada, paper 65-6, p. 63–83.

McLaughlin, G. H., Harvey, H. A., Cartier, W. O., and Robinson, W. A., 1964, Method and means for geophysical prospecting utilizing the earth's magnetic time transients: U. S. Patent 3, 126, 510.

McMurry, H. V., 1958, Exploration of a forty-square mile tract near Cameron Lake, Quebec: in Methods and Case Histories in Mining Geophysics: CIMM, p. 226–236.

Mizyuk, L. YA., 1960, Methods and apparatus for airborne electrical prospecting: Bull. (Izv.) Acad. Sci. U.S.S.R., Geophys. Ser. no. 6, p. 522–528.

Morin, P., Utzmann, R., Favre, B., 1960, Utilisation des modeles metalliques pour l'etude des champs telluriques sur structures cylindriques: Revue de l'Institute Français de Petrole, p. 407–480.

Morreau, M. J., 1957, The loop-frame electromagnetic method of prospecting and its application in Canada, Private report.

Nagata, T., Oguti, T., and Maekawa, H., 1955, Model experiments of electromagnetic induction within the earth: Bull. Earthquake Res. Inst., Tokyo, v. 33, no. 4, p. 561–569.

Parry, J. R., 1965, A theoretical and experimental investigation of finite thin dykes in a uniform electromagnetic field: M.S. Thesis, University of California, Berkeley.

Paterson, N. R., 1959, Comments on paper by Hedstrom and Parasnis: Geophys. Prosp., v. 7, no. 4, p. 435–447.

———— 1961a, Experimental and field data for the dual-frequency phase-shift method of airborne electromagnetic prospecting: Geophysics, v. 26, no. 5, p. 601–617.

———— 1961b, Helicopter EM test, Mobrun orebody, Noranda: Canadian Mining Journal, Nov.

Paterson, N. R., and Stam, J. C., 1960, Report on Hunting dual-frequency airborne EM system: Internal report, Hunting Technical & Exploration Services.

Pemberton, R. H., 1961a, Combined geophysical prospecting system by helicopter: Mining Engineering, Jan.

———— 1961b, Target Mattagami: Trans. CIMM, v. 64, p. 16–23.

———— 1962, Airborne EM in review: Geophysics, v. 27, no. 5, p. 691–713.

Porstendorfer, G., 1959, Direkte Aufzeichnungen tellurischer Vektordiagramme und ihre Anwendungen in Bergbaugebieten, Veröffentlichung Nr. 73 des Instituts für Angewandte Geophysik der Bergakadamie Freiberg/Sa.: Sonderdruck aus "Gerlands Beitrage zur Geophysik" 68 Heft 5, p. 295–307.

———— 1960, Beobachtung linearen tellurischer Polarization während des elektromagnetischen Stormes von 1 April 1960 bei Conradsdorf/Freiberg und die Probleme ihrer Auswertung für geophysikalische Erkundungszwecke in Bergbaugebieten: Monatsberichte der Deutschen Akadamie der Wissenschaften Zu Berlin, Band 2, Heft 8, p. 455–463.

—— 1961, Tellurik: Freiberger Forschungshefte, C107, 186 p.

Rankin, D., Garland, G. D., and Vozoff, K., 1965, An analog model for the magnetotelluric effect: Journal of Geophysical Research, v. 70, no. 8, p. 1939–1946.

Rattew, A. R., 1962, Helicopterborne electromagnetic, magnetic and radiometric survey: Coronation Mine, Trans. CIMM, v. 65, p. 143–150.

Roden, R. B., 1964, The effect of an ocean on magnetic diurnal variations: The Geophysical Journal, v. 8, no. 4, p. 375–388.

Schaub, Yu. B., 1960, The interpretation of results obtained by measuring the angle of inclination of the plane of polarization of the variable natural magnetic field: Bull. (Izvestaya) Acad. Sci., U.S.S.R., Geophys. Series no. 12.

—— 1961a, On a quantitative measure of the information acquired by airborne electromagnetic prospecting methods: Bull. (Izv.) Acad. Sci., U.S.S.R., Geophys. Ser. no. 3, p. 232–236.

—— 1961b, An experimental test of the rotating magnetic field method: Bull. (Izv.) Acad. Sci. U.S.S.R., Geophys. Ser. no. 7, p. 669–673.

—— 1962a, The influence of the specific resistance of the surrounding medium on the form of anomaly curves obtained in aerial electrical prospecting: Bull (Izv.) Acad. Sci., U.S.S.R., Geophys. Series no. 5, p. 423–426.

—— 1962b, Prospecting by the rotating magnetic field method using LI-2 and AN-2 airplanes: Bull. (Izv.) Acad. Sci., U.S.S.R., Geophysics Series no. 7, p. 581–595.

—— 1962c, Efficiency of electromagnetic prospecting by helicopter: Bull. (Izv.) Acad. Sci., U.S.S.R., Geophysics Series no. 8, p. 685–688.

Schmucker, U., 1959, Geomagnetic depth sounding in Germany 1957/59: Magnetograms and first evaluation: Abh. Akad. Wiss. in Goettingen, Math.-Phys. Kl. Beitraege zum Internationalen Geophysikalischen, Heft 5.

Seigel, H. O., Winkler, H. A., and Boniwell, J. B., 1958, Discovery of the Mobrun Copper Limited sulphide deposit, Noranda Mining District, Quebec, in Methods and case histories in mining geophysics: CIMM, p. 237–245.

Shaw, W. W., 1962, AFMAG regional fields; their variation and effects: Abstract in 1962 Yearbook of Society of Exploration Geophysicists.

Sinclair, George, 1948, Theory of models of electromagnetic systems: Proc. I.R.E., v. 36, no. 11.

Slichter, L. B., 1932, Observed and theoretical electromagnetic model response of conducting spheres: A.I.M.E. Geophysical Prospecting, p. 443–459.

—— 1955, Geophysics applied to prospecting for ores: Economic Geology, Fiftieth Anniversary Volume, p. 885–969.

Srivastava, S. P., Douglass, J. L., and Ward, S. H., 1963, The application of the magnetotelluric and telluric methods in central Alberta: Geophysics, v. 28, no.3, p. 426–446.

Strangway, D. W., 1966, Electromagnetic scale modeling, in Methods and techniques in geophysics, ed. by S. K. Runcorn: Interscience Publishers.

Stratton, J. A., 1941, Electromagnetic theory: McGraw-Hill Book Co., Inc.

Sutherland, D. B., 1964, personal communication.

Swanson, H. E., 1960, Model studies of an apparatus for electromagnetic prospecting: Paper presented to A.I.M.E. Annual Meeting.

Tesche, F. R., 1951, Instrumentation of electromagnetic modelling and applications to electromagnetic prospecting: Ph.D. Thesis, University of California, Los Angeles.

Tikhonov, A. N., and Dmitriev, V. I., 1959a, The influence of interference in the induction method of electrical prospecting from the air: Bull. (Izv.) Acad. Sci. U.S.S.R., Geophys. Ser. no. 9, p. 991–992.

—— 1959b, On the possibility of using the induction method of electrical prospecting from the air for geological map-making: Bull. (Izv.) Acad. Sci. U.S.S.R., Geophys. Ser. no. 10, p. 1053–1055.

Tornquist, G., 1958, Some practical results of airborne electromagnetic prospecting in Sweden: Geophysical Prospecting, v. 6, no. 2, p. 112–126.

Utzmann, R., 1954, Prospection electrique et tellurique etudes sur modeles reduits: Bulletin de l'A.F.T.P., no. 107.

Utzmann, R., and Favre, B., 1957, Influence de la noncylindricite des structures sur le champ tellurique. Etude sur modeles reduits pour les anticlinaux resistants: Revue de l'Institut Français du Petrole, p. 135–144.

Wait, J. R., 1960, Mode theory and the propagation of extremely low frequency radio waves: J. Res., National Bureau of Standards, 64D, no. 4, p. 387–404.

—— 1965, Earth-ionosphere cavity resonances and the propagation of ELF radio waves: Jour. Res. Nat. Bureau of Standards, v. 69D, no 8, p. 1057–1070.

Wait, J. R., and Campbell, L. L., 1953, Effect of a large dielectric constant on ground-wave propagation: Canadian Journal of Physics, v. 31, p. 456–457.

Ward, S. H., 1952, A theoretical and experimental study of the electromagnetic method of geophysical prospecting: Ph.D. Thesis, University of Toronto.

———— 1957, Airborne electromagnetic surveying, *in* Methods and case histories in mining geophysics: CIMM Special Volume, p. 71–78.

———— 1959a, AFMAG—airborne and ground: Geophysics, v. 24, no. 4, p. 761–789.

———— 1959b, Unique determination of conductivity, susceptibility, size, and depth in multifrequency electromagnetic exploration: Geophysics, v. 24, p. 531–546.

———— 1960, AFMAG: a new airborne electromagnetic prospecting method: Trans. A.I.M.E., v. 217, p. 333–342.

———— 1961, The electromagnetic response of a magnetic iron ore deposit: Geophysical Prospecting, v. 9, no. 2, p. 191–202.

Ward, S. H., Anderson, G. J., Randolph, E. R., and Blake, R. L., 1955, The inductive electromagnetic method applied to iron exploration: Trans A.I.M.E., v. 202, p. 1121–1126.

Ward, S. H., and Barker, R. A., 1958, Case history of the Juniper Prospect: Transactions A.I.M.E., p. 100–104.

Ward, S. H., Cartier, W. O., Harvey, H. A., McLaughlin, G. H., and Robinson, W. A., 1958, Prospecting by use of natural alternating fields of audio and sub-audio frequencies: Trans. A.I.M.E., v. 61, p. 261–268.

Ward, S. H., and Fraser, D. C., 1966, A conducting permeable sphere and cylinder in an elliptically polarized alternating magnetic field:

Journal of Geomagnetism and Geoelectricity, v. 18, no. 1, p. 23–40.

Ward, S. H., and Gledhill, T. R., 1959, Electromagnetic surveying—ground methods, *in* Methods and case histories in mining geophysics: CIMM, p. 63–70.

Ward, S. H., and Harvey, H. A., 1954, Electromagnetic surveying of diamond drill holes: Canadian Mining Manual, p. 3–8.

Ward, S. H., O'Donnell, J., Rivera, R., Ware, H. G., and Fraser, D. C., 1966, AFMAG—Applications and limitations: Geophysics, v. 31, no. 3.

Ward, S. H., and Ruddock, K. A., 1962, A field experiment with a rubidium-vapor magnetometer: Jour. of Geoph. Res., v. 67, no. 5, p. 1889–1898.

Ware, H. G., 1966, Induced electrical polarization in ground water studies: M.S. Thesis, University of California, Berkeley.

Warren, R. E., 1963, Micropulsation induction effects—period 15 to 40 seconds: M.Sc. Thesis, Department of Mineral Technology, University of California, Berkeley.

West, G. F., 1960, Quantitative interpretation of electromagnetic measurements: Ph.D. Thesis, University of Toronto.

Westcott, E. M., and Hessler, V. P., 1962, The effect of topography and geology on telluric currents: J.G.R., v. 67, no. 12, p. 4813–4824.

Wieduwilt, W. G., 1962, Interpretation techniques for a single frequency airborne electromagnetic device: Geophysics, v. 27, no. 4, p. 493–506.

Yungul, S. H., 1961, Time variations of the ellipticity and preferred direction of the Pc telluric field: Jour. Geophys. Res., v. 66, p. 557–561.

PART D. INDUCED POLARIZATION, A REVIEW

T. R. MADDEN* AND T. CANTWELL**

Investigations into the causes of induced polarization have shown that the largest effects are due to the presence of electronic conducting minerals in the pore system of the rocks. Theoretical studies into the charge transfer reactions involved when current is sent through such mineralized rocks have led to some simple rules concerning the time or frequency structure of the induced polarization effects. There are a few indications that at very low frequencies or at long time scales, deviations from these rules occur that may provide further parameters for evaluating induced-polarization effects.

The greatest difficulties in making field measurements arise from electromagnetic coupling and telluric noise problems. The electromagnetic coupling produces effects that are superimposed on the induced polarization effects, and this sets an upper limit on the frequencies that can be used for the measurement. In most applications one should use frequencies that are less than 10 cps. The telluric noise is more of a problem at the low end of the spectrum, and it sets a limit on the periods that can be used. In typical situations, one must work with periods of less than 60 sec. Filtering techniques are very useful in cutting down the telluric noise effect.

The problems of interpretation are examined briefly and some simple cases are discussed.

Introduction

Most electrical and electromagnetic methods used in mining exploration measure the electrical conductivity of the subsurface. The targets usually are represented by good conductors relative to the background. There are two electrical techniques, however, which are concerned with different electrical properties than mere conductivity. These are (1) the self-potential method, and (2) the induced-polarization method. Both of these have in common the fact that electro-chemical phenomena play an important role, but in this section we will concern ourselves only with the induced-polarization method. As a historical aside it is interesting to note that the Schlumberger brothers, who did so much to advance the techniques of self-potential, actually attempted induced-polarization measurements first, but abandoned this approach in favor of the former method (Schlumberger, 1920).

After the Schlumberger brothers dropped their study of induced polarization, the subject lay dormant for a good many years. The first recognized work in this country was D. F. Bleil's Ph.D. thesis of 1948 (Bleil, 1953). The first extensive geophysical applications of this method, however, should be credited to the geophysical group at Newmont Exploration, Ltd. An excellent review of their research is now available as a monograph (Wait, 1959). By the mid-1950's many other groups were studying these methods independently, so that today a large section of the mining geophysical community, both in this country and abroad, are well versed in the application of these methods to exploration problems and a considerable amount of literature on the subject is available. The term "induced polarization" derives from the fact that the method is mostly concerned with detecting the electrical surface polarization of metallic minerals, which is induced by electrical currents applied to the ground. When these minerals block the pore passages of a rock and an electric current is passed through the rock, an electrochemical barrier must be overcome by the current in order to flow through the interface between the metallic minerals and the solution in the pore passage. The forces which oppose the current flow are said to polarize the interface; and the added voltage necessary to drive the

* Geology and Geophysics Department, MIT, Cambridge, Mass.
** Geoscience Incorporated, Lexington, Mass.

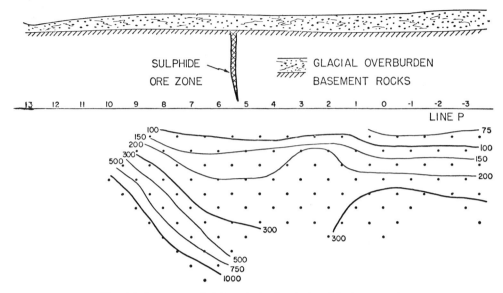

Fig. 1.1. Apparent resistivity $\div 2\pi$ in ohm ft, logarithmic contouring.

current across this barrier is sometimes known as the "overvoltage." When the inducing current is turned off, the overvoltages that were set up decay in time. Observations of these decaying voltages represent one method of detecting the polarization effects within the rock, and the term "overvoltage method" is used by some groups to describe such techniques. Since it also takes a finite time to build up these overvoltages, one finds that the impedance of these zones decreases with increasing frequency, so that measure-

ments may also be made in the frequency domain.

It is found that for a large class of sulfide deposits the induced-polarization methods provide the most diagnostic measure of the presence of such deposits, and this has led to extensive use of these measurements in exploration work. A rather nice example of the increased resolving power of induced-polarization measurements over ordinary resistivity measurements is given in Figures 1.1 and 1.2. They represent one of the authors' first

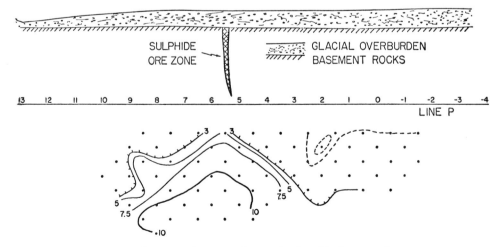

Fig. 1.2. Percent frequency change of ρ_a logarithmic contouring.

IP measurements over a mineralized zone, undertaken in cooperation with P. Hallof.

Sulfide minerals have a polarization effect due essentially to the fact that these minerals are electronic conductors, in contrast to pore fluids, which are ionic conductors. For this reason, any minerals that are electronic conductors can be expected to give IP effects, so that some oxides as well as sulfides and metals are valid IP targets. Graphite and many lower forms of carbon must also be included.

A list of the more common minerals which possess these properties is given in Table 1.1.

Table 1.1. Common minerals with electronic conduction

Oxides	Sulfides	Other
Magnetite	Pyrite	Graphite
Pyrolusite	Pyrrhotite	Native copper
Cassiterite	Marcasite	
	Galena	
	Chalcopyrite	
	Molybdenite	
	Pentlandite	
	Cobaltite	
	Argentite	
	Bornite	
	Chalcocite	
	Enargite	
	Marcasite	

Polarization effects can also be caused by clay minerals, and though in sulfide exploration this represents a source of noise, some progress has been made in applying this effect to problems of water resources (Vacquier et al., 1957). The use of the IP effect in such problems is much more indirect than it is in sulfide mineral exploration, and at present these applications have not been fully developed.

Several different techniques are used to measure IP effects, and even more parameters are used to describe the results of these measurements. When the measurements are made in the time domain, it is a common procedure to turn a current source on for some fixed period of time, and then abruptly turn it off for another fixed period of time, before commencing a new cycle with opposite polarity. The voltage that is found to remain during the "off" period is measured and compared to the "on" period voltage. This voltage is either sampled at fixed intervals after the turn off instant and the ratio is given in millivolts of decay per volt of signal, or the decay voltages are integrated and the ratio is given in millivolt-seconds per volt. The magnitudes that are observed are functions of the charging time, as well as of the decay time used.

When measurements are made in the frequency domain it is usual to compare the ground impedance at some alternating frequency with that measured at some very low frequency. This low frequency is used as a "dc" reference level. The polarization effect is then evaluated in terms of the percentage increase in conductance of the "ac" frequency relative to the dc value. In terms of resistivities the percent frequency effect is given by

$$\text{PFE} = \frac{\rho_{dc} - \rho_{ac}}{\rho_{ac}} \times 100$$

Sometimes phase-shift measurements are made as a function of frequency. These phase shifts are usually less than a degree.

These raw measurement parameters are sometimes further processed to produce other parameters. One common adjustment is to weight the ratio values by the electrical conductivity of the medium. If the millivolt-sec/volt values are multiplied by the conductivity, the product has the units of milli-farads/unit length, and is a measure of the chargeability[1] of the medium. G. V. Keller (1959) of the U. S. Geologic Survey, refers to this parameter expressed in farads/meter as the "specific capacity." Another similar parameter is derived from the frequency effect. If the frequency effect is multiplied by the ac conductivity of the medium, the product is equal to the difference of the ac conductivity and the dc conductivity. Since this is a measure of the amount of conduction that involves polarization blockage, it is sometimes referred to as the "metal factor" or prefer-

---

[1] This is not the "chargeability" as usually defined by geophysicists working in the time domain.

ably as the "metal conduction factor." As used by some groups in the United States and Canada this factor is defined as:

$$MCF = \frac{PFE}{\rho_{dc}} \times 2\pi \times 1000$$

$\rho_{dc} = $ "dc" apparent resistivity in Ω-ft.

The use of the units of feet is an outgrowth of a common resistivity practice.

More sophisticated parameters have also been devised to describe the frequency or time variations of the ratio parameters, but these have not seen wide use as yet (Keller, 1959; Sumi, 1959).

Because time and frequency domain data are related to each other, when the phenomenon is linear, through the Fourier transform, one can expect to derive frequency information from transient measurements and vice versa. In practice, however, the field measurements are much too crude to allow such transformations to be made, so that one cannot determine uniquely one parameter in terms of another. It will be one of our endeavors in this review to examine the physical basis for the induced-polarization effect and attempt to use the physical models to bring out some approximate relationships between these parameters.

The physical models of these induced-polarization effect are also helpful in evaluating the importance of any observed effect in view of the exploration problem involved. It is important to point out, however, that since the electrical properties of geologic materials usually involve only a small fraction of the total rock volume, many unpredictable effects can arise, and one still must rely a good deal on field experiences.

The outline of this review is given as follows:

Section I — The possible causes of induced-polarization effects are examined briefly, and a more detailed examination of the important causes is carried out.

Section II — The features of electrode polarization discussed in the previous section are incorporated into a simple model of mineralized rocks, and the consequences of this model are discussed.

Section III — Certain practical considerations that arise in field procedures are considered.

Section IV — The difficult problem of interpreting the field measurements is examined briefly. This is a subject worthy of much further work, but at present one is still very dependent on the use of type curves and model results.

Section I. The Causes of the Induced-Polarization Phenomenon

In the introduction, the induced-polarization effect was described as a decrease of electrical impedance with increasing frequency or as a decaying voltage residue that lingers on after the energizing current source is turned off. Qualitatively then, these effects behave somewhat as the ordinary dielectric properties of the materials. These effects, however, occur at audio and subaudio frequencies which are much too low for the ordinary displacement currents to be of any significance, and very different phenomena must be involved. This has been discussed in Part B, but we shall briefly repeat some of this material again.

The polarization phenomena involve the storage of energy when a current is applied, and the return of some of this energy as electrical energy after the energizing current is turned off. When the energy is directly stored as electrical energy, we consider the effect as a dielectric property. The known dielectric properties of matter are not capable of producing the large effects observed. It is not necessary for the energy to be stored as electrical energy, however, if mechanisms exist that can couple different types of flows together. Thus, for instance, the electric current flow might cause a fluid flow, and this fluid flow could build up a pressure which would represent a mechanical storage of energy. When the energizing current is turned off the resultant back flow of the fluid could cause a current flow which would represent a polarization effect. By studying these coupling effects, one can deduce the maximum polarization effect that such mechanisms can cause. Such a study has been made for various rock types (Marshall and Madden, 1959) and it was found that only the storage of chemical energy can account for the large effects observed in rocks. The same conclusions were arrived at by quite different arguments in Mayper's study of the background effects in IP (Mayper, 1959).

This storage of chemical energy takes place because the mobilities of various ions through the rocks vary from point to point. When a current is applied across such a rock, excesses or deficiencies of certain ions will occur at the boundaries between zones with different mobilities. The concentration gradients that are thus developed oppose the current flow and cause a polarizing effect.

There are two different situations in rocks that lead to drastic changes in the ionic mobilities. One situation is based on the normal properties of interfaces between rock minerals and interstitial solutions, and the other situation is based on the anomolous conductivity properties of metallic minerals.

Almost all rock minerals absorb a net negative charge when in contact with normal pore fluids, and the resulting potential, called the zeta potential, attracts positive ions close to the surface but repels negative ions away from the surface. This zone of unequal ionic charge extends into the solution for a distance of around 100 angstroms. If the pore passages are small enough so that most of the current must be carried by the positive ions in this diffuse layer, the rock section can be considered as having a low mobility for negative ions. This effect is most pronounced when clay minerals are involved as the extremely small passageways between the clay sheets allow almost *no* movement of negative ions. In order for polarization effects to occur, however, it is necessary for these anion restrictive zones, which we call membrane zones, to be alternated with nonselective zones. Also, in order to keep the time scale of these polarization effects at a finite level, the length of these alternating zones should be very small. Both of these conditions are well met by a dispersion of clay minerals within the pore passages and, therefore, dirty sands

can be expected to give induced-polarization effects. Conversely, it is often found that massive clay zones do not give induced-polarization effects although one cannot guarantee such a result because of the complicated way in which the clay minerals may orient themselves with respect to each other.

The magnitude of the polarization effects produced by these membrane effects is limited to less than 100 percent since the negative ions which are involved cannot carry more than 50 percent of the total current. Some examples of the polarization effects of artificially produced dirty sands are given in (Vacquier et al. 1957).

The frequency scale associated with these membrane polarization effects depends inversely on the square of the length dimension. One cannot give an exact relationship since the ratio of the lengths of the alternating selective and nonselective zones is a factor, but a rule of thumb applicable at room temperature would set the frequency range at around $3 \times 10^{-6}/L^2$ cps if L is expressed in cm.

The polarization effect of metallic or electronic conducting minerals is similar in principle, but very different in detail from the effects of membrane zones. In order for an electric current to flow from a solution through the metallic mineral, a chemical reaction must take place at the mineral-solution interface. If an equal and opposite reaction takes place at the other end of the mineral, we can consider the metallic mineral as having allowed only the passage of the reacting species, and this species may well be only a minor constituent in the pore fluids. It is then possible that the metallic minerals block most of the ions in the solution and this gives the "membrane" effect of the metallic mineral far greater importance than the membrane effect of clay-like zones and allows much greater polarization effects to be produced.

Also the manner in which the excesses or deficiencies of the reactants at the interface oppose the current flow may take a different form. A detailed study of the behavior of such metal-solution interfaces has been made (Madden and Marshall, 1959) and under ordi-

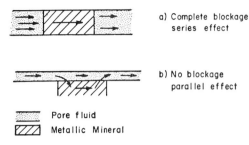

a) Complete blockage
series effect

b) No blockage
parallel effect

Pore fluid
Metallic Mineral

FIG. 2.1. Extreme models of metallic mineral interaction
with pore conduction paths.

nary laboratory conditions a rather striking uniformity of results for various electrodes was observed. It appears that most of the current is carried by minor constituents which react readily at the electrode, and most of the impedance is due to the depletion or excesses of these ions at the electrode which must be supplied by diffusion from the solution. Such an impedance is known as a Warburg impedance. The Warburg impedance shows an $f^{-1/2}$ frequency dependence and is proportional to the concentration of the reacting species. The measured impedance of a group of electrodes which included stainless steel, nickel, copper, graphite, pyrite, galena, and magnetite could all be crudely approximated by

$$Z \cong 1,500 f^{-1/2} \text{ ohms/cm}^2$$

in the range .01–100 cps.

The fits are within a factor of 5 which is a small difference compared to the actual impedance changes that are occurring as a function of frequency. Other steps in the reaction process and other reactions become important at the lower end of this spectrum, and the electrode capacitance becomes important at the higher end. We find, therefore, the greatest differences between the different electrodes outside of this frequency range. It just so happens, however, that this is the frequency range one is usually limited to in field measurements because of practical considerations which will be discussed in Section III.

It is important to point out that these electrode impedances were found to be linear as long as the total voltage drop across the interface was kept below a few millivolts. In the field this will certainly be true, except in the immediate vicinity of the current source, and thus one can still treat rocks having induced-polarization effects as linear impedances.

Section II. Equivalent Circuits for Mineralized Rocks and Their Time-Frequency Relationships

In Section I the frequency dependence of the impedance of metal-solution interfaces was stated to depend on the frequency to the negative $\frac{1}{2}$ power. In order to understand the frequency behavior of a mineralized rock, however, one must consider the interrelation of this impedance with the rest of the electrical conduction paths within the rock. The simplest concept would be to consider the metallic minerals as completely blocking the pore passage ways of the rock. This would result in the Warburg impedance of the metallic mineral interface being in series with the resistive impedance of the pore. Actually, however, pore paths are just as likely to exist between the metallic mineral and its neighboring silicate minerals as between neighboring silicate minerals. In Figure 2.1 we show two extreme cases of emplacement of metallic minerals in the conduction paths of a rock. An intermediate case would have narrow pore passages around the metal, and a thicker one leading to and from the metal. The thickness of the pore passages is not as important as one might expect, however, because of the influence of the diffuse layer. In Section I we described how the negative charge on the rock minerals attracted positive ions and repelled negative ions from the vicinity of the mineral. The number of positive ions attracted, however, exceeds the number of negative ions repelled, and the net result is that an abnormally high ionic concentration exists in the vicinity of the mineral surface. This extra ionic concentration increases the electrical conductivity of the pores, and since it is associated with the mineral surfaces, the extra conductivity is called the surface conductivity. With ordinary dilute pore fluids the surface conductivity predominates over the pore fluid conductivity for pores less than 10^{-4} cm thick. In igneous and metamorphic rocks, where the pores are very thin, the model marked b in Figure 2.1 would appear more appropriate. An analysis of the impedance of such a geometry has been undertaken (Madden and Marshall, 1959) assuming that the solution-mineral interface is a normal Warburg impedance. The result shows that the impedance of the pore alongside the metallic mineral has a frequency dependance to the negative $\frac{1}{4}$ power and is virtually independent of the length of the metallic mineral. Using the typical values of Warburg impedance given in Section I and assuming the surface conduction predominates in the pore passage, this impedance is given as

$$Z_m \cong (2-6)10^6 f^{-1/4}$$

ohms for one cm of pore width.　(2.1)

The pore passage leading to this section will behave as a pure resistance as will any pore passages that bypass the metallic minerals so that a simple circuit to represent a whole rock section would be given by the circuit in Figure 2.2. The rock impedance is then expressed as

$$Z_R = \frac{R_0(R_1 + Z_m)}{R_0 + R_1 + Z_m} \qquad (2.2)$$

and its frequency dependence will depend on

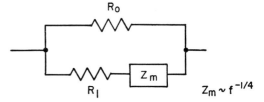

Fig. 2.2. Equivalent circuit for mineralized rock.

the relative magnitudes of the three parameters. If we choose the ratios R_1/R_0 and $Z_m(1 \text{ cps})/R_0$ as parameters and if we assume $R_1 + Z_m(\text{dc}) \gg R_0$, the frequency behavior can be expressed as

$$\frac{Z_R(\text{dc})}{Z_R(f)}$$

$$= \frac{1 + \dfrac{R_1}{R_0} + \dfrac{Z_m(1 \text{ cps})}{R_0} f^{-1/4}}{\dfrac{R_1}{R_0} + \dfrac{Z_m(1 \text{ cps})}{R_0} f^{-1/4}} \cdot \qquad (2.3)$$

The parameters R_1/R_0 and Z_m/R_0 can be determined from the frequency effects at two frequencies. If the model has any validity in representing actual rock impedances, these values can be used to predict the frequency effects at other frequencies. Examples of such extrapolations are given in Table 2.1. The extrapolations of this table are based on the frequency effects measured at three and

Table 2.1. Impedance parameters and extrapolated frequency effects in rock samples

Sample no.	3		13		16		S25	
Rock type	gabbro		dolerite		quartzite (graphitic)		greenstone (pyritic)	
$Z_m(1 \text{ cps})/R_0$	7.3		2.9		5.3		3.7	
R_1/R_0	.40		1.15		.42		.40	
Freq. effects	meas.	pred.	meas.	pred.	meas.	pred.	meas.	pred.
Frequency								
3 cps	1.17	——	1.30	——	1.23	——	1.31	——
10	1.23	1.22	1.34	1.36	1.29	1.29	1.40	1.40
30	1.29	——	1.42	——	1.37	——	1.50	——
100	1.35	1.37	1.48	1.48	1.47	1.48	1.65	1.64
300	1.42	1.47	1.56	1.55	1.56	1.59	1.77	1.78
1,000	1.52	1.59	1.70	1.60	1.71	1.74	1.94	1.95
3,000	1.71	1.73	1.92	1.65	1.88	1.88	2.12	2.11
10,000	2.04	1.89	2.42	1.69	2.05	2.05	2.36	2.30
ρ in Ω-M	7,000		9,000		1,700		5,500	

Table 2.2. Impedance parameters for rock sample groups

Rock group	$Z_m(1\ \text{cps})/R_0$	R_1/R_0
Sedimentary copper ores (White Pine)	25	4
'Duluth' gabbro	3	1.3
Qtz. porphyry, New Mexico (pyrite disseminations)	35	0
Volcanics & conglomerates Keweenaw copper ores	8	1.5
Andesite, Arizona	23	1.8
'Dakota' sandstone	20	3.5
Tuff, Arizona	15	3
Metamorphics, Ontario	10	1

30 cps, which are only a decade apart and are used to predict results of up to three decades beyond. In view of the simplicity of the model, the results seem remarkably good. The only systematic errors of any significance occur at the higher frequencies where the model is expected to break down.

The frequencies used to establish Table 2.1 are too high for field exploration applications, but the model should still be valid at lower frequencies. Using laboratory data on the frequency effects of rock samples measured at .1, 1, and 10 cps, estimates were made of these same parameters for groups of rocks. These results are shown in Table 2.2. From equation (2.3)

$$Z_R(f)$$

$$= \frac{1 + \dfrac{R_1}{Z_m(1)}f^{1/4}}{1 + \dfrac{R_0}{Z_m(1)}f^{1/4} + \dfrac{R_1}{Z_m(1)}f^{1/4}} Z_R(\text{dc}). \quad (2.4)$$

For small values of $[R_0/Z_m]\,f^{1/4}$ and $[R_1/Z_m]f^{1/4}$ this can be approximated by

$$Z_R(f) \cong Z_R(\text{dc})\left[1 - \frac{R_0}{Z_m}f^{1/4}\right]. \quad (2.5)$$

From the values listed in Tables 2.1 and 2.2 we see that this approximation is generally valid for the frequencies that are used in field measurements.

From (2.5) we can express the metal conduction factor as

$$\text{MCF} \cong \frac{2\pi \times 10^5}{Z_R(\text{dc})} \frac{R_0}{Z_m} f^{1/4}$$

$$\cdot \frac{1}{\left[1 - \dfrac{R_0}{Z_m}f^{1/4}\right]} \quad (2.6)$$

and the frequency effect as

$$\text{PFE} \cong 100 \times \frac{R_0}{Z_m} f^{1/4}$$

$$\cdot \frac{1}{\left(1 - \dfrac{R_0}{Z_m}f^{1/4}\right)}. \quad (2.7)$$

Thus both these factors show a $f^{1/4}$ dependence for small $R_0/Z_m f^{1/4}$ values. At higher frequencies the approximations used in deriving equation (2.5) break down, and the frequency effect should level off. This happens very slowly, however, as the examples in Table 2.1 show.

A test of the general validity of equation (2.6) was made by examining the power law that described the frequency behavior of a large group of samples in the frequency range 0.1–10 cps. These results are shown in Figure 2.3. It is evident from Figure 2.3 that the model is still predicting well the observed frequency dependence of the induced polarization properties down to frequencies of 0.1 cps.

There are three consequences of accepting this model that have a bearing on induced-polarization measurements. The first of these relates to the relative importance of the frequency effect or the metal conduction factor as a measure of the polarization properties of the media. From equation (2.7) we see that the frequency effect is essentially a measure of the ratio of the impedance of unblocked conduction paths compared to the impedance of the blocked paths. When there are very few conduction paths, a small amount of metallic mineralization can produce large frequency effects. Conversely, the opening up of unblocked conduction paths, such as occurs when a rock is sheared, will decrease the frequency effect, even though

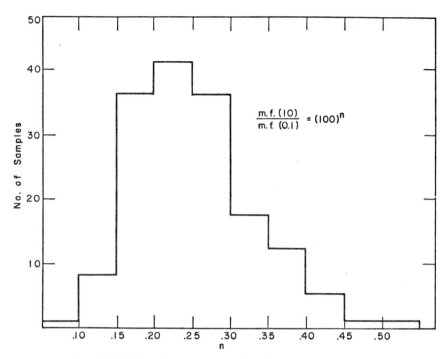

$$\frac{m.f.\,(10)}{m.f.\,(0.1)} = (100)^n$$

FIG. 2.3. Distribution of frequency power laws for rock sample metal factor.

the metallic content is unaltered. In this respect the metal conduction factor, which is just a measure of the conductivity of the blocked paths, appears a truer measure of the importance of metallic mineralization within the rock.

In Table 2.3 we show some typical metal conduction factors that are found in igneous and metamorphic areas.

Unfortunately, the metal conduction factor is strongly dependent on the conductivity of the fluids within the rock pores, and some caution is needed in evaluating this factor in sedimentary areas where large changes in the pore fluids may occur. Also, it is found that frequency effects of two or three percent are not uncommon in rocks without any metallic mineralization (evaluated at 10 cps) due to membrane polarization effects, and metallic conduction factor anomalies based on small frequency effects are sometimes of dubious value. For these reasons it is usual to consider both the frequency effect and the metal conduction factor in evaluating field results.

Another consequence of our model arises in considering the parameter values of the model

as typified by those listed in Table 2.2. The large ratios of Z_m/R_1 implies that the metallic minerals involved are very closely spaced, since R_1 is a measure of the resistance of the paths between the minerals. According to the considerations which led to this model (Madden and Marshall, 1959) a typical length parameter would be something like 10^{-3} cm. Any attempt to explain this result must lead one to accept an important role for a very fine-grained mineralization existing within the rock pores. This would imply that one should be careful in going very far with predictions concerning the gross metallic content of a rock from induced-polarization measurements since the observed properties

Table 2.3. Typical metal conduction factors

Rock type and mineralization	Metal factors
Unmineralized granites	1
Unmineralized basic rocks	1–10
Finely disseminated sulfides	10–100
Disseminated sulfides	100–1,000
Fracture filling sulfides	1,000–10,000
Massive sulfides	>10,000

may be controlled by a rather small volume of metallic minerals. When very large frequency effects and metal conduction factors are encountered, however, there is rarely any doubt of the importance of electronic conducting minerals within the rocks.

The third consequence of our model is the difficulty of attempting detailed frequency studies to differentiate between different mineral occurrences in the frequency range where the model is valid. It appears from equations (2.6) and (2.7) that the frequency effect or metal conduction factor for any frequency can be predicted from its value at just one frequency. This statement will not be true, of course, at frequencies outside the validity range of our model. In the field it is usually not practical to work with frequencies much higher than 10 cps, and here the model is still valid. It is more difficult to set a lower frequency limit for the model, but there is evidence from the time domain data that one can observe deviations from the model at lower frequencies. This evidence will be discussed at the end of this section.

Just as the model was used to relate the measurements at different frequencies, so it may be used to relate measurements made in the time domain to those made in the frequency domain. In principle one can uniquely determine the time behavior from the frequency behavior or vice versa, but in practice one has far too few data points to allow such a unique transformation. The model, however, poses restrictions on the frequency behavior of the induced-polarization effects that allows us to make these transformations.

If we describe the impulse response of the medium as $f_0(t)$, the step function response is given as

$$f_{-1}(t) = \int_0^t f_0(\tau)d\tau. \tag{2.8}$$

The frequency response includes an in-phase and an out-of-phase component, $F_1(\omega) + iF_2(\omega)$. The Fourier relations between the time and frequency domain are then given as

$$f_0(t) = \frac{2}{\pi} \int_0^\infty F_1(\omega) \cos \omega t d\omega \tag{2.9}$$

$$= -\frac{2}{\pi} \int_0^\infty F_2(\omega) \sin \omega t d\omega \tag{2.10}$$

$$F_1(\omega) = \int_0^\infty f_0(t) \cos \omega t dt \tag{2.11}$$

$$F_2(\omega) = -\int_0^\infty f_0(t) \sin \omega t dt. \tag{2.12}$$

Since the phase shifts associated with induced-polarization effects are very small, we are primarily involved with equations (2.9) and (2.11). In fact, we can approximately invert from the frequency domain to the time domain, knowing only the amplitude of the frequency response, $|F(\omega)|$.

$$f_0(t) \cong \frac{2}{\pi} \int_0^\infty |F(\omega)| \cos \omega t d\omega \tag{2.13}$$

$$|F(\omega)| \cong \int_0^\infty f_0(t) \cos \omega t dt. \tag{2.14}$$

Using (2.5)

$$|F(\omega)| \cong Z(\text{dc})\left(1 - \frac{R_0}{Z_m}f^{1/4}\right). \tag{2.15}$$

This expression cannot hold for large frequencies, but, since this frequency range is outside of our interest, we replace (2.15) by $|F(\omega)|$

$$\cong Z_R(\text{dc})\left(1 - \frac{R_0}{Z_m}\left(\frac{\omega}{2\pi}\right)^{1/4}e^{-4\omega}\right). \tag{2.16}$$

The cosine transform of equation (2.16) is known giving us

$$f_0(t) \cong Z_R(\text{dc})\left\{\delta(t) - \frac{2}{\pi} \frac{\Gamma\left(\frac{5}{4}\right)\cos\left(\frac{5}{4}\tan^{-1}\frac{t}{a}\right)}{(2\pi)^{1/4}(a^2 + t^2)^{5/8}} \frac{R_0}{Z_m}\right\}. \tag{2.17}$$

Equation (2.17) is expected to be true for times long compared to a, and short compared to the reciprocal of the lowest frequency at which (2.16) is a valid model.

When $t \gg a$, (2.17) reduces to

$$f_0(t) \cong Z_R(\text{dc}) \left[\delta(t) + \frac{2}{\pi} \frac{\Gamma\left(\frac{5}{4}\right)}{(2\pi)^{1/4}} \cdot \cos\left(\frac{5\pi}{8}\right) t^{-5/4} \frac{R_0}{Z_m} \right] \cdot \quad (2.18)$$

Integrating equation (2.18) gives us the step function response.

$$f_{-1}(t) \cong Z_R(\text{dc}) \left[1 - \frac{1}{1.78} \cdot \frac{R_0}{Z_m(1 \text{ cps})} t^{-1/4} \right] \cdot \quad (2.19)$$

On comparing (2.15) with (2.19), since $(2\pi)^{1/4} = 1.6 \approx 1.78$, we can give as a rule of thumb that the frequency effect at the frequency f is proportional to the step function decay voltage at time $t = 1/2\pi f$.

In the usual units of percent frequency effect and mv/v, we have percent frequency effect at f is approximately given by

$$PFE \cong \frac{1}{10} \frac{mv}{v} \text{ decay at } t = 1/2\pi f. \quad (2.20)$$

Equation (2.19) blows up as $t \to 0$, but the approximation is not valid for $t < a$. It is valid, however, for $t > .01$ sec.

For long times the model that led to (2.19) will no longer hold, and eventually the decay voltages should fall off faster than $t^{-1/4}$.

In practice one does not usually use a step function for the driving source in IP measurements, but rather a sequence of $+$, 0, $-$, 0, $+$ current flows. This can be represented as a sequence of step functions, each delayed by multiples of the switching time as

$$\text{source} = f_{-1}(t) - f_{-1}(t + \tau) - f_{-1}(t + 2\tau)$$
$$+ f_{-1}(t + 3\tau) + f_{-1}(t + 4\tau)$$
$$- f_{-1}(t + 5\tau) \cdots . \quad (2.21)$$

The decay voltage observed during the off times is not then the decay of a step function, but the sum of the sequence of decays associated with the sequence of step functions represented in (2.21). This has the effect of reducing the observed decay voltages, especially at the end of the off periods, but the amount of reduction is dependent on the decay voltages at long times. Thus if deviations from the $t^{-1/4}$ behavior occur for large t, we can feel these effects in the form of the observed decays even though the off periods are not very long.

To test how well equation (2.19) represents the step function response, we have plotted in Figure 2.4 the observed median decays for groups of rock samples. The measurements were made with the typical $+$, 0, $-$, 0, $+$ current source using a 7 sec switching interval, so that an entire cycle took 30 sec. The values are all normalized to the .01 sec value.

Two theoretical decay curves are also shown in Figure 2.4 which represent the extreme cases we should expect. One curve represents the decay that would be observed if the $t^{-1/4}$ step function response continued to $t = \infty$. The other curve represents the expected curve if the $t^{-1/4}$ behavior fell off rapidly beyond 7.5 sec. It is interesting to note that a rapid *fall off* of the decay beyond 7.5 sec actually *increases* considerably the expected decays when sequential switching is used. The rock samples fall in between these extremes. This is taken as evidence that the model we have used does eventually break down at low frequencies. The spread of the rock sample values at the longer decay times would seem to indicate that new parameters could be introduced using the very low frequency or long-time responses which would increase our discrimination of IP responses. Other workers have also observed these variations in the qualitative behavior of IP responses at the low end of the spectrum (Keller, 1959; Sumi, 1959), but more

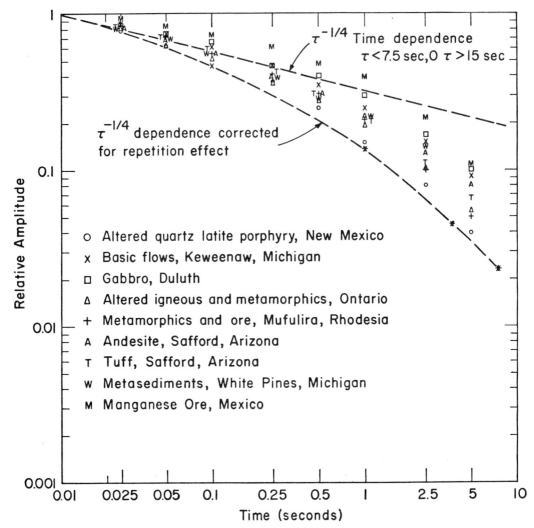

FIG. 2.4. Relative average decay curves for groups of rock samples (normalized to value at 0.01 sec)

work is needed to understand what parameters are involved in producing these variations.

It has been suggested that the metallic mineral composition is involved. It seems likely, however, that geometric factors relating to the emplacement of the metallic minerals within the pore structure are also involved. At present this remains one of the unsolved problems in understanding the IP response of mineralized rocks. Dr. Vacquier attempted to relate similar low-frequency variations in the response of dirty sands to the geometry of the sand grains (Vacquier et al., 1958).

A set of decay curves deviating considerably from the predictions of equation (2.19) are shown for the response of artificially produced samples (Collett, 1959) in the Newmont volume. These results obtained with artificially produced samples are replotted in Figure 2.5. Two factors make these results uncharacteristic of natural responses. First of all, the mixing of grains of a rock matrix with sulfide minerals does not produce the pore geometry we find in consolidated rocks. Secondly, the voltages used were high enough to drive the polarization effects out of the linear response range. The replotting of this data in Figure 2.5 brings out a very system-

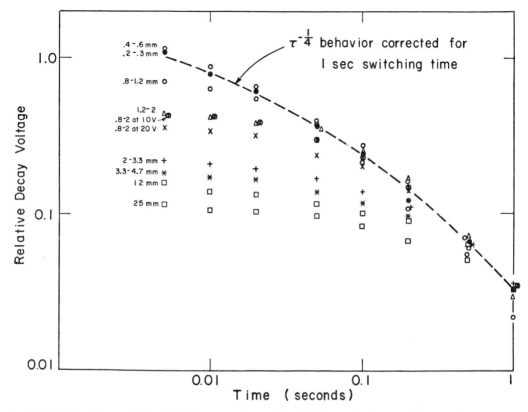

Fig. 2.5. Relative decay of induced polarization voltages of artificial samples using andesite matrix and varying size pyrite grains (after Collett, 1959) 15 volts across sample.

atic behavior for these samples.

The smaller grains did produce decay curves that agreed well with the model, but systematic deviations began to occur as the pyrite grains became as large as the matrix grains and the deviations increased with increasing grain size. These deviations also became more pronounced as the total voltage used was increased. It is difficult to say from these results how much of this effect is due to the nonlinearity and how much is due to the geometry, but it is likely that both effects play a role. If this is the case, then we have examples here of the breakdown of our model in the time or frequency range where we normally expect the model to hold. This breakdown is predictable because of the drastic changes in the pore geometry, but it is not likely that these artificial samples will have many counterparts in naturally occurring mineralized rocks.

In summing, we have tried to show in this section how our electrode impedance studies led to a simple equivalent circuit for mineralized rocks. The frequency or time behavior of this circuit for a wide range of frequencies is dependent on only one parameter, so that an induced-polarization measurement at one frequency or time can be used to predict the effects at other frequencies or times. The deviations from these predictions are most likely to be found at the lower end of the frequency spectrum or for the longer time measurements. At present it is not well known how useful these deviations are in discriminating between different types of IP targets.

In Table 2.4 we summarize the time-frequency interrelationships that the model predicts for various factors used to describe the IP responses, but estimates of the possible deviations based on sample measurements are also included. Keller's "specific capacity" has been omitted, as this factor should be

Table 2.4. IP factors conversion matrix

Measured Values \ Predicted Values	A	B	C	D	E	F	G	H	I	J	K	L
% freq effect at 10cps = A	1	.74	.56	.42	6-5	3-2	2-.5	18-10	6-5	3-2	1.5-.5	10-7
% freq effect at 3cps = B	1.4	1	.77	.56	8-7	4-3	3-.7	25-14	8-7	4-3	2-.7	14-10
% freq effect at 1 cps = C	1.8	1.3	1	.74	11-9	5.5-3.5	3.5-1	32-18	11-9	5.5-3.5	2.5-1	18-13
% freq effect at .3cps = D	2.4	1.8	1.4	1	14-12	7-5	5-1.2	43-24	14-12	7-5	3.5-1	24-17
10 sec T* { mv/v decay .1sec = E	.2-.17	.12-.15	.11-.09	.08-.07	1	.5	.1-.3	2-3	1	.5	.1-.25	1.5
mv/v decay 1sec = F	.5-.3	.4-.25	.3-.2	.2-.15	2	1	.3-.6	5-6	2	1	.25-.5	3
mv/v decay 10sec = G	2-.5	1.5-.4	1-.3	.8-.2	10-3	4-.15	1	20-10	10-3	4-1.5	1	15-5
mv-sec/v 10sec+ = H	.1-.05	.08-.04	.06-.03	.04-.02	.5-.3	.2	.05-.1	1	.5-.3	.2	.05-.08	.7-.6
3 sec T* { mv/v decay .1sec = I	.2-.17	.15-.12	.11-.09	.08-.07	1	.5	.1-.3	2-3	1	.5	.1-.25	1.4
mv/v decay 1sec = J	.5-.3	.4-.25	.3-.2	.2-.15	2	1	.3-.6	5-6	2	1	.25-.5	3
mv/v decay 3sec = K	2-.7	1.5-.5	1-.4	.8-.3	10-4	4-2	1	20-12	10-4	4-2	1	14-7
mv-sec/v 3sec+ = L	.14-.1	.11-.07	.08-.06	.06-.04	.7-.6	.3	.07-.2	1.5-2	.7-.6	.3	.07-.15	1

* T is the quarter period of entire +, 0, -, 0 cycle
or the switching interval

+ The mv-sec integrations are assumed to start
at 0.01 sec after turn-off

based on very long time decay measurements and is not as well predicted as the shorter time scale parameters.

The various parameters are identified by letters, and the relationship between two parameters is given by the entry whose row and column are associated with the appropriate factors. The entries give the column parameter value per unit row parameter value. Thus the 2.4 entry in the 1st column, 4th row indicates that a one-percent frequency effect at .3 cps is equivalent to a 2.4-percent frequency effect at 10 cps.

Section III. Practical Considerations

3.1 General

In this section we treat some of the practical considerations that arise when attempting to make induced-polarization measurements in the field. The topics we will treat include telluric noise, filtering, capacitive coupling, and electromagnetic coupling. The attempt will be made to provide some useful results that can be applied to induced-polarization field programs.

In frequency domain field measurements, the aim is to determine the frequency effect to within 0.5 percent. Since the amount of current injected into the ground determines the voltage set up at the receiver, any fluctuations in current injected will show up as fluctuations in the received voltage. To prevent receiver variations due to this cause,

the transmitter must provide constant current to within the aim of the measurements; in this case 0.5 percent.

It will be worthwhile to estimate typical magnitudes of received signal voltages and to do this we choose an electrode geometry. The choice of the so-called dipole-dipole electrode array, as shown in Figure 3.1, has advantages in field operations and is in common use. The voltage at the receiving electrodes is

$$V = \frac{I\rho_a}{\pi L} \frac{1}{n(n^2 - 1)} \tag{3.1}$$

where ρ_a is in ohm-meters, L in meters, I in milliamps, and v in millivolts. Ln is the dipole-dipole center-to-center distance[2] and ρ_a is the apparent resistivity.

Table 3.1 shows the expected voltages in millivolts for typical apparent resistivities and dipole lengths.

3.2 Telluric noise

The instrumentation to measure such voltages at nearly dc poses no unusual electronic problems. The complication arises because of telluric currents. Figure 3.2 is a plot of the power density of the telluric field as a function of frequency. The data are taken from a thesis by one of the authors

[2] Some geophysicists measure Ln between adjacent ends of the electrode pairs, rather than to their midpoints.

(Cantwell, 1960) and similar data have been collected and reported in the literature (Horton & Hoffman, 1962).

The data shown were all collected in Massachusetts in 1959. Telluric noise is dependent on geographic location, and field operations in high latitudes will encounter increases over the power densities shown in Figure 3.2.

The New England area has rather high resistivities, typically in the range 100–1,000 ohm-m. For lower ground resistivities, as in the Southwest, lower values of telluric noise would be expected, although not in the ratio of the resistivities since more current would flow in the conductive upper layer.

The total power, taken as the integral $\int_{.02}^{1} \phi(f)\, df$, since most of the power lies in this range, is 5.7 (mv/km)² for the maximum telluric noise curve. In this equation $\phi(f)$ is the noise power density in (mv/km)²/cps. Fluctuations on the order of 2–3 mv/km can be expected due to telluric currents and for electrode spreads of 100 m, .2–.3 mv might be found during periods of high telluric activity. Since an induced-polarization measurement requires a determination of voltage to less than one percent, such noise will interfere with field operations when total voltages as in Table 3.1 are typical.

Table 3.1. Voltage at receiving electrodes

$n \backslash \rho_a$	10	100	1,000	ohm meters
2	5.3	53	530	voltage in millivolts
3	1.3	13	130	$L=100$ meters
4	0.5	5	50	$I=1$ amp
5	0.25	2.5	25	
2	1.6	16	160	
3	.4	4	40	$L=300$ meters
4	.16	1.6	16	$I=1$ amp
5	.08	.8	8	

Dipole-dipole electrode configuration.

Various methods to overcome telluric noise are possible. Increasing the signal at the receiver can be done by increasing the current injected into the ground by the transmitter. Currents of 4–5 amperes are upper limits for the usual field instruments, and while larger currents are possible, increased power and voltage requirements lead to safety and logistic problems.

Electrode geometries can also be changed,

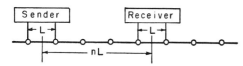

FIG. 3.1(a). Dipole-dipole electrode array.

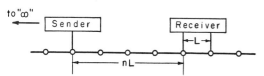

FIG. 3.1(b). Pole-dipole electrode array.

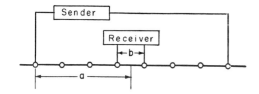

FIG. 3.1 (c). Schlumberger electrode array.

FIG. 3.1. Electrode arrays

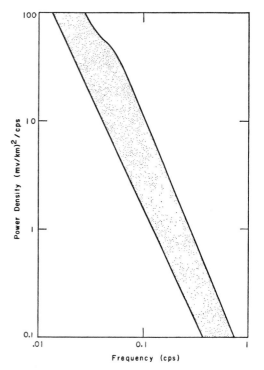

FIG. 3.2. Power density versus frequency. New England data (after Cantwell, 1960).

and both the pole-dipole and the Schlumberger spreads offer the advantage of increased receiver signal for the same injected current. These geometries are shown in Figure 3.1. The formulas for voltages for these geometries are given below; using the units as in equation (3.1).

Pole-dipole

$$V = \frac{I\rho_a}{2\pi L} \frac{1}{n(n+1)} \qquad (3.2)$$

Schlumberger

$$V = \frac{I\rho_a}{\pi} \frac{b}{a^2 - b^2/4} . \qquad (3.3)$$

Since telluric noise is a serious problem, whenever a choice arises the receiving electrode spread should be over the most conductive ground. This will usually reduce the noise, and not affect the signal, at least in those geometries that are symmetric, such as the dipole-dipole arrangement. Another method for reducing the effects of telluric currents is to use some form of filtering to reduce the noise at the receiver. The next section will present the results of certain filtering studies.

Filtering of tellurics

Filtering of telluric noise is done both in the frequency domain method and in the pulse, or time domain, method of induced polarization. In the pulse method the filtering usually takes the form of averaging over a series of decays. In the frequency method, it is possible to analog filter by using frequencies high enough so that a high pass filter can be constructed to cut out much of the noise. Analog filtering is still convenient down to a frequency of around .3 cps. It is also possible to take meter readings at a lower frequency, say .1 or .05 cps, and use a numerical filter. This latter technique amounts to a sampled data system and has advantages in that the frequency effect will be greater at the lower frequency.

In this section we have chosen certain typical problems and will illustrate the application of filtering to these cases. We begin by a short discussion of filtering. A filter system is shown schematically in

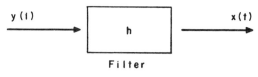

$$\text{MS Voltage} = \int_{.02 \text{ cps}}^{\text{l cps}} \Phi(w) \, dw$$

FIG. 3.3. Filter system schematic.

Figure 3.3. The input is $y(t)$ and the output is $x(t)$. The impulse response is $h(t)$, and the output can be written

$$x(t) = \int_{-\infty}^{t} h(t - \tau)y(\tau)d\tau. \qquad (3.4)$$

Convolution in time is equivalent to multiplication in the frequency domain so that in the frequency domain we have

$$X(\omega) = H(\omega)Y(\omega). \qquad (3.5)$$

The $Y(\omega)$ typical of telluric noise in New England is shown in Figure 3.2. For the raw noise, the maximum MS voltage[3] is 5.7 (mv/km)^2 giving RMS fluctuations of 2.4 mv/km.

One method of reducing telluric noise is to use .3 cps as the lower frequency and high pass filter at the receiver. A filter characteristic cutting off below .3 cps at 12 db per octave is shown in Figure 3.4. The noise output after the filter is shown in Figure 3.5. The noise output has a MS voltage range of .30 to .06 (mv/km)^2, giving RMS fluctuations of .55 to .24 mv/km. The effect of this filter is to reduce the noise amplitude by a factor of about 5–10.

A second technique is to use a numerical filtering scheme, using a frequency in the range .05–.1 cps so that the receiver amplifiers are direct coupled. The rules for such a scheme are:

1) the signal must exceed the noise
2) the receiver voltage must be sampled at the switching frequency and consecutive readings taken.

The numerical filtering technique to be discussed is the polynomial filter. It can be shown that a filter to remove a constant would have the coefficients $(1, -1) \times \frac{1}{2}$. Two

[3] Mean-square voltage.

such filters in series would remove linear terms and would have the coefficients $(1, -2, 1)1/4$. If the sampling interval equals the switching interval of a square wave, however, the square wave is passed without attenuation. The output of such a filter could be written in matrix notation as

$$X = HY \qquad (3.6)$$

with H being $[h_1h_2h_3\ldots h_n]$ and Y being

$$\begin{bmatrix} y_1 \\ y_2 \\ \cdot \\ \cdot \\ \cdot \\ y_n \end{bmatrix}.$$

This is the same as taking a weighted average of the readings, the weighting factors being the coefficients of the operator, h_i.

The polynomial coefficients, the h_i of equation (3.6), are identical to the binomial coefficients, and a five term polynomial filter will have as its terms

$$h_i = \frac{1}{16} \begin{bmatrix} 1 & 4 & 6 & 4 & 1 \end{bmatrix}. \qquad (3.7)$$

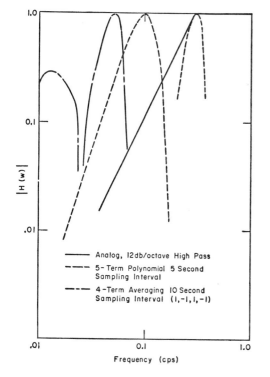

FIG. 3.4. Filter characteristics.

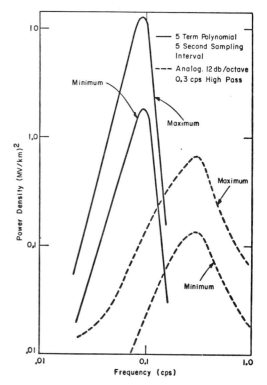

FIG. 3.5. Residual noise after filtering.

The fact that our desired signal alternates in sign makes the coefficients all positive.

The $H(\omega)$ for this filter is shown in Figure 3.4 assuming a .1 cps frequency and taking readings every 5 sec. In Figure 3.5, the residual telluric noise is shown after filtering with a range of MS fluctuations of .19–.65 (mv/km)^2 over the .02–1 cps band. The RMS fluctuations is therefore, .43–.8 mv/km, giving a telluric noise reduction of about a factor of 3–5. By optimizing the five term operator it is possible to improve this figure by another factor of 1.5–2.

In comparing these two techniques, it must be remembered that the frequency effect is increased when the frequency spread is increased by a factor of

$$\left(\frac{f \text{ upper}}{f \text{ lower}}\right)^{1/4}.$$

Also, the sampling technique measures the voltage at its peak just before the switching, which gives the equivalent of an even lower frequency. In actual practice, the peak reading with a 0.1 cps source gives frequency effects about 1.6–2 times greater than those obtained with a .3 cps average reading.

The high frequency readings involve little difficulty as far as filtering is concerned, as the frequency range 1–10 cps is well out of the range of the telluric or power line noise.

In the time domain, or pulse measurements, it is usual to average over several cycles. This is a form of synchronous filtering very similar to the sampled data numerical filtering. The filtering effect of averaging over two complete switching cycles, i.e., four decay sets, is equivalent to the filtering of a $(1, -1, 1, -1)1/4$ operator. For a 5 sec switching interval, the decay periods begin every 10 sec, and the effect of this operator with a 10 sec sampling rate is shown in Figure 3.4.

The examples given are typical of filtering methods used to reduce telluric noise. It would be convenient if some rule could be stated as to the noise variance that could be tolerated with a given signal, but the distribution of noise amplitudes is unknown and probably not stationary. As an example, field measurements could likely be made if the noise arrived as large amplitudes once or twice an hour with quiet periods in between, although the same average noise power distributed over the whole time periods could make the period too noisy for field measurements.

The noise output of the filter sets the lower limit on the frequency effects that can be observed. If the noise output is arbitrarily considered to be equal to the minimum frequency effect voltage observable, then we can compute the minimum frequency effect observable if we are given the total signal voltage.

Minimum frequency effect observable

$$= \frac{\text{noise output}}{\text{signal output}} \cdot$$

Table 3.2 shows the expected output ranges from the filters and allows comparison of these outputs with one and two percent of the signals from Table 3.1.

The noise data in Table 3.2a are based on measurements made in New England where

the apparent resistivity is on the order of 1,000 ohm-m. Noise data from other areas, such as the Southwest, is not readily available. Since the apparent resistivities down to depths of hundreds of meters are generally lower for the Southwest and similar arid regions, a lower noise background can be expected there.

The magnitude of this noise background is difficult to calculate, but field experience indicates that the level is lower by about a factor of ten. This would reduce the noise figures in Table 3.2a by a factor of 10. As an estimate, we will have difficulty in making field measurements around $n=4$ under the assumed conditions of $\rho_a=10$ ohm-m.

3.3 Capacitive coupling

In making measurements of induced-polarization effects, it is important to remove any influences giving rise to polarization voltages not due to the effects being studied. Two such influences are capacitive coupling and electromagnetic coupling. The first couples the transmitter to the receiver through wire-ground or wire-wire capacitance, and the second couples through electromagnetic wave propagation. In this section we treat capacitive coupling and its influence in the three electrode geometries in Figure 3.1.

Coupling can occur in three ways. Capaci-

Table 3.2a. Noise variance summary for line length of 100 meters

	Raw noise	Output of polynomial filter	Output of 12 db/octave filter
Max.	.24 mv	.08 mv	.055 mv
Min.	.12	.04	.024

Noise data from New England; $\rho_a=1,000$ ohm-meters.

Table 3.2b. Normal background frequency effect voltages (see Table 3.1)

$n\backslash\rho_a$	FE in voltage (mv) FE=1%			FE in voltage (mv) FE=2%		
	10	100	1,000	10	100	1,000
2	.053	.53	5.3	.10	1.03	10.3
3	.013	.13	1.3	.026	.26	2.6
4	.005	.05	.5	.01	.10	1.0
5	.003	.025	.25	.005	.05	.50

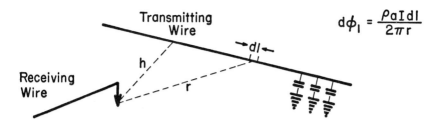

$$d\phi_l = \frac{\rho_a I \, dl}{2\pi r}$$

ϕ_l = leakage potential

I_l = leakage current / unit length

FIG. 3.6. Capacitive coupling case.

tive leakage current from the transmitting wire can be picked up at the receiver electrode; current from the transmitting electrode can capacitively leak into the receiving wire; and current can leak directly from wire to wire. The last coupling method is not important unless the sending and receiving wires are directly next to each other, as in borehole measurements. We will treat the first effect here using Figure 3.6 as the starting point.

The first coupling effect is due to leakage from the transmitting wire. The potential due to the leakage from a length of wire, dl, is

$$d\phi_l = \frac{\rho_a I_l}{2\pi r} \, dL. \tag{3.8}$$

For a length of wire running from L_1 to L_2

$$\phi_l = \int_{L_1}^{L_2} \frac{\rho_a I_l}{2\pi (h^2 + L^2)^{1/2}} \, dL$$

$$= \frac{\rho_a I_l}{2\pi} \ln \frac{L_1 + (h^2 + L_1^2)^{1/2}}{L_2 + (h^2 + L_2^2)^{1/2}}. \tag{3.9}$$

Since we are concerned with the percent change in voltage due to this capacitive leakage from the transmitting line, equation (3.9) will be used to evaluate different electrode geometries, and comparison made with the voltage arising from the current into the transmitting electrode. For the dipole-dipole electrode configuration,

$$V = \frac{\rho_a I}{\pi L} \frac{1}{n(n^2 - 1)} \tag{3.10}$$

$$\phi_l(c) = \frac{\rho_a I_l}{2\pi} \ln \frac{n}{n - 1} \quad (h = 0) \tag{3.11}$$

$$\phi_l(d) = \frac{\rho_a I_l}{2\pi} \ln \frac{n + 1}{n} \tag{3.12}$$

$$V_l = \frac{\rho_a I_l}{2\pi} \ln \frac{n^2}{n^2 - 1}$$

$$\mathrm{FE} = \left(\frac{L}{2} n(n^2 - 1) \ln \frac{n^2}{n^2 - 1} \right)$$

$$\cdot \frac{I_l}{I} \cdot \tag{3.13}$$

A typical value of leakage capacitance to ground is .005 μf/1,000 ft of wire. Using this figure, the impedance to ground at three cps is close to 10 megohms per 1,000 ft. Typical electrode contact resistances would be 500 ohms. With these values Table 3.3 gives typical frequency effects expected from transmitting wire leakage in the dipole-dipole geometry.

For the dipole-dipole case shown in Figure 3.7, Table 3.3 shows that this form of coupling is unimportant. The same would be true for the pole-dipole configuration. For the Schlumberger geometry, the integral in equa-

Table 3.3. Frequency effects from capacitive coupling, dipole-dipole

L (meters)	n	PFE
100	2	1.3×10^{-3}
100	5	4.0×10^{-3}
1,000	2	25×10^{-3}
1,000	5	70×10^{-3}

FIG. 3.7. Dipole-dipole layout.

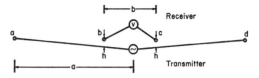

FIG. 3.8. Schlumberger geometry.

tion (3.9) will be evaluated for the geometry in Figure 3.8.

For an estimate of the maximum effect, the transmitter will be placed at the center of the spread and the contribution at electrode c will only be integrated from electrode d to the transmitter. Electrode b will be treated similarly.

The potential at electrode b due to capacitive leakage is

$$\phi_l(b) = \frac{\rho_a I_l}{2\pi}$$

$$\cdot \ln \frac{(a - b/2) + (h^2 + (a - b/2)^2)^{1/2}}{-b/2 + (h^2 + b^2/4)^{1/2}}. \quad (3.14)$$

The voltage at the receiver is

$$V_l = 2\phi_l(b) \quad (3.15)$$

and since

$$V_{\text{Primary}} = \frac{I\rho_a}{\pi} \frac{b}{a^2 - b^2/4}. \quad (3.16)$$

The formula for the frequency effect due to this form of capacitive coupling is:

$$\text{PFE} = 100 \frac{2\phi_l(b)}{V_P} \cdot \quad (3.17)$$

If we assume

$$a = 10\, b = 1{,}000 \text{ m}$$

$$h = 3 \text{ m}$$

then the calculated frequency effect is

$$\text{FE} = -1.4\% \text{ at 3 cps.}$$

The effect of the leakage is to increase the

high frequency reading, giving rise to a negative frequency effect. This represents very nearly the worst case that might be encountered and while 1.4 percent is measurable, it generally is not a significant increase over normal background frequency effects.

Using the approach in this section, capacitive coupling effects can be calculated for any given electrode geometry. Special attention should be paid to wires as they pass electrodes to be sure they are 10 m or more away. Provided the leakage impedance does not increase substantially above that assumed in this section, there seems to be little reason for capacitive coupling to cause large coupling effects as long as care is taken in wire and equipment location during a field survey. When well surveys are made and the wires must be cabled together, however, shielded cabling must be used. This problem is discussed in some detail by Wait (1959).

3.4 Electromagnetic coupling

Electromagnetic coupling is a second form of coupling that will cause frequency dependence in the measurement of resistivity. This leads to false frequency effects not due to polarization effects in the earth. In this subsection we make estimates of these coupling effects and the circumstances under which they become important.

As given in Sunde (1949), for a homogeneous half-space at frequencies where displacement currents are unimportant compared to conduction currents, the coupling between two wire elements dS and ds (Figure 3.9) lying on the half-space is

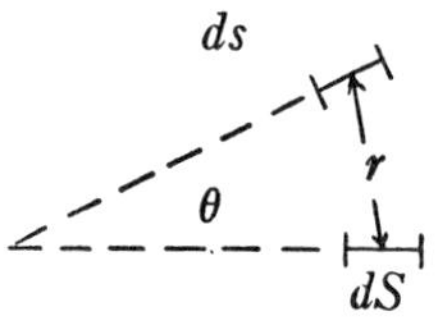

$$dZ_{Ss} = \frac{V}{I} = dSds \left[P(r) \cos\theta + \frac{\partial^2 Q(r)}{\partial S ds} \right] \quad (3.18)$$

FIG. 3.9. Electromagnetic coupling layout.

where

$$Q(r) = \frac{\rho}{2\pi r} \qquad (3.19)$$

and

$$P(r) = \frac{i\mu\omega}{2\pi r} \left\{ \frac{1 - (1 + kr)e^{-kr}}{k^2 r^2} \right\} \qquad (3.20)$$

with

$$k^2 = i\mu\omega/\rho \qquad (3.21)$$

$$I = I_0 e^{i\omega t}. \qquad (3.22)$$

It will be noted that the $Q(r)$ term is the dc coupling term, and $P(r)$ is the electromagnetic coupling term. We can expand equation (3.20) as follows:

$$P(r) = \frac{\rho}{2\pi r^3} \left[1 - (1 + kr)\left(1 - kr \right. \right.$$
$$\left. \left. + \frac{k^2 r^2}{2} - \frac{k^3 r^3}{6} + \cdots \right) \right] \qquad (3.23)$$

$$P(r) \cong \frac{\rho}{2\pi r^3} \left[1 - 1 + kr - \frac{k^2 r^2}{2} + \frac{k^3 r^3}{6} \right.$$
$$\left. - kr + k^2 r^2 - \frac{k^3 r^3}{2} + \cdots \right] \qquad (3.24)$$

$$P(r) \cong \frac{\rho}{2\pi r^3} \left[\frac{k^2 r^2}{2} - \frac{k^3 r^3}{3} \right.$$
$$\left. + \frac{k^4 r^4}{8} + \cdots \right]. \qquad (3.25)$$

We are interested only in small electromagnetic coupling effects in this treatment so the expansion can be terminated after a few terms. Expanding into the real and imaginary parts,

$$P(r) \cong \frac{\rho}{2\pi r^3} \left[\left(\frac{|kr|^3}{3\sqrt{2}} - \frac{|kr|^4}{8} \right) \right.$$
$$\left. + i\left(\frac{|kr|^2}{2} - \frac{|kr|^3}{3\sqrt{2}} \right) \right]. \qquad (3.26)$$

For small $|kr|$ values the imaginary term is the biggest term, but since it is 90 degrees out of phase with the dc coupling term, its effect on the total signal comes in only as $|kr|^4/8$ as long as $P(r) \ll$ total signal. With dipole-dipole coupling this is true for $|kr|$

< 0.7 and we need consider only the real part of $P(r)$.

Our equation for dipole-dipole coupling, from equation (3.18), now becomes approximately

$$dZ_{Ss} = dS ds \left[\frac{|kr|^3 \cos\theta}{3\sqrt{2}} \right.$$
$$\left. - \text{dc term} \right] \frac{\rho}{2\pi r^3} \qquad (3.27)$$

$$\frac{V}{I} \cong \text{dc term} - \frac{e|k|^3}{\pi 6\sqrt{2}} \cos\theta ds dS. \quad (3.28)$$

In equation (3.28) the electromagnetic coupling is approximately independent of the distance, so that it is easy to evaluate the coupling effects for finite length dipoles. The *relative* importance of this coupling term of course increases with distance. The assumption that we used to obtain this result was $|kr| < 0.7$.

For the dipole-dipole electrode geometry the percent coupling becomes

$$\% \text{ coupling} \cong \frac{|kL|^3}{6\sqrt{2}} n(n^2 - 1)100. \quad (3.29)$$

Typical values are listed in Table 3.4.

When we treat the Schlumberger geometry, the distance between wires, r in equation (3.18), can become small. With this in mind, re-examination of equation (3.16) shows that retention of the $i|kr|^2/2$ term will be necessary. That part of the expression for $P(r)$ will have the form:

$$\text{Imaginary}\left[\frac{V}{I} \right]$$
$$= \frac{\rho}{2\pi r^3} \frac{|kr|^2}{2} \cos\theta dS ds. \quad (3.30)$$

Taking the short electrode distance, b, as being small compared to the a distance, equation (3.30) integrates to

$$\text{Imag.} \frac{V}{I} \cong \frac{k^2 \rho b}{\pi} \ln \frac{2a}{h} \qquad (3.31)$$

where h is the distance between the a and b wires and h is assumed to be small compared with a. The wires a and b are assumed parallel.

Table 3.4. Percent coupling effect at three cps. Dipole-dipole geometry

$\rho_a(\Omega\text{-meters})$	a(meters)					
	30	100	300	1,000	3,000	10,000
.3	.2	6.0				
1		1.0				
3		.2	5.2		>5%	
10			0.9			
30			0.2	6.0		
100				1.0		
300				0.2	5.2	
1,000	<.05%				0.9	
3,000					0.2	6.0
10,000						1.0
30,000						0.2

Percent coupling $= |ka|^3/6\sqrt{2}\ 100$.
$a=nl$ (distance between dipole centers).
$n(n^2-1)\approx n^3$ (see equation 3.29).

The in-phase part

$$\frac{\rho}{2\pi r^3}\ \frac{|kr|^3}{3\sqrt{2}}$$

leads to

$$\frac{\rho|k|^3ab}{\pi 3\sqrt{2}}. \qquad (3.32)$$

The percent coupling effect is therefore given as percent coupling out-of-phase

$$= |ka|^2 \ln\frac{2a}{h}\ 100 \qquad (3.33)$$

$$\text{in-phase} = \frac{|ka|^3}{3\sqrt{2}}\ 100. \qquad (3.34)$$

If we again consider only small coupling effects, the total coupling effect is given as:

total coupling effect

$$\cong \frac{|ka|^3}{3\sqrt{2}} + \frac{|ka|^4}{2}\left(\ln\frac{2a}{h}\right)^2. \qquad (3.35)$$

With an a/h ratio of 10–100 the second term predominates for $|ka|>.05$. Since the coupling effects are completely unimportant when $|ka|<.05$, we can ignore the in-phase contribution and consider only the out-of-phase coupling term. When $|ka|>10$, the in-phase term becomes important again, but this extreme case is outside of our range of interest. The complete expression can thus be written as:

Schlumberger geometry percent coupling effect

$$= 100\left[\sqrt{1+\left(|ka|^2 \ln\frac{2a}{h}\right)^2} - 1\right]. \qquad (3.36)$$

Table 3.5. Percent coupling effect at three cps. Schlumberger geometry

ρ_a (ohm-meters)	a(meters)				
	30	100	300	1,000	3,000
.3	.5				
1					
3		.18			
10					>5%
30			2.7		
100					
300		<.05%			
1,000				.5	
3,000					
10,000					.5
30,000					

For $h = 10$ m (distance of closest approach of transmitting wire to receiving electrodes).
"a" is distance to transmitting electrodes (see Figure 3.8).

Since k^2 is proportional to frequency, and since this coupling is an out-of-phase coupling, it behaves similarly to capacitive leakage coupling, but as we see from Table 3.5 this electromagnetic coupling is much more important.

In addition to the other approximations made in obtaining equations (3.29), (3.35) and (3.36) we have assumed a homogeneous earth. Field evidence reveals that large coupling effects can arise from vertical discontinuities of resistivity. Since vertical discontinuities are the rule rather than the exception, it is difficult to attempt to correct for electromagnetic coupling by using theoretical coupling calculations. It is usually preferable in the frequency domain to go to lower frequencies should coupling become a problem, or shift to time domain measurements which involve lower frequencies. A good rule of thumb to follow with dipole-dipole coupling is to keep $a\sqrt{\text{freq}/\rho} < 200$, where a, the separation distance, is given in meters, and ρ is given in ohm-m. For the Schlumberger geometry, the coupling comes in at lower frequencies and one should keep $a\sqrt{\text{freq}/\rho} < 100$.

The conclusions that can be drawn from this section, 3.4, are that for a given a distance the dipole-dipole geometry can handle about 4 times lower resistivities than can the Schlumberger geometry. Also, for a given resistivity, about 2 times larger a's can be used with dipole-dipole geometry before coupling becomes serious.

From Tables 3.4 and 3.5 it is possible to estimate if coupling is a serious problem by observing where in the table field measurements lie. The values in the Tables are approximations only and should not be used to correct field data.

Finally, the pole-dipole geometry mentioned earlier seems to be the best choice for avoiding electromagnetic coupling, but even this geometry cannot guarantee the absence of EM coupling when the resistivity structure is inhomogeneous.

When making measurements in the time domain, coupling affects the transient behavior for times $< [2\pi \text{ (critical frequency)}]^{-1}$.

The critical frequency is the frequency at which coupling becomes important and is approximately given by

$$f_c \approx 10^4 \rho / a^2$$

a = separation distance in meters

ρ = resistivity in ohm-meters

Section IV. Interpretation

The interpretation of induced-polarization field measurements is a complex subject, and it is the intention of this section to treat only certain aspects of the problem.

Hallof (1957) and Seigel (1959) have made valuable contributions by preparing type curves. Seigel has calculated approximate responses for spherical ore bodies and also a number of two layer cases. Hallof gives model results for finite bodies, and theoretical results for vertical contacts and dikes.

The subject of induced-polarization interpretation is intimately associated with that of resistivity interpretation, and it is a problem which is still largely unsolved. We are not prepared to go into this matter in any detail here, but will look very briefly at a few factors, illustrated with some simple model results.

One factor that deserves comment is the saturation effect, which has led some geophysicists to expect no induced-polarization anomalies from massive sulfide zones. This effect is well illustrated in Seigel's approximate treatment for developing theoretical IP anomaly curves (Seigel, 1959). The treatment consists of assuming that the applied field is essentially plane in the vicinity of the anomalous zone, and using the known response of simple shapes in plane fields. For a sphere the induced field is proportional to

$$V_A \propto \frac{\rho_2 - \rho_1}{2\rho_2 + \rho_1} = \frac{\dfrac{\rho_2}{\rho_1} - 1}{2\dfrac{\rho_2}{\rho_1} + 1} \qquad (4.1)$$

where

ρ_1 = background resistivity
ρ_2 = sphere resistivity.

At the surface the receiver sees the sum of the primary field and this induced field. Let

V_0 = primary field

V_{Aa} = induced field at frequency a.

V_{Ab} = induced field at frequency b.

If V_A is frequency dependent, the observed voltage will have a frequency effect given by

$$FE = \frac{V_{Aa} - V_{Ab}}{V_0 + V_{Ab}}$$

$$= \frac{V_{Aa} - V_{Ab}}{V_0} \bigg/ 1 + \frac{V_{Ab}}{V_0}. \qquad (4.2)$$

When the induced field is small compared to the primary field, (4.2) reduces to

$$FE \cong \frac{V_{Aa} - V_{Ab}}{V_0} \qquad (4.3)$$

for small ρ_2/ρ_1 values, (4.1) can be expanded into

$$V_A \propto \left(-1 + 3\frac{\rho_2}{\rho_1} \right) \qquad (4.4)$$

$$FE \cong 3\left(\frac{\rho_{2a} - \rho_{2b}}{\rho_1} \right) \frac{V_A}{V_0}. \qquad (4.5)$$

This expression shows the saturation effect, as large contrasts, i.e. $\rho_2/\rho_1 \ll 1$, give small frequency effects even though ρ_{2a}/ρ_{2b} is a large ratio.

When the induced field becomes appreciable compared to the primary field, the denominator of (4.2) begins to approach zero, and this analysis is no longer correct.

The interactions of the image sources also produce changes that are not accounted for. In the limit of very large targets, i.e, semi-infinite zones, we know that for large enough separations the apparent resistivities are equal to the resistivity of the buried semi-infinite target so that the observed frequency effect reproduces the frequency effects of the target and no saturation phenomenon is observed.

In actual practice one is usually involved with intermediate cases which are the most

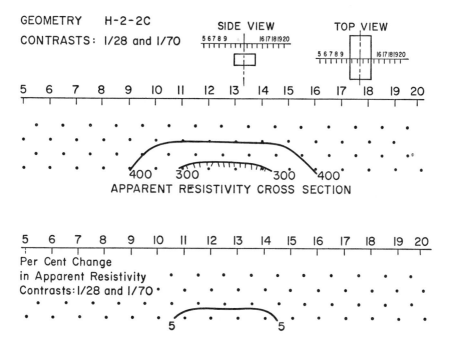

Fig. 4.1. Model results of apparent resistivity and percent change in apparent resistivity.

difficult ones to handle theoretically, and it is usual to resort to modelling techniques.

One modelling technique used by Hallof (1957) is to use identically shaped targets of different resistivities to simulate the change of resistivity with frequency that the IP zones give. This is a valid technique since the phase shifts associated with IP effects are so small that the targets appear essentially as pure resistances. In Figures 4.1 and 4.2 some examples of such modelling derived by Adler (1958) are shown.

The apparent resistivity and frequency effect cross sections which are shown in these figures are obtained by plotting the measured values beneath the center of the spread, at a distance proportional to the spread separation.

The resistivity modelling done by Adler (1958) was for finite geometry bodies having varying resistivity contrasts with the background. In this case the conductive body was modelled using $CuSO_4$-gelatin and the background material was tap water. Adler used the dipole-dipole geometry.

To convert Adler's resistivity curves to induced-polarization curves, the induced-polarization effect is treated as a change in resistivity of the buried body. Since Adler modelled several contrasts for the same geometries, we can combine his plots to show induced-polarization effects by generating the added parameter of frequency effect in the buried body.

The combined curves are shown in Figures 4.1 and 4.2. These curves have been smoothed and made symmetric, and one resistivity curve is shown in each figure to allow comparison of the two parameters. The percent change in apparent resistivity was calculated as

$$\frac{\rho_a(\text{lower contrast}) - \rho_a(\text{higher contrast})}{\rho_a(\text{higher contrast})}. \quad (4.6)$$

For analogy with frequency domain measurements, this is the frequency effect as a fraction of the high frequency receiver voltage reading.

Figure 4.1 shows the percent apparent resistivity change for a body two units thick and buried two units. The percent change rises to approximately six percent at its maximum.

Using the approximate theory discussed

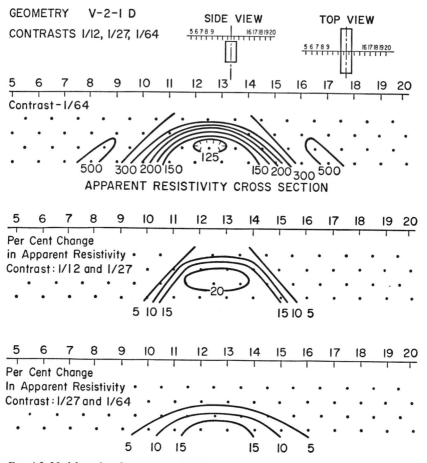

GEOMETRY   V-2-1 D

CONTRASTS 1/12, 1/27, 1/64

SIDE VIEW

TOP VIEW

APPARENT RESISTIVITY CROSS SECTION

Per Cent Change
in Apparent Resistivity
Contrast: 1/12 and 1/27

Per Cent Change
In Apparent Resistivity
Contrast: 1/27 and 1/64

FIG. 4.2. Model results of apparent resistivity and percent change in apparent resistivity.

previously as suggested by Seigel (1959), we note from the upper plot that

$$V_A \text{ must} \cong -.3V_0 \text{ at its maximum, and thus}$$
from 4.6 we predict an FE

$$= 3(.036 - .015) \times .3 \cong 2 \text{ percent}$$

The observed frequency effect is about three times greater than this however.

In Figure 4.2 the body is closer to the surface, being buried one unit deep and extending four units further into the model earth. Here the secondary field V becomes comparable to the primary field, and the approximate treatment is not expected to hold. The observed frequency effects are greatly increased, although they still are a small fraction of the actual frequency effects in the target body. A slight saturation tendency

still exists, however, as the 1/27:1/64 contrast example gives a smaller effect than the 1/12:1/27 contrast example. It is interesting to note the similarity of the IP anomalies with those shown in Figure 1.2, as the ore geometry existing is approximated by the model of Figure 4.2.

In the authors' field experiences it has been found that massive sulfides generally give rise to the largest frequency effects found. In view of the previous discussion this result may very well lead to the conclusion that massive sulfides must have much higher intrinsic frequency effects. To study the reasons for this, one would have to study the jointing and faulting in the ore zones, but it does not appear unreasonable that 'massive' sulfide zones are not truly massive in the electrical sense.

The estimation of depth will be commented on briefly. The induced-polarization type plots of Figures 4.1 and 4.2 give the appearance of arising from deeper targets than the resistivity plots do. In interpreting induced-polarization data, this should be taken into account. In collecting field data, this behavior should be considered when deciding on the dipole lengths and separations at which measurements would be made.

It is the authors' belief that interpretation of induced-polarization data is a fruitful field for investigation as it is difficult to evaluate the importance of observed IP anomalies.

Section V. Conclusions

Despite the difficulties that have been stressed of background IP effects, electromagnetic coupling, and telluric noise, the induced-polarization technique has demonstrated that it has an important role to play in metallic mineral exploration. It is also an area that we believe will benefit from further research. There is a possibility that further parameters for evaluating the induced polarization responses can be obtained from the low end of the frequency spectrum.

The interpretation of induced-polarization field measurements is another area that deserves more attention. Simple approximate techniques are useful in order of magnitude studies, but these techniques break down when more quantitative results are desired.

This review has made no attempt to justify the usefulness of induced-polarization measurements. We believe, from our experiences, that it is an outstanding geophysical tool in exploration for metallic minerals, but good quantitative studies of the effectiveness of such measurements in wide scale exploration applications are needed to properly evaluate these techniques. Other applications of induced polarization are less well established but certain areas show some promise. Extensions of the induced-polarization technique to the determination of such parameters as permeability and grain size have already been attempted (Vacquier et al. 1957; Ward and Keevil, 1960).

It would be very useful if some discrimination between graphite or pyrite and other electronic conducting minerals could be made

from induced-polarization measurements. Unfortunately, at present this does not appear to be the case, but the subject has not yet been exhausted.

As with all geophysical methods, induced-polarization measurements reveal only a limited set of physical parameters, and the proper use of such measurements involves not only the best direct interpretation of the data, but also the use of all the multitudinous indirect evidences with which an exploration group must contend.

Acknowledgments

The authors have been involved off and on with work in induced polarization for the past ten years, and during this time they have benefitted from their contacts with other workers in the field. Among those geophysicists whose help we wish to acknowledge are Dr. Philip Hallof of McPhar Geophysics, Dr. Donald Marshall of Nuclide Analysis Associates, Dr. Keeva Vozoff of the University of Alberta, and Dr. Norman Ness of the Goddard Division of NASA, all former students at MIT. We also wish to acknowledge the help of George Rogers and Dr. Ralph Holmer of Bear Creek Mining Co., and Dr. A. A. Brant of the Newmont Exploration, Ltd. We also wish to express appreciation to Dr. Franc Sumi of the Yugoslavia Geologic Survey, and Dr. Stan Ward and N. B. Keevil, Jr. of the University of California, Berkeley, Dr. Victor Vacquier of the University of California, San Diego, and Dr. G. V. Keller of the U. S. Geologic Survey, for some of their ideas on the subject. Much of the information reported here represents directly the contributions of these geophysicists.

We wish to acknowledge support for some of our researches in the field as well as in the laboratory from the Raw Materials Division of the A.E.C., Bear Creek Mining Company, and Mindamar Metals Ltd.

References

Adler, Paul, 1958, Apparent resistivity cross sections; model results; dipole-dipole coupling: MIT Report.

Bleil, D. F., 1953, Induced polarization: a method

of geophysical prospecting: Geophysics, v. 18, p. 636–661.

Cantwell, T., 1960, Detection and analysis of low frequency magnetotelluric signals: Ph.D. thesis, MIT.

Collett, L. S., 1959, *in* Overvoltage research and geophysical applications: Pergamon Press, Chap. 5.

Hallof, P. G., 1957, On the interpretation of resistivity and induced polarization field measurements: Ph.D. thesis, MIT.

Horton, C. W., and Hoffman, A. J., 1962, Magnetotelluric fields in the frequency range 0.03 to 7 cycles per kilosecond: Jour. of Research of NBS, *66D*, Part I, p. 487–494.

Keller, G. V., 1959, *in* Overvoltage research and geophysical applications: Pergamon Press, Chap. 7.

Madden, T. R., and Marshall, D. J., 1959, Induced polarization; a study of its causes and magnitudes in geologic materials: AEC Report RME-3169.

Marshall, D. J., and Madden, T. R., 1959, Induced polarization: a study of its causes: Geophysics, v. 24, p. 790–816.

Mayper, V., 1959, *in* Overvoltage research and geophysical applications: Pergamon Press, Chaps. 10A and 10B.

Seigel, H. O., 1959, *in* Overvoltage research and and geophysical application: Pergamon Press, Chap. 2.

Sumi, F., 1959, Geophysical exploration in mining by induced polarization: Geophys. Prosp., v. 7, p. 300–310.

Sunde, E. D., 1949, Earth conduction effects in transmission systems: Van Nostrand Company.

Vacquier, V., Holmes, C. R., Kintzinger, P. R., and Lavergue, M., 1957, Prospecting for ground water by induced electric polarization: Geophysics, v. 22, p. 666–687.

Wait, J. R. (editor), 1959, Overvoltage research and geophysical applications: Pergamon Press.

Ward, S. H., and Keevil, N. B., 1962, Electrolyte activity: its effect on induced polarization: Geophysics v. 27, p. 677–690.

PART E. ELECTROMAGNETIC COUPLING OF COLLINEAR DIPOLES ON A UNIFORM HALF-SPACE

FRANK B. MILLETT, JR.*

Introduction

Calculations of the electromagnetic coupling of collinear dipoles on a uniform half-space is a tedious task unless severe restrictions are placed on the limits of the parameter θ (defined by frequency, dipole length, and resistivity of the half-space) and the parameter m (the number of dipole separations center to center). The results of a computer program and the equations used for the calculations are shown below.

Mutual Impedance of Dipoles on a Horizontal Plane

According to Sunde (1949) the mutual impedance, dZ_{Ss}, between two wire elements dS and ds lying in any horizontal plane is

$$dZ_{Ss} = dSds \left[P(r) \cos \epsilon + \frac{\partial^2 Q(r)}{\partial S \partial s} \right] \quad (1)$$

where

$\epsilon =$ angle between the wire elements dS and ds
$r =$ the distance between the wire elements

and where $P(r)$ and $Q(r)$ are functions of the various propagation constants and r. Neglecting propagation effects, the mutual impedance Z_{Ss} between an insulated wire S, which extends from an electrode at A to an electrode at B, and an insulated wire s, which extends from an electrode at a and an electrode at b, (Figure 1) is given by

$$Z_{Ss} = \int_a^b \int_A^B \left[\frac{\partial^2 Q(r)}{\partial S \partial s} \right.$$

$$\left. + P(r) \cos \epsilon \right] dSds. \quad (2)$$

Mutual Impedance of Collinear Dipoles on a Uniform Half-Space

If the wires are on the surface of a uniform earth then

$$P(r) = \left(\frac{j\omega\mu}{2\pi r} \right) \left[\frac{1 - (1 + \gamma r)e^{-\gamma r}}{(\gamma r)^2} \right] \quad (3)$$

$$Q(r) = \frac{\rho}{2\pi r}. \quad (4)$$

Using Sunde's notation, $\cos \epsilon = 1$ for the electrodes configuration shown in Figure 1. The various distances expressed by the limits of integration are

$$(b - A) = (m + 1)L$$
$$(b - B) = mL$$
$$(a - A) = mL$$
$$(a - B) = (m - 1)L$$
$$(B - A) = L$$
$$(b - a) = L$$

where

$L =$ length of wire S and s
$m =$ an integer.

The propagation constant for the low frequencies considered is

$$\gamma = \sqrt{\frac{j\omega\mu}{\rho}}$$

where

$j = \sqrt{-1}$
$\omega =$ angular frequency (radians/second)
$\mu =$ permeability of half-space (henry /meter)
$\rho =$ resistivity of half-space (ohm-m).

* Senior Research Geophysicist, Phelps Dodge Corporation, Douglas, Arizona.

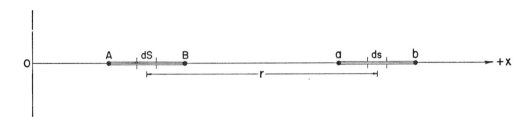

FIG. 1. Collinear dipoles.

Integration of the first term of equation (2) is

$$\iint \frac{\partial^2 Q(r)}{\partial S \partial s} \, dS ds = -\frac{\rho}{\pi L m (m^2 - 1)} . \quad (5)$$

To integrate the second term $P(r)$ is expressed as an infinite series

$$P(r) = \frac{\rho}{2\pi} \left[\frac{\gamma^2}{2r} - \frac{\gamma^3}{3} \right.$$
$$\left. + \sum_{k=4}^{\infty} \frac{(-1)^k (k-1) \gamma^k r^{k-3}}{k!} \right]. \quad (6)$$

To preserve the usual sign convention, equations (5) and (6) must be multiplied by (-1). If a new parameter θ is defined by the expression

$$L\gamma = \sqrt{j}\,\theta = \frac{(1+j)}{\sqrt{2}} \theta \quad (7)$$

then the integration of equation (2), after multiplication by -1, can be written as

$$Z_{S_s} = \frac{\rho}{2\pi L} \left[\left[\frac{2}{m(m^2-1)} - \frac{\theta^3}{3\sqrt{2}} + \text{sum } A \right. \right.$$
$$- \frac{1}{\sqrt{2}} \text{sum } B + \frac{1}{\sqrt{2}} \text{sum } D \right]$$
$$+ j \left[-\frac{\theta^2}{2} \left(m \ln \left(\frac{m^2-1}{m^2} \right) \right. \right.$$
$$+ \ln \left(\frac{m+1}{m-1} \right) \right) + \text{sum } C$$
$$\left. \left. - \frac{1}{\sqrt{2}} \text{sum } B - \frac{1}{\sqrt{2}} \text{sum } D \right] \right] \quad (8)$$

where

$$\text{sum } A = \sum_{k=1}^{k} \frac{(-1)^{k+1} \theta^{4k} f(m^{4k-1})}{(4k-2)(4k)!} \quad (9)$$

$$\text{sum } B = \sum_{k=1}^{k} \frac{(-1)^{k+1} \theta^{4k+1} f(m^{4k})}{(4k-1)(4k+1)!} \quad (10)$$

$$\text{sum } C = \sum_{k=1}^{k} \frac{(-1)^{k+1} \theta^{4k+2} f(m^{4k+1})}{(4k)(4k+2)!} \quad (11)$$

$$\text{sum } D = \sum_{k=1}^{k} \frac{(-1)^{k+1} \theta^{4k+3} f(m^{4k+2})}{(4k+1)(4k+3)!} \quad (12)$$

and where the function of m is defined by the following example

$$f(m^{4k-1}) = [(m+1)^{4k-1} + (m-1)^{4k-1}$$
$$- 2m^{4k-1}]. \quad (13)$$

For the range $m=2$ to $m=9$ and $\theta=0$ to $\theta=0.9$ the sum of the finite series, for an upper limit of $k=7$, approximates the sum of the infinite series to five significant figures.

Results of the Computer Program of EM-Coupling

The normalized value of Z_{S_s}, ($Z_{S_s} / (\rho/2\pi L)$), was calculated for each value of m, in the range $m=2$ to $m=9$, for increments of $\theta=0.01$ for the range $\theta=0$ to $\theta=0.9$. The real and imaginary parts of this normalized value of Z_{S_s} are listed in Table 1 under the column headings "ZREAL" and "IMAG" respectively. The other values listed in Table 1 are calculated from these values according to the following expressions:

$$\text{ABSZ} = \sqrt{(\text{ZREAL})^2 + (\text{IMAG})^2} \quad (14)$$

$$\text{PHASE}^0 = \tan^{-1} \left(\frac{\text{IMAG}}{\text{ZREAL}} \right) \quad (15)$$

(Continued on page 419)

Table 1. EM—coupling dipole-dipole geometry

M	THETA	ZREAL	IMAG	ABSZ	PHASE°	PDMI	PFE
2.0	.00	.33333-00	-.00000	.33333-00	- 0.000	.00	.00
	.01	.33333-00	-.25927-04	.33333-00	- .006	.00	.00
	.02	.33333-00	-.10276-03	.33333-00	- .017	.00	.00
	.03	.33333-00	-.22910-03	.33333-00	- .040	.00	.00
	.04	.33332-00	-.40352-03	.33332-00	- .069	.00	.00
	.05	.33331-00	-.62463-03	.33331-00	- .109	.01	.01
	.06	.33329-00	-.89101-03	.33329-00	- .155	.01	.01
	.07	.33326-00	-.12013-02	.33326-00	- .206	.02	.02
	.08	.33322-00	-.15540-02	.33323-00	- .269	.03	.03
	.09	.33318-00	-.19479-02	.33318-00	- .332	.05	.05
	.10	.33312-00	-.23815-02	.33313-00	- .407	.06	.06
	.11	.33305-00	-.28534-02	.33307-00	- .493	.08	.08
	.12	.33298-00	-.33624-02	.33299-00	- .579	.10	.10
	.13	.33288-00	-.39070-02	.33291-00	- .670	.13	.13
	.14	.33278-00	-.44859-02	.33281-00	- .773	.16	.16
	.15	.33266-00	-.50978-02	.33270-00	- .877	.19	.19
	.16	.33252-00	-.57414-02	.33257-00	- .991	.23	.23
	.17	.33237-00	-.64154-02	.33243-00	- 1.106	.27	.27
	.18	.33220-00	-.71185-02	.33228-00	- 1.226	.32	.32
	.19	.33202-00	-.78495-02	.33211-00	- 1.352	.37	.37
	.20	.33182-00	-.86070-02	.33193-00	- 1.484	.42	.42
	.21	.33160-00	-.93898-02	.33173-00	- 1.621	.48	.48
	.22	.33136-00	-.10197-01	.33152-00	- 1.765	.55	.55
	.23	.33110-00	-.11027-01	.33129-00	- 1.908	.61	.62
	.24	.33083-00	-.11878-01	.33104-00	- 2.057	.69	.69
	.25	.33053-00	-.12750-01	.33078-00	- 2.212	.77	.77
	.26	.33022-00	-.13642-01	.33050-00	- 2.366	.85	.86
	.27	.32988-00	-.14552-01	.33020-00	- 2.527	.94	.95
	.28	.32953-00	-.15478-01	.32989-00	- 2.687	1.03	1.04
	.29	.32915-00	-.16421-01	.32956-00	- 2.853	1.13	1.14
	.30	.32876-00	-.17379-01	.32922-00	- 3.025	1.23	1.25
	.31	.32834-00	-.18351-01	.32886-00	- 3.197	1.34	1.36
	.32	.32791-00	-.19335-01	.32848-00	- 3.375	1.46	1.48
	.33	.32745-00	-.20331-01	.32808-00	- 3.552	1.58	1.60
	.34	.32697-00	-.21338-01	.32767-00	- 3.736	1.70	1.73
	.35	.32647-00	-.22355-01	.32724-00	- 3.919	1.83	1.86
	.36	.32595-00	-.23380-01	.32679-00	- 4.102	1.96	2.00
	.37	.32541-00	-.24414-01	.32633-00	- 4.292	2.10	2.15
	.38	.32485-00	-.25454-01	.32585-00	- 4.481	2.25	2.30
	.39	.32427-00	-.26500-01	.32535-00	- 4.670	2.40	2.45
	.40	.32367-00	-.27552-01	.32484-00	- 4.864	2.55	2.62
	.41	.32304-00	-.28608-01	.32431-00	- 5.059	2.71	2.78
	.42	.32240-00	-.29667-01	.32376-00	- 5.260	2.87	2.96
	.43	.32173-00	-.30728-01	.32320-00	- 5.455	3.04	3.14
	.44	.32105-00	-.31792-01	.32262-00	- 5.655	3.21	3.32
	.45	.32035-00	-.32856-01	.32203-00	- 5.856	3.39	3.51

Table 1 (Continued)

M	THETA	ZREAL	IMAG	ABSZ	PHASE°	PDMI	PFE
2.0	.46	.31962-00	-.33920-01	.32142-00	-6.056	3.58	3.71
	.47	.31888-00	-.34984-01	.32079-00	-6.262	3.76	3.91
	.48	.31811-00	-.36047-01	.32015-00	-6.463	3.96	4.12
	.49	.31733-00	-.37107-01	.31949-00	-6.669	4.15	4.33
	.50	.31653-00	-.38165-01	.31882-00	-6.876	4.35	4.55
	.51	.31571-00	-.39219-01	.31814-00	-7.082	4.56	4.78
	.52	.31487-00	-.40270-01	.31744-00	-7.288	4.77	5.01
	.53	.31402-00	-.41315-01	.31672-00	-7.494	4.98	5.24
	.54	.31314-00	-.42356-01	.31599-00	-7.701	5.20	5.49
	.55	.31225-00	-.43390-01	.31525-00	-7.913	5.42	5.74
	.56	.31134-00	-.44418-01	.31449-00	-8.119	5.65	5.99
	.57	.31042-00	-.45439-01	.31372-00	-8.325	5.88	6.25
	.58	.30947-00	-.46452-01	.31294-00	-8.537	6.12	6.52
	.59	.30851-00	-.47457-01	.31214-00	-8.743	6.36	6.79
	.60	.30754-00	-.48453-01	.31133-00	-8.955	6.60	7.07
	.61	.30655-00	-.49440-01	.31051-00	-9.162	6.85	7.35
	.62	.30555-00	-.50418-01	.30968-00	-9.368	7.10	7.64
	.63	.30453-00	-.51386-01	.30883-00	-9.580	7.35	7.93
	.64	.30349-00	-.52343-01	.30797-00	-9.786	7.61	8.24
	.65	.30244-00	-.53289-01	.30710-00	-9.992	7.87	8.54
	.66	.30138-00	-.54224-01	.30622-00	-10.199	8.13	8.85
	.67	.30031-00	-.55147-01	.30533-00	-10.405	8.40	9.17
	.68	.29922-00	-.56058-01	.30442-00	-10.611	8.67	9.50
	.69	.29812-00	-.56956-01	.30351-00	-10.817	8.95	9.83
	.70	.29700-00	-.57842-01	.30258-00	-11.018	9.22	10.16
	.71	.29588-00	-.58715-01	.30165-00	-11.224	9.51	10.50
	.72	.29474-00	-.59574-01	.30070-00	-11.425	9.79	10.85
	.73	.29360-00	-.60420-01	.29975-00	-11.631	10.08	11.20
	.74	.29244-00	-.61251-01	.29878-00	-11.832	10.36	11.56
	.75	.29127-00	-.62068-01	.29781-00	-12.032	10.66	11.93
	.76	.29009-00	-.62871-01	.29683-00	-12.227	10.95	12.30
	.77	.28891-00	-.63659-01	.29584-00	-12.428	11.25	12.67
	.78	.28771-00	-.64433-01	.29484-00	-12.622	11.55	13.06
	.79	.28651-00	-.65190-01	.29383-00	-12.817	11.85	13.44
	.80	.28529-00	-.65933-01	.29281-00	-13.012	12.16	13.84
	.81	.28407-00	-.66660-01	.29179-00	-13.207	12.46	14.24
	.82	.28285-00	-.67372-01	.29076-00	-13.396	12.77	14.64
	.83	.28161-00	-.68067-01	.28972-00	-13.591	13.08	15.05
	.84	.28037-00	-.68747-01	.28868-00	-13.800	13.40	15.47
	.85	.27912-00	-.69410-01	.28762-00	-13.963	13.71	15.89
	.86	.27787-00	-.70057-01	.28657-00	-14.152	14.03	16.32
	.87	.27661-00	-.70688-01	.28550-00	-14.335	14.35	16.75
	.88	.27535-00	-.71303-01	.28443-00	-14.519	14.67	17.19
	.89	.27408-00	-.71901-01	.28335-00	-14.702	14.99	17.64
	.90	.27281-00	-.72482-01	.28227-00	-14.880	15.32	18.09

Table 1 (Continued)

M	THETA	ZREAL	IMAG	ABSZ	PHASE°	PDMI	PFE
3.0	.00	.83333-01	-.00000	.83333-01	- 0.000	.00	.00
	.01	.83333-01	-.16754-04	.83333-01	- 0.001	.00	.00
	.02	.83332-01	-.66075-04	.83332-01	- 0.005	.00	.00
	.03	.83327-01	-.14655-03	.83327-01	- .103	.01	.01
	.04	.83319-01	-.25677-03	.83320-01	- .178	.02	.02
	.05	.83306-01	-.39535-03	.83307-01	- .269	.03	.03
	.06	.83287-01	-.56088-03	.83289-01	- .384	.05	.05
	.07	.83261-01	-.75200-03	.83265-01	- .516	.08	.08
	.08	.83227-01	-.96733-03	.83233-01	- .665	.12	.12
	.09	.83185-01	-.12055-02	.83194-01	- .831	.17	.17
	.10	.83133-01	-.14653-02	.83146-01	- 1.008	.22	.23
	.11	.83071-01	-.17452-02	.83089-01	- 1.203	.29	.29
	.12	.82998-01	-.20441-02	.83024-01	- 1.409	.37	.37
	.13	.82915-01	-.23606-02	.82948-01	- 1.633	.46	.46
	.14	.82819-01	-.26935-02	.82863-01	- 1.862	.56	.57
	.15	.82711-01	-.30415-02	.82767-01	- 2.108	.68	.68
	.16	.82591-01	-.34035-02	.82661-01	- 2.361	.81	.81
	.17	.82458-01	-.37783-02	.82545-01	- 2.624	.95	.96
	.18	.82312-01	-.41647-02	.82417-01	- 2.899	1.10	1.11
	.19	.82152-01	-.45615-02	.82279-01	- 3.180	1.27	1.28
	.20	.81979-01	-.49678-02	.82130-01	- 3.466	1.44	1.47
	.21	.81793-01	-.53823-02	.81970-01	- 3.764	1.64	1.66
	.22	.81592-01	-.58041-02	.81798-01	- 4.068	1.84	1.88
	.23	.81378-01	-.62322-02	.81616-01	- 4.377	2.06	2.10
	.24	.81150-01	-.66655-02	.81423-01	- 4.698	2.29	2.35
	.25	.80908-01	-.71031-02	.81219-01	- 5.019	2.54	2.60
	.26	.80653-01	-.75441-02	.81005-01	- 5.346	2.79	2.87
	.27	.80384-01	-.79875-02	.80779-01	- 5.672	3.06	3.16
	.28	.80101-01	-.84325-02	.80543-01	- 6.010	3.35	3.46
	.29	.79805-01	-.88783-02	.80297-01	- 6.348	3.64	3.78
	.30	.79495-01	-.93240-02	.80040-01	- 6.692	3.95	4.11
	.31	.79173-01	-.97689-02	.79774-01	- 7.036	4.27	4.46
	.32	.78838-01	-.10212-01	.79497-01	- 7.380	4.60	4.83
	.33	.78490-01	-.10653-01	.79210-01	- 7.729	4.95	5.21
	.34	.78131-01	-.11091-01	.78914-01	- 8.079	5.30	5.60
	.35	.77759-01	-.11526-01	.78608-01	- 8.434	5.67	6.01
	.36	.77375-01	-.11956-01	.78293-01	- 8.783	6.05	6.44
	.37	.76980-01	-.12381-01	.77970-01	- 9.139	6.44	6.88
	.38	.76574-01	-.12801-01	.77637-01	- 9.488	6.84	7.34
	.39	.76158-01	-.13215-01	.77296-01	- 9.843	7.24	7.81
	.40	.75731-01	-.13622-01	.76946-01	-10.199	7.66	8.30
	.41	.75294-01	-.14022-01	.76589-01	-10.548	8.09	8.81
	.42	.74848-01	-.14415-01	.76223-01	-10.903	8.53	9.33
	.43	.74392-01	-.14800-01	.75850-01	-11.253	8.98	9.87
	.44	.73928-01	-.15176-01	.75470-01	-11.602	9.44	10.42
	.45	.73455-01	-.15544-01	.75082-01	-11.946	9.90	10.99

Table 1 (Continued)

M	THETA	ZREAL	IMAG	ABSZ	PHASE°	PDMI	PFE
3.0	.46	.72975-01	-.15903-01	.74687.01	-12.296	10.38	11.58
	.47	.72486-01	-.16253-01	.74286-01	-12.639	10.86	12.18
	.48	.71991-01	-.16592-01	.73878-01	-12.978	11.35	12.80
	.49	.71489-01	-.16922-01	.73464-01	-13.316	11.84	13.43
	.50	.70980-01	-.17242-01	.73044-01	-13.654	12.35	14.09
	.51	.70466-01	-.17551-01	.72619-01	-13.986	12.86	14.75
	.52	.69946-01	-.17849-01	.72188-01	-14.318	13.37	15.44
	.53	.69422-01	-.18137-01	.71752-01	-14.639	13.90	16.14
	.54	.68892-01	-.18413-01	.71311-01	-14.966	14.43	16.86
	.55	.68359-01	-.18679-01	.70865-01	-15.281	14.96	17.59
	.56	.67822-01	-.18933-01	.70415-01	-15.596	15.50	18.35
	.57	.67281-01	-.19175-01	.69960-01	-15.905	16.05	19.12
	.58	.66737-01	-.19406-01	.69502-01	-16.215	16.60	19.90
	.59	.66191-01	-.19626-01	.69040-01	-16.513	17.15	20.70
	.60	.65643-01	-.19833-01	.68574-01	-16.811	17.71	21.52
	.61	.65093-01	-.20030-01	.68105-01	-17.103	18.27	22.36
	.62	.64542-01	-.20214-01	.67633-01	-17.389	18.84	23.21
	.63	.63990-01	-.20386-01	.67159-01	-17.670	19.41	24.08
	.64	.63437-01	-.20547-01	.66681-01	-17.945	19.98	24.97
	.65	.62884-01	-.20696-01	.66202-01	-18.220	20.56	25.88
	.66	.62331-01	-.20834-01	.65721-01	-18.484	21.14	26.80
	.67	.61779-01	-.20959-01	.65237-01	-18.742	21.72	27.74
	.68	.61227-01	-.21074-01	.64752-01	-18.994	22.30	28.70
	.69	.60677-01	-.21176-01	.64266-01	-19.240	22.88	29.67
	.70	.60128-01	-.21268-01	.63779-01	-19.481	23.47	30.66
	.71	.59581-01	-.21348-01	.63290-01	-19.710	24.05	31.67
	.72	.59037-01	-.21416-01	.62801-01	-19.939	24.64	32.69
	.73	.58495-01	-.21474-01	.62312-01	-20.157	25.23	33.74
	.74	.57955-01	-.21521-01	.61822-01	-20.374	25.81	34.80
	.75	.57419-01	-.21557-01	.61332-01	-20.575	26.40	35.87
	.76	.56886-01	-.21582-01	.60843-01	-20.776	26.99	36.97
	.77	.56357-01	-.21597-01	.60354-01	-20.965	27.58	38.08
	.78	.55832-01	-.21601-01	.59865-01	-21.154	28.16	39.20
	.79	.55311-01	-.21595-01	.59377-01	-21.326	28.75	40.35
	.80	.54794-01	-.21579-01	.58890-01	-21.497	29.33	41.51
	.81	.54282-01	-.21553-01	.58405-01	-21.658	29.91	42.68
	.82	.53775-01	-.21518-01	.57921-01	-21.807	30.50	43.87
	.83	.53273-01	-.21473-01	.57438-01	-21.956	31.07	45.08
	.84	.52777-01	-.21419-01	.56957-01	-22.088	31.65	46.31
	.85	.52286-01	-.21356-01	.56479-01	-22.219	32.23	47.55
	.86	.51800-01	-.21283-01	.56002-01	-22.334	32.80	48.80
	.87	.51321-01	-.21203-01	.55528-01	-22.449	33.37	50.07
	.88	.50847-01	-.21114-01	.55057-01	-22.552	33.93	51.36
	.89	.50380-01	-.21016-01	.54588-01	-22.643	34.49	52.66
	.90	.49919-01	-.20911-01	.54122-01	-22.729	35.05	53.97

Table 1 (Continued)

M	THETA	ZREAL	IMAG	ABSZ	PHASE°	PDMI	PFE
4.0	.00	.33333-01	-.00000	.33333-01	- 0.000	.00	.00
	.01	.33333-01	-.12398-04	.33333-01	- .023	.00	.00
	.02	.33332-01	-.48650-04	.33332-01	- .086	.01	.01
	.03	.33327-01	-.10735-03	.33328-01	- .183	.02	.02
	.04	.33319-01	-.18709-03	.33320-01	- .321	.04	.04
	.05	.33307-01	-.28649-03	.33308-01	- .493	.08	.08
	.06	.33289-01	-.40417-03	.33291-01	- .693	.13	.13
	.07	.33264-01	-.53879-03	.33268-01	- .928	.20	.20
	.08	.33232-01	-.68900-03	.33239-01	- 1.186	.28	.28
	.09	.33192-01	-.85351-03	.33203-01	- 1.473	.39	.39
	.10	.33144-01	-.10310-02	.33160-01	- 1.782	.52	.52
	.11	.33087-01	-.12203-02	.33109-01	- 2.114	.67	.68
	.12	.33020-01	-.14201-02	.33051-01	- 2.464	.85	.85
	.13	.32944-01	-.16293-02	.32985-01	- 2.830	1.05	1.06
	.14	.32858-01	-.18467-02	.32910-01	- 3.214	1.27	1.29
	.15	.32762-01	-.20712-02	.32828-01	- 3.615	1.52	1.54
	.16	.32656-01	-.23016-02	.32737-01	- 4.034	1.79	1.82
	.17	.32540-01	-.25371-02	.32638-01	- 4.458	2.08	2.13
	.18	.32413-01	-.27765-02	.32531-01	- 4.899	2.41	2.46
	.19	.32276-01	-.30189-02	.32417-01	- 5.346	2.75	2.83
	.20	.32128-01	-.32633-02	.32294-01	- 5.798	3.12	3.22
	.21	.31971-01	-.35090-02	.32163-01	- 6.262	3.51	3.64
	.22	.31803-01	-.37549-02	.32024-01	- 6.732	3.93	4.09
	.23	.31626-01	-.40005-02	.31878-01	- 7.208	4.37	4.57
	.24	.31439-01	-.42448-02	.31724-01	- 7.689	4.83	5.07
	.25	.31243-٦1	-.44871-02	.31563-01	- 8.170	5.31	5.61
	.26	.31037-01	-.47268-02	.31395-01	- 8.657	5.81	6.17
	.27	.30823-01	-.49632-02	.31220-01	- 9.150	6.34	6.77
	.28	.30601-01	-.51958-02	.31039-01	- 9.637	6.88	7.39
	.29	.30370-01	-.54239-02	.30851-01	-10.124	7.45	8.05
	.30	.30132-01	-.56470-02	.30657-01	-10.617	8.03	8.73
	.31	.29886-01	-.58646-02	.30456-01	-11.104	8.63	9.45
	.32	.29634-01	-.60763-02	.30250-01	-11.585	9.25	10.19
	.33	.29375-01	-.62817-02	.30039-01	-12.072	9.88	10.97
	.34	.29109-01	-.64804-02	.29822-01	-12.554	10.53	11.77
	.35	.28838-01	-.66720-02	.29600-01	-13.029	11.20	12.61
	.36	.28562-01	-.68561-02	.29373-01	-13.499	11.88	13.48
	.37	.28281-01	-.70327-02	.29142-01	-13.963	12.57	14.38
	.38	.27995-01	-.72013-02	.28906-01	-14.427	13.28	15.32
	.39	.27705-01	-.73617-02	.28666-01	-14.880	14.00	16.28
	.40	.27412-01	-.75138-02	.28423-01	-15.327	14.73	17.28
	.41	.27115-01	-.76575-02	.28176-01	-15.768	15.47	18.30
	.42	.26816-01	-.77924-02	.27925-01	-16.203	16.22	19.37
	.43	.26515-01	-.79187-02	.27672-01	-16.627	16.98	20.46
	.44	.26211-01	-.80361-02	.27415-01	-17.046	17.75	21.59
	.45	.25906-01	-.81447-02	.27156-01	-17.452	18.53	22.75

Table 1 (Continued)

M	THETA	ZREAL	IMAG	ABSZ	PHASE°	PDMI	PFE
4.0	.46	.25600-01	-.82443-02	.26895-01	-17.853	19.32	23.94
	.47	.25294-01	-.83350-02	.26631-01	-18.237	20.11	25.17
	.48	.24987-01	-.84168-02	.26366-01	-18.615	20.90	26.43
	.49	.24680-01	-.84896-02	.26099-01	-18.982	21.70	27.72
	.50	.24373-01	-.85536-02	.25831-01	-19.337	22.51	29.05
	.51	.24068-01	-.86089-02	.25561-01	-19.681	23.32	30.41
	.52	.23763-01	-.86554-02	.25291-01	-20.013	24.13	31.80
	.53	.23460-01	-.86934-02	.25019-01	-20.334	24.94	33.23
	.54	.23159-01	-.87228-02	.24748-01	-20.638	25.76	34.69
	.55	.22860-01	-.87439-02	.24476-01	-20.930	26.57	36.19
	.56	.22564-01	-.87567-02	.24204-01	-21.211	27.39	37.72
	.57	.22270-01	-.87615-02	.23932-01	-21.475	28.20	39.28
	.58	.21980-01	-.87584-02	.23660-01	-21.727	29.02	40.88
	.59	.21692-01	-.87475-02	.23390-01	-21.962	29.83	42.51
	.60	.21408-01	-.87291-02	.23120-01	-22.185	30.64	44.18
	.61	.21128-01	-.87033-02	.22851-01	-22.386	31.45	45.87
	.62	.20852-01	-.86704-02	.22583-01	-22.580	32.25	47.60
	.63	.20580-01	-.86305-02	.22317-01	-22.752	33.05	49.36
	.64	.20313-01	-.85839-02	.22052-01	-22.907	33.84	51.16
	.65	.20050-01	-.85308-02	.21790-01	-23.050	34.63	52.98
	.66	.19792-01	-.84713-02	.21529-01	-23.171	35.41	54.83
	.67	.19539-01	-.84058-02	.21271-01	-23.279	36.19	56.71
	.68	.19291-01	-.83345-02	.21015-01	-23.365	36.96	58.62
	.69	.19049-01	-.82575-02	.20761-01	-23.434	37.72	60.55
	.70	.18811-01	-.81752-02	.20511-01	-23.491	38.47	62.51
	.71	.18580-01	-.80878-02	.20264-01	-23.526	39.21	64.50
	.72	.18353-01	-.79954-02	.20019-01	-23.537	39.94	66.51
	.73	.18133-01	-.78984-02	.19778-01	-23.537	40.66	68.53
	.74	.17918-01	-.77970-02	.19541-01	-23.514	41.38	70.58
	.75	.17709-01	-.76915-02	.19307-01	-23.474	42.08	72.65
	.76	.17506-01	-.75820-02	.19077-01	-23.417	42.77	74.73
	.77	.17309-01	-.74688-02	.18851-01	-23.342	43.45	76.82
	.78	.17118-01	-.73521-02	.18630-01	-23.245	44.11	78.92
	.79	.16933-01	-.72322-02	.18412-01	-23.130	44.76	81.04
	.80	.16753-01	-.71093-02	.18199-01	-22.993	45.40	83.16
	.81	.16580-01	-.69836-02	.17991-01	-22.838	46.03	85.28
	.82	.16413-01	-.68554-02	.17787-01	-22.666	46.64	87.40
	.83	.16252-01	-.67249-02	.17589-01	-22.477	47.23	89.52
	.84	.16097-01	-.65922-02	.17395-01	-22.271	47.82	91.63
	.85	.15948-01	-.64576-02	.17206-01	-22.042	48.38	93.73
	.86	.15805-01	-.63214-02	.17023-01	-21.801	48.93	95.82
	.87	.15668-01	-.61837-02	.16844-01	-21.538	49.47	97.89
	.88	.15537-01	-.60447-02	.16671-01	-21.257	49.99	99.94
	.89	.15411-01	-.59046-02	.16504-01	-20.965	50.49	101.97
	.90	.15292-01	-.57636-02	.16342-01	-20.649	50.97	103.97

Table 1 (Continued)

M	THETA	ZREAL	IMAG	ABSZ	PHASE°	PDMI	PFE
5.0	.00	.16667-01	-.00000	.16667-01	- 0.000	.00	.00
	.01	.16666-01	-.98321-05	.16666-01	- .034	.00	.00
	.02	.16665-01	-.38387-04	.16665-01	- .132	.01	.01
	.03	.16661-01	-.84260-04	.16661-01	- .292	.03	.03
	.04	.16653-01	-.14606-03	.16654-01	- .504	.08	.08
	.05	.16641-01	-.22240-03	.16642-01	- .768	.15	.15
	.06	.16623-01	-.31195-03	.16626-01	- 1.077	.24	.24
	.07	.16600-01	-.41337-03	.16605-01	- 1.427	.37	.37
	.08	.16570-01	-.52538-03	.16578-01	- 1.816	.53	.53
	.09	.16532-01	-.64672-03	.16545-01	- 2.240	.73	.74
	.10	.16488-01	-.77617-03	.16506-01	- 2.693	.96	.97
	.11	.16435-01	-.91257-03	.16460-01	- 3.180	1.24	1.25
	.12	.16374-01	-.10548-02	.16408-01	- 3.684	1.55	1.57
	.13	.16306-01	-.12017-02	.16350-01	- 4.217	1.90	1.94
	.14	.16229-01	-.13523-02	.16285-01	- 4.761	2.29	2.34
	.15	.16143-01	-.15056-02	.16213-01	- 5.329	2.72	2.80
	.16	.16050-01	-.16607-02	.16136-01	- 5.907	3.19	3.29
	.17	.15948-01	-.18166-02	.16051-01	- 6.497	3.69	3.83
	.18	.15839-01	-.19726-02	.15961-01	- 7.099	4.23	4.42
	.19	.15722-01	-.21278-02	.15865-01	- 7.706	4.81	5.05
	.20	.15597-01	-.22815-02	.15763-01	- .8.325	5.42	5.73
	.21	.15465-01	-.24330-02	.15655-01	- 8.938	6.07	6.46
	.22	.15326-01	-.25817-02	.15542-01	- 9.563	6.75	7.24
	.23	.15181-01	-.27270-02	.15424-01	-10.181	7.46	8.06
	.24	.15029-01	-.28683-02	.15300-01	-10.806	8.20	8.93
	.25	.14872-01	-.30052-02	.15172-01	-11.425	8.97	9.85
	.26	.14709-01	-.31371-02	.15039-01	-12.038	9.76	10.82
	.27	.14541-01	-.32638-02	.14902-01	-12.651	10.59	11.84
	.28	.14368-01	-.33848-02	.14761-01	-13.258	11.43	12.91
	.29	.14191-01	-.34998-02	.14616-01	-13.854	12.30	14.03
	.30	.14011-01	-.36085-02	.14468-01	-14.444	13.19	15.20
	.31	.13827-01	-.37108-02	.14316-01	-15.023	14.10	16.42
	.32	.13640-01	-.38064-02	.14161-01	-15.590	15.03	17.69
	.33	.13451-01	-.38951-02	.14003-01	-16.152	15.98	19.02
	.34	.13259-01	-.39768-02	.13843-01	-16.696	16.94	20.40
	.35	.13067-01	-.40514-02	.13680-01	-17.229	17.92	21.83
	.36	.12872-01	-.41189-02	.13515-01	-17.745	18 91	23.32
	.37	.12678-01	-.41792-02	.13349-01	-18.243	19.91	24.86
	.38	.12482-01	-.42323-02	.13180-01	-18.730	20.92	26.45
	.39	.12287-01	-.42783-02	.13011-01	-19.200	21.94	28.10
	.40	.12092-01	-.43171-02	.12840-01	-19.647	22.96	29.80
	.41	.11898-01	-.43489-02	.12668-01	-20.077	23.99	31.56
	.42	.11705-01	-.43737-02	.12496-01	-20.489	25.03	33.38
	.43	.11514-01	-.43916-02	.12323-01	-20.879	26.06	35.25
	.44	.11324-01	-.44028-02	.12150-01	-21.245	27.10	37.18
	.45	.11136-01	-.44074-02	.11977-01	-21.595	28.14	39.16

Table 1 (Continued)

M	THETA	ZREAL	IMAG	ABSZ	PHASE°	PDMI	PFE
5.0	.46	.10951-01	-.44056-02	.11804-01	-21.916	29.18	41.20
	.47	.10768-01	-.43976-02	.11631-01	-22.214	30.21	43.29
	.48	.10588-01	-.43834-02	.11460-01	-22.489	31.24	45.44
	.49	.10412-01	-.43634-02	.11289-01	-22.741	32.27	47.64
	.50	.10238-01	-.43378-02	.11119-01	-22.964	33.28	49.89
	.51	.10068-01	-.43066-02	.10951-01	-23.159	34.30	52.20
	.52	.99024-02	-.42703-02	.10784-01	-23.325	35.30	54.55
	.53	.97403-02	-.42289-02	.10619-01	-23.468	36.29	56.96
	.54	.95823-02	-.41828-02	.10455-01	-23.583	37.27	59.41
	.55	.94286-02	-.41321-02	.10294-01	-23.663	38.23	61.90
	.56	.92792-02	-.40772-02	.10135-01	-23.721	39.19	64.44
	.57	.91343-02	-.40182-02	.99790-02	-23.743	40.13	67.02
	.58	.89940-02	-.39554-02	.98253-02	-23.738	41.05	69.63
	.59	.88584-02	-.38890-02	.96745-02	-23.703	41.95	72.27
	.60	.87275-02	-.38193-02	.95266-02	-23.635	42.84	74.95
	.61	.86014-02	-.37466-02	.93819-02	-23.537	43.71	77.65
	.62	.84801-02	-.36710-02	.92406-02	-23.405	44.56	80.36
	.63	.83638-02	-.35929-02	.91028-02	-23.245	45.38	83.09
	.64	.82523-02	-.35123-02	.89687-02	-23.056	46.19	85.83
	.65	.81457-02	-.34297-02	.88383-02	-22.832	46.97	88.57
	.66	.80440-02	-.33452-02	.87119-02	-22.580	47.73	91.31
	.67	.79472-02	-.32589-02	.85895-02	-22.300	48.46	94.04
	.68	.78553-02	-.31713-02	.84713-02	-21.984	49.17	96.74
	.69	.77682-02	-.30824-02	.83574-02	-21.641	49.86	99.42
	.70	.76859-02	-.29924-02	.82479-02	-21.274	50.51	102.07
	.71	.76083-02	-.29017-02	.81428-02	-20.879	51.14	104.68
	.72	.75354-02	-.28103-02	.80423-02	-20.455	51.75	107.24
	.73	.74671-02	-.27184-02	.79465-02	-20.002	52.32	109.74
	.74	.74033-02	-.26263-02	.78553-02	-19.532	52.87	112.17
	.75	.73440-02	-.25340-02	.77689-02	-19.039	53.39	114.53
	.76	.72890-02	-.24419-02	.76871-02	-18.524	53.88	116.81
	.77	.72383-02	-.23500-02	.76102-02	-17.985	54.34	119.00
	.78	.71918-02	-.22584-02	.75381-02	-17.435	54.77	121.10
	.79	.71494-02	-.21674-02	.74707-02	-16.868	55.18	123.09
	.80	.71109-02	-.20771-02	.74081-02	-16.284	55.55	124.98
	.81	.70763-02	-.19875-02	.73502-02	-15.688	55.90	126.75
	.82	.70455-02	-.18989-02	.72969-02	-15.086	56.22	128.41
	.83	.70183-02	-.18113-02	.72483-02	-14.473	56.51	129.94
	.84	.69946-02	-.17249-02	.72042-02	-13.854	56.77	131.35
	.85	.69744-02	-.16397-02	.71645-02	-13.230	57.01	132.63
	.86	.69574-02	-.15559-02	.71292-02	-12.605	57.22	133.78
	.87	.69435-02	-.14735-02	.70981-02	-11.981	57.41	134.80
	.88	.69327-02	-.13925-02	.70712-02	-11.356	57.57	135.70
	.89	.69249-02	-.13132-02	.70483-02	-10.737	57.71	136.46
	.90	.69198-02	-.12356-02	.70292-02	-10.124	57.82	137.11

Table 1 (Continued)

M	THETA	ZREAL	IMAG	ABSZ	PHASE°	PDMI	PFE
6.0	.00	.95238-02	-.00000	.95238-02	- 0.000	.00	.00
	.01	.95236-02	-.81367-05	.95236-02	- .052	.00	.00
	.02	.95220-02	-.31606-04	.95221-02	- .189	.02	.02
	.03	.95180-02	-.69007-04	.95183-02	- .413	.06	.06
	.04	.95106-02	-.11895-03	.95113-02	- .716	.13	.13
	.05	.94988-02	-.18009-03	.95005-02	- 1.089	.25	.25
	.06	.94820-02	-.25109-03	.94853-02	- 1.518	.40	.41
	.07	.94595-02	-.33066-03	.94653-02	- 2.000	.61	.62
	.08	.94311-02	-.41757-03	.94403-02	- 2.532	.88	.88
	.09	.93962-02	-.51061-03	.94101-02	- 3.111	1.19	1.21
	.10	.93547-02	-.60865-03	.93745-02	- 3.724	1.57	1.59
	.11	.93064-02	-.71059-03	.93334-02	- 4.366	2.00	2.04
	.12	.92512-02	-.81539-03	.92870-02	- 5.036	2.49	2.55
	.13	.91891-02	-.92210-03	.92353-02	- 5.730	3.03	3.12
	.14	.91203-02	-.10298-02	.91783-02	- 6.440	3.63	3.76
	.15	.90449-02	-.11376-02	.91161-02	- 7.168	4.28	4.47
	.16	.89630-02	-.12447-02	.90490-02	- 7.907	4.99	5.25
	.17	.88749-02	-.13505-02	.89770-02	- 8.652	5.74	6.09
	.18	.87809-02	-.14541-02	.89005-02	- 9.402	6.54	7.00
	.19	.86813-02	-.15551-02	.88195-02	-10.153	7.40	7.99
	.20	.85765-02	-.16528-02	.87343-02	-10.909	8.29	9.04
	.21	.84669-02	-.17468-02	.86452-02	-11.660	9.23	10.16
	.22	.83528-02	-.18366-02	.85523-02	-12.399	10.20	11.36
	.23	.82346-02	-.19218-02	.84559-02	-13.138	11.21	12.63
	.24	.81129-02	-.20021-02	.83563-02	-13.860	12.26	13.97
	.25	.79880-02	-.20772-02	.82536-02	-14.576	13.34	15.39
	.26	.78603-02	-.21468-02	.81482-02	-15.275	14.44	16.88
	.27	.77303-02	-.22108-02	.80402-02	-15.963	15.58	18.45
	.28	.75984-02	-.22691-02	.79300-02	-16.627	16.74	20.10
	.29	.74651-02	-.23214-02	.78177-02	-17.275	17.91	21.82
	.30	.73308-02	-.23678-02	.77037-02	-17.899	19.11	23.63
	.31	.71958-02	-.24081-02	.75881-02	-18.501	20.33	25.51
	.32	.70607-02	-.24425-02	.74712-02	-19.080	21.55	27.47
	.33	.69257-02	-.24709-02	.73532-02	-19.635	22.79	29.52
	.34	.67912-02	-.24933-02	.72345-02	-20.162	24.04	31.65
	.35	.66577-02	-.25099-02	.71151-02	-20.655	25.29	33.85
	.36	.65254-02	-.25209-02	.69954-02	-21.125	26.55	36.14
	.37	.63947-02	-.25262-02	.68756-02	-21.555	27.81	38.52
	.38	.62658-02	-.25260-02	.67558-02	-21.956	29.06	40.97
	.39	.61391-02	-.25206-02	.66364-02	-22.323	30.32	43.51
	.40	.60148-02	-.25101-02	.65175-02	-22.655	31.57	46.13
	.41	.58931-02	-.24948-02	.63994-02	-22.947	32.81	48.82
	.42	.57744-02	-.24747-02	.62823-02	-23.199	34.04	51.60
	.43	.56587-02	-.24502-02	.61664-02	-23.411	35.25	54.45
	.44	.55462-02	-.24215-02	.60518-02	-23.583	36.46	57.37
	.45	.54373-02	-.23887-02	.59388-02	-23.715	37.64	60.36

Table 1 (Continued)

M	THETA	ZREAL	IMAG	ABSZ	PHASE°	PDMI	PFE
6.0	.46	.53319-02	-.23522-02	.58277-02	-23.806	38.81	63.42
	.47	.52302-02	-.23122-02	.57185-02	-23.852	39.96	66.54
	.48	.51323-02	-.22690-02	.56115-02	-23.852	41.08	69.72
	.49	.50383-02	-.22227-02	.55068-02	-23.806	42.18	72.95
	.50	.49483-02	-.21736-02	.54047-02	-23.715	43.25	76.21
	.51	.48624-02	-.21221-02	.53053-02	-23.577	44.29	79.52
	.52	.47805-02	-.20682-02	.52087-02	-23.394	45.31	82.84
	.53	.47027-02	-.20123-02	.51152-02	-23.165	46.29	86.19
	.54	.46291-02	-.19546-02	.50249-02	-22.890	47.24	89.53
	.55	.45596-02	-.18954-02	.49378-02	-22.575	48.15	92.88
	.56	.44941-02	-.18347-02	.48542-02	-22.208	49.03	96.20
	.57	.44328-02	-.17730-02	.47742-02	-21.801	49.87	99.49
	.58	.43754-02	-.17104-02	.46978-02	-21.348	50.67	102.73
	.59	.43221-02	-.16470-02	.46252-02	-20.861	51.43	105.91
	.60	.42727-02	-.15831-02	.45565-02	-20.329	52.16	109.02
	.61	.42271-02	-.15189-02	.44917-02	-19.767	52.84	112.03
	.62	.41853-02	-.14546-02	.44308-02	-19.166	53.48	114.94
	.63	.41472-02	-.13903-02	.43740-02	-18.535	54.07	117.74
	.64	.41127-02	-.13262-02	.43212-02	-17.871	54.63	120.40
	.65	.40817-02	-.12624-02	.42724-02	-17.189	55.14	122.91
	.66	.40541-02	-.11992-02	.42277-02	-16.478	55.61	125.27
	.67	.40298-02	-.11365-02	.41870-02	-15.751	56.04	127.46
	.68	.40086-02	-.10747-02	.41502-02	-15.006	56.42	129.48
	.69	.39906-02	-.10137-02	.41173-02	-14.255	56.77	131.31
	.70	.39754-02	-.95374-03	.40883-02	-13.493	57.07	132.96
	.71	.39631-02	-.89486-03	.40629-02	-12.725	57.34	134.41
	.72	.39535-02	-.83717-03	.40412-02	-11.958	57.57	135.67
	.73	.39465-02	-.78076-03	.40230-02	-11.190	57.76	136.73
	.74	.39420-02	-.72570-03	.40082-02	-10.434	57.91	137.61
	.75	.39397-02	-.67206-03	.39966-02	- 9.683	58.04	138.30
	.76	.39397-02	-.61991-03	.39881-02	- 8.944	58.12	138.80
	.77	.39417-02	-.56929-03	.39826-02	- 8.216	58.18	139.14
	.78	.39457-02	-.52023-03	.39798-02	- 7.512	58.21	139.30
	.79	.39515-02	-.47280-03	.39797-02	- 6.824	58.21	139.31
	.80	.39590-02	-.42703-03	.39820-02	- 6.154	58.19	139.17
	.81	.39681-02	-.38293-03	.39866-02	- 5.512	58.14	138.90
	.82	.39787-02	-.34052-03	.39933-02	- 4.893	58.07	138.50
	.83	.39907-02	-.29984-03	.40019-02	- 4.297	57.98	137.98
	.84	.40038-02	-.26085-03	.40123-02	- 3.730	57.87	137.36
	.85	.40182-02	-.22358-03	.40244-02	- 3.186	57.74	136.65
	.86	.40336-02	-.18805-03	.40379-02	- 2.670	57.60	135.86
	.87	.40498-02	-.15420-03	.40528-02	- 2.183	57.45	134.99
	.88	.40670-02	-.12204-03	.40688-02	- 1.719	57.28	134.07
	.89	.40849-02	-.91568-04	.40859-02	- 1.283	57.10	133.09
	.90	.41034-02	-.62771-04	.41038-02	- 0.877	56.91	132.07

Table 1 (Continued)

M	THETA	ZREAL	IMAG	ABSZ	PHASE°	PDMI	PFE
7.0	.00	.59524-02	-.00000	.59524-02	- 0.000	.00	.00
	.01	.59522-02	-.69318-05	.59522-02	- .069	.00	.00
	.02	.59506-02	-.26787-04	.59507-02	- .258	.03	.03
	.03	.59467-02	-.58169-04	.59470-02	- .562	.09	.09
	.04	.59394-02	-.99702-04	.59403-02	- .963	.20	.20
	.05	.59280-02	-.15005-03	.59299-02	- 1.450	.38	.38
	.06	.59119-02	-.20791-03	.59156-02	- 2.017	.62	.62
	.07	.58906-02	-.27204-03	.58969-02	- 2.641	.93	.94
	.08	.58638-02	-.34124-03	.58737-02	- 3.329	1.32	1.34
	.09	.58312-02	-.41439-03	.58459-02	- 4.062	1.79	1.82
	.10	.57928-02	-.49042-03	.58135-02	- 4.842	2.33	2.39
	.11	.57484-02	-.56833-03	.57765-02	- 5.644	2.96	3.05
	.12	.56983-02	-.64719-03	.57349-02	- 6.480	3.65	3.79
	.13	.56425-02	-.72613-03	.56890-02	- 7.334	4.42	4.63
	.14	.55812-02	-.80438-03	.56389-02	- 8.199	5.27	5.56
	.15	.55147-02	-.88121-03	.55846-02	- 9.081	6.18	6.58
	.16	.54432-02	-.95598-03	.55265-02	- 9.964	7.15	7.71
	.17	.53672-02	-.10281-02	.54648-02	-10.846	8.19	8.92
	.18	.52870-02	-.10971-02	.53996-02	-11.723	9.29	10.24
	.19	.52030-02	-.11624-02	.53312-02	-12.593	10.44	11.65
	.20	.51156-02	-.12238-02	.52599-02	-13.453	11.63	13.17
	.21	.50252-02	-.12808-02	.51859-02	-14.301	12.88	14.78
	.22	.49323-02	-.13333-02	.51093-02	-15.126	14.16	16.50
	.23	.48373-02	-.13810-02	.50306-02	-15.934	15.49	18.32
	.24	.47406-02	-.14237-02	.49498-02	-16.713	16.84	20.25
	.25	.46428-02	-.14613-02	.48673-02	-17.470	18.23	22.29
	.26	.45441-02	-.14939-02	.47834-02	-18.197	19.64	24.44
	.27	.44450-02	-.15212-02	.46981-02	-18.890	21.07	26.70
	.28	.43460-02	-.15434-02	.46119-02	-19.549	22.52	29.06
	.29	.42473-02	-.15606-02	.45249-02	-20.174	23.98	31.55
	.30	.41494-02	-.15727-02	.44374-02	-20.758	25.45	34.14
	.31	.40526-02	-.15798-02	.43496-02	-21.297	26.93	36.85
	.32	.39571-02	-.15823-02	.42617-02	-21.795	28.40	39.67
	.33	.38634-02	-.15801-02	.41740-02	-22.242	29.88	42.61
	.34	.37717-02	-.15734-02	.40867-02	-22.643	31.34	45.65
	.35	.36821-02	-.15625-02	.40000-02	-22.993	32.80	48.81
	.36	.35951-02	-.15476-02	.39141-02	-23.291	34.24	52.08
	.37	.35107-02	-.15289-02	.38292-02	-23.531	35.67	55.45
	.38	.34292-02	-.15066-02	.37455-02	-23.715	37.08	58.92
	.39	.33507-02	-.14809-02	.36633-02	-23.847	38.46	62.49
	.40	.32753-02	-.14521-02	.35828-02	-23.910	39.81	66.14
	.41	.32032-02	-.14205-02	.35040-02	-23.915	41.13	69.87
	.42	.31344-02	-.13863-02	.34273-02	-23.858	42.42	73.68
	.43	.30691-02	-.13497-02	.33528-02	-23.738	43.67	77.54
	.44	.30073-02	-.13110-02	.32806-02	-23.554	44.89	81.44
	.45	.29490-02	-.12705-02	.32110-02	-23.308	46.06	85.38

Table 1 (Continued)

M	THETA	ZREAL	IMAG	ABSZ	PHASE°	PDMI	PFE
7.0	.46	.28942-02	-.12283-02	.31440-02	-22.999	47.18	89.32
	.47	.28430-02	-.11847-02	.30799-02	-22.620	48.26	93.26
	.48	.27953-02	-.11400-02	.30188-02	-22.185	49.28	97.18
	.49	.27511-02	-.10943-02	.29607-02	-21.692	50.26	101.04
	.50	.27104-02	-.10479-02	.29059-02	-21.136	51.18	104.84
	.51	.26731-02	-.10010-02	.28543-02	-20.529	52.05	108.54
	.52	.26391-02	-.95373-03	.28061-02	-19.870	52.86	112.12
	.53	.26084-02	-.90633-03	.27613-02	-19.160	53.61	115.56
	.54	.25808-02	-.85897-03	.27200-02	-18.409	54.30	118.84
	.55	.25564-02	-.81181-03	.26822-02	-17.619	54.94	121.92
	.56	.25350-02	-.76499-03	.26479-02	-16.793	55.52	124.80
	.57	.25164-02	-.71868-03	.26170-02	-15.940	56.03	127.45
	.58	.25006-02	-.67300-03	.25896-02	-15.063	56.50	129.86
	.59	.24875-02	-.62807-03	.25655-02	-14.169	56.90	132.01
	.60	.24768-02	-.58401-03	.25448-02	-13.270	57.25	133.91
	.61	.24687-02	-.54092-03	.25272-02	-12.359	57.54	135.53
	.62	.24628-02	-.49889-03	.25128-02	-11.453	57.79	136.88
	.63	.24590-02	-.45801-03	.25013-02	-10.548	57.98	137.97
	.64	.24573-02	-.41834-03	.24927-02	- 9.660	58.12	138.80
	.65	.24575-02	-.37994-03	.24867-02	- 8.789	58.22	139.37
	.66	.24596-02	-.34289-03	.24833-02	- 7.935	58.28	139.70
	.67	.24631-02	-.30721-03	.24822-02	- 7.110	58.30	139.80
	.68	.24683-02	-.27295-03	.24834-02	- 6.308	58.28	139.69
	.69	.24749-02	-.24013-03	.24865-02	- 5.541	58.23	139.38
	.70	.24828-02	-.20878-03	.24916-02	- 4.807	58.14	138.90
	.71	.24919-02	-.17891-03	.24983-02	- 4.108	58.03	138.26
	.72	.25020-02	-.15053-03	.25065-02	- 3.443	57.89	137.48
	.73	.25131-02	-.12363-03	.25161-02	- 2.819	57.73	136.57
	.74	.25250-02	-.98232-04	.25269-02	- 2.229	57.55	135.56
	.75	.25377-02	-.74290-04	.25387-02	- 1.679	57.35	134.46
	.76	.25510-02	-.51823-04	.25515-02	- 1.163	57.13	133.29
	.77	.25649-02	-.30793-04	.25650-02	- .688	56.91	132.06
	.78	.25792-02	-.11161-04	.25792-02	- .246	56.67	130.78
	.79	.25939-02	.70557-05	.25939-02	+ .155	56.42	129.47
	.80	.26089-02	.23920-04	.26090-02	+ .527	56.17	128.14
	.81	.26242-02	.39473-04	.26245-02	+ .859	55.91	126.80
	.82	.26396-02	.53719-04	.26401-02	+ 1.163	55.65	125.46
	.83	.26550-02	.66757-04	.26559-02	+ 1.438	55.38	124.12
	.84	.26705-02	.78566-04	.26716-02	+ 1.685	55.12	122.80
	.85	.26859-02	.89198-04	.26874-02	+ 1.902	54.85	121.49
	.86	.27013-02	.98743-04	.27031-02	+ 2.091	54.59	120.21
	.87	.27165-02	.10720-03	.27186-02	+ 2.257	54.33	118.95
	.88	.27315-02	.11463-03	.27339-02	+ 2.401	54.07	117.72
	.89	.27463-02	.12112-03	.27490-02	+ 2.527	53.82	116.53
	.90	.27608-02	.12665-03	.27637-02	+ 2.624	53.57	115.38

Table 1 (Continued)

M	THETA	ZREAL	IMAG	ABSZ	PHASE°	PDMI	PFE
3.0	.00	.39683-02	-.00000	.39683-02	- 0.000	.00	.00
	.01	.39680-02	-.60308-05	.39680-02	- .086	.01	.01
	.02	.39665-02	-.23185-04	.39666-02	- .332	.04	.04
	.03	.39627-02	-.50068-04	.39630-02	- .722	.13	.13
	.04	.39556-02	-.85318-04	.39565-02	- 1.238	.30	.30
	.05	.39446-02	-.12762-03	.39466-02	- 1.851	.54	.55
	.06	.39291-02	-.17570-03	.39331-02	- 2.561	.89	.89
	.07	.39089-02	-.22836-03	.39156-02	- 3.346	1.33	1.35
	.08	.38836-02	-.28446-03	.38940-02	- 4.188	1.87	1.91
	.09	.38533-02	-.34294-03	.38685-02	- 5.088	2.51	2.58
	.10	.38177-02	-.40282-03	.38389-02	- 6.022	3.26	3.37
	.11	.37772-02	-.46320-03	.38054-02	- 6.990	4.10	4.28
	.12	.37317-02	-.52324-03	.37682-02	- 7.981	5.04	5.31
	.13	.36816-02	-.58220-03	.37274-02	- 8.984	6.07	6.46
	.14	.36272-02	-.63942-03	.36832-02	- 9.998	7.18	7.74
	.15	.35688-02	-.69432-03	.36357-02	-11.012	8.38	9.15
	.16	.35068-02	-.74639-03	.35853-02	-12.015	9.65	10.68
	.17	.34415-02	-.79519-03	.35322-02	-13.012	10.99	12.35
	.18	.33734-02	-.84037-03	.34765-02	-13.986	12.39	14.14
	.19	.33030-02	-.88162-03	.34187-02	-14.943	13.85	16.08
	.20	.32307-02	-.91872-03	.33588-02	-15.877	15.36	18.15
	.21	.31568-02	-.95150-03	.32971-02	-16.776	16.91	20.36
	.22	.30819-02	-.97984-03	.32339-02	-17.636	18.51	22.71
	.23	.30064-02	-.10037-02	.31695-02	-18.461	20.13	25.20
	.24	.29306-02	-.10230-02	.31040-02	-19.240	21.78	27.84
	.25	.28550-02	-.10378-02	.30377-02	-19.979	23.45	30.63
	.26	.27799-02	-.10482-02	.29709-02	-20.661	25.13	33.57
	.27	.27057-02	-.10543-02	.29038-02	-21.291	26.82	36.66
	.28	.26327-02	-.10561-02	.28366-02	-21.858	28.52	39.89
	.29	.25612-02	-.10540-02	.27696-02	-22.368	30.21	43.28
	.30	.24915-02	-.10479-02	.27029-02	-22.815	31.89	46.82
	.31	.24238-02	-.10383-02	.26368-02	-23.188	33.55	50.50
	.32	.23583-02	-.10251-02	.25715-02	-23.491	35.20	54.32
	.33	.22953-02	-.10088-02	.25072-02	-23.726	36.82	58.27
	.34	.22349-02	-.98943-03	.24441-02	-23.881	38.41	62.36
	.35	.21773-02	-.96736-03	.23825-02	-23.955	39.96	66.56
	.36	.21225-02	-.94280-03	.23225-02	-23.950	41.47	70.86
	.37	.20707-02	-.91600-03	.22642-02	-23.864	42.94	75.26
	.38	.20219-02	-.88721-03	.22080-02	-23.692	44.36	79.72
	.39	.19762-02	-.85668-03	.21539-02	-23.434	45.72	84.24
	.40	.19336-02	-.82465-03	.21021-02	-23.096	47.03	88.78
	.41	.18941-02	-.79136-03	.20528-02	-22.678	48.27	93.31
	.42	.18577-02	-.75704-03	.20060-02	-22.174	49.45	97.82
	.43	.18244-02	-.72190-03	.19620-02	-21.589	50.56	102.25
	.44	.17941-02	-.68617-03	.19208-02	-20.930	51.59	106.59
	.45	.17668-02	-.65005-03	.18826-02	-20.203	52.56	110.79

Table 1 (Continued)

M	THETA	ZREAL	IMAG	ABSZ	PHASE°	PDMI	PFE
8.0	.46	.17424-02	-.61373-03	.18473-02	-19.406	53.45	114.81
	.47	.17208-02	-.57739-03	.18151-02	-18.547	54.26	118.63
	.48	.17019-02	-.54120-03	.17859-02	-17.641	55.00	122.20
	.49	.16857-02	-.50531-03	.17598-02	-16.685	55.65	125.50
	.50	.16719-02	-.46988-03	.17367-02	-15.699	56.23	128.49
	.51	.16606-02	-.43503-03	.17167-02	-14.679	56.74	131.16
	.52	.16516-02	-.40089-03	.16996-02	-13.642	57.17	133.48
	.53	.16448-02	-.36756-03	.16853-02	-12.599	57.53	135.46
	.54	.16400-02	-.33514-03	.16739-02	-11.551	57.82	137.07
	.55	.16371-02	-.30372-03	.16650-02	-10.508	58.04	138.33
	.56	.16360-02	-.27337-03	.16587-02	- 9.488	58.20	139.24
	.57	.16366-02	-.24416-03	.16547-02	- 8.486	58.30	139.82
	.58	.16387-02	-.21613-03	.16529-02	- 7.512	58.35	140.09
	.59	.16422-02	-.18933-03	.16531-02	- 6.578	58.34	140.06
	.60	.16470-02	-.16380-03	.16551-02	- 5.678	58.29	139.76
	.61	.16529-02	-.13955-03	.16588-02	- 4.824	58.20	139.22
	.62	.16599-02	-.11661-03	.16640-02	- 4.016	58.07	138.47
	.63	.16679-02	-.94976-04	.16706-02	- 3.260	57.90	137.54
	.64	.16767-02	-.74662-04	.16783-02	- 2.550	57.71	136.44
	.65	.16861-02	-.55656-04	.16871-02	- 1.891	57.49	135.22
	.66	.16962-02	-.37935-04	.16967-02	- 1.283	57.24	133.89
	.67	.17068-02	-.21506-04	.17070-02	- .722	56.98	132.47
	.68	.17179-02	-.63255-05	.17179-02	- .212	56.71	130.99
	.69	.17293-02	.76219-05	.17293-02	+ .252	56.42	129.47
	.70	.17409-02	.20392-04	.17410-02	+ .670	56.13	127.93
	.71	.17527-02	.31982-04	.17530-02	+ 1.043	55.82	126.37
	.72	.17646-02	.42461-04	.17651-02	+ 1.381	55.52	124.81
	.73	.17766-02	.51852-04	.17773-02	+.1.673	55.21	123.27
	.74	.17885-02	.60212-04	.17895-02	+ 1.931	54.90	121.75
	.75	.18004-02	.67592-04	.18016-02	+ 2.149	54.60	120.26
	.76	.18121-02	.73988-04	.18136-02	+ 2.338	54.30	118.80
	.77	.18236-02	.79509-04	.18254-02	+ 2.498	54.00	117.39
	.78	.18350-02	.84165-04	.18369-02	+ 2.624	53.71	116.03
	.79	.18461-02	.88014-04	.18482-02	+ 2.727	53.43	114.71
	.80	.18569-02	.91124-04	.18591-02	+ 2.808	53.15	113.45
	.81	.18674-02	.93520-04	.18697-02	+ 2.865	52.88	112.24
	.82	.18775-02	.95248-04	.18799-02	+ 2.905	52.63	111.09
	.83	.18873-02	.96425-04	.18898-02	+ 2.922	52.38	109.99
	.84	.18967-02	.96977-04	.18992-02	+ 2.928	52.14	108.95
	.85	.19057-02	.96954-04	.19082-02	+ 2.911	51.91	107.96
	.86	.19143-02	.96582-04	.19167-02	+ 2.888	51.70	107.03
	.87	.19225-02	.95688-04	.19249-02	+ 2.848	51.49	106.16
	.88	.19303-02	.94436-04	.19326-02	+ 2.802	51.30	105.33
	.89	.19376-02	.92816-04	.19398-02	+ 2.744	51.12	104.57
	.90	.19445-02	.90953-04	.19467-02	+ 2.676	50.94	103.85

Table 1 (Continued)

M	THETA	ZREAL	IMAG	ABSZ	PHASE°	PDMI	PFE
9.0	.00	.27778-02	-.00000	.27778-02	- 0.000	.00	.00
	.01	.27776-02	-.53315-05	.27776-02	- .109	.01	.01
	.02	.27761-02	-.20388-04	.27761-02	- .418	.06	.06
	.03	.27723-02	-.43782-04	.27726-02	- .905	.19	.19
	.04	.27654-02	-.74164-04	.27664-02	- 1.536	.41	.41
	.05	.27548-02	-.11024-03	.27570-02	- 2.292	.75	.76
	.06	.27400-02	-.15077-03	.27441-02	- 3.151	1.21	1.23
	.07	.27208-02	-.19460-03	.27277-02	- 4.091	1.80	1.84
	.08	.26970-02	-.24066-03	.27077-02	- 5.099	2.52	2.59
	.09	.26687-02	-.28796-03	.26842-02	- 6.159	3.37	3.49
	.10	.26359-02	-.33559-03	.26572-02	- 7.254	4.34	4.54
	.11	.25988-02	-.38275-03	.26269-02	- 8.377	5.43	5.74
	.12	.25578-02	-.42872-03	.25934-02	- 9.517	6.64	7.11
	.13	.25130-02	-.47287-03	.25571-02	-10.657	7.95	8.63
	.14	.24648-02	-.51466-03	.25180-02	-11.792	9.35	10.32
	.15	.24137-02	-.55363-03	.24764-02	-12.920	10.85	12.17
	.16	.23601-02	-.58942-03	.24326-02	-14.020	12.43	14.19
	.17	.23044-02	-.62171-03	.23868-02	-15.097	14.08	16.38
	.18	.22470-02	-.65028-03	.23392-02	-16.140	15.79	18.75
	.19	.21884-02	-.67498-03	.22901-02	-17.143	17.56	21.29
	.20	.21290-02	-.69570-03	.22398-02	-18.094	19.37	24.02
	.21	.20692-02	-.71240-03	.21884-02	-18.999	21.22	26.93
	.22	.20094-02	-.72509-03	.21363-02	-19.842	23.09	30.03
	.23	.19501-02	-.73383-03	.20836-02	-20.621	24.99	33.32
	.24	.18915-02	-.73871-03	.20306-02	-21.331	26.90	36.80
	.25	.18339-02	-.73986-03	.19776-02	-21.973	28.81	40.46
	.26	.17778-02	-.73744-03	.19247-02	-22.529	30.71	44.32
	.27	.17233-02	-.73163-03	.18722-02	-23.004	32.60	48.37
	.28	.16707-02	-.72264-03	.18203-02	-23.388	34.47	52.60
	.29	.16201-02	-.71069-03	.17692-02	-23.686	36.31	57.01
	.30	.15719-02	-.69601-03	.17191-02	-23.881	38.11	61.59
	.31	.15260-02	-.67885-03	.16702-02	-23.984	39.87	66.31
	.32	.14828-02	-.65945-03	.16228-02	-23.978	41.58	71.17
	.33	.14421-02	-.63807-03	.15770-02	-23.870	43.23	76.15
	.34	.14042-02	-.61495-03	.15329-02	-23.652	44.81	81.21
	.35	.13690-02	-.59035-03	.14908-02	-23.325	46.33	86.32
	.36	.13366-02	-.56450-03	.14509-02	-22.895	47.77	91.46
	.37	.13069-02	-.53764-03	.14132-02	-22.363	49.13	96.56
	.38	.12800-02	-.50999-03	.13779-02	-21.727	50.40	101.60
	.39	.12558-02	-.48178-03	.13450-02	-20.988	51.58	106.52
	.40	.12342-02	-.45321-03	.13148-02	-20.162	52.67	111.27
	.41	.12153-02	-.42447-03	.12873-02	-19.251	53.66	115.79
	.42	.11988-02	-.39574-03	.12624-02	-18.266	54.55	120.03
	.43	.11847-02	-.36719-03	.12403-02	-17.217	55.35	123.95
	.44	.11730-02	-.33897-03	.12210-02	-16.117	56.05	127.51
	.45	.11634-02	-.31122-03	.12043-02	-14.977	56.64	130.65

Table 1 (Continued)

M	THETA	ZREAL	IMAG	ABSZ	PHASE°	PDMI	PFE
9.0	.46	.11559-02	-.28407-03	.11903-02	-13.808	57.15	133.37
	.47	.11504-02	-.25764-03	.11789-02	-12.622	57.56	135.63
	.48	.11466-02	-.23201-03	.11699-02	-11.436	57.88	137.44
	.49	.11446-02	-.20728-03	.11632-02	-10.262	58.12	138.80
	.50	.11442-02	-.18351-03	.11588-02	- 9.110	58.28	139.71
	.51	.11452-02	-.16079-03	.11564-02	- 7.993	58.37	140.20
	.52	.11475-02	-.13913-03	.11559-02	- 6.916	58.39	140.31
	.53	.11510-02	-.11859-03	.11571-02	- 5.884	58.34	140.06
	.54	.11556-02	-.99200-04	.11599-02	- 4.905	58.25	139.49
	.55	.11611-02	-.80971-04	.11640-02	- 3.988	58.10	138.65
	.56	.11675-02	-.63913-04	.11693-02	- 3.134	57.91	137.57
	.57	.11746-02	-.48030-04	.11756-02	- 2.343	57.68	136.29
	.58	.11823-02	-.33317-04	.11828-02	- 1.616	57.42	134.85
	.59	.11905-02	-.19746-04	.11907-02	- .951	57.14	133.29
	.60	.11992-02	-.73202-05	.11992-02	- .350	56.83	131.64
	.61	.12081-02	.40028-05	.12081-02	+ .189	56.51	129.92
	.62	.12173-02	.14253-04	.12174-02	+ .670	56.17	128.17
	.63	.12267-02	.23460-04	.12269-02	+ 1.094	55.83	126.40
	.64	.12362-02	.31669-04	.12366-02	+ 1.468	55.48	124.63
	.65	.12457-02	.38903-04	.12463-02	+ 1.788	55.13	122.88
	.66	.12552-02	.45229-04	.12560-02	+ 2.063	54.78	121.16
	.67	.12646-02	.50660-04	.12656-02	+ 2.292	54.44	119.49
	.68	.12738-02	.55291-04	.12750-02	+ 2.487	54.10	117.86
	.69	.12829-02	.59143-04	.12842-02	+ 2.641	53.77	116.30
	.70	.12917-02	.62272-04	.12932-02	+ 2.762	53.44	114.80
	.71	.13003-02	.64686-04	.13019-02	+ 2.848	53.13	113.36
	.72	.13086-02	.66496-04	.13103-02	+ 2.911	52.83	112.00
	.73	.13166-02	.67741-04	.13183-02	+ 2.945	52.54	110.71
	.74	.13242-02	.68411-04	.13260-02	+ 2.956	52.26	109.49
	.75	.13315-02	.68624-04	.13333-02	+ 2.951	52.00	108.34
	.76	.13385-02	.68367-04	.13402-02	+ 2.922	51.75	107.26
	.77	.13451-02	.67726-04	.13468-02	+ 2.882	51.52	106.26
	.78	.13513-02	.66746-04	.13529-02	+ 2.830	51.29	105.32
	.79	.13571-02	.65397-04	.13587-02	+ 2.762	51.09	104.45
	.80	.13625-02	.63840-04	.13640-02	+ 2.681	50.89	103.64
	.81	.13676-02	.62011-04	.13690-02	+ 2.596	50.72	102.90
	.82	.13723-02	.59970-04	.13736-02	+ 2.504	50.55	102.22
	.83	.13767-02	.57749-04	.13779-02	+ 2.401	50.39	101.59
	.84	.13806-02	.55391-04	.13817-02	+ 2.298	50.26	101.03
	.85	.13843-02	.52935-04	.13853-02	+ 2.189	50.13	100.52
	.86	.13877-02	.50414-04	.13886-02	+ 2.080	50.01	100.05
	.87	.13906-02	.47811-04	.13914-02	+ 1.971	49.91	99.64
	.88	.13933-02	.45136-04	.13940-02	+ 1.856	49.81	99.26
	.89	.13957-02	.42498-04	.13963-02	+ 1.742	49.73	98.94
	.90	.13977-02	.39849-04	.13983-02	+ 1.633	49.66	98.65

$$PDMI = \left[1 - \frac{ABSZ}{\left(\dfrac{2}{m(m^2 - 1)} \right)} \right]$$
$$\times 100 \qquad (16)$$

$$PFE = \left[\frac{\dfrac{2}{m(m^2 - 1)}}{ABSZ} - 1 \right]$$
$$\times 100 \qquad (17)$$

Acknowledgment

The author wishes to express his appreciation to the management of the Phelps Dodge Corporation for their permission to publish this data.

Reference

Sunde, Erling D., 1949, Earth conduction effects in transmission systems: New York, D. Van Nostrand Co., Inc.

Chapter III

MAGNETIC METHOD

Chapter III

MAGNETIC METHOD

Table of Contents

INTRODUCTION

D. A. HANSEN* AND R. E. MacDOUGALL**

The magnetic method is one of the first geophysical techniques to be applied to mineral exploration. It was used in the location of iron ore bodies as early as 1640. Today, the magnetic method accounts for a major portion of the mining geophysical effort.

This chapter covers two major aspects of the method. The first concerns the characteristics of the earth's magnetic field and the magnetic properties of the rocks and minerals which reside in that field. The second section deals with methods of treatment and interpretation of data obtained in magnetic surveys.

A number of the papers to follow appear in print for the first time; others have been published elsewhere and, because of their significance, have been selected for republication in this volume.

A Selected Bibliography is included as the final contribution to this chapter. The entries have been selected as the most significant contributions in the field of magnetics.

* Formerly with Utah Construction and Mining Co., San Francisco, California; now with Vanguard Exploration Company, San Francisco, California.
** Kennecott Copper Corp., Salt Lake City, Utah.

THE EARTH'S MAGNETIC FIELD

J. A. JACOBS*

The main features of the earth's magnetic field are described and an analysis is given of a uniformly magnetized sphere which gives a first approximation to the earth's field. The origin of the geomagnetic field is discussed in some detail. Time variations of the field are also discussed—both long term (secular) changes and transient variations, including a brief account of magnetic storms.

Introduction

The earth's magnetic field is the subject of one of the earliest scientific treatises ever written, De Magnete, which was published in 1600 by William Gilbert. The discovery of the directive property of a magnetized needle in the earth's field and the invention of the mariner's compass is, however, obscure. The earliest mention in European literature is ascribed to a monk, Alexander Neckham (1157–1217). In spite of this early interest in and practical utilization of the earth's magnetic field, its origin is still uncertain, and has been the subject of much controversy. At its strongest near the poles, the earth's magnetic field is several hundred times weaker than that between the poles of a toy horse-shoe magnet—being less than a gauss (Γ).[1] Thus, in geomagnetism we are measuring extremely small magnetic fields and a more convenient unit is the gamma (γ), defined as $10^{-5}\,\Gamma$.

In a magnetic compass the needle is weighted so that it will swing in a horizontal plane, its deviation from geographical north being called the declination D. D is reckoned positive or negative according as the deviation is east or west of geographical north. The vertical plane through the magnetic force $\mathbf{F}$ (or its horizontal component H) is called the magnetic meridian. Thus, the decli-

nation at any point P is the angle between the magnetic meridian and the geographical meridian through P.

It was also noticed that a nonmagnetic soft-iron needle, which is balanced horizontally on a pivot, becomes inclined to the vertical when magnetized. Over most of the northern hemisphere the north-seeking end of the needle will dip downwards, the angle it makes with the horizontal being called the magnetic dip or inclination I. Over most of the southern hemisphere, the north-seeking end of the needle points upwards and the inclination I is considered negative. The total

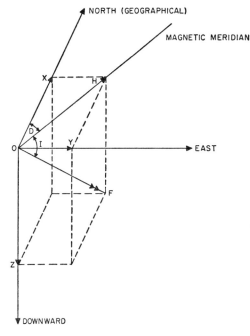

Fig. 1.

---

[1] Strictly speaking the unit of magnetic field strength is the oersted, the gauss being the unit of magnetic induction. The distinction is somewhat pedantic in geophysical applications since the permeability of air is virtually unity in cgs units. The traditional unit used in geomagnetism, the gauss, has thus been retained.

* University of British Columbia, Vancouver.

intensity F, the declination D, and the inclination I completely define the magnetic field at any point, although other components are sometimes used. The horizontal and vertical components of $\mathbf{F}$ are denoted by H and Z. H is always considered positive, whatever its direction, while Z is reckoned positive downwards and thus has the same sign convention as I. H is further resolved into two components X and Y. X is the component along the geographical meridian and is reckoned positive if northward; Y is the orthogonal component and is reckoned positive if eastward. Figure 1 illustrates these different magnetic elements. They are simply related to one another by the following equations:

$$H = F \cos I,$$
$$Z = F \sin I,$$
$$\tan I = Z/H \qquad (1)$$
$$X = H \cos D,$$
$$Y = H \sin D,$$
$$\tan D = Y/X \qquad (2)$$
$$F^2 = H^2 + Z^2 = X^2 + Y^2 + Z^2. \qquad (3)$$

The variation of the magnetic field over the earth's surface is best illustrated by isomagnetic charts, i.e. maps on which lines are drawn through points at which a given magnetic element has the same value. Contours of equal intensity in any of the elements X, Y, Z, H, or F are called isodynamics. Figures 2 and 3 are world maps showing lines of equal declination (isogonics) and lines of equal inclination (isoclinics) for the year 1955. It is remarkable that a phenomenon (the earth's magnetic field) whose origin lies within the earth should show so little relation to the broad features of geography and geology. The isomagnetics cross from continents to oceans without disturbance and show no obvious relation to the great belts of folding or to the pattern of submarine ridges. In this respect the magnetic field is in striking contrast to the earth's gravitational field and to the distribution of earthquake epicenters, both of which are closely related to the major features of the earth's surface.

In 1635 H. Gellibrand discovered that the magnetic declination changed with time, basing his conclusions on observations made in London. This change in the magnetic field with time is called the secular variation and is observed in all magnetic elements. If successive annual mean values of a magnetic element are obtained for a particular station, it is found that the changes are in the same sense over a long period of time, although the rate of change is not usually constant. Over a period of a hundred years or so this change may be considerable. Thus, the H component at Cape Town has decreased by 21 percent in the hundred years following the first observations in 1843. Figure 4 shows the changes in declination and inclination at London, Boston, and Baltimore. A compass needle at London was $11\frac{1}{2}°$ E of true north in 1580 and $24\frac{1}{4}°$ W of true north in 1819, a change of almost 36° in 240 years. Lines of equal secular changes (isopors) in an element form sets of ovals centering on points of local maximum change (isoporic foci). Figures 5 and 6 show the secular change in Z for the years 1922.5 and 1942.5. It is clear that considerable changes take place in the general distribution of isopors even within 20 years. The secular variation is a regional rather than a planetary phenomenon and is anomalously large and complicated over and around the Antarctic. In an area about 1,000 km in linear extent between South Africa and Antarctica, the secular change in the total intensity is at present -220γ/year which is about 18 times as large as the average rate. The secular change is particularly remarkable in the area of East Antarctica where at present there are two isoporic foci, one positive and the other negative, the intensities being $+200\gamma$/year and -100γ/year. On the other hand, the secular variation appears to be markedly smaller in the Pacific hemisphere (between 120° E and 80° W) than over the rest of the earth's surface. The exhaustive analyses of E. H. Vestine and his colleagues (1947) have indicated a clear tendency for the isoporic foci to drift westwards, the mean westward drift of this nondipole field being about 0.18°/year. However, K. Whitham (1958) has examined Canadian isomagnetic

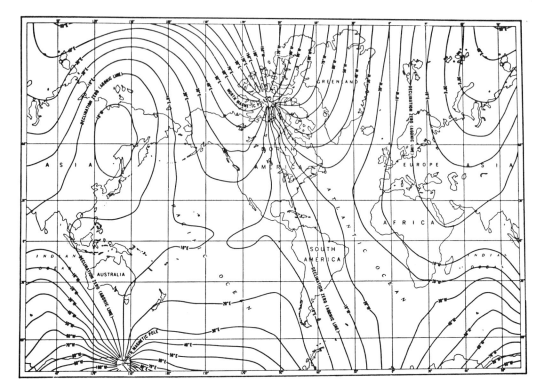

FIG. 2. World map showing contours of equal declination (isogonics) for 1955. Mercator projection (after J. H. Nelson, L. Hurwitz and D. G. Knapp).

and isoporic charts for the epoch 1955.0 and found no evidence for a westward drift of this magnitude. He then reexamined that part of Vestine's data appropriate to Canada and found some evidence of a westward drift in recent years in Canada but some three times smaller than the above figure. Thus, significantly large changes in the rate of the westward drift, as compared to the world average, can be found in a region occupying about four percent of the surface of the earth.

The Field of a Uniformly Magnetized Sphere

William Gilbert published in 1600 the results of his investigations on the variation in direction of the magnetic force over the surface of a piece of the naturally magnetized mineral lodestone which he had cut in the shape of a sphere. He found that the variation of the inclination was in agreement with what was then known about the earth's magnetic field, and he came to the conclusion that the earth behaved substantially as a uniformly magnetized sphere, its magnetic field being due to causes within the earth and not from any external agency as was supposed at that time. In 1839 Gauss showed by a spherical harmonic analysis that the field of a uniformly magnetized sphere, which is the same as that of a geocentric dipole, is an excellent first approximation to the earth's magnetic field.

Since the north-seeking end of a compass needle is attracted towards the northern regions of the earth, those regions must have opposite polarity. Consider, therefore, the field of a uniformly magnetized sphere whose magnetic axis runs north–south, and let P be any external point distant r from the center O and θ the angle NOP, i.e., θ is the magnetic co-latitude (see Figure 7).

The magnetic potential V at P is given by

$$V = \frac{-M \cos \theta}{r^2} \tag{4}$$

where M is the magnetic moment.

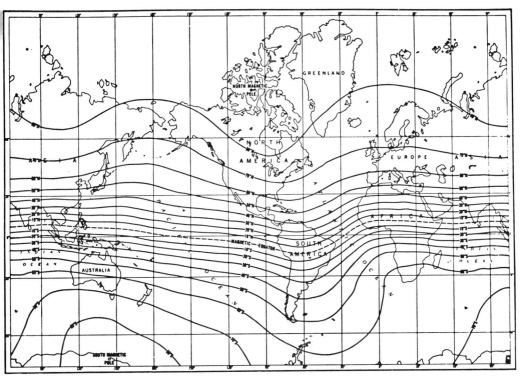

FIG. 3. World map showing contours of equal inclination (isoclinics) for 1955. Mercator projection (after J. H. Nelson, L. Hurwitz and D. G. Knapp).

The inward radial component of force corresponding to the magnetic component Z is given by

$$Z = \frac{\partial V}{\partial r} = \frac{2M \cos \theta}{r^3}. \tag{5}$$

The component at right angles to OP in the direction of decreasing θ, corresponding to the magnetic component H, is given by

$$H = \frac{1}{r} \frac{\partial V}{\partial \theta} = \frac{M \sin \theta}{r^3}. \tag{6}$$

Hence the angle of dip I is given by

$$\tan I = \frac{Z}{H} = 2 \cot \theta \tag{7}$$

and the total intensity

$$F = \sqrt{H^2 + Z^2} = \frac{M}{r^3} \sqrt{1 + 3 \cos^2 \theta}. \tag{8}$$

The maximum value of Z on the surface of the sphere $(r = a)$ is

$$Z_0 = \frac{2M}{a^3} \tag{9}$$

and occurs at the poles. The maximum value of H on the surface is

$$H_0 = \frac{M}{a^3} \tag{10}$$

and occurs at the equator. Thus $Z_0 = 2H_0$, which relationship is approximately true for the earth's field. (The total intensity F of the earth's magnetic field is a maximum near the magnetic poles—its value is just over 0.6 Γ near the northern dip pole and just over 0.7 Γ near the southern dip pole. Its minimum value of about 0.25 Γ is near the Tropic of Capricorn off the west coast of South America. In some areas such as Kursk, south of Moscow, and Berggiesshubel in Germany the magnitude of F may exceed 3 Γ but this is

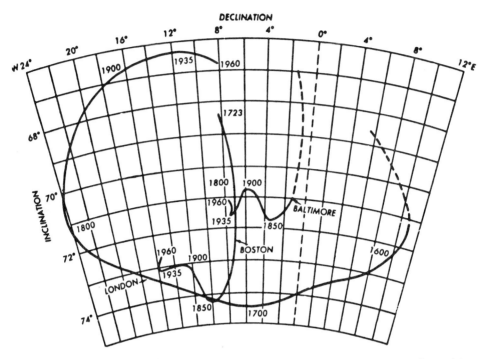

Fig. 4. Secular change of magnetic declination and inclination at London, Boston and Baltimore (after J. H. Nelson, L. Hurwitz, and D. G. Knapp).

entirely due to local concentrations of magnetic ore bodies.)

At points on the earth's surface where the horizontal component of the magnetic field vanishes, a dip needle will rest with its axis vertical. Such points are called dip poles.

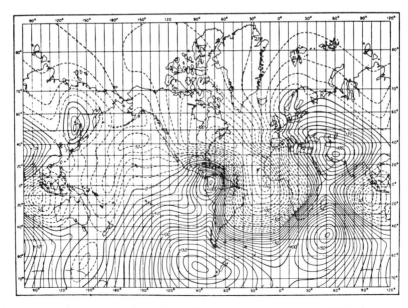

Fig. 5. World map showing the secular variation of the vertical component Z for 1922.5 (after E. H. Vestine, L. Laporte, C. Cooper, I. Lange, and W. C. Hendrix).

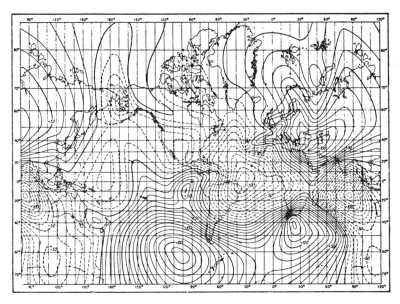

FIG. 6. World map showing the secular variation of the vertical component Z for 1942.5. (After E. H. Vestine, L. Laporte, C. Cooper, I. Lange, and W. C. Hendrix.)

Two principal poles of this kind are situated near the north and south geographical poles and are called the magnetic north and south poles. Their positions at present are approximately 75.5° N 100.5° W and 66.5° S, 139.9° E. They are thus not diametrically opposite,

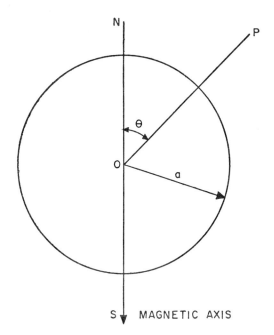

FIG. 7.

each being over 2,500 km from the point antipodal to the other. The magnetic poles must not be confused with the geomagnetic poles which are the points where the axis of the geocentric dipole which best approximates the earth's field, meets the surface of the earth. The geomagnetic poles are situated approximately at 78.5° N, 69° W and 78.5° S 111° E and the geomagnetic axis is thus inclined at about $11\frac{1}{2}°$ to the earth's geographical axis. If the geocentric dipole field were the total field, the dip poles and geomagnetic poles would, of course, be the same. A better approximation to the earth's field can be obtained by displacing the center of the equivalent dipole by about 300 km towards Indonesia.

The Origin of the Earth's Magnetic Field

A magnetic field observed at the surface of the earth could be produced by sources inside the earth, by sources outside the earth's surface or by electric currents crossing the surface. A spherical harmonic analysis of the observed field, however, shows that the source of the field is predominantly internal. Superimposed on this field is a rapidly varying external field giving rise to transient fluctuations. Unlike the secular variation, which is also of internal origin, these transient fluctuations produce no large or enduring changes in the earth's field. They are mostly due to solar effects which disturb the ionosphere and give rise to a number of related upper atmospheric phenomena such as magnetic storms and aurora.

There has been much speculation as to the cause of the earth's main field and no completely satisfactory explanation has as yet been given. A magnetic field could be produced in a number of ways. Consider first the possibility of permanent magnetization. If the field were due to uniform magnetization throughout the earth, the intensity of magnetization would be about 0.075 Γ. The surface layers of the earth are in general not magnetized to anything like this extent. The situation is much worse than this, however. The temperature gradient in the crust is approximately 30°C/km so that, at a depth of about 25 km, a temperature of the order of the Curie point for iron, viz. 750°C, is reached. Thus, unless the Curie point increases with increasing pressure, all ferromagnetic substances will have lost their magnetic properties at greater depths. There is no experimental evidence for a large increase in the Curie point with increasing pressure, and in order to account for the observed value of the earth's magnetic moment, an intensity of magnetization in the earth's crust of about 6 Γ is necessary, which is impossible. For most rocks the intensity is less than 10^{-2} Γ.

A number of attempts have been made to attribute the earth's magnetic field to the earth's rotation, but without success. Likewise, attempts at modifying the equations of electromagnetism or introducing new fundamental physical laws applicable to massive rotating bodies have met with failure. There remains the possibility that electric currents flow in the earth's interior setting up a magnetic field by induction. Such currents may have started originally by chemical irregularities which separated charges and, thus, initiated a battery action. Paleomagnetic measurements have shown that the earth's main field has existed throughout geologic time and that its strength has never differed

widely from its present value. H. Lamb showed in 1883 that electric currents generated in a sphere of radius a, electrical conductivity σ and permeability μ, and left, to decay freely would be reduced by electrical dissipation by Joule heating to e^{-1} of their initial strength in a time not longer than $4\sigma\mu a^2/\pi$. This time is of the order of 10^5 years, whereas the age of the earth is, more than 4×10^9 years. This decay time is even shorter for the higher harmonics so that the geomagnetic field cannot be a relic of the past, and a mechanism must be found for generating and maintaining electric currents to sustain the earth's continuing magnetic field. A process that could accomplish this is the familiar action of the dynamo.

The dynamo theory of the earth's magnetic field is due originally to Sir Joseph Larmor who in 1919 suggested that the magnetic field of the sun might be maintained by a mechanism analogous to that of a self-exciting dynamo. This suggestion was followed up independently by W. M. Elsasser and E. C. Bullard. We know that the earth has a fluid core, the main constituent of which is iron. Thus, the core is a good conductor of electricity and a fluid in which motions can take place, i.e. it permits both mechanical motion and the flow of electric current, and the interaction of these could generate a self-sustaining magnetic field. The secular variation also lends support to a dynamo theory, the variations and changes in the earth's magnetic field reflecting eddies and changing patterns in the motions in the core. It should also be mentioned that paleomagnetic evidence indicates that the earth's dipole field may have reversed its polarity many times in the past. Both normal and reversed fields could equally well exist according to the dynamo theory of the earth's main field.

It has not proved possible to demonstrate the existence of such a dynamo action in the laboratory. If a bowl of mercury some 30 cm in diameter is heated from below, then thermal convection in the mercury will be set up —but no electric currents or magnetism can be detected in the bowl. Such a model experiment fails because electrical processes and mechanical processes do not scale down in the same way. An electric current in the bowl of mercury would have a decay time of about one hundredth of a second. The decay time, however, increases as the square of the diameter of the bowl—and an electric current in the earth's core would last for about 10,000 years before it decayed. This time is more than sufficient for the current and its associated magnetic field to be altered and amplified by motions in the fluid, however slow. The dynamo theory suggests that the magnetic field is ultimately produced and maintained by an induction process, the magnetic energy being drawn from the kinetic energy of the fluid motions in the core. A group of particles moving at different speeds in the fluid may pull laterally on some magnetic lines of force, thus stretching them. In this process of stretching they will gain energy—energy which is taken from the mechanical energy of the moving particles.

Even after the existence of energy sources sufficient to maintain the field has been established, there remains the outstanding problem of sign, i.e. it must also be shown that the inductive reaction to an initial field is regenerative and not degenerative. The question that has to be answered is—do there exist motions of a simply-connected, symmetrical, homogeneous and isotropic fluid body which will cause the body to act as a self-exciting dynamo and produce a magnetic field in the absence of any sustaining field from an external source? In an engineering dynamo, the coil has the symmetry of a clock face in which the two directions of rotation are not equivalent—it is this very feature which causes the current to flow in the coil in such a direction that it produces a field which re-inforces the initial field. A simple body such as a sphere does not have this property —any asymmetry can exist only in the motions.

Both E. C. Bullard and W. M. Elsasser separated the electromagnetic and hydrodynamic problems and attempted to solve the former only, i.e. they assumed a particular motion in the earth's core together with a magnetic field and calculated the electromagnetic interaction occurring within such a

system. As a result of a vast amount of numerical computation using electronic computers, Bullard concluded that the dynamo theory can provide a self-consistent account of the earth's magnetic field. A significant feature of his analysis is that, in order to produce the poloidal field outside the earth, a much more powerful toroidal field must exist in the earth's core. It must be pointed out that Bullard's solution merely shows that one particular set of motions could set up a self-exciting dynamo. It does not follow that his particular solution is the actual one. There has also been some doubt cast on the convergence of his solution.

In 1958 G. Backus and A. Herzenberg, working independently, each showed that it was possible to postulate a pattern of motions in a sphere filled with a conducting fluid in such a way that the arrangement acts as a dynamo producing a magnetic field outside the conductor. In each case the motions were physically very improbable; however, rigorous mathematical solutions were obtained, as was not the case with Bullard's numerical solution. The motions obtained by Backus all involved periods when the fluid is at rest. He needs these periods of rest to insure that other fields generated by induction will not develop in such a fashion that they eventually destroy the whole process. The model of the core obtained by Herzenberg consists of two spheres (which may be pictured as two eddies) each of which rotates as a rigid body at a constant angular velocity about a fixed axis. About a half of all possible configurations can act as dynamos if the velocities, positions, and radii of the rotating spheres are suitably adjusted.

F. J. Lowes and I. Wilkinson (1963) have built a working model of what is effectively a homogeneous self-maintaining dynamo based on Herzenberg's theory. For mechanical convenience they used, instead of spheres, two cylinders placed side by side with their axes at right angles so that the induced field of each is directed along the axis of the other. If the directions of rotation are appropriate, any applied field along an axis of rotation will lead, after two stages of induction, to a parallel induced field. If the velocities are large enough, the induced field will be larger than the applied field which is no longer needed, i.e. the system would be self sustaining.

Other possible causes of electromotive forces deep within the earth are thermoelectric and chemical. A likely place for either would be a major contact between dissimilar materials or between the same substances under markedly different physical conditions. Since the thermoelectric power of materials under the conditions prevailing at depth within the earth is unknown, it is extremely difficult to make a quantitative assessment of the thermoelectric theory. It seems that rather extreme assumptions are necessary to make any theory satisfactory— either an extreme geometry or extreme and implausible values of some of the physical properties of the material in the core and lower mantle. It also appears that the convective heat flow demanded by the theory is excessive and it is not at all certain that the required temperature differences can be realized.

Transient Magnetic Variations

The continuous magnetic records of any observatory show that on some days all three elements exhibit smooth and regular variations, while on other days they are disturbed and show irregular fluctuations. Days of the first kind are called quiet days, and days of the second, disturbed days. At each observatory a figure K between 0 and 9 is assigned to describe the magnetic conditions for each period of three Greenwich hours 0–3, 3–6, etc.

K indices are a measure, for an interval of three hours, of the intensity of magnetic disturbance as shown in the magnetograms at an observatory. Thus, they also incorporate any local effects such as the systematic diurnal variations in geomagnetic activity. There is, therefore, a need for an abstract of the individual K indices to express worldwide features of geomagnetic disturbances over a three-hour period. An average of all individual K indices would not be satisfactory, owing to the inadequate geographical distribution of magnetic observatories. Thus, a new index K_p has been designed to measure

"planetary" variations in magnetic activity. It is based on "standardized" indices which have been freed as far as possible from local features. K_p indices are given to thirds as follows: The intensity interval 1.5 to 2.5, for example, is divided equally into three thirds designated as $2-$, $2o$, and $2+$. This provides 28 grades of K_p from $0o$, $0+$, $1-$, $1o$, $1+$, $\cdots$, $8+$, $9-$, $9o$.

The definition of K_p was chosen so that the whole range of geomagnetic activity from the quietest conditions to the most intense storm could be expressed by a single digit and an affix. This was achieved by a quasi-logarithmic relation between the amplitudes of disturbance in the three-hour interval and K_p. In order to obtain a linear scale, K_p may be converted into a three-hour equivalent

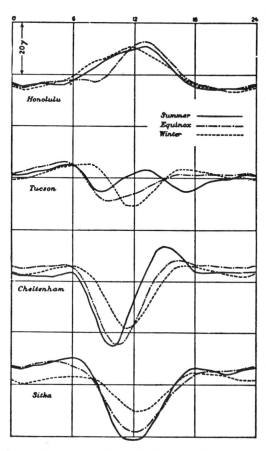

Fig. 8. Quiet-day variation S_q of horizontal intensity H (after J. H. Nelson, L. Hurwitz, and D. G. Knapp).

planetary amplitude, a_p. The average of the eight a_p values for a day is called A_p.

Most days show some magnetic disturbance, but except in periods of very violent activity, it is found that the disturbance D is superposed on a regular daily variation. This is called the solar daily variation S. There is also a regular daily variation L which depends on lunar time. L is of much smaller magnitude than either S or D and cannot usually be recognized at sight on a magnetogram as S and D can. S is seen in its pure form on quiet days when it is denoted by S_q. Figure 8, 9, and 10 show the quiet day variation S_q in H, Z, and D for four well-distributed observatories in the United States of America. (In figures 8, 9 and 10 each curve shows the average variation for a large number of magnetically quiet days for the obser-

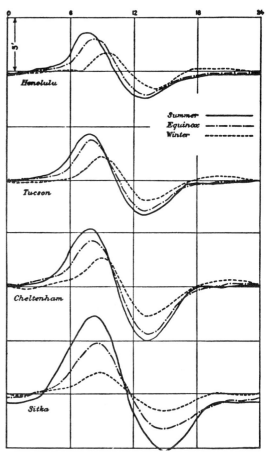

FIG. 10. Quiet-day variation S_q of declination D (after J. H. Nelson, L. Hurwitz, and D. G. Knapp).

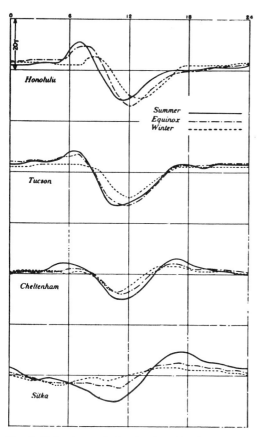

FIG. 9. Quiet-day variation S_q of vertical intensity Z (after J. H. Nelson, L. Hurwitz, and D. G. Knapp).

vatory, season and magnetic element specified. The time is local mean time. For some of the Tucson (Arizona) curves, the quiet days are of two distinct types, and the mean does not well represent either type. The geomagnetic latitudes of the four observatories are Honolulu, 21°; Tucson, 40°; Cheltenham, 50°; Sitka, 60°.) These curves are based on days selected because of their freedom from storms and represent the average of a large number of days so that minor irregularities are smoothed out. The actual curves for any observatory undergo seemingly fortuitous changes from day to day (both in amplitude and shape) so that average curves are hardly ever realized. The S_q variation is greater and more rapid during the hours of daylight than of darkness, in summer than in winter, and the amplitude of S_q is from 50 to 100 percent greater in years of sunspot maximum than in years of sunspot minimum. This emphasizes very clearly that the ultimate cause of S_q is the sun.

A spherical harmonic analysis of the S_q field shows that it is not produced wholly inside the earth (as is substantially the case for the earth's main field and secular variation) nor wholly above it. The major part of the S_q field (some $2/3\sim3/4$) has its origin above the earth, while the minor part has its source inside the earth. The sun is too far away to have any direct magnetic effect, and the most reasonable cause is a system of electric currents flowing in the ionosphere. Changes in these external current systems induce currents within the earth and provide the source for the internal field. The strength and direction of a system of overhead electric currents which could produce the external S_q field have been worked out. Such electric currents are probably induced by the daily periodic motion of the upper atmosphere in the presence of the earth's main magnetic field.

Magnetic Storms

It is found that the intensity of magnetic disturbances increases from low to high latitudes up to about magnetic latitude 65°, the latitude of the auroral zones, i.e., the zones where aurorae are most frequent. Within these zones, the intensity, although considerable, decreases slightly towards the magnetic poles. Magnetograms are seldom completely undisturbed in high latitudes. Although disturbances of low intensity may be confined to a small area of the earth's surface, large disturbances called magnetic storms are world-wide phenomena. Intense magnetic storms usually commence suddenly at almost the same instant (less than one-half minute) all over the earth. Some storms do not begin so abruptly, but their commencement can usually be fixed within an hour.

The records of individual storms differ greatly among themselves, but the changes in the field at the earth's surface may be analyzed into three main parts:

(1) a part depending on time measured from the commencement of the storm. This is known as the storm-time variation D_{st}

(2) a daily variation in addition to that present on quiet days and much greater in intensity and markedly different in character. This is known as the disturbance daily variation S_D.

(3) an irregular part most marked in high latitudes.

In middle and lower latitudes, the storm time part of the horizontal intensity rises to a maximum within an hour or two of the commencement and remains above its initial value for a period of 2–6 hours. This is called the initial phase. H then decreases, attaining after several hours a minimum which is much more below the initial undisturbed value than the maximum was above it. This is called the main phase, and is followed by a gradual recovery which may last for several days. The main phase generally lasts from 12 to 14 hours and tends to be noisy. Often large positive and negative excursions with amplitudes of the order of hundreds of gammas and periods of about one-half hour occur. The greater the storm, the more rapid is the development of these phases.

As in the case of the S_q variation, electric current systems in the upper atmosphere can be postulated to account for the phenomena of an average storm. The D_{st} part is ascribed chiefly to a ring current around the equator at a distance of several thousand kilometers. It can also be attributed to a simple current system in the ionosphere. The S_D variation can only be explained by a much more complex system of currents. Such systems may be no more than a convenient mathematical model whereby the observed magnetic variations can be described.

There are a number of other special types of magnetic disturbance, the most important being a bay which is a departure from an otherwise undisturbed record in the form of a V or bay of the sea. Other special features are micropulsations registered in otherwise quiet intervals and giant pulsations.

In recent years transient variations in the geomagnetic field have been considered from the viewpoint of hydromagnetic waves generated by interactions between the geomagnetic field and solar plasma—i.e. the ionized gas moving out from the sun. This gas, which flows radially outwards, has been called the solar wind. E. N. Parker (1958, 1960) showed that a continuous wind should exist and results from the Mariner 2 space craft and the Imp-I (Explorer 18) satellite have indicated amongst other things that a definite wind blows at all times (with a velocity of approximately 300–500 km/sec.). The wind is very gusty, however, showing fluctuations in energy, energy spread and density in times of the order of hours. Longer term studies with Mariner 2 have shown a striking correlation between the geomagnetic activity index K_p and the daily average solar wind velocity.

Most of the transient variations are due to interactions between the geomagnetic field and the solar wind. The interface between the solar wind and the geomagnetic field is probably unstable and the instabilities will take the form of hydromagnetic waves which propagate through the geomagnetic field and are observed at the earth's surface as small fluctuations in the geomagnetic field. Hydromagnetic waves may also be generated by changes in the pressure on the geomagnetic field boundary when the density or velocity of the solar wind varies.

There have been many attempts to account for the characteristic features of magnetic storms and related phenomena. A hydromagnetic model, due to A. J. Dessler and E. N. Parker (1959) probably gives the best explanation at present. The sudden commencement is initiated by the impact of solar plasma on the geomagnetic field, i.e., a sharp increase in the strength of the solar wind. The effect of the impact is carried down to the lower ionosphere by hydromagnetic waves. The initial phase is due to the increased solar wind pressure on the geomagnetic field. This continues until the diffusion of plasma (trapping of protons) in the geomagnetic field becomes important. The main phase is due to the stresses set up in the geomagnetic field by trapped protons from the solar wind. The major stress term comes from the centrifugal force of the trapped particles

as they oscillate back and forth along the lines of force through the equatorial plane. The large amplitude fluctuations in the field are probably due to changes in the solar wind pressure and/or major instabilities in the flow of the solar wind. The recovery phase is due to the relief of the main phase stress through the transfer of the energy of the trapped protons to neutral hydrogen in the geo-corona.

References Cited

Backus, G. E., 1958, A class of self sustaining dissipative spherical dynamos: Ann. Phys., v. 4, p. 372–447.

Bullard, E. C., 1949, The magnetic field within the earth: Proc. Roy. Soc. A, v. 197, p. 433–453.

——— Electromagnetic induction in a rotating sphere: Proc. Roy. Soc. A, v. 199, p. 413–443.

Bullard, E. C., Freedman, C., Gellman, H., and Nixon, J., 1950, The westward drift of the earth's magnetic field: Phil. Trans. Roy. Soc. A, v. 243, p. 67–159.

Bullard, E. C., and Gellman, H., 1954, Homogeneous dynamos and terrestrial magnetism: Phil. Trans. Roy. Soc. A, v. 247, p. 213–278.

Dessler, A. J., and Parker, E. N., 1959, Hydromagnetic theory of geomagnetic storms: Jour. Geophys. Res., v. 64, p. 2239–2252.

Elsasser, W. M., 1939, On the origin of the earth's magnetic field: Phys. Rev., v. 55, p. 489–498.

——— 1947, Electric modes, Part III *of* Induction effects in terrestrial magnetism: Phys. Rev., v. 72, p. 821–833.

——— 1950, The earth's interior and geomagnetism: Rev. Mod. Phys., v. 22, p. 1–35.

——— 1955, Hydromagnetism I, A review: Amer. J. Phys., v. 23, p. 590–609.

Herzenberg, A., 1958, Geomagnetic dynamos: Phil. Trans. Roy. Soc. A, v. 250, p. 543–585.

Jacobs, J. A., and Westphal, K. O., 1963, Geomagnetic micropulsations: Physics and Chemistry of the Earth, v. 5, p. 253–307, Pergamon Press.

Lowes, F. J., and Wilkinson, I., 1963, Geomagnetic Dynamo: A laboratory model: Nature, v. 198, p. 1158–1160.

Parker, E. N., 1958, Interaction of the solar wind with the geomagnetic field: Phys. Fluids, v. 1, p. 171–187.

——— 1960, The hydrodynamic theory of solar corpuscular radiation and stellar winds: Astrophys. Jour., v. 132, p. 821–866.

Vestine, E. H., Laporte, L., Cooper, C., Lange, I., and Hendrix, W. C., 1947, Description of the earth's main magnetic field and its secular change, 1905–1945: Carnegie Inst. of Washington Publ. No. 578.

Vestine, E. H., Lange, I., Laporte, L., and Scott, W. E., 1947, The geomagnetic field, its description and analysis: Carnegie Inst. of Washington Publ. No. 580.

Whitham, K., 1958, The relationships between the secular change and the non-dipole fields: Can. Jour. Phys., v. 36, p. 1372–1396.

References for General Reading

S. Chapman and J. Bartels, Geomagnetism, Oxford University Press (1940), has been a standard text on geomagnetism for many years. S. Chapman has also published a small book in Methuen's Monographs on physical subjects entitled "The Earth's Magnetism" (1951).

Hide, R., 1956, The hydrodynamics of the earth's core: Physics and Chemistry of the Earth, v. 1, p. 94–137, Pergamon Press.

Hide, R., and Roberts, P. H., 1961, The origin of the main geomagnetic field: Physics and Chemistry of the Earth, v. 4, p. 27–98, Pergamon Press.

Jacobs, J. A., 1963, The earth's core and geomagnetism: Pergamon Press.

MINERAL MAGNETISM

DAVID W. STRANGWAY*

This brief section on mineral magnetism is meant to be a summary of the nature of the magnetic properties of minerals. A description of the nature of magnetism is given considering electron spin and orbital motion. Then a summary of the magnetic properties of naturally occurring minerals is given.

Introduction

The magnetic characteristics of rocks are usually due to the presence of minor amounts of magnetic minerals contained in them. Since these minerals are few in number and yet of considerable importance in magnetic techniques, a discussion of the various minerals and their properties will be given.

All materials are magnetic to some extent. They may be dominantly diamagnetic, paramagnetic, or ferromagnetic depending upon the mechanism causing the magnetic orientations within the specimen. A brief discussion of these forms of magnetization will be given.

Terminology

Before discussing the forms of magnetization, a brief summary of the terms commonly used to describe magnetic properties is given.

We might consider a simple loop of current. Such a loop is equivalent to a magnetic dipole located at the center of the loop. The magnetic moment is given by

$$m = 0.1 i A$$

where

i = current (amperes)
A = cross-sectional area (cm²).

If we extend our picture of a simple loop to the consideration of a solenoid involving many turns of wire, we find that a uniform magnetic field is generated inside the coil. This magnetic field is given by the expression:

$$H = \frac{0.4\pi n i}{l}$$

where

H = field in oersteds
n = number of turns
l = length of solenoid

or

$$H = \frac{4\pi n m}{V}$$

where V is the volume enclosed by the solenoid.

The field of a solenoid, then, depends on the number of turns, the magnetic moment of a single loop, and the volume enclosed by the solenoid.

It is well known that the atomic structure of matter gives a picture of spinning electrons or of circulating currents so that matter itself can contribute to the observed magnetic field. In this case, it is usual to define a magnetic moment per unit volume equivalent to nm/V in the above expression for the field of a solenoid. In this event, matter contributes to the magnetic field the following value:

$H_m = 4\pi M$ where M is the magnetization per unit volume, and $M = nm/V$.

The total induction or flux density (in the presence of an external field, H_o) is given by the expression:

$$B = \mu_0(H_0 + 4\pi M)$$

where

μ_0 = magnetic permeability of free space
H_0 = external field.

* University of Colorado, Boulder, Colo. Now at Dept. of Geology and Geophysics, Massachusetts Institute of Technology, Cambridge, Massachusetts.

It is usual in discussing magnetic properties to use the cgs system of units. In this case, the quantity μ_o has the value of 1, and the value of induction (B) in gauss is numerically equal to the magnetic field (H) in oersteds in the absence of magnetic material. In the mks units used in discussing electromagnetic techniques, the value of $\mu_o = 4\pi \times 10^{-7}$ henries/m so that a careful distinction between magnetic induction and magnetic field needs to be made. In the cgs system the following expression is numerically valid;

$$B = H_O + 4\pi M.$$

In discussing the magnetization of material, it is found that in many instances it is possible to consider the magnetization as proportional to the applied field so that $M \propto H_0$. The constant of proportionality is defined as the susceptibility, K in cgs units /cc or the susceptibility, χ, in cgs units/gm so that

$$M = KH_0$$

where K is in cgs units/cc Then,

$$B = H_0(1 + 4\pi K)$$
$$= H_0 \mu$$

where μ is defined as the magnetic permeability of the material. The susceptibility or the permeability defines the ability of a substance to be magnetized in the presence of an external field. The mechanism by which a substance can be magnetized will now be discussed.

Diamagnetism

We know that an atom is composed of a central positive charge and negatively charged electrons spinning around it. These electrons are constrained to move in an orbit and so act as simple magnets with a magnetic moment as previously defined. When this rotating electron is placed in a magnetic field, a force is exerted on the electron. This force, referred to as the Lorentz force, is given by the following expression:

$$F = \frac{Hev}{c}$$

where

H = magnetic field
e = electronic charge
v = velocity of electron
c = speed of light.

This extra force acting on the electron causes it to rotate with a new frequency. If ω is the new rotational velocity and ω_0 is the rotational velocity in the absence of a magnetic field, the centripetal force exerted on the spinning electron by the field may be written as:

where

$$m_e\omega^2 r - m_e\omega_0^2 r = \frac{Hev}{c}$$

m_e = mass of electron
r = orbital radius
ω_0 = undisturbed rotational frequency
ω = disturbed rotational frequency.

If ω and ω_0 are not greatly different, then the difference

$$\Delta\omega \approx -\frac{eH}{2m_e c}.$$

This is a precessional frequency referred to as the Larmor frequency. This additional frequency gives rise to an excess current. If there are Z electrons in an atom, then the extra current in a single atom is:

$$I = -\frac{Ze^2 H}{4\pi m_e c^2}$$

where Z is the atomic number or the number of electrons associated with each atom.

This excess current moving in an orbit of radius r gives rise to a magnetic moment

$$m = 0.1iA = -0.1\frac{Ze^2 H}{4m_e c^2} r^2.$$

Since the cross-sectional area presented by the orbits to the field is not uniform and on the average less than πr^2, we may write the magnetic moment of a group of atoms as:

$$M = \frac{Ze^2 N H \bar{r}^2}{6m_e c^2}$$

where N is the number of atoms per unit volume and $\bar{r}$ is the mean orbital radius.

The constant of proportionality between the magnetization and the field or the susceptibility is:

$$K = \frac{M}{H} = -\frac{ZeN}{6m_ec^2}\bar{r}^2.$$

These quantities are all measurable, and the diamagnetic susceptibility for a large number of substances has now been measured. The value is negative and very small. Minerals such as quartz, feldspar, and salt are all dominantly diamagnetic and as such cannot contribute significantly to magnetic properties in geologic problems.

Paramagnetism

In addition to the orbital motion of electrons, it is now understood that electrons in orbit also spin on their own axes. This means that an individual spinning electron acts much like a small magnet. When such a magnet is acted upon by a magnetic field, it tends to align itself parallel to the field, but the spinning motion is not modified by the presence of the field. In other words, the spinning electrons act like a distribution of minute permanent magnets in the presence of a magnetic field. In building up the periodic table, it is found that electron spins tend to orient themselves in opposition so that if there is an even number of electrons in an atom, there is no net reaction to a magnetic field. If there is an odd number, however, there is an unpaired electron which can react to a magnetic field and contribute to paramagnetism. In addition to atoms with an odd number of electrons, the transition elements may have several unpaired electron spins. The iron series of transition elements, for example, may have as many as five unpaired spins. Such materials all show paramagnetism.

The development of the susceptibility due to this form of magnetization is due to Langevin. A magnetic field H and a magnet with a dipole moment m have an interaction energy which is a minimum when the two are parallel. The potential energy is given as $V = -mH\cos\theta$ where θ is the angle between

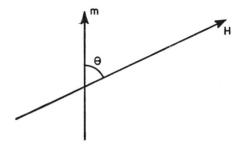

FIG. 1. Relation between magnetic moment m and field H.

m and H (see Figure 1). If we are considering spinning electrons in a solid which are being oriented by the interaction force but disoriented by thermal vibrations, we can derive a value for the mean value of $\cos\theta$. This gives a measure of how completely the electron spins have responded to the applied field. From statistical mechanics, this is given as:

$$\overline{\cos\theta} = \coth a - \frac{1}{a}$$

where

$$a = mH/kT$$

and

$k =$ Boltzmann's constant
$T =$ absolute temperature.

This is a simple function which has the shape shown in the sketch (Figure 2). The curve is linear for small values of a, that is, for small fields or high temperatures. Then at

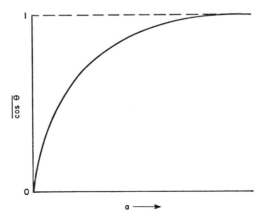

FIG. 2. Langevin function.

higher fields, the value of $\overline{\cos \theta}$ approaches one as all the electron spins become aligned parallel to the field. For such a distribution of electrons the overall magnetization is $M = Nm\,\overline{\cos \theta}$ where N is the number of unpaired electron spins/unit volume. For small values of a, it can be shown that

$$\overline{\cos \theta} \approx \frac{a}{3} = \frac{mH}{3kT}.$$

In this case,

$$M = \frac{Nm^2H}{3kT}.$$

The susceptibility

$$K = \frac{M}{H} = \frac{Nm^2}{3kT} = \frac{C}{T}$$

where C is a numerical constant. The paramagnetic susceptibility, then, is just inversely proportional to temperature unless the field is large enough to cause saturation. The value C is referred to as Curie's constant, since P. Curie first worked out this law. The paramagnetic susceptibility is a measure of the response of spinning electrons to an external magnetic field. It is a temperature dependent quantity decreasing in value as the temperature increases. At low temperatures or high field strengths, the susceptibility becomes independent of temperature. This is the situation when all electrons are lined up parallel to the field.

Many minerals are paramagnetic and, in fact, are sufficiently paramagnetic that they can be separated in high magnetic fields such as exist in a typical magnetic separator. Recently, a series of such minerals have been studied by the Japanese workers. For example, the properties of olivine can be shown to be entirely dependent on the presence of iron ions. Olivine forms a solid solution series between forsterite (Mg_2SiO_4) and fayalite (Fe_2SiO_4). The measured susceptibilities are given in the accompanying graph (Figure 3) after Nagata, Yukutake, and Uyeda. The straight line relationship shows that the iron ion, being the only ion present with an unbalanced spin, controls the magnetic proper-

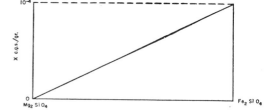

Fig. 3. Magnetic susceptibility of the Olivine solid-solution series (after Nagata, Yukutake, and Uyeda).

ties. Iron is a transition element and, in fact, each atom has approximately five unpaired electrons to contribute to paramagnetism.

Other minerals such as the pyroxenes, biotites, amphiboles, garnets, and cordierites have been similarly studied (see Nagata). These minerals all show paramagnetism contributed by only three ions of natural significance (Fe^{3+}, Fe^{2+}, Mn^{2+}). By determining the number of these ions present, the paramagnetic susceptibility can be accurately calculated.

The unit of magnetic moment used to describe the magnetic properties of electron spins is called the Bohr magneton number (μ_B). This is the magnetic moment of a single spin.

$$\mu_B = \frac{eh}{4\pi m_e c} = 0.927 \times 10^{-20} \text{ erg/gauss.}$$

The description of the magnetic properties of individual ions is often given in terms of the Bohr magneton equivalents or the equivalent number of unpaired spins. For the ions of geologic importance, the magnetic moments are:

$$Mn^{2+} \quad \text{and} \quad Fe^{3+} - 5.59\mu_B$$
$$Fe^{2+} - 5.4\mu_B.$$

These values can be applied directly to the chemical formula of a paramagnetic substance to derive the susceptibility of the substance.

Ferromagnetism

Of more practical importance in studying magnetic data in geology are the ferromagnetic properties of minerals. In discussing orbital and spin effects, we have tacitly ignored the possibility that some of these "magnets" can interact with each other. It is found, however, that as atoms are brought together to form a crystalline solid, there is an energy referred to as the exchange energy, which must be kept to a minimum. In most substances, this exchange energy is kept to a minimum when the atoms are positioned in such a way that electron spins in adjacent atoms are oriented in opposition. In the case of some substances involving the transition elements, however, the parallel configuration of spins is to be preferred and such materials, as a result, are highly magnetic. The classical description of the exchange energy is to consider that acting within the solid there is a strong magnetic field often referred to as the Weiss field. This apparent field is well accounted for in modern quantum-mechanical discussions from a consideration of interfering wave functions. The effect of this apparent field is to line up all the electronic magnets in adjacent atoms in a parallel direction. This means that the substance is highly magnetic, and it is referred to as ferromagnetic.

If we call this field H_E, the energy existing between the electronic magnet and the field is $\mu_B \times H_E$. This energy is the ordering energy while thermal vibrations tend to disorder these electrons. At high temperatures, the thermal disordering energy becomes greater than the ordering energy. This defines a temperature known as the Curie temperature

$$\mu_B H_E = kT_c$$

where

$k =$ Boltzmann's constant 1.38×10^{-16} erg/°K

T_C is the Curie temperature in °K.

At high temperatures, such substances are merely paramagnetic, while at lower tem-

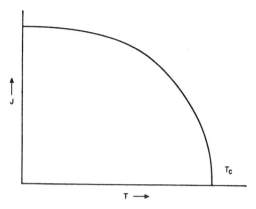

FIG. 4. Temperature dependence of ferromagnetism.

peratures, as the ordering effect becomes greater than the disordering effect, the substance becomes highly magnetic and is ferromagnetic.

When a material is above its Curie temperature it is paramagnetic, but as it cools through the Curie temperature it acquires a spontaneous magnetization as shown in Figure 4. This magnetization represents a maximum possible where all the electron spins are lined up parallel to each other.

If the substance is comprised of a large number of atoms, it is found that the sample does not have the maximum possible magnetization, but rather has some lesser value. In order to explain this phenomenon, the concept of domains has been introduced. It takes a considerable amount of energy to create and maintain a permanent magnet. This magnetostatic energy attempts to maintain itself at a minimum. By putting zones of oppositely directed magnetization adjacent to each other as in Figure 5, the magnetostatic energy required to maintain the magnet is much reduced. Two forces are then competing—the internal field tending to line up all the magnets and the magnetostatic energy tending to make adjacent zones of

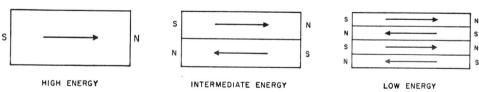

FIG. 5. Typical domain patterns.

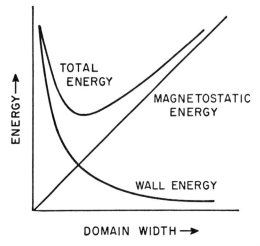

FIG. 6. Relation between wall energy and magnetostatic energy (after Nagata).

reversed magnetization. The sum of these two forms of energy gives rise to a minimum corresponding to a particular size (see Figure 6). This effect then determines the size of domains. In magnetite, this optimum size is in the order of a few microns. The study of ferromagnetism is closely linked to a study of the domains within the solid.

One way of presenting this information is to present the hysteresis loop where the magnetic induction (B) of the sample is plotted against the magnetic field (H) as in Figure 7.

In a sample which is unmagnetized, we find that increasing the field increases the magnetization. As long as the field is kept small, the magnetization is proportional to the field, and we are dealing with the reversible permeability. The slope of the curve is $B/H = \mu = 1 + 4\pi K$. In this part of the hysteresis loop, magnetization takes place by motion of domain walls.

As the field increases, the magnetization starts to saturate and eventually becomes independent of the field. The domain walls move irreversibly across impurities and finally the actual magnetization in the domain rotates. At this stage, the sample has a saturation magnetization (J_s). As the field is decreased, it is seen that the magnetization is not reversible. At zero field there is still a magnetization left, called the remanent magnetization (J_r). It takes a negative field, the coercive force (H_c), to reduce the net magnetization to zero.

The hysteresis loop of magnetic materials contains much of the essential information on the magnetic properties. The permeability, for example, is merely the slope of the hysteresis loop. Since in earth materials the field of usual interest is the earth's field, it is essential that the measurement of the susceptibility of rocks be made in fields with about the same strength as that of the earth's. Larger fields lead to lower susceptibility values as the material starts to saturate. It is also of interest to observe that the susceptibility is dependent on the remanent magnetization. If the material has a high remanent magnetization, the susceptibility in general decreases, as in Figure 8a. A few exceptions to this are known, as in Figure 8b. In natural materials this is probably occasioned by mixtures of minerals.

Antiferromagnetism

Some substances which contain magnetic ions are not magnetic. This occurs in materials in which every oriented spin has an antiparallel spin in a nearby atom so that the net result is zero. Such a substance is familiar

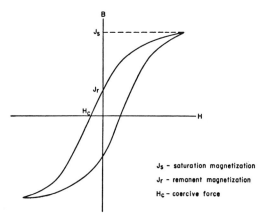

J_s – saturation magnetization
J_r – remanent magnetization
H_c – coercive force

FIG. 7. Typical hysteresis curve.

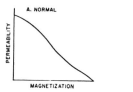
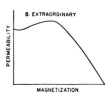

FIG. 8. Relation between total magnetization and permeability.

to us as hematite. Antiferromagnetic substances have a critical temperature below which the negative exchange interaction is dominant. When this exchange interaction is operating, the magnetic spins are rigidly held in opposition, while above this temperature normal paramagnetic behavior is found. This critical temperature is often referred to as the Neel temperature. In Figure 9 we see the temperature variation of the magnetization of hematite.

Ferrimagnetism

The magnetic properties of the natural oxides are due to electrons which have parallel and antiparallel spins but in unequal numbers. For example, the Fe ion has a Bohr magneton number of about five so that Fe_3O_4 should have a magnetic property corresponding to about 15 Bohr magnetons per molecule. When the magnetization is measured, however, it is found that a molecule of magnetite has only four Bohr magnetons per molecule. This observation can be approximately explained if we consider that some of the adjacent electron spins are lined up antiparallel to each other. Magnetite has an inverse spinel structure in which the eight divalent metal ions in the unit cell are in octahedral positions and the sixteen trivalent metal ions are equally divided between octahedral and tetrahedral sites. The trivalent ions are lined up in opposition so that every trivalent ion which is oriented in one direction has a matching ion oriented in the opposite direction and the effects cancel. The only ions left to contribute to the magnetic properties are the divalent ions in the magnetite structure. When spins are lined up in opposi-

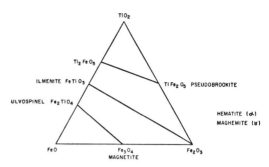

FIG. 10. Composition diagram of natural magnetic minerals.

tion in this way, leaving a net magnetization, the substance is referred to as ferrimagnetic. The natural magnetic oxides of the magnetite-ulvospinel series are all ferrimagnetic. The magnetic properties of ferrimagnetic substances are very similar to those of ferromagnetic substances. In general, ferrites are poorly conducting so that they have important technical applications.

The study of the magnetic properties of rocks and minerals is usually concentrated on the susceptibility and on the natural remanent magnetization. There are various ways in which rocks may acquire a permanent magnetization in nature. These are discussed by Cox and Doell in this chapter.

Magnetic Properties of Minerals

The magnetic minerals of importance are few in number. Those most commonly encountered are the iron and titanium oxides. It is useful to present information concerning these minerals on a composition diagram with FeO, Fe_2O_3, and TiO_2 at the three corners as in Figure 10.

The most common of the minerals are members of the following solid solution series: Magnetite-ulvospinel; hematite-ilmenite and magnetite-maghemite. Very good descriptions of the properties of these minerals have been given recently by Nagata (1961) and by Nicholls (1955). A brief description will be presented here.

Magnetite-ulvospinel

Magnetite and ulvospinel represent the end members of the most commonly occurring magnetic minerals. Magnetite has a

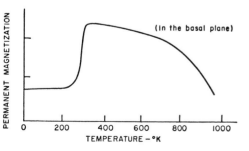

FIG. 9. Magnetization of hematite as a function of temperature (after Nagata).

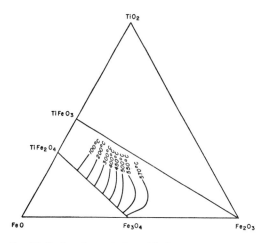

FIG. 11. Curie point variation with chemical composition for titaniferous magnetites (after Nagata).

Curie temperature of 585°C and a saturation magnetization of about 92 emu/gm. The susceptibility of natural magnetites varies considerably depending upon the impurities and imperfections which block the motion of domain walls tending to decrease the susceptibility. Magnetite has a susceptibility in the vicinity of 1.0 with variations from 0.40 to 2.79 (see Werner, 1945). Ulvospinel, although common in natural mineral assemblages, is not often recognized as an independent mineral. It is apparently found as a fine-grained intergrowth. The Curie temperature of ulvospinel is 120°K, well below

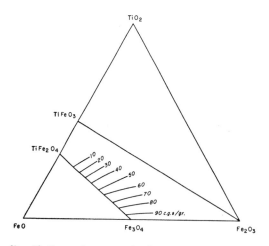

FIG. 12. Saturation magnetization variation with chemical composition for titaniferous magnetites (after Nagata).

normal earth temperatures, so that it does not commonly contribute to the magnetic properties of rocks. However, it forms a complete solid solution series with magnetite, intermediate members having a Curie temperature between that of magnetite and ulvospinel. The composition of this mineral is such that only the trivalent iron ions are present. These ions are the ones that oppose each other in the ferrimagnetic structure of magnetite so that ulvospinel is only very weakly magnetic. The saturation magnetization of solid solutions with compositions between that of magnetite and that of ulvospinel is intermediate between 0 and 92 emu/gm. The properties of saturation magnetization and Curie temperature and their variation with composition are shown in contoured form in the accompanying figures.

Ilmenite-hematite

There is a second series of magnetic minerals which is very important in nature. The end members of this series are only very weakly magnetic. These are antiferromagnetic minerals so that above the Neel temperature (55°K for ilmenite and 953°K for hematite) these substances are paramagnetic. Hematite is, in fact, weakly ferromagnetic in a manner referred to as parasitic ferromagnetism. It is not clear what causes this feeble ferromagnetism with a Curie temperature of 670°C. This ferromagnetism may be a property of antiferromagnetism or it may be due to the presence of impurities or imperfections in the lattice. In any event, hematite has a highly stable permanent magnetization with a coercive force in the order of 7,600 oersteds. The susceptibility is only 20×10^{-6} cgs/gm.

Ilmenite is also antiferromagnetic. It is found, however, that some members of the solid solution series with compositions between ilmenite and hematite may be strongly ferromagnetic. These minerals are occasionally found in nature and must contribute to magnetic anomalies. It is commonly found that samples with reversed magnetizations are in this composition range. For example, the negative anomalies encountered at Allard Lake (Hammond, 1952) are probably due to compositions in the ilmenite-hematite series with a self-reversed magnetization.

Magnetite-maghemite

The composition Fe_2O_3 has two minerals associated with it. The more stable form at high temperatures is hematite or the α form of Fe_2O_3. This hematite has a rhombohedral structure. Below 275°C there is another form of Fe_2O_3 (γ) which is commonly encountered in nature. This has the same inverse spinel structure as magnetite except that there is a lattice vacancy accounting for the change in composition. All compositions between maghemite and magnetite are possible. The Curie temperature of maghemite is probably in the vicinity of 675°C, although its instability at high temperatures makes this almost impossible to determine. The substance is highly magnetic with a saturation magnetization of 83.5 emu/gm.

Pyrrhotite

The sulphide mineral pyrrhotite is quite common in nature and, like magnetite, it is highly magnetic. The pyrrhotite structure is very similar to the hexagonal troilite (FeS), but it has a consistent iron vacancy present so that its composition is written FeS_{1+x} where x may range between 0 and 1/7. The magnetic properties are determined by the x value. For $0 < x < 0.1$, pyrrhotite is antiferromagnetic and for x values greater than 0.1, it is a ferrimagnetic substance with the properties found in ferromagnetic substances. The Curie temperature is usually quoted as between 300° and 325°C and the saturation magnetization is in the order of 62 cgs units. These properties are, however, both dependent on the exact composition of the pyrrhotite, as shown in the accompanying diagram from Nagata (Figure 13). Thus, the $FeS_{1.12}$ shows a susceptibility temperature curve typical of ferromagnets while lower iron deficiencies show intermediate properties with a peak at around 200°C corresponding to a structural transition in pyrrhotite.

Acknowledgments

The author would like to express his appreciation to Kennecott Copper Corporation for assistance in preparation of the manuscript. Maruzen Press, Ltd. of Tokyo and the editors of the *Journal of Geomagnetism and Geoelectricity* of Kyoto kindly permitted the reproduction of several figures.

References

Bozorth, R., 1951, Ferromagnetism: New York, Van Nostrand.

Dekker, A., 1957, Solid state physics: New York, Prentice-Hall.

Hammond, P., 1952, Allard Lake ilmenite deposits: Economic Geology, p. 47.

Kittel, C., 1956, Introduction to solid state physics: New York, John Wiley and Sons.

Nagata, T., 1961, Rock magnetism: Tokyo, Maruzen.

Neel, L., 1955, Some theoretical aspects of rock magnetism: Advances in physics, v. 4, no. 14.

Nicholls, G., 1955, The mineralogy of rock magnetism: Advances in physics, v. 4, no. 14.

Smit, J., and Wijn, H. P. J., 1959, Ferrites: New York, John Wiley and Sons.

Werner, S., 1945, Determinations of the magnetic susceptibility of ores and rocks from Swedish iron ore deposits: Swedish Geological Survey, no. 5, v. 39.

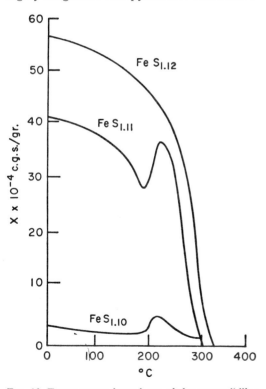

FIG. 13. Temperature dependence of the susceptibility of pyrrhotite (after Nagata).

MAGNETIZATION OF ROCKS†

RICHARD DOELL* AND ALLAN COX*

The magnetization of rocks is made up of an *induced* part, dependent on the ambient magnetic field, and a *remanent* part that is a function of the history of the rock. Induced magnetization is parallel to the ambient magnetic field and its strength is proportional to that of the field and a single constant, the *susceptibility*. Remanent magnetization is a property of magnetic hysteresis and may be acquired under several different processes, separately or in combination. The most important physical property, as regards remanent magnetization, is that of magnetic *coercivity*—expressed as the strength of a magnetic field required to change a remanent magnetization. Because rocks possess a spectrum of coercivities they often contain both "hard" and "soft" remanent magnetizations; moreover, the relative importance of the different magnetizations, including the induced magnetization, varies greatly from rock to rock.

General Statement

The magnetization observed in a rock is determined by two factors, the magnetic field applied to the rock up to the time of observation of the magnetization, and the occurrence of one or more of the several processes by which materials become magnetized. Different magnetizing processes may operate on the rock at different times during its history; the earth's magnetic field may change from time to time, and the magnetization acquired may not in all cases be parallel to the applied field. It is not surprising, therefore, that magnetization is one of the most complex properties that the geologist can study in rocks. Moreover, geologic interpretations of magnetic measurements are critically dependent on the availability of techniques for distinguishing the various magnetic components.

The first two components of magnetization to be distinguished are *remanent* magnetization and *induced* magnetization. Whereas induced magnetization requires the presence of an applied field, remanent magnetization does not. In fields as weak as the earth's, induced magnetization is proportional to the field; the constant of proportionality is called the *susceptibility*. Magnetic-anomaly maps of the earth's field are usually interpreted by assuming that the magnetization in the rocks producing the anomalies is induced magnetization and parallel to the earth's field. However, remanent magnetizations are often not parallel to the earth's field and may be stronger than the induced magnetization. (*See* Nagata, 1953a, p. 128–129, for some typical values.) Therefore, the assumption of a predominance of induced magnetization should be tested by sampling wherever possible.

Each grain of magnetic material in a rock consists of one or more magnetic domains, and although the directions of magnetization are different in different domains, the intensity of magnetization per unit volume, termed the spontaneous magnetization J_S, is the same in all domains of the same mineral. Quantity J_S decreases with increase in temperature and vanishes at the Curie temperature. Sufficiently small grains consist of single domains, and in the absence of an external magnetic field the direction of magnetization in each domain will lie along one of several preferred axes. The directions of these preferred axes and the heights of the magnetic energy barriers that separate them are determined by the shape of the grain, the crystalline anisotropy of the mineral, or both. In an applied magnetic field of increasing intensity the direction of magnetization in the grain is pulled away from the preferred axis toward the field direction. If the energy supplied by the applied field is not greater

† From "Review of Paleomagnetism": G.S.A. Bull., v. 71, p. 645–768. Reprinted by permission of the Geological Society of America.

* U. S. Geological Survey, Menlo Park, California.

than the magnetic energy barriers, the direction of magnetization will return to its former position when the field is removed. This magnetization, which is reversible and depends on the applied field, is by definition an induced magnetization.[1]

When the applied field is increased above a critical value termed the *coercive force*, the direction of magnetization in a single-domain grain crosses over a magnetic energy barrier, and when the field is removed the magnetic vector comes to rest along a new direction. In this case the irreversible change in magnetization is a *remanent* or permanent magnetization. Larger grains contain many domains, and, in an increasing magnetic field, domains with magnetizations nearly parallel to the applied field grow at the expense of others. Magnetic energy barriers again prevent an unlimited reversible growth of domains, and the coercive forces of multidomain grains correspond to the magnetic fields necessary to overcome these energy barriers.

A single rock sample may contain several magnetic minerals with a wide range of grain sizes and a wide coercive force spectrum (Graham, 1953, p. 249). The intensity of natural remanent magnetizations is commonly several orders of magnitude less than the maximum intensity that could be developed if the rock were placed in a magnetic field much larger than any of the coercive forces of the different magnetic constituents. This indicates that only a small fraction of the domains in a naturally magnetized rock has a preferred direction of magnetization causing the observed remanent magnetization; the majority has random directions. Whether the domains with preferred orientations occur in constituents with high or low coercive forces depends on the process by which the remanent magnetization was acquired. The natural remanent magnetization acquired by some process is very "hard" and similar to the remanent magnetization of a good permanent magnet, whereas that acquired by other processes is "soft," corresponding quite closely with the magnetization of soft iron. Because rocks are not homogeneous materials and because many of them have been subjected to several magnetizing processes, both types may be found in the same rock. (*See* Graham, 1953, p. 249–252; Clegg and others 1954a, p. 593.) During the past several decades considerable progress has been made in understanding some of the processes by which natural remanent magnetization is acquired by rocks, and in developing techniques for analyzing the observed magnetizations into components corresponding to the various processes.

In the following paragraphs consideration will be given to the principal processes causing natural remanent magnetization in rocks. Processes leading to remanent magnetizations parallel to the applied field will be discussed first. Then factors leading to remanent magnetizations which are not parallel to the applied field will be considered.

Isothermal Remanent Magnetization

A rock placed in a magnetic field at room temperature and subsequently removed will acquire a remanent magnetization, provided the field is larger than the lowest coercive force of the magnetic minerals in the rock. The process is simply one in which domains having magnetic energy barriers with corresponding coercive forces less than the applied field align their magnetic moments with the field. When the field is removed, the energy barriers prevent these domains from returning to their former positions, and a net magnetization results. Since minerals in rocks usually have coercive forces of the order of 100 oersted or more, the earth's field of about 0.5 oersted is, in general, not strong enough to produce isothermal remanent magnetization (IRM). On the other hand, the large magnetic fields associated with lightning bolts may impart a substantial IRM to rocks (Cox, 1959). The IRM may easily be removed, or changed in direction, by any field as large as that which produced it.

Viscous Magnetization

If a rock remains in a field too weak to cause IRM for a sufficiently long period of

---

[1] The term *induced magnetization* is used, as defined here, in geophysical prospecting applications and should not be confused with *induction*, B, of the usual hysteresis curve.

time, it is often possible to measure a new component of remanent magnetization in the direction of the field (*e.g.*, Rimbert, 1956b, p. 2536; Brynjólfsson, 1957, p. 250–251). Such a magnetization, requiring a relatively long time to form, is termed viscous magnetization. In rocks, as in other materials, it is due to the Boltzmann distribution of thermal energy which, when converted to magnetic energy, allows the magnetic domains to cross energy barriers that they otherwise could not cross in the weak field of the earth. Although the thermal-energy distribution has a random nature, the weak field of the earth provides a slight bias sufficient to cause a net change of magnetization in the direction of the field. The theory of viscous magnetization is similar to that of thermo-remanent magnetization.

Thermo-Remanent Magnetization

Of much more importance for paleomagnetic studies is the process of thermo-remanent magnetization. As a rock cools in the earth's magnetic field it begins to develop spontaneous magnetization at the Curie temperature T_C and a preferential alignment of domains parallel to the field. The resulting magnetization is thermo-remanent magnetization (TRM). It is important to note that not all of the TRM is acquired at the Curie temperature, but rather over a temperature interval extending some tens of degrees below T_C. If, during a cooling experiment, a weak magnetic field is applied only in the temperature interval T_1 to T_2 ($T_2 < T_C$), with zero magnetic field at all other temperatures, a magnetization known as the partial thermo-remanent magnetization (PTRM) is developed. An example of the PTRM acquired in equal temperature intervals on cooling from the Curie temperature is shown in Figure 1a, where the values are plotted as a function of the mean temperature of the interval. Experimentally, it is found that for lavas and baked sediments the PTRM acquired in a weak field over any temperature interval T_1 to T_2 is independent of the magnetization acquired in adjacent temperature intervals (Thellier, 1951, p. 213; Nagata, 1953a, p. 142–153); Thellier reports that the

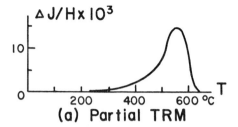

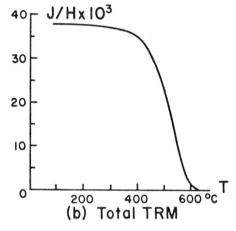

FIG. 1. Acquisition of thermo-remanent magnetization in weak magnetic fields. (a) Partial thermo-remanent magnetization (PTRM) acquired in field H over equal temperature intervals as a function of mean temperature of intervals; (b) Thermo-remanent magnetization (TRM) acquired on cooling from Curie temperature to any temperature T in field H and from T ambient temperature in 0 field (for weak field the quantity J/H is approximately constant).

rock preserves an exact memory of the temperature and field which produced the PTRM (quoted in Néel, 1955, p. 212). If the rock is heated to temperatures up to T_1 no effect on the PTRM acquired between T_1 and T_2 is observed, whereas it is completely destroyed at temperatures above T_2. The total TRM acquired in a given field is very close to the sum of the PTRM's acquired in the same field between the Curie temperature and room temperature. (*Compare* Figures 1a and b.)

The theory of TRM for single-domain particles (Néel, 1955, p. 209–212) explains many of these characteristics. In Néel's model (which will be followed here) each grain has two directions in which the magnetic vector can lie with minimum magnetic energy in the absence of a magnetic field; these directions are 180° apart and are separated by a magnetic barrier of energy

$$E = vH_CJ_S/2 \qquad (1)$$

where v is the volume of the grain, H_C the coercive force, and J_S the spontaneous magnetization of the mineral. When E is greater than the thermal energy (kT), where k is Boltzmann's constant and T the temperature, the thermal fluctuations are not able to move the direction of magnetization across the energy barrier. However, for sufficiently small values of v or sufficiently high values of T, the thermal fluctuations can cause the magnetic moment to move across the barrier. Thus, a total remanent magnetization of initial amount J_0 due to the preferential alignment of a large number of identical single domain grains will, after time t, have decayed to the value J_R given by

$$J_R = J_0 \exp(-t/\tau_0) \qquad (2)$$

where τ_0 is termed the *relaxation time*. As in other decay processes, one may speak of the "half-life" of thermo-remanent magnetization which has the value $0.693 \tau_0$. Quantity τ_0 is given by the equation

$$\begin{aligned} 1/\tau_0 &= A(v/T)^{1/2} \exp(-vH_CJ_S/2kT) \\ &= A(v/T)^{1/2} \exp(-\gamma v/T). \end{aligned} \qquad (3)$$

Quantities A and γ depend on the elastic and magnetic properties of the minerals, and the other quantities are as defined for equation (1).

An important feature of this model for TRM is that a small change in the quantity (v/T) can cause a very large change in τ_0. For example, the physical constants necessary to evaluate A and γ are known for iron (Néel, 1955, p. 211); and values for the quantity (v/T) of 3.2×10^{-21}, 7.0×10^{-21}, and 9.6×10^{-21} correspond respectively to values of 10^{-1} sec, 10^9 sec $(3.4 \times 10^2$ years), and 3.4×10^9 years for τ_0. At room temperature the grain diameters corresponding to these values of (v/T) are roughly 120 Å, 160 Å, and 180 Å. Thus, the direction of magnetization in a grain with a diameter less than 120 Å is easily and quickly changed by the thermal

fluctuations, and the application of a weak field h to a number of such grains causes a net magnetization in the direction of the field. This "equilibrium" "magnetization is given (Néel, 1955, p. 211) by the equation

$$J_E = NvJ_S \tanh(vhJ_S/kT) \qquad (4)$$

where N is the number of grains with volume v.

Because of the strong dependence of τ_0 on (v/T) in equation (3), there is a *critical blocking diameter* for a given mineral, dependent only on the temperature; grains with smaller diameters come to equilibrium very quickly with the magnetization indicated in equation (4), while those with substantially larger diameters maintain their original magnetizations over long intervals of time, regardless of the external field. Similarly, there is a *critical blocking temperature* for all grains of the same diameter.

The acquisition of TRM by single-domain grains is very simple in terms of this model. As a rock cools from its Curie temperature, a given grain assumes the equilibrium magnetization, J_E, until the temperature passes through the critical blocking temperature of the grain. As the temperature goes below this critical value, τ_0 for the grain increases rapidly, and the magnetization becomes "frozen" at the equilibrium level. The independence of partial thermo-remanent magnetizations acquired in different temperature ranges is thus explained as due to the magnetization residing in grains of different diameter. This simple theory explains many of the characteristics of TRM such as its great stability to disturbing fields and its remarkably slow decay.

The acquisition of TRM by most rocks is certainly more complex than indicated here, since many rocks contain magnetic minerals differing in physical properties as well as in grain size. Moreover, rocks containing multidomain grains, and even massive ferromagnetic mineral specimens, also acquire TRM which, commonly, has the characteristics described above. Verhoogen (1959) suggests that the TRM of these materials may reside in small, highly stressed regions within the ferromagnetic crystals.

The Curie temperatures of magnetic materials in igneous rocks lie below 700°C and, in many rocks, below 600°C. The major portion of the natural remanent magnetization measured in many igneous rocks appears to be TRM. (For more complete discussions of TRM *see* Nagata, 1953a, p. 123–192; Néel, 1955, p. 208–218, 225–241; Verhoogen, 1959.)

Depositional Magnetization

As demonstrated in artificially deposited sediments, previously magnetized magnetic particles attain a preferential alignment during deposition and maintain this alignment after consolidation, giving the sediment a remanent magnetization (Nagata and others, 1943, p. 277–279; Johnson and others, 1948, p. 357–360; King, 1955, p. 120). The stability of such a magnetization depends upon the process by which the grains originally acquired their magnetization. (Processes that cause depositional magnetization to have a direction other than that of the applied field will be discussed later.)

Crystallization or Chemical Magnetization

Although the magnetization of some sediments is undoubtedly acquired by the depositional process, studies by Martinez and Howell (1956, p. 205) and by Doell (1956, p. 166) indicate that the magnetization of sediments may also be associated with chemical changes taking place after consolidation. Moreover, Haigh (1958, p. 284–285) and Kobayashi (1959, p. 115–116) have shown in the laboratory that a remanent magnetization is acquired by magnetic materials undergoing a chemical change (*e.g.*, reduction of hematite to magnetite) at constant temperature in a weak magnetic field. These authors also show that the stability of this magnetization, under the effects of higher temperature and demagnetizing fields, is very similar to that for TRM, although the intensity is not so great.

Haigh (1958, p. 278–281) points out 'the theoretical similarity of the processes causing chemical magnetization and TRM of small grains. As the grains of magnetic material grow chemically, the value of the critical quantity (v/T) in the equations for TRM increases because of an increase in v rather than a decrease in T. As the grain grows through the critical blocking diameter appropriate to the temperature at which the chemical reaction occurs, the equilibrium magnetization J_E (equation 4) is, as in the case for TRM, effectively frozen in. Theoretically, the stability properties of crystallization magnetization and TRM should be similar, and laboratory experiments indicate that this is true.

Self-Reversed Magnetization

The most striking example of a magnetization acquired in a direction other than that of the field acting during the acquisition of the magnetization is that of self-reversal. In many paleomagnetic studies directions of magnetization fall into two distinct groups nearly or exactly opposed to each other. Two interpretations of this phenomenon have been proposed: that the earth's magnetic field may periodically reverse itself, or, alternatively, that some rocks may become magnetized in a direction opposite to that of the field acting on them by a process called self-reversed magnetization.

Several mechanisms may theoretically give rise to self-reversed magnetization. The first to be considered requires two magnetic constituents A and B in the rock. Constituent A has a higher Curie temperature than B and acquires a TRM parallel to the applied field. As the rock cools through the Curie temperature of constituent B, the TRM of constituent A acts by one of several interaction mechanisms to order the magnetization of B in a direction exactly opposite to that of A and, hence, reversed with respect to the original applied field. A self-reversal occurs if, after cooling, the total magnetization of B exceeds that of A (Néel, 1951, p. 92), or if constituent A is later selectively removed chemically (Graham, 1953, p. 252–255).

The simplest type of interaction is magnetostatic (Néel, 1951, p. 100; Uyeda, 1958, p. 50–56), in which the field in the region of constituent B at the time the temperature passes through its Curie point is controlled by the magnetization of A, and is reversed with respect to the applied field. The relationship is shown schematically in Figure 2. For this type of interaction to lead to a self-reversal, very stringent requirements are placed on the geometrical arrangement of the two constituents and on the ratio of the applied field to the spontaneous magnetization of constituent A when B becomes magnetized. In rock-forming minerals this mechanism could occur only in very weak applied fields; it is possible, but rather improbable, in fields as strong as the earth's, and no example has been found in nature (Uyeda, 1958, p. 52).

A second type of interaction between the two constituents is an exchange interaction across their common boundary. If good registry exists between the crystal lattices of the two constituents, the spontaneous magnetizations on one side of the boundary will tend to become aligned either parallel or antiparal-

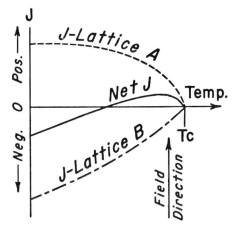

Fig. 3. Self reversal by $J_S - T$ differences in two antiparallel sublattices. On cooling, sublattice A is initially dominant and is aligned with applied field. Sublattice B is locked antiparallel to A and is dominant at low temperatures.

lel to the spontaneous magnetization on the other side. The Weiss-Heisenberg exchange interaction between spinning electrons, which is also responsible for spontaneous magnetization, provides the coupling, which may be very strong. Uyeda (1958, p. 104) finds that members of the ilmenite-hematite series $xFeTiO_3 \cdot (1-x)$ Fe_2O_3, with $.45 < x < .6$, become self-reversed, even when the applied field is as high as 17,000 oersted. This type of interaction appears to be responsible for the reversed magnetization of the Haruna dacite (Uyeda, 1958, p. 120), which is one of the two or three rocks reported to be reproducibly self-reversing.

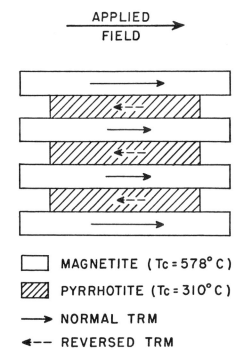

APPLIED FIELD

☐ MAGNETITE (Tc = 578° C)

▨ PYRRHOTITE (Tc = 310° C)

⟶ NORMAL TRM

◀-- REVERSED TRM

Fig. 2. Reversal in pyrrhotite caused by magnetostatic interaction between two different constituents. On cooling, magnetite with higher Curie temperature becomes magnetized first. Further cooling results in magnetization of pyrrhotite in "reversed" field between magnetite layers. Net TRM is "normal." (After experiment by Uyeda, 1958.)

The spontaneous magnetization of some minerals, for example magnetite, is actually made up of two superimposed opposing spontaneous magnetizations, each associated with a separate sublattice in the magnetic mineral. If these two spontaneous magnetizations have different temperature coefficients, the total net spontaneous magnetization may change sign with temperature, as shown in Figure 3. This type of self-reversal mechanism has been demonstrated by Gorter and Schulkes (1953, p. 488) in certain synthetic materials but has not been found in rocks.

A mineral may also undergo self-reversal when cations migrate from disordered to ordered distributions on cooling (Néel, 1955, p. 204; Verhoogen, 1956, p. 208). Moreover, when cooled quickly, cations may be frozen in a disordered state corresponding to a high-temperature equilibrium. Over very long periods of time the cations will then slowly migrate to the equilibrium-ordered positions, and the process may be accompanied by a self-reversal of the TRM. Verhoogen (1956, p. 208) shows that this mechanism is possible for natural magnetites containing impurities; he estimates that the ordering process would require at least 10^5 to 10^6 years. Such a self-reversal mechanism would therefore not be reproducible in the laboratory.

This brief and incomplete review of a rather large field of research serves to emphasize several important points about reversely magnetized rocks. The reversed magnetization of some rocks is now known to be due to a self-reversal mechanism. Moreover, many theoretical self-reversal mechanisms have been proposed, and additional mechanisms will doubtless be suggested in the future. However, in order definitely to reject the field-reversal hypothesis it is necessary to show that *all* reversely magnetized rocks are due to self-reversal. This would be a very difficult task since some of the self-reversal mechanisms are difficult to detect and are not reproducible in the laboratory. A further discussion of this problem will be postponed until some of the relevant paleomagnetic data have been considered.

Other Processes Affecting Remanent Magnetization

King (1955, p. 120), in his experiments on artificially deposited varved silts, found that the inclination measured in the samples ranged some 20 to 30 degrees less than the inclination of the field acting, although the declination was faithfully reproduced. This "inclination error" decreased as the field inclination approached the vertical or horizontal. Like most sedimentary minerals, magnetic mineral grains are rarely uniformly equidimensional; moreover, the common magnetic minerals tend to have directions of magnetization parallel to their longest dimension. The "inclination error" arises dur-

ing the depositional process since the grains will tend to lie with their longest dimension, and hence magnetic direction, parallel to the horizontal bedding plane and not exactly along the applied field direction. King has also demonstrated that an error in the direction of magnetization can occur due to rolling of grains as they settle on the bottom, caused either by deposition on sloping surfaces or by currents.

The magnetic properties of minerals resemble other physical properties in that they are not, in general, completely isotropic; in particular, individual mineral grains usually cannot be magnetized with equal ease in all directions. In all minerals there exist easy and hard directions of magnetization systematically oriented with respect to the crystal lattice, a property called *magneto-crystalline anisotropy*. A single crystal of magnetite, for example, is magnetized more easily along the [111] axes than along the [100] axes, and a crystal of hematite much more easily in the *c* plane than along the *c* axis. A second factor causing anisotropy is the shape of the individual grain. An aggregate of randomly oriented magnetite crystals should have no crystalline anisotropy, but a single grain of the aggregate will be more easily magnetized parallel to its longest dimension. In any of the magnetization processes considered above, except depositional magnetization, in which the grains are already magnetized, the magnetization direction of a single crystal or of an elongated grain will lie between a direction of easy magnetization and the direction of the applied field. However, when preferred-crystal directions or longest-grain dimensions are randomly oriented within a rock sample, the net magnetization direction will be that of the applied field.

Deformation of rocks with a remanent magnetization may also cause a change in the magnetization due to a mechanical rotation of the magnetic particles. A vertical compaction in sediments might, for example, be expected to reduce the inclination of the magnetization vector (Clegg and others, 1954a, p. 596). Graham (1949, p. 156–158) has considered the effects of plastic deformation on remanent magnetization in the limbs of a fold. However, this phenomenon has rarely been cited as a cause of scattered directions of magnetization, probably because highly deformed beds are usually not chosen for paleomagnetic investigations.

Magnetostriction—the effect of stress on magnetization—is another phenomenon which may be important in the magnetization of rocks. In the investigation by Graham and others (1957, p. 471–472) axial compressive stresses of slightly more than 2,500 psi changed the magnetization in the rocks studied (mostly gneisses and iron ores) by as much as 25 percent; moreover, the magnetization of some of the samples did not return to the original state after the stress was removed. Many rocks are subjected to large stresses during their histories—the stresses developed during the cooling of basalt, for example, are sufficient to fracture the rock— and the research described above strongly suggested that magnetostrictive effects might, in general, cause the recorded remanent magnetizations of rocks to be in directions that are not those of the fields acting when remanent magnetization was originally acquired. Stott and Stacey (1959, p. 385) investigated this possibility for TRM by cooling several types of igneous rocks (including basalts, dolerites, andesites, and rhyolites) from above their Curie temperatures in the earth's field while under compressive stresses of 5,000 psi. Identical samples were similarly cooled without an applied stress, and in all cases the resulting TRM, measured at room temperature after the stress had been removed, was parallel to the applied field.

Since some magnetostrictive processes may be time-dependent (Graham and others, 1959), field tests are also of interest in evaluating the role of magnetostriction in paleomagnetism. Different magnetic minerals respond in different ways to the same stresses; thus the consistency of results from rocks of the same period that have different mineral assemblages, or were magnetized by different processes, or have had different stress histories would indicate that, for such rocks, magnetostrictive effects have not been important.

References

Brynjólfsson, A., 1957, Studies of remanent magnetism and viscous magnetism in the basalts of Iceland: Advances in Physics, v. 6, p. 247–254.

Clegg, J. A., Almond, M., and Stubbs, P. H. S., 1954a, The remanent magnetism of some sedimentary rocks in Britain: Philos. Mag., ser. 7, v. 45, p. 583–598.

Gorter, E. W., and Schulkes, J. A., 1953, Reversal of spontaneous magnetization as a function of temperature in LiFeCr spinels: Physical Review, v. 90, p. 487–488.

Graham, J. W., 1949, The stability and significance of magnetism in sedimentary rocks: Jour. Geophys. Research, v. 54, p. 131–167.

——— 1953, Changes of ferromagnetic minerals and their bearing on magnetic properties of rocks: Jour. Geophys. Research, v. 58, p. 243–260.

Graham, J. W., Buddington, A. F., and Balsley, J. R., 1957, Stress-induced magnetizations of some rocks with analyzed magnetic minerals: Jour. Geophys. Research, v. 62, p. 465–474.

——— 1959, Magnetostriction and paleomagnetism of igneous rocks: Nature, v. 183, p. 1318.

King, R. F., 1955, The remanent magnetism of artificially deposited sediments: Royal Astron. Soc. Monthly Notices, Geophys. Supp., v. 7, p. 115–134.

Nagata, T., 1953a, Rock magnetism: Tokyo, Japan, Maruzen Co. Ltd., 225 p.

Néel, L., 1951, L'inversion de l'aimantation permanente des roches: Annales Geophysique, v. 7, p. 90–102.

——— 1955, Some theoretical aspects of rock-magnetism: Advances in Physics, v. 4, p. 191–243.

Rimbert, F., 1956b, Sur l'action de champs alternatifs sur des roches portant une aimantation rémanente isotherme de viscosité: Acad. Sci. (Paris) Comptes Rendus, v. 242, p. 2536–2538.

Stott, P. M., and Stacy, F. D., 1959, Magnetostriction and palaeomagnetism of igneous rocks: Nature, v. 183, p. 384–385.

Thellier, E., 1951, Propriétés magnétiques des terres cuites et des roches: Jour. Physique et Radium, v. 12, p. 205–218.

Uyeda, S., 1958, Thermo-remanent magnetism as a medium of palaeomagnetism, with special reference to reverse thermo-remanent magnetism: Japanese Jour. Geophysics, v. 2, p. 1–123.

Verhoogen, J., 1956, Ionic ordering and self-reversal of magnetization in impure magnetites: Jour. Geophys. Research, v. 61, p. 201–209.

MAGNETIC CHARACTERISTICS OF ROCKS

DAVID W. STRANGWAY*

The magnetic characteristics of rocks are briefly discussed in this article. A discussion of the various factors affecting susceptibility has been included. A short description of various methods of measuring the magnetic properties of rocks is given and then an indication of the magnetic properties of some typical igneous rocks given. In general, basic intrusives and volcanics are found to have strong permanent magnetization which must be important in giving magnetic anomalies. Granitic intrusives, on the other hand, seem to have only weak and scattered remanent magnetizations so that the effect of susceptibility is dominant.

In many geophysical studies, it is found that the magnetic properties of rocks are of interest. It is usual to study both the susceptibility and the remanent magnetism of rocks. In the preceding section of this chapter, Cox and Doell have discussed the physical principles underlying remanent (or permanent) magnetization. In this section, discussions of magnetic susceptibility, of the measurement techniques used in studying the magnetic properties of rocks, and of the magnetic properties of various rock types are presented.

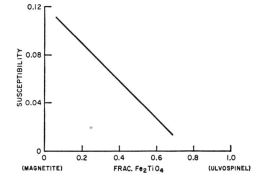

FIG. 1. Susceptibility of the magnetite—ulvospinel series (after Akimoto).

Magnetic Susceptibility

As discussed in a previous section of this chapter on "Mineral Magnetism," the susceptibility of rocks is a measure of their ability to acquire a magnetization in the presence of a magnetic field. This magnetization is commonly given the symbol $M = K\ H_o$ where K is the susceptibility in cgs units/cc and H_o is the applied magnetic field in oersteds. The susceptibility is dependent on many characteristics of the magnetic minerals included in the rock. Some of these factors are considered here.

Dependence on composition

It is, first of all, clear that the magnetic minerals contained in rocks are responsible for the magnetic properties. The susceptibility is, therefore, strongly dependent on the composition and structure of the actual minerals involved. As discussed in "Mineral Magnetism," there are several solid solution series of magnetic minerals commonly found in rocks. The susceptibility of these minerals varies widely as discussed in Akimoto (1957), Nagata (1961), and Akimoto and Nagata (1961). Figure 1, taken from Akimoto, shows, for example, that the susceptibility of the magnetite-ulvospinel series decreases rapidly as the Ti content increases. In many rocks, pure magnetite is a common constituent, but intermediate members of the series are found frequently. Nagata (1961) and others have presented typical compositions of titanomagnetites and ilmenohematites which occur commonly in igneous rocks. Figure 2 gives an indication of the wide compositional variety which can occur in nature in typical igneous rocks. It is clear that considerable variations in the susceptibility of rocks can occur, depending upon the

* Department of Geology, University of Colorado, Boulder, Colorado. Now at Massachusetts Institute of Technology, Cambridge, Massachusetts.

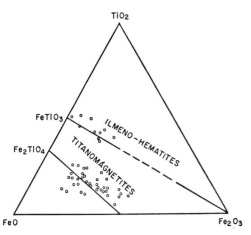

FIG. 2. Chemical composition of minerals from igneous rocks (after Akimoto and Nagata).

exact composition and structure of the magnetic minerals involved.

Dependence on volume fraction

The volume percentage of a rock composed of magnetic minerals is important in determining the overall susceptibility of a rock. The problem of determining the relation between volume percent and susceptibility is, however, not a simple one, since interactions between grains need to be taken into account as the volume fraction increases until finally a rock consisting of a pure magnetic mineral is only a single grain. Several studies, such as those by Slichter (1929), Puzicha (1941), and the monumental work by Werner (1945), have been conducted. To date, only empirical expressions to fit the observed data are available, however.

In deriving a suitable expression to relate volume fraction and susceptibility, several factors must be considered. A single grain of magnetic material contains many magnetic atoms, each of which is acted upon by its neighbors. The result is that the field acting within the grain is less than the external applied field which gives rise to the magnetization. This decrease in the internal field is referred to as demagnetization. The internal field, H int, is given as:

$$H \text{ int} = H_o - NM$$

where

H_o is the applied field
N the demagnetizing factor

and

M the magnetization.

The magnetization can, of course, be a permanent magnetization or a susceptibility. For simplicity, only the effects of susceptibility are considered here. The demagnetizing factor (N) is a function of the shape of the grain. Various workers such as Stoner (1935) have studied this problem in detail. The demagnetizing factor N is given for several shapes.

sphere—$4/3\pi$

infinite cylinder—2π across axis

—0 along axis

infinite slab—4π across short direction

—0 in long directions

In estimating the true susceptibility of a single grain of magnetic material, it is, therefore, necessary to take account of the demagnetizing factor so that the true internal field may be known. If the grain is spherical, the apparent susceptibility is an isotropic property. If, on the other hand, the grain is not spherical, the apparent susceptibility is anisotropic and different corrections need to be applied when the applied field is oriented in various directions with respect to the grains. Crystals also have preferred orientations of magnetization so that the effects of shape and of crystalline anisotropy should not be confused.

In Figure 3, a graph relating the true susceptibility K to the apparent or measured susceptibility K_a is presented. It is readily seen from this that great care must be taken in calculating the true susceptibility of highly magnetic materials. For accurate measurements requiring a minimum of correction, long cylindrical specimens are probably the most suitable. In the grains found in natural rocks, shapes that are nearly spherical or ellipsoidal are probably the most common so that the demagnetizing factor alone, in fact, controls the apparent susceptibility of the grain. For a true susceptibility of 1.0 cgs/cc,

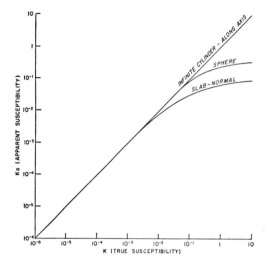

FIG. 3. Effect of shape demagnetization.

for example, an apparent susceptibility of only 0.195 will be measured on a spherical grain.

In considering a rock with an assemblage of grains, it is necessary to take account of the demagnetizing factors of the individual grains, of the demagnetizing factor of the specimen, of the volume percent of magnetic minerals present, and of the interaction between grains. Puzicha (1941) has developed an expression for this, provided the number of grains is small, so that interactions may be ignored. If we let N_s be the demagnetizing factor of the sample as a whole and N the mean demagnetizing factor of the grains, the resultant field operating within a single grain is given by

$$H_o - VN_sM + VNM = NM$$

where V is the volume fraction of magnetic material, M is the magnetization, and H_o the applied field. The expression VNM represents a magnetizing field acting on the individual grain in the presence of other magnetic grains. This is sometimes referred to as the Lorentz field. If the true susceptibility of the magnetic minerals is written as K_m, the magnetization of a single grain is:

$$M = K_m(H_o - VN_sM + VNM - NM).$$

The true susceptibility of the rock specimen is given as $K = VM/H$ int where H int is

the field inside the rock $(H$ int $= H_o - VN_sM)$. The expression for K may then be written

$$K = \frac{VK_m}{1 + K_mN(1 - V)} .$$

This is the expression derived by Puzicha. We see that for highly magnetic minerals such as magnetite, the apparent susceptibility is dependent primarily on the demagnetizing factor of the grains rather than on the true susceptibility of the minerals themselves. By experimenting with powdered materials, Puzicha found that this expression is valid for small percentages of magnetite but that considerable departures are experienced where more than a few percent of magnetite are present. This is because interactions between grains have been ignored.

Werner (1945) has studied a large number of magnetite-rich ores from Sweden. This study enabled him to develop an empirical expression which seems to fit the experimental observations very well. This expression is given as:

$$K = \frac{VK_m}{1 + NK_m(1 - V^{1/6})} .$$

The substitution of $V^{1/6}$ power apparently takes care of the intergranular interactions. In Werner's case, the value of N chosen was $4/3\pi$ or that for a sphere. In Figure 4, an example of data collected by him from the Persberg area of Sweden is shown together with Puzicha's formula, using $N = 4/3\pi$ and $N = 2/3\pi$, and with Werner's modification. It is evident that Werner's empirical expression fits the data well. A second empirical expression is also shown in Figure 4. This is given as

$$K = \frac{K_mV}{1 + K_m(1 - V)} .$$

This expression also fits the experimental data well.

It should be noted that, in order to derive the K value plotted here, it is essential that the correction for the shape of the specimen itself be applied after the apparent susceptibility (K_a) has been measured. In the case of

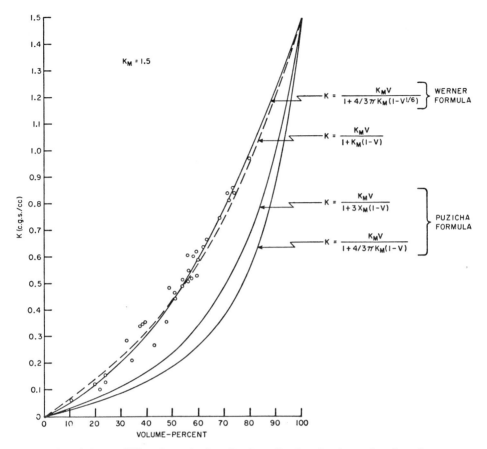

FIG. 4. Susceptibility of samples from Persberg, Sweden, showing various formulas.

many rocks this distinction is small, but in the case of rocks containing much magnetic material this correction is essential.

Slichter (1929) has published some data on a series of artificial samples. These results are shown in Figure 5 and are also compared with the empirical expression

$$K = \frac{K_m V}{1 + K_m(1 - V)}.$$

The fit once again is good. The dependence of susceptibility upon volume fraction of magnetic material is seen to be complicated, but with the various empirical expressions available to us we have a fairly clear picture of the behavior and can predict the dependence of susceptibility on volume fraction.

Other studies of a similar nature have been reported. Jahren (1963) has given a compre-

hensive report on a suite of samples from the iron formations of Minnesota. He gives the expression $K = 0.00116\ V^{1.39}$ for volume percentages of magnetite between 10 and 40 percent. Mooney and Bleifuss (1953) found the relation $K = 0.00289\ V^{1.01}$ for volume percentages between 0.2 and 3.5 percent. It is clear that theoretical expressions are nearly valid for small percentages of magnetite but, with an increase in percentage, departures are due undoubtedly to intergranular interactions. Similar results have been presented by Ponomarev and Glukhikh (1963).

Dependence on field strength

The susceptibility of natural materials depends on many other factors. One of the most interesting of these is the dependence on field strength. Much of the early work was done at fairly high field strengths, but more

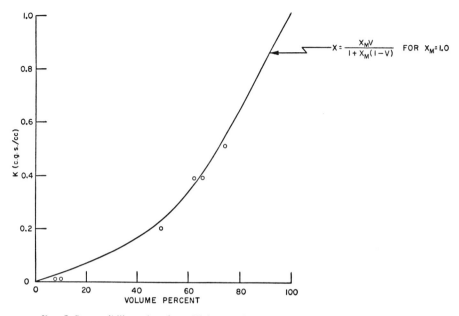

FIG. 5. Susceptibility taken from Slichter and compared with empirical expression.

recently it has been realized that the susceptibility is strongly dependent on the field strength. Since it is most usual in geophysical problems to be interested in the properties of rocks in the presence of the earth's field, a field strength of about 0.5 oersted is commonly used. In any event, susceptibility data must be measured and reported under known field strengths. Werner (1945) has summarized the typical results that one gets as the field strength is varied. In Figure 6, taken from Werner, a typical example is shown. It is interesting to note that the susceptibility becomes very large at a field strength of about 150 oersteds. When one considers a typical hysteresis loop (Figure 7) it is readily seen that this increase is to be expected. The permeability of an initially nonmagnetic sample is given by the slope of the B-H graph. In general, this slope is small, increases as field increases, and finally decreases to zero when the sample is saturated.

In Figure 7, a typical hysteresis loop is shown. Since the slope of the B-H curve is the permeability (μ) and since $\mu = 1 + 4\pi K$,

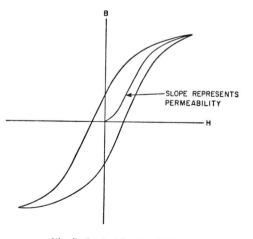

Fig. 7. Typical hysteresis loop.

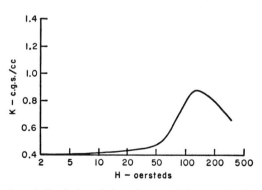

FIG. 6. Typical variation of susceptibility with field strength (after Werner).

it is seen that variations in μ reflect variations in susceptibility. At very weak field strengths, Nagata (1961) and Strangway (1958) have reported on a small decrease in susceptibility observed in the vicinity of 0.5 oersted (see Figure 8). These indicate that a true reversible susceptibility is not observed, even at these very low field strengths. It is important to specify the field conditions used to conduct susceptibility determinations since the measurement is so strongly dependent on the applied field.

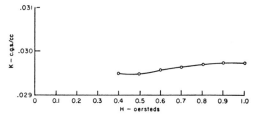

FIG. 8. Weak-field susceptibility variations (from Strangway, 1958).

Dependence on State of Magnetization

It is clear from the preceding discussion that the susceptibility is dependent on the state of magnetization. If a sample has been magnetized to saturation, it cannot be made more magnetic. If the sample has a remanent magnetization, its susceptibility will be different than if it had no permanent magnetization. In general, it is found that susceptibility decreases with an increasing remanence. Although few studies of this nature have been reported on natural materials, a typical curve of this nature is sketched in Figure 9. This curve is taken from Shandley and Bacon (1963). This is the normal type of curve to be expected. In a study by the author (1958), samples of basic intrusives were given a strong permanent magnetization by heating above the Curie temperature and cooling in the earth's magnetic field. It was found that the susceptibility was increased in all cases. When the samples were demagnetized using ac fields, the susceptibility invariably decreased contrary to the normal results. It is not known why this should be, but it seems certain that the samples have a complicated hysteresis loop, probably due to the presence of several magnetic components. Some results of this study are shown in Figure 10.

Dependence on grain size

Many other factors affect the susceptibility of natural materials. Among these is grain size. As a general rule, the larger a grain is the more domains it contains and the

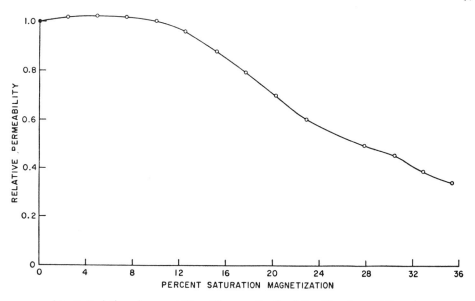

FIG. 9. Variation of permeability with magnetization (after Shandley and Bacon).

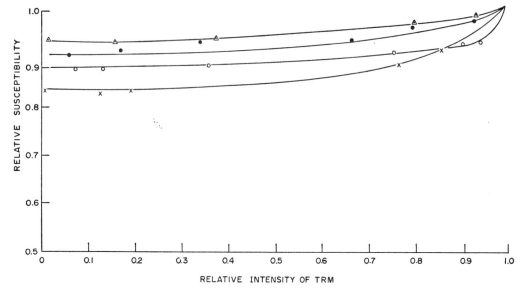

Fig. 10. Increasing susceptibility with decreasing TRM.

easier it is to magnetize. Small grains are magnetically hard and so tend to have low susceptibilities. In general, the easiest way to magnetize a sample is to move a domain wall while much higher fields are required to actually rotate the magnetization within a domain. A particle which is small enough to consist of a single domain is then extremely stable, provided it is also large enough to be above its blocking temperature. As a rough approximation, we may estimate that a single domain grain has a size that is at least the size of a domain wall. Néel has given a theoretical expression to allow one to estimate the minimum expected size of such a grain. This expression is given in terms of a relaxation time, τ_0, given by

$$\frac{1}{\tau_0} = C \exp\left[-\frac{vH_cJ_s}{2kT}\right]$$

where v is the volume of the grain, H_c the coercive, J_s the saturation magnetization, k is Boltzmann's constant, and T is absolute temperature.

The value C is a constant which depends upon the elastic properties of the material

$$C = \frac{eH_c}{2m}\left[3G\lambda + DJ_s^2\right]\left[\frac{2v}{\pi GkT}\right]1/2$$

where e is the charge on an electron, m is the mass of an electron, G is the shear modulus, λ is the coefficient of magnetostriction, and D is a numerical constant, about 3. Using data appropriate for magnetite, we find the following values (Table 1).

The relaxation time is thus strongly dependent on the ratio V/T. If we choose a temperature of 500°C as a blocking temperature, a particle approximately 0.05 micron in diameter will be extremely magnetically stable with a relaxation time of several billion years. It is evident that the susceptibility is a strong function of grain size. It should be noted that this size estimate is a minimum one. The presence of impurities or imperfections in the lattice structure would be expected to make the actual size of a single domain grain considerably larger than

Table 1

V/T	5.52×10^{-21}	11.05×10^{-21}	23.2×10^{-21}	27.6×10^{-21}	33.1×10^{-21}
$\tau_{0(sec)}$	5.83×10^{-2}	9.08	3.04×10^{10}	6.15×10^{13}	1.56×10^{20}

this. A plot showing the typical dependence of susceptibility on grain size is shown in Figure 11 after Shandley and Bacon (1963). It seems probable that these particles of very small size are quite important. It has been pointed out by Strangway (1961) that the presence of single domain grains in a rock could also be the locus of an extremely stable remanent magnetization.

Measurement of Magnetic Properties

Many techniques are available for the measurement of the magnetic properties of rocks, and no attempt could be made in an article of this nature to discuss all of these in detail. Rather, some general comments will be made, and a few representative procedures described in detail.

Susceptibility

In general, it is possible to divide the common techniques of susceptibility measuring into two categories. In the one case, a steady magnetic field is applied to the sample and its change in magnetization measured. In the other, an alternating magnetic field is applied to the sample and the secondary field generated by the sample is measured. In either case, it is usual to conduct measurements in fields that are of the order of 0.5 oersted and it is important to ensure that the sample is immersed in a uniform magnetic field.

ac fields.—In using ac techniques the sample is energized with a low frequency field. It is, of course, essential that this field be of a frequency sufficiently low that no conductivity response of the sample will be obse ved. The response parameter (α) of a sphere in an alternating field is given by $\alpha^2 = \sigma\mu\omega R^2$, where σ is the conductivity (mho/m), μ the permeability (henries/m), ω the rotational frequency, and R the radius (Wait, 1951). In order that the conductivity response of the sample be small, it is essential that the parameter $\alpha \ll 1$. In the case of pure magnetite, the conductivity is approximately 1.5×10^4 mho/m and the permeability $\mu = 1.5 \times 4\pi \times 10^{-7}$ henries/m. For a one-inch diameter sphere and using the condition that $\alpha = 0.1$, we find that the maximum allowable fre-

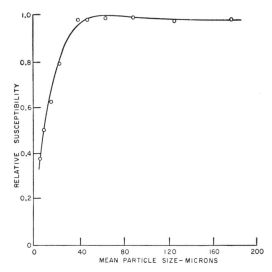

Fig. 11. The dependence of susceptibility on particle size (after Shandley and Bacon).

quency is 2,200 cps.

If the sample is highly magnetic, it is also essential that the demagnetization due to specimen shape be considered. For this reason, many people make use of a long cylindrical specimen and then magnetize it axially so that the effect of shape is reduced to a minimum. In the case of many rocks, however, this correction is negligibly small, and these factors need not be considered.

One technique commonly used has been described by Bruckshaw and Robertson (1949) and by Manley (1954). In this procedure, a set of Helmholtz coils excited by an audio-frequency oscillator and a power amplifier is used. The particular version described here (Strangway, 1958) was operated at a frequency of 200 cps. The amplifier was capable of delivering 50 watts to the field coils. Two receiving coils mounted in opposition in the field were then used. These were connected in opposition and balanced in such a way that no voltage could be detected from the output when no sample was present. In order to achieve this kind of balance, it is necessary to adjust both the number of turns and the capacitance of the coils. Rather than use a variable condenser in the circuit, a single closed loop of copper rod was used. This loop was placed in the vicinity of one of

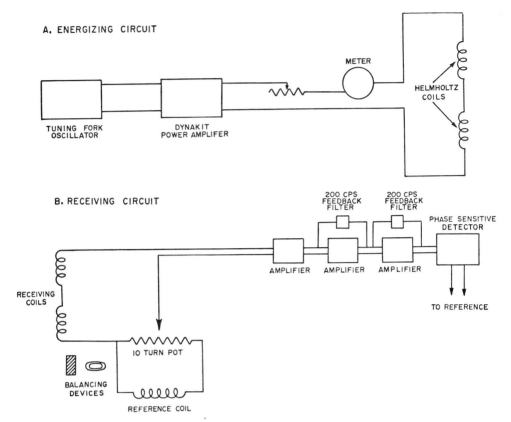

FIG. 12. Circuit of susceptibility measuring device.

the coils and small changes in position allowed a quadrature signal together with some in-phase signal to be introduced into the nearest coil. A small, slightly magnetic slug was moved around in such a way that the remaining in-phase signal was balanced. Thus, no adjustments of the electronic circuit itself were necessary in order to null the instrument. A schematic of the circuit used, together with a table of pertinent coil data, are given in Figure 12 and Table 2. The data have been taken from Strangway (1958).

The instrument is operated as a null detector using a small reference coil and a potentiometer to adjust the null to a minimum. The sensitivity is considerably enhanced by the use of a phase sensitive detector which operates as a very narrow band detector. The system actually built used a furnace for heating the samples, and a limiting sensitivity of about 10×10^{-6} cgs/cc was achieved using a one-cubic-inch sample. At this point it was found that temperature fluctuations limit the stability of the system.

Another system described by Girdler (1961) and others operates on the transformer bridge principle. Such a device has been built at the University of Colorado, and this unit will be described here.

Two arms of the bridge are formed by windings wound on a high permeability toroidal core. It is essential that these two arms be as nearly identical as possible. In order to insure this, the windings are wound in a bifilar manner. Each arm consists of approxi-

Table 2

Coil	ID (cm)	OD (cm)	No. of turns	Wire gauge
ac Helmholtz coils	60	60.8	38	12
Receiver coils	12	18	14,000	36

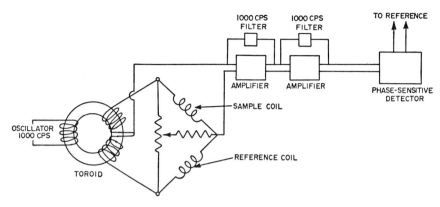

FIG. 13. Transformer-bridge susceptibility meter.

mately 20 turns, and because of the ferrite core, the two arms are almost perfectly coupled. The other two arms of the bridge consist of two air-cored solenoid coils, each with 200 turns of wire. The sample is introduced into one of these coils, and a change in inductance takes place. A ferrite slug is introduced into the second coil so that the bridge can be rebalanced. The distance the slug has to move into the solenoid is calibrated in terms of susceptibility. Balance is again a critical problem and can be achieved with the use of a potentiometer in parallel with the coils and by the use of a movable copper loop as already described. Power is introduced into the bridge by means of an oscillator feeding a separate winding on the toroid, which provides an effective coupling with the transformer arms. As in all devices using ferrite cores, great care has to be taken to ensure that the core is not overdriven so that odd harmonics of the energizing frequency are excited. The bridge is powered at 1,000 cps. The receiving system consists of two highly tuned amplifying stages using amplifiers and feedback filters manufactured by White Instruments, Inc. A reference is taken from the oscillator and a phase-sensitive detector used as the final detector. A sensitivity of 10^{-7} cgs/cc is readily achieved with this system. A sketch of the apparatus is shown in Figure 13.

This system has the advantage of a high degree of stability even for very low values of susceptibility, and the field acting on the sample can be kept at about 0.5 oersted.

Calibration.—The absolute calibration of susceptibility meters can be carried out in several ways. One of the simplest procedures involves the use of a small loop of known geometry in which a known current at the peak frequency of the amplifying circuits is used. This will give the total magnetic moment due to a dipole located in the position of the magnetic sample. If the sample is such that it can be also represented as a dipole, the calibration for total magnetic moment is a simple procedure.

Another alternative is to use a simple closed loop of copper wire and then excite it inductively with the applied field just as would be done in the case of a sample. The response parameters of such a loop have been worked out in detail by West (1957). This type of calibration is quite effective for small values of the response parameter. If a phase-detection system is being used, it is of course essential to measure both the in-phase and the quadrature components of the received signal, since such a loop generates a signal which is partly in-phase and partly in quadrature with the exciting signal.

The more conventional procedure is to use magnetic salts for small values of susceptibility and then to extend the range using sand and magnetite mixtures. Two of the more useful salts are $FeSO_4 \cdot 7H_2O$ and alum (ferrous ammonium sulfate). These have volume susceptibilities of 79.0×10^{-6} cgs/cc and 60.8×10^{-6} cgs/cc, respectively, and are sufficiently stable to be useful for calibrating. By using a very small percentage of magnetite in a sand mixture, it is possible to make a mixture with approximately this susceptibility, and then by increasing the volume percent magnetite the instrument can be calibrated to higher values. As we have already seen, susceptibility is no longer a linear function of volume at more than two percent. These procedures for calibration have been found quite satisfactory for many problems of a geologic nature.

Steady fields.—Other procedures employing a steady field are also in common use. Werner (1945), for example, used an astatic system originally described by Mme. O. Thellier. An astatic magnet system with two magnets mounted in opposition on a fiber is suspended near the sample coil which is a long solenoid with a direct current passing through it. Two identical solenoid coils are mounted in such a way that their effect on the magnet system is approximately cancelled. When a magnetic sample is introduced into one of the coils, the induced magnetic moment in the sample causes the astatic system to deflect. This deflection is dependent on the susceptibility. To ensure that none of the deflection is due to the remanent magnetism of the sample, the sample is placed in a variety of positions with respect to the magnet system and the results averaged. A third coil can be used to null the system when no sample is present.

Astatic magnetometer systems are now in common use in studies of paleomagnetism. It is usual to remove the earth's field while conducting measurements so that the instrument sensitivity can be raised to a maximum. If the same set of readings is also conducted in the presence of a field, a comparison of the two results allows one to determine the susceptibility. One component of the remanent magnetism is determined by rotating the sample directly beneath the suspended magnet system. The remanent magnetism then causes the astatic system to undergo a sinusoidal deflection as the specimen is rotated. If, in addition to the sinusoidal deflection, there is a steady deflection, this is due to susceptibility, and a measurement of susceptibility can be made. The typical results expected, after Collinson, Creer, Irving and Runcorn (1957), are shown in Figure 14. If the sample has a susceptibility anisotropy, the deflections are no longer sinusoidal but are distorted.

Remanent magnetism

Two major categories of measuring procedures are also available in studying the remanent magnetism of rocks. One group uses alternating current procedures while the other uses some form of an astatic magnetometer.

Spinner magnetometer.—Many different spinner magnetometers have been built, especially in the last few years, since there is considerable interest in paleomagnetism. Many ingenious methods of spinning the samples opposite a pickup coil have been devised.

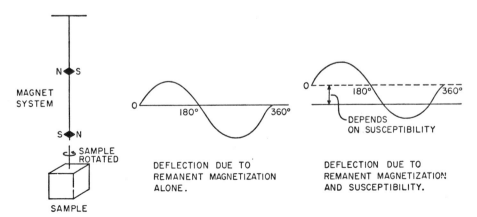

Fig. 14. Determination of susceptibility with astatic magnetometer.

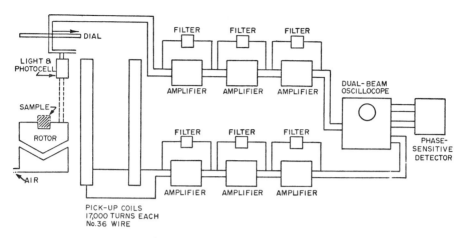

FIG. 15. Schematic of remanent magnetometer.

Most of these are either shaft-driven or air-driven using a Beam's turbine. Since we are interested in knowing the direction as well as the intensity of magnetization, it is essential that some method of obtaining a reference voltage from the spinner be devised. These have commonly consisted of a magnet in the spinning shaft as discussed by Bruckshaw and Robertson (1948) or a photocell picking up an interrupted reflected light signal from the spinning device as described by Graham (1955). A spinner built at the University of Colorado will be discussed briefly to illustrate the techniques.

An air turbine is used to spin one-cubic-inch samples at a rotation speed of 270 cps. This requires an air pressure of approximately 18 psi. The turbine is spun opposite a pair of pickup coils. These coils are mounted in opposition so that any uniform fields present in the laboratory can be reduced to a minimum. The sample in the spinning system introduces a magnetic signal into the nearest coil, and this signal is amplified through a highly tuned circuit. Great care must be taken to ensure that no vibration and no electrostatic noise is picked up. This is achieved by carefully shock mounting all parts involved and by painting all nonmetallic surfaces with silver paint. The rotor inevitably picks up a charge, but this is easily removed by soaking it in salt water between runs.

The rock signal is then amplified and fil-tered by three tuned feedback filters. A light source and photocell pickup are pointed to the top of the rotor which is painted half dark and half light. This signal is passed through a set of amplifiers and filters which are identical to those in the signal channel. These two signals are then monitored on a dual beam oscilloscope which is also used for signal attenuation and their phase compared on a Princeton Applied Research phase sensitive detector. The relative phase of the two signals is adjusted to 0, 90, 180, and 270 degrees by rotating the photocell with respect to the spinning top until a maximum or a minimum is observed on the phase detector. A large dial calibrated in degrees allows one to read the direction of magnetization relative to the markings on the rotor for the component of magnetization in the plane normal to the axis of rotation. The sample is then spun two more times and an accurate measure of the direction of magnetization can be obtained. In some cases, it is necessary to spin the sample six times and average the results. The intensity is measured by the maximum deflection on the phase meter. This instrument will read accurately to about one degree and can be used to measure intensities as low as 5×10^{-7} cgs/cc. A schematic diagram is shown in Figure 15.

Spinner magnetometers can also be used to give a measure of the anisotropy of susceptibility. If the sample is not magnetically isotropic, the local magnetic field is distorted.

This distortion is such that a signal at twice the spinning frequency is observed. By spinning the sample at 135 cps, a signal is observed in the amplifiers tuned to 270 cps. This is dependent on the specimen anisotropy, and is, therefore, a measure of anisotropy.

Astatic magnetometers.—Astatic magnetometers have already been described briefly in the measurement of susceptibility. A comprehensive report by Collinson and Creer (1960) is also available. Curves such as the one shown in Figure 14 are used to measure the direction and intensity of remanent magnetism. By measuring the peak to peak value of the sinusoidal wave form developed by rotating the sample, the intensity of a component of magnetization in one plane can be measured. This is done for off-center orientations, and it is possible to determine the component of magnetization in a second plane. These systems are very rapid to use, and if a quiet environment (both mechanical and electrical) can be found, they are capable of achieving a very high degree of sensitivity. Their disadvantage is that a quiet environment is required, and they are sensitive to components of magnetization other than dipolar so that specimen shape and uniformity are more critical than in spinner magnetometers. Systems of both kinds are commonly operated with a high degree of success.

Calibration of remanent magnetometer systems is essentially the same as calibration of susceptibility meters where one is also attempting to measure a magnetic moment. Coils with known dipole moments and single loops can be used effectively.

Many other experiments in the magnetic properties of rocks can also be conducted. These involve tests of stability, Curie temperature determinations, etc. For additional material, the reader is referred to the book by Nagata (1961) and a forthcoming book on *Procedures in Paleomagnetism* to be published by Elsevier Press under the editorship of Runcorn, Collinson and Creer.

Magnetic properties of rocks.—A great deal of information on the magnetic properties of rocks is available since there has been a great deal of effort in the past few years to compile paleomagnetic information. Many of these studies have concentrated on the remanent magnetism of rocks so that relatively few of the investigators also report on the susceptibility. In view of the large body of literature available, results from only a few representative studies are reported here. For comprehensive bibliographies of the subject, the reader is referred to Cox and Doell (1960) and to a series of articles being published by Irving in the *Geophysical Journal*. The present discussion is limited to igneous rocks since sedimentary rocks are generally only weakly magnetic and do not contribute to observed magnetic anomalies.

Volcanics.—Much of the work done on the magnetic properties of rocks has been concentrated on volcanic rocks. It is found that volcanics are, in general, highly magnetic and, from a paleomagnetic point of view, they are found to be magnetically stable. In addition, it is possible to sample lava flows which have occurred in historical times and compare the observed data with known magnetic fields. In general, it can be said that the lavas have a high remanent magnetization acquired at the time that the flow cooled through its Curie temperature. Rapid cooling rates of these extruded rocks have not allowed the grains to grow very large, and perhaps because of this small grain size, it is often found that the rocks are magnetically stable.

Extensive studies of historical lava flows and of specimens of lava heated in the laboratory and allowed to cool in the present earth's field have been conducted. Studies by Chevallier (1925) and by Thellier and Thellier (1959), for example, show that the direction of magnetization is that of the earth's magnetic field at the location and that the intensity of magnetization acquired by a given sample is proportional to the intensity of the applied field. Many studies have been reported, but perhaps one of the more interesting ones is a study by Cox and Doell (1962) on basalt samples collected from hole EM 7 of the Mohole Project off the coast of

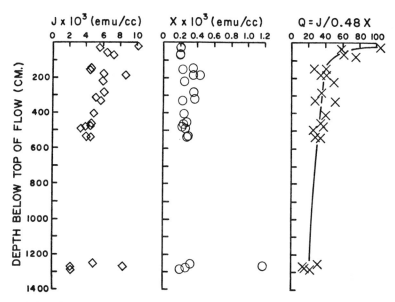

Fig. 16. Variation of depth of remanent magnetization J, susceptibility X, and Koenigsberger ratio Q.

Baja California. These samples were collected from beneath 170 m of Miocene sediments. Twenty-three specimens were collected, and the magnetic data determined from these are shown in Figure 16. The data are plotted as a function of depth below the surface of the flow. It is interesting to observe the extremely high values of remanent magnetization and the correspondingly small values of susceptibility. The result is that Q ratios ranging up to 105 were encountered. There is a strong tendency for high Q ratios to be found at the top of the flow where rapid cooling has produced a very small grain size. Although the declination of magnetization could not be determined, it is clear from the inclination that the sense of magnetization found in these samples is reversed when compared to the present earth's field.

An interesting study of Tertiary and Quaternary basalts was conducted by Irving and Green (1957) and by Green (1960) on samples from Australia. They tabulate the results from 127 samples giving a mean susceptibility of 9.0×10^{-4} cgs/cc and a mean intensity of remanent magnetization of 21.4 $\times 10^{-4}$ cgs/cc. The result is a mean Q ratio approximately equal to 5. Again it is clear that the remanent magnetization is the dominant cause of the magnetic anomalies associated with the basalts. The field problem is considerably complicated by the fact that there are many sections of reversely magnetized material intermixed with sections of normally magnetized material.

An interesting study has been made by Books (1962). He has collected samples and studied airborne magnetic data from an area in north-central Montana close to the Bearpaw Mountains. Several small buttes which are capped with volcanic rocks have been studied and reported as Eocene in age. A total of 455 mafic volcanic rock samples gave a mean intensity of remanent magnetization of 11.1×10^{-3} cgs/cc and a mean susceptibility of about 7×10^{-4} cgs units. The mean Q value for these dark volcanics is thus very high, and all magnetic anomalies associated with these rock units can be expected to be due to remanent magnetization alone. One of these buttes, Squaw Butte, shows a distinct aeromagnetic anomaly as shown in Figure 17. The associated data based on remanent magnetism of samples of the lava itself are shown in Figure 18. It is readily seen that there is a strong tendency for the RNM data to group in a negative sense, and, contrary to the normal situation encountered in the

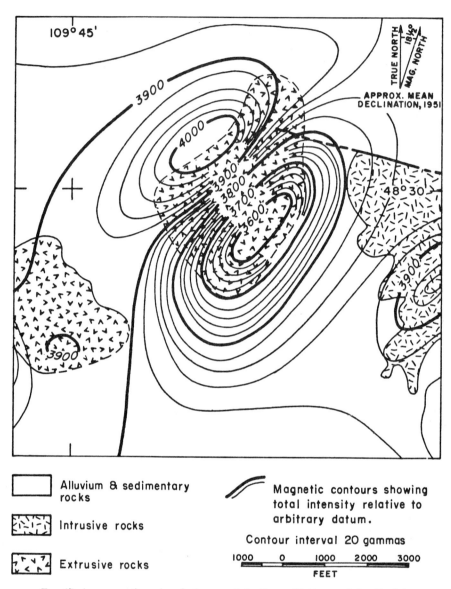

FIG. 17. Aeromagnetic and geologic map of the Squaw Butte area (after Books).

Northern Hemisphere, the negative part of the anomaly is found to the south of the body itself. It is thus clear that both samples and aeromagnetic data show the dominance of the remanent magnetization.

Many other examples of basalt and volcanics have been studied. It is interesting to observe that, in general, the Q ratio appears to be smaller for rocks of greater age. There is not a great deal of information available on the subject, but data collected by Koenigs-

berger and presented by Nagata (1961) support this observation.

Basic intrusives.—Many basic intrusives have been studied paleomagnetically, and for several of these, information on both remanent and induced magnetization is available. Some examples are discussed in this book in the section on "Rock Magnetism and Geologic Correlation."

A study of Precambrian diabase dikes by

Strangway (1961, 1964) has already been presented in Vol. I Chapter 2. In this study the susceptibility varied from about 0.1×10^{-3} to 20×10^{-3} cgs/cc so that, in general, the samples were highly magnetic. It was found that the normal remanent magnetism was fairly uniform in direction and in several cases was an important contributor to magnetic anomalies. It was noted, also, that the remanent magnetism decreased with age so that the younger units, dated at about 10^9 years, had a strong remanence. In sampling these dikes and making measurements on them, it was found that a considerable scatter of directions was present although a good statistical mean could be determined. In Figure 19, the results of the determination of the direction of magnetization are shown on a stereographic net. In Figure 20, the airborne magnetic profiles over these same bodies are shown and compared with calculated curves in which only the effect of susceptibility and only the effect of remanent magnetism were considered. In order to get a good correlation between the observed field and the calculated curves, it is necessary to take account of both kinds of magnetization. It is also necessary to take account of the scatter of the magnetiza-

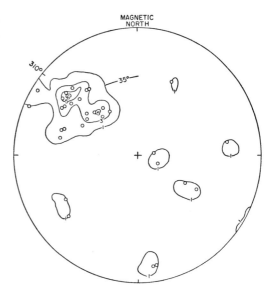

FIG. 18. Density diagram of samples from Squaw Butte that show south-seeking polarizations.

tion. This was simply done by reducing the mean intensity of magnetization by the factor $\overline{\cos \theta}$. This term is a measure of the angular deviation from the mean direction of magnetization, and when this is done, it is found that the calculated and observed

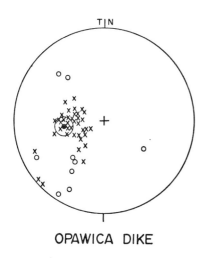

OPAWICA DIKE

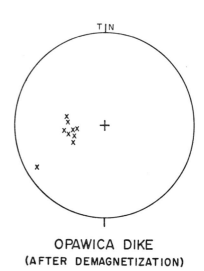

OPAWICA DIKE
(AFTER DEMAGNETIZATION)

○ UPPER HEMISPHERE
× LOWER HEMISPHERE

MEAN DIRECTION OF MAGNETIZATION
SHOWING CIRCLE OF 5% CONFIDENCE

FIG. 19. Stereographic plots of directions of magnetization.

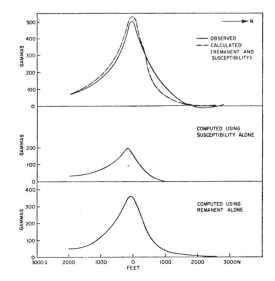

FIG. 20. Observed and calculated airborne magnetic data for the Opawica Dike.

curves over these bodies show a remarkably good agreement.

A similar study has been reported by Green (1960). He has used data compiled by Gough (1956) on the Pilansberg dikes of South Africa. Gough found that the remanent magnetization of these dikes, later dated at 1.3×10^9 years (Schreiner, 1958), is about 4×10^{-3} cgs/cc in an almost negative sense. Ground magnetic studies by Gelletich show that the anomalies encountered are indeed negative, and one is led to the conclusion that the effects of remanent magnetization, even in these very old rocks, far outweigh the effects of susceptibility. The susceptibility is estimated by Green at 1.7×10^{-3} cgs/cc. The net result is that these basic intrusives show an anomaly at the surface of the earth that is negative.

Studies by Vincenz (1954) on some of the Tertiary dikes of northern England show very similar results. Q ratios there range from 0.3 to 3.7, indicating that in many cases the remanent magnetization is important in generating anomalies in the local magnetic field. Graham (1953) studied a series of Precambrian dikes from the northern part of Michigan, and again the Q ratio is found to be considerably greater than one.

There are many studies available now in which the remanent and induced magnetism have been measured. For example, Bull, Irving, and Willis (1962) have studied a suite of dolerite samples from South Victoria Land, Antarctica, which are Mesozoic in age and show a good grouping of direction of magnetization. The mean Q ratio for these dikes for a large number of samples lies between 1.0 and 2.0 so that once again remanent magnetization is important. The work by Hood (1961) in the Sudbury basin of Ontario (probably about 1.7×10^9 years old) gives Q ratios ranging from about 0.1 to 20. There are a sufficient number of samples to indicate that the Q ratio in the Sudbury Basin has a profound effect on the observed aeromagnetic profiles over the area. Intensities of remanent magnetization vary from 1 to about 60×10^{-3} cgs/cc, while the susceptibilities range from 20 to $5,000 \times 10^{-6}$ cgs/cc. Again the grouping of directions of magnetization is good so that the remanent magnetism is an important factor.

Creer, Irving, and Nairn (1959) have reported on a comprehensive study of the Great Whin Sill of north England. As a part of this study, they investigated the intensity and direction of remanent magnetization as well as the susceptibility. These dolerite sills of Upper Carboniferous age have susceptibilities that range from 2.3 to 1.5×10^{-3} cgs/cc and have a remanent magnetization of 1.9 to 4.0×10^{-3} cgs/cc giving a Q ratio in the range of 1.8 to 3.5. Good groupings of directions are found, and again it is necessary to consider that remanent magnetization is of considerable importance. In this case the magnetization is nearly horizontal.

Many other studies are reported in the literature, but it is felt that the examples cited here suffice to indicate that, in the case of basic intrusives, the remanent and the induced magnetization are both important quantities. Even when considering very old rocks, the remanent magnetization can be a dominant factor contributing to the field observed at the surface of the earth.

Acidic intrusives.—A few studies of acidic intrusives in which both the induced and remanent magnetisms were studied have

Table 3. Average Values of Natural Remanence J_n, Susceptibility χ, and Q Factor for Nine Sites, A to J, in emu; N= number of specimens

Site	Granites				Autoliths				Average for all specimens from each site		
	N	$J_n \times 10^4$	$\chi \times 10^4$	Q	N	$J_n \times 10^4$	$\chi \times 10^4$	Q	$J_n \times 10^4$	$\chi \times 10^4$	Q
A	2	3.8	38	.26	13	7.7	42	.40	7.2	41	.38
B	8	6.6	33	.44	13	9.3	32	.64	7.4	32	.62
C	10	4.1	29	.32	11	15	40	.89	9.8	34	.62
D	2	2.2	20	.25	4	4.1	40	.22	3.0	33	.22
E	4	7.5	43	.38	4	8.5	48	.40	8.2	45	.38
F	6	4.2	22	.43	3	3.8	17	.51	4.3	20	.46
G	2	.65	3.3	.44	24	.88	2.3	1.0	0.9	2.4	.95
H	3	1.2	9.3	.29	6	2.5	7.9	.78	2.0	8.3	.65
J	18	2.6	22	.26	2	4.5	28	.36	4.3	23	.26

been reported. Among these are a study by Hawes (1952) of the Spavinaw granite of Oklahoma and one by Currie, Gromme, and Verhoogen (1963) of some granitic plutons in the Sierra Nevada.

In the study by Hawes, 97 samples were studied using a remanent magnetometer. The results obtained were highly variable with directions varying through 360 degrees in azimuth and from $+83$ to -83 degrees in dip. The intensities vary from 0.001 cgs/cc to 0.18 cgs/cc. These values are fairly high and give an overall average of 0.0175 cgs/cc for the remanent magnetization. These intensities, however, are in almost random directions so that the magnetometer profiles flown over this granite area show essentially no effect from the remanent magnetism. Ground profiles taken in the immediate vicinity of the outcrops, on the other hand, show highly erratic values, indicating the presence of these local variations. It is probable that much of the scatter observed is the result of lightning strikes.

The susceptibility of 41 samples was measured, and values ranging from 0.00028 to 0.00198 cgs/cc were found, yielding a mean value of 0.00121. The remanent magnetization of a single specimen is thus much higher than the susceptibility magnetization, but the erratic nature of direction of this magnetization leads to an almost complete cancellation at a height of 675 ft. This is the same effect, as previously discussed, in which the scatter of directions must be included in discussions of the effects of remanent magnetization. In this Precambrian intrusive, the only magnetization that needs to be considered is the susceptibility.

The study by Currie et al. (1963) on some granite plutons which are dated at 79 to 89 million years is of considerable interest. These plutons from the Yosemite Valley of California show a definite remanent magnetization, but the Q ratios are considerably less than one. A table taken from their work is shown here as Table 3. It is readily seen that typical remanent magnetizations of 1 to 8×10^{-4} cgs/cc are typical and susceptibilities of 2 to 45×10^{-4} cgs/cc are typical. Once again, it is interesting to find that, in a few cases, the directions of remanent magnetization scatter widely. At other sites, however, good groupings of remanent magnetic directions were found.

In studying magnetic profiles over these plutons, one would expect that in spite of the young age the susceptibility would determine the nature of the magnetic anomalies encountered.

A study by Allingham and Zietz (1962) of the Climax Stock at the Nevada Test Site has provided useful information on the magnetic properties of granitic rocks. The upper part of a hole drilled in quartz monzonite had a susceptibility of about 1.46×10^{-3} cgs/cc and 0.8 percent magnetite while the lower part in granodiorite had a susceptibility of about 2.94×10^{-3} cgs/cc with about 1.4 percent magnetite by weight. The remanent magnetization of several samples was measured and found to be less than one-eighth of the induced magnetization and with a random scattering of directions. In such cases, the effects of remanent magnetization some distance from the body are clearly of little or no significance.

Other studies of a similar nature have been reported; for example, Ito (1964) studied a series of Miocene granitic intrusives from Japan and found remanent intensities of 1×10^{-5} to 1×10^{-4} cgs/gm. The samples with intensities of about 1×10^{-4} show a stable, well-grouped remanent magnetization. It is still found, however, that the Q ratios are considerably less than one, even for these rocks dated at about 15 million years.

It can, therefore, be seen that the magnetic properties of rock vary widely, and no standard rules for prediction can be used. In general, the dark rocks are more magnetic than light ones; and in general, these rocks have greater Q ratios so that much care needs to be taken in making interpretations of magnetic data based on the assumption of susceptibility magnetization in the earth's fields. In many geophysical problems, of course, one is interested only in the depth to the source. Since this determination can be made independently of the direction of magnetization, the standard techniques are still quite usable. Difficulties in interpretation arise only when one attempts to infer something about the geometry of the causing body.

Acknowledgments

I should like to acknowledge permission to reproduce Figure 2 from the *Philosophical Magazine*, Figures 9 and 11 from L. O. Bacon and P. A. Shandley, Figure 16 from the *Journal of Geophysical Research*, and Figures 17 and 18 from *Geophysics*. I am also indebted to Kennecott Copper Corporation for preparation of the manuscript.

References

Akimoto, S., 1957, Magnetic properties of ferromagnetic oxide minerals as a basis of rock-magnetism: Advances in Physics, v. 6, p. 288.

Akimoto, S., and Nagata, T., 1960, Report on the fundamental basis of rock-magnetism: Report to the International Association of Geomagnetism and Aeronomy presented at Helsinki, Finland.

Allingham, J. W., and Zietz, I., 1962, Geophysical data on the Climax Stock, Nevada Test Site, Nye County, Nevada: Geophysics, v. 27, p. 599.

Books, K. G., 1962, Remanent magnetism as a contributor to some aeromagnetic anomalies: Geophysics, v. 27, p. 359.

Bruckshaw, J. McG., and Robertson, E. I., 1948, The measurement of magnetic properties of rocks: Journal of Scientific Instruments, v. 25, p. 444.

———— 1949, The magnetic properties of the Tholeiite Dykes of North England: Monthly Notices of the Royal Astronomical Society Supplement, v. 5, p. 308.

Bull, C., Irving, E. I., and Willis, I., 1962, Further paleomagnetic results from South Victoria Land, Antarctica: Geophysical Journal of the Royal Astronomical Society, v. 6, p. 320.

Chevallier, R., 1925, L'Aimantation des Lavas de l'Etna: Annales de Physique, v. 4, p. 5.

Collinson, D. W., and Creer, K. M., 1960, Measurements in paleomagnetism: Methods and Techniques in Geophysics, v. I, edited by S. K. Runcorn, Interscience Publishers, London.

Collinson, D. W., Creer, K. M., Irving E., and Runcorn, S. K., 1957, The measurement of the permanent magnetization of rocks: Phil. Trans., v. 250, p. 73.

Cox, A., and Doell, R. R., 1960, Review of paleomagnetism: Bulletin of the Geological Society of America, v. 71, p. 645.

———— 1962, Magnetic properties of the basalt in hole EM 7, Mohole Project: Journal of Geophysical Research, v. 67, p. 3997.

Creer, K. M., Irving, E. I., and Nairn, A. E. M., 1959, Paleomagnetism of the Great Whin Sill: Geophysical Journal Royal Astronomical Society, v. 2, p. 306.

Currie, R. G., Grommé, C. S., and Verhoogen, J., 1963, Remanent magnetization of some upper Cretaceous granitic plutons in the Sierra Nevada, California: Journal of Geophysical Research, v. 68, p. 2263.

Girdler, R. W., 1961, The measurement and computation of anisotropy of magnetic susceptibility of rocks: Geophysical Journal of the Royal Astronomical Society, v. 5, p. 34.

Gough, D. I., 1956, A study of the paleomagnetism of the Pilansberg Dykes: Monthly Notices of the Royal Astronomical Society, v. 7, p. 196.

Graham, J., 1953, Changes of ferromagnetic minerals and their bearing on the magnetic properties of rocks: Journal of Geophysical Research, v. 58, p. 243.

Graham, J. W., 1955, Evidence of polar shift since Triassic times: Journal of Geophysical Research, v. 60, p. 329.

Green, R., 1960, Remanent magnetization and the interpretation of magnetic anomalies: Geophys. Prosp., v. 8, p. 98.

Hawes, J., 1952, A magnetic study of the Spavinaw granite area, Oklahoma: Geophysics, v. 17, p. 27.

Hood, P. J., 1961, Paleomagnetic study of the Sudbury Basin: Journal of Geophysical Research, v. 66, p. 1235.

Irving, E., and Green, R., 1957, The paleomagnetism of the Cainozoic Basalts from Australia: Proceedings of the Royal Society of Victoria, v. 70, p. 1.

Ito, H., 1963, Paleomagnetic study on Kyushu outer zone: 1963 Annual Progress Report of the Rock Magnetism Research Group in Japan.

Jahren, C. E., 1963, Magnetic susceptibility of bedded iron formation: Geophysics, v. 28, p. 756.

Manley, H., 1954, The thermomagnetic properties of the Tholeiite Dikes of Britain: Geofisica Pura e Applicata, p. 29.

Mooney, H. M., and Bleifuss, R., 1953, Magnetic susceptibility measurements in Minnesota: Geophysics, v. 18, p. 383.

Nagata, T., 1961, Rock magnetism: Maruzen Press, Tokyo, 350 p.

Néel, L., 1955, Some theoretical aspects of rock magnetism: Advances in Physics, v. 4, p. 191.

Ponomarev, V. N., and Glukhikh, I. I., 1963, The problem of the determination of iron composition in magnetite ores based upon the magnitude of their magnetic susceptibility: Izvestiya, Academy of Sciences, Geophysics Series, v. 7, p. 742 (translated).

Puzicha, K., 1941, Der magnetismus der gesteine als funktion ihres magnetitgehaltes: Beitrage zur angtewande Geophysik, v. 9, p. 158.

Schreiner, G., 1958, Age of a Pilansberg Dyke of paleomagnetic significance: Nature, v. 181, p. 1330.

Shandley, P. D., and Bacon, L. O., 1963, Analysis for magnetite utilizing magnetic susceptibility: Paper presented at the S.E.G. Meeting, New Orleans, La.

Slichter, L. B., 1929, Certain aspects of magnetic surveying: A.I.M.E., Trans., v. 81, p. 258.

Stoner, E. C., 1935, The demagnetization factor for ellipsoids: Philosophical Magazine, p. 36.

Strangway, D. W., 1958, Measurement of the thermal variation of magnetic susceptibility: M.A. Thesis, University of Toronto.

—————— 1961, Magnetic properties of diabase dikes: Journal of Geophysical Research, v. 66, p. 3021.

—————— 1964, Rock magnetism and dike classification: Journal of Geology, v. 72, p. 648–663.

Thellier, É., and Thellier, O., 1959, Sur l'intensité' du champ magnetique dons le passé' historique et géologique: Annales de Géophysique, v. 15, p. 285.

Vincenz, S. A., 1954, The magnetic properties of some Tertiary intrusives of the Isle of Mull: Monthly Notices of the Royal Astronomical Society Supplement, v. 6, p. 590.

Wait, J. R., 1951, A conducting sphere in a time varying field: Geophysics, v. 16, p. 666.

Werner, S., 1945, Determinations of the magnetic susceptibility of ores and rocks from Swedish iron ore deposits: Swedish Geological Survey.

West, G. F., 1957, Theoretical studies for induction prospecting: M.A. Thesis, University of Toronto.

ELEMENTARY APPROXIMATIONS IN AEROMAGNETIC INTERPRETATION†

D. W. SMELLIE*

Total magnetic intensity anomaly expressions are derived for four simple sources: the point pole, line of poles, point dipole and line of dipoles. Type curves are presented for the point pole and dipole. For all cases, factors are calculated which may be multiplied into the half-maximum distances on the anomaly profiles to yield depth estimates. These methods serve as a first approximation in the interpretation of aeromagnetic data, but their limitations must be kept in mind. Two examples of the application of the methods are given.

Introduction

Although "flux-gate" type total magnetic intensity instruments have been used for aeromagnetic prospecting for some ten years, only a small amount of material has appeared in the literature pertaining to the interpretation of data. Henderson and Zietz (1948) have calculated factors for depth determinations using the point pole and line of poles approximations. This work is modified in the present paper. Vacquier et al. (1951) have used vertical prismatic models for interpreting deep anomalies. Various procedures have been developed for treatment of the data, such as the computation of second vertical derivatives (Henderson and Zietz, 1949a), the upward continuation of anomalies (Henderson and Zietz, 1949b) and the computation of vertical magnetic anomalies from total magnetic field measurements (Hughes and Pondrom, 1947). Peters (1949) has described analytical methods for interpreting vertical magnetic intensity data in deep basement areas which may readily be extended to the total magnetic field case. All these methods depend on the anomalous field being small compared with the normal total intensity of the earth's field, in which case the anomalous field is a harmonic function.

In this paper, four approximate methods are presented—the point pole, line of poles, point dipole and line of dipoles. Type profiles of total magnetic intensity are given for the point sources. For all four types of sources the peak displacement is determined, and

factors calculated for depth determinations using the two distances from maximum to half-maximum along the anomaly profile.

General Considerations

Potential fields of any type are inherently ambiguous. In other words, theoretically an infinite number of solutions may be obtained for the physical property distribution giving rise to a particular anomaly, be it magnetic, gravitational or electrical. Of course, only a limited number would be likely on geological grounds. The present simple models indicate depths to the equivalent pole or dipole of the source.

In aeromagnetic surveying, two general classes of problems present themselves. There are the surveys of sedimentary basins where the strongest anomalies are due to lithologic contrasts within the basement. If sufficient susceptibility contrast exists between the sediments and basement complex, this is reflected in a broad profile which reflects the basement structure. Basement highs then yield local anomalies but unambiguous interpretation of these is difficult. The simple models may be useful as a first approximation for depth estimates, but the prism models of Vacquier et al. (1951) can often give more enlightening results. Surveys of this type are usually flown at constant elevation above sea level and are mainly of interest to the petroleum industry.

The shallow-source problem of interest in mining geophysics, on the other hand, deals with magnetic bodies close to the earth's

† Reprinted from GEOPHYSICS v. 21, no. 4.

* Consultant, Vancouver, B. C., Canada.

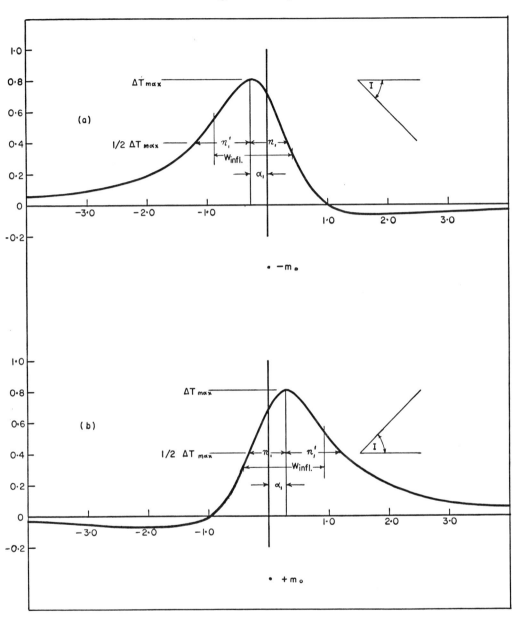

FIG. 1. Total intensity anomaly due to point source in (a) northern and (b) southern magnetic hemispheres, showing profile in units of depth at geomagnetic latitude 45°. The anomalous field component Δt is expressed in units of m_0/ζ^2.

surface, and, hence, surveys are generally conducted at a fixed average height above terrain, usually 500 ft. Rugged terrain can introduce complexities in the profiles, but in country of low topographic relief the results are amenable to analysis. All four approximations have been useful, as well as the two-

dimensional dike and vertical contact problems. Anomalies which duplicate the theoretical model curves are rare, with the result that the models are used only as a guide to qualitative interpretation.

Figure 1 shows the total intensity anomaly on a *meridional* profile passing directly over the point source, in both the northern and southern hemispheres. These illustrate the features of the normal type of profile encountered in practice and the *correspondence between hemispheres*.

The applicability of the approximations depends on the geomagnetic latitude and the dimensions of the source. When the width of the body is small compared to its depth and it is elongated in the direction of polarization, the pole approximations yield the depth to the top. Thus, narrow vertical dikes would yield to a line of poles approximation at high geomagnetic latitudes. However, in low geomagnetic latitudes the dipole moment would make a larger contribution to the observed field. For bodies of limited extent in depth, the dipole approximations yield the depth to the center, the point dipole for bodies approaching a sphere in shape, the line of dipoles a horizontal cylinder. Sources which are wide compared with their depth will give broad profiles, and depth determinations made from them give values that are too large. This is also the case with complex sources consisting of several closely spaced anomalous bodies, whose effects merge to give a single anomaly. The estimated depth will be a maximum value, useful at least for distinguishing shallow from deep-seated sources.

Interpretation of anomalies characterized by nearly circular contours may be approached using a pole or dipole method, while those with contours elongated in one direction require a line of poles or line of dipoles. The choice between pole and dipole approximations is best made by considering the intensity of the minimum in relation to the maximum (Figures 3, 7). Finally, it must be emphasized that the methods serve as a guide to geological reasoning and more elaborate theoretical methods.

Point Pole Approximation

Theory for the total intensity anomaly due to a point pole in the northern hemisphere has been presented (Henderson and Zietz, 1948), but is modified in the present work. In the northern magnetic hemisphere, a narrow body greatly extended in depth whose long axis is close to the direction of polarization, if

polarized normally may be represented by a negative magnetic pole at its upper end.

Using an orthogonal Cartesian coordinate system, z axis vertically downward, pole $-m_0$ at $z = \zeta$, the anomalous magnetic potential ΔV is given by

$$\Delta V = - \frac{m_0}{[x^2 + y^2 + (z - \zeta)^2]^{1/2}} \cdot \quad (1)$$

In the xy plane, the total intensity anomaly $\Delta T(x, y, 0)$ is

$$\Delta T(x, y, 0) = - m_0$$
$$\cdot \frac{x \cos I \cos \beta + y \cos I \sin \beta - \zeta \sin I}{[x^2 + y^2 + \zeta^2]^{3/2}} \quad (2)$$

where the x axis makes an angle β with magnetic north and the y axis is in the northerly half-plane. I is the inclination of the total field T. A profile along the y axis is given by

$$\Delta T(y) = m_0 \sin I \frac{\zeta - ay}{[y^2 + \zeta^2]^{3/2}} \quad (3)$$

where

$$a = \cot I \sin \beta. \quad (4)$$

The peak value ΔT_{max} occurs when $\beta = 90°$ at the point

$$y = - \zeta \alpha_1$$

where

$$\alpha_1 = [(9 + 8 \cot^2 I)^{1/2} - 3]/4 \cot I \quad (5)$$

and its value is

$$\Delta T_{max}$$
$$= m_0 \sin I(1 + \alpha_1 \cot I)/\zeta^2(\alpha_1{}^2 + 1)^{3/2}. \quad (6)$$

The minimum value occurs at

$$y = \zeta \gamma_1$$

where

$$\gamma_1 = [3 + (9 + 8 \cot^2 I)^{1/2}]/4 \cot I \quad (7)$$

and its value is

$$\Delta T_{min}$$
$$= m_0 \sin I(1 - \gamma_1 \cot I)/\zeta^2(\gamma_1{}^2 + 1)^{3/2}. \quad (8)$$

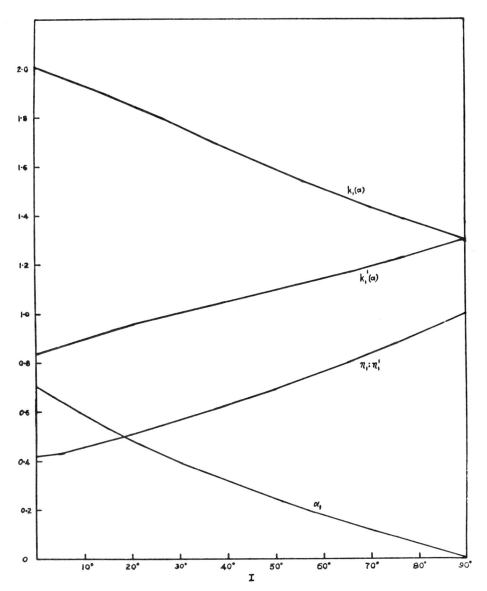

FIG. 2. Total intensity depth factors $k_1(a)$ and $k_1'(a)$, half-maximum distance ratio $\eta_1 : \eta_1'$ and peak displacement α_1 for point source.

Also,

$$\Delta T(y) = 0, \qquad \text{when } y = \zeta \tan I. \quad (9)$$

We wish to calculate factors which, when multiplied into the distance from maximum to half-maximum intensity along a meridional profile, yield the depth to the point pole. We transform our origin to the peak of the anomaly, taking the y axis along the magnetic meridian, obtaining

$$\Delta T(y') = m_0 \sin I$$

$$\cdot \frac{\zeta(1 + \alpha_1 \cot I) - y' \cot I}{[y'^2 - 2\alpha_1 \zeta y' + \zeta^2(1 + \alpha_1^2)]^{3/2}}. \quad (10)$$

Substituting $y' = \zeta/k$ in equation (10) and

equating with $\frac{1}{2}\Delta T_{\max}$ from equation (6), we obtain

$$\frac{1 + \alpha_1 \cot I}{2(\alpha_1{}^2 + 1)^{3/2}k^2}$$

$$= \frac{k(1 + \alpha_1 \cot I) - \cot I}{[1 - 2\alpha_1 k + k^2(1 + \alpha_1{}^2)]^{3/2}}. \quad (11)$$

This may be solved numerically for two real roots, a positive $k_1(a)$ and a negative $-k_1'(a)$. They are to be used with η, the distance from the anomaly maximum to half-

maximum in a northerly direction, and η' in a southerly (in the northern hemisphere). These directions are reversed in the southern hemisphere, cf. Figure 1.

The depth $\zeta = k_1\eta = k_1'\eta'$. The ratio of half-maximum distances $\eta:\eta'$ on the actual anomaly should approximate the theoretical ratio $\eta_1:\eta_1' = k_1':k_1$ if the point pole is an adequate representation of the physical situation. The peak displacement α_1, the factors $k_1(a)$, $k_1'(a)$ and the ratio $\eta_1:\eta_1'$ are given in Figure 2. A family of ΔT profiles corresponding to

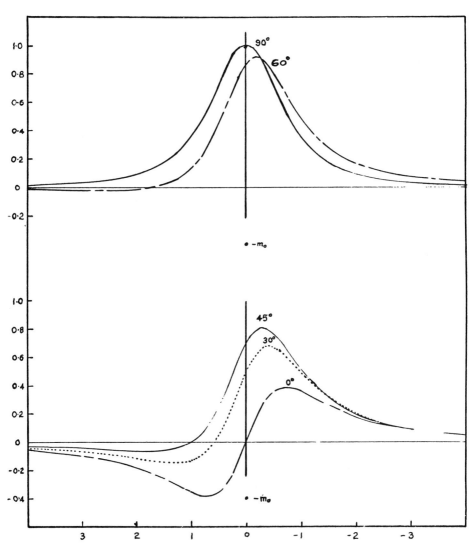

FIG. 3. Total intensity anomaly from a point source at various geomagnetic latitudes (northern hemisphere). Profiles in units of depth on magnetic meridian. The anomalous field component ΔT is in units of m_0/ζ^2.

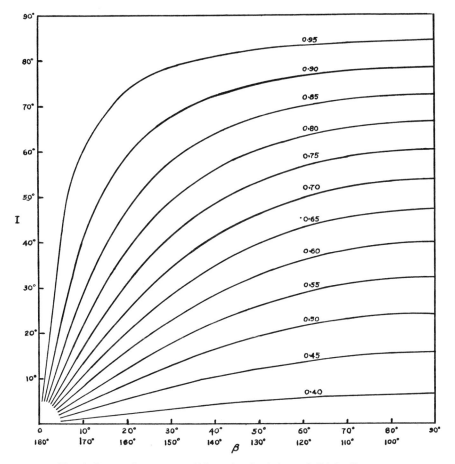

FIG. 4. Curves of constant total intensity depth factor $k_2'(a)$ for line source.

various values of I is presented in Figure 3. Similar notation is used in the subsequent three cases, subscripts 2, 3, 4, corresponding to line of poles, dipole and line of dipoles respectively.

Since a contour aeromagnetic map is normally made up in practice, it was thought sufficient to determine the $k-$ factors for the case $\beta=90°$ corresponding to profiles taken through the anomaly maximum, along the magnetic meridian. In a given practical case, the distances η_1 and η_1' are measured on a meridian profile. These may be multiplied by the factors $k_1(a)$ and $k_1'(a)$, respectively, to yield two depth determinations. If the maximum is difficult to locate, we may measure the distance η'' between points of half-maximum intensity and determine $\zeta=k_1''\eta''$ where

$$k_1''(a) = \frac{k_1(a)k_1'(a)}{k_1(a) + k_1'(a)} \cdot \quad (12)$$

A transverse $(\beta=180°)$ profile through the maximum may serve as a check. This is symmetrical. The width between points of half-maximum intensity η_τ'' per unit depth is given by

$$\eta_\tau'' = 1.533(1 + \alpha_1^2)^{1/2} \quad (13)$$

and, therefore, the depth factor k_τ'' is given by

$$k_\tau'' = 0.652(1 + \alpha_1^2)^{-1/2}. \quad (14)$$

The work of Henderson and Zietz (1948) should be referred to. These authors find the maximum anomaly and one half-maximum point on lines in any direction passing di-

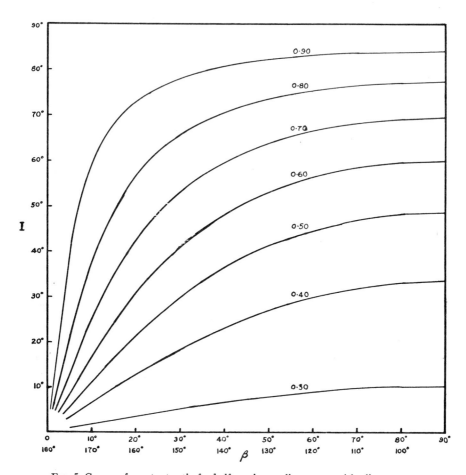

FIG. 5. Curves of constant ratio for half-maximum distance $\eta_2 : \eta_2'$ for line source.

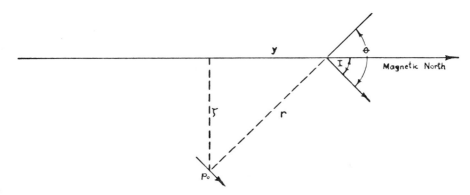

FIG. 6. Geometry of the dipole approximation.

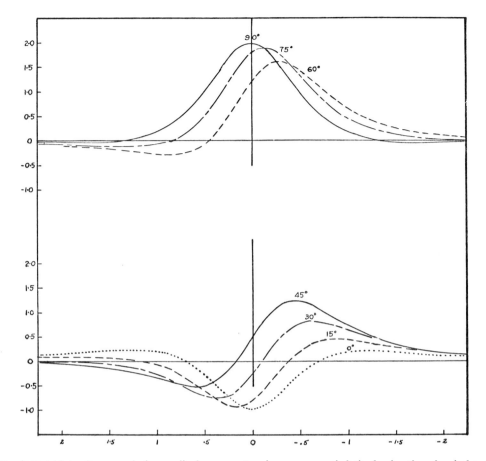

FIG. 7. Total intensity anomaly from a dipole source at various geomagnetic latitudes (northern hemisphere). Profiles in units of depth along magnetic meridian ΔT is in units of p_0/ζ^3.

rectly above the point pole. Of these lines, only that in the magnetic meridian passes through the absolute anomaly maximum, giving the results presented above. For all other directions, the absolute maximum lies to the south of the line (in the northern hemisphere).

In the southern magnetic hemisphere, our type body would be represented by a positive magnetic pole. The magnetic potential is now

$$\Delta V = \frac{m_0}{[x^2 + y^2 + (z - \zeta)^2]^{1/2}} \quad (15)$$

and for a profile along the meridian (y-axis.),

$$\Delta T(y) = m_0 \sin I \, \frac{\zeta + ay}{(y^2 + \zeta^2)^{3/2}}. \quad (16)$$

This expression is merely a mirror image of that for the northern hemisphere. As a result, we may use our northern hemisphere results in the southern hemisphere, provided that we take our distances from maximum to half-maximum η in a southerly direction and η' in a northerly direction.

Line of Poles

The theory for this approximation is also given by Henderson and Zietz (1948), who give factors

$$k_2(a) = \frac{a}{2b} \left[1 + \left(\frac{3b - 1}{b - 1} \right)^{1/2} \right] \quad (17)$$

where

$$b = (a^2 + 1)^{1/2} \quad (18)$$

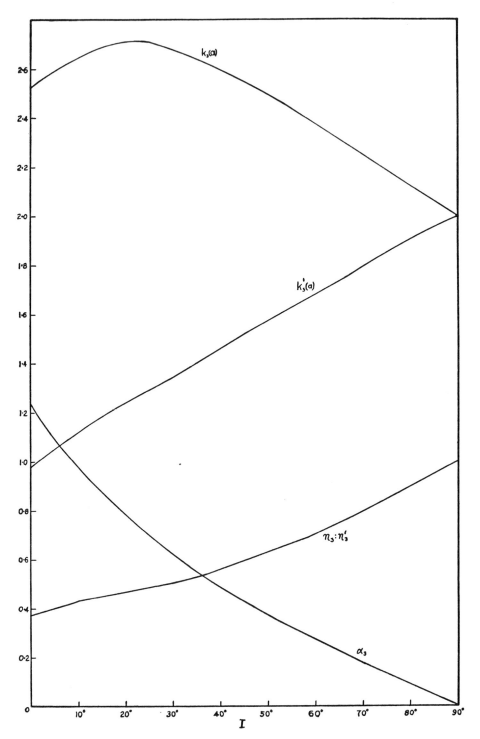

FIG. 8. Total intensity depth factors $k_3(a)$ and $k_3'(a)$, half-maximum distance ratio $\eta_3:\eta_3'$ in peak displacement α^3 for dipole source.

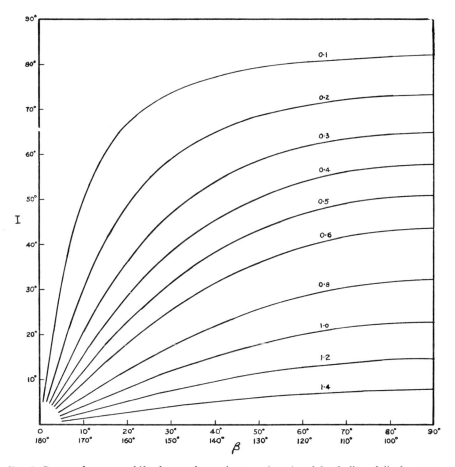

FIG. 9. Curves of constant shift of anomaly maximum α_4 in units of depth, line of dipoles source.

as a function of inclination of the total field I and angle β between strike of body and magnetic north. These factors are for depth determinations using profiles perpendicular to the strike of the anomaly. The half-maximum distance η must be taken northerly in the northern hemisphere and southerly in the southern hemisphere. For the other half-maximum distance,

$$-k_2'(a) = \frac{a}{2b}\left[1 - \left(\frac{3b-1}{b-1}\right)^{1/2}\right]. \quad (19)$$

Values of $k_2'(a)$ as a function of I and β are given in Figure 4.

The ratio of half-maximum distances is given by

$$\eta_2 : \eta_2' = \left[(3b-1)^{1/2} - (b-1)^{1/2}\right]$$
$$/\left[(3b-1)^{1/2} + (b-1)^{1/2}\right] \quad (20)$$

and is plotted in Figure 5. This enables us to compare the measured ratio with a theoretical value and thus see the degree of approximation obtained.

The reflection at the origin for the southern hemisphere anomaly profiles is shown easily for this case.

The shift of the anomaly peak from a position directly above the source is in the negative y-direction and of amount

$$\alpha_2 = (b-1)/a \quad . \quad (21)$$

and the peak value

$$\Delta T_{\max} = \frac{2m_1 \sin I}{\zeta} \frac{1 - a\alpha_2}{1 + \alpha_2^2} \quad (22)$$

where m_1 is the pole strength per unit length,

Point Dipole Approximation

We assume a dipole moment p_0 in the direction of the earth's field at a depth ζ below the plane of observations (Figure 6). The anomalous magnetic potential in the northern hemisphere for a meridional profile passing directly over the source is then

$$\Delta V_3 = p_0 \frac{y \cos I - \zeta \sin I}{(y^2 + \zeta^2)^{3/2}}. \qquad (23)$$

Expressed in units of depth, the total intensity anomaly is

$$\Delta T_3 = f_3(\alpha) p_0 / \zeta^3 \qquad (24)$$

where

$$f_3(\alpha) = [(3 \sin^2 I - 1) - 6 \sin I \cos I \cdot \alpha$$
$$+ (3 \cos^2 I - 1)\alpha^2]/(1 + \alpha^2)^{5/2}. \quad (25)$$

From this expression, $f_3(\alpha)$ has been calculated for representative values of I and the results presented in Figure 7. The mirror images in y of these curves are suitable for application in the southern hemisphere.

To determine the shift of anomaly maximum from the position directly above the source, we set

$$\frac{\partial}{\partial \alpha}(\Delta T) = 0, \quad \text{i.e.}$$

$$(3 \cos^2 I - 1)\alpha^3 - (8 \sin I \cos I)\alpha^2$$
$$+ (7 \sin^2 I - 3)\alpha + 2 \sin I \cos I = 0. \quad (26)$$

The negative real root of this equation yields the required value $-\alpha_3$ at the anomaly maximum. This has been calculated for a number of values of I and the results given in Figure 8.

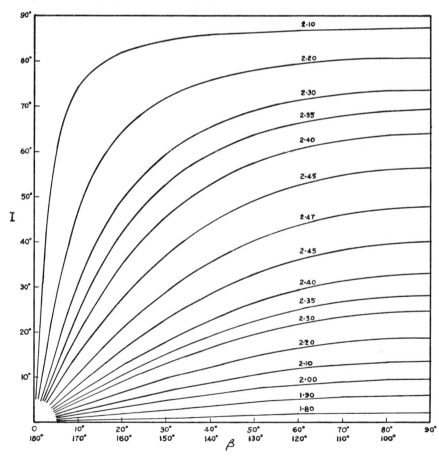

FIG. 10. Curves of constant total intensity depth factor $k_4(a)$ for line of dipoles source.

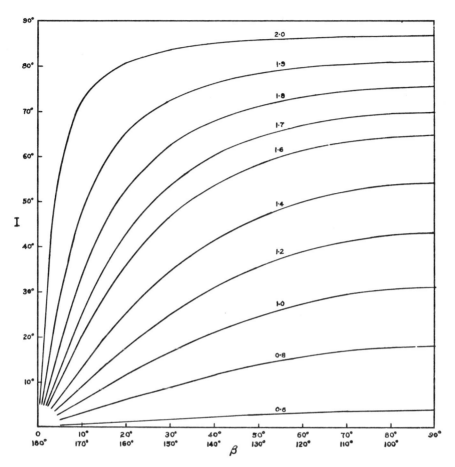

FIG. 11. Curves of constant total intensity depth factor $k_4'(a)$ for line of dipoles source.

The half-maximum depth factors $k_3(a)$ and $k_3'(a)$ were obtained for various values of I by calculating the maximum value $f_3(-\alpha_3)$. Half of this value is then substituted in the expression for $f_3(\alpha)$ and the resulting equation solved for two real roots β_3 and β_3' ($\beta_3 > \beta_3'$). Then

$$k_3(a) = (\beta_3 + \alpha_3)^{-1}$$

$$k_3'(a) = -(\alpha_3 + \beta_3')^{-1}$$

$$\eta_3 : \eta_3' = -(\beta_3 + \alpha_3)/(\alpha_3 + \beta_3'). \quad (27)$$

These factors are given in Figure 8.

Line of Dipoles

Consider a line of magnetic dipoles at depth ζ whose dipole moment is p_1 per unit length in the direction of the earth's field and which strikes at an angle β with magnetic north. We have for the magnetic potential in the northern hemisphere

$$\Delta V_4 = 2p_1[y \cos I \sin \beta + (z - \zeta) \sin I]$$
$$/[y^2 + (\zeta - z)^2] \quad (28)$$

when the y direction is normal to strike and positive in the northerly half-plane. The total intensity anomaly for a profile along the y axis is given by

$$\Delta T_4 = 2p_1 \cos^2 I \sin^2 \beta f_4(\alpha)/\zeta^2 \quad (29)$$

where

$$f_4(\alpha) = [(\alpha^2 - 1)(1 - q^2) - 4\alpha q]$$
$$/(1 + \alpha^2)^2 \quad (30)$$

and

$$q = \tan I \csc \beta = a^{-1}. \tag{31}$$

The method of calculation of the half-maximum depth factors is the same as for the point dipole, the parameter used being q. Families of curves of constant q are used to show the factors in the same manner as for the line of poles. The results for α_4, $k_4(a)$, $k_4'(a)$ and $\eta_4 : \eta_4'$ are shown in Figures 9, 10, 11 and 12, respectively.

Applications

Two field cases will be used as examples of the application of methods outlined in this paper. The first is from a survey in a high northern geomagnetic latitude, the Campbellford area of Canada, and is designated

the Marmora Anomaly. The effect of line spacing on the detection of this anomaly has recently been discussed by Agocs (1955). Data were taken with a Gulf airborne magnetometer and published by the Geological Survey of Canada as Aeromagnetic Sheet No. 31 C/5, Campbellford. A copy of a portion of this map appears as Figure 13.

The anomaly minimum is weak, so a pole approximation is used. The elongation of the contours is not too pronounced, so the point pole model was first tried. Along the magnetic meridian (dotted line) we have distances from anomaly maximum to half-maximum in both north and south directions of 910 ft, indicating a ratio $\eta : \eta' = 1$ as opposed to the theoretical value for the point pole of 0.88 when $I = 75°$ (Figure 2). Estimated depths are $\zeta_1 = k_1(a)\eta = 1,270$ ft from

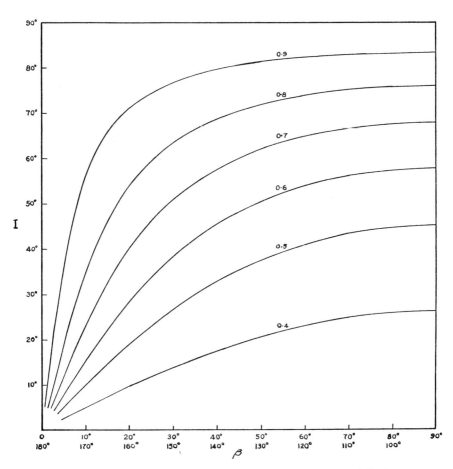

FIG. 12. Curves of constant ratio half-maximum distances $\eta_4 : \eta_4'$ for line of dipoles source.

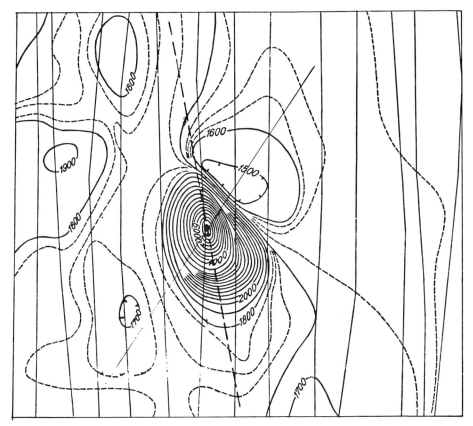

FIG. 13. Total magnetic intensity map showing the Marmora anomaly, a portion of Geological Survey of Canada Aeromagnetic Sheet No. 31C/5, Campbellford. Scale: one inch equals one mile. Flight lines shown.

the northerly distance η and $\zeta_1' = k_1'(a)\eta' = 1,110$ ft from the southerly η^1. If we assume a line of poles striking at $\beta = 45°$ as indicated by the trend of the contours, we have (solid profile) $\eta = 580$ ft, $\eta' = 700$ ft, $\eta : \eta' = 0.82$, the theoretical value (Figure 5, $I = 75°$, $\beta = 45°$). Thus, this approximation seems more suitable. The estimated depths are then $\zeta_2 = k_2(a)\eta = 630$ ft (Henderson and Zietz, 1948, Figure 4), $\zeta_2' = k_2'(a)\eta' = 630$ ft (this paper, Figure 4).

The magnetic ore mass causing this anomaly is 2,400 ft long and 500 ft wide at its maximum width, with a northwest-southeast strike and a dip southwest of 70 to 80 degrees. It is capped by 120 ft of limestone, which added to the flight elevation gives the depth to the top of about 620 ft. From the configuration and depth of the source, the line of poles would be a suitable geophysical

representation of it, as is shown by the agreement between estimated and actual depths. The width of the body would tend to broaden the anomaly slightly in this case, but its finite length would have a narrowing effect.

The second example is from a survey in a low southern geomagnetic latitude, the Katherine-Darwin region of Australia, and is designated Brown's Anomaly. This aeromagnetic anomaly, located southwest of Brown's Deposit, Rum Jungle, Northern Territory, appears on the contour map of Figure 14. This was compiled from data obtained using an AN/ASQ-1 magnetic airborne detector at an average height of 500 ft above terrain and supplied by the Bureau of Mineral Resources, Geology and Geophysics, of the Commonwealth of Australia. Although the anomaly profile changes along strike in distances comparable with the "half-width" of

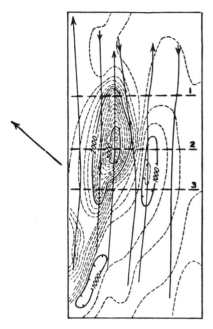

Fig. 14. Total magnetic intensity map showing Brown's anomaly, Rum Jungle, Northern Territory. Figure provided from an airborne magnetometer compilation sheet by the Bureau of Mineral Resources, Geology and Geophysics of the Commonwealth of Australia. Scale: one inch equals one mile. Flight lines shown.

the anomaly, it was considered useful to measure the half-maximum distances on three representative profiles along the anomaly. These are indicated on Figure 14. We find "half-widths," the distances between half-maximum values, on profiles 1, 2, and 3 of 1,320, 1,320 and 990 ft approximately, indicating decrease in either depth or width to the southwest.

On profile no. 1, $\eta = 500$ ft, $\eta' = 820$ ft, hence $\eta : \eta' = 0.61$ which is above the theoretical value 0.47 for a line of poles at $\beta = 120°$, $I = 40°$ (Figure 5). The anomaly minimum is not pronounced, favoring the line of poles. From the two half-maximum distances, estimated depths are $\zeta_2 = 670$ ft, $\zeta_2' = 520$ ft. Using the total half-width, $\zeta_2'' = 570$ ft, indicating that the top of the magnetic body comes close to the surface. On profile no. 2, $\eta : \eta' = 0.8$, rather high for a line approximation, but would correspond to a line of vertical dipoles. For this case, the depth to the

center was found to equal the half-width, i.e., 1,320 ft. Profile No. 3 also has a high $\eta : \eta'$ ratio, 0.7 half-width $= 990$ ft $=$ depth to center for a line of vertical dipoles.

Subsequent ground magnetic work showed a vertical magnetic intensity profile fairly simple to the northeast but developing a double peak to the center giving rise to the increased apparent depth. Drilling at the center revealed a pyrrhotite-bearing body coming close to the surface.

In measuring the η's in both these cases, the half-maximum values is, of course, taken as the median value between the intensity of anomaly maximum and the general level in areas away from the anomaly. Choice of the latter is somewhat arbitrary, the actual values selected being 1,700 γ for the Marmora Anomaly and 1,300 γ for Brown's Anomaly.

A further point of interest is the question of line spacing in order to detect sources of limited extent at a given depth. It appears that the point pole would offer a common case, and it is easily seen from equation (13) that for (magnetic) north-south flight lines, the probability of recording an anomaly from a point source with maximum at least one-half the absolute anomaly, maximum is given by $P = 1.53(1 + \alpha_1^2)^{1/2} \zeta / S$ where S is the flight-line spacing and ζ the depth to the source.

Acknowledgments

It is a pleasure to acknowledge the suggestions for revision of this paper made by Professor J. C. Jaeger. Grateful acknowledgement is due to the Director of the Geological Survey of Canada for permission to use the compilation sheet shown as Figure 13 and to the Director of the Bureau of Mineral Resources, Geology and Geophysics, of the Commonwealth of Australia for the compilation sheet shown as Figure 14.

References

Agocs, W. B., 1955, Line spacing effect and determination of optimum spacing, illustrated by Marmora, Ontario, magnetic anomaly: Trans. C.I.M.M., v. 58, p. 397–400.

Henderson, R. G., and Zietz, I., 1948, Analysis of

total magnetic intensity anomalies produced by point and line sources: Geophysics, v. 13, p. 428–436.

———— 1949a, The computation of second vertical derivatives of geomagnetic fields: Geophysics, v. 14, p. 508–516.

———— 1949b, The upward continuation of anomalies in total magnetic intensity fields: Geophysics, v. 14, p. 517–534.

Hughes, D. S., and Pondrom, W. L., 1947, Computation of vertical magnetic anomalies from total magnetic field measurements: Trans. A.G.U., v. 28, p. 193–197.

Peters, L. J., 1949, The direct approach to magnetic interpretation and its practical application: Geophysics, v. 14, p. 290–320.

Vacquier, V., Steenland, N. C., Henderson, R. G., and Zietz, I., 1951, Interpretation of aeromagnetic maps (memoir 47): New York, Geol. Soc. Am.

MAGNETIC-DOUBLET THEORY IN THE ANALYSIS OF TOTAL-INTENSITY† ANOMALIES

ROLAND G. HENDERSON* AND ISIDORE ZIETZ*

Analysis of horizontal- or vertical-intensity magnetic anomalies in terms of equivalent magnetic doublets has been extensively used for rough estimates of depth and depth extent of disturbing rocks. In this investigation, factors have been theoretically determined by which appropriate total-intensity anomalies can also be analyzed in terms of their magnetic-doublet equivalents. The effectiveness and limitations of the method have been checked by application to anomalies derived from model experiments and to observed anomalies. For satisfactory results the effective radius of the disturbing body must be less than its depth of burial. The calculation of doublet length is not so reliable as the calculation of depth; however, the former is better at low magnetic latitudes.

Introduction

Limitations of magnetic interpretation

The results of aeromagnetic surveys are usually presented in the form of contour maps showing lines of equal total magnetic intensity. The anomalies of interest to exploration geophysicists are departures from smooth regularity, for they are indicative of inhomogeneities in the magnetism of the earth's crust. The relation of anomalies to subsurface geologic structure and to ore bodies is usually uncertain. For this reason interpretations of magnetic anomalies are often qualitative in nature, the map being discussed in terms of "grain" of the anomalies and generalization about likely contrasts in magnetic properties of the basement rocks from which the anomalies probably arise. In general, broad magnetic gradients several tens of miles in linear section represent regional variations in magnetization of the crust; anomalies 10 or 20 miles in lateral extent are associated with more abrupt changes in the magnetic character of the basement rocks; and areally small, high-gradient anomalies are indicative of near-surface concentrations of ferromagnetic materials.

The quantitative interpretation of aeromagnetic maps is at once a complicated and challenging area of geophysical investigation. The complications stem largely from the presence of induced and permanent (sometimes called remanent) magnetism in the disturbing body, from lack of knowledge of the magnetic and geometric parameters of the body, and from an inherent ambiguity affecting interpretation of potential fields. The ambiguity arises from the fact that there are many distributions of magnetic material at various depths which can produce a given anomaly. Supplementary geological and geophysical information is therefore necessary for unequivocal solutions.

Fundamentals of depth estimation

Useful estimates of depths to disturbing bodies are often possible from magnetic anomalies despite these limitations. The relative positions of the maximums, minimums, and inflection points of an anomaly (the so-called shape factors) are functions of the depth and are affected only in a limited way by the remaining geometric parameters of the configuration of the body. These characteristic shape factors are unaffected by blockwise lateral changes in magnetic susceptibility of the basement or by the magnitude of the remanent magnetism when the latter is in the direction of the induced magnetism. Most methods of estimating depth are based on quasi-empirical facts deduced from studies of the shape characteristics of theoretical anomalies. Induction theory is used almost exclusively. It is assumed that the magnetization is the product of the susceptibility contrast and the normal field strength, and that the

† Reprinted from Geological Survey Bulletin 1052-D.

* U. S. Geological Survey, Washington, D. C.

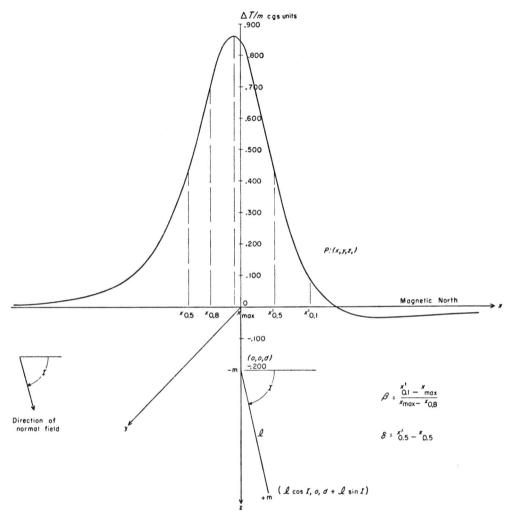

FIG. 1. Total-intensity anomaly for inclined doublet; coordinate system and meaning of β and δ.

direction of magnetization is that of the normal field.

Since the advent of the airborne magnetometer, there have been several papers on methods of depth analysis. In the method outlined by Vacquier and others (1951), the shape characteristics of an observed field are compared with those of prismatic-model fields, the comparison being facilitated by the use of second derivatives of the anomaly which bring the shape characteristics into sharper focus. The method has been used successfully in depth analyses of many broad, large-amplitude anomalies (Zietz and

Henderson, 1956; Henderson and Zietz, 1958).

Purpose and scope of investigation

Where the breadth of the anomaly is comparable to the depth of the source, the Vacquier method is less effective because the shape characteristics become more sensitive to parameters of the geometry other than the depth. Analyses of such anomalies can be made in terms of equivalent magnetic doublets. By equivalent magnetic doublet we mean two magnetic poles of equal strength and opposite sign, whose depths below the surface and mutual displacement in the direction of the earth's normal field are sufficient to account for the shape characteristics of the anomaly. In standard texts on geophysics, such as Heiland (1940), Jakosky (1950), and Nettleton (1940), magnetic doublets are discussed in relation to the anomaly in the vertical component (ΔZ) and the anomaly in the horizontal component (ΔH), but no general treatment for depth calculations is given. Vestine and Davids (1945) presented an ingenious method for analyzing ΔZ in terms of magnetic doublets.

In airborne magnetometry, however, we are interested in the component of the total-intensity anomaly in the direction of the total field vector. It is a linear combination of ΔZ and ΔH and existing theory of the interpretation of doublets is not in general applicable. The work reported here was undertaken to establish a set of model anomaly curves for ΔT doublets and to deduce from them factors that are diagnostic of the doublet parameters. Major interest is centered in the calculation of depth to the upper (or nearer) pole; however, the more intractable problem of doublet length is also considered. There is some latitude in the choice of specific portions of an anomaly profile for formulating the factors. In every case the choice was dictated by considerations of usefulness in practical applications. The method has been tested by application to laboratory magnetic models, and its application to practical anomalies is demonstrated.

Theoretical Doublet Anomalies

Formulation of interpretation factors

In this study it is tacitly assumed that the doublet is produced only by induction in the

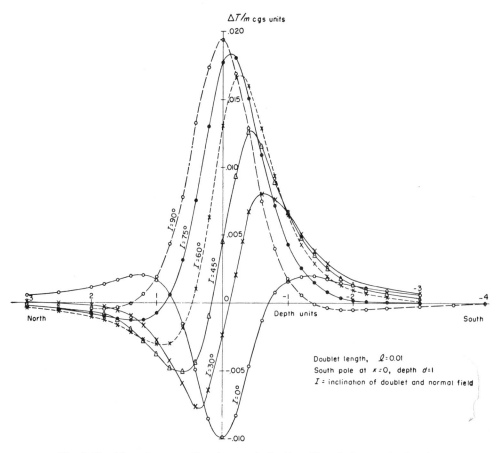

FIG. 2. Total-intensity anomalies of magnetic doublet of length, $l = 0.01$ depth unit.

earth's magnetic field, and that the north dip of the doublet is equal to the magnetic inclination. A right-handed system of coordinates is adopted (Figure 1) with origin at O, x positive to magnetic north, y positive to the east, and z positive vertically downwards. The components of the magnetic field, ΔX, ΔY, and ΔZ, are positive along the respective coordinate axes. The doublet of strength m and length l lies in the xz plane; the coordinates of the pole nearer the origin are $(0, 0, d)$, and those of the remote pole are $(l \cos I, 0, d+l \sin I)$.

The general expression for the anomaly at any point $P : (x, y, z)$ is given by

$$\Delta T(x, y, z) = m \left\{ \frac{(x - l \cos I)}{[(l \cos I - x)^2 + y^2 + (d + l \sin I - z)^2]^{3/2}} - \frac{x}{[x^2 + y^2 + (d - z)^2]^{3/2}} \right\}$$

$$\cdot \cos I + m \left\{ \frac{(d - z)}{[x^2 + y^2 + (d - z)^2]^{3/2}} - \frac{(d + l \sin I - z)}{[(l \cos I - x)^2 + y^2 + (d + l \sin I - z)^2]^{3/2}} \right\} \sin I$$

where it has been assumed that the magnetic inclination is constant over the area. If $y=z=0$, and all linear measures are expressed in units of the depth, a profile along the x axis is given by

$$\frac{\Delta T(x)}{m} = \frac{1}{d^2} \left\{ \frac{\left(\dfrac{x}{d} - \dfrac{l}{d} \cos I\right)}{\left[\left(\dfrac{l}{d} \cos I - \dfrac{x}{d}\right)^2 + \left(1 + \dfrac{l}{d} \sin I\right)^2\right]^{3/2}} - \frac{\dfrac{x}{d}}{\left[\left(\dfrac{x}{d}\right)^2 + 1\right]^{3/2}} \right\} \cos I$$

$$+ \frac{1}{d^2} \left\{ \frac{1}{\left[\left(\dfrac{x}{d}\right)^2 + 1\right]^{3/2}} - \frac{1 + \dfrac{l}{d} \sin I}{\left[\left(\dfrac{l}{d} \cos I - \dfrac{x}{d}\right)^2 + \left(1 + \dfrac{l}{d} \sin I\right)^2\right]^{3/2}} \right\} \sin I. \quad (1)$$

From formula (1), $\Delta T(x)/m$ was computed for doublets with parameters $l/d = 0.01, 0.10, 0.50, 1.00, 1.50, 2.00, 5.00$; and inclinations, $I = 0°, 30°, 45°, 60°, 75°, 90°$. These are shown in Figures 2 to 8, where the depth has been taken as unity.

From an empirical study of theoretical doublet-anomaly curves of this type, it is possible to determine factors, herein designated β and δ, which are useful in estimating l and d from observed anomalies. The dimensionless factor β involves the ratio between certain horizontal distances subtended by the curve, and δ is a horizontal distance, usually between half-maximum abscissas or between nearly inflectional points. In Figure 1, $\beta = (x'_{0.1} - x_{max})/(x_{max} - x_{0.8})$ and $\delta = x'_{0.5} - x_{0.5}$ where x_{max}, $x_{0.1}$, $x_{0.5}$, $x_{0.8}$ are the abscissas of ΔT_{max}, $0.1 \Delta T_{max}$, $0.5 \Delta T_{max}$, and $0.8 \Delta T_{max}$, respectively. Prime marks refer to the more northerly of two points.

Practical considerations require that β be determined from portions of the curve that are easily identifiable and, at most, only slightly affected by nearby disturbances. Peripheral features should be avoided as far as possible. Moreover, β and δ must be so chosen that there will be resolution between successive values of l/d. To satisfy these requirements, β and δ are necessarily different for each inclination. The selection of abscissas is facilitated if the vertical scale of each of the family of $\Delta T(x)$ curves is adjusted so that all maximums have the same amplitude, as is shown in Figure 9 for $I = 75°$. If in this figure, β where chosen in two different ways, say $\beta_1 = (x_{0.5} - x_{max})/(x_{max} - x'_{0.5})$ and $\beta_2 = (x'_{0.1} - x_{max})/(x_{max} - x_{0.8})$, the tabulation would be that shown in Table 1.

Table 1. Comparison of numerical values for two different definitions of β

l/d	0.01	0.10	0.50	1.00	1.50	2.00	5.00
β_1.....	1.24	1.23	1.22	1.17	1.14	1.12	1.08
β_2.....	2.52	2.68	2.79	3.00	3.19	3.21	3.59

The incremental changes in β_1 are too small to permit us adequately to distinguish

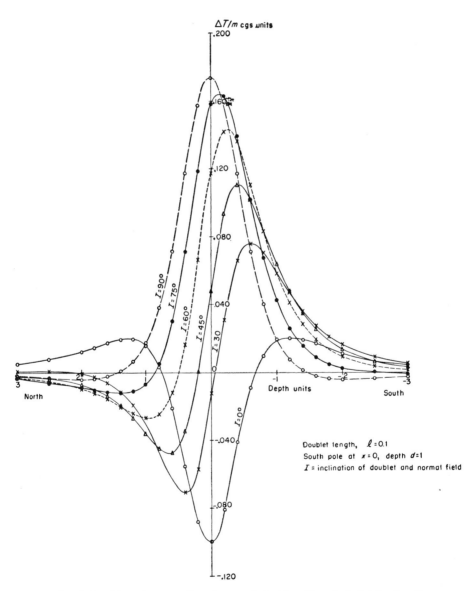

FIG. 3. Total-intensity anomalies of magnetic doublet of length, $l = 0.1$ depth unit.

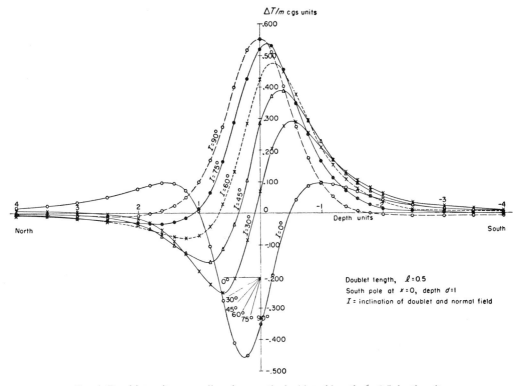

FIG. 4. Total-intensity anomalies of magnetic doublet of length, $l=0.5$ depth unit.

among the different terms l/d, but those of β_2 are satisfactory for this purpose. If the choice were $\beta = (x_{\min} - x_{\max})/(x_{\max} - x_{0.8})$, the increments in β would be larger, but this gain would be offset by uncertainties in the location of the minimum. Similar studies were made of families of theoretical $\Delta T(x)$ profiles for all the remaining inclinations. Abscissas yielding satisfactory values of β and δ are given in Table 2, together with magnitudes of maximum and minimum values of $\Delta T(x)$ and their respective coordinates.

Analysis of anomalies

To determine the magnetic-doublet equivalent of a suitable observed anomaly, a north-south profile is drawn through the maximum at any convenient scale. The zero datum line is drawn by inspection and is based on the mean undisturbed magnetic level. The magnetic inclination for the area is determined from isoclinal charts published by the U. S. Coast and Geodetic Survey

(Deel and Howe, 1948) or from tables by Vestine and others (1947). The abscissas to be used in computing β are taken from Table 2, for the inclination nearest to that observed. If the computed value of β falls within the range of those listed in the table, there is reason to believe that a doublet representation by the method described here is possible. Table 2 is entered for this value of β and a quantity l/d and a depth factor δ are determined by interpolation. The depth d to the near pole is calculated by dividing the corresponding horizontal distance on the observed profile by δ. The doublet length is then obtained from the product of d and l/d.

The calculation is best explained by an example. Consider the total-intensity profile over the inclined cylinder shown in Figure 10, which was obtained from experiments on models. As the inclination is 75 degrees, the abscissas to be used in computing β and δ are $x_{\max}$, $x'_{0.1}$, $x_{0.5}$, $x'_{0.5}$ and $x_{0.8}$, as indicated by Table 2. The maximum value of ΔT is 350 γ;

Table 2. Parameters of magnetic doublets for inclinations, I, and length-to-depth ratios, l/d

[The positions $x_{0.1}$, $x_{0.2}$, $x_{0.3}$ · · · indicate, respectively, abscissas of 10 percent, 20 percent, 30 percent · · · of the maximum value, ΔT_{max}, of a given profile. Prime marks refer to more northerly abscissas. Upper pole is at $x=0$, $d=1$. Pole strength, $m=1$]

l/d	ΔT_{max}	ΔT_{min}	x_{max}	x_{min}	β	δ

Inclination 0°

$[\beta = (x_{min}-x_{max})/(x_{min}-x_{0.5}).\quad \delta = x_0'._5-x_{0.5}]$

0.01	0.002	−0.010	−1.20	0.01	3.16	0.78
.10	.020	−.098	−1.20	.05	3.20	.78
.50	.098	−.452	−1.00	.25	2.91	.83
1.00	.180	−.706	−.90	.50	2.80	1.02
1.50	.235	−.766	−.80	.75	2.46	1.28
2.00	.274	−.707	−.80	1.00	2.14	1.67

Inclination 30°

$[\beta = (x_{min}-x_{max})/(x_{max}-x_{0.5}).\quad \delta = 0'._1-x_{0.1}]$

0.01	0.008	−0.008	−0.60	0.35	1.27	2.67
.10	.076	−.070	−.58	.43	1.31	2.77
.50	.290	−.252	−.53	.60	1.40	2.95
1.00	.440	−.347	−.46	.82	1.45	3.16
1.50	.516	−.332	−.43	1.02	1.61	3.39
2.00	.564	−.306	−.40	1.15	1.67	3.45
5.00	.649	−.185	−.35	1.32	1.72	3.90

Inclination 45°

$[\beta = (x_{min}-x_{max})/(x_{max}-x_{0.6}).\quad \delta = x_0'._2-x_{0.2}]$

0.01	0.013	−0.005	−0.40	0.58	1.60	1.71
.10	.111	−.046	−.35	.65	1.69	1.84
.50	.392	−.154	−.35	.85	2.00	1.94
1.00	.440	−.192	−.35	1.10	2.38	2.16
1.50	.638	−.192	−.35	1.30	2.66	2.30
2.00	.690	−.178	−.35	1.50	2.94	2.40
5.00	.780	−.104	−.35	1.80	3.77	2.66

Inclination 60°

$[\beta = (x_{0.1}-x_{max})/(x_{max}-x_{0.8}).\quad \delta = x_0'._5-x_{0.5}]$

0.01	0.017	−0.003	−0.24	0.85	1.65	1.05
0.10	.142	−.026	−.26	1.00	2.12	1.06
0.50	.480	−.081	−.22	1.20	2.14	1.19
1.00	.662	−.098	−.20	1.40	2.32	1.29
1.50	.750	−.096	−.19	1.68	2.42	1.36
2.00	.801	−.089	−.19	1.80	2.58	1.40
5.00	.882	−.050	−.18	2.50	2.79	1.48

Inclination 75°

$[\beta = (x_0'._1-x_{max})/(x_{max}-x_{0.5}).\quad \delta = x_0'._5-x_{0.5}]$

0.01	0.018	−0.001	−0.12	1.20	2.52	1.01
.10	.163	−.011	−.13	1.40	2.68	1.05
.50	.540	−.033	−.11	1.60	2.79	1.19
1.00	.730	−.040	−.10	2.00	3.00	1.30
1.50	.817	−.038	−.10	2.30	3.19	1.37
2.00	.865	−.043	−.09	2.50	3.21	1.41
5.00	.950	−.021	−.09	3.50	3.59	1.50

Inclination 90°

$[\beta = x_0'._{05}/x_{0.5}.\quad \delta = x_{0.5}]$

0.01	0.020	0.000	0	1.90	2.22	0.51
.10	.174	−.003	0	2.00	2.25	.52
.50	.556	−.019	0	2.50	2.25	.60
1.00	.750	−.011	0	3.00	2.38	.64
1.50	.840	−.011	0	3.50	2.46	.68
2.00	.889	−.010	0	3.50	2.57	.70
5.00	.938	−.005	0	5.70	2.91	.75

therefore the x coordinates for 35, 175, 280 and 350γ are plotted as shown. Then $\beta = (x'_{0.1}-x_{max})/(x_{max}-x_{0.8}) = 3.24$. Entering Table 2 for $\beta = 3.24$ we obtain by interpolation an l/d of 2.2 and a δ of 1.42 inches. As $x'_{0.5}-x_{0.5} = 7.30$ inches on the profile, the depth is $d_c = (x'_{0.5}-x_{0.5})/\delta = (7.30)/(1.42) = 5.1$ inches. The length is $l_c = (l/d)d_c = (2.2)(5.1) = 11.2$ inches. The depth and length are known to be $d_o = 5.05$ inches and $l_o = 10.1$ inches from model experiments. The results are unusually good even for a carefully controlled laboratory experiment.

Other uses of computed anomalies

Although Figures 2 to 8 were computed primarily for determining the β and δ factors, they can be used for qualitative interpretations. For example, they provide information on the general shape of total-intensity anomalies to be expected from different rock masses magnetized by induction. When the horizontal dimensions of the mass are less than the depth to its top, a single doublet can be used to represent it. When the mass has a width less than the depth, but is extensive in the plane of the magnetic meridian, the anomalies of several doublets aligned in parallel in the meridian can be combined to give an equivalent anomaly. This simple addition of two or more anomalies is permissible by the superposition law of potential theory.

The following generalizations based on Figures 2 to 9 are helpful in interpretations:

1. The anomaly of the vertical doublet is symmetric with respect to the axis.

2. For inclined doublets, the maximum of an anomaly is always south of the upper pole, and the amount of the south shift increases with decrease in the inclination.

3. For a given depth and doublet length, a decrease in the inclination diminishes the

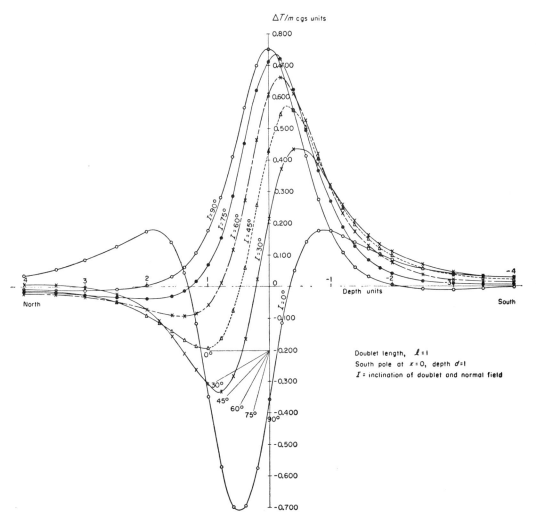

FIG. 5. Total-intensity anomalies of magnetic doublet of length, $l = 1.0$ depth unit.

amplitude of the maximum and increases that of the minimum. The effect on the steepest gradients is practically negligible, and the north slopes of the profile remain parallel for all inclinations. The latter fact suggests that fitting a slope is meaningless, because the diagnostic characteristics of the anomaly are involved in the south slope and minimum as well.

4. If other parameters are equal, an increase in doublet length decreases the steepest gradients of the anomaly, as can be seen explicitly in Figure 9.

5. For an inclination $I = 0$, a double minimum develops when l is about three times the depth, which indicates resolution of the effects of the two poles.

6. For l very large, the theory reduces to that of a point pole, which we have already treated (Henderson and Zietz, 1948).

Magnetic Model Experiments

To investigate the method of study when applied to fields produced by physically realizable bodies, a series of experiments on magnetic models was carried out. Facilities of the Naval Ordnance Laboratory at White Oak, Md., were made available for these and other tests. A detailed account of the experiments is contained in a preliminary report by Zietz and Henderson (1956).

The experimental set up is an elaborate modification of that used by Alldredge and Dichtel (1949) in their interpretation of the Bikini magnetic data. Three large mutually perpendicular Helmholtz-type coils on 30-ft frames are individually energized by an adjustable dc voltage supply. In this way, the magnitude and direction of the uniform field of the earth can be simulated over a relatively large volume about the center of the system. A model is placed at the center and the anomaly field produced by the in-duced magnetism of the model is measured by means of a flux-gate magnetic detector of fixed orientation on a tower having powered vertical positioning. The detector tower is mounted on a carriage which moves in an east-west or a north-south direction. Continuous registration of data is accomplished with a null-type recorder. Once the model has been set up and the detector oriented in the direction of the simulated field, all operations are conveniently effected from control panels mounted in a console. The accuracy of the magnetometer system is $\pm 3\,\gamma$.

The models were prepared from a mixture of gypsum plaster and powdered magnetite

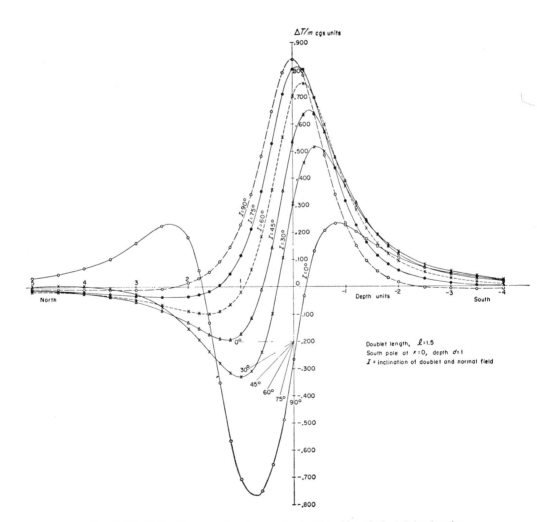

FIG. 6. Total-intensity anomalies of magnetic doublet of length, $l=1.5$ depth units.

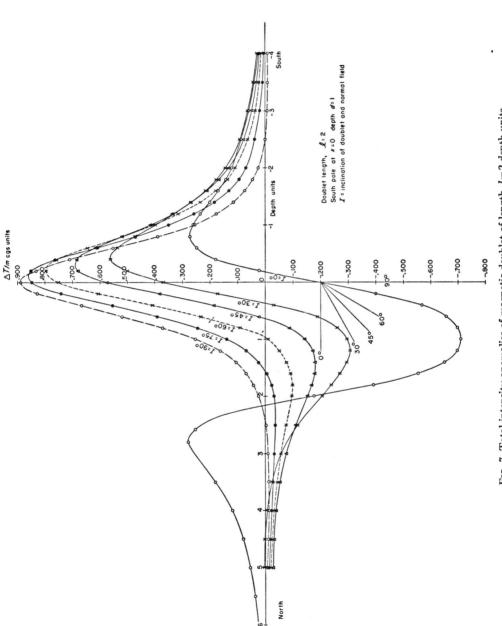

Fig. 7. Total-intensity anomalies of magnetic doublet of length, $l = 2$ depth units.

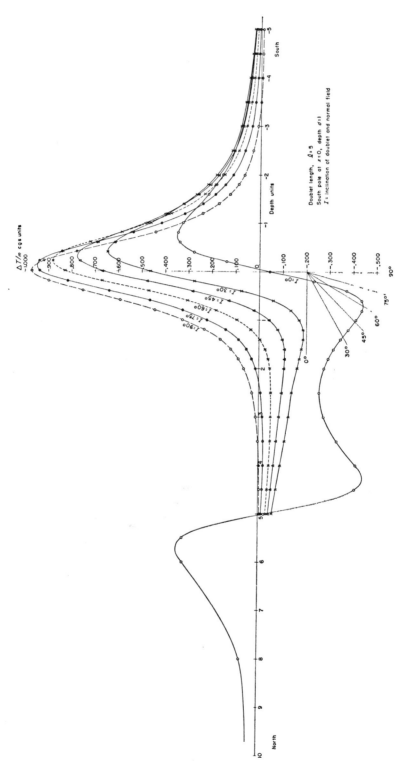

FIG. 8. Total-intensity anomalies of magnetic doublet of length, $l = 5$ depth units.

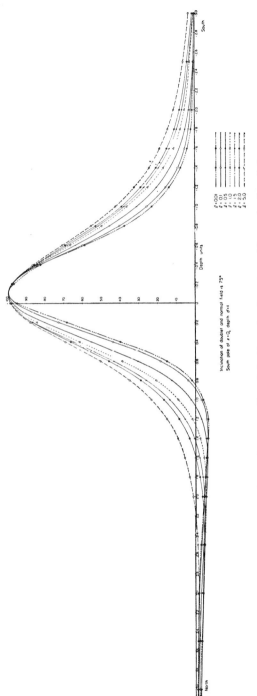

Fig. 9. Total-intensity anomalies of doublets showing effect of increasing length l.

in the ratio of 2:1 by volume. For this study, the models were primarily cylinders; however, a few double-layer models 0.5 inch thick were also used. All remanent magnetism in the models was carefully removed by electrical "shaking" in a zero ambient field. The cylinders and the detector were aligned codirectionally with the field at the center of the Helmholtz system. The applied total field was invariably 53,400 gammas.

Tests on cylindrical models

A profile of a typical ΔT anomaly over a cylinder is shown in Figure 10 together with data for computation. Similar profiles for 5 cylinders in fields of inclinations $I=0$, 75, and 90 degrees were also analyzed and the

results are given in Table 3. The measured length of the cylinder and depth to the center of the base nearer the origin are in columns headed "l_o" and "d_o" and the corresponding computed lengths and depths are in columns "l_c" and "d_c." In general the calculated depths are in better agreement with those measured than are the calculated lengths.

Comparisons of columns $(l/d)_o$ and $(l/d)_c$ also afford some idea of the accuracy involved. Calculations of doublet length are more reliable for low magnetic inclinations than for high inclinations. In low inclinations the more remote source is nearer the surface and can therefore have a greater expression in the data.

Uncertainties in the location of apparent

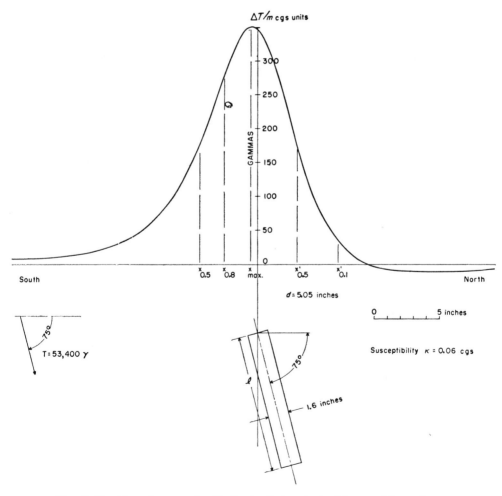

FIG. 10. Total-intensity anomaly of inclined cylinder; obtained from model experiment.

Table 3. Comparison of calculated doublet lengths and depths with those used in model experiments.

[Dip of cylinders equal to inclination of impressed field. Linear dimensions in inches]

Inclination	Cylinder no.	Diameter	Observed values			Computed values		
			l_o	d_o	$(l/d)_o$	$(l/d)_c$	l_c	d_c
0°	I	2.15	5.00	4.90	1.02	1.3	5.5	4.2
		2.15	5.00	6.80	.74	1.0	5.8	5.8
		2.15	5.00	8.50	.59	1.1	7.7	7.0
	II	1.00	5.10	3.70	1.38	1.8	5.4	3.0
		1.00	5.10	5.75	.89	1.8	7.7	4.4
	III	4.05	10.00	9.00	1.11	1.5	11.2	7.5
		4.05	10.00	14.20	.70	1.2	14.8	12.3
	IV	1.60	10.10	6.45	1.57	1.8	10.8	6.2
		1.60	10.10	11.50	.88	1.8	15.1	8.4
	V	1.50	18.00	5.85	3.08	3.8	17.1	4.5
		1.50	18.00	7.35	2.45	2.9	21.5	7.4
30°	I	2.15	5.00	3.75	1.33	1.2	5.2	4.3
		2.15	5.00	5.65	.88	1.1	7.4	7.0
	II	1.00	5.10	3.15	1.62	1.2	4.2	3.5
	III	4.05	10.00	5.00	2.00	1.2	9.5	7.9
	IV	1.60	10.10	5.70	1.77	.8	6.4	7.7
	V	1.50	18.00	4.92	3.66	3.5	20.7	5.9
75°	I	2.15	5.00	5.00	1.00	.9	4.9	5.3
		2.15	5.00	6.65	.75	1.4	9.1	6.4
	III	4.05	10.00	5.00	2.00	2.6	14.6	5.6
	IV	1.60	10.10	5.05	2.00	2.2	11.1	5.1
		1.60	10.10	10.10	1.00	1.1	11.1	10.0
	V	1.50	18.00	4.50	4.00	5.7	25.6	4.5
90°	I	2.15	5.00	4.50	1.11	1.8	7.9	4.5
	II	1.00	5.10	4.60	1.11	1.5	6.6	4.4
	III	4.05	10.10	5.00	2.02	2.6	14.6	5.6
		4.05	10.10	10.00	1.01	1.5	15.0	10.0
	V	1.50	18.00	4.00	4.50	5.0	21.5	4.3
	VI	5.85	9.90	5.05	1.96	1.2	7.8	6.5

poles of a cylindrical body impose limitations on the extent to which comparisons of observed and computed values of l and d can be made. Theoretically, at least, it is expected that d_c will be greater than d_o and l_c will be less than l_o, because the apparent poles must lie within the body. In this particular investigation, the errors developed in the process rendered indiscernible any such systematic trends.

For a given cylinder the errors in computed lengths and depths increase as l/d decreases, which is to be expected. The depth d_c in Table 3 was computed with a mean error of 14 percent; the l_c was computed with a mean error of 29 percent.

Magnetic double-layer models

The method was applied to anomaly fields measured over models consisting of plaster-magnetite horizontal slabs 0.5 inch thick and of different rectangular dimensions. The 5 inches×5 inches model at a depth of 5 inches gave fair results, as shown in Table 4. Here, the doublet length l is logically the slant distance in inches (see inset, Figure 11) measured along the direction of the field between the upper and lower faces, and is given by $l_o = 5/\cos I$ for $0 \gtreqless I \gtreqless 0.032\pi$ and $l_o = 0.5$ inch $\sin I$ for $0.032\pi \gtreqless I \gtreqless \pi/2$. The computed l_o, although not entirely satisfactory for determining the thickness, does in a general way decrease with increasing I and gives the

Table 4. Application of magnetic-doublet theory to field of horizontal slab

[Fields obtained from laboratory measurements on body of dimensions 0.5 inches×5 inches×5 inches at a depth of 5 inches. Linear dimensions in inches]

Incli-nation[1]	l_o	$(l/d)_o$	$(l/d)_c$	l_c	d_c
0°	5.00	1.00	1.12	5.5	4.9
30°	1.00	.20	.60	3.3	5.0
45°	.85	.17	.56	3.2	5.8
60°	.58	.11	.10	.6	6.3
75°	.52	.10	.20	1.2	6.2

[1] Observations over the center line at $I = 90°$ were not made.

order of magnitude. The results suggest that the calculation of depth to the top surface is more accurate at low magnetic inclinations. When applied to double-layer models of larger horizontal dimensions, for example, 0.5 inch×10 inches×10 inches, the method failed, because the β values fell outside the range of Table 2. For models 0.5 inch thick but of plan less than 5 inches×5 inches, the method would very likely be successful.

Some idea of the limits of the size of bodies that can be analyzed in this manner can be gained from the following expression for the ΔZ anomaly on the axis of a vertical cylinder in a vertical field

$$\Delta Z(o) = 2\pi\kappa Z_o\{(d + l)/[(d + l)^2 + \rho^2]^{\frac{1}{2}} - d/(d^2 + \rho^2)^{\frac{1}{2}}\}, \quad (2)$$

where Z_o is the impressed vertical intensity field, ρ the radius, d the depth to the upper base, and κ the susceptibility. If the expression (2) is expanded in a binomial series the result is

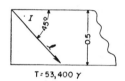

T = 53,400 γ

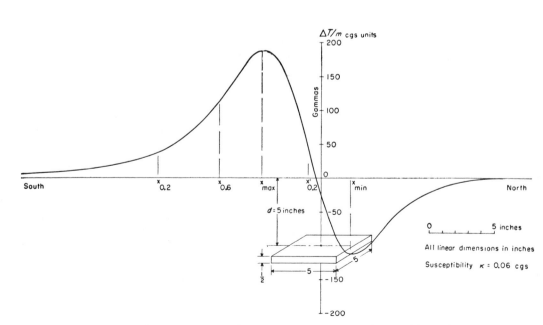

FIG. 11. Total-intensity anomaly of magnetized plate; obtained from model experiment.

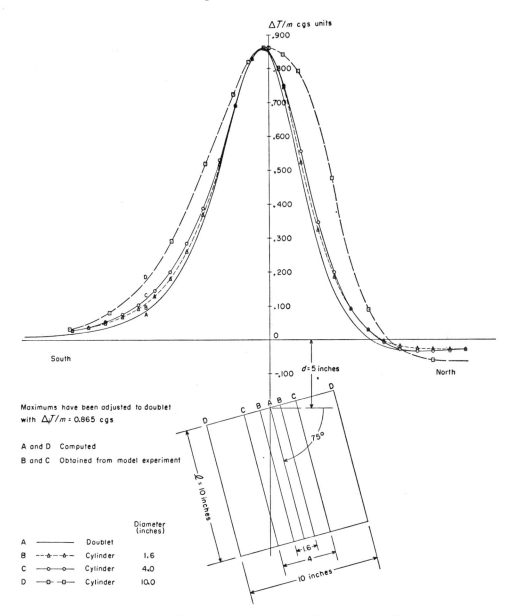

FIG. 12. Anomalies of inclined cylinders showing effect of increased diameter.

$$\Delta Z(o) = 2\pi k Z_o \left\{ \left(\tfrac{1}{2}\right) \left[\rho^2/d^2 - \rho^2/(d+l)^2\right] \right.$$
$$\left. - \tfrac{3}{8}\left[\rho^4/d^4 - \rho^4/(d+l)^4\right] + \cdots \right\} \quad (3)$$

which is valid for $\rho < d$. For $\rho \ll d$ only the first term is significant and (3) may be written

(cylinder) $\Delta Z(o)$

$$\approx \pi \kappa Z_o \rho^2 \left[1/d^2 - 1/(d+l)^2\right]. \quad (4)$$

The expression (4) has the same geometrical form as the formula for a vertical doublet in a vertical field:

$$\Delta Z(o) = m\left[1/d^2 - 1/(d+l)^2\right]. \quad (5)$$

Although (4) and (5) are meaningful only at the origin, and although l for the cylinder is not identical with l for the doublet, the comparison nevertheless suggests that the mean radius of a body must be less than its depth of burial if it is to be successfully represented as a magnetic doublet. The experiment above on the 5 inches×5 inches body at a depth of 5 inches, with an effective radius $\rho = 5/\sqrt{\ }$ confirms this result. In the 10 inches×10 inches body at the same depth, the effective radius is $\rho = 10/\sqrt{\pi}$ and failure is to be expected.

To investigate further the effect of the radius on doublet representation, the anomalies of three coaxial cylinders 10 inches long in a field of inclination 75 degrees were adjusted so that the ΔT_{max} of each was equal to that of a doublet of the same length, as shown in Figure 12. For all, the depth to the center of the top is d and the length $2d$. The radii of cylinders B, C, and D are $\rho = 0.16d$,

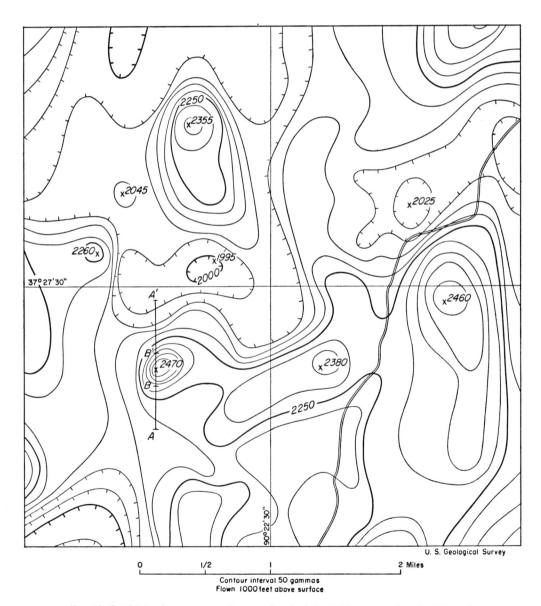

FIG. 13. Total-intensity aeromagnetic map of part of the Coldwater quadrangle, Missouri.

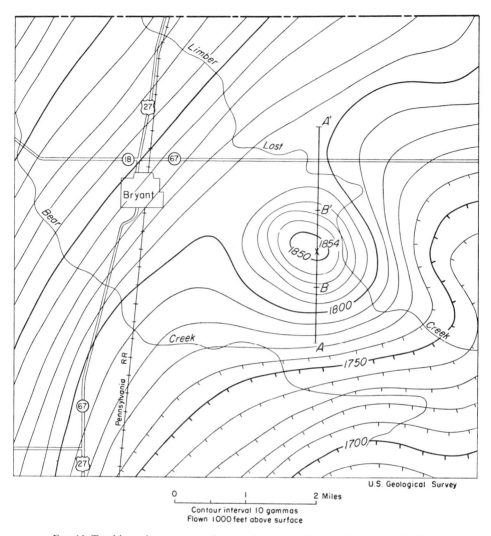

Fig. 14. Total-intensity aeromagnetic map of area near Bryant, Jay County, Indiana.

0.4d, and d. The anomalies of B and C were obtained from model experiments. The doublet anomaly was computed from formula (1). The anomaly for cylinder D was computed numerically by means of a modification (Henderson, R. G., and Zietz, Isidore, 1958) of Gassman's three-dimensional integration process (Gassman, 1951). The latter was checked by application to cylinder C whose anomaly it reproduced faithfully. In Figure 12, it is quite clear that the shape of the anomaly does not alter radically from that of a doublet as the radius increases to 0.4 depth. When the radius equals the depth, the shape

of the anomaly bears little resemblance to that of a doublet; therefore the doublet-analysis method cannot be used. It also appears from Figure 12 that the possibility of determining the radius of a cylinder from a dipolelike anomaly is very remote. A rigorous investigation of this matter is not possible because of the lack of a closed form for calculating the ΔT anomaly of a cylinder.

Practical Applications

Aeromagnetic observations over geologic bodies of known depth, dimensions, and magnetic properties were not available for

testing. The method was therefore applied to
the surveys in areas for which we have some
knowledge, although fragmentary, of the
depth to crystalline magnetic rocks. If the
rocks are exposed, the problem is simply to
determine from magnetic data the altitude of
the surveying airplane above the surface. In
other areas where the crystalline rocks are
buried, the "known" depths can be inferred
from drilling data or from geologic information. Although calculations of l were made,

the results are not included here because
depth-extent data for purposes of comparison were nonexistent.

The anomalies to which we have applied
this method are shown in Figures 13 to 17.
The line $A-A'$ in each figure indicates the
profile across the anomaly, and $B-B'$ indicates the horizontal distance used with the
appropriate δ in the depth calculation. The
values of β are not shown for these applications.

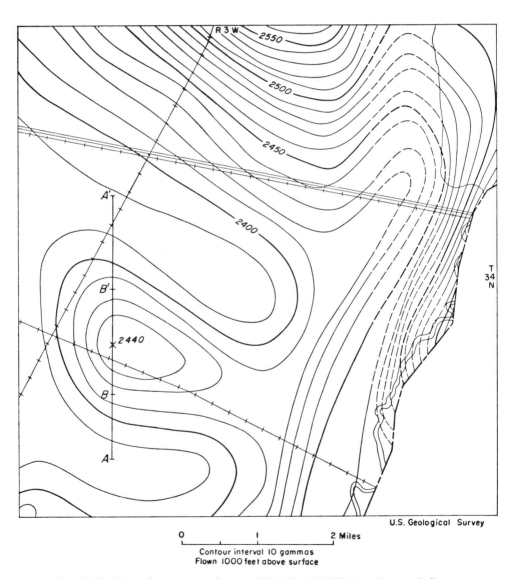

U.S. Geological Survey

0   1   2 Miles

Contour interval 10 gammas
Flown 1000 feet above surface

FIG. 15. Total-intensity aeromagnetic map of T 34 N, R 3 W LaPorte County, Indiana.

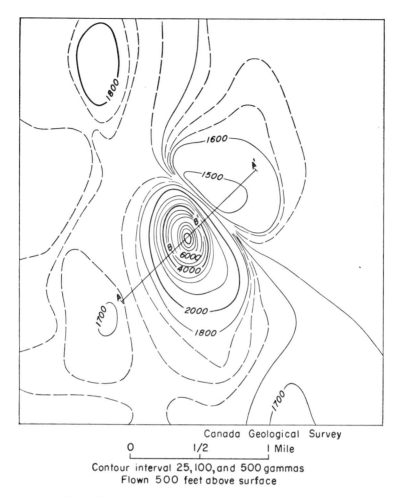

Canada Geological Survey

0   1/2   I Mile

Contour interval 25, 100, and 500 gammas
Flown 500 feet above surface

Fig. 16. Total-intensity aeromagnetic map of the area near Marmora, Ontario, Canada.

Southeast Missouri

On the U. S. Geological Survey aeromagnetic map of the Coldwater quadrangle, in southeastern Missouri (Figure 13), there are several anomalies over exposed felsite, particularly where the felsite is in contact with granite. Calculations of the depth of the source were made on the closed magnetic high about one mile west of Cedar Mountain in the Coldwater quadrangle and a depth of 870 ft was obtained. As the elevation of the airplane above the surface was 800 ft, the calculated value is regarded as satisfactory.

Indiana

The anomaly near Bryant in T 24 N, R 14 E, in Jay County, Ind. (Figure 14), was analyzed by the doublet method and a depth to magnetic rocks of 5,400 ft below the aircraft was found. On the basis of a well in sec. 9, T 24 N, R 13 E, Precambrian igneous rocks in the area are estimated to be at a depth of 3,350 ft, or 4,350 ft below the level of observations.

In La Porte County, Ind. (Figure 15), information on depth to igneous rocks is scanty, as the nearest wells are about 50 miles away. Geologists estimate the depth to the Precambrian is 6,200 ft at the location of the anomaly 6 miles northeast of La Crosse, in T 34 N, R 3 W. The depth calculated by doublet analysis is 6,900 ft below the airplane.

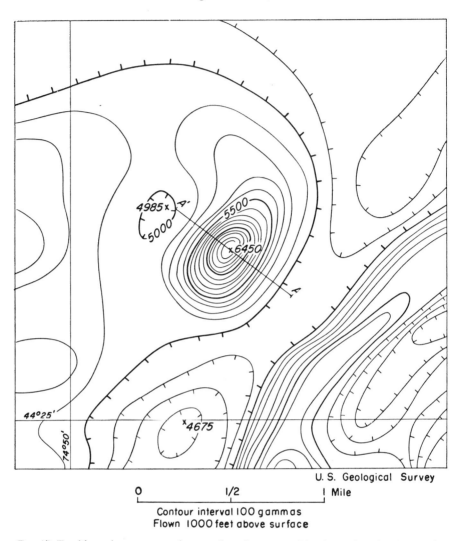

FIG. 17. Total-intensity aeromagnetic map of northern part of Stark Quadrangle, New York.

Ontario, Canada

A prominent magnetic anomaly about one mile southeast of Marmora, Ontario, appears on the Campbellsford aeromagnetic map (Canada Geological Survey, 1950). Drilling information indicates there are 90 to 150 ft of limestone of Paleozoic age overlying iron-bearing Precambrian rocks in the area. The disturbing rocks are known to contain magnetite. A calculation on the northeasterly profile (A–A' in Figure 16) gave a depth of 850 ft below the airplane in comparison with probable depths of 600 to 650 ft.

Adirondack Mountains, N. Y.

Analysis of the isolated magnetic anomaly in the north-central part of the Stark quadrangle in the Adirondack Mountains (Figure 17), indicated a depth of 1,050 ft for the source. The airplane was 1,000 ft above the ground. The rocks in the area have been mapped as hornblende granite with a few layers of metasediment. It is very likely that the disturbing rocks are near the surface.

Conclusions

The application of magnetic-doublet theory has been shown to be reasonably effective for determinations of the depth of cylindrical laboratory models oriented in the direction of the earth's magnetic field. The determination of doublet length is less reliable. In general the method yields better results for bodies in low magnetic inclinations. The method cannot be expected to give satisfactory values in high magnetic inclinations when the mean radius of a horizontal section exceeds the depth of burial. The most practical use of the method is in depth determinations. The anomaly curves of Figures 2 to 8 are also useful qualitatively in obtaining some idea of the anomalies to be expected at various inclinations and the relative displacement of maximums.

Acknowledgments

We acknowledge our indebtedness to Mr. L. R. Alldredge, formerly of the Electricity and Magnetism Division of the Physics Research Department of the Naval Ordnance Laboratory, for the use of the magnetic testing equipment, and to Messrs. C. L. Parsons and K. E. Dornstreich, also of the Naval Ordnance Laboratory, for valuable technical assistance.

References

Alldredge, L. R., and Dichtel, W. J., 1949, Interpretation of Bikini magnetic data: Am. Geophys. Union Trans., v. 30, p. 831–385.

Balsley, J. R., and others, 1954, Total aeromagnetic intensity and geologic map of Stark, Childwold, and part of Russell quadrangles, New York: U. S. Geol. Survey Geophys. Inv. Map GP 117, scale 1 inch = about 1 mile [1955].

Canada Geological Survey, 1950, Aeromagnetic map, Campbellsford sheet, Ontario, No. 315: Canada Geol. Survey Geophysics Paper 13, scale 1 inch = 1 mile.

Deel, S. A., and Howe, H. H., 1948, United States magnetic tables and magnetic charts for 1945: U. S. Coast and Geod. Survey Serial 667, 137 p.

Dempsey, W. J., and Duffner, R. T., 1949, Total intensity aeromagnetic map of Coldwater quadrangle, Madison and Wayne Counties, Missouri: U. S. Geol. Survey Geophys. Inv. Map, scale 1 inch = ½ mile.

Dempsey, W. J., Henderson, J. R., and Duffner, R. T., 1949, Total intensity aeromagnetic map of La Porte County, Indiana: U. S. Geol. Survey Geophys. Inv. Map, scale 1 inch = 1 mile.

Gassman, Fritz, 1951, Graphical evaluation of the anomalies of gravity and of the magnetic field, caused by three-dimensional bodies: 3d World Petroleum Cong., The Hague 1951, Proc., sec., 1, p. 613–621.

Heiland, C. A., 1940, Geophysical exploration: New York, Prentice-Hall Inc., 1013 p.

Henderson, J. R., and Meuschke, J. L., 1951, Total intensity aeromagnetic map of Jay County, Indiana: U. S. Geol. Survey Geophys. Inv. Map GP 86, scale 1 inch = 1 mile.

Henderson, J. R., Jr., and Zietz, Isidore, 1958, Interpretation of an aeromagnetic survey in Indiana: U. S. Geol. Survey Prof. Paper 316-B [in press].

Henderson, R. G., and Zietz, Isidore, 1948, Analysis of total magnetic intensity anomalies produced by point and line sources: Geophysics, v. 13, p. 428–436.

——, 1957, Graphical calculation of total-intensity anomalies of three-dimensional bodies: Geophysics, v. 22, p. 887–904.

Jakosky, J. J., 1950, Exploration geophysics: Los Angeles, Calif., Trija Publishing Co., 1195 p.

Nettleton, L. L., 1940, Geophysical prospecting for oil: New York, McGraw-Hill Book Co., 444 p.

Vacquier, Victor, Steenland, N. C., Henderson, R. G., and Zietz, Isidore, 1951, Interpretation of aeromagnetic maps: Geol. Soc. America Mem. 47, 151 p.

Vestine, E. H., and Davids, Norman, 1945, Analysis and interpretation of geomagnetic anomalies: Terrestrial Magnetism and Atmospheric Electricity, v. 50, p. 1–36.

Vestine, E. H., Laport, Lucile, Lange, Isabelle, Cooper, Caroline, and Hendrix, W. C., 1947, Description of the earth's main magnetic field and its secular change, 1905–1945: Carnegie Inst. Washington Pub. 578, 532 p.

Zietz, Isidore, and Henderson, R. G., 1956, A preliminary report on model studies of magnetic anomalies of three-dimensional bodies: Geophysics, v. 21, p. 794–814.

STANDARD CURVES FOR INTERPRETATION OF MAGNETIC ANOMALIES OVER LONG TABULAR BODIES†

S. PARKER GAY, Jr.*

The magnetic anomalies in Z, H, and T_{I_0} for the thin infinite dike are shown to belong to a single mathematical family of curves for all values of dip and strike of the dike and all values of inclination of the magnetizing field. The complete family of standard curves has been constructed and is incorporated into an interpretational scheme based on superposition with observed magnetic profiles. This technique should give more reliable interpretations than methods based on only a few isolated points of a profile curve.

By integration of the general thin dike response, a general expression of similar form has been derived for thick dikes, and ten sheets of curves for dikes of varying width indices have been constructed. By employing the method of subtraction of curves, these serve for constructing anomaly profiles over bodies of finite depth extent. Additionally, for thin dikes the much-neglected demagnetization corrections have been incorporated in the interpretational method following verification by model studies. One important disclosure of this work is that the depth and location of the apex of an infinite tabular body may be determined without knowing the intensity or direction of magnetization within the body, assuming only that these quantities are constant throughout.

Introduction

Since magnetic surveying was made popular some 30 to 40 years ago by the introduction of the Schmidt-type magnetometer, geophysicists and geologists alike have been concerned with the interpretation of magnetic anomalies over tabular bodies. The tabular, or sheet-like, form is one which Nature has seen fit to distribute about with great regularity, particularly in problems involving mining geology. It is the form taken by dikes, veins, faults, contacts, and layered rocks, which collectively form a substantial percentage of known geological and mineral occurrences. Geophysical literature, since its beginning, has thus contained many contributions to the art of interpreting magnetic anomalies over tabular bodies, and a variety of valuable techniques have resulted.

These interpretation techniques may be grouped into two main classifications:

Class I. Methods based on a few specific points of a magnetic profile.
These include the half-width method, distance between maximum and minimum, cross-overs, points of inflection, points of maximum gradient, and others.

Class II. Methods based on superposition of an entire profile curve, i.e. curve-matching. These include a number of different mathematical and graphical schemes for arriving at anomaly curves, and in some instances utilize curves precomputed for special cases.

The class I methods have the great advantage of being rapid, simple, and easy to apply, but suffer from a lack of accuracy and precision in interpretation. The great variety of forms assumed by anomalies over tabular bodies of different dip and magnetic field inclination makes formulation of general rules difficult. Also, small irregularities in the anomaly curve can greatly alter the position of the critical points, resulting in gross inaccuracies in the interpretation.

The class II methods offer a better solution to the problem of precision since it is natural that a more exact interpretation can be obtained by superposition of an entire curve than by the use of only two or three isolated points on that curve. However, when the curves must be laboriously computed or

† Presented in abbreviated form at the 31st Annual International SEG Meeting, Denver, November 9, 1961. Reprinted from Geophysics v. 28, no. 2.

* American Smelting and Refining Co. Knoxville, Tennessee.

graphically constructed by time-consuming methods, the superposition technique loses its advantage. The geophysicist engaged in operational surveying often does not have the time available for this task, especially when the number of anomalies dealt with is great. *Precomputed* curves, when they are employed, are generally of limited utility, applicable only to special cases usually different from the one at hand. Their forced application may lead to error.

When the writer first attacked the interpretation of magnetic anomalies encountered in his own work, he soon recognized the need of a method that was (1) general enough to cover all cases, (2) accurate enough to furnish diagnostic interpretations, yet (3) simple enough to permit rapid application. It was soon realized that the only existing method which could satisfy these requirements was what we may call subclass IIa: precomputed curves, but in a sufficiently large number to cover all situations.

Of necessity, only tabular bodies of great length and great depth extent could be treated, the so-called "infinite tabular bodies," since to treat the problem of limited length and limited depth extent would be to increase the scope of the study beyond practical limits. All values of the three principal parameters of dip, strike, and field inclination were to be included. A quick appraisal, however, shows this to be a formidable task. Taking values of the above three parameters at intervals of, say, 15 degrees, 735 curves are required for the anomalies in Z, H, or T: a total of 2,205 curves for all three components. That assumes a constant thickness for the body. To include different values of thickness would multiply the above total several times.

Obviously a new approach was necessary or the project would have become too large for an individual person to ever complete. A limited investigation was therefore started to determine if some simplification, or shortcut, could be effected in the mathematics. This investigation was undertaken skeptically, but quite positive results were forthcoming. It was found that a single mathematical family of curves represents all anomalies in Z, H, and T_{I_0}[1] for infinite tabular bodies in any position of dip, strike, and field inclination. This disclosure came about, not as a result of applying complex mathematical techniques, but due to simple trigonometric manipulation of existing formulas.

Basic Derivations

The original derivations were based on formulas presented by Heiland for the magnetic anomalies of a slope (Heiland, 1946, p. 397), which in turn were based on previously derived torsion balance anomalies converted to magnetic anomalies by Poisson's theorem. This approach, although mathematically sound, is not physically lucid and in particular does not lend itself to an understanding of demagnetization effects. Therefore, the concept of magnetic "charge," or pole-strength, will be employed here. A considerable simplification may be made by first treating a very thin tabular body or dike, which will later be generalized to thick tabular bodies by integration.

The thin dike extends to infinity in both strike directions and downdip, and its upper edge, or apex, is a straight line lying at a constant distance z below the horizontal plane of observation (see Figure 1). The requirement of "thinness" is satisfied only by making z much greater than t, the thickness of the dike.

Two left-handed coordinate systems are defined. They share a common origin at any point on the plane of observation directly over the apex and a common z axis, positive vertically downward. The unprimed system has its y axis positive along the magnetic north line; and the primed system has its y' axis perpendicular to the strike of the dike and positive in the northern half-plane of the unprimed system or to the magnetic east. The magnetic anomaly profile derived will be along the y' axis perpendicular to the strike of the dike.

The magnetic azimuth, or strike α is the clockwise angle from the positive y axis to the positive x' axis defined with the following limits:

[1] T_{I_0} is the component of total intensity in the direction of T_0, the undisturbed field.

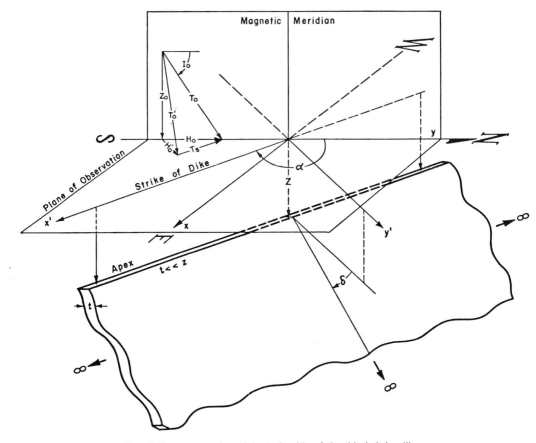

FIG. 1. Geometry and spatial relationship of the thin infinite dike.

$$0° < \alpha \le 180°.$$

The dip δ of the dike is the angle between the positive y' axis and the plane of the dike and has the limits:

$$0° \le \delta \le 180°.$$

Defined thusly it is the "northdip." A dike dipping 30° S, for example, would be considered to have a dip of 150 degrees.

The material comprising the dike has a true magnetic susceptibility k and the surrounding material is assumed to have zero susceptibility. When it is not zero, the susceptibility contrast is used instead of k.

The earth's magnetic field is represented by a vector of magnitude T_0 and inclination I_0 lying in the yz plane. I_0 varies from -90 degrees at the south magnetic pole to $+90$ degrees at the north magnetic pole. T_0 is

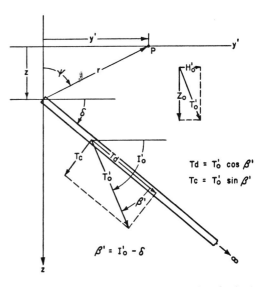

FIG. 2. Geometry of the thin dike in the $y'z$-plane.

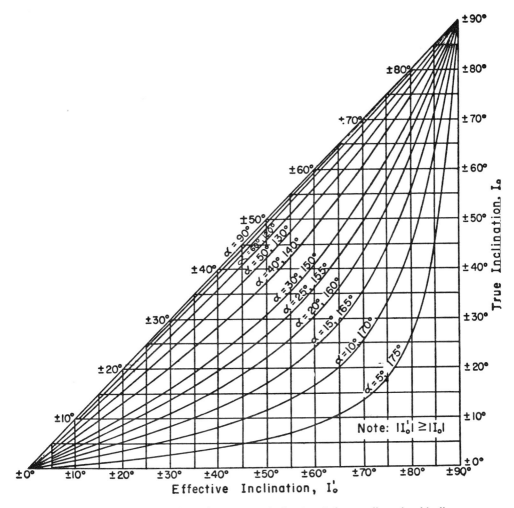

CHART 1. Effective inclination I_0', versus true inclination, I_0 for two-dimensional bodies.

resolved into two components: one lying parallel to the x' axis, and the other lying in the $y'z$ plane. The former, T_s, is parallel to the plane of the dike and may thus be neglected since any magnetic poles that it induces lie on the end faces at infinity. The latter is the component of T_0 that is effective in inducing magnetic poles on the dike's surfaces and so is termed the *effective total intensity* T_0'. Its inclination in the $y'z$ plane is termed the *effective inclination* I_0' (see Figure 2).

The idea of using the effective magnetic field values in the derivations was taken from Koulomzine and Massé (1947) and is an extremely helpful simplification, since it eliminates the azimuth α from further consideration. It is only necessary to use α initially in computing I_0' and T_0', and this is done quickly and simply with nomographs. The nomographs for this are presented in Charts 1 and 2, and are based on the following easily derived relationships:

$$\tan I_0' = \frac{\tan I_0}{\sin \alpha} \qquad (1)$$

$$\frac{T_0'}{T_0} = \frac{\sin I_0}{\sin I_0'}. \qquad (2)$$

The effective magnetic field T_0' is further resolved into two components (Figure 2):

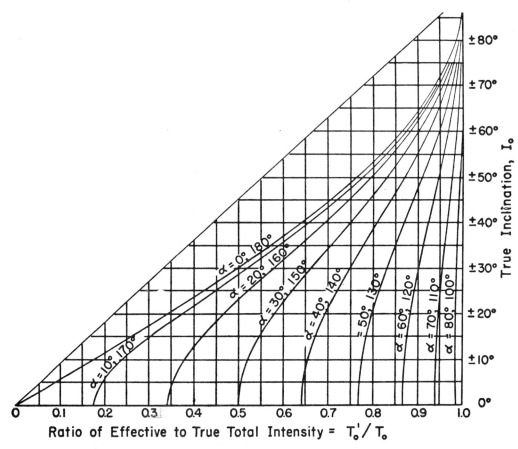

CHART 2. Ratio of effective to true total intensity, T_0'/T_0, versus inclination for two-dimensional bodies.

T_d, the dip-component, parallel to the dip of the dike; and T_c, the cross-component, perpendicular to the plane of the dike. The angle that T_0' makes with the dike is a quantity basic to all dike anomalies and is termed the *effective magnetization angle* β' since it defines the direction of the effective inducing field relative to the dike's plane. Combining the limits of its component quantities, the limits on β' are:

$$-270° \leq \beta' \leq + 90°.$$

The dip- and cross-components of the inducing field create corresponding components of internal magnetization in the dike depending on their independent apparent susceptibilities. These are different from the true susceptibility and from each other because of demagnetization. The magnitudes of the internal magnetization components are

equivalent to the resultant magnetic pole strength per unit area induced on surfaces normal to them. Thus, on the apex of the dike, there is induced a narrow strip of charge of magnetic pole-strength per unit area,

$$m_d = k_d T_d \tag{3}$$

where k_d is the apparent magnetic susceptibility of the dike to T_d. On the upper and lower planar surfaces of the dike there is induced a magnetic pole-strength per unit area,

$$m_c = k_c T_c \tag{4}$$

where k_c is the apparent susceptibility of the dike to T_c. The magnetic anomalies will be derived from the potential due to these distributed magnetic poles.

At a point P on the plane of observation

the long linear distribution of poles on the apical edge gives rise to the so-called "logarithmic potential" which may readily be shown to be:

$$V_d = 2k_dT_dl \log (y'^2 + z^2)^{-1/2}. \quad (5)$$

On the planar surfaces of the dike, the cross-component of magnetization induces two closely spaced sheets of magnetic charge of opposite sign. The potential due to this configuration has been derived by Jakosky (1950, p. 196–197). By making appropriate changes in nomenclature, this can be shown to be:

$$V_c = 2k_cT_cl\left(90° - \delta + \tan^{-1}\frac{y'}{z}\right). \quad (6)$$

By adding equations (5) and (6) and taking the proper derivatives, the vertical and horizontal intensity anomalies may be derived:

$$\Delta Z = -\frac{\partial V}{\partial z} = \frac{2k_dT_dlz}{z^2 + y'^2} + \frac{2k_cT_cly'}{z^2 + y'^2} \quad (7)$$

$$\Delta H' = -\frac{\partial V}{\partial y'} = -\frac{2k_dT_dly'}{z^2 + y'^2} + \frac{2k_cT_clz}{z^2 + y'^2}. \quad (8)$$

$\Delta H'$ is the anomaly in the component of horizontal intensity in the direction of y', not the commonly measured component in the direction of magnetic north. The latter anomaly is designated as ΔH, and is related to $\Delta H'$ as follows:

$$\Delta H = \Delta H' \sin \alpha. \quad (9)$$

One of the most important simplifications in the mathematics may now be made by substituting the angle ψ and eliminating y' from the above expressions (see Figure 2):

$$\Delta Z = + 2k_dT_d\frac{l}{z}\cos^2\psi$$

$$+ 2k_cT_c\frac{l}{z}\cos\psi\sin\psi \quad (10)$$

$$\Delta H' = - 2k_dT_d\frac{l}{z}\cos\psi\sin\psi$$

$$+ 2k_cT_c\frac{l}{z}\cos^2\psi. \quad (11)$$

Finally, by expressing T_d and T_c in terms of T_0' and β'' and simplifying, we have:

$$\Delta Z = 2T_0'\frac{l}{z}\cos\psi(+k_d\cos\psi\cos\beta'$$

$$+ k_c\sin\psi\sin\beta') \quad (12)$$

$$\Delta H' = 2T_0'\frac{l}{z}\cos\psi(-k_d\sin\psi\cos\beta'$$

$$+ k_c\cos\psi\sin\beta'). \quad (13)$$

These are the basic simplified formulas for the magnetic anomaly of the thin infinite dike. It can be shown that, in general, ΔZ and $\Delta H'$ completely define the anomalous magnetic field about any two dimensional body. From these basic expressions several important resultant anomalies may be developed:

ΔT, the anomaly in total intensity,
ΔT_{I_0}, the anomaly in the component of total intensity in the direction of T_0,
$\Delta T_\perp$, the anomaly in the component of total intensity perpendicular to the direction of T_0 and lying in the magnetic meridian,
ΔI, the anomaly in the inclination, and
ΔD, the anomaly in the declination.

Special Case: Demagnetization Neglected

When the true magnetic susceptibility of the dike is small, demagnetization effects are correspondingly small and we can assume:

$$k_c = k_d = k.$$

In this case equations (12) and (13) reduce to the simple forms:

$$\Delta Z = 2kT_0'\frac{l}{z}\cos\psi\cos(\psi - \beta') \quad (14)$$

$$\Delta H' = - 2kT_0'\frac{l}{z}\cos\psi\sin(\psi - \beta'). \quad (15)$$

Equation (14) is equivalent to the formula previously presented by Koulomzine and Massé (1947, p. 10).

It would be desirable at this point to compute the anomaly in total intensity ΔT. However, ΔT is a complex form and it is general practice to use in its place the much simpler form ΔT_{I_0}, the anomaly in the component of T in the direction of T_0, the undisturbed field. It should be remembered that this is a valid approximation only when ΔT is much smaller than T_0, and so must be used with care for large anomalies.

In Figure 3 are presented the relationships between the various anomaly components in total intensity. By substituting equations (14) and (15) into the formula given for ΔT_{I_0}, not forgetting equation (9), it can be shown that,

$$\Delta T_{I_0} = -2kT_0' \frac{t}{z} \frac{\sin I_0}{\sin I_0'} \cos \psi$$
$$\cdot \sin (\psi - \beta' - I_0'). \quad (16)$$

From the equations just derived it is readily seen that the anomalies in ΔZ, $\Delta H'$, and ΔT_{I_0} are very similar forms. The close relationship between them is made more apparent by the following changes in form:

$$\Delta H = 2kT_0' \frac{t}{z} \sin \alpha \cos \psi$$
$$\cdot \cos (\psi - \beta' + 90°) \quad (17)$$

$$\Delta T_{I_0} = 2kT_0' \frac{t}{z} \frac{\sin I_0}{\sin I_0'} \cos \psi$$
$$\cdot \cos (\psi - \beta' + 90° - I_0'). \quad (18)$$

Equations (14), (17), and (18) are the final simplified formulas for the three principal anomalies of the thin infinite dike with demagnetization neglected. It may be observed that all three equations are of the form:

$$\Delta F = C_F \cos \psi \cos (\psi - \theta_F) \quad (19)$$

where

$\Delta F =$ the anomaly in the corresponding component of the magnetic field
$C_F =$ the coefficient term $= f(T_0, I_0, \alpha, k, t, z)$
$\theta_F =$ the index parameter $= f(\beta', I_0')$
$= f(\alpha, \delta, I_0)$.

The values of C_F and θ_F for the three anomalies are tabulated in Table 1 together with the resultant expressions for the dip and thickness of the dike. Also tabulated at the bottom of Table 1 are several interesting

and useful relationships between the different anomalies. A new parameter A is introduced, the *amplitude*, or gamma difference, between maximum and minimum of the measured anomaly curve.

The mathematical family of curves which describe the anomalies of the thin infinite dike is defined by the expression:

$$f(\psi, \theta_F) = \cos \psi \cos (\psi - \theta_F). \quad (20)$$

The complete family of these curves for θ_F between 0 degrees and -360 degrees plotted at 5-degree intervals is presented in Charts 3 to 6. Due to the very small difference between adjacent curves, these charts, for all practical purposes, describe completely the anomalies in ΔZ, ΔH, ΔT_{I_0} for the thin infinite dike.

It is interesting that the relationship between the anomalies in vertical, horizontal, and total intensities for the thin infinite dike was not discovered earlier. In a recent paper, James Affleck (1958) arrived at a related, and in a way, more general, conclusion when he proved that an anomaly curve for a given

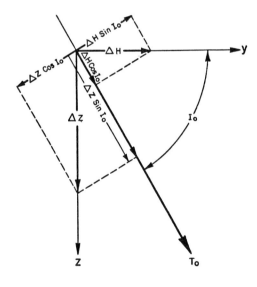

$\Delta T_{I_0} = \Delta Z \sin I_0 + \Delta H \cos I_0$

$\Delta T_{\perp} = \Delta Z \cos I_0 - \Delta H \sin I_0$

$\Delta T = \sqrt{\Delta T_{\perp}^2 + (T_0 + \Delta T_{I_0})^2}$

FIG. 3. The anomalies in the different components of total intensity.

Table 1. Characteristics of anomaly curves with demagnetization neglected

Anomaly ΔF	Coefficient C_F	Index parameter θ_F In terms of β'	Index parameter θ_F In terms of δ	Dip δ	Thickness t
ΔZ	$2kT_0'\dfrac{t}{z}$	β'	$I_0' - \delta$	$I_0' - \theta_Z$	$\dfrac{A_Z}{2kT_0'}$
ΔH	$2kT_0'\dfrac{t}{z}\sin\alpha$	$\beta' - 90°$	$I_0' - \delta - 90°$	$I_0' - \theta_H - 90°$	$\dfrac{A_Z}{2kT_0'\sin\alpha}$
ΔT_{I_0}	$2kT_0'\dfrac{t}{z}\dfrac{\sin I_0}{\sin I_0}$	$\beta' - 90° + I_0'$	$2I_0' - \delta - 90°$	$2I_0' - \theta_T - 90°$	$\dfrac{A_Z}{2kT_0'}\dfrac{\sin I_0'}{\sin I_0}$

When there is more than one type of survey over a given anomaly, the following relationships are useful:

$$\theta_Z = \theta_H + 90° \qquad\qquad \theta_H = \theta_Z - 90° \qquad\qquad \theta_T = \theta_Z - 90° + I_0'$$
$$= \theta_T + 90° - I_0' \qquad\qquad = \theta_T - I_0' \qquad\qquad = \theta_H + I_0'$$

$$A_Z = A_H\frac{z_H}{z_Z}\frac{1}{\sin\alpha} \qquad\qquad A_H = A_Z\frac{z_Z}{z_H}\sin\alpha \qquad\qquad A_T = A_Z\frac{z_Z}{z_T}\frac{\sin I_0}{\sin I_0'}$$

$$= A_T\frac{z_T}{z_Z}\frac{\sin I_0'}{\sin I_0} \qquad\qquad = A_T\frac{z_T}{z_H}\frac{\sin I_0'}{\sin I_0}\sin\alpha \qquad\qquad = A_H\frac{z_H}{z_T}\frac{\sin I_0}{\sin I_0'}\frac{1}{\sin\alpha}$$

body represents the anomaly in another component when the same body is magnetized in a new direction. He states:

" . . . the airborne anomaly can be treated as if it were either the vertical or horizontal intensity anomaly for the same rock mass by replacing the true magnetization by a pseudo-magnetization."

The concept of using a single family of curves to describe the various anomalies for a given body appears to be a new idea, however.

Koulomzine and Massé in 1947 analyzed in detail the many interesting characteristics of the standard family of curves before their general applicability was recognized. The reader is referred to that paper for certain novel properties of the curves. The characteristic points of the standard family are tabulated in Table 2. The most important single property is the fact that all curves in the group are of equal amplitude—unity. This permits the use of the amplitude A as a constant factor in the formulas of Table 1.

Granting that the standard curves are of equal amplitude, all similarity between them ends there. Note the inapplicability of general rules for half-width, points of inflection, cross-overs, etc. The only feasible manner to reliably interpret magnetic profiles over tabular bodies is by superposition of curves.

By reference to the general formula, equation (19), it may be observed that the *shape* of an anomaly for a thin infinite dike depends on the index parameter θ_F, which is a function of strike, dip, and field inclination only. The *amplitude* depends on the coefficient C_F, which is a function of all variables except the dip.

The values of C_F given in Table 1 show that, for a given thin dike striking magnetic east-west, the amplitudes of the ΔZ, ΔH, and ΔT_{I_0} anomalies are equal, whereas for bodies striking in other directions ΔZ is always the greater anomaly. This may come as a surprise to some for it holds true regardless of the value of I_0 and is thus independent of geographic location. This disclosure does not support the popular belief that ΔZ is de-

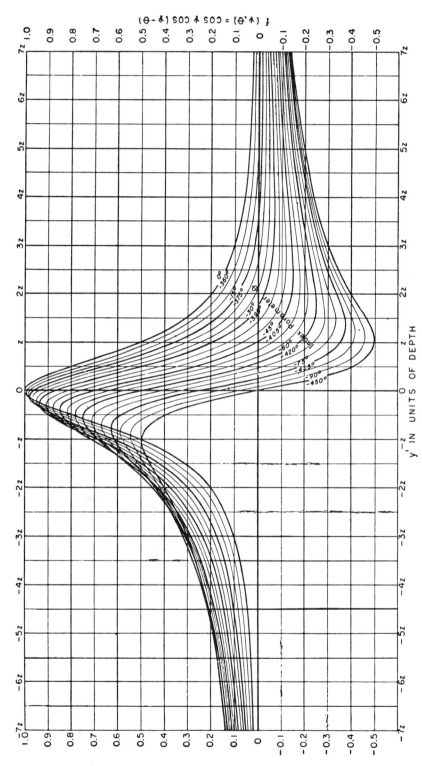

CHART 3. Standard curves for thin infinite dike for values of index parameter from 0° to −90°. Note: For ΔT in Northern Hemisphere, ΔZ and ΔH use upper numbers ($-90° \leq \theta \leq 0°$). For ΔT in Southern Hemisphere use lower numbers ($-450° \leq \theta \leq -360°$).

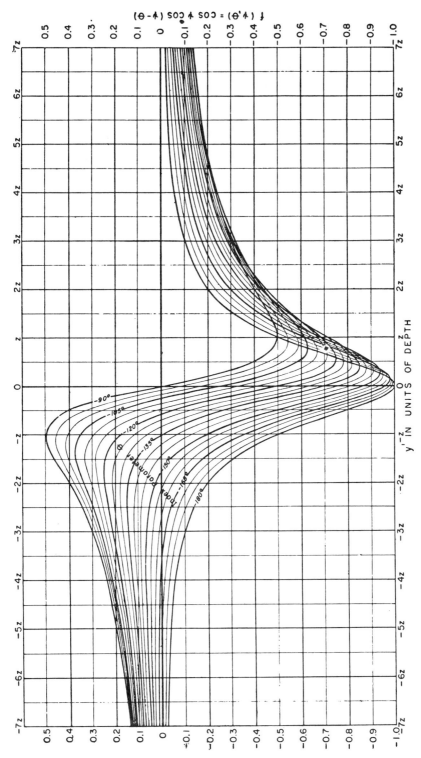

CHART 4. Standard curves for thin infinite dike for value of index parameter from $-90°$ to $-180°$.

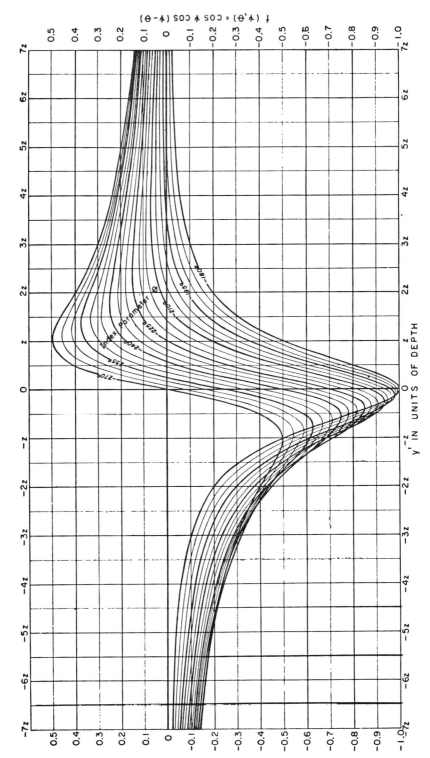

CHART 5. Standard curves for thin infinite dike for values of index parameter from $-180°$ to $-270°$.

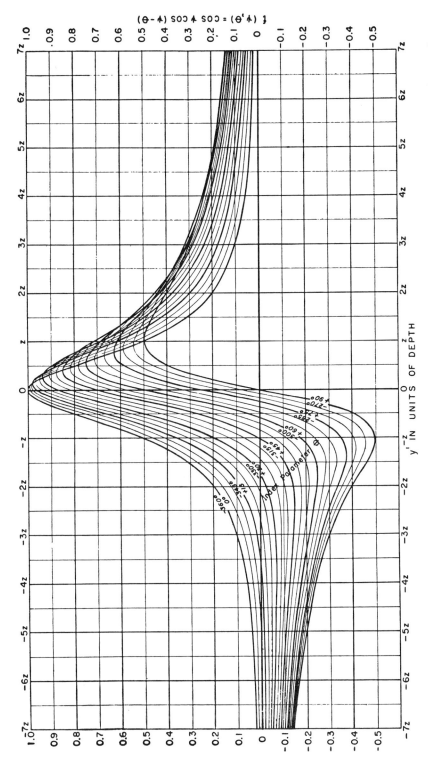

CHART 6. Standard curves for thin infinite dike for values of index parameter from $-270°$ to $-360°$. Note: For ΔZ use lower numbers ($0° \leq \theta \leq 90°$). For ΔT and ΔH use upper numbers ($-360° \leq \theta \leq -270°$).

Table 2. Location and magnitude of characteristic points of standard curves

Characteristic of curve	Location		Magnitude
	In terms of ψ	In terms of y'	
Zero	1. $\psi = 90°, -90°$ 2. $\psi = \theta \pm 90°$	$y_0' = +\infty, -\infty$ $y_0' = -z \operatorname{ctn} \theta$	$f_0 \equiv 0$
Maximum	$\psi_{max} = \dfrac{\theta}{2}$	$y'_{max} = z \tan \dfrac{\theta}{2}$	$f_{max} = \cos^2 \dfrac{\theta}{2}$
Minimum	$\psi_{min} = \dfrac{\theta}{2} \pm 90°$	$y'_{min} = -z \operatorname{ctn} \dfrac{\theta}{2}$	$f_{min} = -\sin^2 \dfrac{0}{2}$

creased in low magnetic latitudes because of a decrease in Z_0. If ΔZ is smaller there, it is only because of the accompanying decrease in T_0. The lower limit on T_0 is found in Brazil at 25,000 gammas—about half the value prevalent in the United States.

Another belief not supported by the foregoing analysis is the idea that the vertical intensity anomaly may decrease or disappear at the so-called subcritical dip, the dip which places the body at right angles to the inducing field (Cook, 1950, p. 682). It is shown here that a given thin tabular body at a given location will produce an anomaly of the same magnitude for all values of dip. (The magnitude of an anomaly is dependent on all parameters *except* the dip.)

It is also of interest to note that regardless of geographic location, and strike direction as well, a ΔZ anomaly due to magnetization solely in the plane of the dike always produces the curve of index parameter 0 degree (or the inverse curve of index parameter -180 degrees at locations south of the magnetic equator). This same situation always produces a ΔH anomaly of index parameter -90 degrees, or its inverse, -270 degrees. For anomalies due to magnetization perpendicular to the plane of the dike only, the opposite situation holds, that is, the ΔZ anomaly is always of index parameter -90 or -270 degrees, and the ΔH anomaly of index 0 or -180 degrees.

Computation of the family of curves presented in Charts 3–6 from equation (20)

proved to be extremely simple. It was carried out to three-place precision in about two hours with the slide rule. It was only necessary to plot points for the primary group of curves shown in Chart 3, since Charts 4, 5, and 6 are images of the primary group reversed top to bottom, left to right, or both, a function carried out on a set of unlabeled curves by the reproduction process. Furthermore, because of symmetry, it was necessary to compute only one fourth the points for the curves of Chart 3.

As may be readily appreciated, the four sheets of curves in Charts 3–6 represent the magnetic anomalies of the thin infinite dike many times more precisely than would have the portfolio of 2,205 curves planned originally.

Thick Dikes

The magnetic anomalies for thick dikes will not be derived here in rigorous fashion, as adequate formulas have been presented before (see Cook, 1950, p. 667). Also, many of the characteristics of thick dike anomalies are similar to those for thin dikes. It is of interest only to observe what happens to the standard formula, equation (19), for a thin dike as the thickness increases.

In Figure 4 is shown a thick dike divided up into a large number of thin dikes of thickness dt, which each produce at P the anomaly:

$$d(\Delta F) = C_w \frac{dt}{z} \cos \psi \cos (\psi - \theta) \quad (21)$$

where $C_w = C_F z/dt$.

It may be shown that $dt/z = \sin \delta \sec^2 \psi d\psi$. Substituting in equation (21) and simplifying:

$$d(\Delta F) = C_w \sin \delta(\cos \theta + \tan \psi \sin \theta)d\psi.$$

This may be integrated between the limits of ψ_2 and ψ_1 to obtain the thick dike anomaly:

$$\Delta F = C_w \sin \delta \left[\cos \theta(\psi_1 - \psi_2) \right.$$

$$\left. + \sin \theta \log \frac{\cos \psi_2}{\cos \psi_1} \right].$$

Since $C_w \sin \delta = C_F/R$, where $R = W/z$, the above formula reduces to a form similar to the thin dike formula:

$$\Delta F = C_F \left[\left(\frac{\psi_1 - \psi_2}{R} \right) \cos \theta_F \right.$$

$$\left. + \left(\frac{1}{R} \log \frac{\cos \psi_2}{\cos \psi_1} \right) \sin \theta_F \right]. \quad (22)$$

The coefficients C_F and the index parameters θ_F are exactly the same as for the thin dike case presented in Table 1. R is the ratio of apical width to depth as shown by Figure 4. The standard curves for thick dikes are thus defined by the expression in brackets in equation (22).

A *complete* family of curves for thick dikes has no meaning, since there are an infinite number of values of the width index R. What was done for the present study, therefore, was to prepare groups of curves of discrete values of R for index parameters at intervals of 10 degrees. Width indices of 0 (thin dike case), 1, 2, 3, and 4 were chosen. The results are shown by the sheets of standard curves given in Charts 7 through 16. These sheets, when reproduced on transparent paper, serve for index parameters in all quadrants by reversing the sheets right to left, top to bottom, or both. The correct index parameter always appears in the upper right hand corner.

It would have been desirable to have constructed charts at a closer index interval, say 5 degrees, as with thin dikes, but there was not sufficient time available. Intermediate

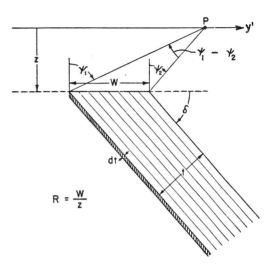

FIG. 4. Geometry of the wide dike in the $y'z$ plane.

curves of sufficient accuracy may readily be prepared by sketching, if needed.[2]

Unlike thin dike curves, the amplitude of the standard curves for thick dikes is not constant but is a number always less than unity, decreasing as the thickness increases. To facilitate curve-matching, the curves were therefore normalized to a constant unit amplitude. The true amplitude a was determined empirically for each curve by plotting points near the maximum and minimum and is tabulated on each sheet. Mathematical computation of a would have been more difficult due to its long, complicated formula.

The variable amplitude of the thick dike curves necessitates the only change needed when utilizing the thin dike formulas (Table 1) for thick dikes: that is, everywhere the amplitude A of an observed profile curve appears in Table 1 the term A/a must be substituted. This results in a greater computed thickness for a thick dike from a given observed amplitude, showing that thick dikes are less efficient producers of anomalies per unit width than thin dikes.

It is of interest to note that the thick dike curves in Charts 7–16 do not begin to depart significantly from thin dike curves $(R=0)$

(*Continued on page 536*)

[2] The intermediate curves have been prepared since first publication of this paper (author).

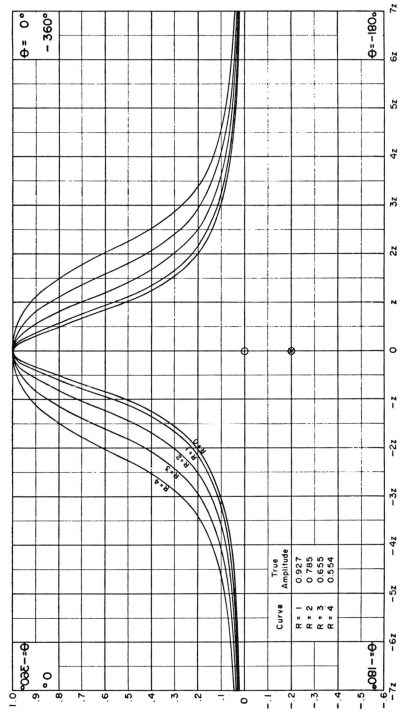

CHART 7. Normalized standard curves for magnetic anomalies over long tabular bodies of varying thickness.

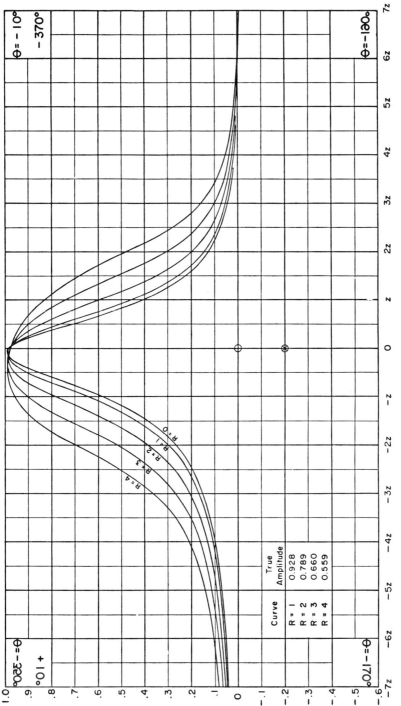

CHART 8. Normalized standard curves for magnetic anomalies over long tabular bodies of varying thickness.

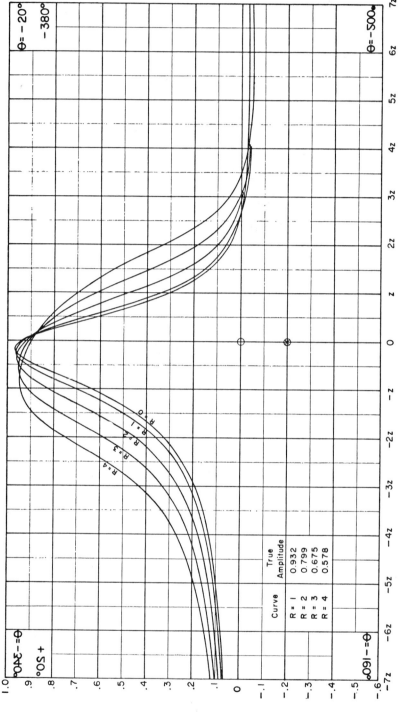

CHART 9. Normalized standard curves for magnetic anomalies over long tabular bodies of varying thickness.

Curve	True Amplitude
R = 1	0.932
R = 2	0.799
R = 3	0.675
R = 4	0.578

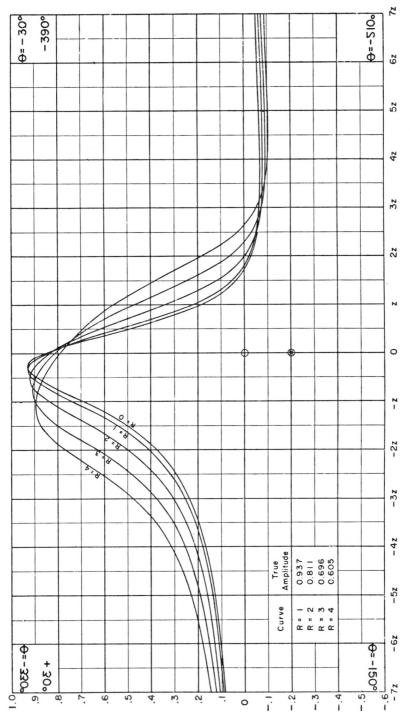

CHART 10. Normalized standard curves for magnetic anomalies over long tabular bodies of varying thickness.

Curve	True Amplitude
R = 1	0.937
R = 2	0.811
R = 3	0.696
R = 4	0.605

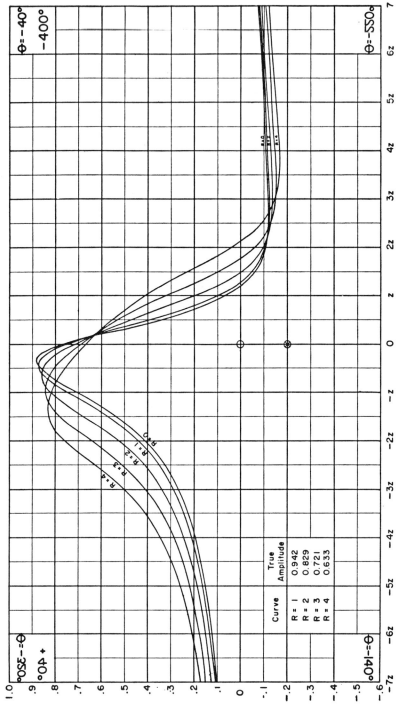

CHART 11. Normalized standard curves for magnetic anomalies over long tabular bodies of varying thickness.

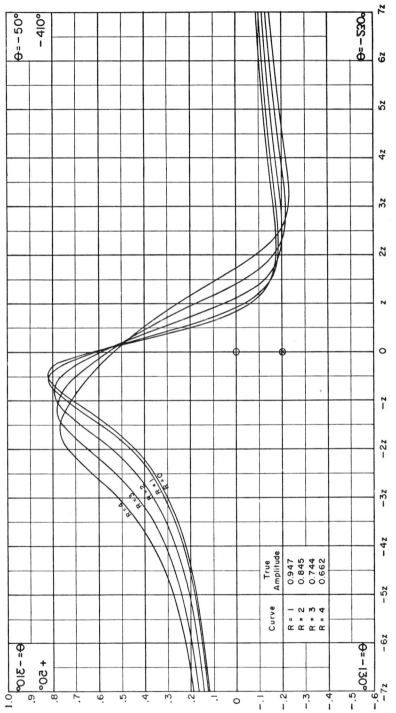

CHART 12. Normalized standard curves for magnetic anomalies over long tabular bodies of varying thickness.

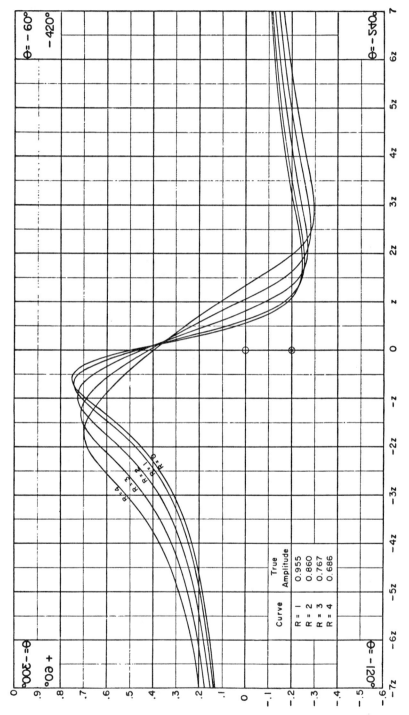

CHART 13. Normalized standard curves for magnetic anomalies over long tabular bodies of varying thickness.

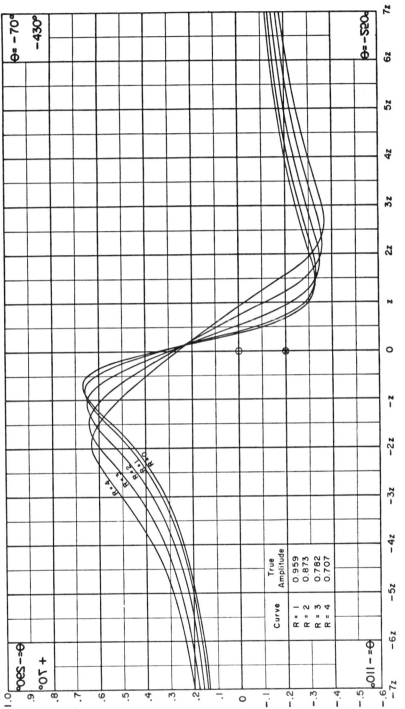

CHART 14. Normalized standard curves for magnetic anomalies over long tabular bodies of varying thickness.

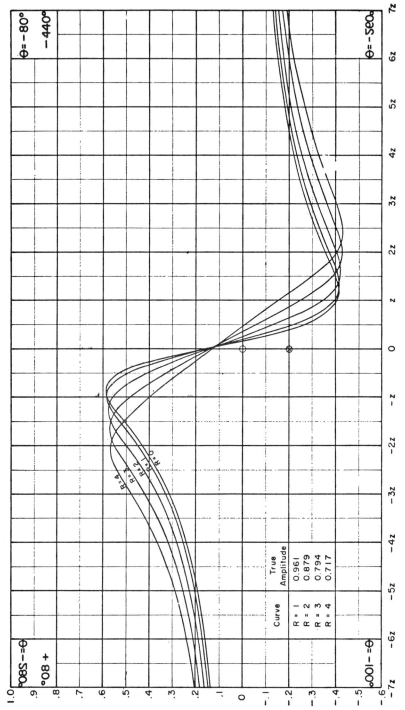

CHART 15. Normalized standard curves for magnetic anomalies over long tabular bodies of varying thickness.

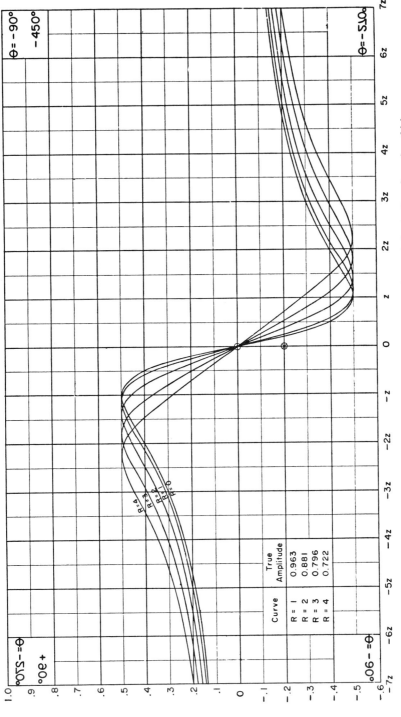

CHART 16. Normalized standard curves for magnetic anomalies over long tabular bodies of varying thickness.

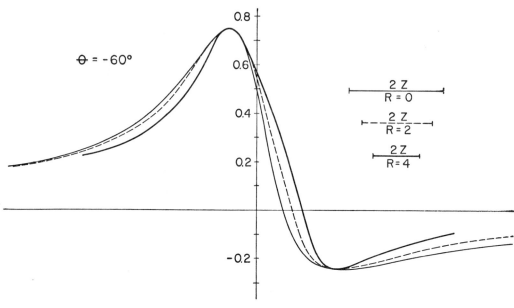

$\Theta = -60°$

Fɪɢ. 5. Dike anomalies plotted with common peaks to illustrate the "pinching" effect shown by wide dike curves.

until the apical width is approximately equal to the depth of burial ($R=1$). The thin dike curves have thus proven to be more universally applicable than previously suspected.

It should be mentioned at this point that the thick dike geometry (Figure 4) breaks down for bodies of near-horizontal dip. For actual geological bodies of shallow dip, however, the geometry of the apex is often quite irregular, resulting in unpredictable variations in the anomaly curve. An equally serious problem in such cases is also that of inhomogenous susceptibility across the width. It was for these practical considerations that standard curves were not constructed for width indices greater than 4.

Another interesting feature, and an important one to interpretation, is that when wide dike curves are superimposed on thin dike curves in such a manner that maxima and minima coincide, the wide dike curves appear to be "pinched," the effect increasing as the width of the body increases (see Figure 5). Anomalies over bodies of shallow depth extent exhibit a similar effect, a fact which calls for much care in performing interpretations.

Demagnetization Effects

Due to the mathematical simplicity of the new formulas derived for the thin dike case, it was decided to attack a problem that has been long ignored: demagnetization. Geophysical instrumentation and operational procedures have advanced far beyond available interpretation schemes when it is always necessary to say: ". . . with demagnetization neglected." There are two fairly recent publications on magnetic interpretation, however, which do include demagnetization corrections as a matter of course, but neither from the United States (Mikov, 1956; Werner, 1953).

For the thin infinite dike, demagnetization computations are simple and exact. It is known that the demagnetization factor N, for components of magnetization in the plane of the infinite sheet is zero, and for components perpendicular to the plane of the sheet 4π. For a thin dike, or semi-infinite sheet, there will be a departure from these values near the edge (apex), but since it is assumed that the thickness of the thin dike is very small compared to the depth of burial this departure is not important. Thus, constant demagnetization factors equal to those for an infinite sheet may be assumed for the thin infinite dike.

For a constant demagnetization factor the apparent susceptibility in terms of susceptibility k is equal to: $k/1+Nk$. The apparent susceptibilities for the dip and cross components of magnetization, respectively, are therefore:

$$k_d = k \tag{23a}$$

$$k_c = k/1 + 4\pi k. \tag{23b}$$

The apparent susceptibility to the dip component remains unaltered, while that for the cross component is decreased. This results in an apparent attenuation of the cross component of magnetization relative to the dip component. The *attenuation constant K* is defined as follows:

$$K = \frac{k_c}{k_d} = \frac{1}{1 + 4\pi k}. \tag{24}$$

This changes the direction and magnitude of the magnetization within the dike, resulting in a new *apparent magnitude* T_0'' for the inducing field and a new *apparent magnetization angle* β'' (see Figure 6).

This consequently modifies the formulas previously derived for the thin infinite dike. Mathematically, the new formulas can be shown to be:

$$\Delta Z = 2kT_0' \frac{l}{z} \frac{\cos \beta'}{\cos \beta''} \cos \psi$$
$$\cdot \cos (\psi - \beta'') \tag{25}$$

$$\Delta H = 2kT_0' \frac{l}{z} \sin \alpha \frac{\cos \beta'}{\cos \beta''} \cos \psi$$
$$\cdot \cos (\psi - \beta'' + 90°) \tag{26}$$

$$\Delta T_{I_0} = 2kT_0' \frac{l}{z} \frac{\sin I_0}{\sin I_0'} \frac{\cos \beta'}{\cos \beta''} \cos \psi$$
$$\cdot \cos (\psi - \beta'' + 90° - I_0'). \tag{27}$$

These anomalies are of the same form as equation (19), the general formula for thin dike anomalies with demagnetization neglected and thus are representable by the standard family of curves. However, the

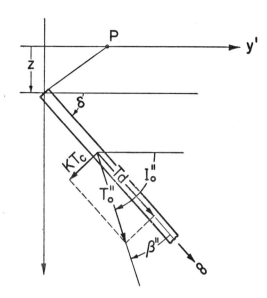

Fig. 6. Apparent magnetic intensity components for a thin infinite dike subject to demagnetization.

coefficients C_F and the index parameters θ_F are different as well as the resultant expressions for dip and thickness. The new values of these quantities are tabulated in Table 3.

In order to facilitate carrying out interpretations of thin dikes with demagnetization included, three auxiliary nomographs have been constructed. Chart 17 was constructed from equation (24) for obtaining the value of the attenuation constant from k, the suspected true magnetic susceptibility. For determining the effective magnetization angle β' from K and the apparent magnetization angle β'' (obtained from curve matching), Chart 18 was constructed from the following easily derived relationship:

$$\tan \beta'' = K \tan \beta'. \tag{28}$$

Finally, the nomograph presented in Chart 19 was constructed for a rapid determination of the *thickness correction factor* C_t, which is the inverse of the modifying expression $\cos \beta'/\cos \beta''$ appearing in the coefficient terms of the anomaly formulas. This expression was converted to a function of β'' and K for construction of Chart 19, as follows:

$$C_\iota = \frac{\cos \beta''}{\cos \beta'}$$

$$= (\cos^2 \beta'' + K^{-2} \sin^2 \beta'')^{1/2}. \quad (29)$$

In carrying out an interpretation, the thickness of the dike is always computed first from the formulas appearing in Table 1, and then corrected for demagnetization by multiplying by C_ι, which is always greater than unity.

It is significant that, in spite of demagnetization effects, the anomalies for ΔZ, ΔH, and ΔT_{I_0} of the thin infinite dike are still representable by the standard family of curves. The effect of demagnetization is only to lower the magnitude of the anomaly and shift it to some other curve in the family.

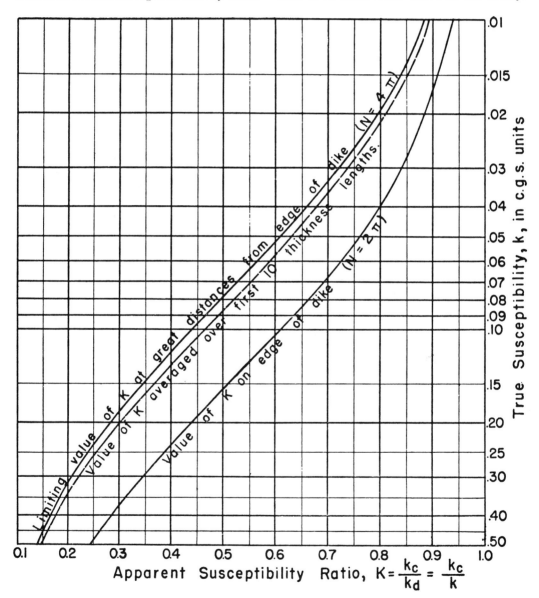

CHART 17. Relative attenuation of the cross-component of magnetization K due to demagnetization versus the true magnetic susceptibility for the thin infinite dike.

Note:

1. For cardinal values $\beta' = \beta''$
2. For $-90° \leq \beta' \leq +90°$, β'' always closer to $0°$ than β'
3. For $-270° \leq \beta' \leq -90°$, β'' always closer to $-180°$ than β'

Limits:
$$-270° \leq \left\{ \begin{array}{c} \beta' \\ \beta'' \end{array} \right\} \leq +90°$$

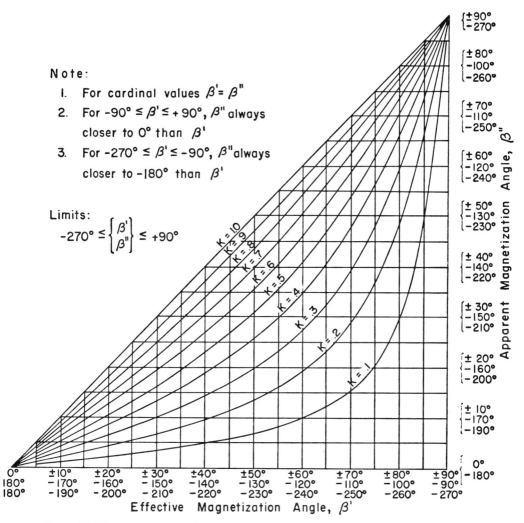

CHART 18. The apparent magnetization angle β'' due to demagnetization versus the effective magnetization angle β' for thin infinite dike.

This means, conversely, that by neglecting demagnetization one arrives at an erroneously small thickness for the body and an erroneous dip. The predictions as to the depth and position of the apex are unaffected by demagnetization, as they depend only upon the curve-matching process.

Analogously, the effects of remanent magnetism on anomalies over tabular bodies may be considered. If the remanent field remains constant in direction and magnitude throughout the body, it will produce effects similar to demagnetization. That is, only the amplitude and shape of the anomaly curve will differ, but the curve will remain a member of the standard family. The depth and position of the body may thus be accurately computed in spite of remanent magnetism. Predictions as to thickness and dip will prove inaccurate, however, unless the amplitude and direction of the remanent component are known. Where, in certain cases, all body parameters are known from geological exploration, then conversely, the characteristics of the remanent field may be determined from the anomaly curve.

The demagnetization effects derived for thin dikes cannot be extended to thick dikes,

Table 3. Characteristics of anomaly curves with demagnetization included

Anomaly ΔF	Coefficient C_F	Index parameter θ_F	Magnetization angle β''	Dip* δ	Thickness t
ΔZ	$2kT_0'\dfrac{t}{z}\dfrac{\cos\beta'}{\cos\beta''}$	β''	θ_Z	$I_0' - \beta'$	$\dfrac{Az}{2kT_0'}\dfrac{\cos\beta''}{\cos\beta'}$
ΔH	$2kT_0'\dfrac{t}{z}\sin\alpha\dfrac{\cos\beta'}{\cos\beta''}$	$\beta'' - 90°$	$\theta_H + 90°$	$I_0' - \beta'$	$\dfrac{Az}{2kT_0'}\dfrac{1}{\sin\alpha}\dfrac{\cos\beta''}{\cos\beta'}$
ΔT_{I_0}	$2kT_0'\dfrac{t}{z}\dfrac{\sin I_0}{\sin I_0'}\dfrac{\cos\beta'}{\cos\beta''}$	$\beta'' - 90° + I_0'$	$\theta_T + 90° - I_0'$	$I_0' - \delta'$	$\dfrac{Az}{2kT_0'}\dfrac{\sin I_0'}{\sin I_0}\dfrac{\cos\beta''}{\cos\beta'}$

* To compute the dip, it is necessary to obtain the correct value of β' from β'' and K with equation (28) or Chart 18.

and in fact, a general solution of demagnetization for thick dikes does not exist. Demagnetization creates an internal magnetization in the near-surface portion of thick dikes that varies both in direction and in magnitude, and a consideration of these effects requires individual treatment of every case, to say nothing of the mathematics in-

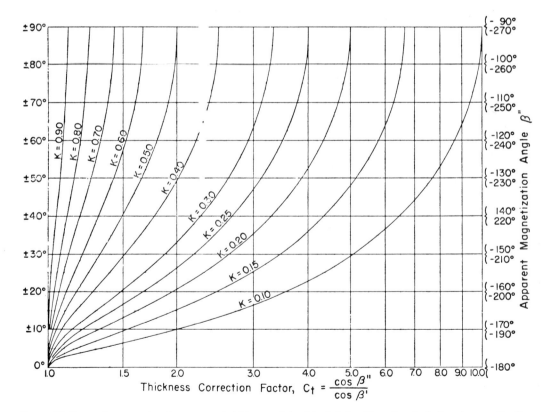

CHART 19. Factor for correcting the computed thickness of the thin infinite dike when including demagnetization.

volved. Needless to say, the anomaly curves for thick dikes subject to demagnetization depart from the standard family.

To a first approximation, nevertheless, it may be considered that the demagnetization constant N, for the cross component of magnetization near the edge of a thick dike, approximates the value 2π. Since the near-surface portion of the dike is relatively more important in producing the anomaly than the deeper portions, the attenuation constant K may be weighted toward the value corresponding to $N = 2\pi$. This approximation can be made directly on Chart 17 when computing K. It is assumed throughout that the dip component of magnetization is unaffected by demagnetization, an assumption that is less correct the greater the thickness of the dike.

Model Studies

To observe the predicted relative attenuation of the cross component due to demagnetization and to check the validity of the demagnetization corrections in general, some simple model studies were undertaken. Two concrete slabs measuring 4 ft $\times$ 7 ft $\times \frac{5}{8}$ inch were prepared using a mixture of sand, cement, and crushed iron ore and backed by plywood. One slab contained approximately 75 percent crushed ore by weight and the other about 10 percent. The ore was a moderately oxidized magnetite.

The models were magnetized only by induction in the earth's field. Any component of remanent magnetism existing in the original magnetite would have been cancelled by the random orientation of the particles in the models.

A number of anomaly profiles were obtained across the slabs inclined at different dip angles and always striking magnetic east-west. Vertical intensity was measured with an Askania Gfz magnetometer in a fixed position, the slabs being moved back and forth underneath (Figure 7). The Gfz magnetometer proved quite suitable for the model work due to the small size of its measuring element. The vertical distance between measuring element and top edge of slab was 4.5 $\pm$ 0.5 inches for all experiments.

Fig. 7. View of movable magnetic model and stationary magnetometer used in experiments for measuring the demagnetization effects of thin tabular bodies.

The inclination I_0 of the earth's field at Palo Alto, California, where the measurements were made is 61.5 degrees, and the total intensity T_0 is 51,600 gammas (from U. S. Coast and Geodetic Survey charts). When inclined at a 60-degree dip angle the slabs were essentially subjected to dip-magnetization only; at a dip angle of 150 degrees (30 degrees) they were subjected to cross-magnetization only. At other inclinations they were magnetized by dip- and cross-components in varying proportions.

The magnetic profiles obtained from the experiments are shown in Figures 8 and 9. The true magnetic susceptibility of the bodies was computed from the amplitude of the two curves for 60-degree dip, and appears on the respective plots. This computation is based on the fact that for thin bodies the dip component is essentially unaffected by demagnetization. The effects of demagnetization on the cross-component ($\delta = 150°$) are quite marked, particularly for the more highly magnetic model (Figure 9). The relative amplitude of the response curve in the latter case was only 40 percent of that obtained with the model inclined at $\delta = 60°$, yielding an attenuation constant $K = 0.40$. The value of K predicted from Chart 17 was 0.44.

For the weakly magnetic model the observed and predicted values of K were 0.96 and 0.87, respectively. Whereas the accuracy in predicting K leaves something to be desired (about 10 percent error in each case), it

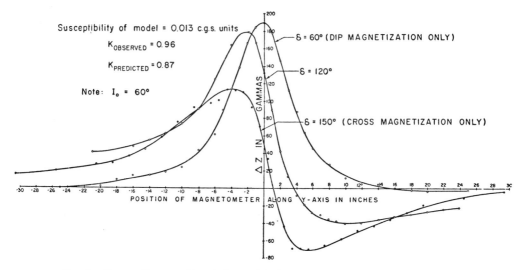

Fig. 8. ΔZ anomalies over thin tabular model of magnetic susceptibility = 0.013 cgs units.

was within the precision of the simple experiments, which were carried out by two people in only three days—including preparation of slabs and framework. A more thorough study of demagnetization effects on models would be advantageous.

In spite of the unsophisticated nature of the foregoing experiments, the results obtained leave no doubt whatsoever of the serious effects of demagnetization on moderately to highly magnetic bodies. With demagnetization absent, the amplitude of anomaly curves for each model inclined at different dip angles would be constant. For weakly magnetic bodies, the difference in

amplitude due to varying dip is slight, as illustrated by Figure 8. For strongly magnetic bodies, however, the differences in amplitude are quite pronounced, showing that the demagnetization suffered by the cross-component is severe. Also, note how demagnetization changes the shape of the intermediate curve of dip angle 150 degrees in Figure 9. Interpretations made from such altered curves would yield incorrect thickness and dip estimates, the result predicted in the previous section.

For highly magnetic deposits of magnetite, true susceptibility values are two to three times that of the more highly magnetic model

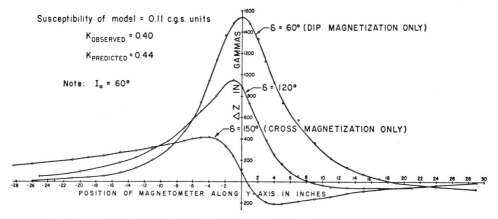

Fig. 9. ΔZ anomalies over thin tabular model of magnetic susceptibility = 0.11 cgs units.

Table 4. Procedure sheet for magnetic interpretation of tabular bodies

Interpreter _____ Date _____ Component _____

Name of	*Results*	11. y' apex = _____ ⎫	Superposition with stan-
Anomaly _____	Depth _____	12. z = _____ ⎭	dard curves
	(No. 14)		
Profile _____	Dip _____	13. Height = _____	
	(No. 15 or 21)		
Description _____	Thickness _____	14. Depth = _____	Subtract: 12–13
	(No. 16 or 23)		
_____	Coordinates of Apex:	15. δ = _____	Table 1
_____	x _____ y _____	16. t = _____	Table 1

Step-by-Step Tabulation			*Demagnetization Corrections*	
Quantity	Reference			
1. T_0 = _____ Gammas ⎫		17. k = _____		
2. I_0 = _____ ⎭	Regional maps of area.	18. K = _____	Chart 17 (With 17)	
3. α = _____	Isogamma map	19. β'' = _____	Table 3	
4. I_0' = _____	Chart 1 (With 2 & 3)	20. β' = _____	Chart 18 (With 18 & 19)	
5. T_0'/T_0 = _____	Chart 2 (With 2 & 3)	21. $\delta_{corr.}$ = _____	$\delta = I_0' - \beta'$	
6. T_0' = _____ Gammas	Multiply: 5×1	22. C_t = _____	Chart 19 (With 18 & 19)	
7. A = _____ Gammas	Magnetic profile	23. $t_{corr.}$ = _____	Multiply: 16×22	
8. R = _____ ⎫	Superposition			
9. θ = _____ ⎬	with standard			
10. a = _____ ⎭	curves			

of these experiments, bringing about a corresponding increase in the demagnetization effects. In such cases accurate quantitative interpretations would be impossible to make from theoretical considerations if demagnetization were neglected.

Interpretational Procedure

To facilitate carrying out magnetic interpretations according to the foregoing analysis, a step-by-step procedure sheet has been prepared and is presented in Table 4. By following this through from beginning to end, the interpreter can readily obtain all the elements desired of an interpretation.

The magnetic field values T_0 and I_0 of the area are tabulated first, and from the isogamma map the magnetic strike α of the anomaly is measured. From these quantities the interpreter determines, with the aid of Charts 1 and 2, the effective magnetic field values T_0' and I_0', in the vertical plane perpendicular to the strike. Next, the amplitude A, the gamma difference between maximum and minimum, is measured on a carefully chosen "best" profile perpendicular to the strike. This magnetic profile is selected so as to minimize the disturbing influence of nearby anomalies, spurious readings, and so on. In some cases smoothing techniques must be employed.

Using the selected, smoothed profile, the curve-matching process is carried out. First, the curve is expanded or reduced in the vertical direction to the constant amplitude of the standard curves and then redrafted. This can be facilitated by using proportional dividers. Next, the curve is reduced and expanded horizontally while its match to different standard curves is checked. The most suitable way so far devised to vary the horizontal scale while keeping the vertical scale constant is with a piece of "one-way stretch" elastic. The curve is represented by a thin strip of soft rubber fastened to the elastic with rubber cement. The elastic is held in its stretched position by using a suitably constructed frame which allows light to pass through from the back for ease of superposition. Undoubtedly, an optical system could be developed which would carry out the curve-matching process much more expeditiously.

From superposition one obtains: θ, the index parameter of the standard curve that provides the closest match; z, the distance of the apex below the plane of observation; and the y' coordinate of the apex. Care must be taken to maintain a known horizontal distance on the profile all the while the horizontal scale is being varied. This known distance is compared to the z units on the y' axis of the final fit for computing z. Equally important, or perhaps more so if the interpretation will lead to the spotting of drill holes, is the maintaining of a known field location on the profile for recuperation of the coordinate of $y' = 0$, the apex of the body in plan view.

From the values obtained by curve-matching, one can compute the depth of the apex below the surface of the ground, and with the aid of Table 1, the dip and thickness of the body. For the last computation, the magnetic susceptibility must be approximately known.

If the magnetic profile matches a thick dike curve, one obtains in addition to the above values, the thickness parameter R and the amplitude a of the matching curve. If the magnetic susceptibility is known, the thickness may then be computed in two ways: (1) from Table 1, remembering to substitute A/a for A; and (2) by substituting the R-value in the following formula (see Figure 4):

$$t = Rz \sin \delta. \tag{30}$$

From experience, the latter has been found to yield only approximate results even in the best cases. When the magnetic susceptibility is unknown, it can be roughly estimated from a thick dike interpretation by equating the appropriate thickness formula in Table 1 with equation (30) and solving for k.

If the magnetic susceptibility is thought to be great and there is a significant cross-component of magnetization, it is necessary to follow through with the demagnetization corrections. From the suspected true susceptibility the attenuation constant K is computed (Chart 17). A certain allowance can be made here for dikes of varying thickness. Then using the index parameter θ, the apparent magnetization angle β'' is determined

(Table 3) and this together with K determines the effective magnetization angle β' (Chart 18). From these quantities, one determines the corrected dip angle (Table 3) and the corrected thickness (Chart 19). Application of demagnetization corrections to thick dikes should be done with caution, as discussed in a previous section.

Due to the many charts and tables used for the interpretation process it has been found convenient to fasten them together into one loose-leaf notebook. An interpretation can be carried out in less than an hour if a proper fit to a standard curve can be made rapidly. However, many factors conspire against a proper fit: spurious readings, nearby or overlapping anomalies, departure of the geometry of the body from the theoretical model, and many others. In some cases the amount and type of mismatch provide an insight into the character of the magnetic source.

One recommended method for improving the accuracy of an interpretation is by performing a second or even third type of survey over the same anomaly. For example, if the original survey was carried out by measuring ΔZ, an independent interpretation could be made from either a ΔH or ΔT profile. For the second anomaly component, readings are only taken along the "best" profile selected from the first survey and not over the whole anomaly, thus affording a considerable savings in field work while at the same time yielding a corresponding amount of information. A variety of new magnetometers marketed in recent years make it possible to accurately measure any component in minimum time.[3]

One suggestion in deciding whether to measure ΔZ, ΔH, or ΔT for the primary area coverage is to decide which of these components yields anomalies over the target bodies that most closely approximate standard curves of index $0°$ (or $-180°$). Anomalies near this index have the classical "high" (or "low") over the disturbing body, a feature more easily understood and explained to interested parties than the more general

---

[3] Of interest in this regard is the new null-reading H magnetometer developed by Askania.

"high-low" combination. Interpretation may, in many cases, be more diagnostic for this type of response curve as well. The index parameter to be expected over a given geological body depends on the strike, inclination, dip, and demagnetization effects and may be computed quite readily from formulas presented in this paper.

Tabular bodies of *limited depth extent* can be treated by subtraction of curves. This method may provide a good depth estimate to the apex of the body, but the estimate for the lower extremity is subject to greater error. The method of subtraction of curves may also be used to treat overlapping anomalies, a very serious problem in many areas.

To obtain more diagnostic interpretations of selected anomalies, the multilevel technique has been employed. When it is suspected that a tabular body is present, the formulas at the bottom of Table 1 allow comparison of multilevel surveys measuring different components at different levels—a ΔZ survey at the surface with an airborne ΔT survey, for example.

Dependent Magnetic Anomalies

In the section on basic derivations, several dependent magnetic anomaly components were mentioned. Figure 3 shows the relationship between the three types of total intensity anomalies: ΔT_{I_0}, the anomaly along the direction of T_0, the undisturbed field; $\Delta T_\perp$, the anomaly in the component perpendicular to T_0 and lying in the magnetic meridian; and ΔT, the component measured by present-day magnetometers. By substituting equations (12) and (17) or (25) and (26) into the formulas shown in Figure 3, complete expressions for these anomalies may be derived for anomalies over thin dikes.

As previously discussed, ΔT_{I_0} may be represented by the standard family of curves, whereas $\Delta T_\perp$ and ΔT may not. When ΔT is much smaller than T_0, ΔT approaches ΔT_{I_0}, an approximation commonly used in petroleum exploration work. For large anomalies of the type encountered in mineral exploration, particularly over iron ore bodies, this assumption is not valid. Thus, techniques based on that assumption, such as second-

derivative methods and upward and downward continuation are not properly applicable to airborne surveys exhibiting large anomalies. Also, in such cases a complete magnetic survey at one level does not completely define the magnetic field at all points in space, an argument which has been used against multilevel methods. It is this writer's opinion that interpretation of the primary data for airborne surveys exhibiting large anomalies is much preferred to that obtained by residual, derivative, or continuation methods, notwithstanding the great success of the latter in petroleum exploration and in basement studies, and that curve-matching techniques, such as those presented in this paper, should be employed wherever possible.

The discrepancy between the directions of ΔT and ΔT_{I_0} that constitutes the basis for the above arguments is defined by ΔI, the anomaly in inclination. This anomaly is of long standing interest to exploration geophysicists, but has seldom, or never, been formulated. For tabular bodies it may readily be computed by substituting formulas presented in this paper into the general expression:

$$\Delta I = \tan^{-1} \frac{\Delta T_\perp}{T_0 + \Delta T_{I_0}} . \qquad (31)$$

One use of ΔI anomalies, for example, would be in computing the theoretical dip needle and superdip anomalies over tabular bodies and in determining the shift of superdip "highs," as discussed by H. L. James in 1948.[4] All these phenomena depend on inclination, as well as on total intensity.

For highly magnetic bodies the ΔI anomaly can be quite impressive. Over one iron ore body at San Juan, Peru ($I_0 = -4°$), the writer measured inclination variations from -28 degrees to $+50$ degrees, a difference of 78 degrees. In Ontario, Canada, a ΔI anomaly was so great that it resulted in negative values of inclination and thus of ΔZ (Ratcliffe, 1957). This was taken as a genuine case of reverse polarization, which was quite difficult to explain, since the adjacent parts of

[4] AIME Technical Paper 2293, March 1948.

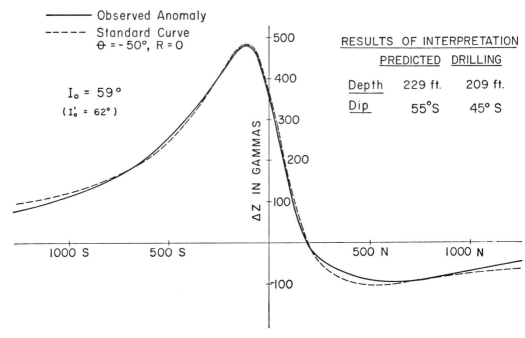

FIG. 10. Interpretation of magnetic anomaly over the Pima copper mine in Arizona.

the anomaly showed even greater values of positive vertical intensity. The anomaly was probably a composite one of the type illustrated by the standard curves presented in this paper but so great that ΔZ exceeded Z_0, a not uncommon occurrence over magnetite deposits, particularly when remanent magnetism is present.

Another interesting anomaly which may be theoretically derived from formulas presented in this paper is the anomaly in declination, ΔD (the "fence-line" anomaly). The expression for ΔD over tabular bodies can be developed from the general formula for the ΔD anomaly over any two-dimensional body:

$$\Delta D = \tan^{-1} \frac{\Delta H' \cos \alpha}{H_0 + \Delta H' \sin \alpha} . \quad (32)$$

This anomaly is theoretically zero for long east-west striking bodies of uniform susceptibility and increases in magnitude as the strike departs from east-west.

Examples

To illustrate the results obtainable with the standard curve method of interpretation,

three brief examples from different geomagnetic latitudes will be presented. The first of these is a profile across a noted geophysical discovery in Arizona, the Pima copper mine (Figure 10).[5] This profile was fitted to a thin dike curve, and it can be seen that the match is quite good, lending weight to the reliability of the interpretation. The predicted depth was 229 ft and the actual depth about 210 ft —an error of only 10 percent. A dip of 68° S was computed with demagnetization neglected, whereas the actual dip was 45° S. Subsequent drilling information showed the mineralized zone to be about 35 ft thick (perpendicular to the dip), so that the magnetic susceptibility of the deposit is about 0.05 cgs units. Demagnetization corrections based on this value of susceptibility yield a corrected dip of 55° S, only 10 degrees different from the observed dip.

An interpretation of a magnetic anomaly near the magnetic equator is shown in Figure 11. The observed curve fitted extremely well to a standard curve of thickness parameter

[5] Constructed from data kindly loaned by W. E. Heinrichs, Jr.

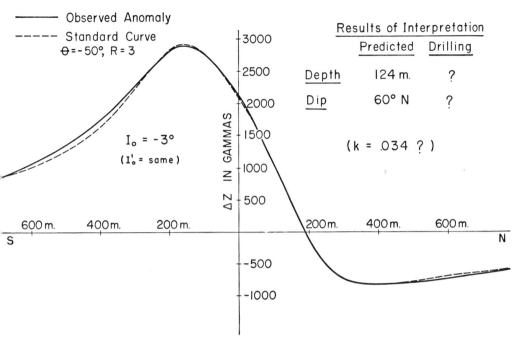

FIG. 11. Interpretation of magnetic anomaly in Marcona district, Peru, near the magnetic equator.

$R=3$, and yielded the results shown. From the R-value and the amplitude of the curve the average susceptibility of the body was estimated to be on the order of 0.034 cgs units. Unfortunately, there are no drilling results to verify the predictions of that particular interpretation, as yet.

An example from south of the magnetic equator is shown in Figure 12. It was difficult to obtain a good match to this profile using the existing standard curves, and the standard curve finally fitted was an intermediate one of parameters $R=1.5$, $\theta=-155°$, constructed by sketch averaging four existing curves. Even so, the curve match cannot be considered excellent in spite of the large amount of time spent on it, yet the depth estimate erred by only 13 percent. This example emphasizes one of the principal advantages of superposition: reliable interpretations can be made many times in spite of irregularities in the anomaly curve that would more seriously affect methods of interpretation based on only a few isolated points of the curve.

The above three examples were chosen for illustration here because of their relatively good fit to the standard curves. It should be pointed out that there have been many more examples that did not match as well, due to a variety of reasons. No claims can be made, therefore, that the standard curve method is a panacea for magnetic interpretations. On the other hand, it is fast, simple, and general, and, it is hoped, will prove to be another step forward in the art of interpreting magnetic anomalies.

Acknowledgments

The writer wishes to acknowledge the helpful criticism received from Dr. Joshua L. Soske, Stanford University, where much of the foregoing comprised a research project for a Master's degree in 1958–59, and in particular to acknowledge Dr. Soske's suggestion to use the Askania Gfz magnetometer for the model studies. The magnetometer was loaned to the writer through the courtesy of Dr. Ralph Holmer, Chief Geophysicist of Bear Creek Mining Company, Denver, who subsequently offered valuable aid and encouragement in the preparation of

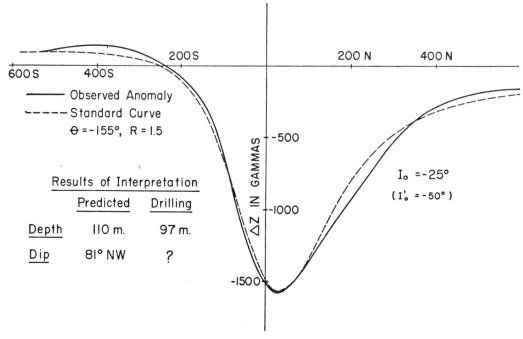

Fig. 12. Interpretation of magnetic anomaly near Vallenar, Chile, south of the magnetic equator.

this paper for presentation. For financial help received while attending Stanford University the writer is indebted to the W. F. Detert scholarship fund. To Marcona Mining Company, San Juan, Peru, the writer is grateful for much time allowed from normal duties for carrying out a large part of the original work and later for computation and preparation of the thick dike curves.

References

Affleck, James, 1958, Interrelationships between magnetic anomaly components: Geophysics, v. 23, p. 738–748.

Cook, Kenneth L., 1950, Quantitative interpretation of vertical magnetic anomalies over veins: Geophysics, v. 15, p. 667–686. (Contains comprehensive bibliography.)

Heiland, C. A., 1946, Geophysical exploration: New York, Prentice-Hall, Inc.

Jakosky, J. J., 1950, Exploration geophysics: Los Angeles, Trija Publishing Co.

Koulomzine, Th., and Massé, L., 1947, Magnetic anomaly of inclined vein of infinite length: American Institute of Mining Engineers Technical Paper No. 2260.

Mikov, D. S., 1956, Atlas of theoretical curves for the interpretation of magnetic and gravitational anomalies (unpublished U. S. Geological Survey translation): Tomsk, State Scientific Technical Press for Literature on Geology.

Ratcliffe, J. H., 1957, Methods and case histories in mining geophysics: 6th Commonwealth Mining and Metallurgical Congress, Montreal.

Werner, S., 1953, Interpretation of magnetic anomalies at sheet-like bodies: Stockholm, Sveriges Geologiska Undersokning.

USE OF PIRSON'S POLAR CHART IN CALCULATING TOTAL-MAGNETIC-INTENSITY ANOMALIES OF TWO-DIMENSIONAL BODIES †

ROLAND G. HENDERSON*

An explanation is given of the use of Pirson's polar chart in calculating the total-intensity anomaly of a two-dimensional body of arbitrary shape. For magnetization by induction in the earth's field the anomaly is obtained in one excursion over the body. Nonparallel magnetizations require two excursions. A dike body is used to illustrate the application.

Introduction

The polar chart shown in Figure 1 was designed by Pirson (1940) for calculating ΔZ and ΔX, the vertical and horizontal components of a magnetic anomaly caused by a finite two-dimensional body. With slight modifications in use it may be employed to calculate ΔT, the component of the total-intensity anomaly in the direction of the earth's normal field, in the case where the body is uniformly magnetized by induction; or in the case where the body is magnetized in a direction different from the earth's present field because of a strong remanent component. Although his paper antedates modern total-intensity magnetometers, Pirson had knowledge of the application of his chart to total-intensity anomalies (personal communication), but he could not be prevailed upon to write the article on the ΔT-application. For the basic theory and details of chart construction, the reader is referred to the original paper. We present here a brief outline of procedures and supplementary material which over the years have facilitated the use of the chart.

Diverging somewhat from Pirson, we take the y axis in the direction of strike of the body. The strike can be inferred from the elongation axis of the anomaly. The angle of strike α is measured from magnetic north over west to the strike direction. This direction defines the negative y axis. The z axis is positive vertically downward. The x axis is along a profile at right angles to the strike and is positive in the direction which makes the system of coordinates right handed. The coordinate system and the basic magnetic quantities are shown in Figure 2.

The chart is shown in Figure 1. The user may construct his own chart from Pirson's equations (11) and (12).[1] The $\Delta \xi$ and $\Delta \eta$ axes are used for orientation purposes. The number of elements counted in the $\Delta \xi$ and $\Delta \eta$ orientations are, for purposes of discussion, designated N_ξ and N_η, respectively. In the normal use of a chart each element contributes at the center an anomaly effect in gammas per unit magnetization equal to the chart constant c. The chart constant is independent of scale, i.e., a large chart and a small chart used on the same vertical section of a body give the same results, within the limits of one's ability to count the elements. The counting may be facilitated by subdividing the chart into groups of ten elements, each group set off by heavy outline. Those who prefer dot charts may easily introduce this modification into Figure 1.

Case I—Induced Magnetization

Magnetic interpretations usually proceed on the assumption that the body is magnetized by induction in the earth's normal field. It is an interesting consequence of induction

[1] Copies of Pirson's Polar Chart may be obtained from the SEG Publication Office, P.O. Box 3098, Tulsa, Oklahoma 74101.

† Publication authorized by the Director, U. S. Geological Survey.

* U. S. Geological Survey, Washington, D. C.

theory that only one excursion over a vertical section of the body with the chart in the $\Delta \xi$-orientation is required for ΔT, while two excursions are required for ΔZ or ΔX.

The earth's normal magnetic field vector $\mathbf{T}_0$ of magnitude T_0 and inclination I in the meridional plane has a component T_1 of inclination ϵ_1 in the xz plane which is responsible for the effective induced magnetization of the body. The parameters necessary for the calculation, expressed in trigonometric form, are

$$\epsilon_1 = \arctan\left(\frac{\tan I}{\sin \alpha}\right) \tag{1}$$

and

$$\left(\frac{T_1}{T_0}\right)^2 = \cos^2 I \sin^2 \alpha + \sin^2 I. \tag{2}$$

Steps in the calculation are as follows:

1) Determine α according to the definition given above.

2) Take as the x axis a representative

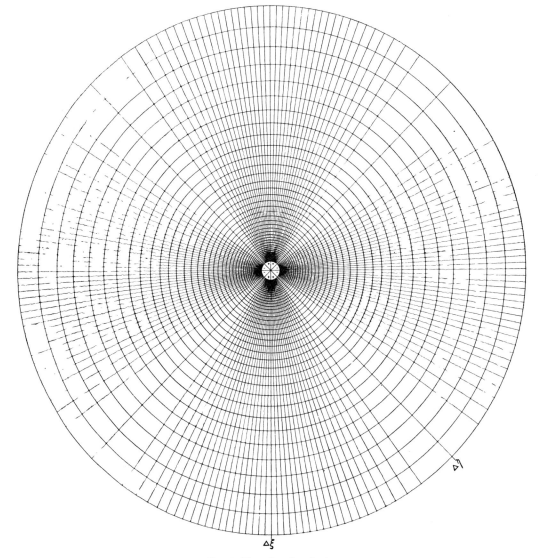

FIG. 1. Pirson's polar chart.

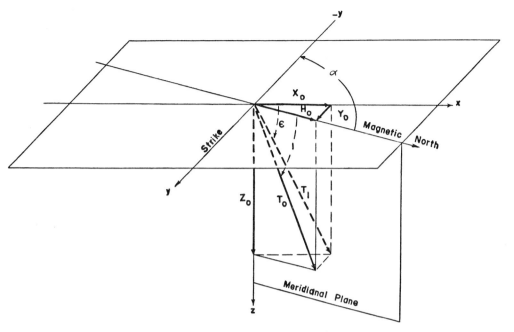

FIG. 2. Coordinate systems and magnetic vectors.

profile perpendicular to the strike. It is positive in a northerly direction.

3) Through the profile take a vertical section of the body including the points to be computed. Draw the point and body configuration to any convenient scale within the compass of the chart. The scale is arbitrary because of the dimensionless character of the chart.

4) From magnetic maps of the earth's field, determine T_0 and I and use them in (1) and (2) to compute ϵ_1 and $(T_1/T_0)^2$.

5) At each point to be computed draw a line making the angle ϵ_1 with the positive x direction. Each such line is in the direction of T_1.

6) Center the chart at the point to be computed, align the $\Delta\xi$ axis with the direction of T_1 and count the elements covering the area of the body, taking into account the algebraic sign of the elements. Estimate fractional elements.

7) Let N_ξ be the number of counts obtained with the chart in the $\Delta\xi$-orientation at a given point, then the total intensity anomaly in gammas is

$$\Delta T = ckT_0 N_\xi [\cos^2 I \sin^2 \alpha + \sin{}^2 I] \quad (3)$$

where k is the susceptibility contrast and c is the chart constant. For the chart shown in Figure 1, $c = 0.00417$ gamma per unit magnetization per sector.

Illustration

Pirson's chart is applicable to any two-dimensional body of arbitrary shape having finite boundaries; however, in order to compare results with exact values, we illustrate its use in calculating the ΔT-anomaly of the theoretical body shown in Figure 3. The parameters and dimensions are as follows: depth = 1, width = 1, vertical depth extent 2, dip $i = \arctan 2$, $\alpha = 60°$, inclination $I = 75°$. With the aid of formulas for a slope given by Heiland (1946), a rigorous formula for the problem is derived in the form

$$\Delta T = 2kT_0 \left[C_1(\phi_2 - \phi_1 + \phi_3 - \phi_4) \right.$$
$$\left. + C_2 \ln \frac{r_2 r_3}{r_1 r_4} \right], \quad (4)$$

where ϕ_j and r_j ($j = 1, 2, 3, 4$) have the meaning given in Figure 3 and where

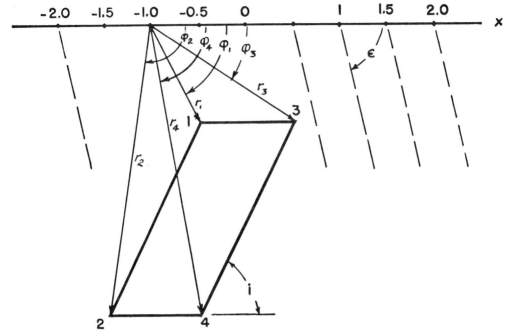

FIG. 3. Theoretical two-dimensional body.

$$C_1 = (\cos^2 I \sin^2 \alpha - \sin^2 I) \sin^2 i$$
$$+ \sin 2I \sin \alpha \sin i \cos i$$

and

$$C_2 = \sin 2I \sin \alpha \sin^2 i$$
$$- (\cos^2 I \sin^2 \alpha - \sin^2 I) \sin i \cos i.$$

The results of calculations by (3) using the Pirson chart and by (4) are given in Table 1 for comparison. The results for the chart are

Table 1. Comparison of polar chart values with exact values for total-magnetic intensity anomaly of body shown in Figure 3

X	$\Delta T/kT_0$ in gammas per unit Magnetization	
	Exact value	Polar chart value
−2.0	0.327	0.321
−1.5	0.567	0.564
−1.0	0.871	0.864
−0.5	1.053	1.053
0.0	0.803	0.795
1.0	−0.148	−0.148
1.5	−0.281	−0.279
2.0	−0.287	−0.284

consistently lower only because of the personal equation of the individual doing the counting. The values were checked independently by another who obtained consistently higher values.

Case II—Total Magnetization

If, through a sampling program or other means, data are available on the uniform bulk remanent magnetization of a two-dimensional body, the Pirson chart may be used to calculate its ΔT anomaly; however, two excursions over the body are required.

Let A and G be the known x and z components of total magnetization (induced+remanent). The magnitude of the component of total magnetization in the xz plane is $\sqrt{A^2+G^2}$ and its inclination is $\epsilon_2 = \arctan (G/A)$.

The calculation is carried out as above, but with the orientation line through each point now making the angle ϵ_2 with the positive x axis. In addition to N_ξ counts, N_η counts obtained with the $\Delta\eta$ axis aligned perpendicular to the orientation axis are required. The total-magnetic intensity anomaly for this case is

$$\Delta T = cN_\xi[A \cos I \sin \alpha + G \sin I]$$

$$+ cN_\eta[G \cos I \sin \alpha - A \sin I]. \quad (5)$$

Equation (5) of course reduces to (3) when A and G involve only components of induced magnetization. Equation (5) was derived by finding ΔX and ΔZ with the aid of Pirson's equations (13) and (14) corrected for an obvious typographical error. Also, when the $\Delta\eta$ axis is aligned at right angles to the direction of magnetization in the xz plane, there is no ambiguity in algebraic sign and the ΔX and ΔZ components are given by

$$\Delta X = \Delta\xi \cos \epsilon + \Delta\eta \sin \epsilon,$$

$$\Delta Z = \Delta\xi \sin \epsilon - \Delta\eta \cos \epsilon.$$

References

Pirson, S. J., 1940, Polar charts for interpreting magnetic anomalies: A.I.M.E. Trans., v. 138, p. 173–192.

Heiland, C. A., 1946, Geophysical exploration: New York, Prentice-Hall, Inc.

POLAR CHARTS FOR CALCULATING AEROMAGNETIC ANOMALIES OF THREE-DIMENSIONAL BODIES†

R. G. HENDERSON* AND ALPHONSO WILSON*

Polar charts have been constructed for seven inclinations of the earth's magnetic field for use in calculating total-intensity anomalies of three-dimensional bodies of arbitrary shape. Starting with a semi-infinite body, the explanation progresses cumulatively, treating finally a laminated body of finite dimensions. The chart at magnetic inclination $I = 90°$ is simply a solid angle chart and can be used for calculating gravity anomalies. Examples are given of applications to observed anomalies.

Introduction

When it is possible to make reasonable assumptions about the depth, size, shape, and magnetization of a three-dimensional body which cannot sensibly be represented by a simple geometric form, recourse must be made to approximation calculations. These may involve analog devices such as graticules, or mechanical or optical integrators; or digital devices such as a desk calculator or an electronic computer.

The method presented here enables one to calculate the aeromagnetic anomaly of three-dimensional bodies of arbitrary shape with the aid of graticules constructed for each of seven inclinations of the earth's magnetic field. This method, which has advantages over the Henderson and Zietz (1957) extension of the Gassmann (1951) method, continues to find use when only a few computed points are desired even though elaborate computer programs and machinery may be available. In fact, quick calculations made with the charts have been used to guide assumptions about the bodies to be simulated on the electronic computer.

A preliminary account of the method was given by Henderson (1960). The entire suite of charts is now complete and is presented in facsimile in Plates 1–7.[1] The method is explained here as it applies to three funda-

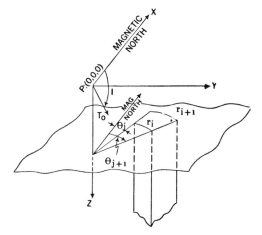

FIG. 1. Elemental semi-infinite vertical cylindrical sector in relation to coordinate system. The effect at P is the basis of the charts.

mental cases; it is also shown how the chart for inclination $I = 90°$ can be used in gravity calculations.

The Charts

In aeromagnetic work we represent the component of the total magnetic intensity anomaly in the direction of the earth's total field vector by ΔT. The graticules are based on the formula for the ΔT anomaly at a point (see Figure 1) due to an elemental semi-infinite vertical cylindrical sector at unit depth below the plane of observations and magnetized by induction in the earth's field. The point P at which the effect is to be deter-

[1] Polar charts are available from the SEG Publication office, P.O. Box 3098, Tulsa, Oklahoma 74101.

---

† Publication authorized by the Director, U. S. Geological Survey.

* U. S. Geological Survey, Washington, D. C.

mined is taken as the origin of a right hand coordinate system with x positive towards magnetic north and z positive downward. All lengths are presumed to have been divided by the depth so that in the discussion which follows the radius r is a dimensionless ratio. The ΔT anomaly per unit magnetization at P due to the element is

$$\left(\frac{\Delta T}{kT_0}\right)_{\text{element}} = (\sin \theta_{j+1} \cos \theta_{j+1} - \sin \theta_j \cos \theta_j)$$

$$\cdot \left\{ \cos^2 I \left[\ln \frac{1 + \sqrt{r_{i+1}^2 + 1}}{1 + \sqrt{r_i^2 + 1}} + \frac{1}{2} \left(\frac{1}{\sqrt{r_{i+1}^2 + 1}} - \frac{1}{\sqrt{r_i^2 + 1}} \right) \right] \right\}$$

$$+ (\sin \theta_{j+1} - \sin \theta_j) \left\{ 2 \sin I \cos I \left[\ln \frac{r_{i+1} + \sqrt{r_{i+1}^2 + 1}}{r_i + \sqrt{r_i^2 + 1}} \right. \right.$$

$$\left. \left. - \left(\frac{r_{i+1}}{\sqrt{r_{i+1}^2 + 1}} - \frac{r_i}{\sqrt{r_i^2 + 1}} \right) \right] \right\} + (\theta_{j+1} - \theta_j)$$

$$\cdot \left\{ \left(\sin^2 I - \frac{1}{2} \cos^2 I \right) \left[\frac{1}{\sqrt{r_i^2 + 1}} - \frac{1}{\sqrt{r_{i+1}^2 + 1}} \right] \right\} . \qquad (1)$$

In (1) k is the magnetic susceptibility of the element and T_0 is the magnitude of the earth's normal field. Using (1) and requiring that each element on a chart have the same prescribed value $(\Delta T/kT_0) = \alpha$ called the chart constant, we constructed graticules for use at magnetic inclinations $I = 0$, 20, 30, 45, 60, 75, and 90°. For a given inclination an α was chosen which would make the chart convenient to use, but where possible it was made a preassigned decimal fraction of the half-space anomaly, $(\Delta T/kT_0) = \pi$ ($2 \sin^2 I - \cos^2 I$). The constants and plate numbers for the various inclinations are given in Table 1.

A typical polar chart, for $I = 45°$ is shown in Figure 2. Each complete element contributes at the center a total magnetic intensity effect of 0.00312 gammas per unit magnetization. The elemental value was not always contained in the extreme ranges of θ an integral number of times, hence some elements have less than full value. A number inserted in a fractional element indicates the percent of a full value it receives. For exam-

ple, the number 38 appearing in an element means that it receives 0.38 of a chart value.

Account must be taken of the algebraic sign of elements. In general, positive and negative areas are set off by broken lines, and are indicated by $+$ and $-$ signs. For $I = 0°$ and $I = 20°$ there is a central area enclosed in a heavy circle in which all the elements are negative. Outside this circle there are positive areas north and south and negative areas east and west. From $I = 30°$ to $I = 75°$ there is one positive area north and one negative area south on each chart. The positive area increases from chart to chart with the inclination until at $I = 90°$, the elements are all positive.

Table 1

Plate number	1	2	3	4	5	6	7
Inclination	0°	20°	30°	45°	60°	75°	90°
α in gammas per unit magnetization	0.00314	0.00306	0.00312	0.00312	0.00393	0.00565	0.00314

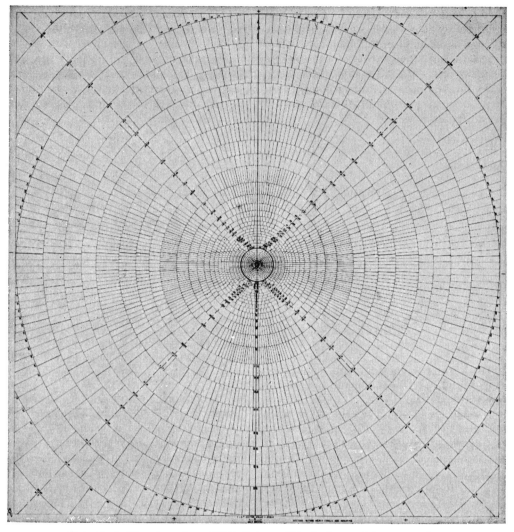

PLATE 1. $I = 0°$, sector value $= .00314$. Sectors within the heavy circle are negative.

Because the ruled radial lines become dense in the neighborhood of the center and tend to obscure its exact location a small area about the center has been arbitrarily deleted from each chart.

The charts can be reproduced on a transparent medium at any convenient scale; however, we have chosen as standard scales one inch equals a depth unit and one-half inch equals a depth unit.

Use of Charts

We explain in detail the application to a basic semi-infinite body. The extension to other bodies is but a corollary.

Semi-infinite vertical cylinder

Consider a vertical cylinder whose upper base, enclosed by a regular contour C_0 as shown in Figure 3, is at depth z_0, and whose lower base, for the moment, is infinitely remote, i.e., the depth extent is infinite. Suppose that the inducing field has an inclination $I = 60°$ and a magnitude T_0; that the susceptibility of the cylinder exceeds that of the surrounding material by an amount k,

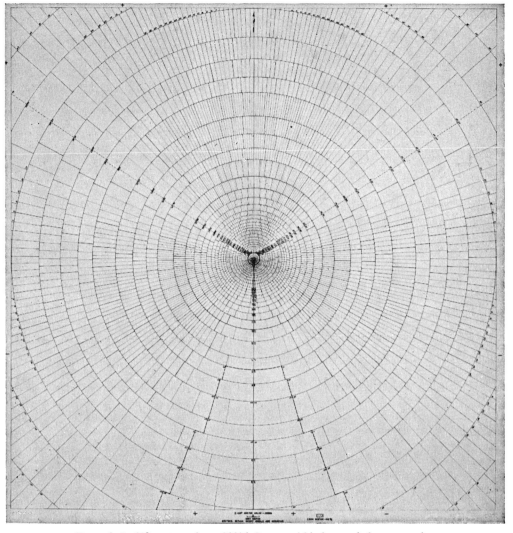

PLATE 2. $I = 20°$, sector value $= .00306$. Sectors within heavy circle are negative.

and that the anomaly is to be computed at points P_1, P_2, and P_3. We should use the graticule at $I = 60°$ which has the more convenient scale. Suppose we choose the one-inch-equals-a-depth-unit chart. The contour C_0 together with the points P_1, P_2, P_3 is plotted at a scale $z_0 = 1$ inch. A straight line in the direction of magnetic north is drawn through each of the points. The chart is centered at a point to be computed, say P_1, with its magnetic axis pointing towards magnetic north. The elements covering the area within the contour are counted with regard

to sign, i.e., a positive element receives a positive count, a negative element receives a negative count. The interior portions of elements cut by the contour C_0 are given a proportionate fractional count. The positive and negative counts are added algebraically. Suppose the summed count is $N(z_0)$. Then the anomaly at P_1 in gammas per unit magnetization is $N(z_0)$. For $I = 60°$ (see Table 1), $\alpha = 0.00393$. The anomaly in gammas is then

$$\Delta T = k T_0 (0.00393) N(z_0).$$

The chart would be similarly centered and

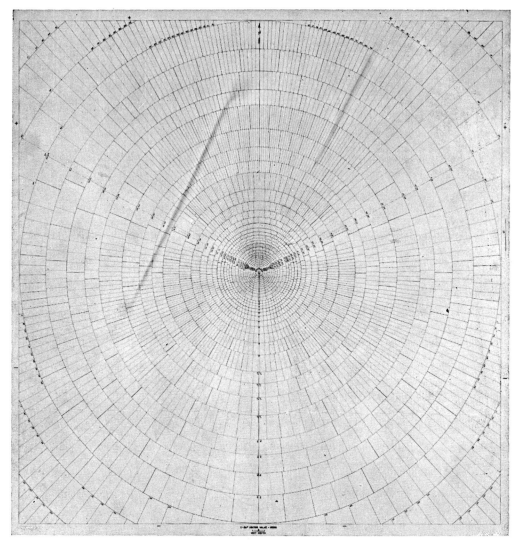

PLATE 3. $I = 30°$, sector value $= .00312$.

alined and the covering elements counted at any subsequent points such as P_2 and P_3.

Finite cylindrical bodies; laminae

Suppose the cylinder in Figure 3 has a finite depth extent t, with lower base at $z_1 = z_0 + t$ as shown also in Figure 3. To compute its anomaly at P_1, we calculate the anomaly of a second semi-infinite cylinder, this time with the depth to the "upper" base equal to z_1 and subtract the effects of the second from the first. The same chart can be used on the second cylinder if we adjust the scale of its configuration so that $z_1 = 1$ inch The configuration consisting of the contour together with all the points to be computed is so reduced to scale, mechanically with a pantograph or optically by photoreduction or use of a projector. The configuration reduced about P_2 is shown in Figure 3 with points to be computed now shown in primed notation. The chart is now used at P_1', P_2', and P_3' in turn. Let $N(z_1)$ be the number of counts for the lower semi-infinite cylinder at

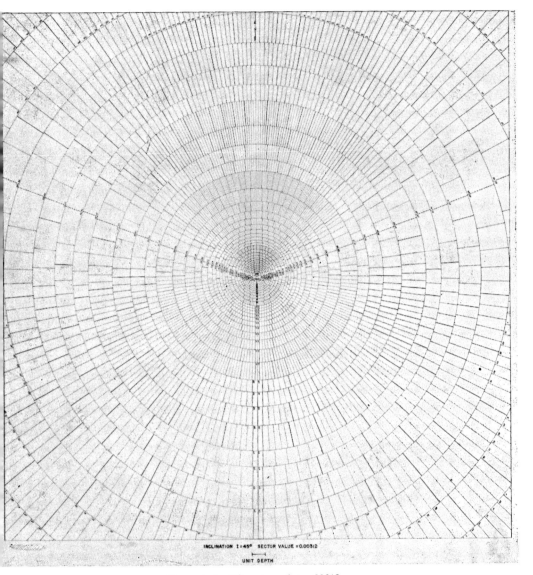

PLATE 4. $I = 45°$, sector value $= .00312$.

P_1', then the anomaly due to the finite cylinder will be

$$\Delta T = kT_0(0.00393)[N(z_0) - N(z_1)],$$

$N(z_0)$ being the number of counts determined for the same point for the upper cylinder.

When the depth extent t is much less than the depth of burial z_0, we have the case of a lamina. Laminae and the superposition prin-

ciple are the bases for the general three-dimensional case discussed below.

Three-dimensional body of arbitrary shape

A three-dimensional body may be approximated by a set of flat lying laminae and represented by a contour map. The laminae need not have the same thickness; in fact it is consistent with the attenuation properties of anomalies to take the layers thicker for in-

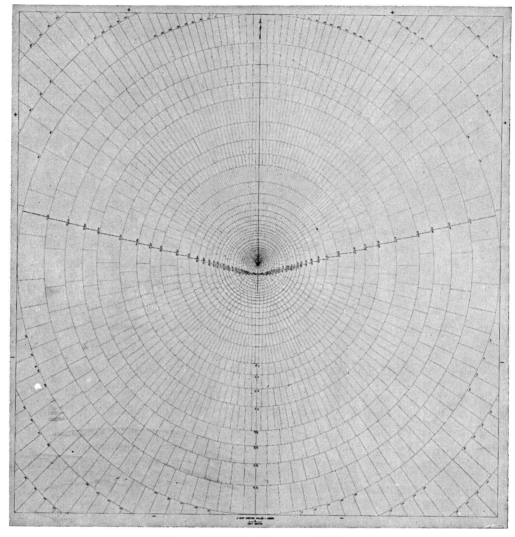

PLATE 5. $I = 60°$, sector value $= .00393$.

creasing z. This results in more rapid computations.

The layered body is initially contoured with z_0 as chart depth as shown in Figure 4a. Configuration reductions to scale are made at each depth z_i and the computations for each layer are performed as explained above. If $N(z_{i-1}, i)$ is the number of counts at P due to the ith layer, then the effect due to the entire body is

$$\Delta T = k T_0 \alpha \sum_{i=1}^{n} N(z_{i-1}, i),$$

where $N(z_{i-1}, i) = N(z_{i-1}) - N(z_i)$ and α is the chart constant.

In cases where the three-dimensional body has considerable depth extent and would involve too many laminae, it is preferable to conceive the body as composed of a nest of vertical (not necessarily circular) cylinders. The chart is then used at the top and bottom of a central cylinder and at the tops and bottoms of several surrounding cylindrical shells. In this way the computations may be effected more rapidly.

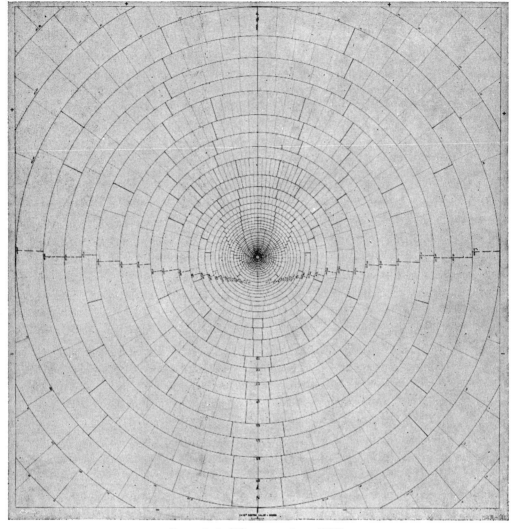

PLATE 6. $I = 75°$, sector value $= .00565$.

Gravity calculations

At inclination $I = 90°$, equation (1) for a magnetic element reduces to

$$\left(\frac{\Delta T}{kT_0}\right)_{\text{mag. element}}$$

$$= (\theta_{j+1} - \theta_j)\left(\frac{1}{\sqrt{r_i^2 + 1}} - \frac{1}{\sqrt{r_{i+1}^2 + 1}}\right). \quad (2)$$

The right member of (2) is a numeric which can be shown to be proportional to Δg, the vertical component of gravity at P due to an element dz units thick. More precisely, for a mass element

$$\left(\frac{\Delta g}{G\rho dz}\right)_{\text{mass element}}$$

$$= (\theta_{j+1} - \theta_j)\left(\frac{1}{\sqrt{r_i^2 + 1}} - \frac{1}{\sqrt{r_{i+1}^2 + 1}}\right) \quad (3)$$

where G is the gravitational constant, and ρ is the density of the element. In view of the equivalence of (2) and (3), the chart at $I = 90°$, with some change in concept, may

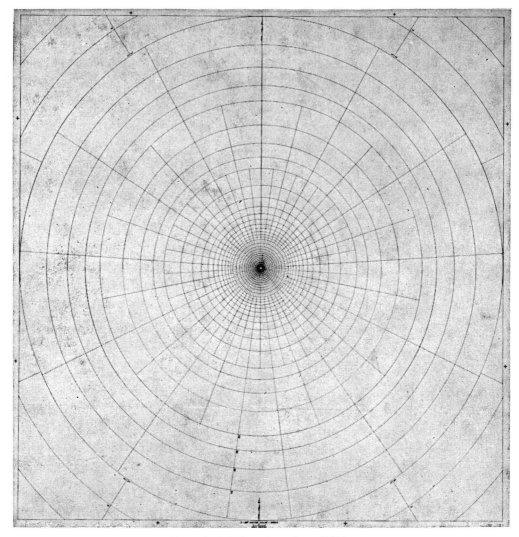

PLATE 7. $I = 90°$, sector value $= .00314$.

be used in three-dimensional gravity calculations. In fact, it becomes simply a solid-angle chart not unlike one designed by Lachenbruch (1957) for certain heat conduction problems. The accuracy of the $I = 90°$ graticule as a solid-angle chart can be readily established by applying it to a circular disc and comparing the resulting values with those given by Masket and Rodgers (1962).

The gravity application is so well known that it needs little or no elaboration. The body is divided into horizontal laminae, but the chart is used at the median plane (Figure 4c) rather than at the top and bottom of a lamina, and the depths z_i are to this plane. The chart element is 2.089×10^{-5} mgal/m per unit density. The gravity anomaly for a lamina is then

$$\Delta g = 2.089 \times 10^{-5} \rho N(z_i) dz_i$$

where $N(z_i)$ is the number of elements counted at the median plane. In a mathematically rigorous sense the lamina should have infinitesimal thickness, but practically it need not be so. Nettleton (1942) discusses the error due to finite thickness in certain special cases.

FIG. 2. Polar chart for computing the magnetic anomaly of three dimensional bodies magnetized in a field of inclination $I = 45°$.

For an approximation to the gravity effect at P due to the entire body, one could add up the effects of the various laminae, i.e.,

$$\Delta g = 2.089 \times 10^{-5} \sum_{i=1}^{n} \rho_i N(z_i) dz_i.$$

The density ρ_i has been placed after the summation sign to allow for layerwise changes in density.

For more accurate values of the gravity effect one can follow Talwani and Ewing (1960) and perform a numerical integration after determining $N(z_i)$ at the various levels. It should be observed that our expression $2.089 \times 10^{-5} \rho N(z)$ corresponds to the V of Talwani and Ewing (1960). Their three-level system of integration can therefore be used once the values $2.089 \times 10^{-5} \rho N(z)$ have been determined.

Practical Application

The following illustration of an application to a semi-infinite cylinder of irregular horizontal section is due to John W. Allingham of

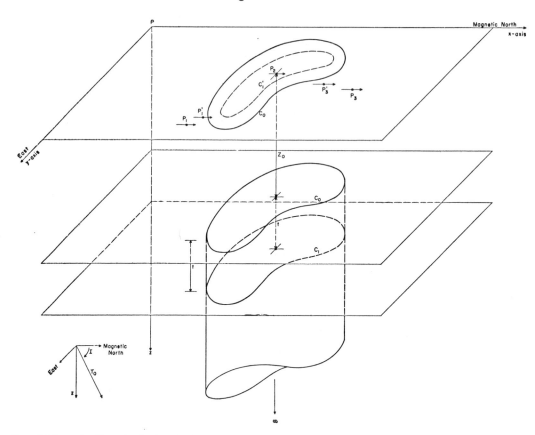

FIG. 3. Magnetic effect of cylinder of thickness t derived from effects of two semi-infinite cylinders at depth z_0 and z_0+t. Configuration for lower figure given by primes after reduction to scale by applying factor z_0/z_0+t.

the U. S. Geological Survey. Figure 5 is an aeromagnetic map of the Pea Ridge anomaly in Washington County, southeast Missouri. The crystalline basement rocks are overlain by about 1,100 ft of Paleozoic sedimentary rocks. The buried contact between the rhyolitic volcanic rocks and the granite host rock, shown in heavy outline, was inferred from the magnetic map by the method given by Vacquier et al. (1951). The magnetic susceptibility of the granite was determined from drill hole samples and from outcrops in the neighboring St. Francois Mountains. Susceptibilities for the volcanic rocks were based on subsurface measurements in the Indian Creek area and in the area of Pilot Knob. Drilling has established the existence of a magnetite ore body. The shape of the body shown in the rectangle is essentially conjectural. The chart for $I=75°$ at a scale one inch equals one depth unit was used to compute profile $A-A'$ as discussed above for a vertical cylinder, except that the body here is composite. The separate profiles computed for the volcanic rocks and the magnetite body in Figure 6, when combined, give an anomaly which closely fits the observed profile. In view of the ambiguity of such interpretations, this can only be regarded as one of many possible solutions.

For practical examples of "layer cake" type approximations to three-dimensional bodies, the reader is referred to Henderson (1960) or Allingham and Zietz (1962).

Acknowledgments

The authors are grateful to John W. Allingham of the U. S. Geological Survey, whose persistent requests provided the early stimulus for this work, and whose practical

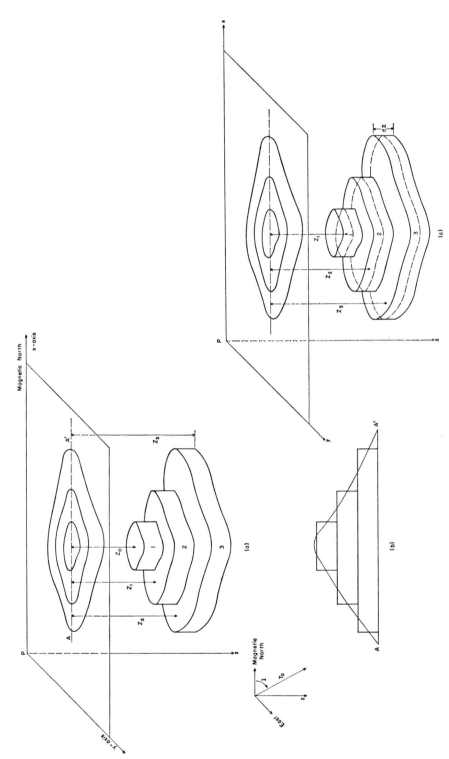

Fig. 4. Three-dimensional body approximated with laminae. (a) Magnetic body; graticule is used at top and bottom of each lamina, (b) vertical section A–A', (c) gravity body; solid angle chart ($I = 90°$) is used at median plane of lamina.

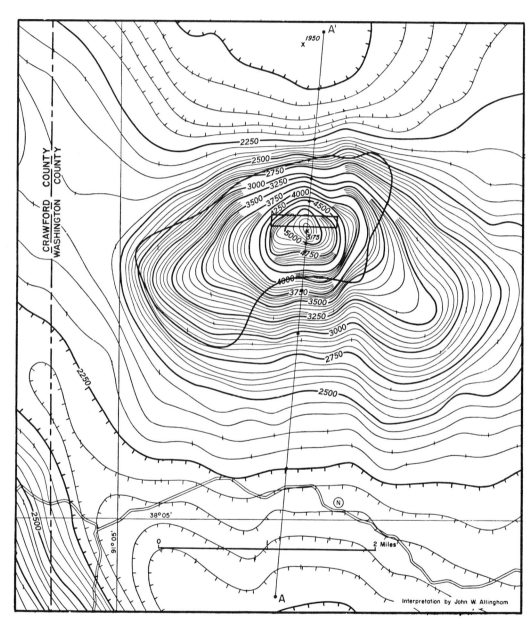

FIG. 5. Aeromagnetic map of Pea Ridge anomaly, southeast Missouri. Inferred contact between volcanic rocks and granite host rock shown by heavy irregular line. Rectangle is conjectured outline of ore body.

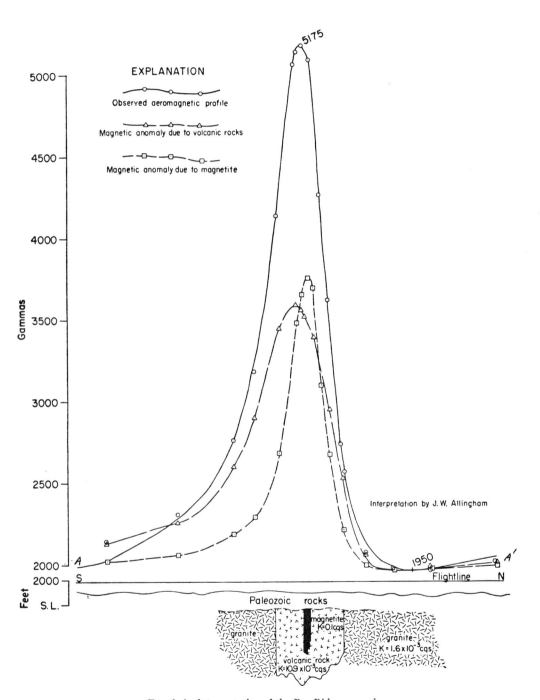

FIG. 6. An interpretation of the Pea Ridge anomaly.

applications were generously made available to them. Thanks are due to Emil Seginak who assisted in the drafting and to H. R. Joesting, Andrew Griscom, and other coworkers in the Survey who used the charts extensively and contributed valuable suggestions leading to their improvement.

References

Allingham, J. W., and Zietz, Isidore, 1962, Geophysical data on the Climax Stock, Nevada Test Site, Nye County, Nevada: Geophysics, v. 27, p. 599–610.

Gassmann, Fritz, 1951, Graphical evaluation of the anomalies of gravity and of the magnetic field caused by three-dimensional bodies: World Petroleum Congress, 3d, The Hague, Proc., sec. 1, p. 613–621.

Henderson, R. G., 1960, Polar charts for evaluating magnetic anomalies of three-dimensional bodies: Article 52, in U. S. Geol. Survey Prof. Paper 400-B, p. B112–B114.

Henderson, R. G., and Wilson, Alphonso, 1963, Polar charts for calculating aeromagnetic anomalies of three-dimensional bodies: U. S Geological Survey open-file report, 7 charts.

Henderson, R. G., and Zietz, Isidore, 1957 Graphical calculation of total-intensity anomalies of three-dimensional bodies: Geophysics v. 22, p. 887–904.

Lachenbruch, A. H., 1957, Three-dimensional heat conduction in permafrost beneath heated buildings: U. S. Geol. Survey Bull. 1052-B, p. 50–69.

Masket, A. V. H., and Rodgers, W. C., 1962, Tables of Solid Angles: U. S. Atomic Energy Commission Rept., TID-14975.

Nettleton, L. L., 1942, Gravity and magnetic calculations: Geophysics, v. 7, p. 293–310.

Talwani, Manik, and Ewing, Maurice, 1960, Rapid computation of gravitational attraction of three-dimensional bodies of arbitrary shape: Geophysics, v. 25, p. 203–225.

Vacquier, Victor, Steenland, N. C., Henderson, R. G., and Zietz, Isidore, 1951, Interpretation of aeromagnetic maps: Geol. Soc. America Mem. 47

REMANENT MAGNETIZATION AND AEROMAGNETIC INTERPRETATION†

ISIDORE ZIETZ* AND G. E. ANDREASEN*

Quantitative interpretation of aeromagnetic anomalies has been based for the most part on the use of physical models in which the direction of magnetization is parallel to that of the earth's field, although laboratory results show that this assumption is invalid for many rock units. Magnetic fields have been calculated for inclinations of magnetization significantly different from that of the earth's present field. The calculations are for a rectangular flat-topped mass with finite and infinite vertical sides and a 75 degree inclination of the earth's field. Several significant empirical relationships between the physical model and the computed fields have been obtained. For low dips of magnetization, the maximum and minimum points, rather than the points of inflection, mark the edges of the rock masses. The dip of the magnetization vector may be estimated from the ratio between the maximum and minimum anomaly amplitudes. The depth calculation techniques described in Geological Society of America Memoir 47 are based on the assumption of induced polarization, but these same empirical rules can be applied equally well to the total intensity field when remanent magnetization is present. This probably explains the success of the Memoir methods when applied to observed aeromagnetic anomalies over sedimentary basins.

Introduction

The interpretation of magnetic anomalies has been based principally on the assumption that the anomalous field results solely from induction in the earth's field and that remanent magnetization, if present, is either negligible or codirectional with the earth's field (among many investigators are Peters, 1949; Pirson, 1940; Vacquier and others, 1951). If relatively strong remanent magnetization is present and not codirectional with the earth's field the methods of interpretation are not applicable. Although these assumptions are often reasonable, it is becoming increasingly evident that many rock units, some of wide geographic extent, possess important components of remanent magnetization in directions significantly different from that of the earth's field. In this connection, the contribution of remanent magnetization to magnetic anomalies has been demonstrated by several investigators including Green (1960), who, in an aeromagnetic study of the Australian Kainozoic basalts and the Pilansberg dikes, showed that the anomalies were produced by remanent magnetization. He then determined the geometric configuration of the rocks, knowing the intensity and direction of remanence from a paleomagnetic survey. Watkins (1961), measured reverse remanent vectors in samples of granitic gneiss from the Bayonet area in Alberta, Canada. In an investigation of aeromagnetic anomalies in north-central Montana, Books (1962) showed that remanent magnetization is the dominant factor in anomalies over the volcanic rocks and a contributing factor in anomalies over the intrusive rocks. DuBois (1962, 1963) demonstrated that remanent magnetization was an important contributor in anomalies over the massive hematite body near Egremont, England, and over the serpentine rocks of the Sierra Nevada Mountains, California. The authors have noted remanent magnetization seems to be an important contributor to aeromagnetic anomalies over alkalic rocks. The correlation of remanence with alkalic rocks has been observed in many areas including the North Carolina Piedmont, the Black Hills, the stocks and ring dikes of the White Mountains in New Hampshire, small circular alkalic extrusives in the Canadian Shield, and over an igneous plug in the Shenandoah

† Publication authorized by the Director, U. S. Geological Survey.

* U. S. Geological Survey, Washington, D.C.

Valley. Significantly the magnetization of these alkalic rocks is essentially uniform, and the remanent magnetic anomalies are characteristically of large amplitude and are generally isolated.

Previous investigators, including those cited above, have determined magnitude and direction of remanence by laboratory measurements of rock samples. The present paper describes a method of determining remanent direction from operations on the observed field only. In order to examine observed total intensity fields qualitatively and quantitatively in areas where remanence is present theoretical magnetic fields were calculated for a suite of rectangular prisms, under various directions of total magnetization. Only the total magnetization or vector sum is considered, and no differentiation is made between the induced and remanent components. The fields were calculated from an exact mathematical formula. If the remanent magnetization relative to the induced magnetization is small, the formula reduces to the case for induced magnetization, and the three-dimensional magnetic fields generated would be similar to those published by Vacquier and others (1951), differing only by the demagnetization factor. It is the purpose of this paper to: 1) present a brief mathematical development of the formula used in computing the magnetic fields; 2) present some significant empirical relationships between the physical prism and the computed field; and 3) illustrate how the prisms may be used in the interpretation of observed magnetic anomalies.

A few investigators have developed methods for the determination of remanent magnitudes and directions in rocks from observed data. Vacquier (1962) computes the direction and magnitude of remanence in a uniformly magnetized body by high-speed computer, knowing configuration and the total magnetic intensity of the body. Henderson and Allingham (1964) applied a modified version of the Vacquier method to a study of Square Butte, Montana. Hall (1959) has determined the direction of magnetization from magnetic profiles for the point-pole, horizontal line of

dipoles, thin and thick dipping sheets, and a sloping step. Zietz (1961) presented computed three-dimensional fields for various directions of magnetization and prism thicknesses and showed how the fields can be used in aeromagnetic interpretation.

In a recent article, Bhattacharyya (1964) has taken the same view as the authors in an initial approach to the study of remanent magnetization. He has calculated aeromagnetic anomalies for prismatic bodies using arbitrary directions of polarization but admits "the problems of interpretation of anomalies may thus become exceedingly difficult in cases where magnetization due to induction plays an insignificant role compared to that due to remanence. Attempts to simplify this problem look to be futile." The authors take a contrary view. We believe that a study of remanent fields provides an excellent approach for determining both the direction of magnetization and areal extent of the structure producing the anomaly qualitatively and quantitatively.

The Magnetic Prism

The magnetic prism is assumed to be a rectangular block with an upper surface one depth unit below the x-y plane of observation (see Figure 1). The length, width, and thickness of the prism are expressed in depth units. The prism is assumed to be made up of elementary dipoles all aligned in the same direction and possessing the same magnetic moment. The potential V at any point $P(x, y, z)$ due to an elemental volume dv $= dx'dy'dz'$ at a distance r and a total magnetization $\mathbf{I}_t$ is

$$V = \int_v \frac{\mathbf{I}_t \cdot \mathbf{r}}{r^3} \, dv. \tag{1}$$

The magnetization $\mathbf{I}_t$ is the vector sum of the magnetization ($\mathbf{I}_i$) resulting from induction in the earth's field and the remanent magnetization ($\mathbf{I}_\rho$), i.e.,

$$\mathbf{I}_t = \mathbf{I}_i + \mathbf{I}_\rho. \tag{2}$$

The direction of $\mathbf{I}_t$ is defined by two angles, α and δ, as shown in Figure 2. The axes of the

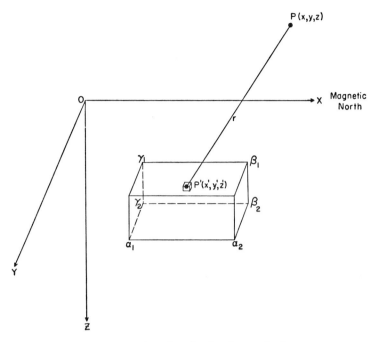

FIG. 1. Rectangular prism showing elemental volume.

rectangular coordinate system are chosen so that the z axis is directed positively downwards and the x axis is in the direction of magnetic north.

Completing the scalar product in (1),

$$V = \int \frac{I_t r \cos \theta}{r^3}\, dv \qquad (3)$$

where θ is the angle between $\mathbf{I}_t$ and $\mathbf{r}$ and

$$\cos \theta = \frac{(x - x')}{r} \cos \delta \cos \iota$$

$$+ \frac{y - y'}{r} \sin \delta \cos \iota + \frac{z - z'}{r} \sin \iota$$

substituting

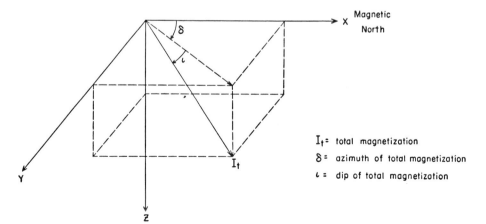

$I_t =$ total magnetization

$\delta =$ azimuth of total magnetization

$\iota =$ dip of total magnetization

FIG. 2. Total magnetization I_t.

$$V = \int_v \frac{I_t[(x - x') \cos \delta \cos \iota + (y - y') \sin \delta \cos \iota + (z - z') \sin \iota]}{r^3} \, dv \qquad (4)$$

where

$$r = \sqrt{(x - x')^2 + (y - y')^2 + (z - z')^2}.$$

The component of magnetic intensity in the direction of the earth's field, i.e., the value measured by a total field magnetometer is

$$\Delta T = \Delta X \cos I + \Delta Z \sin I, \qquad (5)$$

where I is the angle of dip of the earth's field. As

$$\frac{\partial V}{\partial x} = -\frac{\partial V}{\partial x'} \quad \text{and} \quad \frac{\partial V}{\partial z} = -\frac{\partial V}{\partial z'}$$

equation (5) becomes

$$\Delta T = \frac{\partial V}{\partial x'} \cos I + \frac{\partial V}{\partial z'} \sin I. \qquad (6)$$

The anomalous field ΔT contains parameters of the inducing field (H), the susceptibility of the magnetizable material (k), and the remanent magnetization (I_ρ). The parameters may be eliminated and the field normalized by computing the ratio $\Delta T/I_t$ which is dependent only on the geometry of the magnetic mass (Zietz and Henderson, 1956). Then equation (6) becomes

$$\frac{\Delta T}{I_t} = \frac{\partial}{\partial x'}\left(\frac{V}{I_t}\right) \cos I$$

$$+ \frac{\partial}{\partial z'}\left(\frac{V}{I_t}\right) \sin I. \qquad (7)$$

The substitution of (4) into (7) yields

$$\frac{\Delta T}{I_t} = \left\{ \int_v \left[\cos \delta \cos \iota \, \frac{\partial}{\partial x'}\left(\frac{x - x'}{r^3}\right) \right.\right.$$

$$+ \sin \delta \cos \iota \, \frac{\partial}{\partial x'}\left(\frac{y - y'}{r^3}\right)$$

$$\left.\left. + \sin \iota \, \frac{\partial}{\partial x'}\left(\frac{z - z'}{r^3}\right) \right] dv \right\} \cos I$$

$$+ \left\{ \int_v \left[\cos \delta \cos \iota \, \frac{\partial}{\partial z'}\left(\frac{x - x'}{r^3}\right) \right.\right.$$

$$+ \sin \delta \cos \iota \, \frac{\partial}{\partial z'}\left(\frac{y - y'}{r^3}\right)$$

$$\left.\left. + \sin \iota \, \frac{\partial}{\partial z'}\left(\frac{z - z'}{r^3}\right) \right] dv \right\} \sin I. \qquad (8)$$

Upon reducing the volume integral to a surface integral and carrying out the integration, the final expression for the normalized field at any point in the x-y plane becomes

$$\frac{\Delta T(x, y, 0)}{I_t} = \cos \iota \cos \delta \cos I \tan^{-1} \frac{y - \beta_2}{x - \alpha_1} - \cos \iota \cos \delta \cos I \tan^{-1} \frac{y - \beta_1}{x - \alpha_1}$$

$$- \cos \iota \cos \delta \cos I \tan^{-1} \frac{(y - \beta_2)\gamma_1}{(x - \gamma_1)\sqrt{(x - \alpha_1)^2 + (y - \beta_2)^2 + \gamma_1^2}}$$

$$+ \cos \iota \cos \delta \cos I \tan^{-1} \frac{(y - \beta_1)\gamma_1}{(x - \alpha_1)\sqrt{(x - \alpha_1)^2 + (y - \beta_1)^2 + \gamma^2}}$$

$$- \cos \iota \cos \delta \cos I \tan^{-1} \frac{y - \beta_2}{x - \alpha_2} + \cos \iota \cos \delta \cos I \tan^{-1} \frac{y - \beta_1}{x - \alpha_2}$$

$$+ \cos \iota \cos \delta \cos I \tan^{-1} \frac{(y - \beta_2)\gamma_1}{(x - \alpha_2)\sqrt{(x - \alpha_2)^2 + (y - \beta_2)^2 + \gamma_1^2}}$$

$$- \cos \iota \cos \delta \cos I \tan^{-1} \frac{(y - \beta_1)\gamma_1}{(x - \alpha_2)\sqrt{(x - \alpha_2)^2 + (y - \beta_1)^2 + \gamma_1^2}}$$

$$+ \sin \iota \sin I \tan^{-1} \frac{(x - \alpha_1)(y - \beta_1)}{\gamma_1 \sqrt{(x - \alpha_1)^2 + (y - \beta_1)^2 + \gamma_1^2}}$$

$$+ \sin \iota \sin I \tan^{-1} \frac{(x - \alpha_2)(y - \beta_2)}{\gamma_1 (x - \alpha_2)^2 + (y - \beta_2)^2 + \gamma_1^2}$$

$$- \sin \iota \sin I \tan^{-1} \frac{(x - \alpha_2)(y - \beta_1)}{\gamma_1 \sqrt{(x - \alpha_2)^2 + (y - \beta_1)^2 + \gamma_1^2}}$$

$$- \sin \iota \sin I \tan^{-1} \frac{(x - \alpha_1)(y - \beta_2)}{\gamma_1 \sqrt{(x - \alpha_1)^2 + (y - \beta_2)^2 + \gamma_1^2}}$$

$$+ \sin \iota \cos I \log \frac{(y - \beta_2) + \sqrt{(x - \alpha_2)^2 + (y - \beta_2)^2 + \gamma_1^2}}{(y - \beta_1) + \sqrt{(x - \alpha_2)^2 + (y - \beta_1)^2 + \gamma_1^2}}$$

$$- \sin \iota \cos I \log \frac{(y - \beta_2) + \sqrt{(x - \alpha_1)^2 + (y - \beta_2)^2 + \gamma_1^2}}{(y - \beta_1) + \sqrt{(x - \alpha_1)^2 + (y - \beta_1)^2 + \gamma_1^2}}$$

$$- \cos \iota \cos \delta \log \frac{(y - \beta_2) + \sqrt{(x - \alpha_1)^2 + (y - \beta_2)^2 + \gamma_1^2}}{(y - \beta_1) + \sqrt{(x - \alpha_1)^2 + (y - \beta_1)^2 + \gamma_1^2}}$$

$$+ \cos \iota \cos \delta \sin I \log \frac{(y - \beta_2) + \sqrt{(x - \alpha_2)^2 + (y - \beta_2)^2 + \gamma_1^2}}{(y - \beta_1) + \sqrt{(x - \alpha_2)^2 + (y - \beta_1)^2 + \gamma_1^2}}$$

$$- \cos \iota \sin \delta \cos I \log \frac{-\gamma_1 + \sqrt{(x - \alpha_2)^2 + (y - \beta_1)^2 + \gamma_1^2}}{-\gamma_1 + \sqrt{(x - \alpha_1)^2 + (y - \beta_1)^2 + \gamma_1^2}}$$

$$+ \cos \iota \sin \delta \cos I \log \frac{-\gamma_1 + \sqrt{(x - \alpha_2)^2 + (y - \beta_2)^2 + \gamma_1^2}}{-\gamma_1 + \sqrt{(x - \alpha_1)^2 + (y - \beta_2)^2 + \gamma_1^2}}$$

$$- \cos \iota \sin \delta \sin I \log \frac{(x - \alpha_2) + \sqrt{(x - \alpha_2)^2 + (y - \beta_1)^2 + \gamma_1^2}}{(x - \alpha_1) + \sqrt{(x - \alpha_1)^2 + (y - \beta_1)^2 + \gamma_1^2}}$$

$$+ \cos \iota \sin \delta \sin I \log \frac{(x - \alpha_2) + \sqrt{(x - \alpha_2)^2 + (y - \beta_2)^2 + \gamma_1^2}}{(x - \alpha_1) + \sqrt{(x - \alpha_1)^2 + (y - \beta_2)^2 + \gamma_1^2}} \cdot \quad (9)$$

Equation (9) is an exact expression for the normalized field due to a rectangular magnetic prism at any point in the x-y plane. If the remanent magnetization is negligible, the equation reduces to an expression for a normalized field caused by induction only.

Normalized fields have been computed for several prisms ranging in length and width from 3×3 (depth units) to 12×12. The thickness of the prisms (in depth units) is 0.1, 0.25, 0.5, 1.0, and infinity. The upper surface of all the prisms is 1.0 depth unit below the x-y plane of observation. The azimuths of angles of total magnetization (with respect to magnetic north) are 0, 30, 60, and 90 degrees, and the dip angles are 0, 20, 30, 45, 60, 75, 90, 120, and 150 degrees. The inclinations of the earth's normal fields are 0, 30, 60, 75, and 90 degrees.

Exact values of the normalized field at 1,369 grid points in the plane of observation above each prism may be obtained in about 15 sec on an IBM 7094 Computer. A modification of the curve-drawer program developed by the U. S. Weather Bureau interpolates the data, which is then automatically contoured on an Electronic Associates Inc. model 3410 Dataplotter. The interpola-

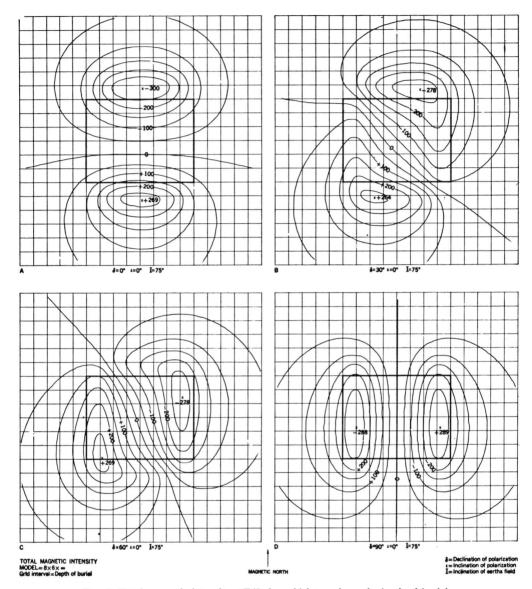

FIG. 3. Total magnetic intensity $\Delta T/I_t$ for grid interval equals depth of burial.

tion requires about 15 sec on the IBM 7094, and approximately 35 sec are required for the contouring.

Only the normalized fields for two prisms are presented here. One is $8\times6\times0^\infty$ (depth units) and the other is $3\times3\times0.25$ (depth units). The azimuth of magnetization (δ) ranges from 0 degrees to 90 degrees and the dip of magnetization (ι) ranges from 0 de-

grees to 150 degrees. The earth's field (I) is inclined at 75 degrees. The normalized fields are shown in Figures 3 to 6 and 8 to 11.

Discussion of prism fields

The configuration of the normalized magnetic fields for a particular prism depends upon the direction of total magnetization (azimuth and dip). For each direction of

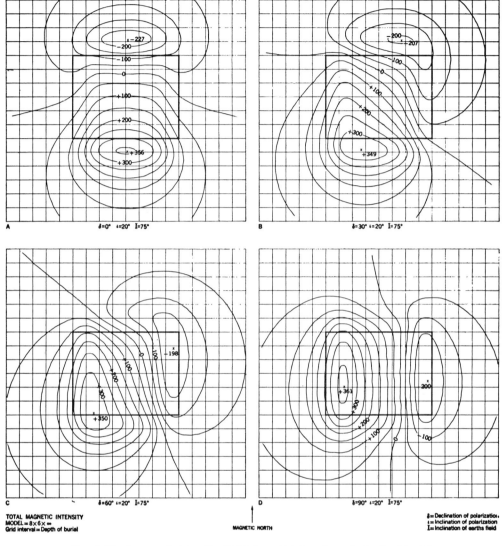

A $\delta=0°$ $\iota=20°$ $I=75°$

B $\delta=30°$ $\iota=20°$ $I=75°$

C $\delta=60°$ $\iota=20°$ $I=75°$

D $\delta=90°$ $\iota=20°$ $I=75°$

TOTAL MAGNETIC INTENSITY
MODEL = 8 × 6 × ∞
Grid interval = Depth of burial

MAGNETIC NORTH

δ = Declination of polarization
ι = Inclination of polarization
I = Inclination of earth's field

FIG. 4. Total magnetic intensity $\Delta T/I_t$ for grid interval equals depth of burial.

magnetization there is associated a distinct field with a spatial relationship between the maximum and minimum values and the geometry of the prism. For certain directions of magnetization the fields will display symmetry about some axis (for example, when $\delta = 0$ all fields are symmetrical with respect to the x axis).

The fields presented here are arranged in sequence to show the effect of varying the azimuth of magnetization (δ) for particular dips (ι).

When the azimuth of magnetization is in the direction of magnetic north and the dip is less than 90 degrees, a characteristic minimum develops on the north side of the prism. The magnitude of the minimum is greatest when the dip is zero degrees and becomes less

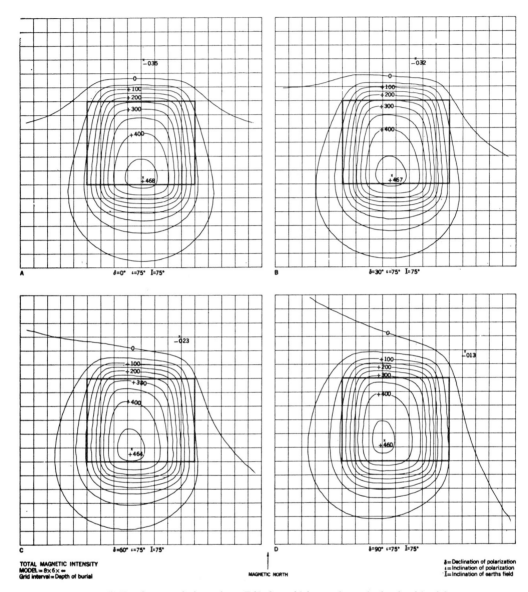

FIG. 5. Total magnetic intensity $\Delta T/I_t$ for grid interval equals depth of burial.

as the dip approaches 90 degrees. For dips greater than 90 degrees (and ≤ 180 degrees) the minimum is located on the south side of the prism and its magnitude increases with an increase in dip, becoming greatest when $\iota = 180°$. For a prism of finite thickness the minimum surrounds the body for a dip of 90 degrees.

As the azimuth is increased from 0 to 90 degrees the minimum migrates in the direction of the increase for dips less than 90 degrees, and the maximum migrates in the direction of the increase for dips greater than 90 degrees.

For reasonably low dips of magnetization ($0° < \iota \leq 60°$ and $150° \leq \iota \leq 180°$) there exists a spatial relationship between the field and the prism such that the maxima and minima are positioned approximately over the edges of the prism.

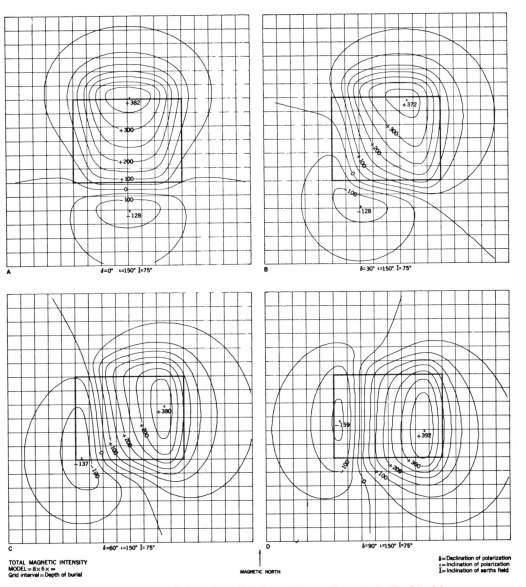

FIG. 6. Total magnetic intensity $\Delta T/I_t$ for grid interval equals depth of burial.

These relationships may be observed in Figures 3 to 6. For a dip $\iota = 0°$, the minimum and maximum are nearly over the north and south edges of the prism (Figure 3A). As the azimuth increases, the minima and maxima migrate in the direction of the increase and are still positioned approximately over the edges (Figures 3B, 3C, and 3D). The fields display symmetry about the x-axis (magnetic north) in Figures 3A and 3D. For a dip $\iota = 20°$,

essentially the same spatial relationships are seen to exist (Figures 4A–4D). The magnitude of the minimum is diminished with the increased dip angle.

As the dip angle increases, the minima and maxima move away from the edges, and the magnitude of the minimum diminishes. At about $\iota = 75°$, the spatial relationships described above no longer exist, as may be seen in Figures 5A–5D. For dips greater than 75

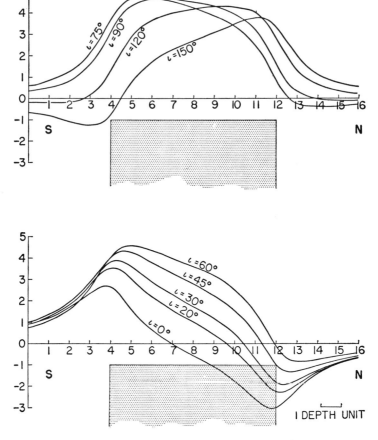

FIG. 7. Aeromagnetic profiles for various dip angles ι.

degrees, the minimum appears on the south side of the prism. At a dip angle of $\iota = 150°$, the minima and maxima are fairly near the edges of the prisms for the various azimuths shown in Figures 6A–6D. A similar suite of fields for $\iota = 180°$ (not shown) would be identical to the suite shown in Figures 3A–3D, except that the minima and maxima would be reversed.

The correspondence of the maximum and minimum values of $\Delta T/I_t$ to the edges of the prism $6 \times 8 \times \infty$ can also be seen in Figure 7. The azimuth is $\delta = 0°$ and the dip (ι) is varied from 0 to 150 degrees to produce the nine north-south profiles shown. The maxima and minima occur nearly over the edges of the prism for angles of $\iota \leq 60°$ and $\iota \geq 150°$. The

profile for $\iota = 180°$ is not shown but is identical to the profile for $\iota = 0°$, except that the maxima and minima are reversed.

The spatial relationship between the maximum and minimum $\Delta T/I_t$ and the edges of the prism also holds for all sizes of prisms of finite depth extent. To illustrate, a suite of magnetic fields is presented in Figures 8 to 11 for the model $3 \times 3 \times 0.25$ (in depth units). The minimum and maximum occur over the north and south edges of this thin prism when $\delta = 0°$ and $\iota = 0°$ (Figure 8A), and when $\delta = 45°$ the minimum and maximum occur nearly over the northeast and southwest corners of the prism, as shown in Figure 8B. When the azimuth angle is $\delta = 90°$ (Figure 8C) the minimum and maximum fall

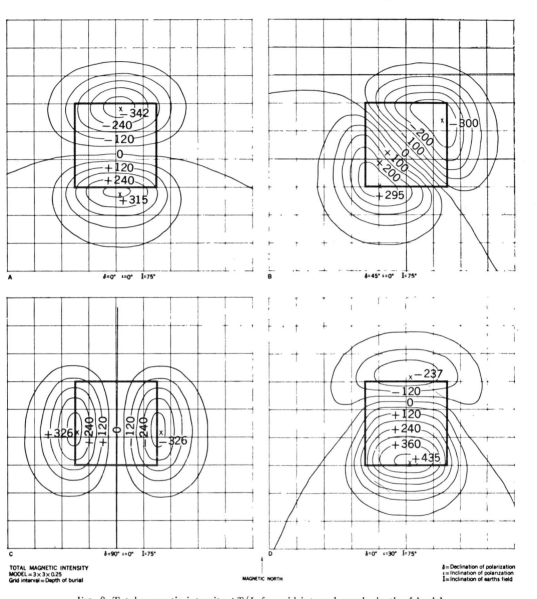

FIG. 8. Total magnetic intensity $\Delta T / I_t$ for grid interval equals depth of burial.

over the east and west edges, respectively, and there is symmetry about both axes.

The normalized magnetic fields shown in Figures 8D, 9A, and 9B are for a constant dip of magnetization $\iota = 30°$ and azimuths of 0, 45, and 90 degrees, respectively. The correspondence of the minima and maxima to the edges of the prisms is good. For a constant dip of $\iota = 60°$ and azimuths of 0, 45, and 90

degrees, the correspondence is only fair, as may been seen in Figures 9C, 9D, and 10A. Figure 10B shows the field for a dip $\iota = 90°$ (the field is independent of the azimuth). Here the maxima occur near the center of the prism and the minima far to the north.

The next suite of fields are computed using a constant dip of total magnetization $\iota = 120°$ with azimuths of 0, 45, and 90 degrees (Fig-

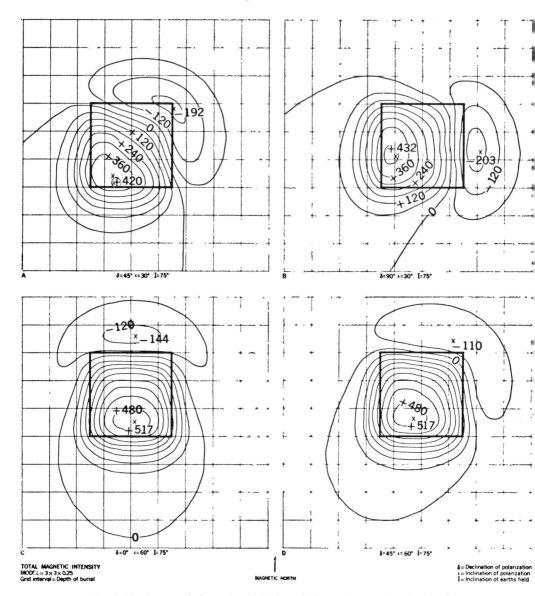

FIG. 9. Total magnetic intensity $\Delta T/I_t$ for grid interval equals depth of burial.

ures 10C, 10D, and 11A). The minima migrate in the direction of the increasing azimuth as before; however, the location
correspondence to the edges of the prisms is
poor. As the dip angle becomes smaller (relative to the horizontal) the minima and maxima are more nearly positioned over the
edges of the prism. The fields developed for a
low dip angle of 150 degrees and azimuth of
0, 45, and 90 degrees are shown in Figures

11B, 11C, and 11D. The maxima and minima
are seen to occur nearly over the edges of
the prism.

Determination of Magnetization Directions

The azimuth of magnetization may be
approximated directly from the normalized
magnetic field. As previously noted, the
migration of the maxima and minima is in

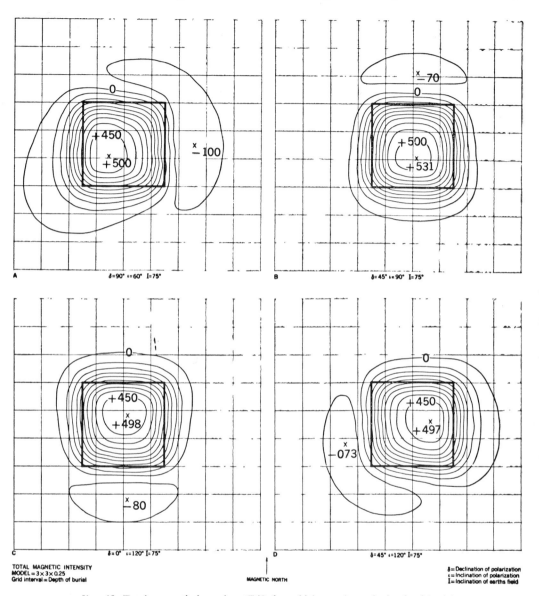

Fig. 10. Total magnetic intensity $\Delta T / I_t$ for grid interval equals depth of burial.

the direction of the increasing azimuth (δ). If the maximum and minimum $\Delta T / I_t$ are connected by a straight line, then the angle formed by this line and magnetic north (X axis) is an approximation of the azimuth angle of the magnetization vector. This approximation, however, is valid only for low dip angles. As the dip angle approaches 90 degrees the approximation is not applicable.

A comparison between the true azimuth and the measured azimuth for the two prisms is shown in Table 1. The correspondence is best for very small angles, but generally fair for all angles $\delta < 60°$. The approximation for the azimuth of the magnetization vector is generally valid for most sizes of prisms whether of infinite or finite depth extent, providing the dip angles are low.

The approximate dip (ι) of the magnetiza-

Table 1. Azimuths determined from prism fields

True Azimuth (δ)	Type of prism										
	8×6×∞				4×6×∞				3×3×0.25		
	0°	30°	60°	90°	0°	30°	60°	90°	0°	45°	90°
0	0	26	54	90	0	42	70	90	0	52	90
20	0	22	52	85	0	38.5	65	90	0	*	*
30	0	20	51	83	0	37	72	85	0	45	81
45	0	19	49	78	0	26	62	85	0	*	*
Dip 60	0	18	41	71	0	23.5	54	80	0	26	81
(ι) 75	0	11	27	44	0	18	46	49.5	0	*	*
90	0	0	0	0	0	0	0	0	0	0	0
120	0	33	72	108	0	42	73	100.5	0	52	99
150	0	28	55	96	0	41.5	69	95	0	52	99

* Fields for these prisms not computed.

tion may be determined from the normalized theoretical magnetic field, though somewhat less directly than the azimuth. The procedure involves forming the ratio (ρ) of the maximum $\Delta T/I_t$ to the minimum $\Delta T/I_t$. The ratio thus formed varies according to the dip. The relationship between ρ and ι for an 8×6×∞, a 4×6×∞ (field not shown), and a 3×3×.25 prism for azimuth angles $\delta = 0°$, 30°, 60°, and 90° is shown in Table 2. For a specific dip angle less than 60 degrees, the ratio of maximum to minimum remains about constant for the three prisms and for all azimuth angles. Forming the ratio $\Delta T_{max}/ \Delta T_{min}$, the approximate dip may be read directly from the table. The procedure is not applicable for steeply dipping magnetizations, except that ratios greater than ten would indicate dips of more than 60 degrees. This empirical procedure for determining the

approximate dip of magnetization is particularly useful as, for low-dip angles, it is essentially independent of the size (areal extent and thickness) of the prism and the azimuth of magnetization.

All of the analyses in this report are based on magnetic fields calculated for the case of an earth's field with dip 75 degrees. For this case, the techniques for determining the areal distribution of the body and the direction of magnetization are most valid when the dip of magnetization is low.

Theoretical considerations validated by calculation of the field for other dip angles of the earth's field suggest that it is the angle between the direction of the earth's field and the total magnetization that really contributes to our understanding of the magnetic field for blocklike prisms. For small angles, prism-field relationships are similar to those

Table 2. Ratios between maximum and minimum of the magnetic field

Azimuth (δ)	Type of prism							
	8×6×∞				4×6×∞	3×3×0.25		
	0°	30°	60°	90°	0°	0°	45°	90°
0°	.9	.9	.9	1.0	.9	.9	.9	1.0
20°	1.6	1.6	1.7	1.8	1.5	*	*	*
30°	2.1	2.3	2.4	2.5	2.3	1.9	2.2	2.1
Dip 45°	3.3	3.7	4.2	4.5	3.5	*	*	*
(ι) 60°	5.7	6.7	8.0	10.0	6.4	3.7	4.6	5.1
75°	13	15	20	34	19.0	*	*	*

* Fields for these prisms not computed.

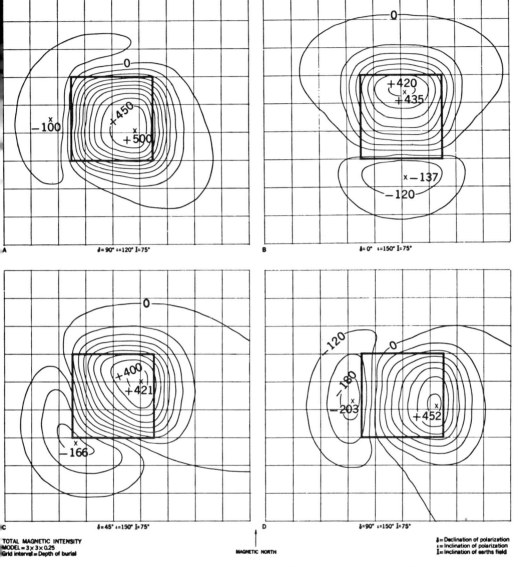

FIG. 11. Total magnetic intensity $\Delta T/I_t$ for grid interval equals depth of burial.

for induced magnetization. For large angles, the relationship between field and prism is analogous to the case described previously for low-angle magnetization when $I = 75°$.

Remanent Magnetization and Aeromagnetic Interpretation

From the study of the theoretical fields for the various models, it is apparent that the magnetic maxima and minima approximately define the location of the edges of the prism, provided the dip of the magnetization is low and the dip of the earth's field is approximately 75 degrees. The angle then formed by magnetic north and the line connecting the maximum and minimum is an approximate measure of the true angle of azimuth of the total magnetization. By form-

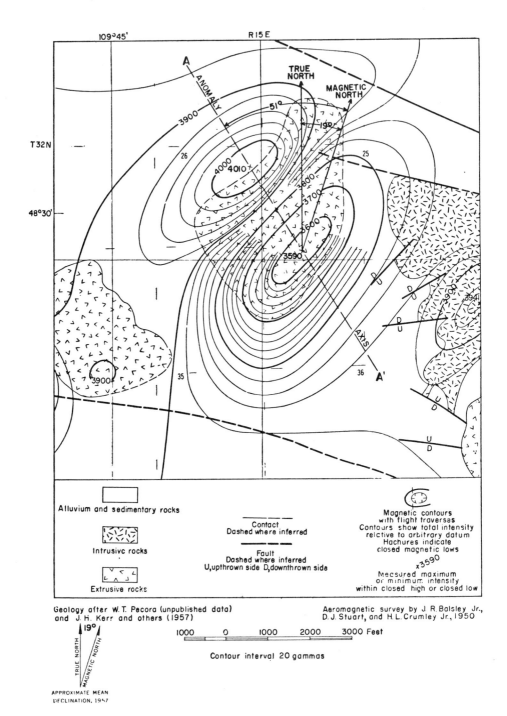

FIG. 12. Aeromagnetic and generalized geology map of the Squaw Butte area, Montana.

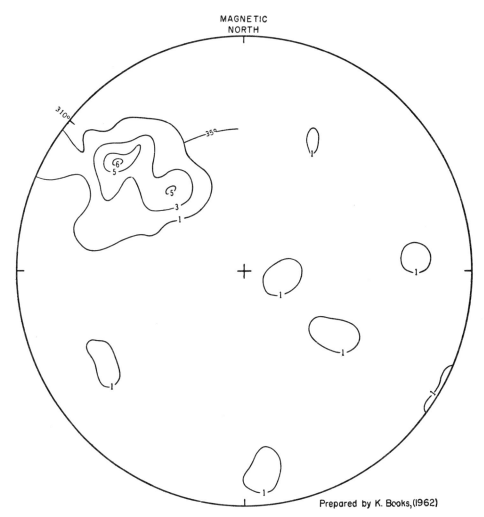

Fig. 13. Density diagram of samples from Squaw Butte that show south-seeking magnetizations. Contours are based on number of points within a counter circle representing one percent of the total area of the diagram.

ing the ratio $\Delta T_{max}/\Delta T_{min}$ it is sometimes possible to determine the dip (ι) of the magnetization through the use of Table 2.

As an example, the method of analysis is applied to total-intensity aeromagnetic maps of Squaw Butte and Wild Horse Ridge, Montana. The magnetic map for Squaw Butte is shown in Figure 12.

This map was compiled from data observed at a flight elevation of 1,000 ft above ground surface. Squaw Butte is a low-lying topographic feature, composed of mafic volcanic rocks of Eocene age, that rises (about 250 ft) above the surrounding countryside. The magnetic anomaly associated with the Butte is dominated by a large negative closure of 3,600 gammas on the southeast side and a smaller positive closure of 4,000 gammas to the northwest. The magnetic high on the northern side indicates the presence of a remanent magnetization direction substantially different from earth's field. An analysis of 113 samples of the alkalic rocks showed that the induced magnetization was small in comparison with a strong remanent magnetization which averaged 9.91×10^{-3} cgs

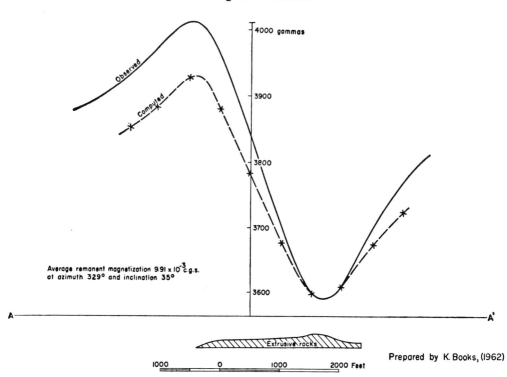

Average remanent magnetization 9.91 x 10⁻³ c.g.s.
at azimuth 329° and inclination 35°

Prepared by K. Books, (1962)

FIG. 14. Computed and observed total intensity anomalies at Squaw Butte, Montana.

(Books, 1962). The induced magnetization may be considered negligible, so that effectively the anomaly is caused solely by remanence. A density diagram of equal-area plots (Figure 13) for the samples shows greatest concentrations near an azimuth of 31 degrees (measured counterclockwise from magnetic north) and a dip of the south-seeking magnetization is 35 degrees, which corresponds to an ι of 215 degrees.

Profile AA' (Figure 14) compares the observed magnetic anomaly over the strongly permed alkalic rocks of Squaw Butte with a theoretical magnetic profile that was computed using the azimuth, dip, and intensity of remanence determined from the sample study. Only remanence data were used in this calculation. The fit is reasonably good, indicating that the assumptions of the calculation were essentially correct and that the body possessed uniform rather than random magnetization.

From simple operations on the observed total field alone, the azimuth and dip of the remanent magnetization may be approximated. The azimuth is approximately equal to the angle formed by the line joining the observed $\Delta T_{\max}$ to $\Delta T_{\min}$ and magnetic north. In Figure 12 AA' joins the magnetic high and low. The angle formed by AA' and magnetic north is found to be about 51 degrees. This is very close to the 310-degree azimuth determined from the sample analysis.

From Table 2 we may empirically determine the dip of magnetization. An inspection of the aeromagnetic map for Squaw Butte (Figure 12) shows that a reasonable average intensity in this area is about 3,880 gammas. The ratio ρ of $\Delta T_{\max}/\Delta T_{\min}$ then becomes 130/290. But this table was developed for $\iota < 180°$. For $\iota > 180°$ the ratio is 290/130 or about 2.2. From the ratio table it is seen that $\rho = 2.2$ corresponds to a dip angle of about 30 degrees. This compares very well with 35 degrees for south-seeking poles determined by rock-sample analyses.

If the flight elevation over Squaw Butte

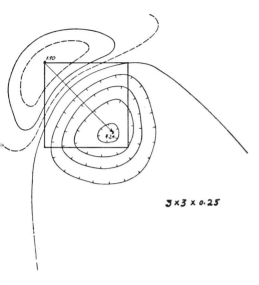

$3 \times 3 \times 0.25$

FIG. 15. $\Delta T/I_t$ for an I_t declined 315 degrees and dipping 210 degrees. Dip of the earth's field is 75 degrees.

(1,000 ft) corresponds to one depth unit, and its dimensions, though not rectangular in shape, are taken to be about $3{,}000 \times 3{,}000$ ft, the butte may be approximated by a prism 3×3 depth units. The thickness of the body is 250 ft which corresponds to a prism thickness of 0.25 depth unit. Figure 15 shows the field produced by a prism with an azimuth of magnetization that most nearly meets these requirements $3 \times 3 \times 0.25$. This model has a $\delta = 315°$ and an $\iota = 210°$. This dip corresponds to a dip of 30 degrees, except that the polarity has reversed, thus interchanging the maximum and minimum.

The similarity of the theoretical and observed fields is quite close, considering the irregular shape of Squaw Butte. Moreover, the location of the edges of the Butte with respect to the $\Delta T_{\max}$ and $\Delta T_{\min}$ is nearly identical with that of the prism. The ob-

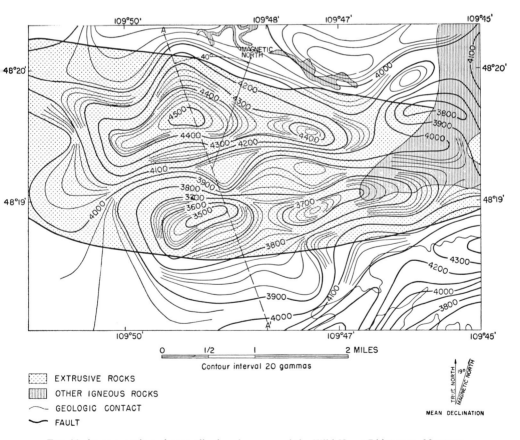

EXTRUSIVE ROCKS
OTHER IGNEOUS ROCKS
GEOLOGIC CONTACT
FAULT

Contour interval 20 gammas

MEAN DECLINATION

FIG. 16. Aeromagnetic and generalized geology map of the Wild Horse Ridge area, Montana.

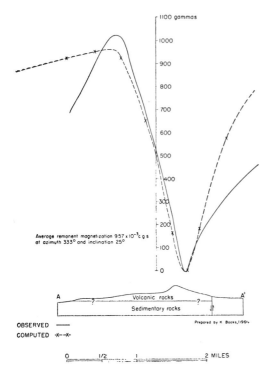

Prepared by K. Books, 1961.

FIG. 17. Computed and observed total intensity anomalies at Wild Horse Ridge, Montana.

served ΔT_{max} coincides almost exactly with the edge of the butte.

Let us consider as a further illustration the Wild Horse Ridge area in Montana. The aeromagnetic map is shown in Figure 16. The ridge is dominated by a large positive anomaly on the north side and an equally large negative anomaly on the south side, indicating, as in the previous illustration, a remanence direction substantially different than that of the earth's field.

Wild Horse Ridge is a prominent ridge of mafic volcanic rock that covers a wide area. The thickness of the rock is unknown but is presumably small, except in the area of the magnetic anomaly. The highest part of the ridge falls near the minimum magnetic value as shown in section AA' of Figure 17. An analysis of 172 samples by Books (personal communication) adequately defines the azimuth, dip, and intensity of the remanent magnetization of this rock mass. Figure 18 is a density diagram based on the sample

analyses. The cluster of points near azimuth 333 degrees indicates south-seeking poles (plotted on the lower hemisphere), and the points near azimuth 153 degrees indicate north-seeking poles (also plotted on the lower hemisphere). The average orientation of the north and south-seeking poles is approximately at an azimuth of 333 degrees and a dip of zero degrees. The azimuth 333 degrees corresponds to a δ of 314 degrees (taking the mean declination to be 19 degrees).

Induced magnetization in Wild Horse Ridge is very small compared with the remanent magnetization, so that the anomaly may be assumed to be caused by remanence only. Using the azimuth, dip, and intensity of magnetization determined from the sample analysis, a theoretical profile was computed. This profile, shown in Figure 17, compares fairly well with the observed profile. From this it is concluded that the basic assumptions of uniform remanent magnetization and dip and azimuth of the remanence are valid.

Operating only on the observed magnetic field associated with Wild Horse Ridge, the azimuth and dip of magnetization may be determined with fair accuracy. The azimuth is approximately equal to the angle formed by a line joining ΔT_{max} and ΔT_{min} on the aeromagnetic map (Figure 16) and magnetic north. This measured angle is 320 degrees, which compares favorably with 314 degrees as determined from the analysis of the rock samples.

The dip of magnetization is approximated by first quantitatively determining the average field intensity in the area of the anomaly and then forming the ratio $\rho = \Delta T_{max}/\Delta T_{min}$. The average intensity in the vicinity of Wild Horse Ridge is very nearly 4,000 gammas, and the ratio ρ then is about 1.0. Referring to Table 2 it is seen that this ratio corresponds to a dip of 0 degrees, the same value of dip as determined by rock-sample analyses.

It is significant to note that even though the anomalies are not "clean" (i.e., isolated) and the theoretical magnetic field only roughly equivalent to the observed field, the method is nevertheless usable for approxi-

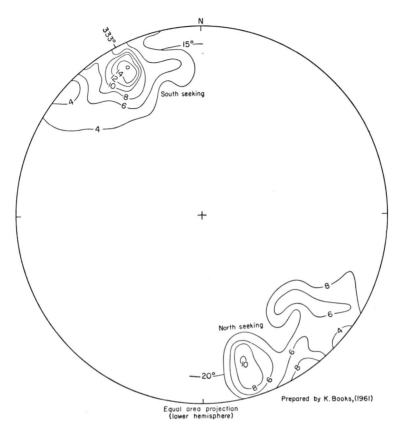

Fɪɢ. 18. Density diagram of samples from Wild Horse Ridge that show north- and south-seeking magnetizations. Contours are based on number of points within a counter circle representing one percent of the total area of the diagram.

mate determinations of the dip and azimuth of the remanent magnetization.

It should be noted also that even though the magnetic field associated with the rocks of Wild Horse Ridge is rather complex and the geometry of the Ridge essentially unknown, the empirical methods developed here for determining the azimuth and dip of the remanent magnetization directly from the total magnetic field are nonetheless valid.

References

Bhattacharyya, B. K., 1964, Magnetic anomalies due to prism-shaped bodies with arbitrary polarization: Geophysics, v. 29, p. 517–553.

Books, K. G., 1962, Remanent magnetism as a contributor to some aeromagnetic anomalies: Geophysics, v. 27, p. 359–375.

DuBois, R. L., 1962, Magnetic characteristics of a massive hematite body: Jour. Geophys. Research, v. 67, p. 2887–2894.

——— 1963, Remanent, induced, and total magnetism of a suite of serpentine specimens from the Sierra Nevada, California: Jour. Geophys. Research, v. 68, no. 1, p. 267–278.

Green, R., 1960, Remanent magnetization and the interpretation of magnetic anomalies: Geophys. Prosp., v. 8, p. 98–110.

Hall, D. H., 1959, Direction of polarization determined from magnetic anomalies: Jour. Geophys. Research, v. 64, p. 1945–1959.

Henderson, Roland G., and Allingham, John W., 1964, The magnetization of an inhomogeneous laccolith calculated on a digital computer: Proceedings Third Annual Conference, Computers in the Mineral Industries: Stanford Univ., Pub., Geol. Sci., v. 9, no. 2.

Peters, Leo J., 1949, The direct approach to magnetic interpretation and its practical application: Geophysics, v. 15, p. 290–321.

Pirson, Sylvain J., 1940, Polar charts for interpreting magnetic anomalies: A.I.M.E., v. 138 (Geophysics), p. 173–192.

Vacquier, V., 1962, A machine method for computing the magnitude and direction of magnetization of a uniformly magnetized body from its shape and a magnetic survey, *in* Benedum earth magnetism symposium, Pittsburgh, Pa.: 1962, Proc., Pittsburgh, Univ. Pittsburgh Press, p. 123–137.

Vacquier, V., Steenland, N. C., Henderson, R. G., and Zietz, Isidore, 1951, Interpretation of aeromagnetic maps: Geol. Soc. America, Mem. 47, 151 p.

Watkins, N. D., 1961, The relative contributions of remanent and induced magnetism to the observed magnetic field in northeast Alberta: Geophys. Prosp., v. 9, p. 421–426.

Zietz, Isidore, 1961, Remanent magnetization and aeromagnetic interpretation [abs]: S.E.G. Yearbook, p. 235.

Zietz, Isidore, and Henderson, R. G., 1945, Model studies of magnetic anomalies: Geophysics, v. 21, p. 794–814.

THE (SIN X)/X·(SIN Y)/Y METHOD FOR CONTINUATION OF POTENTIAL FIELDS*

C. H. G. OLDHAM

The (sin x)/x· (sin y)/y method provides a convenient way for the upward and downward continuation of potential fields. Tables of coefficients facilitating the application of this method to three dimensional problems are presented, and the method evaluated using several theoretical models. For downward continuation the method is sensitive to random fluctuations in the potential field data, and appears limited to continuation to rather shallow depths. For upward continuation the method works well, and as an illustration of its use the gravity field over an area of exposed Precambrian rocks is projected upward to different elevations; thus illustrating the anomalies which would result from basement rocks had this area been covered by up to four miles of sediments.

Introduction

Tomoda and Aki (1955) used the properties of the function (sin x)/x as the basis of a new method for the downward continuation of two-dimensional potential fields. Tsuboi (1956, 1957) used this method in his interpretation of gravity data from California and the East Indies. In principle, the extension of the method to three dimensions was simple (Tsuboi and Tomoda, 1958) but without an electronic computor the numerical computations were prohibitive. When Professor Tsuboi visited the California Institute of Technology in 1956 the California Research Corporation assisted him by computing the coefficients needed for three-dimensional downward continuation (Tsuboi, Oldham, and Waithman, 1958). Coefficients were also computed for upward continuation and the method was evaluated by applying it to several artificial problems.

The tables of coefficients for upward continuation and the results of the evaluation are presented here for the first time. For the sake of completeness, the tables for downward continuation are also reproduced.

The Method

The method was originally proposed as an aid to gravity interpretation, and all the examples in this paper are gravity examples. It should be realized, however, that the method is equally valid for the continuation of magnetic fields.

Basically the method consists of approximating the potential field by the sum of surfaces each generated by an expression of the type b_{ij}(sin x)/x· (sin y)/y. One such surface is centered at each of the points $(x_i y_j)$ on a uniform grid. The b_{ij} coefficients are numerically equal to the potential field values at the (i, j) points of the uniform grid about which the surfaces are centered. The grid interval is scaled so as to be equivalent to π. Under these conditions each of the surfaces has the numerical value b_{ij} at the grid point about which it is centered, and 0 at all other grid points. The sum of all such surfaces therefore gives the potential field values at all the grid points, and hence is an approximation to the actual potential field.

At first sight this seems to be an unnecessarily complicated way of approximating the potential field. But, there is a good reason. It is a fairly straight forward matter to continue the field represented by a single (sin x)/ x· (sin y)/y surface to any specified distance above or below the original plane. The total field at each grid point on this new plane is then obtained by adding the contributions from each component surface.

Tsuboi (1958) has shown that the gravity field due to a single b_{ij}(sin x)/x· (sin y)/y surface at any point (x, y) on an horizontal plane at a depth D below the surface is given by

$$g_D(x, y) = b_{ij} \int_0^1 \int_0^1 \cos mx$$
$$\cdot \cos nye^{\pi\sqrt{m^2+n^2}\,D/a}dmdn. \quad (1)$$

* Unit for the Study of Science Policy, University of Sussex, England

If the points at which g_D is to be evaluated are equispaced with an interval equal to a, then

$$g_D(ra, sa) = b_{ij} \int_0^1 \int_0^1 \cos m\pi(ra)$$

$$\cdot \cos n\pi(sa) e^{\pi\sqrt{m^2+n^2}\,D/a}\; dm dn. \quad (2)$$

If $d = D/a$ is specified, i.e. if the depth D is a given ratio of the grid spacing, say one half, or one, then the double integral may be evaluated. A set of coefficients will then be obtained, one for each r, and s value. These when multiplied by b_{ij} give the gravity field at the new depth. The total field due to all component surfaces is obtained by simple summation at each grid point.

The double integral (2) does not appear to be integrable analytically and numerical methods had to be used for its evaluation. The Weddle method of numerical integration was used and the intervals from $m=0$ to $m=1$ and $n=0$ to $n=1$ were divided into 36 equal sections. The integral was evaluated for values of r and s from 0 to 15, and for values of $D/a = 0.5$, 1.0, -0.5, -1.0. (The negative sign indicates upward continuation.) The corresponding coefficients are reproduced in Tables 1 to 4. They represent only the bottom right-hand quadrants of the array of coefficients actually used in a given problem. The rest of the coefficients are obtained by symmetry. The listed coefficients are first reflected about the vertical and then about the horizontal axes, to give the coefficients for all four quadrants.

Application

The use of the tables is simple in principle. Values of the gravity or magnetic field are interpolated onto, or measured at, the intersections of a square grid. The grid interval must be either equal to, or twice the depth to which the field is to be projected.

The appropriate table of coefficients is written down as a rectangular mesh on a transparent stencil (say A). The gravity values are also written down on a piece of paper (say B) having a square mesh with the same spacing as A. Overlay A on B so that the meshes coincide. Calculate the products

of values which appear at the same grid points and add them up. The sum represents the gravity field at the required depth and immediately below the central point of $A(x=0, y=0)$. Shift the overlay A one step relative to B and repeat the calculation. Continue until the whole area has been covered.

Evaluation

The satisfactory evaluation of methods for improving the resolution of potential field data poses a serious problem. This is equally true whether the methods be for computing residuals, second derivatives, or for downward continuation. Two approaches to solving this problem are frequently used. The first consists of applying the method to be evaluated to artificial problems, the answer to which can also be analytically computed. The other approach is to apply the method to field data. Neither approach is entirely satisfactory. The first deals with idealized simple bodies that are rarely met within nature. They are "too artificial" to satisfy the practicing geophysicist. The second approach is unsatisfactory because the correct answer is never known. All we can say is that the method appears reasonable (or unreasonable). A third approach which partially gets around the objection to artificial problems is to add random numbers to the artificially created data before applying the method. These random numbers simulate the random errors in actual field data, which may be due to instrumental error, or to near-surface density (or susceptibility) inhomogeneities.

All three approaches were used in the evaluation of the method discussed in this paper.

Evaluation using an artificial example

The artificial body chosen for this study was an infinite horizontal plate. It was chosen because the gravity anomaly due to such a plate is the same irrespective of height above the plate. This suggests a simple way of evaluating the method, since under the above conditions, the sum of the coefficients in each of Tables 1 to 4, should tend to unity. (They should only equal unity if the tables had been extended all the way to

Table 1. Tsuboi coefficients for $d = +0.5$

r \ s	0	1	2	3	4	5	6	7	8	9	10	11	12	13	14	15
0	+3.65742	-0.74169	+0.19159	-0.09485	+0.05113	-0.03430	+0.02309	-0.01750	+0.01309	-0.01059	+0.00843	-0.00712	+0.00593	-0.00519	+0.00450	-0.00412
1	-0.74169	+0.02208	-0.01953	+0.00340	-0.00441	+0.00153	-0.00182	+0.00086	-0.00098	+0.00055	-0.00061	+0.00038	-0.00042	+0.00028	-0.00032	+0.00023
2	+0.19159	-0.01953	+0.00040	-0.00335	+0.00009	-0.00112	+0.00012	-0.00052	+0.00010	-0.00029	+0.00008	-0.00019	+0.00006	-0.00013	+0.00005	-0.00010
3	-0.09485	+0.00340	-0.00335	-0.00025	-0.00106	-0.00012	-0.00045	-0.00004	-0.00024	-0.00001	-0.00014	0	-0.00009	+0.00001	-0.00007	+0.00001
4	+0.05113	-0.00441	+0.00009	-0.00106	-0.00019	-0.00046	-0.00010	-0.00023	-0.00005	-0.00013	-0.00002	-0.00008	-0.00001	-0.00006	-0.00001	-0.00004
5	-0.03430	+0.00153	-0.00112	+0.00012	-0.00046	-0.00012	-0.00024	-0.00007	-0.00013	-0.00004	-0.00008	-0.00002	-0.00005	-0.00001	-0.00004	-0.00001
6	+0.02309	-0.00182	+0.00012	-0.00045	-0.00010	-0.00024	-0.00008	-0.00014	-0.00005	-0.00008	-0.00003	-0.00005	-0.00002	-0.00004	-0.00001	-0.00003
7	-0.01750	+0.00086	-0.00052	-0.00004	-0.00023	-0.00007	-0.00014	-0.00005	-0.00009	-0.00004	-0.00006	-0.00002	-0.00004	-0.00002	-0.00003	-0.00001
8	+0.01309	-0.00098	+0.00010	-0.00024	-0.00005	-0.00013	-0.00005	-0.00009	-0.00004	-0.00006	-0.00003	-0.00004	-0.00002	-0.00003	-0.00002	-0.00002
9	-0.01059	+0.00055	-0.00029	-0.00001	-0.00013	-0.00004	-0.00008	-0.00004	-0.00006	-0.00003	-0.00004	-0.00002	-0.00003	-0.00001	-0.00002	-0.00002
10	+0.00843	-0.00061	+0.00008	-0.00014	-0.00002	-0.00008	-0.00003	-0.00006	-0.00003	-0.00004	-0.00002	-0.00003	-0.00002	-0.00002	-0.00001	-0.00001
11	-0.00712	+0.00038	-0.00019	0	-0.00008	-0.00002	-0.00005	-0.00002	-0.00004	-0.00002	-0.00003	-0.00002	-0.00002	-0.00001	-0.00002	-0.00001
12	+0.00593	-0.00042	+0.00006	-0.00009	-0.00001	-0.00005	-0.00002	-0.00004	-0.00002	-0.00003	-0.00002	-0.00002	-0.00001	-0.00002	-0.00001	-0.00001
13	-0.00519	+0.00028	-0.00013	+0.00001	-0.00006	-0.00001	-0.00004	-0.00002	-0.00003	-0.00001	-0.00002	-0.00001	-0.00001	-0.00001	-0.00001	-0.00001
14	+0.00450	-0.00032	+0.00005	-0.00007	-0.00001	-0.00004	-0.00001	-0.00003	-0.00001	-0.00002	-0.00001	-0.00002	-0.00001	-0.00001	-0.00001	-0.00001
15	-0.00412	+0.00023	-0.00010	+0.00001	-0.00004	-0.00001	-0.00003	-0.00001	-0.00002	-0.00001	-0.00002	-0.00001	-0.00001	-0.00001	-0.00001	-0.00001

Table 2. Tsuboi coefficients for $d = +1$

$r \backslash s$	0	1	2	3	4	5	6	7	8	9	10	11	12	13	14	15
0	+15.78495	-5.84713	+2.18517	-1.08956	+0.63200	-0.41449	+0.28900	-0.21440	+0.16400	-0.13029	+0.10541	-0.08761	+0.07381	-0.06367	+0.05575	-0.05025
1	-5.84713	+1.35318	-0.48663	+0.22434	-0.13492	+0.08545	-0.06161	+0.04485	-0.03535	+0.02781	-0.02315	+0.01917	-0.01660	+0.01432	-0.01287	+0.01160
2	+2.18517	-0.48663	+0.15329	-0.07843	+0.04144	-0.02851	+0.01833	-0.01408	+0.00998	-0.00809	+0.00606	-0.00508	+0.00395	-0.00340	+0.00273	-0.00247
3	-1.08956	+0.22434	-0.07843	+0.03557	-0.02328	+0.01390	-0.01107	+0.00771	-0.00668	+0.00512	-0.00464	+0.00381	-0.00355	+0.00306	-0.00294	+0.00264
4	+0.63200	-0.13492	+0.04144	-0.02328	+0.01042	-0.00756	+0.00420	-0.00346	+0.00200	-0.00174	+0.00098	-0.00087	+0.00043	-0.00038	+0.00012	-0.00011
5	-0.41449	+0.08545	-0.02851	+0.01390	-0.00756	+0.00543	-0.00465	+0.00315	-0.00297	+0.00222	-0.00217	+0.00175	-0.00175	+0.00149	-0.00150	+0.00134
6	+0.28900	-0.06161	+0.01833	-0.01107	+0.00420	-0.00465	+0.00165	-0.00145	+0.00067	+0.00066	+0.00022	-0.00025	-0.00001	-0.00002	-0.00015	+0.00011
7	-0.21440	+0.04485	-0.01408	+0.00771	-0.00346	+0.00315	-0.00145	+0.00160	-0.00158	+0.00113	-0.00116	+0.00089	-0.00093	+0.00076	-0.00080	+0.00069
8	+0.16400	-0.03535	+0.00998	-0.00668	+0.00200	-0.00297	+0.00067	-0.00158	+0.00049	-0.00052	+0.00024	-0.00029	+0.00011	-0.00015	-0.00003	-0.00008
9	-0.13029	+0.02781	-0.00809	+0.00512	-0.00174	+0.00222	-0.00066	+0.00113	-0.00052	+0.00043	-0.00047	+0.00029	-0.00033	+0.00021	-0.00025	+0.00017
10	+0.10541	-0.02315	+0.00606	-0.00464	+0.00098	-0.00217	+0.00022	-0.00116	+0.00024	-0.00047	+0.00048	-0.00053	+0.00040	-0.00044	+0.00035	-0.00039
11	-0.08761	+0.01917	-0.00508	+0.00381	-0.00087	+0.00175	-0.00025	+0.00089	-0.00029	+0.00029	-0.00053	-0.00021	+0.00017	-0.00027	+0.00023	-0.00029
12	+0.07381	-0.01660	+0.00395	-0.00355	+0.00043	-0.00175	-0.00001	-0.00093	+0.00011	-0.00033	+0.00040	-0.00017	+0.00072	-0.00076	+0.00069	-0.00072
13	-0.06367	+0.01432	-0.00340	+0.00306	-0.00038	+0.00149	-0.00002	+0.00076	-0.00015	+0.00021	-0.00044	-0.00027	-0.00076	+0.00063	+0.00063	-0.00068
14	+0.05575	-0.01287	+0.00273	-0.00294	+0.00012	-0.00150	-0.00015	-0.00080	-0.00003	-0.00025	+0.00035	+0.00023	+0.00069	+0.00063	+0.00098	-0.00100
15	-0.05025	+0.01160	-0.00247	+0.00264	-0.00011	+0.00134	+0.00011	+0.00069	-0.00008	+0.00017	-0.00039	-0.00029	-0.00072	-0.00068	-0.00100	-0.00096

Table 3. Tsuboi coefficients for $d = -0.5$

$\frac{i}{s}$	0	1	2	3	4	5	6	7	8	9	10	11	12	13	14	15
0	+0.33342	+0.07452	+0.00323	+0.00546	-0.00028	+0.00158	-0.00030	+0.00072	-0.00022	+0.00040	-0.00016	+0.00026	-0.00012	+0.00018	-0.00010	+0.00015
1	+0.07452	+0.08833	-0.00559	+0.00292	+0.00082	+0.00078	+0.00022	+0.00052	-0.00008	+0.00016	-0.00003	+0.00010	-0.00001	+0.00007	+0.00001	+0.00005
2	+0.00323	+0.00559	+0.00345	+0.00160	-0.00050	+0.00049	+0.00032	+0.00020	+0.00015	+0.00010	+0.00008	+0.00005	+0.00005	+0.00003	+0.00003	+0.00003
3	-0.00546	+0.00292	+0.00160	+0.00104	+0.00061	+0.00040	+0.00025	+0.00018	+0.00012	+0.00010	+0.00007	+0.00006	+0.00004	+0.00004	+0.00003	+0.00003
4	-0.00028	+0.00082	+0.00090	+0.00061	+0.00044	+0.00029	+0.00021	+0.00015	+0.00011	+0.00008	+0.00006	+0.00005	+0.00004	+0.00003	+0.00003	+0.00002
5	-0.00158	+0.00078	+0.00049	+0.00040	+0.00029	+0.00023	+0.00016	+0.00013	+0.00009	+0.00007	+0.00006	+0.00005	+0.00004	+0.00003	+0.00003	+0.00002
6	-0.00030	+0.00022	+0.00032	+0.00025	+0.00021	+0.00016	+0.00013	+0.00010	+0.00008	+0.00006	+0.00005	+0.00004	+0.00003	+0.00003	+0.00002	+0.00002
7	+0.00072	+0.00032	+0.00020	+0.00018	+0.00015	+0.00013	+0.00008	+0.00008	+0.00006	+0.00005	+0.00004	+0.00004	+0.00003	+0.00002	+0.00002	+0.00002
8	-0.00022	+0.00008	+0.00015	+0.00012	+0.00011	+0.00009	+0.00006	+0.00006	+0.00005	+0.00004	+0.00004	+0.00003	+0.00003	+0.00002	+0.00002	+0.00002
9	+0.00040	+0.00016	+0.00010	+0.00010	+0.00008	+0.00007	+0.00006	+0.00005	+0.00004	+0.00004	+0.00003	+0.00003	+0.00002	+0.00002	+0.00002	+0.00002
10	-0.00016	+0.00003	+0.00006	+0.00007	+0.00006	+0.00006	+0.00005	+0.00004	+0.00004	+0.00003	+0.00003	+0.00002	+0.00002	+0.00002	+0.00002	+0.00001
11	+0.00026	+0.00010	+0.00005	+0.00006	+0.00005	+0.00005	+0.00004	+0.00004	+0.00003	+0.00003	+0.00002	+0.00002	+0.00002	+0.00002	+0.00001	+0.00001
12	-0.00012	+0.00001	+0.00005	+0.00004	+0.00004	+0.00004	+0.00003	+0.00003	+0.00003	+0.00002	+0.00002	+0.00002	+0.00002	+0.00002	+0.00001	+0.00001
13	+0.00018	+0.00007	+0.00003	+0.00004	+0.00003	+0.00003	+0.00003	+0.00002	+0.00002	+0.00002	+0.00002	+0.00002	+0.00001	+0.00002	+0.00001	+0.00001
14	-0.00010	+0.00001	-0.00003	+0.00003	+0.00003	+0.00003	+0.00002	+0.00002	+0.00002	+0.00002	+0.00002	+0.00001	+0.00001	+0.00001	+0.00001	+0.00001
15	+0.00015	+0.00005	+0.00003	+0.00003	+0.00002	+0.00002	+0.00002	+0.00002	+0.00002	+0.00002	+0.00001	+0.00001	+0.00001	+0.00001	+0.00001	+0.00001

Table 4. Tsuboi coefficients for d = —1.0

r \ s = 0	1	2	3	4	5	6	7	8	9	10	11	12	13	14	15
0	+0.13718	+0.05965	+0.01242	+0.00590	+0.00176	+0.00153	+0.00047	+0.00062	+0.00017	+0.00032	+0.00007	+0.00019	+0.00003	+0.00013	+0.00002	+0.00010
1	+0.05965	+0.03260	+0.01036	+0.00461	+0.00193	+0.00123	+0.00061	+0.00049	+0.00026	+0.00024	+0.00013	+0.00014	+0.00007	+0.00009	+0.00005	+0.00007
2	+0.01242	+0.01036	+0.00590	+0.00303	+0.00166	+0.00097	+0.00061	+0.00040	+0.00028	+0.00020	+0.00015	+0.00011	+0.00009	+0.00007	+0.00006	+0.00006
3	+0.00590	+0.00461	+0.00303	+0.00193	+0.00119	+0.00077	+0.00051	+0.00035	+0.00025	+0.00018	+0.00014	+0.00011	+0.00008	+0.00007	+0.00006	+0.00005
4	+0.00176	+0.00193	+0.00166	+0.00119	+0.00084	+0.00058	+0.00041	+0.00029	+0.00022	+0.00016	+0.00013	+0.00010	+0.00008	+0.00007	+0.00006	+0.00005
5	+0.00153	+0.00123	+0.00097	+0.00077	+0.00058	+0.00044	+0.00032	+0.00024	+0.00018	+0.00014	+0.00011	+0.00009	+0.00007	+0.00006	+0.00005	+0.00005
6	+0.00047	+0.00061	+0.00061	+0.00051	+0.00041	+0.00032	+0.00025	+0.00020	+0.00016	+0.00012	+0.00010	+0.00008	+0.00007	+0.00005	+0.00005	+0.00004
7	+0.00062	+0.00049	+0.00040	+0.00035	+0.00029	+0.00024	+0.00020	+0.00016	+0.00013	+0.00010	+0.00009	+0.00007	+0.00006	+0.00005	+0.00004	+0.00003
8	+0.00017	+0.00026	+0.00028	+0.00025	+0.00022	+0.00018	+0.00016	+0.00013	+0.00011	+0.00009	+0.00007	+0.00006	+0.00005	+0.00004	+0.00004	+0.00003
9	+0.00032	+0.00024	+0.00020	+0.00018	+0.00016	+0.00014	+0.00012	+0.00010	+0.00009	+0.00008	+0.00006	+0.00005	+0.00005	+0.00004	+0.00003	+0.00003
10	+0.00007	+0.00013	+0.00015	+0.00014	+0.00013	+0.00011	+0.00010	+0.00009	+0.00007	+0.00006	+0.00005	+0.00005	+0.00004	+0.00003	+0.00003	+0.00003
11	+0.00019	+0.00014	+0.00011	+0.00011	+0.00010	+0.00009	+0.00008	+0.00007	+0.00006	+0.00005	+0.00005	+0.00004	+0.00004	+0.00003	+0.00003	+0.00002
12	+0.00003	+0.00007	+0.00009	+0.00008	+0.00008	+0.00007	+0.00007	+0.00006	+0.00005	+0.00005	+0.00004	+0.00004	+0.00003	+0.00003	+0.00002	+0.00002
13	+0.00013	+0.00009	+0.00007	+0.00007	+0.00007	+0.00006	+0.00005	+0.00005	+0.00004	+0.00004	+0.00003	+0.00003	+0.00002	+0.00002	+0.00002	+0.00002
14	+0.00002	+0.00005	+0.00006	+0.00006	+0.00006	+0.00005	+0.00005	+0.00004	+0.00004	+0.00003	+0.00003	+0.00003	+0.00002	+0.00002	+0.00002	+0.00002
15	+0.00010	+0.00007	+0.00006	+0.00005	+0.00005	+0.00005	+0.00004	+0.00004	+0.00003	+0.00003	+0.00003	+0.00002	+0.00002	+0.00002	+0.00002	+0.00001

$r = \infty$, $s = \infty$). The actual sums of the coefficients for Tables 1 and 2 are shown in Table 5, which also shows the effect of including different numbers of terms in the summation. The sums of Tables 3 and 4 are shown in Figure 1. It will be noted that for $D/a = 0.5$ the sum of coefficients tends quite rapidly towards unity, whereas for $D/a = 1$ the trend towards unity is much less rapid and hence less satisfactory. The same is also true for the upward continuation tables. For example, when 9 terms are included in both x and y directions, the method underestimates the true value by about 5 percent when $D/a = -0.5$, and by about 10 percent when $D/a = -1.0$.

Evaluation using artificial examples plus random error

The example selected for this test was the gravity field due to three buried spheres. The spheres each had a radius of one km, a density contrast of one gm/cm³, and were buried at a depth of 4 km below the surface. The horizontal disposition of the spheres is indicated by the points A, B, and C, in Figure 2. To the values of gravity due to these three spheres at each point on a one-km square grid were added random numbers, taken from a book of random numbers, and scaled to have a standard deviation of 0.25 gravity units. This standard deviation was about one part in 130 of the maximum gravity effect of the three spheres. Tables 1 and 2 were used to project the field down by depths of one-half km and one km. The computations were also repeated using different numbers of coefficients, but only the results of using the 19×19 array of coefficients are shown here, in Figure 2(b) and 2(c). No significant improvements were obtained by using the full 31×31 array of coefficients. The theoretical field for three spheres buried at a depth of three km was also computed analytically and is shown in Figure 2(d). For the method to be considered successful, Figures 2(c) and 2(d) should have been the same.

The conclusions are clear. A satisfactory result is obtained when the projected depth is one half the grid spacing, but when the depth is equal to the grid spacing the effect of the

Table 5. Summation of Tsuboi coefficients for $d=0.5$ and $d=1.0$

	Number of terms included in the summation (in both x and y directions)	Sum of coefficients
$d=0.5$	3	1.0107
	4	1.1714
	5	1.0324
	6	1.1045
	7	1.0332
	8	1.0739
	9	1.0306
	10	1.0568
	11	1.0277
	12	1.0461
	13	1.0248
	14	1.0387
	15	1.0220
$d=1.0$	3	0.2213
	4	1.8569
	5	0.7269
	6	1.4511
	7	0.8936
	8	1.2802
	9	0.9629
	10	1.1937
	11	0.9936
	12	1.1468
	13	1.0048
	14	1.1219
	15	1.0036

random error distorts the projected field to such an extent that the results are quite unsatisfactory. It would be interesting to know how other techniques for downward continuation behave under similar tests.

As might be expected, much better results were obtained with the upward continuation tests. The three spheres gravity field plus random error was projected up to heights of one-half km and one km above the surface. The field due to the three spheres now buried at 4.5 km and 5.0 km were also computed analytically. The contoured results are shown in Figure 3. The agreement between the continued field and the theoretical field at the same height is good.

Evaluation using field data

As an example of the use of the method for upward continuation, the Bouguer gravity field over an area of Precambrian rocks in Southeastern Ontario was projected upwards to heights of one and two miles. The field at a height of two miles was then projected up-

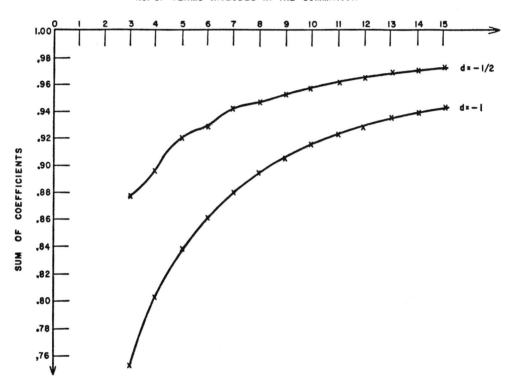

FIG. 1. The summation of the Tsuboi coefficients for $d = -\frac{1}{2}$ and $d = -1.0$.

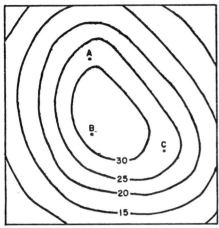

(a) GRAVITY FIELD DUE TO THREE SPHERES PLUS THE EFFECT OF RANDOM ERRORS.

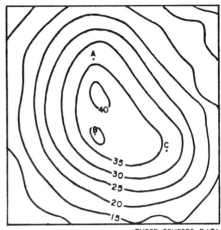

THREE SPHERES DATA
(b) PLUS RANDOM ERRORS, PROJECTED DOWNWARD BY D = ½ KM, USING 19 × 19 COEFFICIENTS.

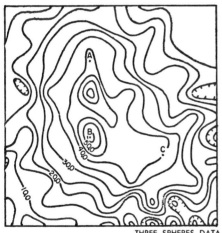

THREE SPHERES DATA
(c) PLUS RANDOM ERRORS, PROJECTED DOWNWARD BY D = 1 KM, USING 19 × 19 COEFFICIENTS.

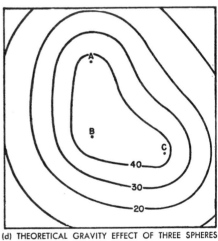

(d) THEORETICAL GRAVITY EFFECT OF THREE SPHERES BURIED AT DEPTH OF 3 KM.

EXPLANATION:
RADII OF SPHERES = 1 KM
DEPTH CENTER OF SPHERES = 4 KM
DENSITY OF SPHERES = 1 GM/CC
STANDARD DEVIATION OF RANDOM ERROR = 0.25 GRAVITY UNITS
CONTOUR INTERVAL = 5 GRAVITY UNITS

0   5 km.

FIG. 2. Downward continuation of gravity data due to three buried spheres.

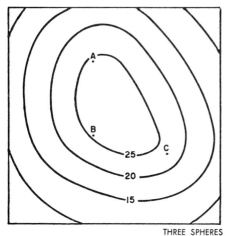

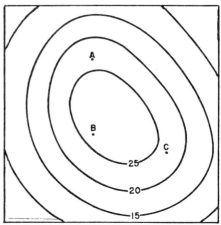

THREE SPHERES
(a) DATA PLUS RANDOM ERRORS PROJECTED UPWARD
BY $D = -\frac{1}{2}$ KM.

(b) GRAVITY EFFECT OF THREE SPHERES BURIED AT
DEPTH OF 4.5 KM.

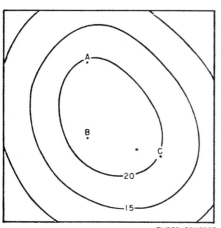

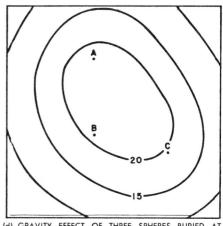

THREE SPHERES
(c) DATA PLUS RANDOM ERRORS PROJECTED UPWARD
BY D   1 KM.

(d) GRAVITY EFFECT OF THREE SPHERES BURIED AT
DEPTH OF 5 KM.

EXPLANATION:
RADII OF SPHERES = 1 KM
DEPTH CENTER OF SPHERES = 4 KM·
DENSITY OF SPHERES = 1 GM/CC
STANDARD DEVIATION OF RANDOM ERROR
.. 0.25 GRAVITY UNITS
CONTOUR INTERVAL = 5 GRAVITY UNITS

0   5 km.

FIG. 3. Upward continuation of gravity data due to three buried spheres.

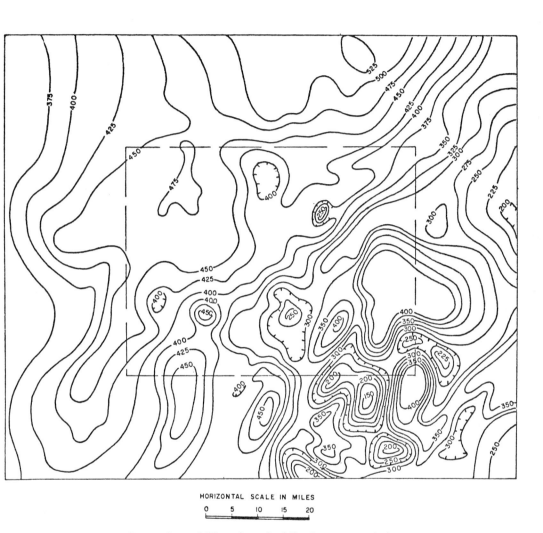

HORIZONTAL SCALE IN MILES

0   5   10   15   20

Contour interval 25 gravity units (all values are negative).

FIG. 4. Bouguer anomaly gravity map of an area of Precambrian rocks in southeastern Ontario. (Area outlined in center of map is area shown in Figure 7.)

Contour interval 25 gravity units (all values are negative).

FIG. 5. Ontario gravity data projected to a height of one mile above sea level.

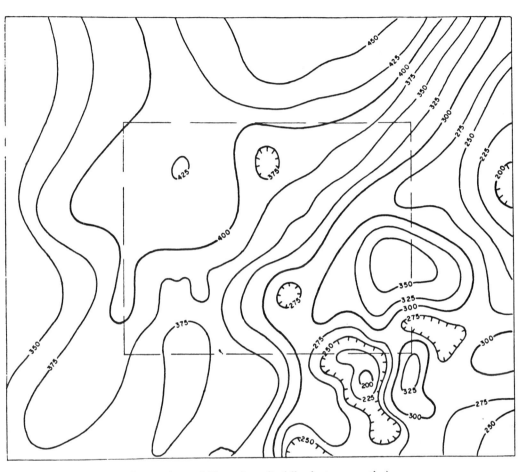

Contour interval 25 gravity units (all values are negative).

Fig. 6. Ontario gravity data projected to a height of two miles above sea level.

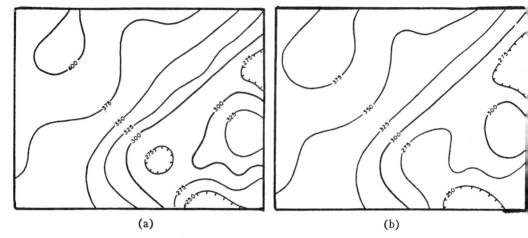

(a)   (b)

Contour interval 25 gravity units (all values are negative).

FIG. 7. Ontario gravity data projected to heights of: (a) three miles above sea level, (b) four miles above sea level

ward by an additional one and two miles. The resulting contour maps are shown in Figures 4 to 7, and northwest-southeast profiles across the area are shown in Figure 8.

This example is of particular interest to the oil geophysicist since it illustrates the gravity anomalies which can be due to lithology changes within the basement, even when the basement may be buried by up to 4 miles of sediments.

Conclusions

Theoretically the (sin x)/x method provides a convenient way for the upward and downward continuation of potential fields. In practice, however, the method is rather sensitive to error in the observed data and, for downward continuation, appears to be limited to a depth not exceeding one half the grid spacing. It is well suited for upward continuation.

Acknowledgments

I am grateful to Professor C. H. Dix, of the California Institute of Technology, for suggesting the cooperation between Professor Tsuboi of the University of Tokyo and California Research Corporation in the compu-

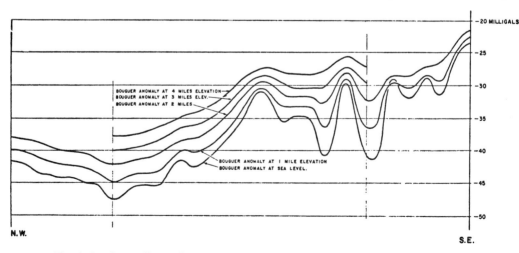

FIG. 8. Gravity profiles at different heights across an area of Precambrian rocks in Ontario.

tation of the tables for downward continuation. I especially wish to thank Professor Tsuboi for the valuable discussions on this and other gravity problems which we had during his visit to California. The work was done when I was on the staff of the California Research Corporation, and I am grateful to this organization for permission to publish the paper.

References

Tomoda, Y., and Aki, K., 1955, Use of the function (sin x)/x in gravity problems: Proc. Japan Acad., v. 31, p. 443–448.

Tsuboi, C., 1956, Crustal structure in Northern and Middle California from gravity pendulum data: G.S.A. Bull., v. 67, p. 1641–1646.

—— 1957, Crustal structure along a certain profile across the East Indies as deduced by a new calculation method: Gedenkbock, F. A., Vening Meinesz, p. 287–294.

Tsuboi, C., Oldham, C. H. G., and Waithman, V. B., 1958, Numerical tables facilitating three dimensional gravity interpretations: Journal of Physics of the Earth, v. 6, p. 7–13.

Tsuboi, C., and Tomoda, Y., 1958, The relation between the Fourier series method and the (sin x)/x method for gravity interpretations: Journal of Physics of the Earth, v. 6, p. 1–5.

THE COMPUTATION OF SECOND VERTICAL DERIVATIVES OF GEOMAGNETIC FIELDS†

ROLAND G. HENDERSON* AND ISIDORE ZIETZ*

Second vertical derivatives of magnetic fields, because of their high resolving power, are often very useful in interpreting magnetic anomalies. Formulas are developed which permit their ready numerical computation. Comparisons are made between the resulting approximate values and the rigorous values obtained for simple idealized fields. The similarity between maps of second vertical derivatives of fields and those of certain types of residual fields is discussed.

Introduction

The airborne magnetometer, as employed in mapping geomagnetic anomalies, has been in extensive use by the U. S. Geological Survey for many years. The quantitative use of magnetics is limited because of the low resolving power of the method and because of the ambiguity in magnetic interpretations. Despite these limitations, there is justification for getting as much out of the data as possible. An advantage of the method is its use in preliminary surveys to disclose areas in which geophysical methods of higher resolving power may be used.

Qualitative and quantitative interpretations can be made more objective by constructing second vertical derivative maps or so-called residual maps of the observed field. H. M. Evjen (1936) demonstrated the higher resolving power of the first vertical derivative of the two-dimensional gravitational anomaly field produced by two parallel line sources. Even greater resolution is afforded by the second vertical derivatives of the field. V. Vacquier et al. (1951) use second derivatives in conjunction with prismatic models to estimate depths to the basement from total magnetic intensity anomalies.

Second vertical derivative maps have been computed for aeromagnetic surveys over regions where the geology was fairly well known. The interesting feature about such maps is the manner in which they tend to delineate geologic formations known to be magnetic. Also, the presence of magnetic rocks in sediments is disclosed more prominently than is possible with the observed field. Second vertical derivatives also are useful in the analytical continuation of magnetic fields toward sources, although such uses are limited by the accuracy both of the data and of the method of computing.

The recognized importance of these derivatives led the authors to study the means by which they may be computed. The accuracy and limitations of the approximation formulas developed herein are examined in relation to rigorous values obtained from elementary fields.

Mathematical Theory

If ΔV is the anomaly in magnetic potential, at all points of free space it satisfies the Laplace equation

$$\nabla^2(\Delta V) = 0. \tag{1}$$

The component of the total-intensity anomaly ΔT in the direction of the earth's normal field (assumed invariant over the area) is given by

$$\Delta T = -\frac{\partial(\Delta V)}{\partial t} \tag{2}$$

where t is the unit vector in the direction of the earth's undisturbed field. The equation

† Presented at the 19th Annual SEG Meeting in St. Louis, March 16, 1949. Reprinted from GEO-PHYSICS v. 14. Published by permission of the Director, U. S. Geological Survey.

* U. S. Geological Survey.

(2) is valid as long as $\Delta T \ll T_0$ where T_0 is the magnitude of the total field. Operating on each side of equation (2) with

$$\nabla^2 \equiv \frac{\partial^2}{\partial x^2} + \frac{\partial^2}{\partial y^2} + \frac{\partial^2}{\partial z^2}$$

in consequence of equation (1) we have

$$\nabla^2(\Delta T) = \frac{\partial^2(\Delta T)}{\partial x^2} + \frac{\partial^2(\Delta T)}{\partial y^2}$$

$$+ \frac{\partial^2(\Delta T)}{\partial z^2} = 0. \qquad (3)$$

Therefore ΔT, on the bases assumed, satisfies the Laplace equation and admits of analysis by the methods of potential theory.

$\Delta T(x, y, 0)$ is known at most at an infinite number of points on a finite number of flight lines spaced generally from one-quarter mile to one mile apart. After preparation of a magnetic-contour map, the anomaly is known approximately over the plane of observations. The second vertical derivative at a point may be computed with the aid of a function which satisfies equation (3), vanishes at infinity, and reduces approximately to the contoured values of ΔT on the plane of observations.

Suppose a right-handed system of coordinates is adopted in which the origin is taken at the center of the anomaly and the z axis is taken positive vertically upward. A satisfactory solution to equation (3) in terms of a Fourier-Bessel expansion is

$$\Delta T(z, r, \phi) = \sum_{k=1}^{K} \sum_{n=0}^{N} e^{-\mu_k z} [A_{kn} \cos n\phi$$

$$+ B_{kn} \sin n\phi] J_n(\mu_k r) \qquad (4)$$

where $x = r \cos \phi$, $y = r \sin \phi$, k and n are positive integers, A_{kn} and B_{kn} are constants to be determined; $J_n(\mu_k r)$ is a Bessel function of the first kind, and μ_k are positive roots of $J_n(\mu_k a) = 0$ where a is a large value of the radius r at which the anomaly ΔT is effectively zero, or has been arbitrarily made so.

Differentiating equation (4) and allowing z to approach zero we have

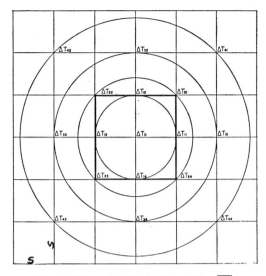

Fig. 1. Values of $\Delta T(r)$ for determining $\overline{\Delta T}$.

$$\frac{\partial^2 \Delta T}{\partial z^2} = \sum_{k=1}^{K} \sum_{n=0}^{N} \mu_k^2 [A_{kn} \cos n\phi$$

$$+ B_{kn} \sin n\phi] J_n(\mu_k r). \qquad (5)$$

The constants A_{kn}, B_{kn} of equation (5) can be obtained from equation (4) when $z = 0$; however, the computation is time consuming and laborious. Equation (4) is greatly simplified when dependence on ϕ is eliminated. This can be effected approximately in the following manner: A square grid of mesh length S is superimposed and the value of ΔT interpolated at each grid corner (see Figure 1). On the first circle, radius S, about the origin there are four values ΔT_{11}, ΔT_{12}, ΔT_{13}, ΔT_{14}; on the second circle, radius $S\sqrt{2}$, there are the four values ΔT_{21}, ΔT_{22}, ΔT_{23}, ΔT_{24}, and on the jth circle the values ΔT_{j1}, ΔT_{j2}, ΔT_{j3}, ΔT_{j4}. By taking the average value of ΔT on each circle, it can easily be shown that dependence on ϕ is eliminated, and, as a consequence, only Bessel functions of zero order, i.e., $J_0(\mu_k r)$, remain in the expansion (4). It has been assumed that four points are adequate for representing the average value of ΔT on each circle. With these modifications, we have

$$\overline{\Delta T}(r) = \sum_{k=1}^{K} A_k J_0(\mu_k r) \qquad (6)$$

where $A_{k0} \equiv A_k$, and $\overline{\Delta T}$ represents the average value of ΔT on the circle of radius r. Equation (4) can now be written

$$\Delta T(z, r) = \sum_{k=1}^{K} A_k z^{-\mu_k z} J_0(\mu_k r) \qquad (7)$$

where

$$\Delta T(0, r) \equiv \overline{\Delta T}(r).$$

From equation (7) the required derivative at the origin is

$$\frac{\partial^2 \Delta T}{\partial z^2} = \sum_{k=1}^{K} \mu_k{}^2 A_k J_0(\mu_k 0) = \sum_{k=1}^{K} \mu_k{}^2 A_k. \qquad (8)$$

Equation (8) affords a means of computing the second vertical derivative of ΔT at the origin. The coefficients A_k can be evaluated by solving K equations in K unknowns involving the value of the anomaly at the center and the average values of ΔT on $K-1$ circles about the origin.

There is no loss in generality if the origin is taken at the point where $\partial^2 \Delta T / \partial z^2$ is desired. There is wide latitude in the choice of $r=a$, the value where ΔT is essentially zero, as we are concerned with fitting values of ΔT in the neighborhood of the origin. Usually ΔT on two or three circles about the origin yields values of sufficient accuracy.

To put equation (8) into a form more convenient for computation let ΔT_0 be the value of the field at the point where the derivative is sought, and $\overline{\Delta T}_1 \overline{\Delta T}_2$ the average values of the field on circles of radii r_1 and r_2 respectively. Then from equation (6)

$$\Delta T_0 = A_1 \qquad + A_2 \qquad + A_3$$
$$\overline{\Delta T}_1 = A_1 J_0(\mu_1 r_1) + A_2 J_0(\mu_2 r_1) + A_3 J_0(\mu_3 r_1)$$
$$\overline{\Delta T}_2 = A_1 J_0(\mu_1 r_2) + A_2 J_0(\mu_2 r_2) + A_3 J_0(\mu_3 r_2). \qquad (9)$$

In solving for the coefficients A_1, A_2, A_3 in equations (9) it is convenient to use a nine-point system consisting of ΔT_0 and eight neighboring points. Then $r_1 = S$, $r_2 = S\sqrt{2}$ as shown in Figure 1. Suppose we take $a = 10S$ as the radius at which the idealized anomaly is arbitrarily smoothed to zero. Then from $J_0(\mu_k 10S) = 0$ we have (Jahnke, E., and

Emde, F., 1945) $\mu_1 = 0.2405/S$, $\mu_2 = 0.5520/S$, $\mu_3 = 0.8654/S$, and

$$J_0(\mu_1 r_1) = 0.9856$$
$$J_0(\mu_2 r_1) = 0.9253$$
$$J_0(\mu_3 r_1) = 0.8215$$
$$J_0(\mu_1 r_2) = 0.9713$$
$$J_0(\mu_2 r_2) = 0.8534$$
$$J_0(\mu_3 r_2) = 0.6592.$$

Inserting these values in (9), we determine A_1, A_2, A_3. Equation (8) then becomes

$$\frac{\partial^2 \Delta T}{\partial z^2} = [6.185 \Delta T_0 - 8.374 \overline{\Delta T}_1 + 2.189 \overline{\Delta T}_2] \frac{1}{S_2} \qquad (10)$$

which is a working formula for computing the indicated derivative.

By expanding $J_0(\mu_k r)$ in equation (6) in its defining power series, we derive a second and simpler expression for $\partial^2 \Delta T / \partial z^2$:

$$\overline{\Delta T}(r) = \sum_{k=1}^{K} A_k J_0(\mu_k r)$$
$$= \sum_{k=1}^{K} A_k - \frac{r^2}{4} \sum_{k=1}^{K} \mu_k{}^2 A_k$$
$$+ \frac{r^4}{64} \sum_{k=1}^{K} \mu_k{}^4 A_k + \cdots . \qquad (11)$$

In consequence of equation (6) and equation (8), equation (11) may be written

$$\overline{\Delta T}(r) = \Delta T_0 - \frac{r^2}{4} \frac{\partial^2 \Delta T}{\partial z^2}$$
$$+ \frac{r^4}{64} \sum \mu_k{}^4 A_k + \cdots . \qquad (12)$$

Using a nine-point system with $r = S$ and $r = S\sqrt{2}$ in equation (12), we have two simultaneous equations from which $\partial^2 \Delta T / \partial z^2$ can be obtained. The solution is:

$$\frac{\partial^2 \Delta T}{\partial z^2} = \frac{2}{S^2} (3\Delta T_0 - 4\overline{\Delta T}_1 + \overline{\Delta T}_2). \qquad (13)$$

Table 1. Comparisons of values of $\frac{1}{4}(\partial^2 \Delta T/\partial z^2)$ computed from derived formulas. Field is that of a point pole at various depths.

Depth, $\zeta = 10$

x	y	True value $\dfrac{1}{4}\dfrac{\partial^2 \Delta T}{\partial z^2}$	Unit grid spacing Values by formula		
			I	II	III
0	0	0.15	0.15	0.16	0.16
2	1	0.11	0.10	0.10	0.10
2	3	0.07	0.06	0.06	0.06
3	3	0.06	0.06	0.06	0.06

Depth, $\zeta = 5$

x	y	True value $\dfrac{1}{4}\dfrac{\partial^2 \Delta T}{\partial z^2}$	Unit grid spacing Values by formula		
			I	II	III
0	0	2.40	2.41	2.36	2.41
1	1	1.61	1.62	1.61	1.63
2	2	0.47	0.52	0.51	0.53
2	3	0.12	0.12	0.12	0.15

Depth, $\zeta = 2.5$

x	y	True value $\dfrac{1}{4}\dfrac{\partial^2 \Delta T}{\partial z^2}$	Unit grid spacing Values by formula			0.5 Unit grid spacing Values by formula			0.25 Unit grid spacing Values by formula		
			I	II	III	I	II	III	I	II	III
0	0	38.40	37.02	36.61	37.63	38.36	38.24	38.38	38.40	38.40	38.33
1	1	7.56	8.81	8.78	9.26	7.94	7.94	8.26	7.76	7.76	7.88
2	0	0.27	−1.25	−1.10	−0.58	−0.27	−0.22	−0.67	0.23	0.24	0.16
2	2	−1.98	−0.73	−0.79	0.28	−1.68	−1.70	−1.37	−1.96	−1.96	−1.86
3	1	−1.90	−2.21	−2.18	−2.42	−2.03	−2.02	−2.10	−1.92	−1.92	−1.94

Applications of the Second Vertical Derivative Formulas

Either formula may be applied to determine the derivatives on the plane of observation. In practice, however, the use of equation (13) greatly simplifies the calculations, the values differing negligibly from those obtained by using equation (10).

To investigate the accuracy of the methods, a theoretical anomaly ΔT, due to a point pole in a magnetic field of inclination 90 degrees, has been computed for depths of 2.5, 5.0, and 10.0 units, respectively. A check on the accuracy of the process is provided since the formula for the rigorous computation of $d^2\Delta T/dz^2$ is obtained by differentiating the mathematical expression (Henderson and Zietz, 1948) for ΔT. The formula is

$$\frac{\partial^2 \Delta T}{\partial z^2} = -\frac{15m\zeta^3}{(x^2 + y^2 + \zeta^2)^{7/2}}$$

$$+ \frac{9m\zeta}{(x^2 + y^2 + \zeta^2)^{5/2}} \quad (14)$$

where x, y, o are the coordinates of the point at which ΔT is evaluated and o, o, ζ are the coordinates of the point pole of strength m. Computations using the various methods are tabulated and presented in Table 1 for $m = 1,000$. For a grid of one-half unit spacings, the formulas are modified by multiplying the right-hand members by four.

It should be observed that for decreasing depths, the horizontal gradient and curvature of the ΔT anomaly increase and the agreement between true and computed values becomes less favorable. When $\zeta = 2.5$ and the grid spacing is unity, satisfactory checks are no longer obtained. The situation is remedied by reducing the grid spacing by one half. As a result, the determinations obtained from the formulas agree with the true value for the derivative. By including a third circle, slightly different values are obtained. The formula is derived by inserting into equation (12) the average values ΔT_0, $\overline{\Delta T_1}$, $\overline{\Delta T_2}$, $\overline{\Delta T_3}$ on circles of radii 0, S, $S\sqrt{2}$, $2S$, respectively. This leads to three simultaneous equations which are easily evaluated. The solution is:

$$\frac{\partial^2 \Delta T}{\partial z^2}$$

$$= \frac{21\Delta T_0 - 32\overline{\Delta T_1} + 12\overline{\Delta T_2} - \overline{\Delta T_3}}{3S^2}. \quad (15)$$

When a half-unit grid is used, the right-hand member is multiplied by four. Referring to Table 1, it is evident that the addition of a third circle does not significantly increase the accuracy of the derivative.

Generally, the finer the grid spacing, the better the fit and the more accurate is the computed value of the second derivative as was shown for the point pole. However, in certain types of exploration, the local or shallow anomalies are of little or no interest because of their industrial or sedimentary character and theoretically should be removed before the derivatives are calculated. Practically the latter can be effected by increasing the grid spacing to a size commensurate with the magnetic features to be studied.

As an illustration of the effect of grid size, consider the aeromagnetic map of the Clearfield-Philipsburg area in central Pennsylvania in Figure 2. The second derivative of this field computed on a one-mile grid is shown in Figure 3. This map is characterized by numerous foci, some of which are doubtless due to industrial installations and to near-surface magnetic material. The closed high in the lower right-hand corner occurs over Pennsylvania State College. The second derivative map, Figure 4, of the same area is computed on a three-mile grid. These anomalies are broader and are probably associated with deep magnetic features. A very similar second derivative map (not shown here) was obtained for a grid of two miles.

Relationship Between the Second Vertical Derivative and Residual Maps

It has already been established that in the neighborhood of the point the anomaly may be represented by a power series of the form

$$\overline{\Delta T}(r) = \sum_{k=1}^{K} A_k - \frac{r^2}{4} \sum_{k=1}^{K} A_k \mu_k^2$$

$$+ \frac{r^4}{64} \sum_{k=1}^{K} A_k \mu_k^4 + \cdots$$

(see equation (11)) where $\overline{\Delta T}(r)$ is the average value of the field at a distance r from the point at which the second vertical derivative is to be evaluated. Neglecting terms of the fourth order and higher, in equation (11) we have

$$\overline{\Delta T}(r) = \Delta T_0 - \frac{r^2}{4} \frac{\partial^2 \Delta T}{\partial z^2}. \quad (16)$$

The average values of the field at $r = S$ and $r = S\sqrt{2}$, respectively, become

$$\overline{\Delta T_1} = \Delta T_0 - (S^2/4) \frac{\partial^2 \Delta T}{\partial z^2}$$

$$\overline{\Delta T_2} = \Delta T_0 - (S^2/2) \frac{\partial^2 \Delta T}{\partial z^2}. \quad (17)$$

These equations imply that the solutions for $\partial^2 \Delta T/\partial z^2$ are numerous, as the computation involves the solution of two linear equations with only one unknown. Multiplying the first of equations (17) by 4 and the second by 1 we have

$$\frac{\partial^2 \Delta T}{\partial z^2} = \frac{2}{S^2} (3\Delta T_0 - 4\overline{\Delta T_1} + \overline{\Delta T_2}). \quad (18)$$

Similarly, other expressions for $\partial^2 \Delta T/\partial z^2$ may be found provided r in $\overline{\Delta T}(r)$ is chosen in the neighborhood of the point.

Of particular interest is the similarity between second vertical derivative and residual maps. Residual maps have been used extensively by geophysicists to bring into focus local features which tend to be obscured by the broad features of the field. Various methods have been recommended for obtaining residual fields. One well-known procedure consists of averaging the field values in the neighborhood of a point and subtracting this average from the value at the point. If the averaging process employs a nine-point system as was used in the computations above, a definite relationship can be shown to exist between the residual and second derivative maps.

Consider the outline square consisting of

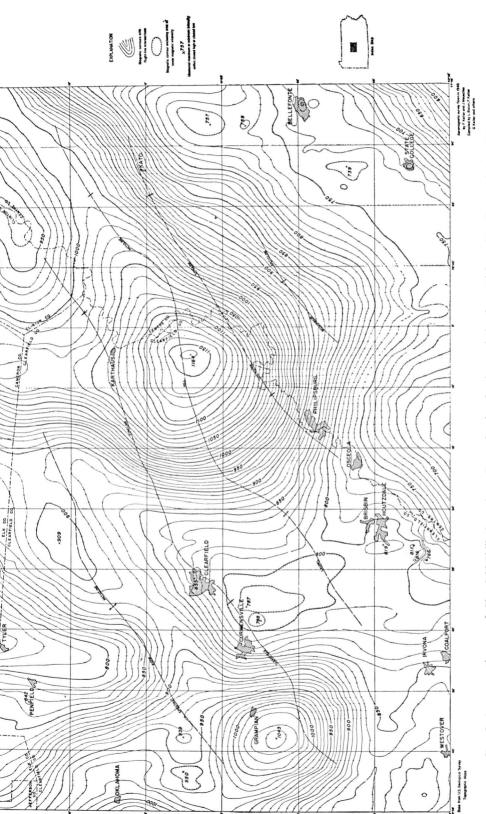

FIG. 2. Aeromagnetic map of Clearfield-Philipsburg Area, Pennsylvania, showing variation in total intensity. Contour interval 10 gammas. Flown approximately 1,000 ft above the surface.

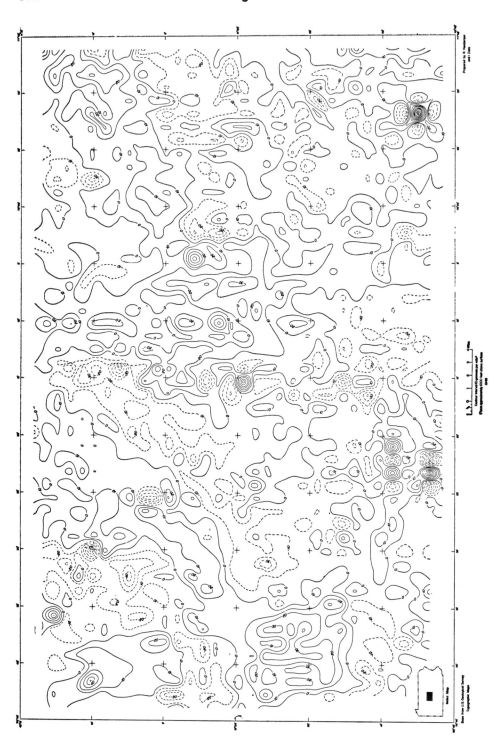

FIG. 3. Aeromagnetic map of Clearfield-Philipsburg Area, Pennsylvania, showing second vertical derivatives of total magnetic intensity computed on a one mile grid.

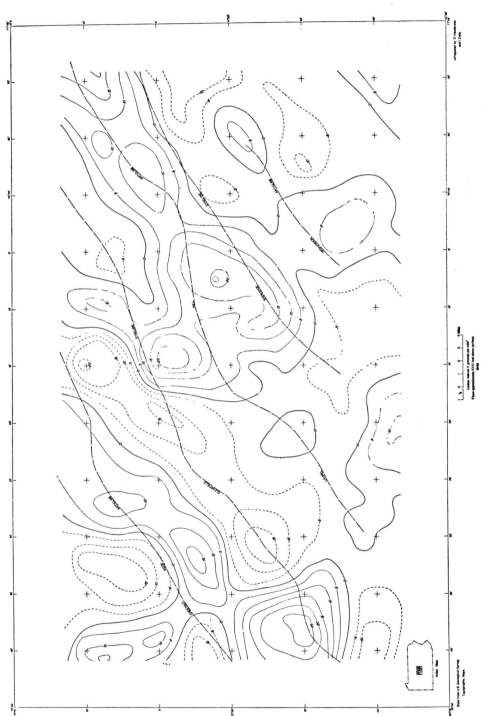

FIG. 4. Aeromagnetic map of Clearfield-Philipsburg Area, Pennsylvania, showing second vertical derivatives of total magnetic intensity computed on a three-mile grid.

four unit squares as shown in Figure 1. The average of the nine grid corner values subtracted from the value at the center gives the residual value at the center. In this case the residual, R, at ΔT_0 becomes

$$R = \Delta T_0 - 1/9(\Delta T_0 + \Delta T_{11} + \Delta T_{12}$$

$$+ \Delta T_{13} + \Delta T_{14} + \Delta T_{21} + \Delta T_{22}$$

$$+ \Delta T_{23} + \Delta T_{24}) \tag{18}$$

or

$$R = 1/9(8\Delta T_0 - 4\overline{\Delta T_1} - 4\overline{\Delta T_2}). \tag{19}$$

Multiplying both equations in (17) by four and adding, we have

$$\frac{\partial^2 \Delta T}{\partial z^2} = \frac{1}{3S^2}(8\Delta T_0 - 4\overline{\Delta T_1} - 4\overline{\Delta T_2}). \tag{20}$$

Consequently,

$$\frac{\partial^2 \Delta T}{\partial z^2} = \frac{3R}{S^2} . \tag{21}$$

It follows from equation (21) that the derivative and residual maps of the same area differ only in the magnitude of the horizontal gradient. The location of the maximum as well as the minimum and zero contours will appear in exactly the same positions.

References

Evjen, H. M., 1936, The place of the vertical gradient in gravitational interpretations: Geophysics, v. 1.

Vacquier, V., Steenland, N. C., Henderson, R. G., and Zietz, I., 1951, Interpretation of aeromagnetic maps: Geol. Soc. America, memoir 47.

Jahnke, E., and Emde, F., 1945, Tables of functions: Dover Publications.

Henderson, R. G., and Zietz, I., 1948, Analysis of total magnetic-intensity anomalies produced by point and line sources: Geophysics, v. 13, p. 428–436.

SELECTED BIBLIOGRAPHY

Introduction

A number of investigators have aided the editors in the selection of the following bibliography. Entries were chosen as the most significant and most useful for those interested in the application of the magnetic method to mining problems. The entries have been grouped as follows: General, Magnetic Field of The Earth, Magnetic Properties of Rocks and Minerals, Magnetic Interpretation, and Case Histories.

General

Cox, A., and Doell, R. R., 1960, Review of paleomagnetism: Bull. G.S.A., v. 71, p. 645–768.

deWet, J. P., Editor, 1957, Methods and case histories in mining geophysics: 6th Commonwealth Mining and Metallurgical Congress, Montreal, Mercury Press.

Dobrin, M. B., 1960, Introduction to geophysical prospecting, 2nd edition: New York, McGraw-Hill Book Company, Inc.

Haalck, H., 1934, Lehrbuch der Angewandten Geophysik: Berlin.

Heiland, C. A., 1940, Geophysical exploration, reprinted 1963: New York, Hafner Publishing Company.

Jakosky, J. J., 1957, Exploration geophysics: Los Angeles, Trija Publ. Co.

Nettleton, L. L., 1940, Geophysical prospecting for oil: New York, McGraw-Hill Book Company, Inc.

Parasnis, D. S., 1962, Principles of applied geophysics: New York, John Wiley & Sons, Inc.

Reford, M. S., and Sumner, J., 1964, Review article—aeromagnetics: Geophysics, v. 29, p. 482–516.

Runcorn, S. K., Editor, 1960, Methods and techniques in geophysics: v. 1, 374 p., New York, Interscience Publishers Inc.

Magnetic Field of the Earth

Bullard, E. C., 1958, 9th Charles lecture; The secular variation of earth's magnetic field: p. 47–60.

Chapman, S., 1951, The earth's magnetism, 2nd Edition: New York, John Wiley and Sons, Inc., p. 127.

Chapman, S., and Bartels, J., 1940, Geomagnetism, 2 vol.: New York, Oxford University Press.

Deel, S. A., and Howe, H. H., 1948, United States magnetic tables and magnetic charts for 1945: U. S. Coast and Geodetic Survey, Serial 667; p. 137.

Fleming, J. A., 1939, Terrestrial magnetism and electricity, in Physics of the earth; Series 8: New York, McGraw-Hill Book Co., Inc.

Hide, R., and Roberts, P. H., 1961, The origins of the main geomagnetic field: Physics and Chemistry of the Earth, v. 4, p. 27–98.

Jacobs, J. A., 1963, The earth's core and geomagnetism: The Commonwealth and International Library of Science, Technology, Engineering and Liberal Studies, Geophysics Division, New York, The Macmillan Company, v. 1.

———, 1964, The earth's core and geomagnetism: New York, Pergamon Press, p. 137.

Lundy, A. K., and Howe, H. H., 1962, Magnetism of the earth: Publ. 40-1, U. S. Coast and Geodetic Survey, Wash. D.C., p. 79.

Runcorn, S. K., 1956, The magnetism of the earth's body: Handbuch der Physik (J. Bartels, ed.), v. 47, p. 498–533.

U. S. Navy, 1954, World magnetic charts for the year 1955, Hydrographic office, Dept. of Navy.

Vestine, E. H., Laporte, L., Cooper, C., Lange, I., and Hendrix, W. C., 1947, Description of the earth's main magnetic field and its secular change, 1905–1945: Carnegie Inst. of Washington Publ., no. 578, p. 532.

Vestine, E. H., Lange, L., Laporte, L., and Scott, W. E., 1947, The geomagnetic field, its description and analysis: Carnegie Inst. of Washington Publ., no. 580.

Whitham, K., and Loomer, E. I., 1957, Irregular magnetic activity in Northern Canada with special reference to aeromagnetic survey problems: Geophysics, v. 22, p. 646–659.

Whitham, K., and Niblett, E. R., 1961, The diurnal problem in aeromagnetic surveying in Canada: Geophysics, v. 26, p. 211–228.

Magnetic Properties of Rocks and Minerals

Balsley, J. R., and Buddington, A. F., 1954, Correlation of reverse remanent magnetism and negative anomalies with certain minerals: Jour. Geomagnetism and Geoelectricity, v. 6, p. 176–181.

Balsley, J. R., and Buddington, A. F., 1958, Iron-titanium oxide minerals, rocks and aeromagnetic anomalies of the Adirondack area, New York: Econ. Geol., v. 53, p. 777–805.

Bersudsky, L. D., 1937, On the causes of the inverse polarity of magnetite deposits in the Angarallim region: Irkutsk, East Siberian Geol. Trust, Trans., no. 2, p. 66.

Books, Kenneth G., 1962, Remanent magnetism as a contributor to some aeromagnetic anomalies: Geophysics, v. 27, p. 359–375.

Bruckshaw J. M., 1953, Magnetic properties of rocks: Nature, v. 171, no. 4351, p. 500–502. Review by Thomas A. Elkins: Geophysics, v. 18, p. 960.

Bruckshaw, J. M., and Robertson, E. I., 1949, The magnetic properties of the Tholeiite dikes of North England: Mon. Not. Royal Ast. Soc., Geoph. Suppl. 5, v. 8, p. 308.

Green, R., 1960, Remanent magnetization and the interpretation of magnetic anomalies: Geophys. Prosp., v. 8, p. 98–110.

Girdler, R. W., and Peter, G., 1960, An example of the importance of natural remanent magnetization in the interpretation of magnetic anomalies: Geophys. Prosp., v. 8, p. 474–483.

Haalck, J., 1942, Der Gesteinsmagnetismus; seine Beziehungen zur den Erscheinungen des Ferromagnetismus und zum Erdmagnetischen Feld (The magnetism of rocks: its relations to the phenomena of ferromagnetism and to the earth's magnetic field): Akademische Verlagsgesellschaft Becker & Erler Kom-Ges, Leipzig, Lithoprint ed. published by J. W. Edwards, Ann Arbor, Michigan, 90 p., 1945. Review by R. A. Geyer: Geophysics, v. 12, p. 285–287.

Hargraves, R. B., 1959, Magnetic anisotropy and remanent magnetism in hemoilmenite from ore deposits at Allard Lake, Quebec: Jour. Geophys. Res., v. 64, p. 1565–1578.

Hawes, J., 1952, A magnetic study of the Spavinaw granite area, Oklahoma: Geophysics, v. 17, p. 27.

Hays, W. W., and Scharon, L., 1963, An example of the influence of remanent magnetization on magnetic intensity measurements: Geophysics, v. 28, p. 1037–1048.

Howell, L. G., Martinez, J. D., Frosch, A., and Statham, E. H., 1960, A note on chemical magnetization of rocks: Geophysics, v. 25, p. 1094–1099.

Howell, L. G., Martinez, J. D., and Statham, E. H., 1958, Some observations on rock magnetism: Geophysics, v. 23, p. 285–298.

Hyslop, R. C., 1945, A field method for determining the magnetic susceptibility of rocks: A.I.M.E. Geophysics, p. 242. Tech. Pub. No 1285, 4 p., Feb. 1941.

Koenigsberger, J. G., 1938, Natural residua magnetism of eruptive rocks: Terrestrial Mag netism and Electricity, v. 43, p. 309.

Laurila, E., 1963, On the measurements of th susceptibility and conductivity of rocks sur rounding a bore: Acta Polytechnica Scandi navia, n. 25.

Mooney, H. M., 1952, Magnetic susceptibilit measurements in Minnesota, Part I, techniqu of measurement: Geophysics, v. 17, p. 531–543

Mooney, H. M., and Bleifuss, R., 1953, Magneti susceptibility measurements in Minnesota Part II, analysis of field results: Geophysics v. 18, p. 383–393.

Nagata, T., 1961 (Revised Edition), Rock-magne tism: Maruzen Co., Ltd., Tokyo.

Nicholls, G. D., 1955, The mineralogy of rock magnetism: Advances in Physics, v. 4, p. 113-190.

Petrova, G. N., and Yuknovets, N. I., 1953 Changes in the magnetic properties of rocks ir the vicinity of fractures (in Russian): Akad Nauk SSSR Isv., Ser. Geofiz., no. 2, p. 115–123

Runcorn, S. K., 1955, Rock magnetism—Geo physical aspects: Advances in Physics, v. 4, p 224–291.

Slichter, L. B., 1942, Magnetic properties of rocks *in* Handbook of physical constants: G.S.A Special Paper No. 36, p. 293–298.

Stacey, F. D., 1963, The physical theory of rock magnetism: Advances in physics, (Phil. Mag Supplement), v. 12, p. 45–133.

Strangway, D. W., 1961, Magnetic properties o diabase dikes: Jour. of Geoph. Res., v. 66, no. 9 p. 3021–3032.

Taylor, G. L., and Reno, D. H., 1948, Magnetic properties of "Granite" wash and unweathered "Granite": Geophysics, v. 13, p. 163–181.

Tucker, P. M., 1952, High magnetic effect o lateritic soil in Cuba: Geophysics, v. 17, p. 753–755.

Uyeda, S., Fuller, M. D., Belshé, J. C., and Girdler, R. W., 1963, Anisotropy of magnetic susceptibility of rocks and minerals: Jour. of Geoph. Res., v. 68, p. 279–291.

Werner, S., 1945, Determinations of the magnetic susceptibility of ores and rocks from Swedish iron ore deposits: Sveriges Geologiska Undersokning, v. 39, n. 5, 79 p., Stockholm, P. A. Norstedt and Soner.

Magnetic Interpretation

Affleck, J., 1958, Interrelationships between magnetic anomaly components: Geophysics, v. 23, p. 738–748.

Andreasen, G. E., and Zietz, I., 1962, Limiting parameters in the magnetic interpretation of a geologic structure: Geophysics, v. 27, p. 807–814.

Baranov, V., 1953, Calcul du gradient vertical du champ de gravité ou du champ magnetique mesuré á la surface du sol: Geophys. Prosp., v. 1, p. 121–191.

———— 1957, A new method for interpretation of aeromagnetic maps: Pseudo gravimetric anomalies: Geophysics, v. 22, p. 359–383.

Bhattacharyya, B. K., 1964, Magnetic anomalies due to prism-shaped bodies with arbitrary polarization: Geophysics, v. 29, p. 517–531.

Eott, M. H. P., 1963, Two methods applicable to computers for evaluating magnetic anomalies due to finite three dimensional bodies: Geophys. Prosp., v. 11, p. 292–299.

Bruckshaw, J. M., and Kunarutnam, K., 1963, The interpretation of magnetic anomalies due to dykes: Geophys. Prosp., v. 11, p. 509–522.

Cook, K. L., 1950, Quantitative interpretation of magnetic anomalies over veins: Geophysics, v. 15, p. 667–686.

Daneš, Z. F., and Oncley, L. A., 1962, An analysis of some second derivative methods: Geophysics, v. 27, p. 611–615.

Dean, W. C., 1958, Frequency analysis for gravity and magnetic interpretation: Geophysics, v. 23, p. 97–127.

Egyed, L., 1948, The determination of an infinite inclined dike from the results of gravity and magnetic surveys: Geophysics, v. 13, p. 437–442.

Elkins, T. A., and Hammer, S., 1938, The resolution of combined effects, with applications to gravitational and magnetic data: Geophysics, v. 3, p. 315–331.

Eve, A. S., 1932, A magnetic method of estimating the height of buried magnetic bodies: Geophys. Prosp., Trans. A.I.M.E., v. 97, p. 200–215.

Fisher, J. W., 1941, Limiting values of gravitational and magnetic anomalies due to a subterranean structure bounded by a single differential surface: Geophysics, v. 6, p. 1–12.

Gamburzeff, G. A., 1928, Bestimung der Elemente eines Durch Einen Unendlich Langen Homogenen Zylinder Hervorgerufenen Magnetischen Feldes und eines Gravitationfeldes: Beitrage zur Geophysik von Gerland 19, p. 210–230.

Garland, G. D., 1951, Combined analysis of gravity and magnetic anomalies: Geophysics, v. 16, p. 51–62.

Gassman, F., 1951, Graphical evaluation of the anomalies of gravity and magnetic field caused by three-dimensional bodies: Third World Petroleum Cong. The Hague 1951 Proceedings, p. 613–621.

Giret, R., 1963, Précision dans les etudes magnétiques aériennes, son incidence sur la qualité des resultats: Geophys. Prosp., v. 11, p. 19–38.

Grant, F. S., 1954, A theory for the regional correction of potential field data: Geophysics, v. 19, p. 23–45.

———— 1957, A problem in the analysis of geophysical data: Geophysics, v. 22, p. 309–344.

Green, R., 1960, Remanent magnetization and the interpretation of magnetic anomalies: Geophys. Prosp., v. 8, p. 98–110.

Gulatee, B. L., 1938, Magnetic anomalies: Geol. Sur. of India Professional Paper 29.

Haalck, H., 1926, Theorie der magnetischen aufschlussmethode; Zeit. Geophysics, v. 2, p. 1–11 and p. 49–62.

———— 1929, Die magnetischen Methoden der angewandten Geophysik: Handbuch der Experimental Physik, v. 25, p. 320–347.

Hall, D. H., 1959, Direction of polarization determined from magnetic anomalies: Jour. Geophys. Res., v. 64, p. 1945–1949.

Hammer, S., 1956, Modern methods of gravity and magnetic interpretation: Rome, Fourth World Petroleum Contress Proc., p. 635.

Heirtzler, J. R., Peter, G., Talwani, M., and Zurflueh, E. G., 1962, Magnetic anomalies caused by two-dimensional structure: their computation by digital computers and their interpretation: Tech. Rept. no. 6, Lamont Geol. Obs., Columbia University, New York.

Helbig, K., 1964, Graticules for the complete determination of the magnetic field of homogeneously magnetized cylindrical bodies with arbitrary cross section and finite lateral extension: Geophys. Prosp., v. 12, no. 2, p. 147–169.

Henderson, R. G., 1960, A comprehensive system of automatic computation in magnetic and gravity interpretation: Geophysics, v. 25, p. 569–585.

Henderson, R. G., and Allingham, J. W., 1963, The magnetization of an inhomogeneous laccolith calculated on a digital computer: Transactions, 3rd Annual Stanford-Arizona Computer Conference. G. A. Parks, General Editor.

Henderson, R. G., and Zietz, I., 1948, Analysis of total magnetic intensity anomalies produced by point and line sources: Geophysics, v. 13, p. 428–436.

———— 1949, The computation of second vertical derivatives of geomagnetic fields: Geophysics, v. 14, p. 508–516.

———— 1949, The upward continuation of anomalies in total magnetic intensity fields: Geophysics, v. 14, p. 517–534.

—————— 1957, Graphical calculation of total-intensity of three-dimensional bodies: Geophysics, v. 22, p. 887–904.

—————— 1958, Magnetic doublet theory in the analysis of total intensity anomalies: U. S. Geol. Sur. Bull. 1052-D.

Hutchison, R. D., 1958, Magnetic analysis by logarithmic curves: Geophysics, v. 23, p. 749–769.

Hughes, D. S., and Pondrom, W. L., 1947, Computation of vertical magnetic anomalies from total magnetic field measurements: A.G.U. Trans., v. 28, p. 193–197.

Kazinskii, V. A., 1960, Mathematical tables for the approximation of geophysical anomalies and reduction by interpolation: New York, Pergamon Press, 94 p.

Keys, D. A., 1937, A survey of methods for determining the depths of magnetic ore bodies: A.I.M.E. Tech. Pub. No. 830, p. 1–8.

Koenigsberger, J., 1928, Zur Deutung der Karten Magnetischer Isanomalen und Profile: Beitrage zur Geophysik von Gerland 18–19, Band 19, p. 241–291.

Kogbetliantz, E. G., 1944, Quantitative interpretation of magnetic and gravitational anomalies: Geophysics, v. 9, p. 463–493.

Koulomzine, T., and Massé, L., 1949, Magnetic anomaly of inclined dike of infinite length: A.I.M.E. Trans., v. 181, p. 51–67.

Logachev, A. A., 1940, An experimental application of the aeromagnetic survey to the determination of depths in magnetic masses: Russia, Central Geological & Prospecting Institute, Materials Geophysic, f. 8, p. 35–38.

Mikov, D. S., 1956, Atlas of theoretical curves for the interpretation of magnetic and gravitational anomalies: State Scientific Technical Press for Literature on Geology and Conservation of Mineral Resources, Tomsk. (From unpublished U. S. Geol. Sur. Trans.)

Nettleton, L. L., 1942, Gravity and magnetic calculations: Geophysics, v. 7, p. 293–310.

Oldham, C. H. G., and Sutherland, D. B., 1955, Orthogonal polynomials: their use in estimating the regional effect: Geophysics, v. 20, p. 295–306.

Paterson, N. R., 1962, Geological mapping by magnetometer surveys: Proceedings of the benedum earth magnetism symposium.

Pentz, H. H., 1940, Formulas and curves for the interpretation of certain two-dimensional magnetic and gravitational anomalies: Geophysics, v. 5, p. 295–306.

Peters, L. J., 1949, The direct approach to magnetic interpretation and its practical application: Geophysics, v. 14, p. 290–320.

Price, C. E., 1959, Magnetic dipole nomograms: Geophysics, v. 24, p. 330–334.

Reford, M. S., 1964, Magnetic anomalies over thin sheets: Geophysics, v. 29, p. 532–536.

Roman, I., 1946, Resolving power of magnetic observations: A.I.M.E. Min. Tech., Tech. Paper 2097, v. 10, 18 p., New York. Review by Thomas A. Elkins: Geophysics, v. 12, p. 284.

Sen, Janshi, 1945, Calculation of the depth of a magnetic deposit: Geophys. Prosp., Trans. A.I.M.E., v. 164, p. 186–188.

Skeels, D. C., and Watson, R. J., 1949, Derivation of magnetic and gravitational quantities by surface integration: Geophysics, v. 14, p. 133–150.

—————— 1956, Correlation of geological and geophysical data: Rome, Fourth World Petroleum Congress Proc., Sec. 15, p. 665–673.

Slichter, L. B., 1929, Certain aspects of magnetic surveying: Geophys. Prosp., Trans. A.I.M.E., v. 81, p. 238–260.

Smellie, D. W., 1956, Elementary approximations in aeromagnetic interpretation: Geophysics, v. 21, p. 1021–1040.

Smith, R. A., 1959, On the depth of bodies producing local magnetic anomalies: Quart. Jour. Mech. and Applied Math., v. 12, pt. 3, p. 354–364.

—————— 1961, Some theorems concerning local magnetic anomalies: Geophys. Prosp., v. 9, p. 399–410.

Solaini, L., 1954, Methodi moderni di studio delle anomalie gravitazionali e magnetiche: Milano Seminario Mat. 3 Fis. Rend., v. 24, p. 1–20.

Sokolov, K. P., 1956, Geological interpretation of Magneto-surveying data: Moscow, Gosgeoltekhizdat, 128 p.

Stam, J. C., 1960, Geological reconnaissance mapping with the help of aeromagnetic surveys: Copenhagen, International Geological Congress, XXI Session, Norden, 1960.

Strakhov, V. N., 1959, Theory of the two-dimensional problem of magnetic exploration: Akad. Nauk SSSR, Izvestiya, Geophysics Ser., no. 2, p. 244–253.

Vacquier, V. W., Steenland, N. C., Henderson, R. G., and Zietz, I., 1951, Interpretation of aeromagnetic maps: Geol. Soc. Amer., Memoir No. 47.

Vacquier, V. W., 1963, A machine method for computing the magnitude and direction of magnetization of a uniformly magnetized body from its shape and a magnetic survey: Benedum symposium on paleomagnetism. T. Nagata, Editor.

Vestine, E. H., and Davids, N., 1945, Analysis and interpretation of geomagnetic anomalies:

Terr. Magnetism and Atmospheric Electricity, v. 50, p. 1–36.

Wantland, D., 1944, Magnetic interpretation: Geophysics, v. 9, p. 47–59.

Watson, R. J., 1952, Chart to estimate magnitude of magnetic anomalies (Nomogram): Geophysics, v. 17, p. 960–961.

Werner, S., 1953, Interpretation of magnetic anomalies at sheet-like bodies: Sveriges Geologiska Undersokning, Arsbok 43 (1949), n. 6, Stockholm.

Zietz, I., and Henderson, R. G., 1956, Model studies of magnetic anomalies: Geophysics, v. 21, p. 794–814.

Case Histories

Agocs, W. B., 1955, Line spacing effect and determination of optimum spacing illustrated by Marmora Ontario magnetic anomaly: Geophysics, v. 20, p. 871–885.

Allingham, J. W., and Zietz, Isidore, 1962, Geophysical data on the Climax Stock, Nevada Test Site, Nye County, Nevada: Geophysics, v. 27, p. 599–610.

Balsley, J. R., James, H. L., and Wier, K. L., 1949, Aeromagnetic survey of parts of Baraga, Iron and Houghton Counties, Michigan, with preliminary geologic interpretation: Geoph. Inv. Sheet, U. S. Geol. Sur. Review by Kenneth L. Cook: Geophysics, v. 16, p. 289.

Barnes, V. E., and Romberg, F., 1943, Gravity and magnetic observations on Iron Mountain magnetite deposit, Llano County, Texas: Geophysics, v. 8, p. 32–45.

Barret, W. N., 1931, Magnetic disturbance caused by buried casing: Bull. A.A.P.G., v. 15, no. 11, p. 1371–1399.

Bath, G. D., 1962, Magnetic anomalies and magnetizations of the Biwabik, iron formation, Mesabi area, Minnesota: Geophysics, v. 27, p. 627–650.

Blum, V. J., 1945, The magnetic field over igneous pipes: Geophysics, v. 10, p. 368–375.

Bourret, W., 1949, Aeromagnetic survey of the Allard Lake district, Quebec: Econ. Geol., v. 44, no. 8, p. 732–740. Review by Kenneth L. Cook: Geophysics, v. 16, p. 290.

Bower, M. E., Geophysical interpretation of the magnetic anomaly at Marmora, Ontario: Canada Geol. Sur. Paper 59-4, 11 p.

Buomeny, R. W., 1962, Geologic interpretation of the aeromagnetic map of the Levanon quadrangle, Linn and Marion Counties, Oregon: U. S. Geol. Sur. Map, G P 212.

Cook, K. L., 1950, Magnetic surveys in the Iron Springs District, Iron County, Utah: U. S. Bureau of Mines Report Inv. 4586, p. 78. Re-

view by Jack W. Peters: Geophysics, v. 16, p. 290–291.

——— 1955, Magnetic surveys over serpentine masses, Riley County, Kansas: Min. Eng., v. 7, p. 481.

Duffell, S., MacLaren, A. S., and Holman, R. H. C., 1963, Red Lake-Lansdowne House area, Northwestern Ontario, bedrock geology, geophysical and geochemical investigations: Geol. Sur. Canada, Paper 63-5.

Galbraith, F. M., 1945, The magnetometer as a geological instrument at Sudbury: Geoph. Trans. A.I.M.E., p. 98–106.

Grant, C. K., 1950, Magnetic surveys in the Middleback Range: South Australia Dept. of Mines, Min. Rev. 90, p. 163.

Haalck, H., 1929, Zur Frage der Erklarung der Kursker Magnetischen und Gravimetrischen Anomalie: Beitrage zur Geophys., Gerlands, v. 22, p. 241–255 and 385–399.

Hammond, P., 1952, Allard Lake ilmenite deposits: Econ. Geology: v. 47, no. 6, p. 634–649. Review by Nelson C. Steenland: Geophysics, v. 18, p. 475.

Hawkes, H. E., 1951, Magnetic exploration for chromite: U. S. Geol. Sur. Bull. 937-A, p. 1–21. Review by Kenneth L. Cook: Geophysics, v. 18 p. 716–717.

——— et al, 1953, Geologic investigation of the Boyertown magnetite deposits in Pennsylvania: U. S. Geol. Sur. Bull. 995d, p. 135–149.

Heinrichs, W. E., Jr., and Thurmond, R. E., 1956, A case history of the geophysical discovery of the Pima Mine, Pima County, Arizona: SEG Geophysical Case Histories, v. 2, p. 607–610.

Joesting, H. R., 1945, Magnetometer and direct-current resistivity studies in Alaska: Trans. A.I.M.E. Geophysics, p. 66–87.

Joesting, H. R., Bacon, L. O., and Getz, J. H., 1948, Geophysical investigations of manganiferous iron deposits, Boston Hill, Grant County, New Mexico: U. S. Bur. Mines, R. I. 4175. 12p.

Johnson, H. R., et al, 1940, Tracing a basic dike by geoelectrical and geomagnetic methods: Trans. A.I.M.E. Geophysics, p. 160.

Keys, D. A., 1940, Magnetic survey of the Ivry Ilmenite deposit: Trans. A.I.M.E. Geophysics, p. 153.

Koulomzine, T., and Brossard, L., 1947, The use of geophysics in prospecting gold and base metals in Canada: Geophysics, v. 12, p. 651–662.

Menshikov, P. N., 1957, Oypt primeneniya geofizicheskikh metodov razvedki pri poiskakh kimberlitovykh trubok (Attempt at the application of geophysical methods of exploration in prospecting for kimberlite pipes): Razvedka i okhrana nedr, no. 4, p. 42–49.

Mumme, W. G., 1963, Aeromagnetic prospecting for iron ore on Eyre Peninsula, South Australia: Geophysics, v. 28, p. 593–607.

—— 1964, Negative total-intensity magnetic anomalies in the southeast of South Australia: Jour. Geoph. Res., v. 69, p. 309–315.

Pearson, W. J., 1957, An investigation into the geological significance of some magnetic anomalies in the Lac la Ronge area of northern Saskatchewan: Sask. Dept. Min. Res., Report No. 29, 52 p.

Pemberton, R. H., 1961, Target Mattagami: Trans. Can. Inst. Min. Met., v. 64, p. 16–23.

Savrasov, D. I., 1962, Nekotoryye svedeniya ob effektivnosti primeneniya metadov magnitorazvedki pri poiskakh korennykh mestorozhdeniy almazov (Some information on the effectiveness of the use of magnetic survey methods in the search for bedrock deposits of diamonds): Akad. Nauk SSSR, Sibirskoye Otdeleniye, Geologiya i Geofizika, n. 8, p. 96–102.

SEG, 1948, 1956, Geophysical Case Histories, v. 1, v. 2.

Steenland, N. C., and Brod, R. J., 1960, Basement mapping with aeromagnetic data—Blind River basin: Geophysics, v. 25, p. 586–601.

Sutton, P. J., and Mumme, W. G., 1957, The effect of remanent magnetization on aeromagnetic interpretation: Austr. Jour. Physics, v. 10, p. 547–557.

Vincenz, S. A., 1955, Magnetic prospecting for iron ores in Jamaica: Geophysics, v. 20, p. 593–614.

Zietz, I., and Henderson, R. G., 1955, The Sudbury aeromagnetic map as a test of interpretation methods: Geophysics, v. 20, p. 307–317.

Zurbrigg, H. G., 1963, Thompson mine geology: Trans. Can. Inst. Min. Met., v. 66, p. 227–236.

Magnetic Instruments and Survey Techniques

Balsley, J. R., 1952, Aeromagnetic surveying, in Advances in geophysics: New York, Academic Press, Inc., v. 1, p. 313–349.

Bruckshaw, J. M., 1954, Magnetic variometers of the Schmidt type: London, Hilger & Watts Ltd., Hilger Division.

Collinson, D. W., and Creer, K. M., 1960, Measurements in palaeomagnetism, in Methods and techniques in geophysics: ed. S. K. Runcorn,

New York, Interscience Publishers, Inc., p 168–210.

Giret, R., and Malnar, L., 1963, A new airborn magnetometer: the caesium vapour magnetometer (Abstract): Geophys. Prosp., v. 11, p. 372

Haalck, F., 1956, A torsion magnetometer fo measuring the vertical component of the earth's magnetic field: Geophys. Prosp., v. 4 p. 424–441.

James, H. L., 1948, Field comparisons of some magnetic instruments with analysis of superdip performance: A.I.M.E. Tech. Pub. 2293, in Mining Tech., v. 12.

Jensen, H., 1961, The airborne magnetometer Scientific American, June 1961, p. 151–162.

Joyce, J. W., 1937, Manual on geophysical prospecting with the magnetometer: U. S Bureau of Mines Publication. Revised edition 1948, reproduced by Hobart Publishing Co Wash. 15, D. C. 129 p.

Keyser, A. R., Rice, J. A., and Schearer, L. D. 1961, A metastable helium magnetometer for observing small geomagnetic fluctuations: Jour Geoph. Res., v. 66, p. 4163–4169.

Levanto, A. E., 1959, A three component magnetometer for small drill holes and its use in ore prospecting: Geophys. Prosp., v. 7, p. 183–195.

Packard, M., and Varian, R., 1954, Free nuclear induction in the earth's magnetic field (Abstract): Phys. Rev., v. 93, p. 941.

Serson, P. H., Mack, S. Z. and Whitham, K., 1957, A three component airborne magnetometer: Ottawa. Dom. Obs. Pub., v. 19, p. 15–97.

Skilman, T. E., and Bender, P., 1958, Measurements of the earth's magnetic field with a rubidium vapor magnetometer: Jour. Geoph. Res., v. 63, p. 513–515.

Stearn, N. H., 1929, Dip needle as a geological instrument: A.I.M.E. Geophysics, p. 345–363.

Waters, G. S., and Phillips, G., 1956, A new method of measuring the earth's magnetic field: Geophys Prosp., v. 4, p. 1–9.

Werner, S., 1963, Aeromagnetic mapping by the Geological Survey of Sweden, methods and general considerations: Geoexploration, v. 2, p. 21–31.

Whitham, K., 1960, Measurement of the geomagnetic elements, in Methods and techniques in geophysics: ed. S. K. Runcorn, New York, Interscience Publishers, Inc.

Wickerham, W. E., 1954, The Gulf airborne magnetic gradiometer: Geophysics, v. 19, p. 116–123.

Chapter IV

GRAVITY METHODS

Chapter IV

GRAVITY METHODS

Table of Contents

INTRODUCTION

JOHN S. SUMNER*

Gravity methods are a useful primary and supplementary exploration technique in mining geophysics, accounting for about ten percent of the total effort over recent years.

Newtonian potential theory provides a necessary foundation for understanding the nature of gravity fields. Laplace's equation describes the field outside of gravitating matter, and Poisson's equation holds for the fields within a mass.

Gravity fields due to simple geometric shapes are derived to illustrate uses of basic principles. Gauss' law demonstrates the field of a cylinder, and the Bouguer effect.

Fundamental information and theory are provided in this introduction to the Gravity Chapter, for the papers by Morris and Sultzbach, Millett, and Fuller which follow.

General

Gravity methods of exploration have a definite place in mining geophysics, and are becoming increasingly useful for several purposes. Table 1 gives the gravity surveying activity in mining exploration over the past several years (from SEG Geophysical Activities Committee's Reports).

Regional surveys with readings spaced at one- to 10-mile intervals usually bring out the major structural and lithological variations in an area. More closely spaced gravity station coverage reveals finer geological detail which is usually apparent without extensive interpretation. Some gravity investigations can directly indicate the presence of more massive mineralized bodies such as iron ore, chromite, and valuable sulfides. Several such case histories are described elsewhere in Volume I of this publication, giving interpretational methods.

Gravimetric prospecting is a very useful adjunct to other exploration methods, thereby providing a different set of parameters for the more complete solution of a subsurface problem. Special gravity surveys such as underground, drill-hole, or engineering applications are closely related to normal gravity exploration problems.

Gravity surveys can be interpreted to give the most probable subsurface density structure, using boundary conditions imposed by the limits of geological reasonableness. Al-

Table 1

	Manpower			USA Expenditure		
	Rank	Man-months	Percent	Rank	Dollars	Percent
1964	6	598	10.4	6	$760 k	9.6
1963	5	764	13.9	3	879 k	14.6
1962	4	539	12.2	6	704 k	12.6
1961	5	485	13.0	6	422 k	8.6
1960	5	836	9.5	7	757 k	6.9
1959	5	890	8.4	7	710 k	7.5

though there are an infinite number of possible solutions to potential field problems, giving an inherent ambiguity to gravity interpretation, there is also a certain uniqueness in the magnitude of the causative mass. Thus the usual gravity problem is to solve for the most probable distribution of density contrast σ and associated volume V which will satisfy both the form of the gravity anomaly and their mass product M. Thus it can be written that the area under a gravity anomaly curve is proportional to the causative mass, and the anomalous mass is proportional to the product, density contrast times volume.

In this regard, density measurements of materials from a problem area are most useful. It is often risky to use handbook information or guess work for subsurface density contrasts. In-situ or laboratory measurements are the best and certainly most reliable

* University of Arizona, Tucson, Arizona.

623

values for these purposes, and are worth the effort to obtain them.

History

Our understanding of the force of gravity begins with Kepler's laws of planetary motion. From these quantitative observations Newton (1642–1727) derived the gravitational law of force

$$F = G \frac{Mm}{r^2}. \tag{1}$$

In terms of gravitational field intensity, which is force per unit mass,

$$g = G \frac{M}{r^2} \tag{2}$$

Where G is the gravitational constant and r is the distance between bodies of mass M and m. The units of gravity are those of acceleration; one centimeter per second^2 is one gal. The milligal is more commonly used in exploration.

This form of Newton's Gravitational Law can be proved to hold for spherical masses, and of course in cases where the distance between gravitating particles is much larger than their size. The simple form of the inverse square law given in (2) will not be valid where the geometric shape of bodies is planar or linear, except for discrete particles of such bodies.

The gravitational constant G was not measured experimentally until 1790, when Cavendish (1731–1810) determined its value and thereby gave a value for the density of the earth.

Newton himself did not completely feel that gravity is a direct property of mass or that he had explained gravitational attraction, which indeed he had not. Equation (1) is an empirical observation of gravitational forces in nonrelativistic situations, and holds closely within limits of observation.

The modern physical concept of a gravity field is that masses distort space which surrounds them, and that a gravitational force is the apparent result. Thus gravitational attraction at a distance is due to the geometric properties of space rather than matter itself.

Instruments

The first portable gravity measuring devices, which came into being during the 19th century, were the pendulum and torsion balance. These instruments were capable of measuring absolute gravity, and precise gravity gradients. This equipment was complex and bulky, and individual readings took several hours to complete.

Modern gravity meters are of the null-reading, astatic (semi-stable) type, employing a system of optical and mechanical levers to obtain their remarkable sensitivity. Such mechanisms must be made of low thermal coefficient material and be thermally insulated and compensated to avoid effects due to temperature variations. Thermostatic control is often necessary to reduce thermal drift effects.

The more popular instruments being used in North America employ a mechanical principle known as the "zero length spring." At the instrument's balance point the restoring spring constant k is proportional to the spring length AB, i.e., if there were no tension on the spring, its length would be zero. Tension on this balancing spring is proportional to the weight of the mass element $mg \propto kAB$, thus small changes in gravity are proportional to small variations in the length AB. The mass element is returned to a null position with a micrometer screw, and the length variation is calibrated in terms of gravity differences.

Thus gravity meters only measure small changes in gravity between nearby stations rather than absolute gravity itself. Readings change slowly with time due to nonelastic stretch or drift of the spring. Instrument calibration is not easily adjusted or changed because of the delicate nature of the elastic balance system.

Data processing

Before the advent of high-speed digital computers, about half the effort necessary in doing a gravity survey was involved in extensive computations in the reduction of field data. These data corrections are necessary because of the fairly large effects due to changes with latitude, elevation, and topogaphy. Also, the gravity meter reading changes slowly with time, and there are tidal effects to be reckoned with. These calculations are not difficult to make but are tedious and time consuming when done with only a desk calculator.

Gravity data processing with the digital computer has made this geophysical method much more feasible to mining exploration. Topographic effects are noticeably large in many mining areas, and are quite laborious to make when done by hand, but are rapidly made at low cost by the computer methods.

Thus the next paper in this chapter, by Morris and Sultzbach, is important from the emphasis it places on computer processing of gravity data. The automatic interpretation technique that they describe takes much of the drudgery from routine data analysis.

Potentials and Fields

The concept of potential is frequently convenient in studying gravity fields because it is a simpler mathematical function and does not usually involve the use of vectors. A potential function describes the energy of a system and its directional derivative will give the field. Difference in potential between points in a field is the work done in moving a unit mass from one point to the other. The potential function U is dependent on point coordinates only, thus the work done is independent of the path between points. Potential is not time dependent in a conservative field, such as in gravity. The gravitational scalar potential relative to some arbitrary (sometimes symmetrical) position in space is

$$U = - G \frac{M}{r} . \tag{3}$$

There are inherent limitations to the resolution of potential fields which lead to uncertainty in interpretation of gravity data. Solutions are possible after boundary values have been established for the particular problem.

A mass gives rise to "lines of force," a description of which is frequently useful in visualizing gravity fields. Lines of force are normal to equipotential surfaces, in isotropic media. One must take care not to ascribe radiation characteristics to lines of force, which are only a convenient means of viewing a field. Such a line is a curve whose direction coincides with that of the force field acting at a point. If the components of the force along x, y, and z axes are given by F_x, F_y, and F_z, then the equations of the lines of force are

$$\frac{dx}{F_x} = \frac{dy}{F_y} = \frac{dz}{F_z} . \tag{4}$$

A field is directed in the same sense as a line of force at that point. The mapping of a force field by means of lines of force provides not only the force direction but also will give the magnitude of the force.

A note of caution in the measurement of force fields by test particles: too large a particle can distort the field which it is to measure, and too small a mass may lose the isotropic properties of matter which it is to represent.

The number of lines of force Φ which pass through a unit area ds in a normal plane defines field intensity

$$g = \frac{\Phi}{ds} . \tag{5}$$

The gradient of potential is the negative of force per unit mass, or field intensity. Thus if $\mathbf{i}$, $\mathbf{j}$, and $\mathbf{k}$ are unit vectors and ∇ is the gradient operator,

$$\mathbf{g} = - \left[\mathbf{i} \frac{\partial U}{\partial x} + \mathbf{j} \frac{\partial U}{\partial y} + \mathbf{k} \frac{\partial U}{\partial z} \right]$$

$$= - \nabla U \tag{6}$$

where

$$\nabla = \left[\mathbf{i} \frac{\partial}{\partial x} + \mathbf{j} \frac{\partial}{\partial y} + \mathbf{k} \frac{\partial}{\partial z} \right] .$$

Gauss' Law and Laplace's Equation

The ideas of a gravitational field and potential can be usefully extended by Gauss' law of force flux. The total flux Φ of gravitational force through any closed surface is defined as the surface integral of the normal component of the intensity of the gravitational field.

$$\Phi = \oint_s \mathbf{g} \cdot \mathbf{ds} \qquad (7)$$

where **ds** is a vector normal to the surface ds and of magnitude equal to the area of ds. The direction of the vector **ds** determines the sign of the integral function in (7). If the integral is taken over the whole surface Gauss' law says

$$\Phi = -4\pi GM \qquad (8)$$

where M is the total mass enclosed by the surface and G is the constant of gravitation $(6.67 \times 10^{-8}$ cm³/gram sec²). The surface integral can be transformed into a volume integral by means of the divergence theorem

$$\Phi = \oint_s \mathbf{g} \cdot \mathbf{ds} = \oint_v \mathbf{\nabla} \cdot \mathbf{g} dV. \qquad (9)$$

where

$$\mathbf{\nabla} \cdot \mathbf{g} = \frac{\partial g_x}{\partial x} + \frac{\partial g_y}{\partial y} + \frac{\partial g_z}{\partial z}$$

and dV is an element of volume. Combining equations (6) and (8) we have

$$\oint_v \mathbf{\nabla} \cdot \mathbf{\nabla} U dV = 4\pi GM = 4\pi G \oint_v \sigma dV \qquad (10)$$

where σ is the density of mass distribution enclosed by the surface. Since equation (10) must hold for any closed surface in the field, which encloses mass, then

$$\mathbf{\nabla} \cdot \mathbf{\nabla} U = 4\pi G\sigma. \qquad (11)$$

This is Poisson's equation, which is very useful to the analysis of gravity problems. Replacing $\mathbf{\nabla} \cdot \mathbf{\nabla} U$ by $\nabla^2 U$ where

$$\nabla^2 U = \frac{\partial^2 U}{\partial x^2} + \frac{\partial^2 U}{\partial y^2} + \frac{\partial^2 U}{\partial z^2}$$

gives the Laplacian of U. Thus the Laplacian of the potential of a gravitational field is equal to a constant times the density of the distribution of matter in the field. The nature of a gravity field may therefore be thought of as completely determined by this second order partial differential equation, which is Poisson's equation. In an area of a field where

σ is zero, this reduces to

$$\nabla^2 U = 0 \qquad (12)$$

which is Laplace's equation, and describes the field outside of gravitating matter.

Equation (12) is the general solution of gravity field problems, specific solutions of which must be made by application of appropriate boundary conditions. In solving special problems it is useful to observe an important uniqueness theorm, which states that if potential has an assigned value U along spacial boundaries, there is a unique solution to Laplace's equation. This is the counterpart of the nonuniqueness of a field, being produced by any possible density distribution of particles.

Laplace's equation is important in gravitational, magnetic, and electrical fields used in geophysics, and is basic to applications of potential theory.

Derivation of the Gravity Field of Simple Shapes

Gauss' law is a convenient formulation for deriving the gravity field of several simple geometric shapes. In the case of a sphere of uniform density we first write Gauss' law as

$$\oint_s \mathbf{g} \cdot \mathbf{ds} = -4\pi GM. \qquad (13)$$

Our Gaussian surface can simply be concentric with the spherical mass, with the two surfaces coincident and at a radius r from the center. The Gaussian surface is then oriented such that lines of force are either normal to it, or do not penetrate the surface. Equation (13) then becomes

$$g \cdot 4\pi r^2 = 4\pi GM.$$

Thus

$$g = \frac{GM}{r^2} \qquad (14)$$

which is of course the law of Newtonian attraction for a sphere.

By differentiating equation (14) with respect to the earth's radius r, we obtain the change of gravity with respect to elevation

$$\frac{dg}{dr} = -2\frac{GM}{r^3} = -\frac{2g}{r} \qquad (15)$$

which is the Free Air Effect of gravity, amounting to $-.09406$ mgals per foot. The Free Air correction is opposite in sign to the effect, to compensate for this change. The Free Air Anomaly, which is the result from correcting data for latitude and Free Air effect, does not vary greatly on the earth. This relative consistence of Free Air Anomaly over the earth is an expression of isostasy.

In the case of the gravity field about a line element, a Gaussian surface can take the simple form of a cylinder concentric about the linear mass. The line can be given a density of ρ per unit length, over a length L. Substituting in equation (13)

$$g \cdot 2\pi rL = 4\pi G\rho L$$

and

$$g = \frac{2G\rho}{r} . \qquad (16)$$

If the mass per unit length ρ is translated to mass per unit volume or density σ, then $\rho = \pi R^2\sigma$, where R is the radius of a cylinder of density σ. Then

$$g = \frac{2\pi R^2 G\sigma}{r} \qquad (17)$$

which is the more familiar form for the gravity field of a circular cylinder. This is the basic equation of the gravity field of a two dimensional body. It can be transformed to the very useful interpretative relationship as discussed in the paper by F. Millett which is contained in this Chapter on Gravity Methods.

Equation (17) shows that the gravity field of a linear element has an inverse first power distance dependence. The mass of the cylinder can be assumed to be concentrated on the cylinder's axis, which can be proved, as also in the case of a sphere, by Gauss' law.

In the earth's field, gravity anomaly measurements are superimposed on the much larger field of the earth, thus only a vector component of the anomaly field is measured. This fact must be always taken into account

when interpreting the mass distribution causing an anomaly.

Bouguer Effect

The "stone slab" correction to gravity data takes into account the gravity field of a plane sheet of density δ per unit area, extending infinitely in two dimensions. A Gaussian surface would be conveniently constructed with the flat, circular sides parallel to and on opposite sides of the infinite sheet. The gravitational flux is everywhere normal to the infinite sheet, thus is normal to and penetrates flat, circular sides of the pillbox. No flux passes through the curved sides of the pillbox which are normal to the sheet and to the flux lines.

Using Gauss' law of equation (13) we can write

$$g \cdot 2\pi R^2 = 4\pi G\pi R^2\delta$$

where R is the radius of the Gaussian pillbox, and thus

$$g = 2\pi G\delta. \qquad (18)$$

The density per unit area δ is also the thickness t times the mass per unit volume σ of the slab, which on substitution gives the Bouguer gravity effect

$$g = 2\pi G\sigma t \qquad (19)$$

which does not fall off with distance from the slab.

The Bouguer effect is $0.01277\ \sigma$ mgals per foot, which is about one milligal for a 78-ft slab with a density of one; a convenient rule of thumb value to remember for estimating thickness of overburden or horizontal strata.

The Bouguer correction is opposite in sign to the Bouguer effect, and is frequently combined with the Free Air correction in order to make an elevation correction to data.

A Bouguer gravity anomaly is an observed value which has been corrected for latitude and elevation. This is usually the anomaly, perhaps based on some relative datum, which is plotted on a map and interpreted in terms of probable subsurface geology. The assumed density used to plot a gravity map should always be noted early in an analysis of data.

Ficticious, topographic-caused anomalies can result if an erronous density value is selected.

The complete Bouguer gravity anomaly also includes a correction for terrain effects in the vicinity of the station. Fortunately, the terrain correction is always of one algebraic sign, that is, a value to be added to compensate for either an adjacent hill or valley.

Note that "anomaly" when used in the context of a data reduction method such as "Bouguer gravity anomaly," is different from a bump on a gravity profile curve.

Shape of the Earth

The form of a nonrotating earth would be very close to that of a sphere, with sea level being an equipotential, equal-gravity surface. Our rotating earth sets up a rotational potential ψ which when combined with gravitational potential U defines an observed family of geoidal or equipotential surfaces which would have a value

$$V = U - \psi. \tag{20}$$

The earth's sea level geoid is not an equal-gravity surface, but a surface of constant potential V.

Solution to potential equation (20) becomes complex because the earth no longer has a spherical shape, thus the simple potential function (3) must be modified. This problem was first treated by the French mathematician Clairaut (1713–1765) to give the theoretical gravity on the earth as a function of latitude. To a first approximation, sea-level gravity g can be given in the form

$$g = g_0(1 + \beta \sin^2 \phi) \tag{21}$$

where g_o is gravity at the equator, ϕ is latitude, and β is Clairaut's solution for a density stratified earth. Here $\beta = 5/2K - k$, where K is gravitational flattening and f is geometric flattening.

The International Gravity Formula, adopted in 1924, as used by most geodesists and geophysicists, is

$$g = g_0[1 + .005288 \sin^2 \phi$$
$$- .0000059 \sin^2 2\phi] \tag{22}$$

where sea-level equatorial gravity, g_o is 978.049 gals. This equation gives the earth's

accepted spheroidal shape. By differentiation the variation of gravity with latitude is

$$\frac{dg}{dx} = 1.308 \sin 2\phi \text{ milligals per mile} \tag{23}$$

which is a very meaningful factor in mining surveys.

Tides

Lunar tides of the oceans and the earth are large enough to affect gravity survey measurements, having maximum amplitudes of about 0.3 mgals. Tidal effects are due to variations in distance and direction to the axis of rotation of the earth-moon system. This rotational axis is contained within the earth and is defined by the center-of-mass of the earth-moon orientation. By looking at the tidal problem in this frame of reference one can readily appreciate why the principal tidal period is about half a day, while the apparent lunar period is about one day.

Corrections for tidal effects can be made from theoretical (as published yearly in *Geophysical Prospecting*) or observed data, or can be removed by including these variations with instrument drift. There are local differences between actual and theoretical tidal effects due to elastic inhomogeneities in the earth's crust.

Interpretation of Data

Usually the ultimate end in obtaining gravity data is for the purpose of interpreting subsurface geological conditions in some area of interest. In mining problems without other geophysical or geological guidelines this can be a difficult matter. Let us assume that we have some idea of density contrasts and subsurface structure.

First of all the geophysicist should have a good background knowledge of the many idealized gravity curves over basic geometric shapes. This enables him to intelligently choose a solution without making a number of preliminary computations. Next the anomaly curve for the assumed conditions is calculated and compared to the observed curve. This procedure is repeated to obtain a fairly good fit of observed and calculated curves. There is a point of diminishing returns in making more than a few adjustments to the curve fitting process, because one can fit an observed curve exactly but use fallacious assumptions.

Machine interpretive methods are gaining in popularity in mining geophysics; these are based on a number of different approaches depending on the objective of the survey. The concluding paper in this chapter by B. Fuller is a good example of a new, versatile approach to frequency analysis of data, and the use of operators.

References for General Reading

Garland, G. D., 1965, The earth's shape and gravity: New York, Pergamon Press.

Goguel, J., 1954, A universal table for the prediction of the lunar-solar correction in gravimetry: Geophys. Prosp., v. 2, supplement, p. 1-6.

Heiskanen, W. A., and Vening Meinesz, F. A., 1958, The earth and its gravity field: New York, McGraw-Hill Book Co., Inc.

Kellogg, O. D., 1953, Foundations of potential theory: New York, Dover Publications, Inc.

Ramsey, A. S., 1959, An introduction to the theory of Newtonian attraction: Cambridge, University Press.

GRAVITY DATA REDUCTION AND INTERPRETATION USING A DIGITAL COMPUTER, A CASE HISTORY

DAVID B. MORRIS*

AND

ROBERT A. SULTZBACH**

A large-scale gravity survey program produces a continuing flow of data which must be computed, interpreted, and stored for future reference. Computer methods developed to facilitate the processing of these data are discussed.

A gravity data-reduction program performs processing and computation of gravimeter and elevation field notes. The computation of instrument drift, scale correction factor, observed gravity, theoretical gravity, station elevation, and Bouguer gravity at several densities is accomplished by the program. Base station observed gravity values required for the computations are maintained on a magnetic disk file which is automatically updated with the newly computed stations. The results are printed in a standard format and preserved for future reference in a punched-card history file.

A specialized gravity profile interpretation program computes the depth to bedrock for two dimensional alluvial valleys from the Bouguer gravity profile. The alluvial cross section is approximated by a series of vertical rectangular strips. Depth to bedrock is computed by an iterative procedure. As an optional feature, the regional correction is automatically determined as a function of the Bouguer profile by the iterative procedure. The interpreted section is plotted along with the Bouguer gravity profile with an on-line plotter.

The computer methods are competitive costwise with manual methods, and they provide the additional advantages of speed, accuracy, and versatility.

The first steps toward automated processing of gravity data at Kennecott were taken in conjunction with regional gravity work. In 1958 a gravity data history file was established on punched cards. Each gravity station was represented by a card containing station identification, coordinates, and the pertinent gravity data.

The regional gravity program was recently expanded into an extensive reconnaissance gravity project. With full time gravity crews in the field, the manual data processing task became excessive. Fortunately, a computer with the capability to substantially relieve the data processing burden was available within the company. This computer, an IBM 1620 with 60K core storage, two direct access magnetic disk drives and an on-line X-Y plotter, was applied in two areas. The initial implementation was a Gravity Field Data Reduction System which became operational in January, 1965. By March, 1965, a Gravity Profile Interpretation System was also in use.

Gravity Data Processing

The flow of gravity data from field observation to final report is traced in Figure 1. The data collected in the field must be processed in several stages to prepare it for evaluation by the geophysicist. The intermediate processing has been accomplished in the past by tedious manual methods. Today, much of the data processing burden is assumed by the electronic digital computer.

A computer is suited for handling well-structured tasks, tasks that can be fully and uniquely specified by an explicit set of rules. Many of the tasks involved in processing gravity data are obviously well structured.[1] Gravity data reduction, for example, is routine work which follows a well-established computational pattern. Other tasks are less

[1] Complex or involved.

* Senior Computer Programmer, Scientific and Engineering Computer Center, Kennecott Copper Corporation, Salt Lake City, Utah.

** Senior Geophysicist, Geophysics Division, Kennecott Copper Corporation, Salt Lake City, Utah.

well structured and may require the talents of highly skilled personnel. In some cases, however, a detailed analysis leads to a reformulation of the problem in a well-structured framework. The interpretation of certain gravity profiles is an example of this situation.

If gravity data are processed sporadically, in small amounts, or under widely different conditions, automated processing may be difficult to justify. However, if large amounts of data are produced by a continuing gravity survey project, computer processing offers significant advantages.

Two program systems are being used in support of Kennecott's gravity survey work. The first of these, the Gravity Field Data Reduction System, performs computations on the raw field data and maintains and continuously updates a gravity station history file. The second is a specialized Gravity Profile Interpretation System designed for the interpretation of gravity surveys over alluvial filled valleys. Although these program systems are tailored to the needs of a specific project and are designed to take advantage of the capabilities of a particular computer configuration, the basic framework is sufficiently general to be applied to other gravity data processing situations.

Related work in computer-oriented gravity data processing is reported in the literature. Tanner and Buck (1964) and Heinrichs et al. (1964) describe data reduction programs. Automated gravity profile interpretation is discussed by Bott (1960), Healy and Press (1964), and Corbato (1965).

Gravity Field Data Reduction System

The reconnaissance gravity surveys performed by Kennecott are tied to a regional network established with stations located approximately every five miles along U.S.G.S. and Coast and Geodetic level lines. Aneroid barometers are used to maintain elevation control in conjunction with known elevation points, such as bench marks, road elevations and section corners. The Bouguer gravity is computed using an absolute datum. An accuracy of 0.5 milligals is considered adequate for the purpose of these surveys.

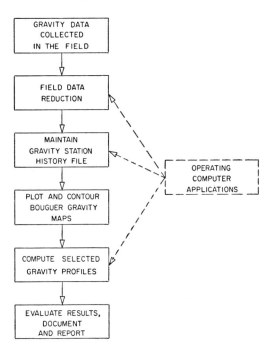

Fig. 1. The collection and processing of gravity survey field data.

The flow of gravity data from field observation through the data reduction steps is diagramed in Figure 2.

Gravity data are collected by field crews using a gravimeter and two aneroid surveying altimeters. Gravimeter and altimeter field notes are kept separately as illustrated in Figures 3 and 4. Each line of the notes represents a station occupied by the field crew. Stations are identified by numbers assigned consecutively within a state. Base stations are indicated by an asterisk.

Both the gravimeter and altimeter traverses are tied to base stations, for which the observed gravity values or elevations are known. Base ties are made as often as possible, and a survey always begins and ends at a base station. Instrument drifts are computed between base ties. Base station values also provide an absolute reference level for computing observed gravity and elevation.

The field notes are mailed to the head office on a daily basis. Office personnel check for obvious errors and omissions. The notes are then transferred to punched cards, and computer input decks are assembled for each

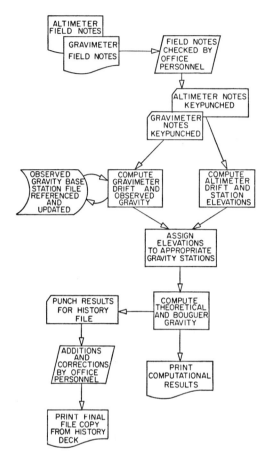

FIG. 2. Information flow through the Gravity Field Data Reduction System.

day's survey (see Figure 5). Although several input decks are stacked for continuous processing, the "day's survey" constitutes the basic processing unit considered by the data reduction system. From the standpoint of program logic, the initial processing of the gravimeter and altimeter notes is carried out independently. Subsequently, the computed elevations are matched to the gravity stations by station number, final computations are performed, and the results are printed and punched.

To facilitate the gravimeter computations, observed gravity base station values are maintained on a direct access magnetic disk file, ordered by state and station number. Whenever a gravity base station is encountered, the appropriate observed gravity value is retrieved from the disk file. Instrument drift, assumed linear, is computed between successive base ties (see Appendix for computational formulas). Instrument readings are drift corrected and the instrument scale factor is applied. The corrected readings are referenced to the base station values to obtain the observed gravity for each station.

The observed gravity base station file is continuously updated with the addition of the newly computed observed gravity values. These new values may serve as base stations for future surveys. Important future base stations are occupied several times. In this case, the average of the observed gravity values is recorded on the base station file.

The altimeter computations are similar to those performed for the gravimeter. The altimeter base station elevations are recorded by the field crews. Temperature-humidity scale correction factors, determined from wet- and dry-bulb thermometer readings, are also noted. Altimeter drift and scale correction factors are interpolated linearly between successive altimeter base stations. The altimeter readings are drift corrected and the scale correction factor is applied. The observed elevation is computed using the base station value as a reference. Since two altimeters are carried, the station elevation is taken as the average of the two observed elevations.

By cross-referencing station numbers, the computed elevations are paired with the appropriate gravity stations.

The final computations are performed for each station. Theoretical gravity is computed using the given latitudes. The free air and Bouguer corrections are applied and the Bouguer gravity is computed for several desired densities. The computational formulas are given in the Appendix.

The computational results for each day's survey are printed as in Figure 6. The instrument drift corrections are included to aid in detecting errors and to act as a guide to the reliability of the survey. Other results listed are as follows:

1) Identifying header with location of survey,

INST. __WW 108__
INST. CODE __6__
K __.992 GU/DD__
OPERATOR __RS__

PAGE __1__
DATE __5-24-65__
AREA __AREA "H"__
STATE __2__

GRAVITY FIELD NOTES

STATION	ELEVATION CONTROL	MILE.	TIME	DIAL	LATITUDE	LONGITUDE	REMARKS
*2384	BM	3.0	10:53	575.7	33° 13.79'		ELEV. 3322 BENCH MARK
17051	ALT	4.1	11:00	567.2	33° 13.92'		
17052	BM	5.0	11:12	631.4	33° 14.46'		ELEV. 3299 BENCH MARK
17053	ALT	6.0	11:20	666.0	33° 14.94'		
17054	BM	7.0	11:40	670.8	33° 15.48'		ELEV. 3269 BENCH MARK
17055	BM	8.1	11:56	661.0	33° 15.75'		ELEV. 3286 BENCH MARK
17056	ALT	8.9	12:08	631.4	33° 15.32'		
17057	ALT	9.5	12:23	614.9	33° 14.88'		SW COR. SEC. 3
17058	ALT	0.1	12:30	565.2	33° 14.59'		VOLCANICS
*2384	BM	7.7	13:25	576.5	33° 13.79'		ELEV. 3322 BENCH MARK

FIG. 3. Typical gravimeter notes collected by a field crew.

ALTIMETER 1. __D__
ALTIMETER 2. __A__
OPERATOR __D.M.__
WEATHER __Clear. Windy__

PAGE __2__
DATE __5-24-65__
AREA __AREA "H"__
STATE __2__

ALTIMETER NOTES

STATION	ELEVATION CONTROL	MILE.	TIME	ALT. 1	ALT 2	DRY/WET	C.F.	ELEV.	REMARKS
*2384	BM	3.0	10:54	3449	3251	71/54	1.045	3322	
17051	ALT	4.1	10:59	3470	3269				
*17052	BM	5.0	11:12	3432	3229			3299	
17053	ALT	6.0	11:20	3415	3214				
*17054	BM	7.0	11:40	3417	3215			3269	
*17055	BM	8.1	11:57	3442	3243	78/56	1.060	3286	
17056	ALT	8.9	12:08	3505	3305				
17057	ALT	9.5	12:23	3540	3338				
17058	ALT	0.1	12:30	3592	3391				
*2384	BM	7.7	13:25	3511	3308	85/59	1.08	3322	

FIG. 4. Altimeter Field notes collected in conjunction with the gravity data shown in Figure 3.

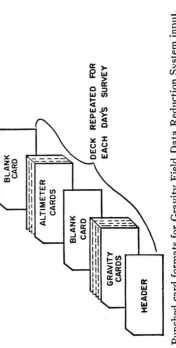

FIG. 5. Punched card formats for Gravity Field Data Reduction System input.

```
*** GRAVITY METER COMPUTATIONS ***              LOCATION - AREA H
--------------------------------------------------------------------------------
       STA. ELEV.                           ELEVATION   AVE.    THEO.    OBS.     BOUGUER GRAVITY
  LOC  NO.  CONTROL  DATE    LATITUDE  LONGITUDE ALT.1 ALT.2 ELEV.  GRAVITY  GRAVITY D=2.67  D=2.33  D=2.00

    2  2384 BM       05-24-65 GRAVITY BASE STATION (DRIFT CORRECTION=     0.0DD) 3.28580
    2 17051 ALT      05-24-65 33-13.92         3343  3341 3341.7 3.59759  3.28495  -.1122  -.0977  -.0836
    2 17052 BM       05-24-65 33-14.46         ALT.  BASE 3299.0 3.59833  3.29132  -.1091  -.0948  -.0809
    2 17053 ALT      05-24-65 33-14.94         3277  3279 3278.0 3.59899  3.29474  -.1076  -.0934  -.0796
    2 17054 BM       05-24-65 33-15.48         ALT.  BASE 3269.0 3.59974  3.29521  -.1084  -.0942  -.0805
    2 17055 BM       05-24-65 33-15.75         ALT.  BASE 3286.0 3.60011  3.29423  -.1088  -.0945  -.0807
    2 17056 ALT      05-24-65 33-15.32         3348  3348 3347.9 3.59952  3.29129  -.1074  -.0929  -.0788
    2 17057 ALT      05-24-65 33-14.88         3379  3378 3378.8 3.59891  3.28964  -.1066  -.0919  -.0777
    2 17058 ALT      05-24-65 33-14.59         3432  3431 3431.6 3.59851  3.28471  -.1079  -.0931  -.0786
    2  2384 BM       05-24-65 GRAVITY BASE STATION (DRIFT CORRECTION=    -.8DD) 3.28580
```

```
** ALTIMETER DRIFT COMPUTATIONS **
AREA H                      05-24-65

BASE        DRIFT CORRECTION
STATION     (DIAL DIVISIONS)
NUMBER      ALT. 1      ALT. 2

 -2384
 -17052       -4.9        0.0
 -17054      -13.4      -14.4
 -17055       -8.9      -11.9
 -2384       -35.6      -31.6
```

FIG. 6. The computer output document printed by the Gravity Field Data Reduction System. The results are for the field data of Figures 3 and 4.

2) Gravimeter identifying number,
3) State identifying number,
4) Station number and elevation control,
5) Date of survey,
6) Position by latitude and longitude,
7) Station elevation,
8) Theoretical gravity,
9) Observed gravity, and
10) Bouguer gravity at three densities.

A card is punched for each gravity station with the data reduction results. These cards form a history file. As the results are reviewed by office personnel, corrections and additions are incorporated in the history file. Periodically, a listing of the history file is generated on the computer to provide a permanent record of the stations occupied. The Bouguer gravity values are plotted and contoured manually. The contoured maps are reviewed and interpreted by a geophysicist. As part of the interpretation, he may select several gravity profiles for computation. In the case of the alluvial filled valley the profile computation is performed on the computer

Gravity Profile Interpretation System

A Bouguer gravity anomaly may be attributed to an infinite number of mass distributions. Since the mass distribution related to the anomaly is not unique, the interpretation hinges on the availability of other geophysical or geologic information. With sufficient additional information, a single interpretive model is determined.

In general, the gravity interpretation problem is not well structured. In some instances, however, the geologic setting is such that the geophysical model can be described within a framework suitable for computer solution. The interpretation of gravity anomalies over alluvial filled valleys is an example of a well-structured interpretive problem.

Under suitable conditions and assumptions a Bouguer gravity profile provides a means of estimating the depth to bedrock through the alluvial cover. The gravity profile is selected on a line perpendicular to the Bouguer gravity contours. The underground structure is assumed to be of uniform cross section extending infinitely in the direction perpendicular to the profile. In addition, the following factors are specified to insure a unique interpretation:

1. The locations of the surface bedrock-alluvium contacts are given,
2. The alluvium-bedrock density contrast is specified, and

3. The underlying bedrock is not undercut at any point by the alluvial fill.

The interpretive procedure is derived from the method described by Bott (1960) for direct gravity interpretation of sedimentary basins. The alluvial cross section is approximated by a set of adjacent vertical rectangular strips. The upper ends of the strips coincide with the land surface and the lower ends define the underground bedrock-alluvium contact. Hence, the length of a strip represents the depth to bedrock.

The strip lengths or depths are computed by an iterative procedure. An initial estimate of the strip depth provides a trial body. The anomaly over this trial body is computed and subtracted from the observed anomaly, giving a residual anomaly. Using the residual anomaly the depth estimates are refined and the anomaly over the new trial body is recomputed giving a new and smaller residual. The procedure cycles until the residual anomaly is reduced to a specified tolerance.

The versatility of the program is enhanced by several features. Surface topographic irregularities need not be approximated by a level surface, since the upper edges of the approximating strips are allowed to follow the fluctuations of the land surface. In addition, a laterally varying density pattern within the alluvium may be accommodated by assigning a separate density contrast to each strip.

Sometimes a gravity survey extends only part of the way across a very wide valley. A gravity profile extracted from this information is open ended, since it crosses a bedrock-alluvium contact at only one end. For computation, the alluvial cross section beyond the open end of the profile is approximated by a semi-infinite rectangular cross section. The depth of the semi-infinite rectangle is computed by the iterative procedure along with the depth computations for the finite strips.

The gravity profile is specified in terms of the terrain corrected Bouguer gravity. A regional correction is subtracted from the Bouguer profile to give the local anomaly, which is ascribed to the density contrast of the alluvial fill. This local anomaly, sometimes called the regionally corrected anomaly, is the basis for the computation of the depth to bedrock.

The interpretation of the profile is highly sensitive to the value of the regional correction; therefore, this value should be determined as accurately as possible. To satisfy this accuracy requirement, the regional correction should be determined separately for each profile, based on information in the proximity of the profile.

The profile interpretation program expresses the regional correction as a linear function of position along the profile.[2] The value of the regional correction may be explicitly specified as input to the program, or it may be determined automatically from the Bouguer profile as part of the computational procedure.

Automatic determination of the regional correction can be accomplished if the Bouguer profile extends over bedrock, beyond the surface bedrock-alluvium contacts. The value of the regional correction is refined with each step of the iterative determination of strip depth. It is adjusted to bring the bedrock values of the regionally corrected anomaly into agreement with the values of the computed anomaly over the current trial body.

A flowchart of the Gravity Profile Interpretation System is diagrammed in Figure 7. The program input, shown in the first box, includes the following identifying information at the strip midpoints: surface coordinate and elevation, Bouguer gravity, and density contrast. The regional correction is also given if it is not to be determined by the program. The strip depths are initially set to zero in the second box and the iterative procedure begins and recycles until a satisfactory solution is achieved.

The computation points used to define the profile are located at the midpoints of the approximating strips and at selected bedrock points. As the initial step of the iterative procedure, the anomaly due to the strips is computed at each computation point. The regional correction is then adjusted—if not

[2] See Appendix for computational formulas.

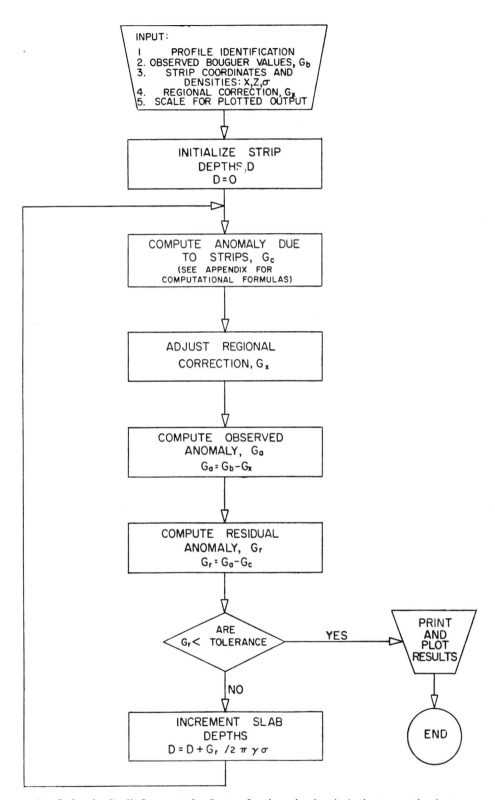

Fig. 7. Gravity Profile Interpretation System flowchart showing the basic computational steps.

specified in the input—to produce a best fit, in the least-squares sense, between the computed and the regionally corrected anomaly at the bedrock computation points. Since the regional correction is expressed as a linear function of position, this is computationally equivalent to fitting a least-squares line through several points.

The regionally corrected anomaly is computed by subtracting the regional correction from the observed Bouguer values. The difference between the observed anomaly and the computed anomaly due to the strips gives the residual anomaly. The residual at each strip midpoint is tested. If all residuals are less than a specified tolerance, control is transferred to the output section. If the residuals are not within the specified tolerance, the strip depths are adjusted. The adjustment to a given strip (or semi-infinite rectangle) is proportional to the value of the residual computed at the midpoint of that strip. Specifically, this depth adjustment equals the thickness of the infinite Bouguer slab required to compensate for the residual. After each strip is adjusted the iterative cycle begins again.

The results of the profile computations are printed and automatically plotted by an on-line digital X-Y plotter. Typical plotted output is shown in Figure 8. The interpreted section is smoothed by plotting the midpoints of the rectangular approximating strips rather than the corners. An appropriate standard frame size is selected according to the size of the plotted profile and interpreted section. A border and title block are drawn by the plotter along with appropriate labeling information and coordinate scales. The result is a finished product which is reproduced and incorporated into gravity survey reports.

The validity of the method used by the gravity interpretation program is tested by computing a profile having a known interpretation. For example, a gravity profile calculated over a triangular cross section for a given density contrast supplies the input to the interpretation program. The comparison of the resulting interpreted section with the original triangular cross section gives an indication of the effectiveness of the method. Test cases have shown the interpreted sections to be essentially identical with the original test body. The validity of the procedure has been additionally verified by experience. To date, over 100 profiles have been computed with acceptable results.

Difficulties have been encountered in computing a few of the Bouguer profiles. The procedure sometimes requires an excessive number of iterations to converge to a solution. In some cases, the interpreted sections display extreme depth oscillations between successive strips, giving an interpretation that is unlikely from a geologic standpoint. These difficulties are attributed to several factors. The assumed model may be a poor approximation to the field situation and a solution may be nonexistent. Measurement error may cause erroneous anomalies. The interpretive procedure itself may be unstable under conditions in which the thickness of the infinite Bouguer slab is a poor approximation to the required depth adjustment.

Conclusions

Automated gravity data reduction offers several advantages over manual methods. The most important is the ability of the computer to accommodate a varying work load. Doubling the amount of gravity data processed makes a negligible change in the computer's total work load. Accuracy is another advantage. A certain percentage of errors is to be expected in manual processing, even with the most conscientious personnel. In contrast, the electronic computer is virtually error-free. The only significant source of error is key punching of the field notes. Even here, the probability of error is slight since all punched data are mechanically verified by a second key punch operator. The punched card history file is an additional benefit of computer processing. This file is a permanent easily referenced source of gravity data useful for a variety of geophysical studies.

Over a year of experience has proven computer processing of gravity data to be competitive costwise with manual methods. It is estimated that computer costs to date, including programming, key punching, com-

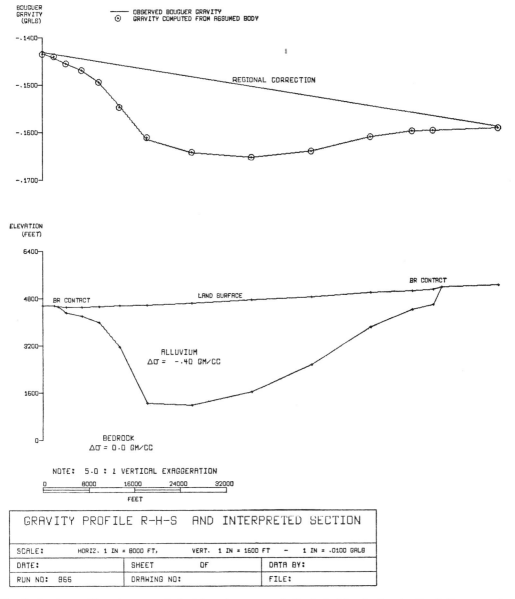

FIG. 8. Gravity profile and computed alluvial section automatically drafted by the Gravity Profile Interpretation System on an on-line digital X-Y plotter.

puter time and overhead, are about 50¢ per station. As the programming costs are spread over more stations, this cost should drop to about 35¢ per station. Manual processing, including overhead, costs approximately 50¢ per station. Although no significant cost advantage is realized with computer processing, the other advantages more than justify the change. It should be noted, however, the success of this computer application resulted from the high volume of data processed and the uniformity of the data collection procedure. Small gravity survey projects, using a variety of methods, could not be expected to support the costs of program development.

Some of the advantages mentioned above

also apply to the Gravity Profile Interpretation System. A varying work load is easily accommodated and the computer results are essentially error-free. Perhaps even more important, the speed and ease with which the program can be used frees the geophysicist to perform a more thorough interpretive job than he would if he were confronted with the time consuming drudgery of hand computation. A profile is set up for automatic computation in about half an hour. Manual computations take two to three hours. The plotting routine saves additional hours of drafting time required to prepare the interpreted profiles for reports. Automated profile computation encourages the interpretation of more profiles, making better use of the gravity data, while releasing the geophysicist from computational restrictions for the more important task of evaluating the results.

Appendix

Computational formulas used in the processing of gravity data are given below.

Data reduction formulas

Drift.—Gravimeter and altimeter drifts are computed using the formula

$$\beta = \frac{(R_{b2} - R_{b1}) - (V_{b2} - V_{b1})/K_{b2}}{T_{b2} - T_{b1}}$$

where β is the drift rate; R_{b1} and R_{b2}, V_{b1} and V_{b2}, and T_{b1} and T_{b2} are the instrument readings, base station values, and times, respectively, at the first and second base station. K_{b2} is the instrument scale constant in the case of the gravimeter or the scale correction factor at time T_{b2} in the case of the altimeter.

Observed gravity or elevation.—The observed gravity or elevation is computed by the formula

$$V_a = V_{b1} + K_a[(R_a - R_{b1}) - \beta(T_a - T_{b1})]$$

where V_a, R_a, and T_a are the observed gravity, instrument reading, and time, respectively, at the station being computed. In the case of gravimeter computations, K_a is the instrument scale constant. For altimeter computations it is the correction factor obtained by linear interpolation;

$$K_a = K_{b1} + (K_{b2} - K_{b1})(T_a - T_{b1})/(T_{b2} - T_{b1}).$$

Theoretical gravity—The International Gravity Formula used to compute theoretical gravity is given by the equation

$$G_t = 978.049\,(1 + 0.0052884\,\sin^2\phi$$
$$- 0.0000059\,\sin^2 2\phi$$

where G_t is the theoretical gravity in gals and ϕ is the latitude of the point.

Bouguer anomaly.—The Bouguer anomaly is given by the following expression:

$$G_b = G_{obs} - G_t + E_{obs}\,(dg/dE - 2\pi\gamma\rho)$$

where G_b is the Bouguer gravity, G_{obs} is the observed gravity, E_{obs} is station elevation, γ is the universal gravitational constant, dg/dE is the vertical gradient of gravity, and ρ is the assumed crustal density. Substituting constant values the following formula is obtained

$$G_b = G_{obs} - G_t$$
$$+ E_{obs}\,(.00009406 - .00001276\rho).$$

Profile interpretation formula.

Rectangular cross section.—The gravitational effect of an infinite body with a rectangular cross section is given by the expression

$$G = 2\gamma\sigma\left\{x_1 \ln\left(\frac{z_2^2 + x_1^2}{z_1^2 + x_1^2}\right)^{1/2}\right.$$
$$- x_2 \ln\left(\frac{z_2^2 + x_2^2}{z_1^2 + x_2^2}\right)^{1/2}$$
$$+ z_2[\tan^{-1}(x_1/z_2) - \tan^{-1}(x_2/z_2)]$$
$$\left. - z_1[\tan^{-1}(x_1/z_1) - \tan^{-1}(x_2/z_1)]\right\}$$

where G is the gravitational effect, σ is the density of the rectangular section, x_1 and x_2 are the horizontal distances of the observer from the edges of the rectangle, and z_1 and z_2 are the vertical distances of the observer from the upper and lower edges respectively.

Semi-infinite rectangle.—The formula for the semi-infinite rectangular cross section is obtained from the rectangular formula by letting x_2 approach infinity in the negative direction, resulting in the equation

$$G = 2\gamma\sigma \left[x_1 \ln \left(\frac{z_2^2 + x_1^2}{z_1^2 + x_1^2} \right)^{1/2} \right.$$

$$+ z_2 \tan^{-1}(x_1/z_2) - z_1 \tan^{-1}(x_1/z_1)$$

$$\left. + \pi/2(|z_2| - |z_1|) \right].$$

Infinite Bouguer slab.—In the iterative procedure the strip depths D are adjusted at each iteration by the thickness of the infinite Bouguer slab required to compensate for the residual anomaly G_r over the strip. The magnitude of the adjustment ΔD is given by

$$\Delta D = G_r/2\pi\gamma\sigma.$$

Regional Correction.—The regional correction G_x is expressed as a linear function of position along the profile in the form

$$G_x = a + bx$$

where x is the distance along the profile from an arbitrary reference point and a and b are determined by a least-squares fit, such that the sum of the squares of the residual anomaly at the bedrock computation points is minimized.

References

Bott, M. H. P., 1960, The use of rapid digital computing methods for direct gravity interpretation of sedimentary basins: Roy. Astron. Soc. Geophys. Jour., v. 3, p. 63–67.

Corbato, Charles E., 1965, A least-squares procedure for gravity interpretation: Geophysics, v. 30, p. 228–233.

Healy, J. H., and Press, Frank, 1964, Geophysical studies of basin structures along the eastern front of the Sierra Nevada, California: Geophysics, v. 29, p. 337–359.

Heinrichs, Walter E., Jr., Gaines, J. E., Carey, W. W., and Spaulding, J. D., 1964, Successful computer application by a small exploration consulting firm: Quarterly of the Colorado School of Mines, Applications of statistics, operations research and computers in the mineral industry, v. 59, p. 81–90.

Tanner, J. G., and Buck, R. J., 1964, A computer-oriented system for the reduction of gravity data: Publications of the Dominion Observatory, Ottawa, v. 31, p. 57–65.

A DOT CHART FOR THE CALCULATION OF GRAVITATIONAL AND MAGNETIC ATTRACTION OF TWO-DIMENSIONAL BODIES

FRANK B. MILLETT, JR.*

Introduction

The dot chart described in this paper is an adaptation of Hubbert's graticule (1948). Like Hubbert's graticule, it offers the field man, who does not have ready access to digital computers, a rapid method of calculating theoretical profiles due to two-dimensional bodies of infinite length. Since many geological features may be treated as two-dimensional bodies, the dot chart is a useful tool instead of a geophysical curio.

The dot chart retains the capability of lineal integration provided by Hubbert's graticule while, at the same time, it offers an intuitive insight to profile matching. The chart may be modified for bodies of finite length by the addition of partitioning circles. The body's cross section may be modified for calculation of magnetic attraction.

Principle of the Dot Chart

Mathematical basis for the dot chart

Vertical component of gravity due to a small mass.—The vertical component of gravity, at the origin (0) of Figure 1, due to a small mass, $dm = \rho(dx\,dy\,dz)$, at (x, y, z) is given by

$$dg_z = G(dm/r^2)\sin\alpha$$
$$= G\rho(z/r^3)dx\,dy\,dz \qquad (1)$$

where

$G =$ the universal gravitational constant

$\rho =$ density (assumed to be constant over the volume $dx\,dy\,dz$)

$\sin\alpha = z/r$

$r = (x^2 + y^2 + z^2)^{1/2}$.

Equation (1) is the basic expression which may be integrated to obtain the vertical component of gravity at the origin (0) due to a body of any shape.

Vertical component of gravity due to a two-dimensional body of cross section dx dz.—For the special class of "two-dimensional bodies" the form of equation (1) is reduced to two coordinate axes. If the body extends from $y = -\infty$ to $y = +\infty$ then the element of volume is a two-dimensional body of infinite length having a cross section $dx\,dz$. The vertical component of gravity due to the mass of such an element of volume is

$$dg_z = G\rho z\,dx\,dz \int_{-\infty}^{+\infty} (a^2 + y^2)^{-3/2}dy \qquad (2)$$

where

$$a^2 = x^2 + z^2$$

is constant for this integration.

Integration of equation (2) gives

$$dg_z = 2G\rho(x^2 + z^2)^{-1}z\,dx\,dz. \qquad (3)$$

Vertical component of gravity due to a two-dimensional body bounded by planes θ_1 and θ_2 and planes z_1 and z_2.—The cross section of this body is shown in Figure 2. Integration of equation (3) over this cross section gives

$$g_z = 2G\rho \int_{z_1}^{z_2} z\,dz \int_{z\,\text{ctn}\,\theta_2}^{z\,\text{ctn}\,\theta_1} (x^2 + z^2)^{-1}dx$$

or

$$g_z = 2G\rho(\theta_2 - \theta_1)(z_2 - z_1). \qquad (4)$$

The value computed from equation (4) depends only on the change in θ and z over the cross section of the body and not on the absolute values of their limits. Equation (4)

* Formerly Assistant Senior Engineer with Oceanic Production Division, Aerojet General Corp.; presently, Senior Research Geophysicist with Phelps Dodge Corp.

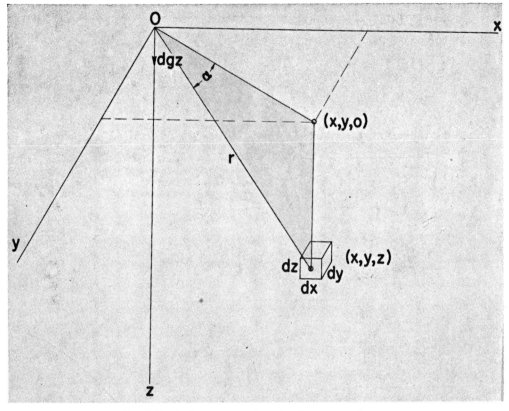

FIG. 1. Vertical component of gravity due to a small mass.

applies to any size area bounded by θ planes and z planes and forms the basis for Hubbert's graticule and the dot chart.

Description of the dot chart

Figure 3 shows a scaled down version of a dot chart with a scale ratio vertical/horizontal of 1:1. The charts may be constructed for any size $\Delta\theta\Delta z$ cross section (Hubbert's solenoids) and for any scale ratio. The larger scale ratios are particularly useful for dot charts designed for making terrain corrections.

The dots are placed at the corners of Hubbert's $\Delta\theta\Delta z$ solenoids formed by the intersection of the θ and z planes. The number labeled "n" just outside the border of the chart is the ray number and θ is calculated as

$$\theta = n\Delta\theta$$

where

$\Delta\theta$ = angular separation of the radial planes ($1\text{-}\tfrac{1}{2}°$ in Figure 3).

For angles $\theta > 90°$ ($n > 60$) two numbers are shown at each ray. The upper number is the value of n and the lower number is the value of $(120-n)$. The value of n is used for lineal integration while the numbers

$$n \quad \text{for } n \leq 60$$

and

$$(120 - n) \quad \text{for } n \geq 60$$

are used for determining the number of dots remaining on any horizontal plane from the edge of the chart to infinity.

The number labled "k" is the horizontal plane number and z is calculated from

$$z = k\Delta z \tag{6}$$

where

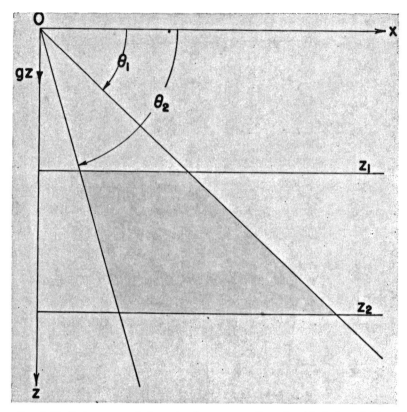

FIG. 2. Vertical component of gravity due to a two-dimensional body bounded by planes θ_1 and θ_2 and planes z_1 and z_2.

Δz = vertical separation of the horizontal planes.

Figure 3, at full scale, was constructed for a model scale 1 inch = 400 ft. The value of Δz (94 ft) was selected so that a $\Delta\theta\Delta z$ solenoid, $1\frac{1}{2}$ degree wide, drawn to this model scale, would produce 0.01 mgal of vertical component at the origin for a density contrast of one gm/cm³. Selection of a different density contrast or model scale would give an attraction of

$$\Delta g_z/\text{dot} = 0.01\rho(\Delta z)_m/94 \ (\text{mg/dot}) \quad (7)$$

where

ρ = density contrast in gm/cm³
$(\Delta z)_m$ = the value of dot chart Δz as measured by the model scale.

Integration by the use of the dot chart

Areal integration.—Hubbert (1947) divided the entire xz plane into equal $\Delta\theta\Delta z$

solenoids each having a value

$$\Delta g_z = 2G\rho\Delta\theta\Delta z. \quad (8)$$

The vertical component of gravity due to a body of cross section (S) in the xz plane is obtained by the integration of equation (3) over the area of S. By use of equation (8) this can be approximated by

$$g_z = 2G \iint_S \rho(x^2 + z^2)^{-1}z \, dx \, dz$$

$$\doteq 2G \sum_S \rho\Delta\theta\Delta z. \quad (9)$$

If the density ρ is constant throughout S then

$$g_z \doteq 2G\rho \sum_S \Delta\theta\Delta z = 2G\rho N'\Delta\theta\Delta z \quad (10)$$

where

N' = the number of $\Delta\theta\Delta z$ solenoids counted in S.

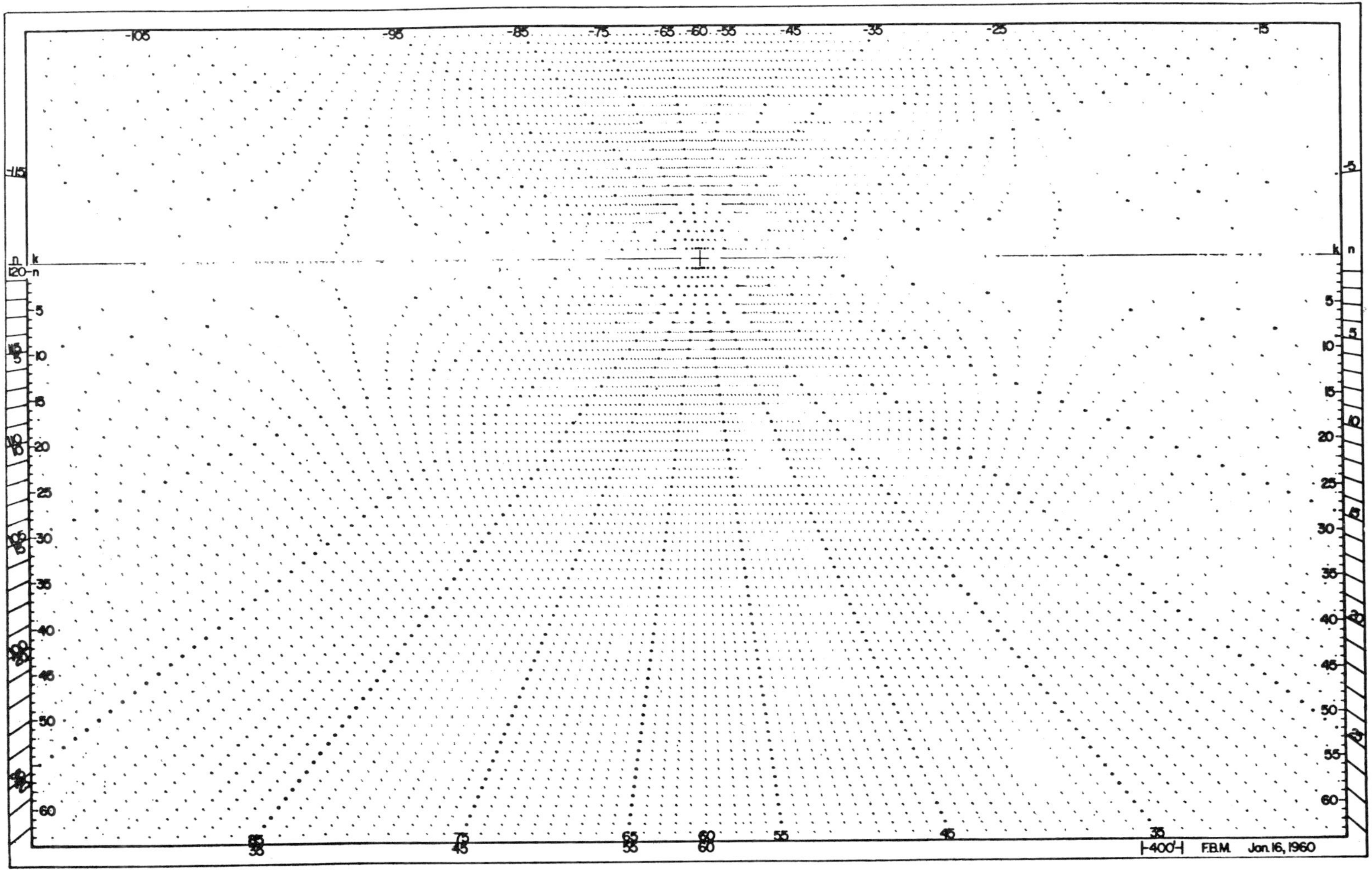

FIG. 3. Dot chart.

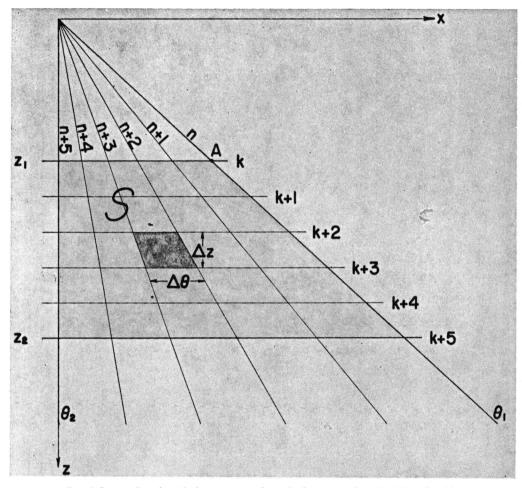

FIG. 4. Integration of vertical component of gravity by summation of $\Delta\theta\Delta Z$—solenoids.

If a dot is placed at the center of each $\Delta\theta\Delta z$ solenoid and if the fractional solenoids of S are neglected, then the number of dots would be identical to the number of solenoids. The true dot count using the chart shown in Figure 3 may differ slightly from N', but for an adequate model scale the value of g_z may be approximated just as closely by

$$g_z = 2G\rho\Delta\theta\Delta z N \qquad (11)$$

where

$N =$ the number of dots counted in S.

The counting of dots or solenoids is an approximation of the areal integration of equation (3) over S.

Lineal integration.—The line integral for

an area S can be found by the integration

$$\oint \theta dz \quad \text{or} \quad \oint z d\theta$$

over its bounding surface.

In Figure 4 the line integral $\oint \theta dz$ starting from point A and traversing the boundary of S in the counterclockwise sense is

$$\oint \theta dz = \int_{z_1}^{z_1} \theta dz + \int_{z}^{z_2} \theta_2 dz + \int_{z_2}^{z_2} \theta dz$$

$$+ \int_{z_2}^{z_1} \theta_1 dz$$

$$= 0 + \theta_2(z_2 - z_1) + 0 + \theta_1(z_1 - z_2)$$

$$= (\theta_2 - \theta_1)(z_2 - z_1). \qquad (12)$$

The evaluation by this method is identical to the results obtained by the areal integration $\int sd\theta\ dz$. Traversing the boundary in a clockwise sense will give a negative value for the integral $\oint \theta\ dz$.

The line integral $\oint z\ d\theta$ taken in a clockwise sense from point A is

$$\oint z\ d\theta = \int_{\theta_1}^{\theta_1} z\ d\theta + \int_{\theta_1}^{\theta_2} z_2\ d\theta + \int_{\theta_2}^{\theta_2} z\ d\theta$$
$$+ \int_{\theta_2}^{\theta_1} z_1\ d\theta$$
$$= 0 + z_2(\theta_2 - \theta_1) + 0 + z_1(\theta_1 - \theta_2)$$
$$= (\theta_2 - \theta_1)(z_2 - z_1) \tag{13}$$

which is identical to $\oint \theta\ dz$ taken in the counterclockwise direction. Reversing the direction of the traverse in the integration $\oint z\ d\theta$ to counterclockwise will give a negative value for the line integral.

Exact value of the above integrations may readily be determined for a simple boundary of S shown in Figure 4, but for more complicated boundaries the integrations are approximated by traversing the boundaries of small solenoids which lie close to S. The line integrals are expressed in terms of these solenoids by the following approximations

$$\oint_S \theta\ dz \doteq \sum_S \theta\Delta z \tag{14}$$

$$\oint_S z\ d\theta \doteq \sum_S z\Delta\theta. \tag{15}$$

If all Δz's are equal and all $\Delta\theta$'s are equal, then the above formulas may be written as

$$\oint_S \theta dz \doteq \Delta z \sum_S \theta = \Delta z\Delta\theta \sum_S n \tag{16}$$

$$\oint_S z d\theta \doteq \Delta\theta \sum_S z = \Delta\theta\Delta z \sum_S k \tag{17}$$

where

$$\theta = n\Delta\theta$$
$$z = k\Delta z.$$

If equation (16) is used the boundary of S must be traversed in a counterclockwise direction and the value of n is tabulated each

time z changes by Δz. The sign is positive if Δz is positive and negative if Δz is negative. For Figure 4, starting at A, this summation is

$$\Delta z\Delta\theta \sum_S n = \Delta z\Delta\theta[(n+5) + (n+5)$$
$$+ (n+5) + (n+5) + (n+5)$$
$$- n - n - n - n - n]$$
$$= 25\Delta z\Delta\theta. \tag{18}$$

Using equation (17) and traversing S in a clockwise sense the summation is

$$\Delta z\Delta\theta \sum_S k = \Delta z\Delta\theta[(k+5) + (k+5)$$
$$+ (k+5) + (k+5) + (k+5)$$
$$- k - k - k - k - k]$$
$$= 25\Delta\theta\Delta z. \tag{19}$$

Substitution of the following equalities

$$\theta_1 = n\Delta\theta$$
$$\theta_2 = (n+5)\Delta\theta$$
$$z_1 = k\Delta z$$
$$z_2 = (k+5)\Delta z$$

in equation (12) or (13) will give results identical to those obtained in equations (18) and (19) above.

Dot density at a point in the xz plane

The dot density (Ψ) at any point ($k\Delta z$, $n\Delta\theta$) in the xz plane is defined as the number of dots per unit area in the vicinity of the point. Figure 5 shows a dot at the center ($k\Delta z$, $n\Delta\theta$) of a $\Delta\theta\Delta z$ solenoid bounded by the θ planes $(n-\frac{1}{2})\Delta\theta$ and $(n+\frac{1}{2})\Delta\theta$ and the z planes $(k-\frac{1}{2})\Delta z$ and $(k+\frac{1}{2})\Delta z$. The area of the solenoid $ABCD$ is

Area $ABCD$ = Area DOC − Area AOB
$$= 1/2(k + 1/2)\Delta z \cdot (k + 1/2)\Delta z$$
$$\cdot [\text{ctn}\ (n - 1/2)\Delta\theta - \text{ctn}\ (n + 1/2)\Delta\theta]$$
$$- 1/2(k - 1/2)\Delta z \cdot (k - 1/2)\Delta z$$
$$\cdot [\text{ctn}\ (n - 1/2)\Delta\theta - \text{ctn}\ (n + 1/2)\Delta\theta]$$
$$= k(\Delta z)^2[\text{ctn}\ (n - 1/2)\Delta\theta$$
$$- \text{ctn}\ (n + 1/2)\Delta\theta]$$

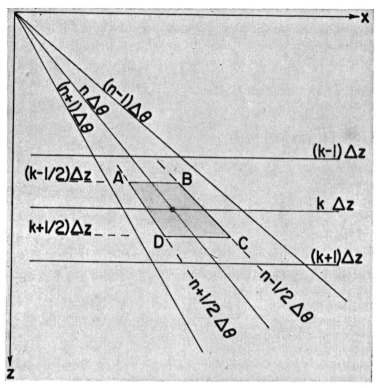

FIG. 5. Dot density at a point in the xz plane.

or

Area $ABCD = k(\Delta z^2) \sin \Delta\theta / [\sin (n-1/2)\Delta\theta$

$\cdot \sin (n+1/2)\Delta\theta]$.   (20)

The value of dot density (Ψ) is

$\Psi = 1$ dot/Area $ABCD = \sin (n - 1/2)\Delta\theta$

$\cdot \sin (n = 1/2)\Delta\theta / [k(\Delta z)^2 \sin \Delta\theta]$

or since $(\sin \Delta\theta = \Delta\theta)$

$\Psi = \sin (n - 1/2)\Delta\theta$

$\cdot \sin (n + 1/2)\Delta\theta / [k\Delta\theta(\Delta z)^2]$.   (21)

The values of n and k may be treated as continuous variables and need not be restricted to integers. The function $F(n, \Delta\theta)$, defined as

$F(n, \Delta\theta) = \sin (n - 1/2)\Delta\theta \cdot \sin (n + 1/2)\Delta\theta$

$= 1/2[\cos \Delta\theta - \cos 2n\Delta\theta]$ (22)

is plotted as a function of n in Figure 6.
    If the approximation

$\sin (n\Delta\theta) \doteq \sin (n - 1/2)\Delta\theta$

$\doteq \sin (n + 1/2)\Delta\theta$

is used, then it can be shown that the locus of points of equal dot density $(\Psi = \text{constant})$ is a circle tangent to the x axis and centered on the z axis. The polar equation of the circle is

$r = (C/\Psi) \sin (n\Delta\theta) = 2R \sin (n\Delta\theta)$ (23)

where

$C = (\Delta\theta)^{-1}(\Delta z)^{-2}.$

The value of R and r are measured in terms of the row number k of the dot chart.

Locus of dot density for bodies of finite cross section

    For a body of finite cross section S, the average dot density $(\overline{\Psi})$ is defined as

$$\overline{\Psi} = \iint_S \Psi dA / \iint_S dA = N/A$$ (24)

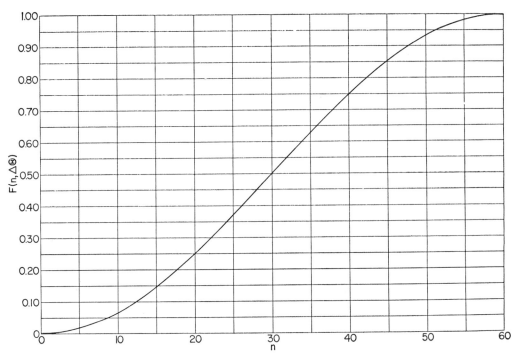

FIG. 6. Plot of $F(n, \Delta\theta)$ as a function of n.

where

N = the number of dots in S
A = the area of S.

For a body of circular cross section the locus of $\overline{\Psi}$ passes through the center of the cross section regardless of the position of the center in the xz plane. For other symmetrical cross sections, the locus of $\overline{\Psi}$ does not, in general, pass through their centers. While the concept of dot density is generally useful in the derivation of mathematical expressions for dot chart evaluation, a particular application of its use for depth estimates will be discussed in a later section.

Gravitational Attraction

Calculation of attraction of bodies of infinite length

To compute the vertical component of gravity g_z, for a body of infinite length, the dot chart is used without modification. The integration may be carried out by any of the methods previously described, since they all give the number of dots or $\Delta\theta\Delta z$ solenoids (N)

in any cross section S. The value of Δg_z/dot is determined by the scale chosen for the construction of the dot chart and the scale chosen for the model (equation 7). The value of g_z is given by

$$g_z = N \cdot \Delta g_z / \text{dot}. \qquad (25)$$

Calculation of attraction of bodies of finite length

To compute g_z for bodies of finite length both the dot chart and procedure must be modified. For a two-dimensional body of finite length extending from y_1 to y_2 the vertical component of gravity $(dg_z)_f$ is

$$(dg_z)_f = Gpz\,dx\,dz \int_{y_1}^{y_2} (a^2 + y^2)^{-3/2}dy$$

$$= G\rho a^{-2}z\,dx\,dz[y(a^2 + y^2)^{-1/2}]_{y_1}^{y_2} \qquad (26)$$

where

$$a^2 = x^2 + z^2.$$

For a body of infinite length the above integration gives

$$(dg_z)_\infty = 2G\rho a^{-2} z \, dx \, dz. \qquad (27)$$

and

The attraction $(dg_z)_f$ may be expressed in terms of $(dg_z)_\infty$ and the "end corrections" (Nettleton, 1940) as

$$(dg_z)_f = 1/2[y(a^2 + y^2)^{-1/2}]_{y_1}^{y_2} \, (dg_z)_\infty$$

$$= F(a/y_2) \cdot (dg_z)_\infty \qquad (28)$$

where

$$F(a/y_2) = 1/2[y(a^2 + y^2)^{-1/2}]_{\alpha y_2}^{y_2}$$

$$y_1 = \alpha y_2.$$

The vertical component of gravity $(g_z)_f$, due to a body of finite length and cross section S is

$$(g_z)_f = \iint_S (dg_z)_f = \iint_s F(a/y_2) \cdot (dg_z)_\infty. \qquad (29)$$

To integrate equation (29) graphically, the

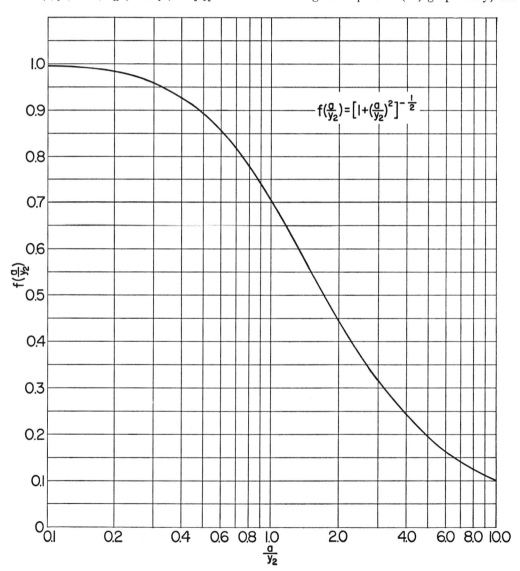

$$f\left(\frac{a}{y_2}\right) = \left[1 + \left(\frac{a}{y_2}\right)^2\right]^{-\frac{1}{2}}$$

FIG. 7. Plot of the general partitioning function $f(a/y_2)$.

lot chart is partitioned by a family of circles centered at the origin. Each circle is the locus of

$$F(a/y_2) = \text{constant.}$$

It is assumed that the partitioning is consistent with the accuracy desired, and that for the area between the ith circle and the $(i+1)$th circle (called the ith zone) the function

$$F(a/y_2)_i = 1/2[F(a_i/y_2) + F(a_{i+1}/y_2)] \quad (30)$$

can be considered constant. The value of the integral $\int\int_{\Delta S_i}(dg_z)_f$ over a subarea ΔS_{si}, common both to S and the ith zone, is approximated as

$$\int\int_{\Delta S_i}(dg_z)_f = \int\int_{\Delta S_i}F(a/y_2)\cdot(dg_z)_\infty$$

$$= F(a/y_2)_i \int\int_{\Delta S_i}(dg_z)_\infty. \quad (31)$$

The value of $\int\int_{\Delta S_i}(dg_z)_\infty$ is $2G\rho\Delta\theta\Delta z$ times the number of dots in ΔS_i. The multiplier $F(a/y_2)_i$ is determined by the dot chart partitioning. This process is repeated for each subarea of S and $(g_z)_f$ is approximated as

$$(g_z)_f = \int\int_S (dg_z)_f$$

$$\doteq \sum_S F(a/y_2)_i \int\int_{\Delta S_i}(dg_z)_\infty. \quad (32)$$

As an example, a dot chart (Figure 3) is to be partioned for a profile across a body 1,880 ft long with

$$y_2 = 1,410 \text{ ft}$$

and

$$y_1 = -470 \text{ ft} = -y_2/3.$$

The function $F(a/y_2)$ is given by

$$F(a/y_2) = 1/2[y(a^2 + y^2)^{-1/2}]^{y_2}_{-y_2/3}$$

which may be written in normalized form as

$$F(a/y_2) = 1/2[[1 + (a/y_2)^2]^{-1/2} + [1 + (3a/y_2)^2]^{-1/2}].$$

A master curve shown in Figure 7 shows the function

$$f(a/y_2) = [1 + (a/y_2)^2]^{-1/2}$$

plotted against a/y_2. From this master curve the function

$$F(a/y_2) = 1/2[f(a/y_2) + f(3a/y_2)]$$

can be easily calculated and plotted as shown in Figure 8.

If a scale of 1 inch $= 400$ ft is selected for the model then the value of y_2 may be written in terms of Δz for the dot chart shown, as

$$y_2 = 15\Delta z \quad (\Delta z = 94 \text{ ft})$$

and the radius of the ith circle can be written as

$$a_i = k_i\Delta z.$$

For any chosen value of $F(a_i/y_2)$, the value of a_i/y_2 can be determined from the curve shown in Figure 8. The radius of the ith circle can be drawn to scale or measure in terms of the number k_i of the dot chart, as a radius

$$k_i = 15(a_i/y_2).$$

Table 1 shows a_i/y_2 and the calculated radius of the partitioning circle (k_i) for the chosen value of $F(a_i/y_2)$. Figure 9 shows the partitioning circles and the mean value of $F(a/y_2)_i$ for zones drawn on the dot chart. The value of $(g_z)_f$ for the cross section S shown is determined from the following expression

$$(g_z)_f = \sum_{i=5}^{8} F(a/y_2)_i \int\int_{\Delta S_i}(dg_z)_\infty$$

$$= (\Delta g_z/dot)_\infty \sum_{i=5}^{8} F(a/y_2)_i \cdot N_i$$

$$= (\Delta g_z/dot)_\infty \cdot (0.55N_5 + 0.45N_6 + 0.35N_7 + 0.25N_8)$$

where

$N_i =$ the number of dots in the subarea ΔS_i.

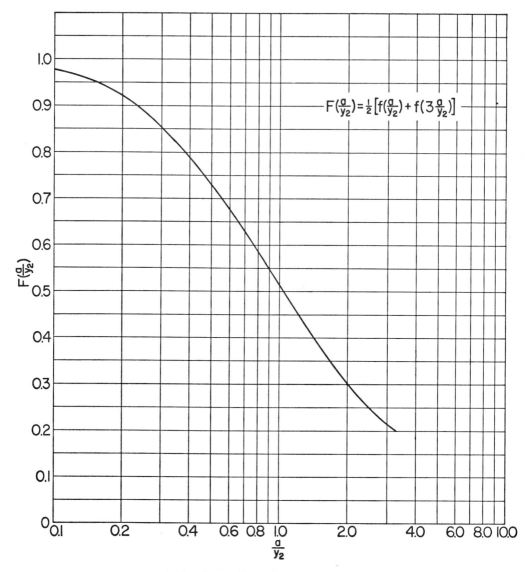

$$F\left(\frac{a}{y_2}\right)=\tfrac{1}{2}\left[f\left(\frac{a}{y_2}\right)+f\left(3\frac{a}{y_2}\right)\right]$$

Fig. 8. Plot of a specific partitioning function $F(a/y_2)$.

Depth determination

The concept of dot density is useful for making depth determinations from symmetrical profiles of long cylinders. Various formulas may be developed, but all assume that the average dot density is equal to the dot density at the center of the cross sectional area S. Except for the circular cylinder, this is not generally true.

A simple example to consider is the symmetrical anomaly whose total relief is known.

It is assumed that the average dot density is equal to the dot density at the center of the cross sectional area $(\overline{\Psi}=\Psi_c)$. If the peak value $g_0(x=0)$ is known and the gravity value is g_i at some point x_i on the profile, then the gravity values may be expressed as

$$g_0 = CA\Psi_0$$

$$g_i = CA\Psi_i$$

where

C = a constant
A = the cross sectional area of the body
Ψ_0 = dot density at the center of the body at $x=0$
Ψ_i = dot density at the center of the body at $x=x_i$.

The ratio g_i/g_0 calculated from the gravity profile may be expressed in terms of dot density as

$$g_i/g_0 = (CA\Psi_i)/(CA\Psi_0) = \Psi_i/\Psi_0$$
$$= (F(n_i, \Delta\theta)/k_i)/(F(n_0, \Delta\theta)/k_0). \quad (33)$$

If g_i and g_0 are measured from the same plane then $k_i=k_0$ and since the value of $F(n_0, \Delta\theta)$ $\doteq 1$ the gravity ratio may be written as

$$g_i/g_0 = F(n_i, \Delta\theta). \quad (34)$$

With the aid of Figure 6 the value of n_i can be determined and the depth Z_i calculated from

$$Z_i = x_i \tan (n_i\Delta\theta),. \quad (35)$$

If the anomaly is due to a circular cylinder then for all Z_i's

$$Z_i = Z_{i+1} = \cdots = Z_t$$

where

Z_t = the true depth to the center of the cylinder.

If the anomaly is not that of a circular cylin-

Table 1. Dot chart partitions

$F(a_i/y_2)$	$F(a/y_2)_i$	a_i/y_2	k_i
1.0		0	0
	.95		
0.9		.23	3.45
	.85		
0.8		.38	5.70
	.75		
0.7		.55	8.25
	.65		
0.6		.76	11.40
	.55		
0.5		1.04	15.60
	.45		
0.4		1.42	21.30
	.35		
0.3		2.00	30.00
	.25		
0.2		3.25	48.75

der, then in general

$$Z_i \neq Z_{i+1} \neq \cdots \neq Z_t$$

however,

$$\lim_{x_i \to \infty} Z_i = Z_t$$

where

Z_t = true depth to the center of the body.

A formula may be developed for determining the depth from profiles whose true peak value is unknown. To derive this formula the ratio $(g_0-g_i)/(g_0-g_2)$ is formed and expressed in terms of dot density as

$$(g_0 - g_i)/g_0 - g_j)$$
$$= CA(\Psi_0 - \Psi_i)/CA(\Psi_0 - \Psi_j)$$
$$= (\Psi_0 - \Psi_i)/(\Psi_0 - \Psi_j) \quad (36)$$

where

g_0 = peak value of gravity at $x=0$
g_i = gravity value at $x=x_i$
g_j = gravity value at $x=x_j$

and the Ψ's are the corresponding dot densities at the above stations.

Since differences are taken, all of the above gravity values may include the same additive constant without affecting the calculation.

Magnetic Attraction

Mathematical basis for the method

Calculation of magnetic attraction by use of the dot chart is based on the relationship of magnetic and gravitational potential. If U is the gravitational potential due to the mass of a body with uniform density ρ, and if this body is uniformly polarized in a direction i, with an intensity of magnetization I, then the magnetic potential W, according to a theorem of Poisson, is

$$W = - (I/(\rho G))\partial U/\partial i \quad (37)$$

where G is the universal gravitational constant. The magnetic force F_s, in any direction s, is by definition,

$$F_s = - \partial W/\partial s = I/(\rho G)\frac{\partial}{\partial s}\left(\frac{\partial U}{\partial i}\right). \quad (38)$$

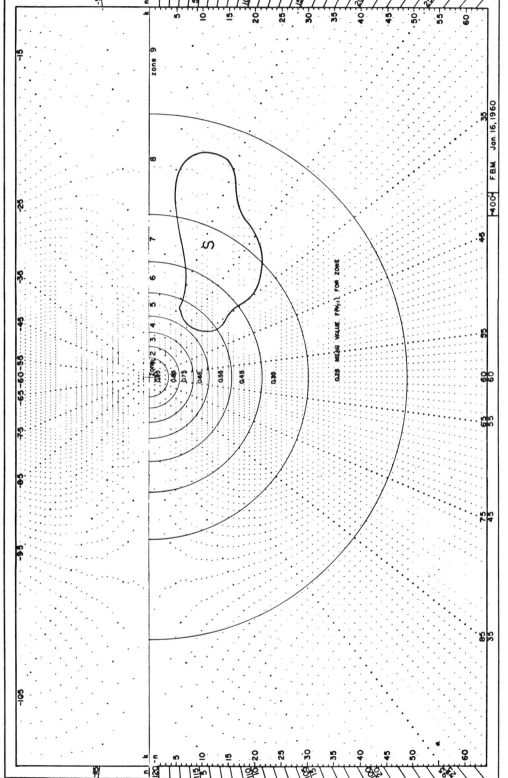

Fig. 9. A partitioned dot chart.

While the emphasis is on a graphical method of performing these calculations the methods employed in the use of the dot chart can be used to derive mathematical formulas which check those found in the geophysical literature. However, like all such formulas, the condition of uniform polarization is assumed even if it can not be met for bodies with sharp corners. The only limitation to the dot chart method is how well the derivatives of equation (38) can be approximated.

All magnetic polarization vectors are assumed to be in the xz plane. For long bodies the projection of the true polarization vectors on the xz plane may be used, but for short bodies (partitioned dot chart) the xz plane must be parallel to the polarization vectors.

Calculation of the magnetic attraction of infinite length bodies for any direction of magnetization i

The shaded portion of Figure 10 shows a graphical model used for calculating the magnetic attraction of a body of cross section S located at point A and uniformly magnetized in a direction i. If uniform polarization is assumed, then the shape of S need not be restricted to the circular cylinder and Poisson's theorem may be used.

$U_A =$ the gravitational potential of the body at position A.

$U_B =$ the gravitational potential of the body if displaced in the direction of magnetic north by a small distance δx to position B.

$U_C =$ the gravitational potential of the body, if displaced downward a small distance δz to position C.

$U_D =$ the gravitational potential of the body if displaced in the direction of the earth's magnetic field, i (Northern hemisphere assumed), a small distance δi.

The change in gravitational potential experienced moving from A to D can be calculated for the various paths available as follows:

Path ABD

$$U_B = U_A + \frac{\partial U_A}{\partial x}\, \delta x$$

$$U_D = U_B + \frac{\partial U_B}{\partial z}\, \delta z = U_A + \frac{\partial U_A}{\partial z}\, \delta x$$

$$+ \frac{\partial U_B}{\partial z}\, \delta z$$

and

$$(\delta U_{AD})_{ABD} = U_D - U_A = \frac{\partial U_A}{\partial x}\, \delta x$$

$$+ \frac{\partial U_B}{\partial z}\, \delta z. \qquad (39)$$

Path ACD

$$U_C = U_A + \frac{\partial U_A}{\partial z}\, \delta z$$

$$U_D = U_C + \frac{\partial U_C}{\partial x}\, \delta x = U_A + \frac{\partial U_A}{\partial z}\, \delta z$$

$$+ \frac{\partial U_C}{\partial x}\, \delta x$$

and

$$(\delta U_{AD})_{ACD} = U_D - U_A = \frac{\partial U_A}{\partial z}\, \delta z$$

$$+ \frac{\partial U_C}{\partial x}\, \delta x. \qquad (40)$$

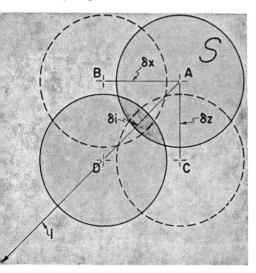

FIG. 10. Graphical model for calculating magnetic intensity.

Path AD

$$U_D = U_A + \frac{\partial U_A}{\partial i}\,\delta i$$

$$(\delta U_{AD})_{AD} = U_D - U_A = \frac{\partial U_A}{\partial i}\,\delta i. \quad (41)$$

Since the gravitational field is conservative then

$$\delta U_{AD} = (\delta U_{AD})_{AD} = (\delta U_{AD})_{ABD}$$
$$= (\delta U_{AD})_{ACD} \quad (42)$$

or

$$\delta U_{AD} = (\delta U_{AD})_{AD}$$
$$= 1/2[(\delta U_{AD})_{ABD} + (\delta U_{AD})_{ACD}]$$
$$= 1/2\left[\left(\frac{\partial U_A}{\partial x} + \frac{\partial U_C}{\partial x}\right)\delta x\right.$$
$$\left. + \left(\frac{\partial U_A}{\partial z} + \frac{\partial U_B}{\partial z}\right)\delta z\right]. \quad (43)$$

The rate of change of potential in the direction of polarization i is

$$\frac{\delta U_{AD}}{\delta i} = \frac{1}{2}\left[\left(\frac{\partial U_A}{\partial x} + \frac{\partial U_C}{\partial x}\right)\frac{\delta x}{\delta i}\right.$$
$$\left. + \left(\frac{\partial U_A}{\partial z} + \frac{\partial U_B}{\partial z}\right)\frac{\delta z}{\delta i}\right].$$

If δi is small, then the derivative at A is

$$\frac{\partial U}{\partial i} = \lim_{\delta i \to 0} \frac{\delta U_{AD}}{\delta i} \doteq \frac{\delta U_{AD}}{\delta i}$$
$$= \frac{1}{2}\left[\left(\frac{\partial U_A}{\partial x} + \frac{\partial U_C}{\partial x}\right)\frac{\delta x}{\delta i}\right.$$
$$\left. + \left(\frac{\partial U_A}{\partial z} + \frac{\partial U_B}{\partial z}\right)\frac{\delta z}{\delta i}\right] \quad (44)$$

where the ratios $\delta x/\delta i$ and $\delta z/\delta i$ are constant regardless of the magnitude of δi.

The vertical component of the magnetic intensity V from equation (38) is given by

$$V = F_z = [I/(\rho G)]\frac{\partial}{\partial z}\left(\frac{\partial U}{\partial i}\right). \quad (45)$$

The partial derivative $\partial/\partial z(\partial U/\partial i)$ of equation (45) can be approximated as

$$\frac{\partial}{\partial z}\left(\frac{\partial U}{\partial i}\right) \doteq \frac{1}{2}\left[\left(\frac{\partial}{\partial z}\left(\frac{\partial U_A}{\partial x}\right)\right.\right.$$
$$\left. + \frac{\partial}{\partial z}\left(\frac{\partial U_C}{\partial x}\right)\right)\frac{\delta x}{\delta i} + \left(\frac{\partial}{\partial z}\left(\frac{\partial U_A}{\partial z}\right)\right.$$
$$\left.\left. + \frac{\partial}{\partial z}\left(\frac{\partial U_B}{\partial z}\right)\right)\frac{\delta z}{\delta i}\right]. \quad (46)$$

The order of partial differentiation for these functions is immaterial and since $\partial U/\partial z = g$ then equation (46) may be written as

$$\frac{\partial}{\partial z}\left(\frac{\partial U}{\partial i}\right) \doteq \frac{1}{2}\left[\left(\frac{\partial}{\partial x}(g_z)_A\right.\right.$$
$$\left. + \frac{\partial}{\partial x}(g_z)_C\right)\frac{\delta x}{\delta i} + \left(\frac{\partial}{\partial z}(g_z)_A\right.$$
$$\left.\left. + \frac{\partial}{\partial z}(g_z)_B\right)\frac{\delta z}{\delta i}\right]. \quad (47)$$

The partial derivatives of the form $\partial/\partial x(g_z)_A$ and $\partial/\partial z(g_z)_A$ are approximated as shown in the following examples:

$$\frac{\partial}{\partial x}(g_z)_A = \frac{\partial}{\partial x}(2G\rho\Delta\theta\Delta z N_{Az})$$
$$= 2G\rho\Delta\theta\Delta z \frac{\partial N_{Az}}{\partial x}$$
$$= 2\,G\rho\Delta\theta\Delta z \lim_{\delta x \to 0}(N_A - N_B)_z/\delta x$$
$$\doteq 2G\rho\Delta\theta\Delta z(N_A - N_B)_z/\delta x \quad (48)$$

and similarly

$$\frac{\partial}{\partial z}(g_z)_A = 2G\rho\Delta\theta\Delta z(N_A - N_C)_z/\delta z \quad (49)$$

where

N_{Az} is the number of dots in S when the body is at position A and the dot chart is used with the $n = 60$ ray in the direction of the positive z axis,

and

$(N_A - N_B)_z$ means that the number of dots in S at B is subtracted from the number of dots in S at A. The subscript z gives the orientation of the dot chart.

Using the results of equations (48) and (49) then equation (47) may be rewritten as

Table 2. Equations of horizontal and vertical intensity for horizontal and vertical polarization

i	H (analytical)	H (dot chart)	V (analytical)	V (dot chart)
$+z$	$H = \dfrac{I}{\rho G}\dfrac{\partial}{\partial x}\left(\dfrac{\partial U}{\partial z}\right)$	$H = 2I\Delta\theta\Delta Z\dfrac{(N_A - N_B)_z}{\delta x}$	$V = \dfrac{I}{\rho G}\dfrac{\partial}{\partial z}\left(\dfrac{\partial U}{\partial z}\right)$	$V = 2I\Delta\theta\Delta Z\dfrac{(N_A - N_C)_z}{\delta z}$
	$H = \dfrac{I}{\rho G}\dfrac{\partial}{\partial z}\left(\dfrac{\partial U}{\partial x}\right)$	$H = 2I\Delta\theta\Delta Z\dfrac{(N_A - N_C)_x}{\delta z}$		
$+x$	$H = \dfrac{I}{\rho G}\dfrac{\partial}{\partial x}\left(\dfrac{\partial U}{\partial x}\right)$	$H = 2I\Delta\theta\Delta Z\dfrac{(N_A - N_B)_x}{\delta x}$	$V = \dfrac{I}{\rho G}\dfrac{\partial}{\partial z}\left(\dfrac{\partial U}{\partial x}\right)$	$V = 2I\Delta\theta\Delta Z\dfrac{(N_A - N_C)_x}{\delta z}$
			$V = \dfrac{I}{\rho G}\dfrac{\partial}{\partial x}\left(\dfrac{\partial U}{\partial z}\right)$	$V = 2I\Delta\theta\Delta Z\dfrac{(N_A - N_B)_z}{\delta x}$

$$\frac{\partial}{\partial z}\left(\frac{\partial U}{\partial i}\right) \doteq \frac{1}{2}\,(2G\rho\Delta\theta\Delta z)$$

$$\cdot\left[\left[\frac{(N_A - N_B)_z}{\delta x} + \frac{(N_C - N_D)_z}{\delta x}\right]\frac{\delta x}{\delta i}\right.$$

$$\left. + \left[\frac{(N_A - N_C)}{\delta z} + \frac{(N_B - N_D)_z}{\delta z}\right]\frac{\delta z}{\delta i}\right]$$

$$\frac{\partial}{\partial z}\left(\frac{\partial U}{\partial i}\right) \doteq 2G\rho\Delta\theta\Delta z(N_A - N_D)_z/\delta i. \quad (50)$$

The vertical component of magnetic intensity V is

$$V = [I/G\rho]\frac{\partial}{\partial z}\left(\frac{\partial U}{\partial i}\right)$$

$$= 2I\Delta\theta\Delta z(N_A - N_D)_z/\delta i. \quad (51)$$

In a similar manner, the horizontal component of magnetic intensity H, for the direction of polarization i, is

$$H = 2I\Delta\theta\Delta z(N_A - N_D)_x/\delta i. \quad (52)$$

To calculate H, the same model is used but the chart is rotated 90 degrees so that ray $n = 60$ ($\theta = 90°$) is in the direction of the positive x axis. With the chart rotated to this new position, a dot may have a positive or negative value as the x coordinate of dot is positive or negative. To avoid any ambiguity of positioning of the model, the midpoint of the vector δi should be considered as the center of the model.

Caution should be used in the choice of the magnitude of δi for it must be as small as possible and still give an accurate value for the difference $(N_A - N_D)$.

From equations (51) and (52) special equations may be written as summarized in Table 2. The units of these equations are cgs when I is in cgs. If gamma values are desired, then the results must be multiplied by 10^5.

Acknowledgments

The author wishes to express his appreciation to the management of the Aerojet-General Corporation for their permission to publish this paper which is based on lecture notes prepared by the author while in their employ.

He would also like to thank the management of the Phelps Dodge Corporation for the opportunity to publish this paper and to express his gratitude to Mr. George Rogers, Chief Geophysicist of Phelps Dodge, for his encouragement and support in the preparation of the first lecture course offered by Aerojet.

References

Hubbert, M. King, 1948, A line-integral method of computing the gravitational effects of two-dimensional masses: Geophysics, v. 13, p. 215–225.

Nettleton, L. L., 1940, Geophysical prospecting for oil: New York, McGraw-Hill Book Co., Inc.

TWO-DIMENSIONAL FREQUENCY ANALYSIS AND DESIGN
OF GRID OPERATORS

BRENT D. FULLER*

Grid operators designed to accomplish specific purposes on potential field data may be interpreted as filters with frequency responses in a two-dimensional frequency domain. Such an interpretation allows a convenient analysis of the effects of grid operators and provides a means for their design.

Existing operators for obtaining second and fourth vertical derivations, residuals, and analytic continuation are analyzed and compared in the frequency domain. Operators are designed to accomplish continuation, band-pass, low-pass, and high-pass filtering, and to filter according to strike direction.

Introduction

Since the inception of magnetic and gravitational subsurface investigation, several types of operations have been devised by which uninteresting variations may be removed from a two-dimensional set of potential field data in order to emphasize those variations which may prove more interesting. By such operations, regional trends may be removed to investigate variations of small areal extent or, conversely, local variations may be removed in order to explore deeper or larger geologic structure. Among these operations are the derivative methods, the so-called "residual" methods, and analytic continuation, although the latter may have a different or broader objective.

All of these operations involve the convolution of data with a mathematical function, or set of "weights," which may be interpreted as a numerical filter. Several sets of weights have been derived by different techniques for each of the above operations and some comparison of their effects is necessary. Early comparisons (Griffin, 1949; Peters and Elkins, 1953; Rosenbach, 1953; Rosenbach, 1954) were made on the basis of particular sets of data resulting in the unhappy circumstance that, of two sets of weights, one might look more favorable one time and the other more favorable another time (Peters and Elkins, 1953; Rosenbach, 1953). Clearly, a more general type of comparison, and one which is not dependent on data, is desirable. The interpretation of operators as filters

allows a comparison to be made in terms of their effects on various frequencies present in the data to be operated upon. Dean (1958) recognized the utility of frequency domain interpretation of such operators and discussed the frequency responses of certain analytic continuation schemes. Byerly (1965) included response curves for certain of the second derivative schemes. Meskó (1965) presented frequency curves for several second derivative operators and general residual schemes.

All the frequency analyses to date, however, have been one-dimensional (radial). Dean (1958) showed that a function which is radially symmetric has a radially symmetric Fourier transform, leading to the conclusion that a one dimensional frequency analysis is sufficient to specify the frequency response of a radially symmetric operator. In actual practice, however, operators for geophysical data are convoluted with *discrete* data specified on a square grid, which is exactly equivalent to discrete, square grid specification of the operator. The result is that radial symmetry is lost, although the operator, and hence its frequency response, remains symmetric about each cartesian coordinate axis. This loss of radial symmetry makes necessary a two-dimensional frequency analysis for complete specification of the frequency response.

It is convenient to treat the operators as numerical filters applied to an equi-spaced grid of data in an *x-y* plane. The frequency

---

* University of California, Berkeley, California.

esponse may then be obtained by Fourier transformation with respect to both the x and y coordinates and presented as contours in an f_x-f_y plane, where f_x is frequency (or avenumber) in the x direction, and f_y is frequency (or wavenumber) in the y direction. In this manner, the averaging procedures normally employed with radial operators and the loss of radial symmetry due to discrete data specification are included in the operator and their effects included in the two-dimensional frequency response.

Certain attention has been given to the grid spacing of data submitted to the operations discussed here (Reford, 1961). By choosing the frequency axes of the frequency response plots to be in units of cycles/data interval, grid spacing is eliminated as a variable to be considered when speaking of the effect of the operators. Changing the grid spacing (or data interval) simply moves the frequency domain representation of a particular waveform in space to a different location in a frequency response plot. One may vary grid spacing so that a particular anticipated waveform lies in a desirable region of the frequency response of a particular operator.

The concept of a two-dimensional frequency domain also allows the design of other useful filters which might otherwise be overlooked. The frequency response plots presented herein are intended as a catalog from which to choose filter operators for particular purposes and for particular data, as a means of determining how data has been, or will be, affected by the use of these operators, and as a guide for design of special purpose two-dimensional filters.

General Theory

Grid or two-dimensional filtering may be described by the two-dimensional convolution integral,

$$\phi'(x, y)$$

$$= \int_{-\infty}^{\infty} \int_{-\infty}^{\infty} f(\alpha, \beta)\phi(x - \alpha, y - \beta)d\alpha d\beta \quad (1)$$

where

$\phi(x, y)$ is the input data

$\phi'(x, y)$ is the filtered output
$f(x, y)$ is the filtering function.

In order that a filtering function be useful, it must be of a finite extent. If $f(x, y)$ becomes zero for $|x| \geq X$ and $|y| \geq Y$, then (1) may be replaced by

$$\phi'(x, y)$$

$$= \int_{-X}^{X} \int_{-Y}^{Y} f(\alpha, \beta)\phi(x - \alpha, y - \beta)d\alpha d\beta. \quad (2)$$

Denoting the Fourier transform of a function by the corresponding capital letter with a frequency argument and taking the Fourier transform of (2), we have

$$\Phi'(f_x, f_y) = F(f_x, f_y)\Phi(f_x, f_y). \quad (3)$$

Equation (3) makes clear the filtering effect of the function $f(x, y)$. The spectrum of the input is modified by multiplication by the function $F(f_x, f_y)$ in order to arrive at the output. Convolution in the space domain is equivalent to multiplication in the frequency domain. The Fourier transform of $f(x, y)$, also known as the frequency response, is given by

$$F(f_x, f_y)$$

$$= \int_{-X}^{X} \int_{-Y}^{Y} f(x, y)e^{-2\pi i(f_x x + f_y y)}dydx. \quad (4)$$

If $f(x, y)$ is even with respect to both the x and y coordinates, equation (4) becomes

$$F(f_x, f_y) = 4 \int_{0}^{X} \int_{0}^{Y} f(x, y) \cos 2\pi f_y y$$

$$\cdot \cos 2\pi f_x x dydx. \quad (5)$$

If we choose the space dimensions in units of data intervals, then f_x and f_y are in units of cycles per data interval. In the instance of discrete sampled data, the integral convolution of equation (2) is replaced by

$$\phi'(x, y) \cong \sum_{n=-Y/\Delta y}^{Y/\Delta y} \sum_{k=-X/\Delta x}^{X/\Delta x} f(k\Delta x, n\Delta y)$$

$$\cdot \phi(x - k\Delta x, y - n\Delta y)\Delta x \Delta y \quad (6)$$

or, replacing $f(k\Delta x, n\Delta y)\Delta x \Delta y$ by $W(k, n)$ and letting

$$\Delta x = \Delta y = 1 \text{ data interval}$$

then

$$\phi'(x, y)$$

$$\cong \sum_{n=-Y}^{Y} \sum_{k=-X}^{X} W(k, n)\phi(x - k, y - n). \quad (7)$$

If we constrain $f(x, y)$ to be even with respect to both coordinate axes, the frequency response of equation (5) may be approximated by

$$F(f_x, f_y) \cong 4 \sum_{n=0}^{Y} \sum_{k=0}^{X} W(k, n) \cos 2\pi n f_y$$

$$\cdot \cos 2\pi k f_x. \quad (8)$$

$W(k, n)$ are the set of weights to be given to the data values at coordinates (k, n) with respect to the point at which filtered output is desired. Equations (7) and (8) are readily amenable to computer techniques.

In filter design, we specify $F(f_x, f_y)$ and obtain $f(x, y)$, and subsequently $W(k, n)$, by inverse transformation of equation (4). Considering continuous functions, $f(x, y)$ is given by

$$f(x, y) = \int_{-f_{o_y}}^{f_{o_y}} \int_{-f_{o_x}}^{f_{o_x}} F(f_x, f_y)$$

$$\cdot e^{2\pi i (f_x x + f_y y)} df_x df_y \quad (9)$$

where f_{o_x} and f_{o_y} are cutoff frequencies beyond which the Fourier transform $F(f_x, f_y)$ is specified to be zero. For discrete weights it is convenient to choose these cutoffs as the Nyquist frequency or 0.5 cycles per data interval. Specifying $F(f_x, f_y)$ digitally, choosing $F(f_x, f_y)$ (and hence $f(x, y)$) to be even, (9) gives, in the discrete approximation,

$$W(k, n) \cong 4 \sum_{l=0}^{.5/\Delta f_x} \sum_{m=0}^{.5/\Delta f_y} F(l\Delta f_x, m\Delta f_y)$$

$$\cdot (\cos 2\pi l \Delta f_x k)(\cos 2\pi m \Delta f_y n)\Delta f_x \Delta f_y. \quad (10)$$

Equation (10) may be used in conjunction with a digitally specified frequency response in order to arrive at a set of weights with which to convolute the given data. $W(k, n)$ may be limited in its usefulness by extreme length or extent, in which case it must be shortened in some manner. This point will be discussed further in a later section.

The choice of operators which are constrained to be even with respect to the x and y axes requires the Fourier transform to be real and even. The possibility of phase shift (except for 180-degree phase shift) is thus obviated and there is no loss of generality as regards amplitude response.

Analysis of Operators

General considerations

All operators analyzed here have been presented by their respective authors as sets of radial weights $W(r_l)$ to be applied to average data values $\bar{\phi}(r_l)$ about a circle of radius r_l centered on the point at which filtered output is desired. The filtered output at a point (x, y) is then given by the sum of the products of $W(r_l)$ and $\bar{\phi}(r_l)$,

$$\phi'(x, y) = \sum_{l=0}^{N} \bar{\phi}(r_l) W(r_l) \quad (11)$$

where $N+1$ is the number of averaging circles employed and the circle r_0 is the point (x, y) at which filtered output is desired. The operation may be transformed to cartesian coordinates by distributing the radial weight for a particular circle among the discrete grid points which enter into the computation of average data about that circle. Then

$$\bar{\phi}(r) = \frac{1}{m} \sum_{p} \sum_{q} \phi(p, q) \quad (12)$$

where m is the number of data points on the particular circle and where the summation is over all p and q such that $\sqrt{p^2+q^2}=r$. Using (12), $\bar{\phi}(r)W(r)$ may be written

$$\bar{\phi}(r)W(r) = \sum_{p} \sum_{q} \phi(p, q)W(p, q) \quad (13)$$

where

$$W(p, q) = \frac{1}{m} W(r); \quad r = \sqrt{p^2 + q^2}. \quad (14)$$

The relation between the averaging circles and the cartesian grid points is represented graphically in Figure 1. By transformation to cartesian coordinates, the filtered output

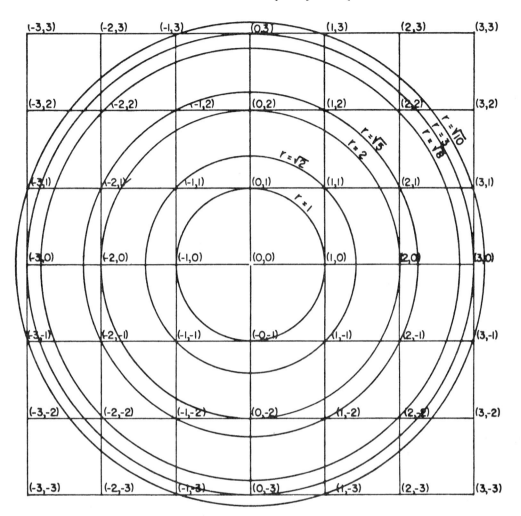

Fɪɢ. 1. Graphical relation between averaging rings and cartesian coordinate points for small radii.

may be concisely represented by the two-dimensional discrete convolution,

$$\phi'(k, n)$$

$$=\sum_{p=-Y}^{Y} \sum_{q=-X}^{X} \phi(k - p, n - q)W(p, q) \quad (15)$$

where X and Y are the coordinates of the nonzero weight which is farthest removed from the point (k, n). Where the choice of averaging circles by an author results in a particular grid point being ignored in the computation, that point has a cartesian weight of value zero.

The radial weights specified by the authors were converted to cartesian weights by (14) for the analysis here. The division of equation (14) results in some instances in small round off errors. Where this occurred, the cartesian weights were finely adjusted in the least significant figure in order that certain criteria of the scheme being investigated are met (i.e. for analytic continuation, $F(o, o) = 1$; for derivative schemes, $F(o, o) = 0$).

Tables 1 through 3 and Tables 4 through 6 list, respectively, the radial weights specified by the various authors and the calculated cartesian weights for the operators investigated. To compute frequency responses of

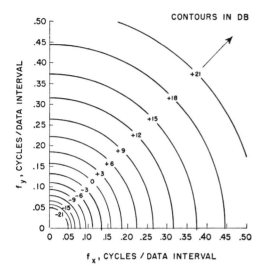

CONTOURS IN DB

FIG. 2. Analytic frequency response for an ideal second vertical derivative operator, in decibels.

the operators, direct use is made of equation (8). Computer programs were designed to calculate and plot $F(f_x, f_y)$ in decibels (db) where

$$F(f_x, f_y) \text{ in db} = 20 \log_{10} |F(f_x, f_y)|. \quad (16)$$

The symmetry of all the operators analyzed constrains $F(f_x, f_y)$ to be real, thus precluding the possibility of phase shift. It is still possible for phase reversal $(F(f_x, f_y) < 0)$ to occur and the presentation of frequency response or, more properly, amplitude response in decibels, prevents recognition of such an occurrence. $F(f_x, f_y)$ was included in printed computer output, however, and checked for phase reversals. Where these occur, it will be noted in the text.

In all computer plots, maximum and minimum contour values were chosen as ± 21 db. Hence the absence of contours above and below these values does not imply a flat response.

Derivative methods

The derivative methods analyzed are: the second vertical derivative operators due to Henderson and Zietz (1949), Peters (1949), Elkins (1951), Rosenbach (1953), Henderson (1960), and the center-point, one-ring technique mentioned in Nettleton (1954); the

fourth vertical derivative operator of Peters (1949).

The theoretical response of a true second derivative operator may be obtained in the following manner. Let a set of potential field data $\bar{\phi}(x, y)$ be represented in terms of its Fourier transform $\Phi(f_x, f_y)$ as follows:

$$\phi(x, y, z)\Big|_{z=0} = \int_{-\infty}^{\infty} \int_{-\infty}^{\infty} \Phi(f_x, f_y)$$
$$\cdot e^{2\pi i (f_x x + f_y y)} df_x df_y. \quad (17)$$

Differentiating (17) twice with respect to x and twice with respect to y, we obtain

$$\frac{\partial^2 \phi(x, y, z)}{\partial x^2}\Big|_{z=0} = -\int_{-\infty}^{\infty} \int_{-\infty}^{\infty} 4\pi^2 f_x^2 \Phi(f_x, f_y)$$
$$\cdot e^{2\pi i (f_x x + f_y y)} df_x df_y \quad (18)$$

$$\frac{\partial^2 \phi(x, y, z)}{\partial y^2}\Big|_{z=0} = -\int_{-\infty}^{\infty} \int_{-\infty}^{\infty} 4\pi^2 f_y^2 \Phi(f_x, f_y)$$
$$\cdot e^{2\pi i (f_x x + f_y y)} df_x df_y. \quad (19)$$

For measurements outside of the region of sources, as is the case with magnetic or gravity measurements at the surface of the earth, Laplace's equation holds, so that

$$\frac{\partial^2 \phi(x, y, z)}{\partial z^2}\Big|_{z=0} = -\frac{\partial^2 \phi(x, y, z)}{\partial x^2}\Big|_{z=0}$$
$$-\frac{\partial^2 \phi(x, y, z)}{\partial y^2}\Big|_{z=0}. \quad (20)$$

Substituting (18) and (19) into (20), we have

$$\frac{\partial^2 \phi(x, y, z)}{\partial z^2}\Big|_{z=0} = \int_{-\infty}^{\infty} \int_{-\infty}^{\infty} 4\pi^2 (f_x^2 + f_y^2) \Phi$$
$$\cdot (f_x, f_y) e^{2\pi i (f_x x + f_y y)} df_x df_y. \quad (21)$$

Comparison of equations (17) and (21) clearly indicates that, if we designate the Fourier transform of the second vertical derivative as $\Phi''(f_x, f_y)$, then

$$\Phi''(f_x, f_y) = 4\pi^2 (f_x^2 + f_y^2) \Phi(f_x, f_y) \quad (22)$$

which, letting

$$F(f_x, f_y) = 4\pi^2 (f_x^2 + f_y^2) \quad (23)$$

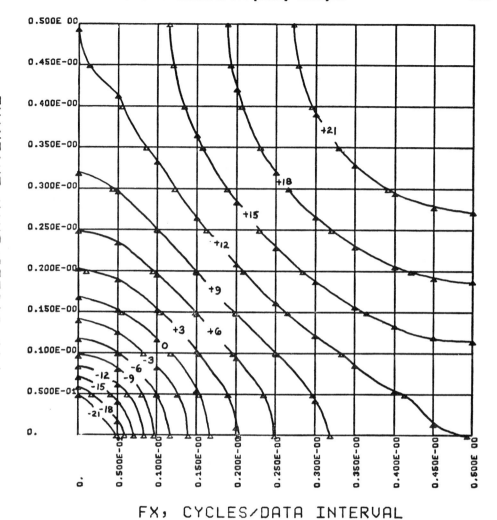

FY, CYCLES/DATA INTERVAL

FX, CYCLES/DATA INTERVAL

FIG. 3. Frequency response for Henderson and Zietz (1949, equation 10) second vertical derivative operator, in decibels.

may be written

$$\Phi''(f_x, f_y) = F(f_x, f_y)\Phi(f_x, f_y). \quad (24)$$

Equation (23), then, describes the frequency response of the filter or operator which gives, as output, the second derivative of the input. This is plotted in Figure 2 with a contour interval of three db and maximum and minimum contours of ± 21 db. By virtue of their name, second vertical derivative operators would be expected to have frequency responses similar to that of Figure 2.

Figures 3 through 5 illustrate the fre-

quency responses of three very similar operators proposed by Henderson and Zietz (1949) and repeated in this volume p. 606–614. By comparison with Figure 2, it is seen that the behavior of the response is generally close to ideal except for a reversal in curvature of high-frequency contours. This effect appears in several of the frequency responses considered in this paper and, although also dependent upon the particular operator, is a result of the loss of radial symmetry discussed earlier.

The responses of the Henderson and Zietz operators increase monotonically though at a

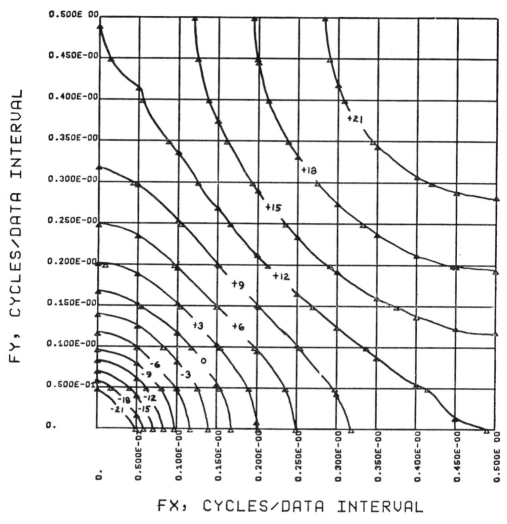

F<small>IG</small>. 4. Frequency response for Henderson and Zietz (1949, equation 13) second vertical derivative operator, in decibels.

somewhat slower rate than the theoretical response of Figure 2 would predict. Small variations, consisting of higher frequencies, will be amplified and emphasized at the expense of lower frequencies. Attention is called to the earlier remarks regarding the grid spacing of data to be operated upon. If grid spacing is chosen to be so small that random reading or correction errors appear as the high frequencies, then these will receive the maximum amplification and the resulting contour map may have closures about every point. On the other hand, choosing a larger grid spacing to smooth out the

random errors and place anomalous waveforms at the high end of the frequency axis leads to aliasing. On the assumption that random errors are small compared to the amplitudes of anomalous waveforms, the latter choice seems most desirable in the case of the Henderson-Zietz operators.

Figure 6 depicts the frequency response of the second vertical derivative scheme proposed by Peters (1949). This response is quite unlike that of a true second derivative and might better come under the heading of an imperfect high-pass filter. However, this scheme lessens the difficulty of extreme am-

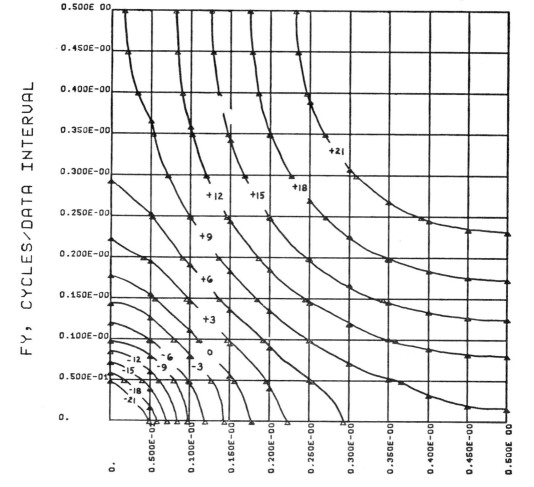

Fɪɢ. 5. Frequency response for Henderson and Zietz (1949, equation 15) second vertical derivative operator, in decibels.

plification at the higher frequencies. In general, the amplification at any frequency of Peters' operators is less than that of the Henderson and Zietz operators. Grid spacing of data to be operated upon should be chosen so that anomalous waveforms lie in the region of maximum amplification. Since anomalies consist of a wide band of space frequencies, this choice is not simple but some optimum grid spacing may be chosen. The dissimilarity of Peters' scheme to an ideal second vertical derivative operator does not preclude its usefulness.

The frequency responses of three second vertical derivative operators due to Elkins (1951) are depicted in Figures 7 through 9. The operator of Figure 7 provides a quite good high-pass filter with a wide band of zero db response and would be better classed with residual operators. The wide band of zero db response allows further quantitative determinations on the filtered output data. The operators of Figures 8 and 9 have a zero db pass band in the mid-frequency range, fall off slowly with increasing frequency, and rise again to zero db at the Nyquist frequencies to form a type of band-pass filter. The general contour shape of the Elkins operators is

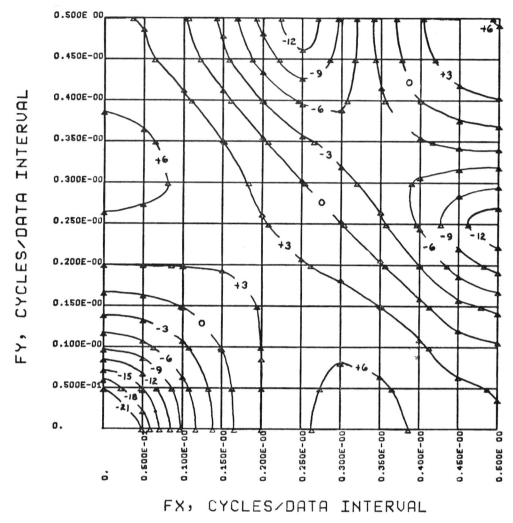

Fɪɢ. 6. Frequency response for Peters (1949, equation 27) second vertical derivative operator, in decibels.

similar to that of Peters' operators and the same remarks apply. In both cases, the description as "second vertical derivative operator" is somewhat of a misnomer.

The scheme of Rosenbach (1953), the center-point, one-ring scheme, and that of Henderson (1960) depicted in Figures 10, 11, and 12 respectively, are all similar to the previously described Henderson and Zietz system, in that they all have monotonically increasing responses. In this respect they approach the true second derivative. The remarks regarding extreme amplification of high frequencies also apply here.

The theoretical frequency response of a fourth vertical derivative is obtained in the same manner as that for the second vertical derivative by recognizing that Laplace's equation holds for derivatives of potentials outside of the region of sources. In this manner we find that the frequency response of a theoretical operator, which converts a set of data into its true fourth vertical derivative, is

$$F(f_x, f_y) = 16\pi^4(f_x^2 + f_y^2)^2. \qquad (25)$$

Equation (25) is plotted in Figure 13 and represents the goal of operators which ascribe to be fourth derivative operators.

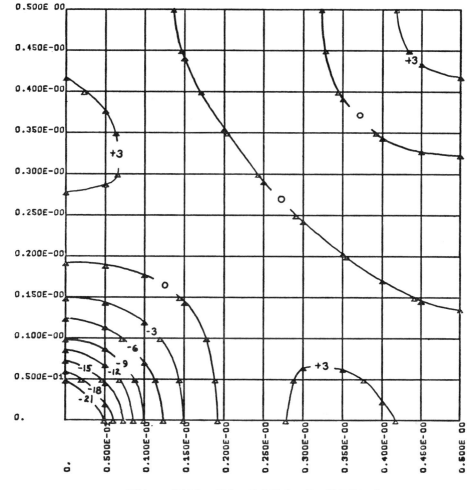

Fɪɢ. 7. Frequency response for Elkins (1951, equation 13) second vertical derivative operator, in decibels.

Only one fourth vertical derivative operator is considered here, that of Peters (1949), and its response is plotted in Figure 14. The contours of the response surface are similar in shape to those of the Peters' second derivative responses except for steeper gradients. The response bears little resemblance to the theoretical fourth derivative response, but, again, the operator may still be desirable in certain applications.

Residual methods

The goal of residual operators is to remove low frequency regional trends from a set of

data, leaving, presumably with a minimum of distortion, the higher frequency variations due to local geologic trends. In this respect, a residual operator is simply a high-pass filter. The three operators analyzed here have become popular through usage.

The frequency responses are shown in Figures 15 through 17. The center-point, one-ring method has a relatively narrow band of zero db response and hence its output would be distorted somewhat and not conducive to further quantitative determinations. The center-point, 2-ring and nine-point operators are better high-pass filters with wide bands of

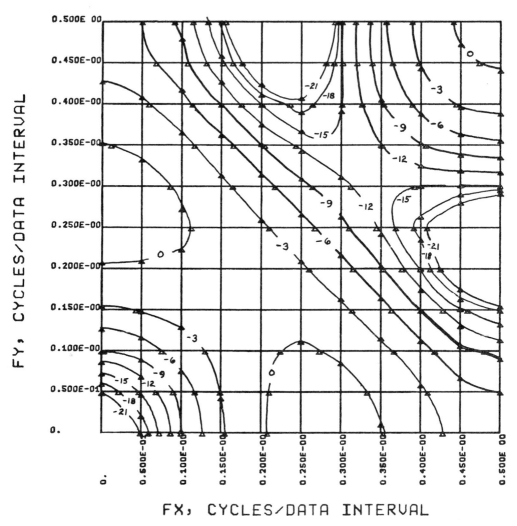

FIG. 8. Frequency response for Elkins (1951, equation 14) second vertical derivative operator, in decibels.

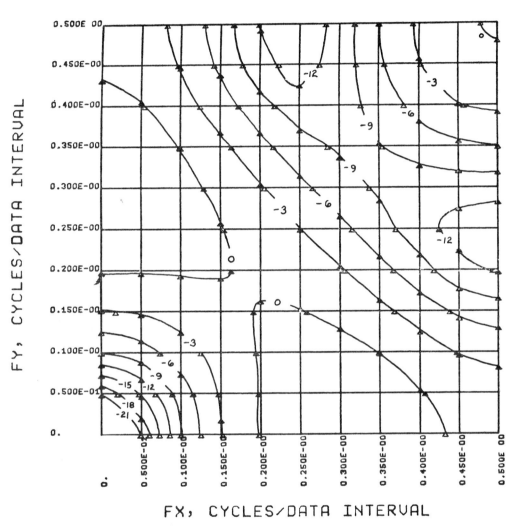

FIG. 9. Frequency response for Elkins (1951, equation 15) second vertical derivative operator, in decibels.

zero db response. These would be better suited to quantitative work after filtering. All three operators could be improved upon by making the gradient between the pass and reject bands steeper. This point will be considered in the section on operator design.

Analytic continuation

From the results of potential theory, the upward continuation of a potential $\phi(x, y, 0)$ in a source-free region to a height h above the plane $z=0$ is given by (Henderson and Zietz, 1949)

$$\phi(x, y, h) = \int_{-\infty}^{\infty}\int_{-\infty}^{\infty} \frac{h\phi(\alpha, \beta, 0)d\alpha d\beta}{2\pi[(x - \alpha)^2 + (y - \beta)^2 + h^2]^{3/2}}. \qquad (26)$$

Comparison of (26) with (1) and realization that the convolution integral is commutative allows recognition of (26) as a two-dimensional convolution and hence a filtering operation. The potential data $\phi(x, y, 0)$ is operated upon by the filtering function $f_u(x, y, h)$, in order to arrive at $\phi(x, y, h)$, where

$$f_u(x, y, h) = \frac{h}{2\pi[x^2 + y^2 + h^2]^{3/2}}. \qquad (27)$$

The theoretical frequency response of a true upward continuation operator may then be obtained by Fourier transformation of (27) or solution of the integral

$$F_u(f_x, f_y, h) = \int_{-\infty}^{\infty}\int_{-\infty}^{\infty} \frac{he^{-2\pi i(f_x x + f_y y)}}{2\pi[x^2 + y^2 + h^2]^{3/2}}\, dxdy. \qquad (28)$$

Since the function to be transformed is even with respect to x and y, equation (28) becomes

$$F_u(f_x, f_y, h) = 4\int_{0}^{\infty}\int_{0}^{\infty} \frac{h \cos 2\pi f_x x \cos 2\pi f_y y}{2\pi[x^2 + y^2 + h^2]^{3/2}}\, dxdy. \qquad (28a)$$

Reference to Erdelyi [1954, p. 11, equation (7)] yields the integration with respect to x after which (28a) becomes

$$F_u(f_x, f_y, h) = \frac{2\pi^{1/2}hf_x}{\Gamma(3/2)}\int_{0}^{\infty} \frac{K_1(2\pi f_x\sqrt{y^2 + h^2})}{\sqrt{y^2 + h^2}}\, dy. \qquad (28b)$$

The y integration is obtained by reference to Erdelyi [1954, p. 56, equation (44)] and (28b) becomes

$$F_u(f_x, f_y, h)$$
$$= \frac{\pi^{1/2}}{2\Gamma(3/2)} e^{-2\pi h(f_x^2 + f_y^2)^{1/2}}. \qquad (28c)$$

But, from Abramowitz and Stegun (1965, p. 255, equation 6.1.9),

$$\Gamma(\tfrac{3}{2}) = \tfrac{1}{2}\pi^{1/2} \qquad (29)$$

so that equation (28) finally becomes

$$F_u(f_x, f_y, h) = e^{-2\pi h(f_x^2 + f_y^2)^{1/2}}. \qquad (30)$$

Equation (30) describes the desired frequency response of an upward continuation operator. To arrive at a similar relation for downward continuation, we need only recognize that, if we upward continue a set of data a distance h and then downward continue the same distance h, we should arrive at the same data we started with. Then the following relation must hold in the frequency domain,

$$\Phi(f_x, f_y)$$
$$= F_d(f_x, f_y, h)F_u(f_x, f_y, h)\Phi(f_x, f_y). \qquad (31)$$

Substituting (30) in (31), we have, for the desired frequency response of a downward

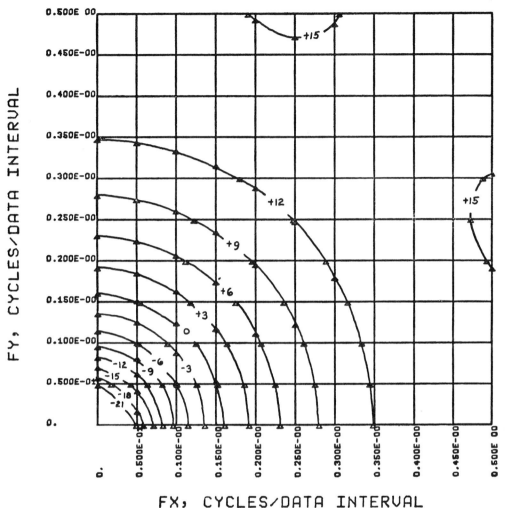

FIG. 10. Frequency response for Rosenbach (1953, Equation 16) second vertical derivative operator, in decibels.

continuation operator (source-free regions only),

$$F_d(f_x, f_y, h) = e^{2\pi h(f_x^2+f_y^2)1/2}. \quad (32)$$

Equation (30) is plotted in decibels in Figure 18 for $h=1$ data interval to depict the desired upward continuation response for that value of h. Because of the decibel presentation, changing signs on the contour values will convert the plot to that of the frequency response for downward continuation to $H=1$ data interval.

The frequency responses for Peters' (1949) operators for upward and downward con-

tinuation to $h=1$ data interval are presented, respectively, in Figures 19 and 20. Figure 19 resembles the ideal upward continuation response only in the very general sense that attenuation increases with increasing frequency. Figure 20, as the response of Peters' downward continuation ($h=1$) operator, behaves properly only at the very low frequencies. At the higher frequencies, where an ideal operator would continue to amplify, Peters' operator attenuates. Close inspection of the downward continued maps in Peters' (1949) original work reveals that the data interval was chosen such that

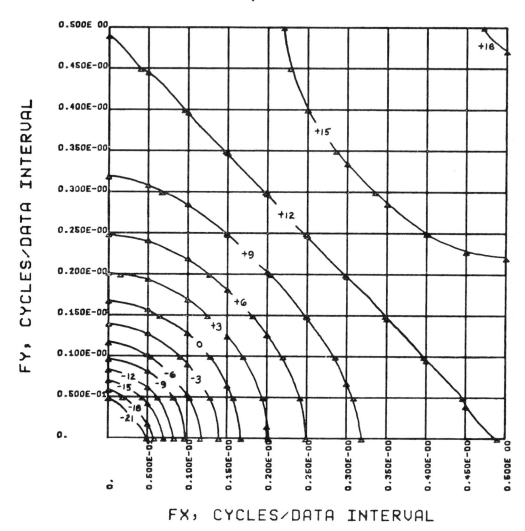

FX, CYCLES/DATA INTERVAL

Fɪɢ. 11. Frequency response for center-point, one-ring second vertical derivative operator, in decibels.

features of interest would lie at the low frequency end and thus be amplified. The attenuation at higher frequencies then becomes a noise elimination technique and, though dissimilar to the ideal response, not at all undesirable. Some phase reversals occur in Peters' $(h=1)$ operators, the most serious occurring when amplitude response is -12 db. Others occur where attenuation is greater. All the phase reversals occur at the higher frequencies, however, and, by the previous remarks, are irrelevant since they do not affect features of interest.

Figures 21 and 22 illustrate frequency responses for the upward and downward continuation $(h=1$ data interval) schemes of Henderson (1960). Again, upward continuation response is generally correct, except for contour shape, in that attenuation increases with increasing frequency. The downward continuation operator response is quite similar to that of the corresponding ideal operator, although the gradient is slightly smaller. Henderson's downward continuation operator would require a different choice of data interval than that of Peters in order to place features of interest in the region of greatest amplification. Phase

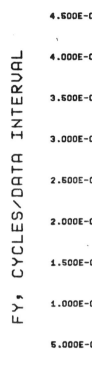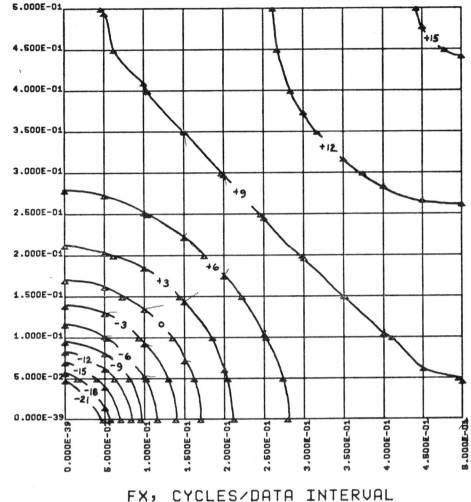

FIG. 12. Frequency response for Henderson (1960) second vertical derivative operator, in decibels.

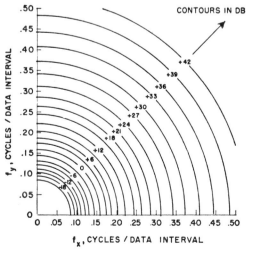

FIG. 13. Analytic frequency response for an ideal fourth vertical derivative operator, in decibels.

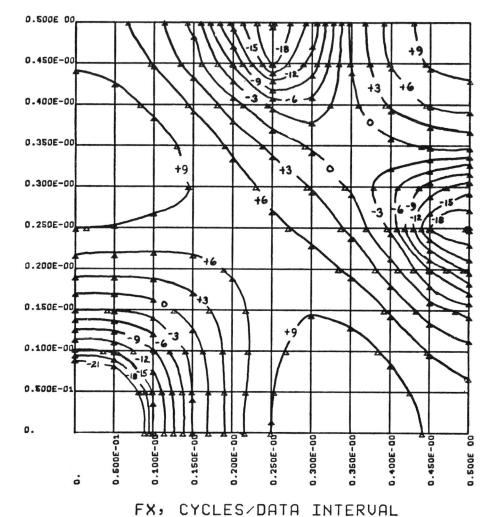

FIG. 14. Frequency response for Peters (1949, equation 28) fourth vertical derivative operator, in decibels.

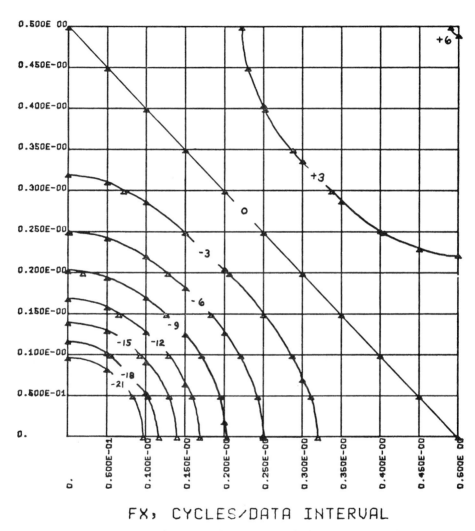

FIG. 15. Frequency response for center-point, one-ring residual operator, in decibels.

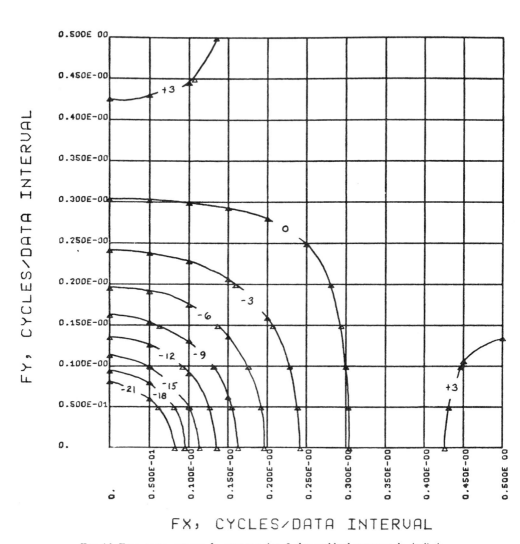

FIG. 16. Frequency response for center-point, 2-ring residual operator, in decibels.

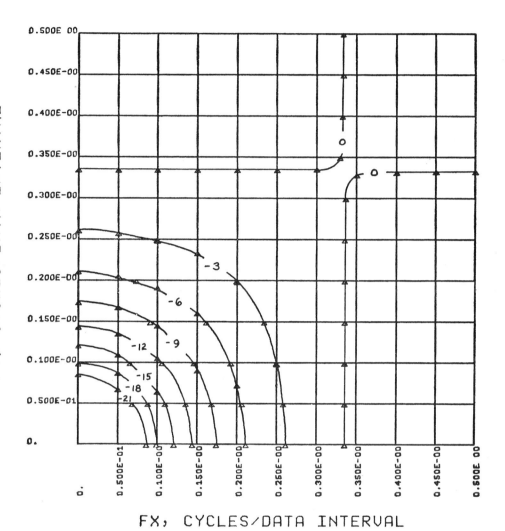

FIG. 17. Frequency response for nine-point residual operator, in decibels.

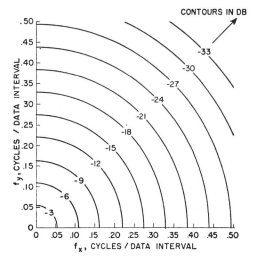

FIG. 18. Analytic frequency response for an ideal upward continuation ($h=1$ data interval) operator, in decibels.

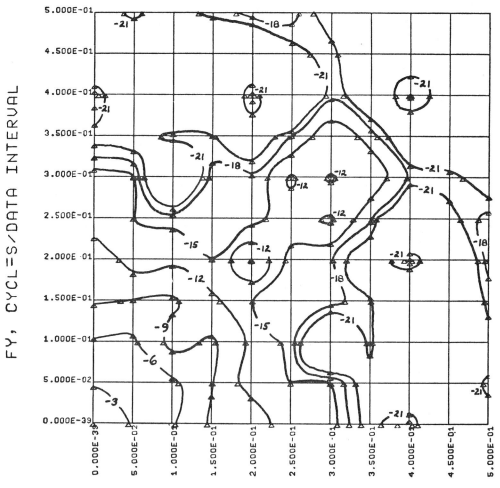

FIG. 19. Frequency response for Peters (1949) upward continuation ($h=1$ data interval) operator, in decibels.

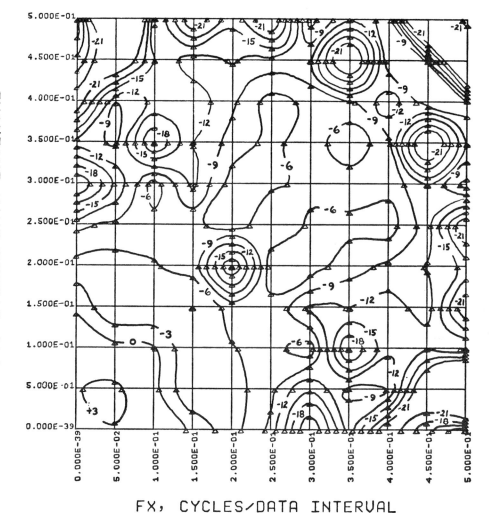

FIG. 20. Frequency response for Peters (1949) downward continuation ($h=1$ data interval) operator, in decibels.

eversals occur in Henderson's upward continuation ($h=1$) operator, the most serious occurring when amplitude response is -9 db. No phase reversals occur in his downward continuation ($h=1$) operator.

In Figure 23, equation (30) is plotted for $h=2$ data intervals, thus presenting the response of the corresponding ideal upward continuation operator. The ideal response for downward continuation may be obtained by mentally changing signs on the contours of Figure 23.

Figures 24 and 25 are the frequency responses of Peters' (1949) upward and downward continuation operators, respectively, to $h=2$ data intervals. Much the same remarks as made for Peters' $h=1$ data interval schemes apply. Upward continuation is only generally correct and downward continuation is correct only at the low frequencies. The worst phase reversals occur at -12 db amplitude response in the upward continuation operator and at -3 db amplitude response in the downward continuation operator and occur at the higher frequencies.

Figures 26 and 27 represent the frequency responses for the upward and downward continuation operators, respectively, of Hen-

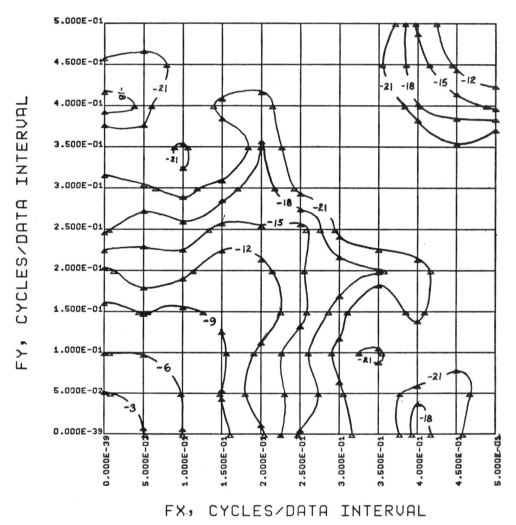

FIG. 21. Frequency response for Henderson (1960) upward continuation ($h=1$ data interval) operator, in decibels.

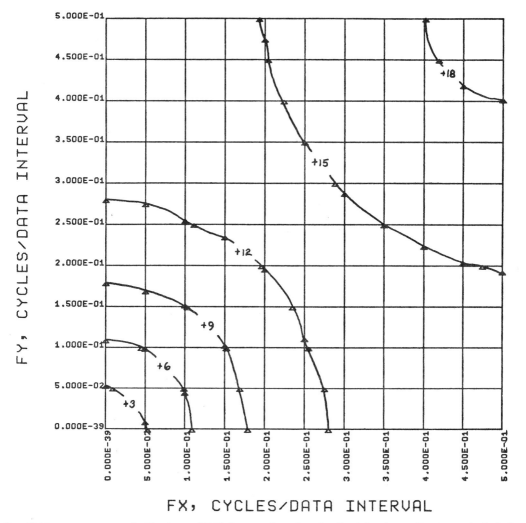

FIG. 22. Frequency response for Henderson (1960) downward continuation ($h=1$ data interval) operator, in decibels.

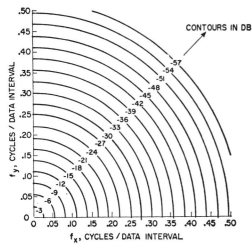

FIG. 23. Analytic frequency response for an ideal upward continuation ($h=2$ data intervals) operator, in decibels.

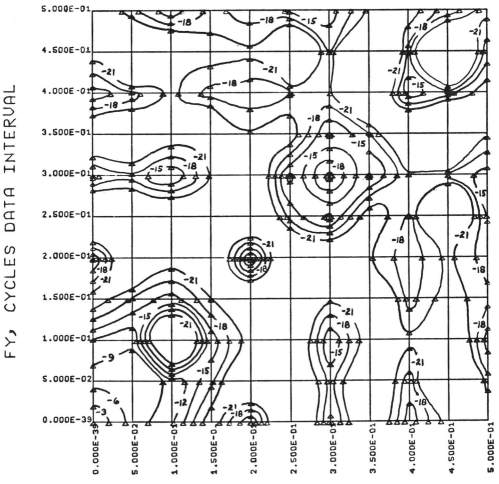

FIG. 24. Frequency response for Peters (1949) upward continuation ($h=2$ data intervals) operator, in decibels.

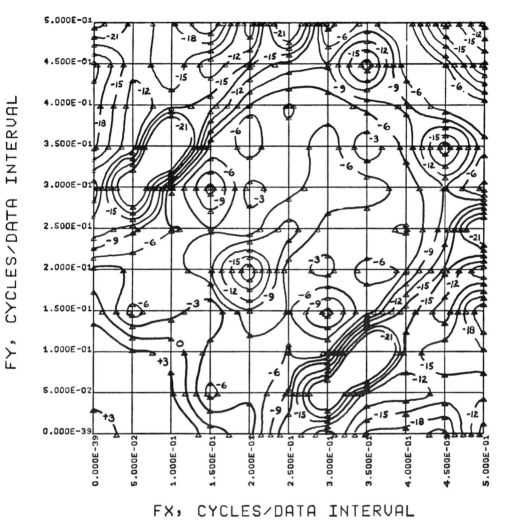

FIG. 25. Frequency response for Peters (1949) downward continuation ($h=2$ data intervals) operator, in decibels.

derson (1960) for continuation to $h=2$ data intervals. It is interesting to note that Henderson's downward continuation operator is consistently more accurate than his corresponding upward continuation operator although downward continuation is inherently a more difficult problem. The worst phase reversal in Henderson's upward continuation ($h=2$ data intervals) operator occurs where amplitude response is -12 db and no phase reversals occur in the downward continuation operator.

Design of Operators

General considerations

The design of filter operators may be accomplished by utilization of equation (9). Computer programs were designed to accept, as input, a digital specification of the desired frequency response and to inverse transform the desired frequency response by approximate evaluation of (9), thus giving, as output, a set of discrete weights which will accomplish the desired purpose. In most

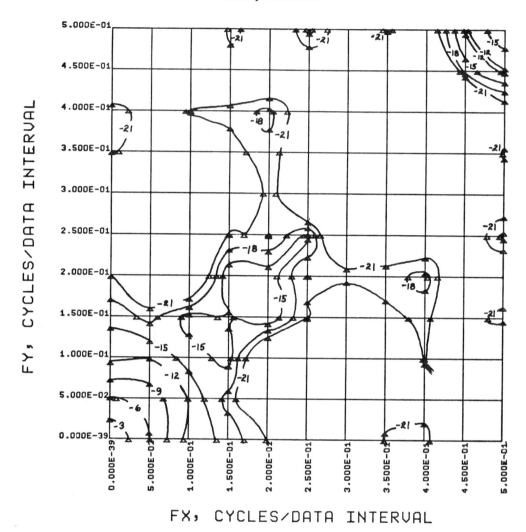

FIG. 26. Frequency response for Henderson (1960) upward continuation ($h=2$ data intervals) operator, in decibels.

instances, the set of weights will be too large in areal extent to be of practical value and must be shortened in some manner. To accomplish this purpose, the derived operator may be multiplied by the function

where X and Y are the tolerated x and y (or K and n) extents, in data intervals, of the operator. For all operators derived here, X and Y have been chosen as seven data inter-

$$S(K, n) = \begin{cases} \dfrac{1}{2}\left\{1 + \cos\left[\dfrac{\pi(K^2 + n^2)^{1/2}}{(X^2 + Y^2)^{1/2}}\right]\right\} & \text{for } \begin{cases} |K| \leq X \\ |n| \leq Y \end{cases} \\[20pt] 0 & \text{for } \begin{cases} |K| > X \\ \quad\text{or} \\ |n| > Y \end{cases} \end{cases} \qquad (33)$$

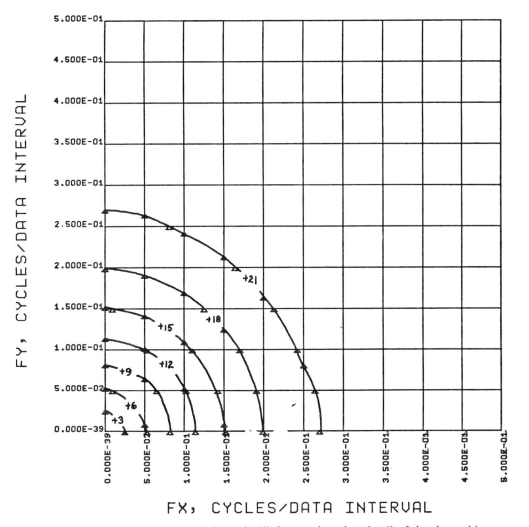

FX, CYCLES/DATA INTERVAL

FIG. 27. Frequency response for Henderson (1960) downward continuation ($h = 2$ data intervals) operator, in decibels.

vals so that maximum loss of record due to operator extent will be six data points on each edge of the record. Then, if we let $W'(K, n)$ be the operator derived directly by inverse transform, the final shortened operator is

$$W(K, n) = W'(K, n)S(K, n). \quad (34)$$

The shortening of the operator will, of course, affect the frequency response. A Fourier transform is then carried out upon $W(K, n)$ in order to obtain the actual response of the shortened operator. This procedure constitutes a check on whether the choice of X and Y is large enough to provide an adequate approximation of the desired frequency response.

Plotting procedures are identical to those used in the analysis of operators. Contour interval is 3 db and the maximum and minimum contours plotted are ± 21 db. All derived operators are tabulated in Table 6 of Appendix A.

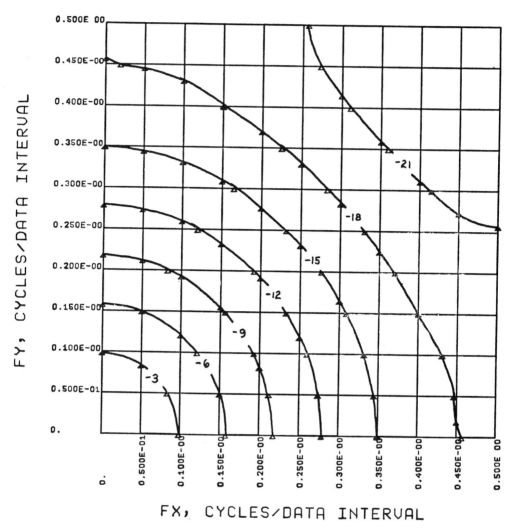

FY, CYCLES/DATA INTERVAL

FX, CYCLES/DATA INTERVAL

FIG. 28. Frequency response for derived upward continuation ($h=1$ data interval) operator.

Analytic continuation

By use of equation (27), an upward continuation operator may be directly calculated. In terms of data intervals, and including the required shortening, the upward continuation operator becomes

$$W_u(K, n, h) = \frac{hS(K, n)}{2\pi[K^2 + n^2 + h^2]^{3/2}}. \quad (35)$$

Subsequent Fourier transformation of the derived operator according to equation (8) results in a frequency response which may be compared to the theoretical response of

equation (30) to judge the accuracy and desirability of the operator.

By use of equation (35), an operator is designed for upward continuation to one data interval and tabulated in Table 6. The corresponding frequency response is illustrated in Figure 29. The comparison with the theoretical response of Figure 19 is favorable although not exact. It is noted that, although the general form of the response agrees well with Figure 19, the gradient of the surface formed by the operator response is less steep than that of the theoretical response. In view of the small areal extent of the operator,

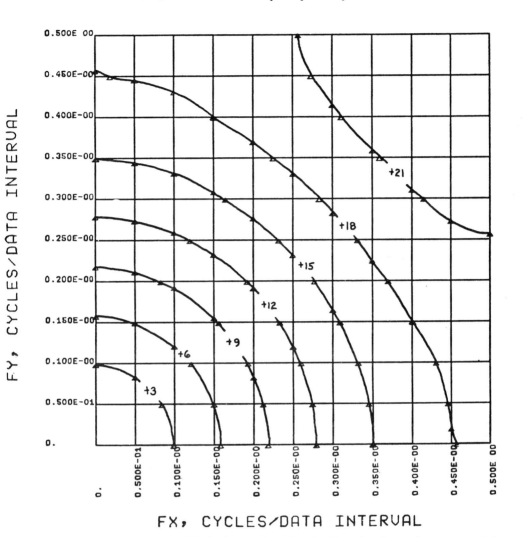

FX, CYCLES/DATA INTERVAL

Fig. 29. Frequency response for inverse of derived upward continuation ($h=1$ data interval) operator or design criterion for downward continuation ($h=1$ data interval) operator, in decibels.

however, it is both sufficient and practical for most purposes and appears to be preferable to previously accepted upward continuation operators.

To obtain a corresponding downward continuation operator, we recognize from equation (31) that

$$F_d(f_x, f_y, h) = \frac{1}{F_u(f_x, f_y, h)}. \quad (36)$$

The desired frequency response for a downward continuation operator then is given by the inverse of the corresponding upward continuation operator response. In the decibel presentation, the inverse operation is accomplished by changing the signs of the contour values. Figure 29 represents the desired frequency response or design specification for an operator which accomplishes downward continuation to $h=1$ data interval. Subsequent inverse Fourier transform and shortening yields the desired operator. Figure 30 illustrates the frequency response of an operator obtained in this manner. Though the response is not exactly accurate, the operator is again sufficient and practical

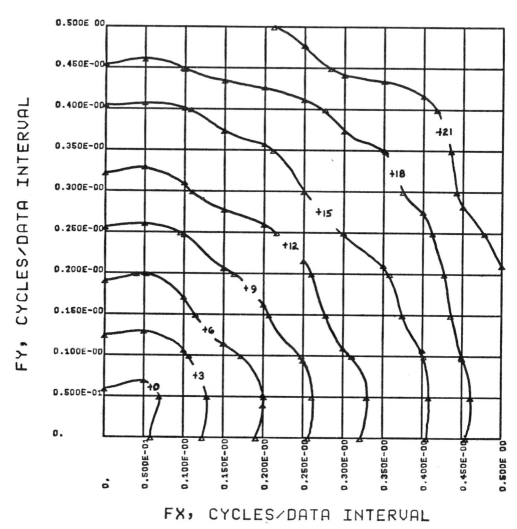

FIG. 30. Frequency response for derived downward continuation ($h=1$ data interval) operator, in decibels.

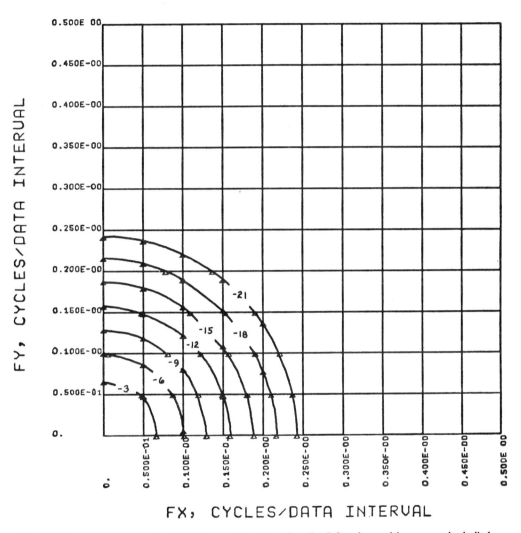

FIG. 31. Frequency response for derived upward continuation ($h=2$ data intervals) operator, in decibels.

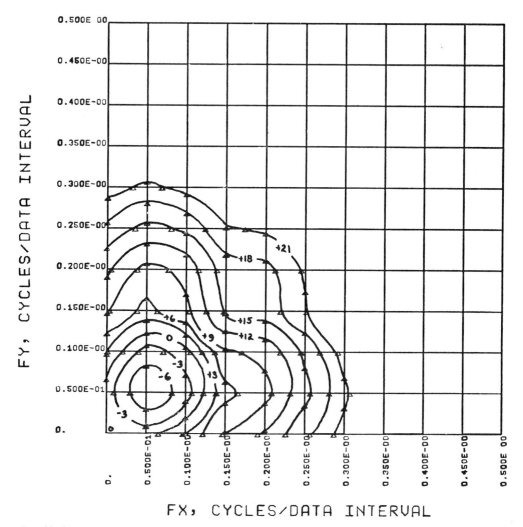

Fɪɢ. 32. Frequency response for derived downward continuation ($h=2$ data intervals) operator, in decibels.

for most purposes and, especially in view of its small size, may be easily applied to potential field data.

Figure 31 illustrates the frequency response for an operator designed to upward continue potential data to $h=2$ data intervals. The response closely approximates that of Figure 23. Using the inverse of Figure 31 as a design criterion, as in the previous case, response of the derived downward continuation operator is illustrated in Figure 32. Figure 32 is not an adequate approximation to the inverse of Figure 31 because of too severe shortening. The choice of X and Y is too small to allow the high amplification

necessary in the low frequencies. For continuation to greater depths, the problem becomes more difficult and larger operators are required. Figure 32 is retained as an example of an incorrect choice of X and Y in design. Phase reversals are entirely absent in all the derived continuation operators.

Conventional filtering

The concepts of low-pass, high-pass and band-pass filtering commonly applied to one-dimensional filtering may be easily extended to two-dimensional filtering and, in fact, may be a more descriptive terminology than the use of terms such as regional or residual

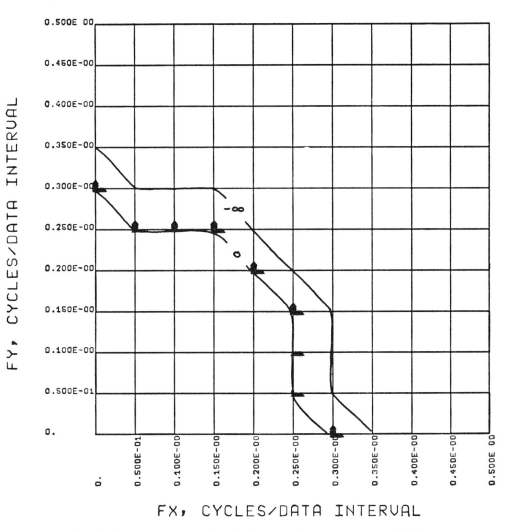

Fig. 33. Frequency response of an ideal low-pass filtering operator, in decibels.

operators. It has already been mentioned that residual operators ascribe to being high-pass filters. An operator which retains only the regional variations is then a low-pass filter. Band-pass filtering may find application in removing the regional variations and the very high frequency variations, retaining a band of frequencies, with minimum distortion, within which the sought-after geologic information may be found.

Design is accomplished by (a) digital specification of the desired frequency response, (b) inverse Fourier transform according to equation (9), (c) shortening of the operator according to equations (33) and (34), and (d) Fourier transform according to equation (8) in order to check the actual frequency response of the derived operator.

Figure 33 is the desired frequency response for a low-pass filter. The cutoff frequency may be varied at will. The rather odd shape of the contours is due to specification of the response on a square grid and the "stacking" of computer-plotted points is due to the specified sharp cutoff. Figure 34 illustrates the actual response of the derived operator, after shortening. The passband (zero db response) is relatively flat and the cutoff between pass and reject bands is sharp, as desired.

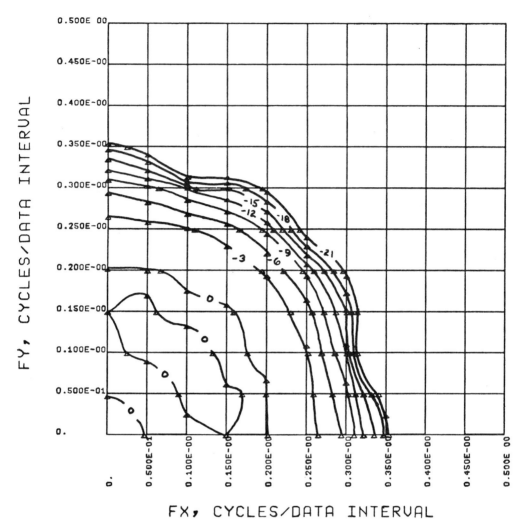

FIG. 34. Frequency response of derived low-pass filtering operator, in decibels.

In a similar manner, one can propose a desired high-pass response and derive a high-pass operator. The response for the derived operator is illustrated in Figure 35. The cutoff is sharp and the passband is relatively flat except at very high frequencies where there is some amplification. The transition between the pass and reject bands is sharper than that of the residual operators analyzed in a previous section although the latter, with the exception of the center-point, one-ring operator, do not exhibit the undesirable amplification at high frequencies.

The desired response for a band-pass filter is depicted in Figure 36. The actual re-

sponse of the derived operator is illustrated in Figure 37. The passband is reasonably flat and cutoffs on both sides of the passband are sharp. The location of the cutoffs in the frequency domain may be varied at will during design in order to fulfill particular purposes.

Small phase reversals occur in these filters, the largest occurring where amplitude response is −26 db. Such phase reversals may be considered negligible.

A special purpose strike sensitive filter

By modification of the concept of velocity filtering (Embree et al., 1963) currently

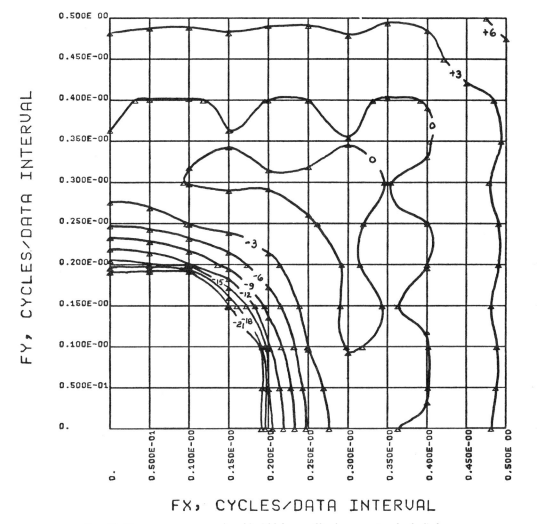

FIG. 35. Frequency response of an ideal high-pass filtering operator, in decibels.

employed in seismic data processing, a filter which is sensitive to the strike of linear trends may be derived. Such a filter may prove useful in an area of more than one linear trend, only one of which is known to control mineralization or one of which is known to be irrelevant.

Consider the data on an x-y plane as a set of traverses in the x direction with the y coordinate of the traverse varying from $-Y$ to $+Y$. Figure 38 represents a hypothetical situation with a single linear feature which is of the same form from trace to trace. Let the traverse for $y=0$ be designated $f(x)$ and have a Fourier transform (with respect to x only)

of $F(f_x)$. The slope of the linear trend in the x-y plane is S and the strike $N\theta E$ so that

$$S = \frac{\Delta x}{\Delta y}$$
$$\theta = \mathrm{Tan}^{-1}S.$$

The entire set of data in the x-y plane may be represented in terms of the $y=0$ traverse as

$$\phi(x, y) = f(x - sy).$$

The two-dimensional Fourier transform of $\phi(x, y)$ is then

$$\phi(f_x, f_y)$$
$$= \int_{-Y}^{Y} \int_{-\infty}^{\infty} f(x - sy)e^{-2\pi i(f_x x + f_y y)}dxdy. \quad (37)$$

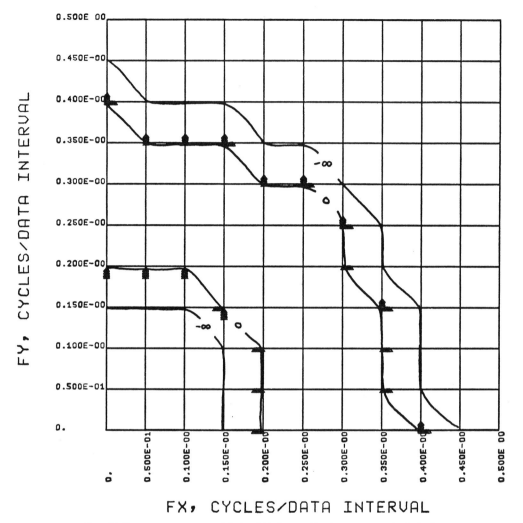

FIG. 36. Frequency response of derived high-pass filtering operator, in decibels.

By hypothesis,

$$f(x) = \int_{-\infty}^{\infty} F(f)e^{2\pi i f_x x} df_x$$

which demands that

$$f(x - sy) = \int_{-\infty}^{\infty} F(f)e^{-2\pi i f_x ys}e^{2\pi i f_x x}.$$

By the Fourier transform pair relationship, then,

$$F(f)e^{-2\pi i f_x sy} = \int_{-\infty}^{\infty} f(x - sy)e^{-2\pi i f_x x}. \quad (38)$$

Substituting equation (38) in equation (37), we have

$$\Phi(f_x, f_y) = \int_{-Y}^{Y} F(f)e^{-2\pi i y (f_x s + f_y)} dy.$$

Integrating with respect to y, the two dimensional Fourier transform becomes

$$\Phi(f_x, f_y) = 2YF(f)\frac{\sin\left[2\pi Y(f_x s + f_y)\right]}{\left[2\pi Y(f_x s + f_y)\right]} \cdot \quad (39)$$

Equation (39) is a function of the form $\sin x/x$ with a maximum at $x=0$. The maxi-

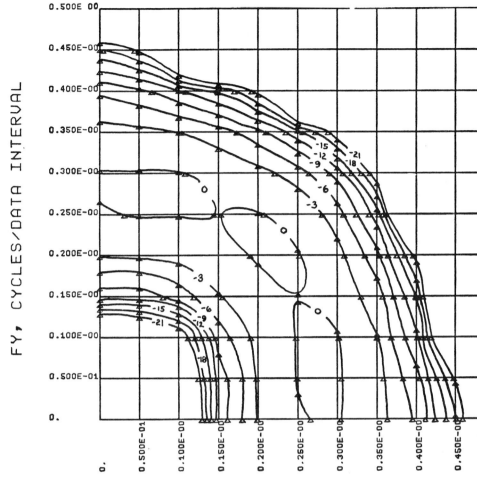

FIG. 37. Frequency response of derived band-pass filtering operator, in decibels.

num in the f_x-f_y plane is along the line

$$sf_x + f_y = 0$$

or

$$\frac{f_y}{f_x} = -\frac{\Delta x}{\Delta y}. \qquad (40)$$

Thus a linear trend in the space domain will be evidenced by a linear trend in the frequency domain. The fact that the positive slope transforms to a negative slope is of no concern since, in all filters designed here, the frequency response is specified to be even with respect to both axes. However, a simple

redefinition of the Fourier transform with respect to only one of the coordinate axes would cause positive slopes in the space domain to transform to positive slopes in the frequency domain.

On the basis of (40), a filter may be designed to pass or reject certain linear features of varying strikes. Figure 39 is the design specification for a filter which will pass linear features with north to northeast strikes. By inverse Fourier transformation and shortening, the weights of Table 7 are obtained. Subsequent Fourier transformation results in the actual frequency response of Figure 40.

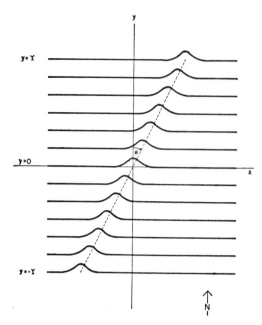

FIG. 38. Representation of two dimensional data over a linearly striking body as a sequence of one-dimensional profiles.

tion and an operator of larger areal extent, resulting in better results, i.e. more complete rejection of the unwanted trend and more complete retention of the trend to be retained.

This technique of "strike filtering" is presented here only as an interesting application of the design of special purpose filters in a two-dimensional frequency domain. Its intended effect on data differs markedly from that of previously discussed operators which have become familiar through usage. A detailed discussion should include, as well as the theoretical effect on linear features, theoretical and experimental results on many types of features. Clearly, the utility of such a device depends on the characteristics of the features to be excluded and those to be retained. It is anticipated that further investigations will be pursued in the near future. Until then, the operators for strike filtering presented in Table 6 should be used only with considerable discretion and awareness.

Figure 41 represents a similar procedure for a filter which passes strikes from northeast to east.

In Figure 42, the cylinder and fault are added to give an artificial gravity map with two distinct linear trends. All data are generated on a 50×50 equi-spaced grid.

The filter of Figure 41 (east-northeast pass) is applied to the data of Figure 42 and results in the filtered gravity map of Figure 43. Although some character in the fault has been lost, the characteristic gradient remains and the cylinder feature has been almost entirely removed.

The application of the filter of Figure 40 (north-northeast pass) to the data of Figure 42 results in the filtered output of Figure 44. Only a slight gradient remains as evidence of the fault, and the essential features of the cylinder response are retained.

Attention should be called to the fact that the strike filtering operators derived here were designed to be of such a size that "filter loss" of data points amounts to only six data points on each edge of the record. Larger sets of data would allow relaxation of this restric-

Conclusions

The concept of a two-dimensional frequency domain allows a unique and practical interpretation of operators designed to filter a two-dimensional grid of data. The design of operators may be accomplished by simple Fourier transform techniques, and computer methods allow fast and efficient means of calculation and presentation.

Many of the operators discussed here were derived before the advent of computer techniques and had to consider, in addition to operator accuracy and extent, the factor of ease of computation, since computations were accomplished largely by hand and by desk calculator. This last consideration may be somewhat relaxed today with the aid of high-speed computers, allowing more emphasis upon the ability of an operator to accomplish a specified purpose with a minimum loss of data due to operator size.

No single filter or operator should be considered routine or necessary to the interpretation of all data. Cautious and intelligent choices from the many operators available

(Continued on page 703)

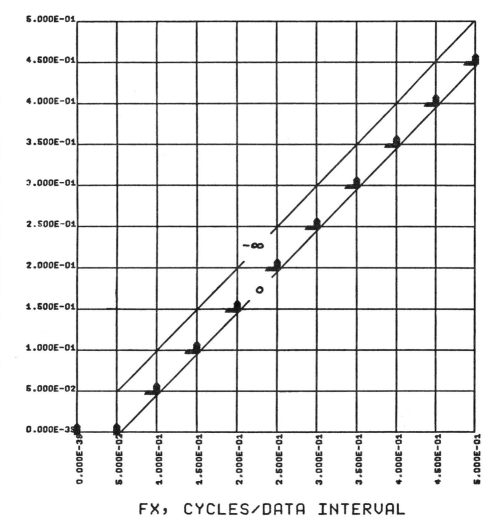

FIG. 39. Frequency response of an ideal north-northeast pass strike filtering operator, in decibels.

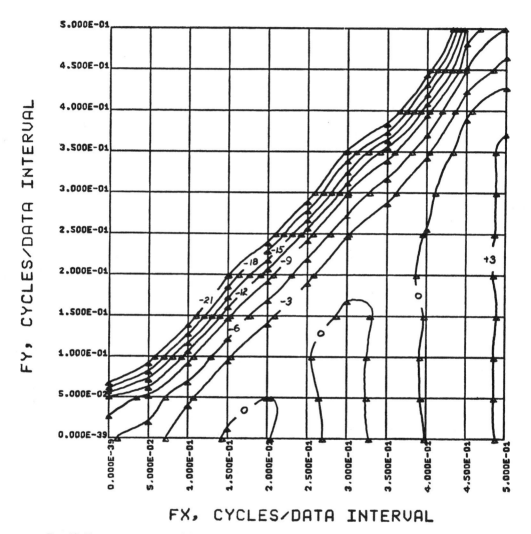

FIG. 40. Frequency response of derived north-northeast pass strike filtering operator, in decibels.

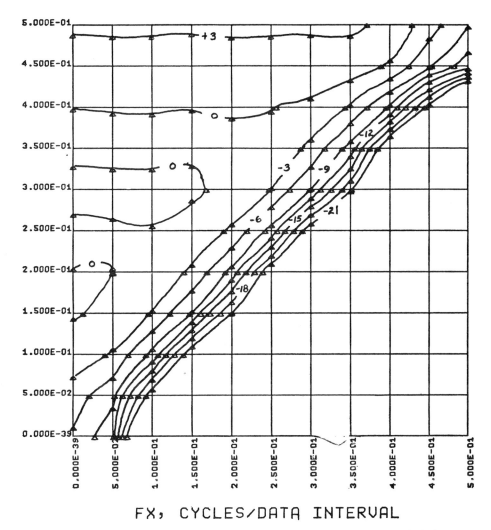

FIG. 41. Frequency response of derived east-northeast pass strike filtering operator, in decibels.

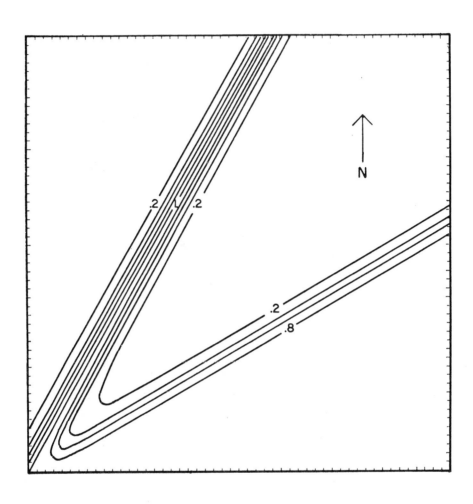

GRAVITY, FAULT + CYLINDER
CONTOUR INTERVAL .2 MGAL

FIG. 42. Simulated gravity over horizontal cylinder striking N 30° E and vertical fault striking N 60° E.

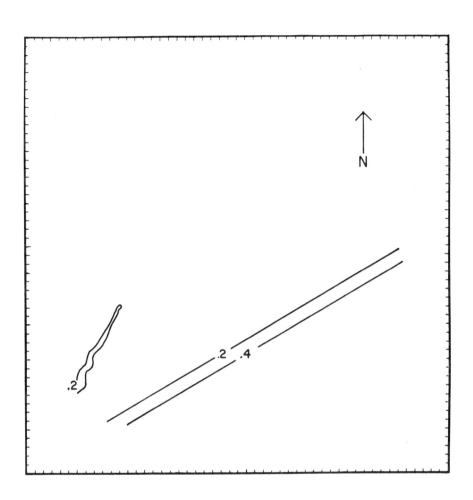

OUTPUT, ENE PASS FILTER
CONTOUR INTERVAL .2 MGAL

FIG. 43. Gravity over cylinder and fault after filtering with east-northeast pass strike filtering operator.

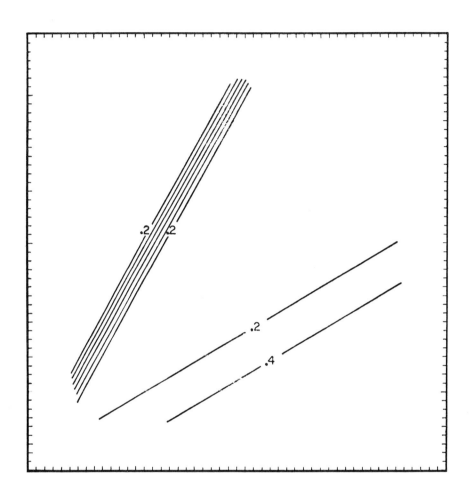

NNE PASS FILTER
CONTOUR INTERVAL .2 MGAL

FIG. 44. Gravity over cylinder and fault after filtering with north-northeast pass strike filtering operator.

nd use of design principles for particular ets of data should be foremost in the data rocessing procedure. Too often, maps are beled simply as "residual" or "second de-vative" with an utmost confidence that the perator employed accomplishes the stated esult and a seeming disregard for the details f the method used. A knowledge of the frequency response of any operator employed is ital to a well-informed interpretation.

Acknowledgments

The author wishes to express his gratitude o the National Science Foundation for con-inued support under a National Science 'oundation Graduate Fellowship and to the Computer Center of the University of Cali-ornia at Berkeley for the donation of com-uter services necessary to accomplish this roject.

Sincere thanks are due Dr. S. H. Ward, cientific advisor and chairman of the thesis ommittee for his encouragement and criti-isms through this project. Drs. D. Sakrison nd L. Cohen, as members of the thesis com-nittee, offered valuable criticisms prior to ompletion. The encouragement of fellow raduate students is also gratefully acknowl-dged.

Last, although certainly not least, the uthor wishes to thank his wife, Mrs. Beryl Fuller, for the long hours spent in typing of he manuscript, and Mr. Dick Heidemann or drafting of the figures.

References

Abramowitz, M., and Stegun, I. A., 1965, Handbook of mathematical functions: National Bureau of Standards.

Byerly, P. E., 1965, Convolution filtering of gravity and magnetic maps: Geophysics, v. 30, no. 2, p. 281–283.

Dean, W. C., 1958, Frequency analysis for gravity and magnetic interpretation: Geophysics, v. 23, no. 1, p. 97–127.

Elkins, T. A., 1951, The second derivative method of gravity interpretation: Geophysics, v. 16, no. 1, p. 29–50.

Embree, P., Burg, J. P., and Backus, M. M., 1963, Wide band velocity filtering—The pie slice process: Geophysics, v. 28, no. 6, 948–976.

Erdelyi, A., editor, 1954, Bateman manuscript project, tables of integrals transforms, Vol. I: New York, McGraw-Hill Book Co. Inc.

Henderson, R. G. and Zietz, I., 1949 and this volume, The computation of second vertical derivatives of geomagnetic fields: Geophysics, v. 14, no. 4, p. 508–516.

Henderson, R. G., 1960, A comprehensive system of automatic computation in magnetic and gravity interpretation: Geophysics, v. 25, no. 3, p. 569–585.

Griffin, W. R., 1949, Residual gravity in theory and practice: Geophysics, v. 14, no. 1, p. 39–56.

Meskó, A., 1965, Some notes concerning the frequency analysis for gravity interpretation: Geophys. Prosp., v. 13, no. 3, p. 475–488.

Nettleton, L. L., 1954, Regionals, residuals, and structure: Geophysics, v. 19, no. 1, p. 1–22.

Peters, L. J., 1949, The direct approach to magnetic interpretation and its practical application: Geophysics, v. 14, no. 3, p. 290–319.

——— 1954, Letter to the Editor on "The Use and Accuracy of Second Derivative Coefficients": Geophysics, v. 19, no. 2, p. 341–342.

Peters, L. J., and Elkins, T. A., 1953, Discussion of "A Contribution to the Computation of the 'Second Derivative' from Gravity Data": Geophysics, v. 18, no. 4, p. 894–912.

Reford, M. S., 1961, Airborne magnetometer surveys for petroleum exploration: Aero Service Corporation Publication.

Rosenbach, O., 1953, A contribution to the computation of the "second derivative" from gravity data: Geophysics, v. 18, no. 4, p. 894–909.

——— 1953, Reply to Peters, L. J. and Elkins, T. A., Geophysics, v. 18, no. 4, p. 909–912.

——— 1954, Quantitative studies concerning the vertical gradient and second derivative methods of gravity interpretation: Geophys. Prosp. v. 2, no. 2.

Steenland, N. C., 1954, Review of "Quantitative Studies Concerning the Vertical Gradient and Second Derivative Methods of Gravity Interpretation," Geophysics, v. 19, no. 4, p. 836, 837.

Appendix A

Table 1. Radial weights

Operator	W (0)	W (1)	$W(\sqrt{2})$	W (2)	$W(\sqrt{5})$	$W(\sqrt{9.23})$
Second derivative						
H and Z* eqn. (10)	6.185	−8.374	2.189			
H and Z eqn. (13)	6.000	−8.000	2.000			
Peters eqn. (27)	1.156	0.256	−0.445		−1.359	0.392
H and Z eqn. (15)	7.000	−10.667	4.000	−0.333		
Elkins eqn. (13)	1.067	−0.133	−0.267		−0.667	
Elkins eqn. (14)	0.571	0.286			−0.857	
Elkins eqn. (15)	0.710	0.258	−0.194		−0.774	
Rosenbach eqn. (16)	4.000	−3.000	−1.333		0.333	
Center-point, 1-ring	4.000	−4.000				
Fourth derivative						
Peters eqn. (28)	1.753	0.170	−1.036		−2.384	1.497
Residual						
Center-point, 1-ring	1.000	−1.000				
Center-point, 2-ring	1.000	−0.500	−0.500			
Nine point	0.890	−0.445	−0.445			

* Henderson and Zietz.

NOTE: $W(\sqrt{9.23})$ is the weight applied to the average about circles of radius $\sqrt{8}, \sqrt{9}, \sqrt{10}$.

Table 2. Peters' continuation radial weights

		Upward		Downward	
		$h=1$	$h=2$	$h=1$	$h=2$
k	r_k	$W(r_k)$	$W(r_k)$	$W(r_k)$	$W(r_k)$
0	0	.1464	.0528	.3969	.4197
1	1	.2113	.0918	.3026	.3532
2	$\sqrt{2}$	.1494	.1139	.3356	.5460
3	$\sqrt{5}$	.1264	.1153	.2749	.4071
4	$\sqrt{8.5}$	.0862	.1151	.2234	.2668
5	$\sqrt{17}$	.0778	.1207	.0356	−.0442
6	$\sqrt{34}$	.0528	.0902	−.2194	−.3762
7	$\sqrt{58}$	.0346	.0637	−.3413	−.6236
8	$\sqrt{99}$	.0206	.0400	.1248	.3130
9	$\sqrt{125}$	.0949	.1965	−.1331	−.1395

h is the extent of continuation, in data intervals.
$r = \sqrt{8.5}$ indicates average about radii of $\sqrt{8}$ and $\sqrt{9}$
$r = \sqrt{17}$ indicates average about radii of $\sqrt{16}$ and $\sqrt{18}$
$r = \sqrt{34}$ indicates average about radii of $\sqrt{36}$ and $\sqrt{32}$
$r = \sqrt{99}$ indicates average about radii of $\sqrt{100}$ and $\sqrt{98}$

Table 3. Henderson (1960) radial weights

			$W(r_i)$		
r_i	Upward continuation $h=1$	Upward continuation $h=2$	Downward continuation $h=1$	Downward continuation $h=2$	Second derivation
0	0.11193	0.04034	4.8948	16.1087	2.82994
1	0.32193	0.12988	−3.0113	−13.2209	−2.49489
$\sqrt{2}$	0.06062	0.07588	0.0081	−0.4027	0.05173
$\sqrt{5}$	0.15206	0.14559	−0.5604	−1.9459	−0.39446
$\sqrt{8}$	0.05335	0.07651	−0.0376	−0.0644	0.00932
$\sqrt{13}$	0.06586	0.09902	−0.0689	−0.0596	−0.00732
$\sqrt{25}$	0.06650	0.11100	−0.0605	−0.0522	0.00304
$\sqrt{50}$	0.05635	0.10351	−0.0534	−0.0828	0.00219
$\sqrt{136}$	0.03855	0.07379	−0.0380	−0.0703	0.00040
$\sqrt{274}$	0.02273	0.04464	−0.0227	−0.0443	0.00004
$\sqrt{625}$	0.03015	0.05998	−0.0302	−0.0600	0.00000

Table 4. Cartesian grid weights

Second derivative

Operator	$W(0,0)$	$W(1,0)$	$W(2,0)$	$W(3,0)$	$W(0,1)$	$W(1,1)$	$W(2,1)$	$W(3,1)$	$W(0,2)$	$W(1,2)$
H and Z eqn. (10)	6.184	−2.094			−2.094	0.548				
H and Z eqn. (13)	6.000	−2.000			−2.000	0.500				
H and Z eqn. (15)	7.000	−2.667	−0.083		−2.667	1.000			−0.083	
Peters eqn. (27)*	1.156	0.064		0.025	0.064	−0.111	−0.171	0.025		−0.171
Elkins eqn. (13)	1.068	−0.034			−0.034	−0.067	−0.083			−0.083
Elkins eqn. (14)	0.572	0.071			0.071		−0.107			−0.107
Elkins eqn. (15)	0.710	0.065			0.065	−0.049	−0.097			−0.097
Rosenbach eqn. (16)	4.000	−0.750			−0.750	−0.334	0.042			0.042
Center-point, 1-ring	4.000	−1.000			−1.000					

Fourth derivative

Operator	$W(0,0)$	$W(1,0)$	$W(2,0)$	$W(3,0)$	$W(0,1)$	$W(1,1)$	$W(2,1)$	$W(3,1)$	$W(0,2)$	$W(1,2)$
Peters eqn. (28)*	1.752	0.041		0.094	0.041	−0.259	−0.298	0.094		−0.298

Residual

Operator	$W(0,0)$	$W(1,0)$	$W(2,0)$	$W(3,0)$	$W(0,1)$	$W(1,1)$	$W(2,1)$	$W(3,1)$	$W(0,2)$	$W(1,2)$
Center-point, 1-ring	1.000	−0.250			−0.250					
Center-point, 2-ring	1.000	−0.125			−0.125	−0.125				
Nine point	0.888	−0.111			−0.111	−0.111				

* Peters' operators include the further weights tabulated below:

	$W(2,2)$	$W(0,3)$	$W(1,3)$
Peters eqn. (27)	0.025	0.025	0.025
Peters eqn. (28)	0.094	0.094	0.094

Table 5. Peters (1949). Analytic continuation nonzero cartesian weights

	Upward continuation $h=1$	Upward continuation $h=2$	Downward continuation $h=1$	Downward continuation $h=2$
$W(0,0)$	0.1464	0.0528	0.3969	0.4197
$W(1,0)$	0.0528	0.0229	0.0756	0.0883
$W(3,0)$	0.0108	0.0144	0.0279	0.0334
$W(4,0)$	0.0097	0.0151	0.0045	-0.0055
$W(6,0)$	0.0066	0.0113	-0.0274	-0.0470
$W(10,0)$	0.0013	0.0025	0.0078	0.0196
$W(0,1)$	0.0528	0.0229	0.0756	0.0883
$W(1,1)$	0.0376	0.0285	0.0839	0.1365
$W(2,1)$	0.0158	0.0144	0.0344	0.0509
$W(1,2)$	0.0158	0.0144	0.0344	0.0509
$W(2,2)$	0.0108	0.0144	0.0279	0.0334
$W(0,3)$	0.0108	0.0144	0.0279	0.0334
$W(3,3)$	0.0097	0.0151	0.0045	-0.0055
$W(7,3)$	0.0043	0.0080	-0.0427	-0.0779
$W(0,4)$	0.0097	0.0151	0.0045	-0.0055
$W(4,4)$	0.0066	0.0113	-0.0274	-0.0470
$W(10,5)$	0.0119	0.0246	-0.0166	-0.0174
$W(0,6)$	0.0066	0.0113	-0.0274	-0.0470
$W(8,6)$	0.0013	0.0025	0.0078	0.0196
$W(3,7)$	0.0043	0.0080	-0.0427	-0.0779
$W(7,7)$	0.0013	0.0025	0.0078	0.0196
$W(6,8)$	0.0013	0.0025	0.0078	0.0196
$W(0,10)$	0.0013	0.0025	0.0078	0.0196
$W(5,10)$	0.0119	0.0246	-0.0166	-0.0174

Table 6. Henderson (1960) nonzero cartesian weights

	Upward continuation $h=1$	Upward continuation $h=2$	Downward continuation $h=1$	Downward continuation $h=2$	Second vertical derivative
$V(0, 0)$	0.11193	0.04034	4.8948	16.1087	2.82994
$V(1, 0)$	0.08048	0.03247	−0.7528	−3.3052	−0.62372
$V(5, 0)$	0.00554	0.00925	−0.0050	−0.0044	0.00025
$V(25, 0)$	0.00151	0.00300	−0.0015	−0.0030	0.00000
$V(0, 1)$	0.08048	0.03247	−0.7528	−3.3052	−0.62372
$V(1, 1)$	0.01515	0.01897	0.0020	0.1007	0.01293
$V(2, 1)$	0.01901	0.01820	−0.0701	−0.2432	−0.04931
$V(7, 1)$	0.00470	0.00863	−0.0044	−0.0069	0.00018
$V(1, 2)$	0.01901	0.01820	−0.0701	−0.2432	−0.04931
$V(2, 2)$	0.01334	0.01913	−0.0094	0.0161	0.00233
$V(3, 2)$	0.00823	0.01238	−0.0086	−0.0074	−0.00092
$V(2, 3)$	0.00823	0.01238	−0.0086	−0.0074	−0.00092
$V(4, 3)$	0.00554	0.00925	−0.0050	−0.0044	0.00025
$V(3, 4)$	0.00554	0.00925	−0.0050	−0.0044	0.00025
$V(0, 5)$	0.00554	0.00925	−0.0050	−0.0044	0.00025
$V(5, 5)$	0.00470	0.00863	−0.0044	−0.0069	0.00018
$W(10, 6)$	0.00482	0.00922	−0.0048	−0.0088	0.00005
$V(1, 7)$	0.00470	0.00863	−0.0044	−0.0069	0.00018
$W(15, 7)$	0.00284	0.00558	−0.0028	−0.0055	0.00000
$W(24, 7)$	0.00151	0.00300	−0.0015	−0.0030	0.00000
$W(6, 10)$	0.00482	0.00922	−0.0048	−0.0088	0.00005
$W(7, 15)$	0.00284	0.00558	−0.0028	−0.0055	0.00000
$W(20, 15)$	0.00151	0.00300	−0.0015	−0.0030	0.00000
$W(15, 20)$	0.00151	0.00300	−0.0015	−0.0030	0.00000
$W(7, 24)$	0.00151	0.00300	−0.0015	−0.0030	0.00000
$W(0, 25)$	0.00151	0.00300	−0.0015	−0.0030	0.00000

Table 7. Derived operators

	Upward continuation $h=1$	Downward continuation $h=1$	Upward continuation $h=2$	Downward continuation $h=2$	Low pass	High pass	Band-Pass	North-northeast pass	East-northeast pass
$W(0,0)$	0.21045	6.33260	0.07014	76.0219	0.28250	0.90000	0.38000	0.50250	0.50250
$W(0,1)$	0.07255	−1.87262	0.04893	−43.2376	0.16965	−0.19156	0.10069	0.20165	−0.24065
$W(0,2)$	0.01699	0.62523	0.02238	20.9871	0.00139	0.01978	−0.10568	0.00226	0.04739
$W(0,3)$	0.00526	−0.40022	0.00946	−11.4951	−0.02910	−0.01693	0.01212	0.02114	−0.05274
$W(0,4)$	0.00195	0.30572	0.00407	7.1712	0.00710	0.04415	0.02222	0.00162	0.03404
$W(0,5)$	0.00078	−0.22966	0.00177	−4.7578	0.00861	−0.03444	0.00000	0.00615	−0.02583
$W(0,6)$	0.00031	0.15635	0.00075	3.0669	−0.00136	0.01113	0.00575	0.00084	0.01766
$W(1,0)$	0.07255	−1.87262	0.04893	−43.2376	0.16965	−0.19156	0.10069	−0.24065	0.20165
$W(1,1)$	0.03850	0.18694	0.03629	21.2085	0.09179	−0.09144	−0.03713	−0.02139	−0.02139
$W(1,2)$	0.01259	−0.08015	0.01827	−9.3036	−0.01608	−0.01388	−0.08606	0.06259	−0.05380
$W(1,3)$	0.00443	0.07013	0.00823	5.1458	−0.02189	0.02381	0.01730	0.00192	0.00192
$W(1,4)$	0.00174	−0.06177	0.00367	−3.4007	0.00799	0.00582	0.01001	0.01114	−0.00484
$W(1,5)$	0.00071	0.04727	0.00163	2.4115	0.00440	−0.00486	0.00038	0.00119	0.00119
$W(1,6)$	0.00029	−0.03255	0.00069	−1.6306	−0.00411	−0.00400	0.00281	0.00332	−0.00008
$W(2,0)$	0.01699	0.62523	0.02238	20.9871	0.00139	0.01978	−0.10568	0.04739	0.00226
$W(2,1)$	0.01259	−0.08015	0.01827	−9.3036	−0.01608	−0.01388	−0.08606	−0.05380	0.06259
$W(2,2)$	0.00633	0.03079	0.01096	3.7050	−0.02579	0.01343	−0.00860	−0.01826	−0.01826
$W(2,3)$	0.00284	−0.02782	0.00566	−2.0314	−0.00225	0.00986	0.02125	0.03067	−0.02360
$W(2,4)$	0.00126	0.02150	0.00275	1.2841	0.00931	0.00144	−0.00322	0.00144	0.00144
$W(2,5)$	0.00055	−0.01627	0.00128	−0.8785	−0.00067	−0.00349	0.00564	0.00590	−0.00159
$W(2,6)$	0.00023	0.01067	0.00056	0.5678	−0.00433	0.00217	0.00217	0.00072	0.00072
$W(3,0)$	0.00526	−0.40022	0.00946	−11.4951	−0.02910	−0.01693	0.01212	−0.05274	0.02114
$W(3,1)$	0.00443	0.07013	0.00823	5.1458	−0.02189	0.02381	0.01730	0.00192	0.00192
$W(3,2)$	0.00284	−0.02782	0.00566	−2.0314	−0.00225	0.00986	0.02125	−0.02360	0.03067
$W(3,3)$	0.00155	0.01941	0.00332	1.2214	0.01083	−0.00036	0.00141	−0.01375	−0.01375
$W(3,4)$	0.00078	−0.01538	0.00177	−0.7869	0.00432	−0.00733	−0.00315	0.01524	−0.01032
$W(3,5)$	0.00037	0.01130	0.00087	0.5684	−0.00212	−0.00025	0.00358	0.00090	0.00090
$W(3,6)$	0.00016	−0.00742	0.00038	−0.3737	0.00057	0.00115	−0.00273	0.00267	−0.00032
$W(4,0)$	0.00195	0.30572	0.00407	7.1712	0.00710	0.04415	0.02222	0.03404	0.00162
$W(4,1)$	0.00174	−0.06177	0.00367	−3.4007	0.00799	0.00582	0.01001	−0.00484	0.01114
$W(4,2)$	0.00126	0.02150	0.00275	1.2841	0.00931	0.00144	−0.00322	0.00144	0.00144
$W(4,3)$	0.00078	−0.01538	0.00177	−0.7869	0.00432	−0.00733	−0.00315	−0.01032	0.01524
$W(4,4)$	0.00043	0.01149	0.00101	0.4458	−0.00412	−0.00352	0.00412	−0.00875	−0.00875
$W(4,5)$	0.00021	−0.00824	0.00052	−0.3023	−0.00304	−0.00053	0.00000	0.00657	−0.00380
$W(4,6)$	0.00009	0.00503	0.00023	0.1794	0.00181	0.00102	−0.00405	0.00043	0.00043
$W(5,0)$	0.00078	−0.22966	0.00177	−4.7578	0.00861	−0.03444	0.00000	−0.02583	0.00615
$W(5,1)$	0.00071	0.04727	0.00163	2.4115	0.00440	−0.00486	0.00038	0.00119	0.00119
$W(5,2)$	0.00055	−0.01627	0.00128	−0.8785	−0.00067	−0.00349	0.00564	−0.00159	0.00590
$W(5,3)$	0.00037	0.01130	0.00087	0.5684	−0.00212	−0.00025	0.00358	0.00090	0.00090
$W(5,4)$	0.00021	−0.00824	0.00052	−0.3023	−0.00304	−0.00053	0.00000	−0.00380	0.00657
$W(5,5)$	0.00011	0.00564	0.00027	0.2041	−0.00141	0.00188	0.00000	−0.00424	−0.00424
$W(5,6)$	0.00005	−0.00316	0.00011	−0.1119	0.00043	0.00033	0.00020	0.00198	−0.00092
$W(6,0)$	0.00031	0.15635	0.00075	3.0669	−0.00136	0.01113	0.00575	0.01766	0.00084
$W(6,1)$	0.00029	−0.03255	0.00069	−1.6306	−0.00411	−0.00400	0.00281	−0.00008	0.00332
$W(6,2)$	0.00023	0.01067	0.00056	0.5678	−0.00433	0.00217	0.00217	0.00072	0.00072
$W(6,3)$	0.00016	−0.00742	0.00038	−0.3737	0.00057	0.00115	−0.00273	−0.00032	0.00267
$W(6,4)$	0.00009	0.00503	0.00023	0.1794	0.00181	0.00102	−0.00405	0.00043	0.00043
$W(6,5)$	0.00005	−0.00316	0.00011	−0.1119	0.00043	0.00033	0.00020	−0.00092	0.00198
$W(6,6)$	0.00002	0.00147	0.00004	0.0502	0.00009	0.00054	0.00003	−0.00111	−0.00111